KU-596-519

The
Which? Hotel Guide 1999

The
Which? Hotel
Guide 1999

Edited by
Patricia Yates & Kim Winter

CONSUMERS' ASSOCIATION

The Which? Hotel Guide 1999 was researched by *Holiday Which?*,
part of Consumers' Association, and published by
Which? Ltd, 2 Marylebone Road, London NW1 4DF

Email address: guide.reports@which.co.uk

Distributed by The Penguin Group:
Penguin Books Ltd, 27 Wrights Lane, London W8 5TZ

First edition September 1998
Copyright © 1998 Which? Ltd

Reprinted in January 1999

Base mapping © Map Marketing Ltd/AND Map Graphics Ltd 1998
Map information © Which? Ltd 1998

British Library Cataloguing in Publication Data
A catalogue record for this book is
available from the British Library

ISBN 0 85202 732 X

Warm thanks to Sophie Butler, Sophie Carr, Clare Haworth-Maden,
Lindsay Hunt, Andrew Leslie, Fred Mawer, Erica Quan, Kevin
Rushby, John Wheelwright; also to Dick Vine for the illustrations; and
to Kyzen Creative Consultants for the cover design.

For a full list of Which? books, please write to
Which? Books, Castlemead, Gascoyne Way, Hertford X, SG14 1LH
or access our web site at http://www.which.net/

Photoset by Tradespools Ltd, Frome, Somerset
Printed in England by Clays Ltd, St Ives plc

Holiday Which? regularly inspects holiday destinations in both
Britain and abroad, as well as reporting on airfares, hotel safety and
other issues of interest to holiday-makers. To keep up to date with
the best information, take out a magazine subscription. For details of
a free trial, write to *Holiday Which?*, Consumers' Association, PO
Box 44, Hertford SG14 1SH, tel (01992) 822804.

Contents

How to use the *Guide*

The *Guide*'s main entries are divided into four sections: London, England, Scotland and Wales. In the London section, hotels are listed alphabetically by name; in all other sections, they are listed under the nearest town or village. The maps in the centre section can be used as a starting point for planning your trip. (The London map locates hotels by name.) Alternatively, if you know the name of a hotel but are unsure about its precise location, use the index at the back of the book. Don't forget that other hotels worth considering are listed in our Round-ups; these also appear on the maps.

All the entries in this year's *Guide* have been rewritten between April and June 1998. The narrative about each hotel is based on an inspection by a professional hotel inspector and is backed up by reports sent in by readers over the past year. The *Guide* relies on proprietors for the factual information about the hotel; they fill in a questionnaire giving details of the number of rooms, facilities offered, restrictions on children, dogs and smoking, prices for rooms and meals, and so on. Telephone and fax numbers, email and web site addresses were all checked just before we went to press but may change.

Key to symbols

This denotes somewhere where you can rely on a good meal – either the hotel features in the main section of the 1999 edition of *The Good Food Guide* or our inspectors were impressed, whether by particularly competent home cooking or by more lavish cuisine.

This denotes that the hotel is in an exceptionally peaceful location, where you should expect to have a restful stay. We give this symbol to a few city hotels that are relatively peaceful, considering their location.

This denotes that the hotel offers all its twin or double rooms (not including four-posters or suites) for £35 or less *per person per night*, including breakfast, at the standard rate. (Many hotels advertise special breaks, and weekend and out-of-season offers, which can mean cheaper room rates than those quoted.) Where the rate includes dinner, the price of dinner at that hotel has been taken into account.

NEW ENTRY This denotes that the entry is new to the *Guide* as a main entry in the 1999 edition.

This denotes that the hotel has been singled out for one of our special awards for 1999: see the centre colour section.

Other symbols are used to organise our factual information:

◖ Opening and closing periods of both the hotel and any restaurant or dining-room.

▨ Directions to help you find the hotel and details of parking facilities, including any charge for public and private car parks.

⇌ Details of the number and type (single, double, four-poster, etc.) of bedrooms, bathrooms, shower-rooms and other facilities in the rooms. 'Twin/double' may mean that the beds are of the 'zip-link' type: let the hotel know when booking whether you want the beds arranged separately or together. All bedrooms have tea/coffee-making equipment unless we specify to the contrary. 'Some in annexe' means some of the rooms are in a separate cottage, converted coach-house or other building. 'Family rooms available' means that an extra bed can be made available in a twin or double room.

✍ Details of the public rooms available and other special facilities, including function and conference facilities (residential and non-residential), facilities for children, sports and games at the hotel. Where 'conferences' precedes the residential capacity, the number is for single occupancy of rooms; otherwise the number is for full occupancy (e.g. three in a family room). Nearby leisure facilities are mentioned only if the hotel offers guests access to these free or at reduced rates. Hotels in England and Wales that are licensed for civil weddings in accordance with the Marriage Act 1949 (as amended) are indicated. In Scotland, religious weddings may be held at any hotel or indeed anywhere else; civil weddings, however, can be held only in registrars' offices save in exceptional circumstances.

♿ We have not inspected hotels specifically from the point of view of disabled readers. The information given here is that supplied by the proprietor, who has confirmed that the entrance to the hotel is at least 80cm wide and passages at least 120cm across, in accordance with British Standard recommendations. Always telephone to check that the hotel can meet your particular requirements.

● Restrictions on children, dogs, smoking. In addition to specifying minimum ages for children or not allowing them in the restaurant or dining-room in the evening – both of which are indicated – some hotels have restrictions on children in bars, which may not be shown. Guide dogs are often not included in the restriction on dogs; any charge for accommodating dogs in bedrooms is indicated. Since proprietors do change their rules, it is wise to check on restrictions and charges at the time of booking.

▭ Details of credit, debit and charge cards accepted at the hotel. Some hotels may levy a surcharge on payment by card.

£ Prices you can expect to pay up to April 1999 (if the hotel has told us prices are likely to rise before then, we say so). We give prices *per room for one night*, whether for one person in a single room, for one person alone in a twin or double room, for two people sharing a twin or double room, or for a family sharing a room. 'Deposit required' may mean that the hotel will take your credit card number as a surety when you book a room.

Meal prices are given next: breakfast (B), if it is not included in the room price, lunch (L) and dinner (D) if available. When bar/bistro meals are mentioned, lunch prices may be for just a main course, while dinner may be for two or more courses. Set meal and à la carte (alc) meal prices are given where applicable; these are usually of three or more courses. Room prices are rounded up to the nearest £1, meal prices to the nearest 50p.

We also indicate whether the hotel offers special-priced breaks; these might include cheaper rates at weekends, or in low season, or for stays longer than a couple of days, and can offer a considerable saving on the standard room rate quoted.

If you are travelling by train, you can phone 0345 484950 for queries about timetables, fares, special promotions, etc. You cannot make a booking on this number, but will be given the number for the appropriate train operating company, which will sell tickets and book your seat. There is also a web site at www.rail.co.uk that offers a timetable planning service.

Introduction

To many of you *The Which? Hotel Guide* is by now an old friend. The thrill of anticipation with this new edition will come in turning the pages and seeing which hotel is in and which is out, and which places have won our coveted Hotel of the Year special award – see the new colour section in the centre of the book.

But every year as we stand in pristine formation on the bookshop shelves, we are picked up, flicked through, bought and taken home by a new set of readers for whom it is worth reinforcing their good judgement in choosing this particular guide. Even our faithful followers might like to be reminded of what makes us different.

The Which? Hotel Guide exists to serve its readers. We take no payments for inspecting a hotel, turning up unannounced, staying anonymously and paying the bill just like any other customer. Hoteliers do not see what we have written before publication, nor is the length of their entries or their prominence related to a fee paid to us. For there is no charge to be in this *Guide*, no way of slipping in – apart from passing our inspection, which is designed to cream off the best places. It is, of course, an expensive business for us – we use a team of experienced hotel inspectors who work for Consumers' Association and are used to looking at hotels all over the world.

Similarly, it is not possible for hoteliers to pass through our net just by getting a few friends to write in – we always go to see for ourselves. We also have a truly wonderful readership, who are genuinely interested in letting us know the good and bad, and even sharing their new finds with us (that takes selflessness). These readers tell us where the gold stars are still shining, and where the laurels are being rested on, and help us run an efficient monitoring service. We also, of course, consult our sister publication, *The Good Food Guide*, for expert assessments of the quality of food and service in the restaurant or dining-room. To everyone who has sent us their feedback on a hotel visit, let us say thank you. If you would like to become one of our hundreds of regulars, just fill in one of the forms at the back of the book and send it Freepost, or email us on guide.reports@which.co.uk – it couldn't be simpler.

The view from the bridge

We were delighted to be invited to join the Tourism Forum by the Department of Culture, Media and Sport in order to wrestle with some of the issues relating to tourism in Britain. On the 'quality' working party the topics of hotels and grading systems were naturally a major talking point. Over the twelve-month life of this guide we should see the fruits of the unified grading system (by the English Tourist Board, AA and RAC) in England, while the Scottish and Wales Tourist Boards press on with their own variations of the star rating system.

Small hoteliers continue to voice their concerns that a concerted push for uniformity should not end up dominating and driving out the utterly charming mild eccentricity that many of the entries in the *Guide* rightly celebrate. It seems to us that in an industry made up of small players, excellence should be cherished and rewarded, not squeezed into regimented boxes. That sort of thinking leads to those awful fixed coat hangers (they look tidier when you open the door, apparently) and the inevitable ten minutes of muted swearing before the dress is flung back into the suitcase. For the small hotelier, too, the focus has now switched from 'Which inspection system should I join?' to 'Where should I go to promote myself?' and 'How big a space should I pay for?' as the organisations involved in grading direct their energies to selling space within their guides. We were truly astonished when talking to one lady starting up a farmhouse B&B, with just two rooms costing £20 per person a night, to find out that she forked out nearly £800 this year to be graded by the tourist board and included in a small farmhouse B&B marketing consortium. She looked on these costs as necessary start-up payments, but of course any sort of paying concern will eventually have to pass these costs on to the customer. It did rather bring home to us the reason why even the biggest names ask us how to get into the *Guide* and tell us what a service we perform in promoting the best – just because they are the best, not because they have paid us to say they are.

An individual view of progress

Also during the course of the past year we took part in a research programme led by Professor Theodore Zeldin, an Oxford academic, and ended up being interviewed about the forms that progress takes in the hotel industry. We were somewhat disconcerted when, at the end of the interview, the researcher switched off the tape and said: 'That was really interesting. You said the exact opposite of everyone else I've spoken to.' What we had argued is that change and progress come about from the actions of individuals – whether Francis Coulson (sadly lost to us this year) with his vision of the Country House Hotel at Sharrow Bay, Ken McCulloch changing hotel standards in city centres at One Devonshire Gardens in Glasgow and now rolling out the Malmaison chain, and Anouska Hempel showing the way into a new era with the minimalism of her latest London venture, Hempel. That statement seems so self-evident that we still can't quite believe that ours was a solo voice.

Returning to results

At the other end of the scale there is the problem of those hoteliers who will never voluntarily enter any grading system, but depend on trapping the unwary. They give Britain a bad name. Although the tourist boards have as part of their agenda the raising of standards at the bottom end, it is hard to see how the same aim could get on to the agenda of the more commercially driven AA and RAC. Yet this is one of the key issues that a national grading system has to address.

Nowhere is the problem more apparent (outside London) than at our large seaside resorts. The nation's favourites have now largely degenerated into the ugly sisters. The natural choice for the summer holiday is no longer two weeks at Great Yarmouth or Clacton, where we spent holidays as girls. How can we hold our heads up knowing it is on the Spanish costas that the resort and hotel standards are set? Stroll along the prom nowadays and you will be more likely to despair at the derelict piers and decaying Victorian piles, as you trip over litter from the fast-food joints, than to hear the brass band play. We think it is a cause for national shame that we are allowing our beautiful coastline to spiral into decline. Look at resort guides and you will see that a large number of the hotels are not opting for any grading system. Why should they? It is an extra cost, on a probably already financially fragile business, that brings little apparent benefit – and not going in for it clearly does not exclude a hotelier from advertising in the local authority guide. Yet who would come here who could afford to go elsewhere? Resorts know that they have to adapt or die. Some have made the change – like Brighton, which now concentrates on the conference visitor – but they are the rarities. We are delighted to have some resort hotels in the *Guide* – the Riviera at Sidmouth, Carlton House and Langton Manor at Bournemouth and a new entry, the Royal at Ventnor, 'rescued' from the Forte empire – but they are few and far between.

As we went to press it emerged that the Department of Culture, Media and Sport had recommended the axing of the English Tourist Board. The ETB already operates at a significant disadvantage to the Scots and Welsh, getting £9.73m grant-in-aid (representing £0.25p per head of population), as against £18.3m (£4.81) and £74.6m (£6.31) respectively. It is true that the ETB and the regional tourist boards have in the past not sufficiently differentiated their roles, which has resulted in excessive bureaucracy, but surely it is self-evident that some sort of central leadership is necessary to drive the industry in England? Perversely, there was a rapid announcement that the Scottish Tourist Board was quite safe. We cannot see that there is any hope at all for the unified grading system, let alone any of the other initiatives that the ETB has started, if the ETB is simply zapped.

Would you want to work here?

There has been a great deal of navel-gazing about why a business that employs seven per cent of the workforce and creates one in five of all new jobs is regarded as little better than a sweat shop – long hours for little pay – and not a worthwhile career. We have heard a lot of debate about the issue of the minimum wage too – that it will mean more cuts in housekeeping and it's 'fine to pay graduates a proper wage, but not the washer-upper'. How refreshing, then, to talk to one of the small hoteliers (meant only as an adjective applied to the hotel, not to the size of the personality) in the *Guide* who declared 'it will make absolutely no difference to us – we pay our staff properly!' When gently prodded about the washer-upper, the Trotskyist tendencies came to the fore. 'I pay the washer-upper £6.50 an hour, more than I pay the graduates who will go on to be high flyers and earn good salaries. You have to pay people doing the unpopular and dirty jobs – they are the backbone of the industry.' And you can see the point. Gliding over the parquet is all very well, but clean plates and a vacuumed bedroom are rather more fundamental.

Sometimes the minimum wage gets mixed up with tipping and service charges too. Research shows us that tipping is in decline – with the value of tips falling to less than five per cent of the bill, and one third of guests not tipping at all. Count us in on that third: we're of the generation (it is generational: father always left something on the bedside table in an envelope) that thinks service is part and parcel of staying in a hotel. We are irritated by seeing 15 per cent 'service charge' added to the hotel bill. Why not divide up the laundry bill, too, given that you'll have to change the sheets? (Please don't – that's a joke.) Consumers want a clear pricing system, not big surprises when checking out. If the way to do that is by paying staff a fair salary and sharing out the occasional voluntarily given tip, so be it.

Competing for business

The cost of staying at British hotels continues to make the headlines – and it is no news to regular travellers that our hotels are some of the most expensive in Europe. One of the underlying reasons given for this is that British hotels, particularly the larger groups, strongly rely on their corporate guests who are not picking up the tab personally and are less concerned with 'value' than private individuals. But all businesses today are forced to be leaner and meaner and that includes reviewing the corporate travel account. Rather than stick to the predictably safe, business folk are shopping around and finding not only good value in smaller hotels but friendly and personal service too. Many of the small hoteliers we talk to are now competing for corporate business – and winning it. We also get some lovely letters from salespeople who keep a copy of the *Guide* in the glove compartment, and are delighted to find a good recommendation even when they are travelling in the back of beyond. Our inspection team, who do a fair few business miles themselves, are always on the lookout for good business hotels as well as places for a weekend break – we've given awards to some of the best at the start of the colour section in the middle of the book. If you're a regular business traveller, don't forget to let us know of any we should look at.

Get them while they're young

Should children be banned? Just think of the outcry if we substituted any other age group or nationality or racial group in that sentence. Yet many hoteliers would answer 'yes' to that question – and a segment of the great British public concurs. We'd like to think that the European acceptance of all ages, whereby children are welcomed as part of the family group, is a trend we will adopt, but that continental drift seems a slow old process. My own children (4 and 6 now) shape my view. They are regular hotel visitors, love the experience – and have never crayoned on the walls or broken a precious ornament! If we want our young to learn how to behave in society we have to let them experience being out in public and being expected to behave properly. My children's delight in the excitement of a hotel stay is part of my enjoyment of a weekend away – and I must admit a touch of parental pride when a guest at the Swan, Southwold complimented me on their behaviour at breakfast. Thank you, madam, you quite made my day.

If we look at taking the children away as an experience in civilised behaviour for them, why do hotel kitchens insist on offering menus based solely on cheap fish fingers and chips? Ask for vegetables (my two love broccoli and cauliflower) and the reaction is like one of those Heath cartoons, with waiters' eyes on stalks. Children nowadays have travelled the world with their parents; my 6-year-old thought his garlic frogs' legs the height of sophistication in a French café last year. So why not offer small helpings of real food to delight their palate and make them long to go to good restaurants. It might even be better if we returned to the days of shepherd's pie, roast chicken and proper vegetables – real nursery food now enjoying a resurgence for grown-ups.

Wary of weddings

Weddings are big business for hoteliers, particularly now that they can play host to the actual ceremony, too. But it's clear from our postbag that there is a certain conflict between running large (and often boisterous) functions and creating a relaxed and peaceful environment for the rest of the guests. One hotel we stayed at this year was planning to close the hotel on the Saturday and Monday of the May bank holiday for wedding parties – that's one way of doing it. More typical is the weekenders' letter that goes: 'We were beginning to feel a nuisance, with staff having little time for us. When we complained we were told that they had two weddings over the weekend and were under a lot of pressure. We felt they should not have accepted our booking if they could not cope.' Another reader writes: 'The dining-room and lounge were out of bounds and it was apparent that we were in the way... We cannot understand why our booking was accepted.' At the very least, guests should be told when booking that there will be a wedding party. One hotelier has gone a step further and no longer holds functions throughout the summer. 'They tend to take over the place. Arrive at two, are meant to finish at six, but of course guests get drunk, as people do, and hang around the bars and lounges.' He felt this wasn't the atmosphere his weekend visitors were looking for and he also had an eye to his staff: 'if they've worked a 15-hour day on Saturday, they are not going to come in for Sunday breakfast and smile at people and say "How are you?" – they'll just be exhausted.' However, he reckons he has lost £150,000 worth of wedding business this year, and says cautiously, 'Only time will tell if it's the right decision'.

Before moving on from this subject, we cannot resist recounting the moan of the couple who went to relax at a country house hotel and found themselves in the middle of a corporate clay pigeon shoot. Outraged, they returned home – although they had booked only three days in advance the hotel hadn't thought to mention the event.

Managerial style

After celebrating the joys of English eccentricity, it's only fair to tell the tales of what happens when charm tips over into Basil Fawlty parodies. One reader reported: 'Our evening's entertainment was hearing the owners taking a young waiter to task for asking permission to go home, having completed his three hours. This request triggered a lengthy lecture as to their expectations of their staff and how this young man should aspire to exude confidence and a professional style when carrying a spoon and fork so that he could engage in conversation with his guests.'

That conversation probably wasn't half as much fun as one forced on another reader: 'We were wakened at about 2 a.m. by loud voices debating the various merits and demerits of '70s pop groups. This continued for about an hour and a half, when I went downstairs and asked the owners if they would mind lowering their voices a little.' We are constantly amazed at the number of hotels that have put a great deal of effort into ensuring the place *looks* right, but very little into ensuring that the owners and staff make it a pleasant place to stay. Perhaps these letters illustrate the point.

'No sooner had you risen from a chair, or from a chair you had moved an inch or two to be nearer to someone, than someone dashed over, plumped up cushions and put the chair back in its rightful position. Not an attitude designed to make you feel at home and, what is more, the staff were often so busy fretting over such things that they did not have any time left to attend to the needs of the guests.'

More typical is the total vacuum – where is mine host? 'It's difficult to put a finger on, but whilst the staff were very welcoming and friendly if you needed them (and could find them), we didn't feel as though anyone was in charge, no maître d' or friendly owner. It didn't feel as though anyone really cared. I'm not one to like being fussed over, but I suppose we didn't feel pampered, and for £100 a night I think we should have been.'

And with a tinge of sadness for a missed opportunity, we read: 'Personally, I would have been glad of the chance to have a little conversation here and there, even only a few sentences, such as "Are you enjoying the Folk Festival?".'

And still these little aggravations continue, like breakfast tables being set around the diners (earliest sighting this year, 8.20 p.m.) and this lovely story: 'I asked for a bottle of still water. The water came in a jug and tasted like flat fizzy water. I asked the waitress and she assured me that it was still water. I called the proprietor and was finally told that it was flat fizzy water from the night before. The waitress had understood that I had asked for such a thing!" How fortunate that the hotelier had happened to save it from the night before.

Cancellation charges conflict

Here is another area where the rights of the consumer and the hotelier are confused. If you book a hotel, even by telephone, you make a contract with that hotel. If you subsequently cancel, the hotel is entitled to charge you for its loss of profit. From readers we get outraged letters like: 'In all my time, we have never experienced being charged for rooms cancelled with over a week's notice' after cancelling five rooms in a small hotel with 10 days' notice – the hotelier had in fact not charged for the two rooms he managed to re-let.

On the other side, one small hotelier told us how three rooms were left empty on an August bank holiday after a party failed to turn up - and six months later she is still no nearer getting any money. In such cases, consumers clearly have obligations to go with their rights and one or two guests failing to turn up can make the difference between a profit and loss. Hoteliers do need to be clear what the cancellation policies are but, equally, consumers need to play fair. For more on rights and responsibilities in hotels, see overleaf.

Mirror, mirror on the wall

And just in case you think we've omitted all those small niggles that so worry the guest, let us name our choice of the year as ... the make-up mirror. The problem is put succinctly by one reader: 'Like nearly every hotel we have stayed in there was nowhere sufficiently well lit to apply make-up. Do men decide the lighting?'

Finally, do keep the reports coming. We read all the letters and we've had some hilarious ones this year. The best quotes are dotted through the *Guide*. Perhaps our favourite is the one that finishes: 'Fantastic stay, loads of fun and thoroughly recommended', and starts: 'The building is fabulous, and lives in a world I can only describe as a cross between Disneyland and *The X-Files*. The staff belong in neither, of course, but are in fact representatives of the United Nations (being from every corner of the globe), probably behaving better, for between constant onslaughts of main courses and wave after wave of murderous desserts, they were at my side to mop my brow, and ease my pain and suffering by pouring gallons of the house cellar contents down my now distended throat.'

Which seems to bring us back to where we started, in praise of that touch of eccentricity that makes a stay at the hotel an event to remember. All your reports are read, filed and avidly referred to, so do let us know what you think of our selection this year. We've a new face in the office this year: our thanks to Joan Brown for keeping the administration going.

Patricia Yates and Kim Winter
Editors

Your rights and responsibilities in hotels

A few days away at a hotel is a special treat for many of us, so we don't want anything to spoil it. And when we're travelling on business we don't want any hotel hassles that might distract us. But sometimes things do go wrong, and the hotel doesn't live up to expectations.

Below we set out your rights in dealing with hotels and answer some of the questions regularly asked by our readers. This should help you put things straight on the spot, but if it doesn't, we suggest ways to go about claiming your rights.

When I arrived at the city-centre hotel where I'd booked a weekend break I was told that they had made a mistake and the hotel was full. Owing to a popular conference, the only room I could find was in a more expensive hotel at the other side of town, so I'm out of pocket. What are my rights?

The hotel accepted your booking and was obliged to keep a room available for you. It is in breach of contract and liable to compensate you for additional expenses arising out of that breach – the difference in cost between what you were expecting to pay and what you ended up having to pay, plus any travelling expenses. Write to the manager explaining what happened, and enclose copies of receipts for your additional expenditure. (See also points 1–5 on page 18.)

After booking I found that I had to cancel. I immediately wrote to advise the owners, but they refuse to return my deposit, and say they expect me to pay additional compensation.

When you book a room and the hoteliers accept your booking you enter into a binding contract with them – they undertake to provide the required accommodation and meals for the specified dates at the agreed price, and you commit yourself to paying their charges. If you later cancel or fail to turn up, the hotel may be entitled to keep your deposit to defray administrative expenses, although it should be possible to challenge this if the deposited amount is a very high proportion of the total cost.

If a hotelier is unable to re-let the room you have booked – and he or she must try to do so – he or she can demand from you the loss of profit caused by your cancellation, which can be a substantial proportion of the total price. It's important to give as much notice as possible if you have to cancel: this increases the chances of your room being re-let. If after cancelling you find that the full amount has been charged to your credit card you should raise the matter with your credit card issuer, who will ask the hotel whether the room was re-let, and to justify the charge made.

When I phoned to book a room the receptionist asked for my credit card number. I offered to send a deposit by cheque instead, but the receptionist insisted on taking the number.

Hotels have increasingly adopted this practice to protect themselves against loss when guests fail to turn up. It's reasonable for hotels to request a deposit, and where time permits a cheque should be acceptable.

After a long drive I stopped off at a hotel and asked for a room for the night. Although the hotel was clearly not full the owners refused to give me a room. Can they do this?

Hotels and inns are not allowed to refuse requests for food and shelter providing accommodation is available and the guest is sober, decently dressed and able to pay. If you meet these requirements and are turned away by a hotel with a vacancy you are entitled to sue for damages. If proprietors want to be able to turn away casual business, or are fussy about the sort of people they want to stay in their establishment, they are likely to call it 'guesthouse' or 'private hotel'. In any event, it's illegal to exclude anyone on the grounds of race or sex.

When I called to book they told me I would need to pay extra if I wanted to pay by credit card. Is this legal?

Yes. Dual pricing was legalised early in 1991 and some hoteliers have elected to charge guests who pay by credit card extra to recover the commission payable to the card company. You can challenge this if you're not told when you book, or if it's not indicated on the tariff displayed in reception.

I arrived at a hotel in winter and found I was the only guest. Both my bedroom and the public rooms were distinctly chilly. I was uncomfortable throughout my stay and asked the management to turn up the heating, but things didn't improve.

It's an implied term of the contract between you and the hotel that the accommodation will be of reasonable standard, so it should be maintained at a reasonable temperature. You can claim compensation or seek a reduction of the bill. You were right to complain at the time. You are under a duty to 'mitigate your loss' – to keep your claim to a minimum. The most obvious way of doing this is to complain on the spot and give the management a chance to put things right.

I was very unhappy when I was shown to my room. It hadn't been vacuumed, the wastebins were full, the towels hadn't been changed and I found dog hairs in the bed.

You are entitled to a reasonable standard of accommodation having regard to the price paid. But no hotel, however cheap, should be dirty or unsafe. Ask for things to be put right, and if they're not, ask for a reduction of the bill.

While I was in bed a section of the ceiling caved in. I was injured, but I could have been killed.

Under the Occupiers' Liability Act hotel owners are responsible for the physical safety of their guests. You have a claim for compensation, and would be wise to seek legal advice to have it properly assessed.

The hotel brochure promised floodlit tennis courts. When we arrived the lawns had been neglected and the nets were down. We couldn't play.

A hotel must provide advertised facilities. If it doesn't you can claim compensation, or ask for an appropriate deduction from your bill in respect of the disappointment suffered. You might also want trading standards officers to consider bringing a case against the hotel under the Trade Descriptions Act.

While I was staying at a hotel my video camera was stolen from my room.

Hotel owners owe you a duty of care and must look after your property while it is on their premises. They are liable for any loss and damage as long as it wasn't your own fault – you would be unlikely to succeed if you left it clearly visible in a ground-floor room with the door and window unlocked. However, under the Hotel Proprietors Act, providing hotel owners display a notice at reception, they can limit their liability to £50 per item or £100 in total. They can't rely on this limit if the loss was caused by negligence of their staff, although you will have to prove this.

My car was broken into while parked in the hotel car park. I want compensation.

The Hotel Proprietors Act doesn't cover cars. Your claim is unlikely to succeed.

My dinner was inedible. Do I have to pay for it?

The Supply of Goods and Services Act obliges hotels to prepare food with reasonable skill and care. The common law in Scotland imposes similar duties. If food is inedible, you should tell the waiter and ask for a replacement dish. If things aren't put right you can ask for a reduction of the billed amount. If you pay in full, possibly to avoid an unpleasant scene, write a note at the time saying that you are doing so under protest and are 'reserving your rights'. This means that you retain your right to claim compensation later.

Asserting your rights

1 Always complain at the time if you're unhappy. It's by the far the best way, and necessary to discharge your obligation to mitigate your loss.

2 If you reach deadlock you can deduct a sum from the bill in recognition of the deficient service received. Remember that the hotel might try to exercise its rights of 'lien' by refusing to release your luggage until the bill is paid. It's probably easier to pay in full, but give written notice that you are paying under protest and are reserving your rights to claim compensation through the courts.

3 Legal advice is available from a number of sources. Citizens Advice Bureaux, Law Centres and Consumer Advice Centres give free advice on consumer disputes. In certain cases your Local Trading Standards Department might be able to help. If instructing a solicitor be sure to sort out the cost implications at the outset. Or you can write to Consumers' Association's Which? Legal Service, Castlemead, Gascoyne Way, Hertford SG14 1LH, who, for a fee, may be able to help you. For details on how to join, phone (0800) 252100.

4 Once you know where you stand, write to the hotel setting out your claim.

5 If this fails to get things sorted out and you feel that you have a strong case, you can sue for sums of up to £3,000 (due to increase to £5,000 by mid-1999) under the small claims procedure in the county court. In the sheriff court in Scotland the limit is £1,000. You shouldn't need a solicitor.

LONDON

SANDRINGHAM HOTEL

NW3

Abbey Court

20 Pembridge Gardens, London W2 4DU
TEL: 0171-221 7518   FAX: 0171-792 0858
EMAIL: abbeyhotel@aol.com

Bijou hotel in a fine, Victorian mansion off Notting Hill Gate.

Abbey Court is one of a number of well-proportioned, free-standing houses on this quiet side-street. With its country-house-style look, it is a classic example of London's plethora of small town-house hotels. The bedrooms range from impressive, four-poster affairs to cosy little standard doubles. All are daintily furnished with a smattering of antiques, mini-buttonback armchairs and a dressing-table, and all but one have a whirlpool bath in their swish marble bathrooms. A hairbrush, magazines, books, an old-fashioned radio and complimentary mineral water and biscuits invest them with a homely air. The public areas lack the roominess of some other town-house establishments, with only a small lounge area off the reception. Downstairs, the conservatory, with its wooden floors and dining tables, is less sophisticated than the rest of the house, but is earmarked for a revamp. It's used for breakfast (£7 extra if brought to your room) and is then laid out with an honesty-bar arrangement later in the day. The management is keen, and appears to have thoroughly investigated one correspondent's strong criticism about the service provided by the reception staff.

◗ Open all year   ⚇ Nearest tube station is Notting Hill Gate (Central, District and Circle lines). On-street parking (metered); public car park (£26 per day)   ⤙ 6 single, 6 twin, 7 double, 3 four-poster; family rooms available all with bathroom/WC, exc 1 single with shower/WC; all with TV, room service, hair-dryer, trouser press, direct-dial telephone; no tea/coffee-making facilities in rooms   ⌔ Conservatory/bar, garden; conferences (max 10 people residential/non-residential); leisure facilities nearby (reduced rates for guests); babysitting   ⅙ No wheelchair access   ⬤ No dogs; no smoking in some bedrooms   ▭ Amex, Delta, Diners, MasterCard, Switch, Visa   £ Single £88, single occupancy of twin/double £110 to £118, twin/double £130 to £145, four-poster £175, family room £156 (prices valid till Sept 1998); deposit required. Cooked B £9.50

Abbey House

11 Vicarage Gate, London W8 4AG
TEL: 0171-727 2594

Simple B&B in a grand Victorian house, in an up-market location on a quiet street close to Kensington's smart shops and Kensington Palace.

It may not be as gracious as the nearby former residence of Princess Diana, but this six-storey mansion does have a certain stateliness. On arrival, you pass through a portico flanked by marble pillars, and proceed down a fine, black-and-white-tiled hall, and up a handsome staircase decorated with busts, pot-plants, paintings of royalty and architectural prints. After such impressiveness, the nuts and bolts of the B&B bring you down to earth with a bump. The bedrooms are definitively basic, with worn, cheap furniture. However, they are generally spacious and sport a house plant or two, and some have high, corniced ceilings. None is *en suite*, though all have a basin; a bathroom or shower-room, often with a separate toilet, is shared by every two or three rooms. Breakfast is served in modest, but cheerful, surroundings in the basement, alongside which is an area where you can make hot drinks – it's a pity that UHT sachets rather than fresh milk are provided. Abbey House's low prices make it extremely popular, so book well in advance, especially for weekend stays.

◐ Open all year ⓩ Nearest tube station is High Street Kensington (District and Circle lines). On-street parking (metered); public car park nearby (£12 per day) ⌸→ 2 single, 5 twin, 5 double, 4 family rooms; all with TV; hair-dryer on request; no tea/coffee-making facilities in rooms ⊘ Breakfast room; babysitting ఉ No wheelchair access ⊜ No dogs; no smoking in public rooms ⊟ None accepted £ Single £40, twin/double £65, family room £78 to £90; deposit required. Special breaks available

---

Academy Hotel

17–25 Gower Street, London WC1E 6HG
TEL: 0171-631 4115   FAX: 0171-636 3442

Town-house hotel that is a smart, modern conversion of five interconnecting Georgian houses.

In easy walking distance of Oxford Street, the British Museum and Covent Garden, the dapper Academy is very much in the town-house mould, though without the antique-rich preciousness of many of the comparable West London set-ups. Rather, parquet floors and pleasing contemporary paintings set a fresh, unaffected tone. In the basement, a club restaurant used by local business people as well as hotel guests, with a short but interesting dinner menu, was being revamped when we inspected. Upstairs lie two cosy little sitting-rooms that open on to the hotel's paved and walled small gardens. If you like to open your bedroom window, it's definitely worth asking for a garden-facing room: those at the front are double-glazed, as they have to endure the plentiful traffic along Gower Street. Rooms vary in size from compact singles to very spacious one-room suites, but in terms of décor they are very similar – appealingly uncluttered, and featuring attractive reproduction furniture, coronet drapes over double beds and spruce, modern bathrooms. A correspondent judged his room – as well as the service – to be excellent, the only niggle being a tiny shower-room 'with an exceedingly small wash-basin'.

◐ Open all year; restaurant closed Sat & Sun eves ⓩ Nearest tube stations are Goodge Street and Tottenham Court Road (Northern line and Central line) and Russell Square (Piccadilly line). Public car park nearby (£28 per day) ⌸→ 13 single, 8 twin, 19 double, 8 suites; family rooms available; most with shower/WC, some with bathroom/WC, suites with bath/shower/WC; all with TV, room service, direct-dial telephone, some with trouser press; hair dryer available ⊘ Restaurant, bar, 2 sitting-rooms, conservatory, 2 patio gardens; conferences (max 40 people residential/non-residential), functions; early suppers for children; cots, high chairs, babysitting ఉ No wheelchair access ⊜ No dogs ⊟ Amex, Delta, Diners, MasterCard, Switch,

Visa　£ Single £100 to £115, single occupancy of twin/double £115 to £130, twin/double £125 to £145, suite £185; deposit required. Continental B £8, cooked B £10; set L, D £14.50; alc L, D £20.50. Special breaks available

The Ascott

49 Hill Street, London W1X 7FQ
TEL: 0171-499 6868　FAX: 0171-499 0705
EMAIL: ascottmf@scotts.com.sg
WEB SITE: www.scotts.com.sg/

High-quality, serviced apartments in the heart of Mayfair.

A small, Singapore-based hotel chain has turned this uninviting-looking, 1920s brick apartment block into a luxurious hideaway, which is popular with visitors from America and the Middle East. Using the building's art-deco style as a starting-point, the group has decorated the apartments in a 'neo-deco' look, notably in the atmospheric use of blinds and sleek, wooden furniture. All the apartments come with first-rate business, leisure and domestic facilities – from a desk with a fax and computer link-up, to a CD player and video, as well as a washing-machine, dryer and microwave. The one-, two- and three-bedroom apartments have a proper kitchen, and only really differ from each other in their number of bedrooms. In the studio apartments, however, you sleep on a sofa-bed, and the kitchen facilities are hidden behind cupboard doors. All are rentable on a nightly basis, although stays for a week or longer are more common. Continental breakfasts are included in the rates, and can be taken either in the smart breakfast room or in the spruce patio off the lobby; the professional staff can also arrange the delivery of meals from a selection of nearby restaurants.

◑ Open all year　◲ Nearest tube station is Green Park (Jubilee, Piccadilly and Victoria lines). On-street parking (metered); public car park nearby (£22 per day)　⌸ 56 suites; all with bathroom/WC; all with satellite TV, video, fax, voice mail, modem point, CD player, room service, safe, hair-dryer, direct-dial telephone, air-conditioning, kitchen, iron, washing-machine, dryer, microwave　⦸ Breakfast room, bar, lounge, terrace; conferences (max 8 people residential/non-residential); gym, sauna, solarium; cots, high chairs, babysitting, play area　♿ No wheelchair access　● No dogs
▭ Amex, Delta, Diners, MasterCard, Switch, Visa　£ Suite £193 to £570; deposit required.

Basil Street Hotel

Basil Street, London SW3 1AH
TEL: 0171-581 3311　FAX: 0171-581 3693
EMAIL: thebasil@aol.com
WEB SITE: www.absite.com/basil/

A traditional, English country-house-hotel atmosphere transported into the centre of Knightsbridge.

This privately owned, rather quirky and thoroughly old-fashioned London institution has been taking guests for almost the full span of the twentieth century. With Harrods at one end of the street and Harvey Nichols yards away, the hotel is a favourite of the tweed set, up from the country for a bout of serious shopping. During the day, the hotel's mellow and secluded public rooms, such as the women-only Parrot Club and the main lounge – both furnished with homely antiques and Persian rugs on their parquet floors – are popular with local shoppers too, who come here to recuperate with snacks and tea. Greater sustenance is available in the peaceful, upper-floor restaurant, which concentrates on such unmodish fare as roast duckling served in an orange sauce and roast beef and Yorkshire pudding. The undemonstrative, yet soothing, bedrooms eschew some of the hi-tech facilities and extras that are commonly found in other major London hotels. Suites do not exist (the biggest room is Room 315A), and a number of singles are not *en suite* (but are very popular, thanks to their bargain rates). Many rooms have recently been refurbished, but plenty of bathrooms are still enjoyably dated – some have venerable wooden loo seats, others sauna-like, pine-panelled walls. If you like sleeping with an open window, ask for a more peaceful, interior-facing room.

○ Open all year ☑ Nearest tube station is Knightsbridge (Piccadilly line). Private car park (£22 per day, must book); on-street parking (metered); public car park nearby (£27 per day) ⇨ 41 single, 21 twin, 21 double, 2 family rooms; most with bathroom/WC exc 11 singles; all with TV, room service, hair-dryer, direct-dial telephone; no tea/coffee-making facilities in rooms ⌀ Restaurant, lounge; functions (max 300 people incl up to 131 residential), conferences; early suppers for children; cots, high chairs, babysitting ⓖ No wheelchair access ● No dogs in public rooms; no smoking in some bedrooms ▭ Amex, Delta, Diners, MasterCard, Switch, Visa £ Single £79 to £141, twin/double £211, family room £281 (1998 prices); deposit required. Continental B £9.50, cooked B £13.50; set L £13.50, D £16.50; alc L £18, D £25 . Special breaks available

The Beaufort

33 Beaufort Gardens, London SW3 1PP
TEL: 0171-584 5252   FAX: 0171-589 2834
EMAIL: thebeaufort@nol.co.uk
WEB SITE: www.thebeaufort.co.uk/index.htm

One of London's most relaxed, up-market town-house hotels, with a host of extras included in the tariff.

Diana Wallis' well-established hotel, run by a posse of eager young women, spreads through two Victorian houses on a refined cul-de-sac terrace round the corner from Harrods. The décor is both bold and pretty throughout. There are an abundance of flower arrangements and striking, original English floral watercolours on display, both in the fetching sitting-room (the only public area) and the bedrooms. Though few of these are particularly large, they are highly individual and carefully stylised affairs, maybe featuring light star patterns on the walls, and mottled-beige bathrooms. The choicest face the quiet street and have floor-to-ceiling french windows. All are stuffed with pampering extras, such as a personal stereo, umbrella, shortbread, chocolates and a mini-decanter of brandy. One of the hotel's major selling points is that almost everything is included in the rates; the exceptions are phone and laundry bills, VAT, and, in the less de-luxe rooms, room-service snacks. That cream teas, continental breakfasts, all beverages (from champagne to soft drinks) and even one airport transfer are not charged for makes the establishment good value compared with its rivals. It also means that the sitting-room, where the bar is located, is a far more used and convivial spot than in many other town-house set-ups.

◑ Open all year 🔁 Nearest tube station is Knightsbridge (Piccadilly line). On-street parking (metered); public car park nearby (£20 per day) 🛏 3 single, 5 twin, 13 double, 7 suites; most with bathroom/WC exc 3 singles with shower/WC; TV, room service, hair-dryer, direct-dial telephone, CD player, video; no tea/coffee-making facilities in rooms ⚘ Sitting-room; leisure facilities nearby (free for guests); cots, high chairs ♿ No wheelchair access ● No children under 3; no dogs ▭ Amex, Delta, Diners, MasterCard, Visa £ Single £150, single occupancy of twin/double £180, twin/double £170 to £260, suite £295; deposit required. Special breaks available

---

Bedknobs [see map 3]

58 Glengarry Road, East Dulwich, London SE22 8QD
TEL: 0181-299 2004   FAX: 0181-693 5611
EMAIL: gill@bedknobs.co.uk
WEB SITE: www.bedknobs.co.uk/

Homely, prettily furnished B&B in a south London suburb.

Perhaps understandably, you get considerably more comfort for your money in Bedknobs than in B&B accommodation in central London. Its down side is not being near a tube station; overground trains take about ten minutes to London Bridge from East Dulwich station, which is about a ten-minute walk away. Gill Jenkins' home is on a fairly quiet, typical suburban London street made up of late-Victorian terraced houses. Victorian fireplaces, some antiques and pine furnishings invest the house with much period character, while such details as family photos and mobiles over the stairs give the place a very homely atmosphere. Downstairs lies an enjoyably cluttered breakfast room, where guests eat round a communal table. Upstairs are three bedrooms, which share a smart bathroom and shower room. The 'Big Blue Room', with a magnificent, antique, walnut bed, is the best, though the smaller rooms at the rear are also very attractive, and quieter. In Gill's mother's house next door are three further, slightly simpler bedrooms, but one of these has a private bathroom. Gill's commitment to helping her guests is best exemplified in the bedrooms' detailed information books, full of local restaurant menus, train timetables and so forth. 'An outstanding host... beautifully decorated and immaculately fresh rooms', enthuses an Australian correspondent.

◑ Open all year 🔁 Glengarry Road is opposite Dulwich Hospital in East Dulwich Grove. On-street parking (free) 🛏 2 single, 1 twin, 3 double; family rooms available; some in annexe; 1 double with bathroom/WC; all with TV, hair-dryer ⚘ Breakfast room ♿ No wheelchair access ● No dogs; no smoking ▭ Delta, MasterCard, Switch, Visa £ Single £32, single occupancy of twin/double £35 to £45, twin/double £50 to £60, family room £60 to £75; deposit required

Blakes Hotel

33 Roland Gardens, London SW7 3PF
TEL: 0171-370 6701 FAX: 0171-373 0442
EMAIL: blakes@easynet.co.uk
WEB SITE: www.blakeshotel.co.uk/

An extraordinary, visual tour de force *of a hotel, designed by the owner, Anouska Hempel.*

Hidden away from the hoi polloi on a residential, South Kensington side-street, this daringly conceived fantasyland attracts the glitterati in their droves: Liam Gallagher and Patsy Kensit, to name but two, spent their honeymoon night in the all-white, four-poster suite. Virtually every inch of the interior looks startling. The lobby adopts a colonial style, all wooden shutters and old trunks. In the basement restaurant, artichokes decorate the tables and Thai-warrior costumes the walls. The closest Blakes comes to a sitting-room – an oriental den piled high with cushions – is also downstairs. The bedrooms, variously suffused in indulgent black, gold, grey and white colour schemes, are showy enough to have graced many a fashion shoot – particularly the dazzlingly opulent suites, which are replete with many *objets d'art*. The singles and small doubles are, surprisingly, relatively affordable. Most of the state-of-the-art mod cons (oxygen cannisters are the latest gimmick) are hidden from view so as not to spoil the overall effect. The food is as exotic as the surroundings: breakfast could include Bayonne ham and fresh figs or quail's eggs, while the eclectic dinner menu offers the likes of lobster ravioli in a lemon-grass bisque. Despite the hotel's indisputable trendiness, the extremely obliging staff are not at all snooty.

◑ Open all year ⟦⟧ Nearest tube station is Gloucester Road (Piccadilly, District and Circle lines). On-street parking (metered); public car park nearby �)→ 14 single, 3 twin, 19 double, 7 four-poster, 9 suites; some in annexe; most with bathroom/WC exc 4 singles with shower/WC; all with TV, 24-hour room service, hair-dryer, mini-bar, direct-dial telephone, some with CD player, video, air-conditioning; no tea/coffee-making facilities in rooms ⊘ Restaurant, bar, sitting-room, garden; conferences (max 20 people residential/non-residential), functions; leisure facilities nearby (reduced rates for guests); early suppers for children; cots, high chairs, babysitting ⅋ No wheelchair access ● No dogs ▭ Amex, Diners, MasterCard, Switch, Visa ⟦£⟧ Single £153, twin/double £183, four-poster £353, suite £560 to £817; deposit required (prices valid till Oct 1998). Continental B £14, cooked B £17; alc L £55, D £85. Special breaks available

Bryanston Court

56–60 Great Cumberland Place, London W1H 8DD
TEL: 0171-262 3141 FAX: 0171-262 7248

A thorough revamp for this inexpensive, family-run hotel near Marble Arch.

If you're looking for a dignified, but modest, base close to Oxford Street, Bryanston Court, which is spread along a handsome, Georgian terrace, might fit the bill. All its bedrooms have recently been completely refurbished, and are now cheerfully decked out in yellow-and-red-dotted wallpaper and floral bedspreads. There is, however, little that the owners – the hands-on Theodore family, which has been at the helm for 20 years – can do about their size. Many of them are definitively small: a good deal of shuffling is needed to get round the beds; the basins can often be found in the bedrooms; and the simple shower-rooms are box-like. The rear-facing bedrooms are a better bet for light sleepers. The spacious public areas have a certain elegance: battered old leather armchairs and spotlit paintings set the tone in the lounge and bar, while the dining-room (which serves decent buffet breakfasts only) adopts a lighter, more Regency style. Prices have risen by 15 to 20 per cent since last year, in reflection of the smartening-up of the bedrooms; for something cheaper, consider the Concorde Hotel (see entry) three doors along, which is under the same ownership.

◑ Open all year   🔽 Nearest tube station is Marble Arch (Central line). On-street parking (metered); public car park nearby (£20 per day)   🛏 20 single, 26 twin, 8 double; all with shower/WC; all with TV, hair-dryer, direct-dial telephone   ✅ Bar, lounge, dining-room   ⅙ No wheelchair access   ● No dogs in bedrooms
▭ Amex, Delta, Diners, MasterCard, Switch, Visa   💷 Single £85, single occupancy of twin/double £95, twin/double £110; deposit required. Cooked B £6

The Cadogan

75 Sloane Street, London SW1X 9SG
TEL: 0171-235 7141   FAX: 0171-245 0994
EMAIL: info@the cadogan.u-net.com

Unflashy, quintessentially English hotel, in the heart of Knightsbridge.

Occupying most of a whole block near Sloane Street's ritzy shops, the appeal of this mid-sized, late-Victorian hotel is carefully understated. Though it has a past intriguing enough to make a PR team weep – Lillie Langtry's drawing-room and dining-room were here, and Oscar Wilde was arrested in 1895 in Room 118 – it does not overplay its history. Langtry's rooms are now meeting rooms, sporting pictures of the actress, while Room 118 has become the Oscar Wilde Room, in which, for a surcharge, you can sleep surrounded by portraits of the dramatist. Historic House Hotels, the owner, has gained plenty of experience in restoring old buildings, as can be seen in the trio of fine, country-house hotels that appear in the *Guide* (Bodysgallen Hall, Hartwell House and Middlethorpe Hall: see entries) and its lengthy renovation of the Cadogan is nearing completion. The public rooms, notably a softly lit, panelled lounge and a cosy restaurant, with a beautiful, stuccoed ceiling, are restful; signs ban laptops and mobile phones. The restaurant's modern and traditional British cuisine is reasonably priced, considering the hotel's location. An antique cage lift takes you up to bedrooms that are also pleasingly soothing, kitted out as they are in subdued, tasteful schemes; all are double glazed, but the most peaceful face Pavilion Street. Staff provide keen-as-mustard, unaffected service.

◑ Open all year 🚇 Nearest tube stations are Knightsbridge and Sloane Square (Piccadilly line and District and Circle lines). Public car park nearby (£24 per day) 🛏 26 single, 9 twin, 14 double, 13 suites; family rooms available all with bathroom/WC; all with TV, room service, hair-dryer, mini-bar, trouser press, direct-dial telephone, voice mail, modem point, some with air-conditioning; no tea/coffee-making facilities in rooms ✅ Restaurant, bar, lounge; functions (max 40 people incl up to 20 residential), conferences; tennis; leisure facilities nearby (reduced rates for guests); early suppers for children, by arrangement; cots, babysitting ♿ Wheelchair access to hotel (1 step, ramp available) and restaurant (2 steps, ramp), WC (unisex), lift to bedrooms, 2 rooms specially equipped for disabled people ⦿ No children under 10 in restaurant eves; dogs by prior arrangement; no smoking in some bedrooms ▭ Amex, Delta, MasterCard, Switch, Visa £ Single £150, single occupancy of twin/double £185 to £200, twin/double £195 to £230, family room £270, suite £350; deposit required. Continental B £11, cooked B £15.50; set L £18, D £25.50; alc L, D £33. Special breaks available

Cannizaro House [see map 3]

West Side, Wimbledon Common, London SW19 4UE
TEL: 0181-879 1464 FAX: 0181-879 7338

Fairly authentic rendition of an up-market country-house hotel, with as countrified a setting as a London hotel can offer.

Cannizaro House's chief selling point is its position: on the edge of Wimbledon Common, with lawns running up to the back door, but still just a stone's throw from central London. The handsome house, which has hosted prime ministers, royalty and glitterati through the centuries, dates from 1705, but was largely rebuilt in 1900. Now it's part of the Thistle Hotel chain, and the service is correct, yet personal.

The interior is enjoyably grand, both in the restaurant and especially the lounge, with its jade-coloured pillars, *trompe l'oeil* over the fireplace and lavish flower displays. A strict dress code is rigidly enforced, and one young mother with a babe-in-arms was firmly banished to the hotel car park when arriving to pick up her conference-attending husband. The lounge is the only sitting area in a hotel with 46 bedrooms, and is a busy thoroughfare which doubles as the bar; the hotel definitely lacks a further quiet sitting-room. Matters improve in the summer, when the house's large terrace comes into play.

The best (and considerably more expensive) bedrooms, featuring antiques and individual, warm-coloured design schemes, lie in the original building; Room 219, with a four-poster, is said to be haunted by a former housekeeper, who sometimes pipes up when she hears the jangling of keys. Over half the bedrooms lie in the adjoining new wing; they have good-quality reproduction furniture and fancy marble bathrooms, but are unexciting.

◑ Open all year 🚇 From A3 turn south on to A219 towards Wimbledon; after about 1½ miles turn right into Cannizaro Road; second right is Westside and hotel is 50 yards on left. Private car park 🛏 15 twin, 24 double, 4 four-poster, 3 suites; all with bathroom/WC; all with TV, room service, hair-dryer, trouser press, direct-dial telephone, some with ironing facilities ✅ Restaurant, bar, lounge; functions (max 100 people residential/non-residential), conferences; civil wedding licence; leisure facilities nearby (reduced rates for guests) ♿ Wheelchair access to hotel and restaurant, WC (unisex), 4 ground-floor bedrooms ● No children under 8; no dogs; no smoking in restaurant and some bedrooms ⌧ Amex, Delta, Diners, MasterCard, Switch, Visa £ Single occupancy of twin/double £150 to £186, twin/double £173 to £249, four-poster £290 to £370, suite £310 to £435; deposit required. Continental B £10.50, cooked B £13.50; set L, D £26.50; alc L, D £40

Cliveden Town House

26 Cadogan Gardens, London SW3 2RP
TEL: 0171-730 6466   FAX: 0171-730 0236

Arguably the most indulgent of London's bevy of plush town-house hotels.

Tucked away on a quiet street just behind Sloane Square, the urban progeny of Cliveden, one of Britain's grandest country-house hotels, is fittingly grand in its own, well-mannered way. As is usual with such town-house establishments, its gabled, late-Victorian façades give little hint of the opulence – fine antiques and imposing works of art – that lies within. With the recent addition of ten new suites in another adjoining house, it is, by London town-house standards, relatively large, and therefore feels less intimate than some. However, this also means that it is roomier, with several gorgeous public spaces, namely a new, part-panelled breakfast room, a cosy library sporting a Joshua Reynolds portrait, and a hugely relaxing and elegant drawing-room, where a landscape of Cliveden occupies pride of place above the mantelpiece. Complimentary afternoon teas and early evening champagne are served here, and steps lead down to a secluded garden which is shared with the adjoining houses. The bedrooms run the full gamut of size, price and ostentation, though all benefit from such pleasing touches as having the guest's name posted on the door, as well as their own fax and music system. All but the singles have gas fires. There is, of course, 24-hour room service, although the prices are high (£8 for a bowl of soup, for example); the service itself was rather stretched when we inspected. As we went to press, the group that owns Cliveden had been sold to another consortium – reports please.

◗ Open all year ⊿ Nearest tube station is Sloane Square (District and Circle lines). Public car park nearby (£28 per day) ⊨ 8 single, 16 twin/double, 11 suites; family rooms available all with bathroom/WC; all with satellite TV, 24-hour room service, hair-dryer, mini-bar, direct-dial telephone, fax, voice mail, CD player, video, air-conditioning, some with trouser press; no tea/coffee-making facilities in rooms ⚡ Drawing-room, breakfast room, library, garden; conferences/functions (max 12 people residential/non-residential); gym; early suppers for children; cots, toys, babysitting ♿ No wheelchair access ● No dogs in public rooms ⌧ Amex, Delta, Diners, MasterCard, Switch, Visa £ Single £147, single occupancy of twin/double from £247, twin/double from £247, family room £453, suite £423 to £741; deposit required. Continental B £14.50, cooked B £18.50; alc L £19, D £36. Special breaks available

Prices are what you can expect to pay in 1999, except where specified to the contrary. Many hoteliers tell us that these prices can be regarded only as approximations.

Concorde Hotel

50 Great Cumberland Place, London W1H 7FD
TEL: 0171-402 6169   FAX: 0171-724 1184

Basic B&B in need of sprucing up, but low rates and several superb-value apartments.

Difficulties in obtaining an extended lease are preventing the owners of the Concorde (sister to Bryanston Court – see entry) from giving it a face-lift. Although wallpaper may be peeling here and there, and basic bedroom furnishings and shower-rooms have long seen better days, the rates are also healthily low. The accommodation can also be rather cramped, and, as there is no double glazing, rooms facing the street (which runs straight down from Marble Arch) can be noisy. Yet the place has the character you'd expect of a Georgian building, with creaky floors and plenty of light through long sash windows, and fairly appealing public rooms – namely a pleasant, leather-furnished lounge, a diminutive bar and a pine-furnished, basement breakfast room. Moreover, long-serving staff such as Alex, the elderly factotum who has worked here for 20 years, cultivate a friendly air. But without doubt the Concorde's best feature is its one- to three-bedroom serviced apartments, several of which are located in the next-door houses, with a few more in a quiet mews behind. Though not smart, they are roomy, comfortably furnished and amazing value, given the space and facilities they provide.

◗ Closed Chr and New Year   ⤢ Nearest tube station is Marble Arch (Central line). On-street parking (metered), public car park nearby (£18 to £35 per day)   ⨼ 10 single, 13 twin, 3 double, 2 family rooms; most with shower/WC, some with bathroom/WC; all with TV, room service, hair-dryer, direct-dial telephone   ⬥ Bar, lounge, breakfast room   ♿ Wheelchair access to hotel (1 step) and restaurant   ● No dogs   ▭ Amex, Delta, Diners, MasterCard, Switch, Visa   £ Single £72, single occupancy of twin/double £82, twin/double £82, family room £92; deposit required. Cooked B £6

The Connaught

Carlos Place, Mayfair, London W1Y 6AL
TEL: 0171-499 7070   FAX: 0171-495 3262
EMAIL: info@the-connaught.co.uk
WEB SITE: www.savoy-group.co.uk/

This outstanding hotel is a Mayfair bastion of old-fashioned values and impeccable service.

The Connaught's motto, *placere placet* – 'pleasure to please' – sums up what's best about this wonderful, 101-year-old institution. Its bedrooms – antique-laden suites excepted – may look surprisingly ordinary given their punitive rates, with a jug of iced water about the only sustenance provided. Its sitting-rooms may seem almost fusty in these days when many London hotels occupy the cutting edge of fashionable design. But the hotel has no equal in the capital when it comes to service. Traditionally uniformed in tailcoats and the like, the staff are masterful at anticipating guests' needs, while every floor has its own room-service kitchen, and every room a set of buttons marked 'maid', 'valet' and 'waiter'. The aim is to maintain bedrooms as if by magic: housekeeping trolleys and vacuum cleaners in the corridors are noticeable by their absence. The ambience feels more late nineteenth-century than late twentieth-century, not least in the hotel's clubby restaurant, where formal attire is required. Fitting seamlessly into the surroundings is the much-praised cuisine, classic French and English in style in such dishes as boeuf en croûte and boiled silverside brisket and pickled tongue with dumplings.

○ Open all year ◪ Nearest tube station is Green Park (Piccadilly, Victoria and Jubilee lines). On-street parking (metered); public car park nearby ⛟ 30 single, 36 double, 24 suites; all with bathroom/WC; all with TV, room service, hair-dryer, direct-dial telephone; no tea/coffee-making facilities in rooms ⌀ 2 restaurants, bar, 2 lounges; functions (max 22 people residential/non-residential), conferences; leisure facilities nearby (free for guests); cots, high chairs, babysitting ♿ Wheelchair access to hotel (ramp) and restaurant, WC (unisex), no ground-floor bedrooms, but lift ⬤ No dogs ▭ Amex, Diners, MasterCard, Visa £ Single £250, single occupancy of twin/double £310 to £340, twin/double £335 to £365, suite £600 to £1,110; deposit required. Continental B £13, cooked B £15; set L £27.50, D £55; alc D £50. Special breaks available

County Hall Travel Inn   NEW ENTRY

Belvedere Road, London SE1 7PB
TEL: 0171-902 1600   FAX: 0171-902 1619

Superb value, good-quality budget hotel chain accommodation at a prestigious, central London address.

This new Travel Inn, with over three hundred bedrooms, beats virtually any of London's no-frills B&Bs hands down for comfort and value for money. Taking up part of the monumental County Hall building on the south side of the Thames, its position is enviably central – a short walk from Waterloo, the South Bank, even the Houses of Parliament. Bedrooms are paragons of smartness and spaciousness for their price, which is the same however many occupy the room (up to two adults and two children under 17). All are furnished in identical style, with light-wood units and plain walls; larger rooms come with a sofa-bed. Top-notch bathrooms all have a bath and shower; toiletries, however, do not extend beyond a plain bar of soap. As well as a decent range of mod cons in the rooms (to use phones you need to pre-purchase a card), each floor has communal ironing facilities. Downstairs is a busy but efficient reception, a shop selling newspapers, soft drinks and so forth, and a large, cheerful – if unsophisticated – restaurant and bar. Buffet breakfasts are not included in the room rates but are keenly priced, and later in the day there is an extensive selection of mainstream fare: pasta, salads, burgers and the like. The surrounding building sites are all that presently mar the hotel: many rooms are double-glazed, but it may still be worth asking for a room facing the interior courtyard.

◐ Open all year ⏻ Nearest tube station is Waterloo (Northern, Bakerloo and Waterloo & City lines). Public car park nearby (£8 to guests between 5pm and 11am) 🛏 201 double, 112 family rooms; all with bathroom/WC; all with TV ⟡ Restaurant, bar ♿ No wheelchair access ⊝ No dogs; smoking in some bedrooms only ☐ Amex, Delta, Diners, MasterCard, Switch, Visa £ All rooms £55, single occupancy £55; deposit required. Continental B £4, cooked B £6; bar/bistro L, D £8 to £15

Covent Garden Hotel

10 Monmouth Street, London WC2H 9HB
TEL: 0171-806 1000   FAX: 0171-806 1100
EMAIL: covent@firmdale.com
WEB SITE: www.firmdale.com/

Dramatically furnished, ultra-stylish hotel in the heart of theatreland.

Tim and Kit Kemp's clutch of London hotels all look fabulous, and none more so than this conversion of a former hospital, which is a visual masterpiece throughout. The bedrooms bask in luxurious fabrics – co-ordinated with very individual and vivid designs – and the bathrooms in swanky, grey-flecked marble. All but the single rooms house a dressed mannequin, which is appropriate given that many models stay here. Downstairs, off the lobby, lies the little Brasserie Max, an eye-catching, Parisian-looking café serving a voluminous breakfast menu – from fresh strawberries to waffles – and a short, multi-ethnic dinner menu. The *pièce de résistance* is, without doubt, the vast lounge (which is secluded away up on the first floor), with its honey-coloured panelling, the plushest of soft furnishings and a few magnificent antiques. Off it lies a small library and a huge, self-service drinks selection – more honesty kitchen than honesty bar. If you feel the need to keep in trim in order to live up to your surroundings, there's also a little narcissistic, mirror-lined gym. The keen staff, who are nattily dressed in shades of grey, are as well turned out as the hotel.

◐ Open all year ⏻ Nearest tube stations are Leicester Square and Covent Garden (Piccadilly and Northern lines). On-street parking (metered); public car park nearby 🛏 8 single, 30 twin, 8 double, 1 four-poster, 3 suites; family rooms available all with bathroom/WC; all with TV, 24-hour room service, hair-dryer, mini-bar, direct-dial telephone, fax/modem point, mobile phone, CD player, video, mini safe, some with trouser press; no tea/coffee-making facilities in rooms ⟡ Restaurant, bar, drawing-room, library; conferences/functions (max 40 people residential); gym; leisure facilities nearby (free for guests); early suppers for children; cots, babysitting ♿ No wheelchair access ⊝ No dogs ☐ Amex, MasterCard, Visa £ Single £206, single occupancy of twin/double £235 to £299, twin/double £235 to £299, four-poster £347, family room £317 to £346, suite £440 to £646 (1998 prices); deposit required. Continental B £13, cooked B £16.50; alc L, D £30. Special breaks available

'Like nearly every hotel we have stayed in there was nowhere sufficiently well lit to apply make-up. Do men decide on the lighting?'
On a hotel in Renfrewshire

Dorset Square Hotel

39 Dorset Square, London NW1 6QN
TEL: 0171-723 7874   FAX: 0171-724 3328
EMAIL: dorset@firmdale.com
WEB SITE: www.firmdale.com/

Exuberant décor and cricketing associations feature in this seductive town-house hotel near Regent's Park.

The longest-established of Tim and Kit Kemp's five London hotels lies just off the busy Marylebone Road, and plenty of traffic rumbles past it down Gloucester Place. But taking up as it does two houses of the fine Regency terraces that surround this square's lovely, arboreal gardens (to which guests have access), the hotel feels removed from urban life. Before the terraces were built, the square was the site of Thomas Lord's first cricket ground – hence the cricketing caps, bats and stumps on display in some of the rooms. More significant to guests, however, is the liberal deployment of fine antiques and rich and bold soft furnishings in the refined sitting-room – where you can help yourself to drinks from an honesty bar – and throughout the bedrooms. These vary considerably in size and price (the cheaper ones are pretty small and views over the square cost extra), but all look enchanting and have smart, granite bathrooms. The basement's Potting Shed Restaurant and Bar, which is popular with business people on weekdays, and lays on live jazz a couple of nights a week, adopts a different, modern-rustic look, with flower-pots and garden equipment providing a quirky backdrop. Its eclectic menu might offer lobster and crab ravioli, or Thai fish-cakes served on a bed of stir-fry noodles. The breakfasts are extensive, and room service includes a bedroom picnic: a tray of such edible goodies as chocolates and strawberries.

◐ Open all year; restaurant closed Sat eve   ☑ Nearest tube station is Baker Street (Circle, Jubilee, Metropolitan and Bakerloo lines). On-street parking (metered); public car park nearby.   ⟞ 7 single, 10 twin, 18 double, 2 four-poster, 1 suite; family rooms available all with bathroom/WC; all with TV, 24-hour room service, hair-dryer, mini-bar, direct-dial telephone, fax/modem point, some with trouser press, safe; no tea/coffee-making facilities in rooms   ⊘ Restaurant, bar, sitting-room, garden; functions (max 30 people residential/non-residential), meetings; early suppers for children; cots, babysitting   ⟐ No wheelchair access   ● No dogs   ☐ Amex, MasterCard, Visa   £ Single £116, single occupancy of twin/double £147 to £218, twin/double £147 to £218, four-poster £230, family room £253 to £265, suite £230 (1998 prices); deposit required. Continental B £10.50, cooked B £14; set L £16.50, D £21; alc L, D £22. Special breaks available

---

The Guide *for the year 2000 will be published in the autumn of 1999. Reports on hotels are welcome at any time of the year, but are extremely valuable in the spring. Send them to* The Which? Hotel Guide, FREEPOST, 2 Marylebone Road, London NW1 1YN. *No stamp is needed if reports are posted in the UK. Our email address is: "guide.reports@which.co.uk".*

Durley House

115 Sloane Street, London SW1X 9PJ
TEL: 0171-235 5537   FAX: 0171-259 6977
EMAIL: durley@firmdale.com
WEB SITE: www.firmdale.com/

A small block of serviced one- and two-bedroom apartments offering discreet luxury.

This is the most expensive of the Kemps' London establishments (see also the Covent Garden, Dorset Square and Pelham hotels and the Fox Club), and it is popular with moneyed Americans – often Daddy stays here on business, with his family in tow. Compared with hotel accommodation, Durley House loses out in terms of public rooms, there being just a stylish little drawing-room. However, the highly professional service is far more personal: the 24-hour room service runs the gamut from Häagen-Dazs ice-cream and smoked-salmon sandwiches to pasta and steak, and the apartments are stocked with enough booze to lubricate a fair-sized party. For a charge, staff will even go shopping for you. The apartments (called 'suites') are highly individual. The grandest are very elaborate, with carved fireplaces and even, in one, a grand piano, while others are far less ostentatious and more homely. All share such traits as tasteful, rich soft furnishings, antiques, works of art, king-size beds, a proper kitchen equipped with a cooker and fridge, and a fax machine. The only off-putting factor – apart from the rates – is that most suites overlook noisy Sloane Street (but also the substantial private gardens beyond, to which guests have access). The double glazing is fairly effective, however, and the bedrooms (the main bedroom in the two-bedroom apartments, at least) are located at the much quieter rear of the building.

◑ Open all year   ⊿ Nearest tube station is Sloane Square (District and Circle lines). On-street parking (metered); public car park nearby   ⌌→ 11 suites; all with bathroom/WC; all with TV, 24-hour room service, hair-dryer, mini-bar, direct-dial telephone, kitchen, fax, some with trouser press   ⊘ Drawing-room, garden; conferences (max 30 people incl some residential), functions; tennis; cots, babysitting   ♿ No wheelchair access   ● No dogs   ▭ Amex, MasterCard, Visa   £ Suite £282 to £511 (1998 prices); deposit required. Continental B £9.50, cooked B £15; snacks L, D £7.50, alc L, D £26.50. Special breaks available

Durrants Hotel

George Street, London W1H 6BJ
TEL: 0171-935 8131   FAX: 0171-487 3510

Competitively priced and ultra-traditional hotel, run by the same family for over 70 years.

Paying guests have been staying at this establishment in a Georgian block at the southern end of Marylebone High Street since 1790, and since 1921 they have been welcomed by the Miller family. The full force of the hotel's considerable pedigree is felt in its venerable public areas, which are ennobled by an abundance of old prints, paintings and antique nick-nacks. The most atmospheric are the extremely snug bar and pump room (once men-only, thanks to its racy portraits of nudes), and the fairly formal, panelled restaurant, with its leather banquette seating. Its keenly priced, limited-choice menus, as well as an extensive à la carte menu, centre appropriately on traditional roasts and grills. Breakfast is, unfortunately, served in a separate, less characterful room. A warren of creaky corridors leads to a large variety of bedrooms, some featuring antiques, but most furnished with good-quality reproduction units and light, but restrained, décor. The larger rooms face the street, while the quieter ones are found to the rear of the building. The service is generally deemed to be good, though younger staff can be inexperienced.

○ Open all year; restaurant closed 25 Dec ⊿ Nearest tube station is Marble Arch (Central line). On-street parking (metered); public car park nearby ⟟ 16 single, 37 twin, 32 double, 3 family rooms, 4 suites; all with bathroom/WC; all with TV, room service, hair-dryer, trouser press, direct-dial telephone, some with mini-bar, air-conditioning; no tea/coffee-making facilities in rooms ✓ Restaurant, bar, 3 lounges, drying-room; functions (max 100 people residential/non-residential), conferences; early suppers for children; cots; high chairs, babysitting ⟐ No wheelchair access ● No dogs ▭ Amex, Delta, MasterCard, Switch, Visa £ Single £88, single occupancy of twin/double £130, twin/double £135, family room £175, suite £250; deposit required. Continental B £9.50, cooked B £12.50; set L, D £17; alc L, D £25

Egerton House Hotel

17–19 Egerton Terrace, London SW3 2BX
TEL: 0171-589 2412   FAX: 0171-584 6540
EMAIL: bookings@theegerton.force9.net

Staid, restful and extremely elegant town-house accommodation, popular with business people.

The discreet brass plaque and Union Jack at the entrance to this handsome Victorian building, on a fairly quiet side-street between the V&A and Harrods, accurately convey the refined, English atmosphere to be found within. At the reception very correct staff wait to meet guests' needs. Beyond lies a formal drawing-room with imposing marble fireplace, oil paintings, plump, soft furnishings, delicate stuccoed walls and a beautifully presented honesty bar. Downstairs you'll find a graceful breakfast room, best suited, perhaps, for impressing business clients; the menus offer everything from kippers to muffins and prunes. Upstairs, the bedrooms are extremely tasteful if slightly dauntingly pristine, rigged out with antiques and white bedspreads. Mini-bars are hidden away in cupboards or under drapes, while the smart marble bathrooms are equipped with power showers and robes. Room service is extensive – from afternoon tea with crumpets to lamb cutlets.

See also the entry for the nearby Franklin – under the same ownership and in similar style, but with a wider variety of bedrooms and a somewhat better position.

○ Open all year ⊿ Nearest tube stations are South Kensington and Knightsbridge (Piccadilly, District and Circle lines). On-street parking (metered); public car park nearby (£22 per day) ⟟ 9 single, 4 twin, 15 double, 1 four-poster; all with bathroom/WC; all with satellite TV, room service, hair-dryer, mini-bar, direct-dial telephone, radio, air-

conditioning; no tea/coffee-making facilities in rooms ✓ Bar, lounge, breakfast room; leisure facilities nearby (reduced rates for guests) ⚿ No wheelchair access
● No children under 8; no dogs ▭ Amex, Delta, Diners, MasterCard, Visa
£ Single £150, single occupancy of twin/double £200, twin/double £200 to £260, four-poster £260 (prices valid till late 1998); deposit required. Continental B £9, cooked B £14; alc L, D £22.50 (room service only)

Elizabeth Hotel

37 Eccleston Square, London SW1V 1PB
TEL: 0171-828 6812

Simple, yet characterful, B&B accommodation overlooking a fine Pimlico square, seven minutes' walk from Victoria Station.

Eccleston Square is one of the most attractive parts of Pimlico, with its stately terraces of neoclassical buildings around large and mature private gardens (to which hotel residents have access). The Elizabeth, occupying two of the houses, has been run by the present owners since 1974, and they have imbued it with considerable old-fashioned character. They have achieved this above all by coating the maze of stairs and corridors, as well as the inviting lounge, with dozens of historical cartoons and prints, and the basement breakfast room with old photos of the square and its famous former visitors and residents (Winston Churchill, for example, once lived two doors down from the hotel). The small bedrooms, with their velour headboards and no-frills pine furniture, are much plainer, though they are immaculately maintained and very competitively priced. Those at the rear of the buildings are peaceful, while four at the front have french windows opening on to terraces.

◑ Open all year ⌷ Nearest tube station is Victoria (District, Circle and Victoria lines). On-street parking (metered); public car park nearby (£8.50 per 24 hours for guests)
⇤ 8 single, 8 twin, 8 double, 14 family rooms; most with bathroom/WC, some with shower/WC; all with TV; no tea/coffee-making facilities in rooms ✓ Breakfast room, lounge, garden; conferences (max 25 people residential/non-residential); tennis; cots, high chairs, babysitting ⚿ No wheelchair access ● No dogs; no smoking in breakfast room ▭ None accepted £ Single £40 to £55, single occupancy of twin/double £55 to £80, twin/double £62 to £80, family room £96 to £115; deposit required

Five Sumner Place

5 Sumner Place, London SW7 3EE
TEL: 0171-584 7586   FAX: 0171-823 9962
EMAIL: no.5@dial.pipex.com
WEB SITE: dspace.dial.pipex.com/

A top-notch South Kensington B&B, and the best in its price range – relatively cheap in this upmarket area.

Lots of punters seem to know how good Five Sumner Place is, so book well in advance, particularly at weekends. The B&B is ideally placed on a rather grand Victorian residential terrace (all porticoes and railings), a short stroll from South

Ken tube and local shops and restaurants. The owner and his long-serving Polish manager Tom run a tight, civilised ship. Though the establishment lacks a lounge, the spacious conservatory breakfast room is lovely, decked out in yellow cloths, bentwood chairs and lots of house plants, and can be used as a sitting-room during the day. Alongside lies a pretty little courtyard garden. Buffet breakfasts are extensive, tea and coffee is available during the day, and there is a full set of broadsheet newspapers to browse through. Bedrooms feature good-quality dark reproduction furniture, high ceilings, pleasant prints, a flourish of drapes over double beds, and good mod cons – for example ironing boards, and fridges on request. Room 6, with long windows opening on to a balcony, is worth asking for. Other garden-facing rooms are more peaceful, though there is limited traffic noise.

◑ Open all year ⚡ Nearest tube station is South Kensington (District, Circle and Piccadilly lines). On-street parking (metered); public car park nearby (£20 per day) 🛏 3 single, 5 twin, 5 double; most with shower/WC exc 2 with bathroom/WC; all with TV, room service, hair-dryer, trouser press, direct-dial telephone, some with mini-bar; no tea/coffee-making facilities in some rooms ✓ Breakfast room/conservatory, garden ♿ No wheelchair access ● No children under 6; no dogs; no smoking in public rooms and some bedrooms ▭ Amex, MasterCard, Switch, Visa £ Single £82 to £88, single occupancy of twin/double £110 to £120, twin/double £130 to £141, family room £142 to £165; deposit required

The Fox Club [NEW ENTRY]

46 Clarges Street, London W1Y 7PJ
TEL: 0171-495 3656   FAX: 0171-495 3626
EMAIL: fox@firmdale.com

A tiny, beautifully furnished Mayfair club, with a conservative clientele.

As this is a club, you're asked to sign in as you enter this Georgian town house – the latest, and smallest, of Tim and Kit Kemp's highly imaginative creations. Only residents, club members and their guests can eat and drink here; members get a discount on the accommodation. At lunch-time, blazered business people on first-name terms with the professional young staff populate the single public room: a sophisticated, pine-boarded space serving as bar, sitting-room and dining-room. A chrome-topped bar dominates one end, while the other is laid out with half-a-dozen wooden tables and also a sitting-room in miniature that faces a real fire. An extensive breakfast menu, as well as bar snacks and such unfussy dishes as steak and suprême of chicken, are on offer (and are also available in bedrooms at certain times). The six bedrooms and three suites are named after the lovers of the wife of politician Charles James Fox (Britain's first foreign secretary); the couple lived here in the late eighteenth century. Each bears the meticulously designed trademark Kemp look, namely antiques coupled with acres of fine, striking fabrics, softened by such homely touches as games and books. Tall people should avoid the suites, whose beds are not full length.

◗ Open all year; dining-room closed Sat & Sun eves ⓩ Nearest tube station is Green Park (Piccadilly, Victoria and Jubilee lines). On-street parking (metered); public car park nearby (£30 per day) 🛏 6 double, 3 suites; all with bathroom/WC; all with TV, room service, hair-dryer, mini-bar, direct-dial telephone, voice mail, video, safe; no tea/coffee-making facilities in rooms ⊘ Dining-room/bar/sitting-room; functions (max 60 people incl up to 18 residential); early suppers for children; cots, babysitting ♿ No wheelchair access ⬤ No children under 12; no dogs ▭ Amex, Delta, MasterCard, Switch, Visa 💷 Double £190, suite £220; deposit required. Continental B £9.50, cooked B £12.50; bar/bistro L, D £11.50; alc L, D £29. Special breaks available

The Franklin

28 Egerton Gardens, London SW3 2DB
TEL: 0171-584 5533   FAX: 0171-584 5449
EMAIL: bookings@thefranklin.force9.co.uk

Top-of-the-range town-house hotel in Kensington, backing on to pretty gardens.

The younger, and larger, sister of the Egerton House Hotel (see entry) takes up four tall Victorian houses on a quiet residential street; Brompton Road's chic shops and cafés are seconds away. The hotel is very similar to Egerton House in most respects, not least in its graceful and elegant (if a touch stiff) traditional English atmosphere. But the Franklin has the added benefit of backing onto lovely, private, communal gardens (shared with neighbouring houses), which are full of towering trees and blossoms in the spring. The serene drawing-rooms, which are decked out with stern paintings and draped and ruched curtains, enjoy this view, as do the best, and priciest, bedrooms. These aptly named 'Garden' rooms all have floor-to-ceiling windows and four-poster, or half-tester, beds; Room 5 offers direct access to the gardens. All the bedrooms are extremely swish, boasting luxurious fabrics and antiques, along with marble bathrooms. The cheapest options are a couple of titchy singles. There is 24-hour room service, or, if you're feeling more sociable, you can head for the intimate, clubby bar and smart basement breakfast room. Note that the rates decrease by over a third in some winter- and summer-holiday periods.

◗ Open all year ⓩ Nearest tube station is South Kensington (Piccadilly, District and Circle lines). On-street parking (metered); public car park nearby (£21 per day) 🛏 10 single, 10 twin, 10 double, 7 four-poster, 5 family rooms, 5 suites; all with bathroom/WC; all with satellite TV, air-conditioning, room service, hair-dryer, mini-bar, direct-dial telephone; no tea/coffee-making facilities in rooms ⊘ Sitting-room, 2 drawing-rooms, bar, breakfast room, garden; conferences (max 20 people residential/non-residential); leisure facilities nearby (reduced rates for guests); early suppers for children; cots, high chairs, babysitting, outdoor play area ♿ No wheelchair access ⬤ No dogs; no smoking in some bedrooms ▭ Amex, Delta, Diners, MasterCard, Visa 💷 Single £140, single occupancy of twin/double £165 to £210, twin/double £165 to £210, four-poster £275, family room £225 to £275 + £30 per child, suite £225; deposit required. Continental B £9, cooked B £14; bar/bistro L £7.50, D £10.50; alc L £20, D £30. Special breaks available

See page 6 for a brief explanation of how to use the Guide.

La Gaffe

107–111 Heath Street, London NW3 6SS
TEL: 0171-435 8965   FAX: 0171-794 7592
EMAIL: la-gaffe@msn.com

Simple accommodation in a convivial, family-run restaurant-with-rooms in Hampstead.

La Gaffe is something of a Hampstead institution. The courteous Stella family, originally from the Abruzzo area of Italy, have been feeding customers here for 36 years; they claim their restaurant is the oldest in the village. Downstairs divides into the restaurant, with art-nouveau murals on the walls, a small bar area and the wine bar, decked out with basic wooden tables, rattan chairs and theatrical posters. The atmosphere is entirely unpretentious and down-to-earth, as is the decent Italian food. The menu runs from Parma ham and melon to home-made pasta and tiramisù, and locals often just pop in for a cappuccino. Upstairs reflects more clearly the building's history, which dates back to the eighteenth century when apparently it was a shepherd's cottage. Some bedrooms, as well as the rather gloomy corridor, were earmarked for a needed face-lift when we inspected, and the whole hotel was being redecorated as we went to press. The Stellas readily, and accurately, describe the rooms as compact (expect box-like shower- rooms too). However, their cheerfulness – a Hockney print here, drapes over the beds there – compensates for simplicity and lack of space. Avoid front-facing rooms: La Gaffe is right on the busy main road through the village. The Tube is just a couple of hundred yards away.

❶ Open all year   🚇 Nearest tube station is Hampstead (Northern line). Private car park (very limited, £5 per day); on-street parking (free and metered)   🛏 4 single, 4 twin, 6 double, 1 four-poster, 1 family room, 2 suites; 7 in annexe; most with shower/WC, 3 with bathroom/WC; all with TV, hair-dryer, direct-dial telephone   ⚓ Restaurant, bar, roof terrace; early suppers for children from 6.30pm   ♿ No wheelchair access   ● Children welcome; no dogs or smoking in bedrooms   ▭ Amex, MasterCard, Switch, Visa   💷 Single £55, single occupancy of twin/double £65, twin/double £80, four-poster £115, family room £115, suite £115; deposit required. Cooked B £4; bar/bistro L, D £7.50; alc L, D £17.50

The Gainsborough

7–11 Queensbury Place, London SW7 2DL
TEL: 0171-957 0000   FAX: 0171-957 0001
EMAIL: gainsborough@eeh.co.uk
WEB SITE: www.eeh.co.uk/

Presentable town-house accommodation in traditional English mode, with affordable rates.

This hotel is a sister to the Gallery (see entry), which lies directly opposite. The two hotels are similar in ambience and standard, and both are pitched primarily at business people looking for comfortable, but unluxurious, lodgings in intimate, town-house-style surroundings. The Gainsborough takes its name from (rather awful) reproductions of the artist's paintings in an otherwise smart,

Regency-style sitting-room area next to the reception. More prints appear in the attractive and light breakfast room/bar. The bedrooms are decorated in fancy fabrics and busy colour schemes; the bathrooms have showers only – some good quality, others in need of upgrading. As in the Gallery, the cheaper double rooms and their beds can be small for two people. Unlike the Gallery, however, here there are a number of keenly priced little single rooms. Several front-facing rooms have lofty french windows opening on to small balconies. The back-facing rooms are generally quieter, though they have to put up with playground noise from the *lycée* attached to the Institut Français, a cultural centre just three doors away.

◑ Open all year ☒ Nearest tube station is South Kensington (Piccadilly, District and Circle lines). On-street parking (metered); public car park nearby (£24 per day)
⤶ 9 single, 15 twin, 16 double, 5 family rooms, 4 suites; all with shower/WC; all with TV, room service, hair-dryer, direct-dial telephone, safe, some with mini-bar, trouser press ✅ Breakfast room/bar, sitting-room; leisure facilities nearby (free for guests); cots, high chairs, babysitting ♿ No wheelchair access ● No dogs ▭ Amex, Diners, MasterCard, Switch, Visa £ Single £77, single occupancy of twin/double £100, twin/double £136, family room £159, suite £218; deposit required

---

The Gallery

8–10 Queensberry Place, London SW7 2EA
TEL: 0171-915 0000   FAX: 0171-915 4400
EMAIL: gallery@eeh.co.uk
WEB SITE: www.eeh.co.uk/

Good-quality, mid-range, town-house hotel – reasonably priced for this style of accommodation in an expensive part of town.

London has a plethora of far fancier town-house hotels, but the Gallery is a decent choice if you want a discreet South Kensington base without paying a fortune. It takes up two nineteenth-century houses on a fairly busy side-street; across the road at one end of the street lies the Natural History Museum, while South Kensington tube station is a three-minute walk away in the other direction. With its mahogany panelled walls, reproductions of famous paintings and floor-to-ceiling purple drapes over the windows, the hushed and clubby reception/bar/lounge feels cosy in the winter. Downstairs, hot and cold buffet breakfasts are served in a breakfast room, which is jollily decorated in blues and yellows and with Impressionist prints. The bedrooms feature rich colour schemes and well-equipped granite bathrooms. Some, to the front, have small balconies, but those to the rear are more peaceful. There are only two single rooms and no single-occupancy rates, and some doubles can be cramped, with the bed as narrow as double beds can be. By contrast, the two 'junior' suites are palatial, and have whirlpool baths and private, rooftop terraces to boot. See also entry for the Gainsborough.

◑ Open all year ☒ Nearest tube station is South Kensington (Piccadilly, District and Circle lines). On-street parking (metered); public car park nearby (£24 per day)
⤶ 2 single, 10 twin, 22 double, 2 suites; family rooms available all with bathroom/WC; all with satellite TV, room service, hair-dryer, direct-dial telephone, some with mini-bar,

trouser press, fax, video, air-conditioning ⊘ Breakfast room, bar/lounge, TV room; conferences; leisure facilities nearby (free for guests); cots, high chairs, babysitting &. No wheelchair access ● No dogs ▭ Amex, Diners, MasterCard, Switch, Visa £ Single £136, twin/double £147, family room £177, suite £235; deposit required

The Generator

Macnaghten House, Compton Place, London WC1H 9SD
TEL: 0171-388 7666   FAX: 0171-388 7644
EMAIL: generator@lhdr.demon.co.uk
WEB SITE: www.lhdr.demon.co.uk/

Giant, youth-oriented, industrial-styled hostel in Bloomsbury.

The Generator offers the most basic accommodation of anywhere in the *Guide*. However, given the astronomical cost of staying in central London, it's also the only entry in the capital that falls within most student budgets. Bedrooms are spartan in the extreme, with little more than beds and a wash-basin. Most sleep four in bunk-beds – the majority of guests are young groups – but some rooms sleep two, three, five, six or eight. You can't share with strangers. Single-sex shower and toilet facilities (racily identified by a nut for females, a bolt for males) are well maintained, as is the whole enterprise, and youthful staff are ubiquitous and keen. Great effort has gone into making the public areas look a little different. The self-service cafeteria (for independent travellers, continental breakfast only) and bar (open to 2am) are brutally futuristic, with neon and metal pillars to the fore, and MTV, pin-ball and pool for entertainment. Popular culture posters – *Silence of the Lambs*' grisly Hannibal Lecter is sure to clear your head fast first thing in the morning – adorn corridor walls. And, just in case you were in any doubt that this is not exactly the Ritz, numbers are branded on bedroom doors as on prison inmates' uniforms.

◗ Open all year ⊠ Nearest tube stations are Russell Square and King's Cross (Piccadilly, Victoria, Northern, Circle, Metropolitan and Hammersmith & City lines). Public car park nearby (£25 per day) ⊨ 26 twin, 38 3-bed rooms, 116 4-bed rooms, 6 5-bed rooms, 8 6-bed rooms, 13 8-bed rooms; no tea/coffee-making facilities available in rooms ⊘ Bar, cafeteria, lounge/games room; pool tables, games machines &. No wheelchair access ● No dogs; no smoking in bedrooms ▭ MasterCard, Visa £ Single occupancy of twin £36 to £38, twin £45 to £52, 3-bed room £57 to £66, 4-bed room £76 to £88, 5-bed room £95 to £110, 6-bed room £114 to £132, 8-bed room £144 to £164 (prices valid till Nov 1999); deposit required

The Gore

189 Queen's Gate, London SW7 5EX
TEL: 0171-584 6601   FAX: 0171-589 8127
EMAIL: sales@gorehotel.co.uk

One of the Guide's favourite London hotels: a buzzing bar and bistro, and antiques and paintings galore.

Out on a limb away from Kensington's shops and restaurants, but close to the Royal Albert Hall, the Gore's two Victorian mansions have been welcoming guests for over a hundred years. Well-heeled non-residents now come in droves to its panelled, grand-looking but casual bar, and to Bistrot 190, an airy, stylishly simple, wooden-floored and wood-tabled affair, making them far more lively than most London hotels' drinking and dining spots. The bistro's food – carefully presented, swiftly served, large portions of multi-ethnic fare – is recommended. The formal, pricier Restaurant at One Ninety Queen's Gate is in the basement. A cascade of paintings, prints and antiques can be found everywhere in the hotel, including the serene sitting-room and all the bedrooms. The fanciest bedrooms, such as the Tudor Room, with its seventeenth-century bed and throne loo, and the Venus Room, with its gilded bed, are completely over the top. Yet far cheaper rooms – even the small singles – still boast some wonderful antique pieces, notably magnificently carved bedheads. Service is professional, but, in keeping with such an upbeat hotel, not in the least bit starchy.

◑ Closed 25 & 26 Dec; main restaurant closed Sun eve ⧈ Nearest tube station is Gloucester Road (Piccadilly, District and Circle lines). On-street parking (metered); public car park nearby (£14 per day) ⊫ 26 single, 3 twin, 14 double, 5 four-poster, 6 suites; some with bathroom/WC, most with shower/WC; all with TV, room service, hair-dryer, mini-bar, safe; no tea/coffee-making facilities in rooms ⊘ restaurant, bistro, bar, sitting-room; leisure facilities nearby (reduced rates for guests); cots, high chairs, babysitting ⅍ No wheelchair access ● No dogs in public rooms ▭ Amex, Delta, Diners, MasterCard, Switch, Visa £ Single £147, single occupancy of twin/double £176, twin/double £191, four-poster £191, suite £265 (prices valid till Apr 1999); deposit required. Continental B £6.50, cooked B £9

The Goring

Beeston Place, London SW1W 0JW
TEL: 0171-396 9000   FAX: 0171-834 4393
EMAIL: reception@goringhotel.co.uk
WEB SITE: www.goringhotel.co.uk/

Long-established, family-run Edwardian hotel – one of London's classiest traditional establishments.

'A Very Special Place' is the (justified) first part of the title of a new book recounting the history of the Goring. Founded in 1910, this is a place that, perhaps above all else, excels due to the continuity of its history. The present owner, George Goring, is the grandson of the founder, and some senior members of staff are well into their third decade of service here. While the Goring has considerable pedigree – in the past royalty used it, thanks to its proximity to Buckingham Palace, and it was the world's first hotel with a private bathroom and central heating in every bedroom – it's not at all stuffy. The staff members aren't as formal as their dress (morning suits and the like) would lead you to expect, and it looks jollier than a rather grand Edwardian hotel should. For example, the marble-floored lobby is painted a strong yellow, and large, woolly sheep appear in the soothing lounge (which is very popular for its full-scale afternoon teas) and also in bedrooms, all of which adopt pleasing, light tones. These are of a uniformly high quality (Mr Goring tries to sleep in every one over time to check that it's up to scratch): the standard doubles, and even the singles, are generally massive, and the bathrooms are superb, marbled affairs. The best-placed rooms overlook the large garden (to which there is no access) at the rear. As you would expect, there is 24-hour room service, but the restaurant, with its wonderful plasterwork, is worth experiencing; comfort food such as roasts, mixed grills and fish-cakes feature strongly.

◑ Open all year   ⤢ Nearest tube station is Victoria (Victoria, District and Circle lines). Private car park (£17.50 per day); on-street parking (metered)   ⌸ 21 single, 4 twin, 43 double, 7 suites; family rooms available all with bathroom/WC; all with TV, 24-hour room service, air-conditioning, hair-dryer, direct-dial telephone, some with fax, trouser press; no tea/coffee-making facilities in rooms   ✅ Dining-room, bar, lounge; conferences (max 50 people residential/non-residential), functions; civil wedding licence; leisure facilities nearby (free for guests); cots, high chairs, babysitting   ♿ Wheelchair access to hotel and dining-room (ramp), lift to WC (unisex), lift to bedrooms   ⬤ No dogs   ▭ Amex, Delta, Diners, MasterCard, Switch, Visa £ Single £159 to £183, single occupancy of twin/double £194 to £218, twin/double £194 to £218, family room £224 to £247, suite £282 to £224; deposit required. Continental B £11, cooked B £15; bar/bistro L, D £7.50; set L £26, D £33. Special breaks available

---

Green Park Hotel

Half Moon Street, London W1Y 8BP
TEL: 0171-629 7522   FAX: 0171-491 8971
EMAIL: greenparkhotel@btinternet.com

Unintimidating, mid-priced, mid-sized hotel on the southern edge of Mayfair.

The Green Park Hotel is a good option for those wanting a central base with the full gamut of hotel facilities (such as a concierge and 24-hour room service), but who don't wish to pay the earth for a room in one of the capital's grand establishments. Popular with the corporate trade, but also attracting a fair number of tourists, it takes up much (14 houses to be exact) of one side of an attractive, terraced Georgian street. The public areas aspire to elegance: the cosy, but roomy, bar has tartan and striped sofas, and Claude's Restaurant is graced by Monet prints on its walls. The bedrooms are a mixed bag: about a third (called 'executives') are kitted out in quality reproduction furnishings and have marble bathrooms; the rest are cheaper and smaller, with rather tired and dated décor. The hotel's new owners (it changed hands in the summer of 1997) are planning to overhaul them all, installing air-conditioning, and our inspector was shown a template room in the appealing new style, with fresh pine furniture and stripey fabrics. Haggle over the rates: in less busy periods you may be able to clinch a room for around £100 a night.

◑ Open all year; restaurant closed Sat & Sun L   ⤢ Nearest tube station is Green Park (Piccadilly, Victoria and Jubilee lines). On-street parking (metered); public car park nearby (£31 per day)   ⌸ 44 single, 40 twin, 67 double, 1 four-poster, 9 suites; family rooms available all with bathroom/WC; all with TV, 24-hour room service, hair-dryer, trouser press, direct-dial telephone, voice mail, some with fax/modem points, spa-bath/jacuzzi   ✅ Restaurant, bar, lounge, 2 conservatories; conferences (max 130 people residential/non-residential); cots, high chairs, babysitting   ♿ No wheelchair access ● No dogs; no smoking in some bedrooms ⬜ Amex, Diners, MasterCard, Switch, Visa £ Single £145, single occupancy of twin/double £165, twin/double £165, four-poster £250, family room £200, suite £250 (1998 prices); deposit required. Continental B £10, cooked B £12; bar/bistro L, D £6; set L £11, D £18 to £22; alc L, D £28

The Halkin

5 Halkin Street, London SW1X 7DJ
TEL: 0171-333 1000   FAX: 0171-333 1100
EMAIL: res@halkin.co.uk

Cutting-edge design and technology in a slick Belgravia pad.

Christina Ong's newer London hotel, the trendy Metropolitan, has been getting all the publicity of late, but serious business people prefer the Halkin, which is smaller and more discreet. Hidden away from the hoi polloi on a side-street between Hyde Park Corner and Belgrave Square, this is a sensational-looking place, decked out along minimalist, Italian lines. In the sleek, calm bedrooms, black, white and cream combine most strikingly with the rosewood panelling (those on the top floor, with their curved walls and ceilings, are particularly memorable), while, in the lobby, natty black armchairs sit decoratively on pink marble floors beneath beige walls. Attention to presentation continues in the restaurant, in Stefano Cavallini's much-praised, light, modern, Italian cuisine, on the tables (each may sport a single pale rose of uniform colour) and in the marbled and pillared surroundings. The superbly attentive young staff are even dressed for effect, kitted out as they are in dark Armani suits. But the Halkin doesn't intend merely to impress visually: the bedrooms pander to business people's needs with two phone lines (a flat surcharge can reduce the phone bill by 50 per cent) and a fax machine, and to everyone's whims with such ultra-mod cons as heated bathroom mirrors (to stop them misting up).

◑ Open all year ⬛ Nearest tube station is Victoria (District, Circle and Victoria lines). On-street parking (metered); public car park nearby ⬅ 30 double, 11 suites; family rooms available all with bathroom/WC; all with satellite TV, video, room service, hair-dryer, mini-bar, direct-dial telephone, fax, air-conditioning; no tea/coffee-making facilities in rooms ⬗ Restaurant, bar, lounge; functions, conferences ♿ Wheelchair access to hotel and restaurant, WC (unisex), lift to bedrooms ● No dogs ⬜ Amex, Delta, Diners, MasterCard, Switch, Visa £ Double £300 to £382, suite £465 to £647 (1998 prices); deposit required. Continental B £13, cooked B £16; set L £25, D £45; alc L £26, D £50. Special breaks available

Hampstead Village Guesthouse   `NEW ENTRY`

2 Kemplay Road, London NW3 1SY
TEL: 0171-435 8679   FAX: 0171-794 0254
EMAIL: hvguesthouse@dial.pipex.com

Unconventional home-from-home B&B; not in the least bit smart, though many hotel comforts have not been overlooked.

Annemarie van der Meer's B&B is quintessential liberal, bookish Hampstead. Her handsome, detached late-Victorian house stands in a quiet residential street about 400 yards from the Heath, not much further from the Tube and village centre. Street parking is for Hampstead residents only, but special arrangements can be made for £10 a day. Over the last two decades, as her offspring have grown up, Annemarie has gradually converted their bedrooms into lettable accommodation. But she's left them with much of their clobber – piles of books, old files and various pictures – so occupying one feels very much like staying in a friend's spare room. They also come with off-beat antiques – from a blue Victorian bath plonked in the middle of David's Room to a small double bed on runners that originated in a German castle in Mark's Room (which has the added bonus of a private roof terrace). The other bedroom of note is the large Garage, the most expensive and utterly different from the rest, decked out in modern furnishings such as a leather recliner. Not all rooms are *en suite*, but all have a panoply of mod cons, including fridge, hot-water bottle and ironing board, and some intriguing antique cons such as wonderful old basins. Breakfast is served as late as you want, either on pine tables in the kitchen or in the lovely big courtyard garden, where an outdoor power supply allows each table to have its own toaster.

○ Open all year ⚡ Nearest tube station is Hampstead (Northern line). Private car park and on-street parking (both £10 per day) 🛏 1 single, 5 double, 1 four-poster, 1 suite; family rooms available; 1 with bathroom/WC, 4 with shower/WC; all with TV, hair-dryer, trouser press, direct-dial telephone, fridge, ironing facilities ✓ Breakfast room, garden; cots, high chairs, babysitting, baby-listening, playroom, outdoor play area ♿ No wheelchair access ● No dogs; no smoking ▭ None accepted £ Single £35 to £50, single occupancy of double £40 to £50, double £55 to £65, family room £70 to £80, suite £90; deposit required. Cooked B £6

Hazlitt's

6 Frith Street, London W1V 5TZ
TEL: 0171-434 1771 FAX: 0171-439 1524

A hugely characterful, classy but informal B&B in the heart of Soho; book well in advance.

Named after the essayist, who died here, Hazlitt's is still much favoured by literary types. Bill Bryson claims it to be his preferred London base, and it is frequented by many other authors, such as Roddy Doyle and Ted Hughes (signed works of sometime guests fill a cabinet in the sitting-room). The three adjacent, early Georgian town houses ooze character from every creaking and often alarmingly sloping board. Even more alluring are the furnishings. Bedrooms (quieter at the back, lighter at the front) hold antiques galore; some have eye-poppingly carved, antique bedheads. Many bathrooms are often as big as the bedrooms themselves and contain magnificent Victorian claw-foot baths. It is features such as these that you're paying a premium for, as opposed to mod cons, which are pretty limited for such pricey accommodation. Busts and old paintings and prints abound throughout the buildings, including in the little clubby sitting-room, which is the only public area. The atmosphere is laid back, as are the engaging staff – no uniforms or servile fawning here. Sustenance

45

doesn't extend much beyond continental breakfast (croissants, yoghurt, freshly squeezed orange juice), but with a gallimaufry of bars, cafés and restaurants a short stroll away this should be no hardship.

○ Closed 24 to 26 Dec ⊠ Nearest tube station is Tottenham Court Road (Central and Northern lines). Public car park nearby (£30 per day) ⊨ 5 single, 1 twin, 11 double, 5 four-poster, 1 suite; family rooms available; all with bathroom/WC exc 1 single with shower/WC; all with TV, room service, hair-dryer, direct-dial telephone; no tea/coffee-making facilities in rooms ⊘ Sitting-room; early suppers for children; cots, babysitting ⅙ No wheelchair access ● None ⊟ Amex, Delta, Diners, MasterCard, Switch, Visa £ Single £147, single occupancy of twin/double £192, twin/double/four-poster £192, family room £227, suite £276; deposit required. Continental B £8.50

The Hempel

31–35 Craven Hill Gardens, London W2 3EA
TEL: 0171-298 9000   FAX: 0171-402 4666
EMAIL: the-hempel@easynet.co.uk
WEB SITE: www.hempelhotel.com/

Perhaps Britain's most extraordinary looking hotel – a bravura exercise in oriental minimalism taken to extremes.

Since it opened in 1996, more column inches seem to have been written about the Hempel – named after its designer owner, Anouska Hempel – than any other hotel in the country. Tucked away in a Victorian terrace in Bayswater, it's most easily identified by the doormen who hang around outside in their designer coats, looking like hit men from a Tarantino movie. Inside, every element of the hotel is intended to be a sensually provocative statement: the ante-room is filled with nothing but orchids, for example. The lobby is a vast, blindingly white space, with little to focus on but the flickering flames that rise out of a bed of white grit. Translucent stairs lead down to the I-Thai restaurant, where the fusion of Italian, Thai and Japanese cuisine is just as theatrical in taste and presentation as the stark, black-and-white surroundings. The bedrooms turn the principle of form following function on its head. Guests are given a lengthy tour of their rooms when they arrive – if they weren't, they might have difficulty locating even the toilet, let alone all the hi-tech gadgets that are available. Decked out in a limited palette of white, cream, grey and black, and furnished with bare wood, granite, steel and matting, as aesthetic creations they are indisputably wonderful. One that we were shown even has its bed suspended in a cage from the ceiling. However, whether they are comfortable or not is a moot point.

○ Open all year ⊠ Nearest tube stations are Paddington, Bayswater and Lancaster Gate (District, Circle, Bakerloo, Hammersmith & City lines and Central line). On-street parking (metered); public car park nearby (£20 per day) ⊨ 2 twin, 33 double, 6 suites; all with bathroom/WC; all with TV, room service, hair-dryer, mini-bar, direct-dial telephone, fax, modem, air-conditioning, safe; no tea/coffee-making facilities in rooms ⊘ Restaurant, bar, 2 libraries, garden; functions (max 150 people incl up to 82 residential), conferences; civil wedding licence; leisure facilities nearby (reduced rates for guests); cots, babysitting ⅙ Wheelchair access to hotel (ramp) and restaurant (lift)

lift to bedrooms, 1 room specially equipped for disabled people ● Children discouraged from restaurant eves; no dogs ☐ Amex, Diners, MasterCard, Visa ⒠ Single occupancy of twin/double £259 to £300, twin/double £259 to £300, suite £435 to £910; deposit required. Continental B £15, cooked B £20; alc L £40, D £60

L'Hotel

28 Basil Street, London SW3 1AS
TEL: 0171-589 6286   FAX: 0171-823 7826
EMAIL: levin@capitalhotel.co.uk
WEB SITE: www.capitalhotel.co.uk/

Classy, imaginatively designed shoppers' haven, just 50 yards from Harrods.

Aesthetics are all in this swanky B&B. Stencilled walls and an artfully displayed bowl of apples immediately catch the eye in the reception area, as do the delicate, fabric-coated walls, the shuttered and thickly draped windows, the country-pine furniture and the pretty, cork-tiled bathrooms in the 12 extremely appealing bedrooms. Those at the front, overlooking a busy back-street next to Harrods, are larger, and may have a gas fire, while those at the rear are quieter. Breakfast, as well as the well-regarded, unelaborate dishes on the pithy lunch and dinner menus, can be taken in the Le Metro wine bar in the basement. As carefully conceived as the rest of the establishment, here the style is minimalist chic, with chrome, leather and bare wood to the fore. And that's it, as far as L'Hotel's facilities are concerned: there is no sitting-room, no room service other than for breakfast, no concierge service, and the reception is not always staffed. If you want more (indeed, much more) pampering, and a top-flight gourmet experience, consider staying and/or eating at the intimate but grand Capital, which is next door but one, and under the same ownership.

◐ Open all year; wine bar closed Sat & Sun eves ⊠ Nearest tube station is Knightsbridge (Piccadillly line). On-street parking (metered); public car park nearby ⌂ 11 twin, 1 suite; all with bathroom/WC; all with TV, mini-bar, direct-dial telephone; room service (breakfast only) ⊘ Wine bar; functions (max 50 people incl up to 12 residential); early suppers for children; cots, babysitting ⟁ Wheelchair access to hotel (3 steps), 1 ground-floor bedroom ● No dogs in public rooms ☐ Amex, Delta, Diners, MasterCard, Switch, Visa ⒠ Single occupancy of twin/double £165, twin/double £165, suite £188; deposit required. Cooked B £6.50; alc L, D £15.50

The Howard

Temple Place, London WC2R 2PR
TEL: 0171-836 3555   FAX: 0171-379 4547
EMAIL: reservations@thehowardhotel.co.uk
WEB SITE: www.thehowardhotel.co.uk/

Opulently furnished, business-oriented hotel, with a conservative ambience, overlooking the Thames.

Built in the architecturally uninspired 'seventies, the Howard Hotel closely resembles a multi-storey car park. Don't let this put you off: its interior, in a *faux* classical vein, could hardly be more elegant. The lobby – all ornate, multi-coloured, Adam-style friezes and marble pillars – is jaw-droppingly ostentatious. The same could be said of the Quai d'Or Restaurant (serving serious French cuisine, with predictably high prices) and bar, both dripping with moulded ceilings, chandeliers and ruched curtains, and overlooking a sunken Italian garden. Efficient staff hovering around in morning suits add to the hotel's sense of formality. The bedrooms are as soothingly understated as the public areas are over the top, though the bathrooms, the majority in black-and-white marble, are pretty snazzy. Most suites enjoy a panoramic vista of the Thames from private terraces; standard rooms cost the same whether they face the river or the office blocks behind the hotel, so it's worth asking for one with a river view. With the hotel's proximity to the City, the Law Courts and two of the Inns of Court, not surprisingly most guests are here for work (there is also a well-equipped business centre). In order to fill the rooms on Friday to Sunday nights, rates can drop by over a third, with a bottle of champagne thrown in.

◑ Open all year　☑ Nearest tube station is Temple (District and Circle lines). Private car park　⇱ 4 single, 67 twin, 38 double, 25 suites; all with bathroom/WC; all with TV, 24-hour room service, hair-dryer, direct-dial telephone, some with mini-bar; no tea/coffee-making facilities in rooms　✓ Restaurant, bar, lounge, garden; functions (max 200 people residential/non-residential), conferences; civil wedding licence; early suppers for children; cots, high chairs, babysitting　&. Wheelchair access to hotel and restaurant, WC (unisex), lift to bedrooms　● None　▭ Amex, Delta, Diners, MasterCard, Switch, Visa　£ Single £255, twin/double £285, suite £305 to £565; deposit required. Continental B £14.50, cooked B £19.50; set L, D £28.50. Special breaks available

Knightsbridge Green Hotel

159 Knightsbridge, London SW1X 7PD
TEL: 0171-584 6274　FAX: 0171-225 1635
EMAIL: thekghotel@aol.com

Super, hideaway B&B accommodation which is pretty good value for its prime location – yards from both Harrods and Hyde Park.

With its unpromising, low-key entrance squeezed between a carpet shop and an electronics shop, the Knightsbridge Green promises little from the outside. Its 27 smart bedrooms therefore feel like a rather exciting discovery. They come close to matching standards in far pricier establishments nearby, in their size (even singles are spacious), tasteful, upbeat décor (Impressionist prints hang on walls, fun animal prints appear on some curtains) and well-equipped bathrooms (most have power showers with big heads). Housekeeping standards, under the meticulous eye of the keen manager Paul Fizia, are high. Though the street outside is very noisy, rooms are air-conditioned and the double glazing works well, and anyway half the rooms overlook a pedestrian alley or an interior courtyard. The only public room is a lounge – by the time the *Guide* goes to press, the old first-floor sitting-room should have disappeared and a new one been created next to the entrance. However, a short walk away there are pubs, cafés and restaurants aplenty. Breakfast (a choice of a hot drink and a croissant, full continental or full English) is served in the bedrooms.

◐ Closed 24 to 26 Dec   ⏚ Nearest tube station is Knightsbridge (Piccadilly line)
⏦ 7 single, 5 twin, 3 double, 12 suites; most with bathroom/WC, 1 suite with shower/WC; all with TV, hair-dryer, trouser press, direct-dial telephone   ⌔ Lounge
♿ Wheelchair access to hotel, lift to bedrooms, 1 specially equipped for disabled people, no ground-floor bedrooms   ⬤ No dogs   ▭ Amex, Diners, MasterCard, Visa
£ Single £100, single occupancy of twin/double £135, twin/double £135, suite £160; deposit required. Continental B £3.50 to £6, cooked B £9.50

The Leonard

15 Seymour Street, London W1H 5AA
TEL: 0171-935 2010   FAX: 0171-935 6700
EMAIL: the.leonard@dial.pipex.com

Luxurious town-house hotel with an informal atmosphere, close to Oxford Street.

Part of a refurbished Georgian terrace a short walk from Marble Arch tube station and the department stores on Oxford Street's smarter western end, the Leonard is ideally placed for shoppers. Most guests, however, turn out to be business people, no doubt due to its high rates. Attentive, round-the-clock service from the youthful staff and, above all, lavish, often period, furnishings and very spacious accommodation justify the prices. Downstairs, you can wind down in the so-called 'Café Bar', an elegant, multi-purpose room, with squashy sofas, dining tables and a proper bar. As well as breakfasts, fairly priced, simple dishes, such as sandwiches, salads and pasta, can be eaten here – or in the privacy of the bedrooms at any hour of the day. These are indulgent, extremely plush and boldly furnished: expect CD players and videos, and anti-mist mirrors in the swanky marble bathrooms. Most of the accommodation comes in the form of suites – some with kitchenettes, others vast and opulent (one even sports a fake marble pillar). Of the standard bedrooms, the massive Room 9, with its gas fire, is a good choice. Light sleepers may, however, prefer a room at the back, since plenty of traffic plies up and down Seymour Street.

◐ Open all year   ⏚ Nearest tube station is Marble Arch (Central line). On-street parking (metered); public car park nearby (£20 per day)   ⏦ 8 twin/double, 1 four-poster, 20 suites; all with bathroom/WC; all with TV, room service, hair-dryer, mini-bar, direct-dial telephone, CD player, video; no tea/coffee-making facilities in rooms   ⌔ Bar; conferences (max 15 people residential/non-residential); gym; leisure facilities nearby (reduced rates for guests); early suppers for children; cots, high chairs, toys, babysitting, baby-listening   ♿ No wheelchair access   ⬤ No dogs   ▭ Amex, Diners, MasterCard, Switch, Visa   £ Single occupancy of twin/double £188, twin/double £212, four-poster £212 to £435, suite £265 to £459; deposit required. Continental B £12, cooked B £16; alc L, D £16.50. Special breaks available

---

It is always worth enquiring about the availability of special breaks or weekend prices. The prices we quote are the standard rates for one night – most hotels offer reduced rates for longer stays.

London Outpost

69 Cadogan Gardens, London SW3 2RB
TEL: 0171-589 7333   FAX: 0171-581 4958
EMAIL: londonoutpost@dial.pipex.com

Refined town-house hotel in a smart location, round the back of Sloane Square.

The hotel's full name, The London Outpost of the Carnegie Club, conveys its exclusive, clubby atmosphere well. The club in question turns out to be a sporting retreat in Scotland, hence the blue-and-white flag flying over the door of this handsome, terraced Victorian house. Inside, ticking clocks, sepia prints, oil paintings by English masters, swagged curtains and well-worn antiques set the ultra-traditional tone, both in the library and drawing-room, where complimentary champagne is served in the evenings. The bedrooms, named after artists and writers with local associations, are, if anything, even better looking, in a co-ordinated, stylised way. The best – and most expensive – is Turner, which has a magnificent four-poster bed; it also has a gas fire in an impressive fireplace, as do all but the smallest two rooms. Though there isn't that much traffic passing along the street, the bedrooms at the rear of the building are quieter. Breakfasts, afternoon teas, salads and sandwiches can be served in your room, or taken in a pretty conservatory off the library. Being such a small establishment, the service is intended to be very personal (3 per cent is added to the total bill).

◗ Open all year   🚇 Nearest tube station is Sloane Square (District and Circle lines). On-street parking (metered)   🛏 6 twin, 4 double, 1 four-poster; all with bathroom/WC; all with TV, room service, hair-dryer, mini-bar, trouser press, direct-dial telephone; no tea/coffee-making facilities in rooms   ⊘ Drawing-room, library, conservatory, garden   ⚒ No wheelchair access   ⬤ No dogs; no smoking in bedrooms   ▭ Amex, Diners, MasterCard, Switch, Visa   £ Twin/double £177 to £235, four-poster £277; deposit required. Continental B £12, cooked B £17

Miller's | NEW ENTRY |

111A Westbourne Grove, London W2 4UW
TEL: 0171-243 1024   FAX: 0171-243 1064
EMAIL: millersuk@aol.com

New, informal, Notting Hill B&B that amounts to an extraordinary antiques emporium.

Martin Miller, founder of the eponymous antiques guides, and owner – as well as sometimes resident – of Miller's, uses the term 'rooming house' to encapsulate its laid-back, period atmosphere. You enter, inauspiciously, through a door next to a launderette; a sedan chair greets you, then old rugs adorning the walls over the stairs leading up to the first floor. Here you'll find a little breakfast room and a vast, wondrous drawing-room, redolent of a fusty antiques shop where you hope to find a prize piece that the dealers have overlooked. A giant Jacobean fireplace, brass chandeliers, busts, vases, gilt frames, more rugs and much, much more besides – all are piled higgledy-piggledy, along with stacks of books (including many of Miller's own). Beyond are seven bedrooms – also furnished with antiques galore, but in a somewhat more orderly fashion – with smart, new bathrooms. Each is named after a Romantic poet and comes with a poem on one side of its door, which is expressed in a rather ghastly mural on the other. Keats is a palatial, four-poster room; Byron is Baroque in style; while Shelley – one of the quietest, since it faces a side-street rather than the busy Westbourne Grove – is vaguely oriental. A congenial American manager is on hand for much of the day, but the idea is that you come and go as you please, using your own front-door key, helping yourself to drinks from an honesty bar, and to breakfast (eaten round a communal table) from a buffet spread.

◐ Open all year ⃣ Nearest tube station is Bayswater (District and Circle lines). On-street parking (metered) ⃔ 2 twin, 4 double, 1 four-poster; all with bathroom/WC; all with TV, direct-dial telephone, voice mail; no tea/coffee-making facilities in rooms ⃠ Drawing-room, breakfast room; functions (max 50 people incl up to 14 residential) ⃗ No wheelchair access ● No dogs ⃞ Amex, MasterCard, Visa £ Single occupancy of twin/double £123 to £135, twin/double £141 to £152, four-poster £146 to £170; deposit required. Special breaks available

---

Morgan House

120 Ebury Street, London SW1W 9QQ
TEL: 0171-730 2384   FAX: 0171-730 8442

Fetching, few-frills B&B in Victoria that is younger sister to Woodville House (see entry).

That Morgan House bears many similarities to Woodville House is hardly surprising, given that they are a few hundred yards apart on the same street, occupy similar tall, thin buildings in Georgian terraces and, most importantly, are under the same ownership. Here, proprietors Rachel Joplin and Ian Berry have installed a manager, but the place is still run on Woodville's caring lines. This is the newer of their two enterprises, and is more freshly decorated. Hallway and stairs are ennobled by gilt mirrors and a soothing floral scheme, while the basement breakfast room is an upbeat blue and yellow affair. Bedrooms have Victorian fireplaces and sport simple but natty colours and furnishings such as director's chairs and rattan bedheads. As at Woodville, they are generally small and only three have facilities *en suite*; the shared bathroom facilities are pretty rudimentary. Room 9, a family room with a bunk-bed, has welcoming teddies and smart shower-room. Ebury Street is pretty busy, and most windows are not double-glazed, so it's best to ask for a rear-facing room, which should be fairly peaceful.

◐ Open all year ⃣ Nearest tube station is Victoria (Victoria, Circle and District lines); by junction of Elizabeth Street and Ebury Street. On-street parking (metered); public car park £6 per day ⃔ 2 single, 3 twin, 3 double, 3 family rooms; 3 with bathroom/WC; all with TV, hair-dryer ⃠ Breakfast room, drying-room, library, garden; babysitting, toys, patio play area ⃗ No wheelchair access ● No dogs; no smoking in public rooms ⃞ MasterCard, Visa £ Single £39, single occupancy of twin/double £48, twin/double £58 to £80, family room £75 to £100; deposit required

Number Sixteen

16 Sumner Place, London SW7 3EG
TEL: 0171-589 5232   FAX: 0171-584 8615
EMAIL: reservations@numbersixteenhotel.co.uk
WEB SITE: www.numbersixteenhotel.co.uk/

*Graceful but informal country-house-style B&B in the heart of
South Kensington.*

The name is the only dull element in Number Sixteen. This loveable B&B has the
refinement of some of the capital's more fashionable small town-house hotels,
but without their stuffiness. Here, the staff are young and at times inexperienced,
but keen and friendly. Set on a smart residential street, the four pristine,
porticoed terraced houses, through which the enterprise spreads, bode well. Its
beguiling sitting-room and library, both with polished antiques, fine paintings,
bold flower displays and cornicing, live up to expectations, added to which is the
bonus of a conservatory overlooking an award-winning courtyard garden set
round a fish pond. The bedrooms, rigged out with well-worn antiques and
restful, traditional, yet individual, design schemes, score highly for their
character; the bathrooms, however, tend to be a little dated. One of the best
rooms is 'Garden', with french windows opening on to its own terrace. The
cheapest are a couple of small singles, whose loos are down the corridor.
Breakfasts (generous versions of continental plus porridge and boiled eggs are
included in the rates) are normally served in the rooms. Room service is
otherwise limited to tea and coffee; drinks are available from mini-bars and an
honesty bar in the library.

◐ Open all year   ⊿ Nearest tube station is South Kensington (Piccadilly, District and
Circle lines). On-street parking (metered); public car park nearby (£25 per day)
⊨ 9 single, 23 twin/double, 4 family rooms; most with bathroom/WC, some with
shower/WC; all with TV, hair-dryer, mini-bar, direct-dial telephone, safe, clock radio; no
tea/coffee-making facilities in rooms; limited room service   ⌛ Bar, sitting-room,
library, conservatory, garden; leisure facilities nearby (reduced rates for guests); cots
♿ No wheelchair access   ● No children under 12; no dogs   ▭ Amex, Delta, Diners,
MasterCard, Switch, Visa   £ Single £85 to £120, single occupancy of twin/double
£155 to £185, twin/double £155 to £185, family room £195; deposit required. Cooked B
£8. (Prices valid till Mar 1999.)

Park Lane Hotel

Piccadilly, London W1Y 8BX
TEL: 0171-499 6321   FAX: 0171-499 1965
WEB SITE: www.sheraton.com/parklane

*One of London's top long-established grand hotels, now with the
Sheraton chain at the helm.*

Opened in 1927 and built to impress, the Park Lane (actually located near the
Hyde Park Corner end of Piccadilly) is at its best in its fabulous public rooms.
The most lavish, the art-deco ballroom, has appeared in many a costume drama
(including 'Brideshead Revisited'), and is usually open for a peek. You're more

likely to spend time in the Palm Court lounge, a vast, serene conservatory sitting-room used for afternoon teas, and the two restaurants – the chandeliered and panelled Bracewell's, and the less formal Brasserie on the Park, which serves more moderately priced French fare amid deco décor.

The bedrooms are generally less characterful than these public areas, though most have fancy marble bathrooms. Cheaper rooms can be a bit pokey and gloomy. For a special occasion ask for an Executive room or suite – the latter enjoy expansive views over Green Park. Try bargaining over the rates, which can drop dramatically when occupancy levels are low.

Sheraton, which took over in 1996, has been improving business facilities, setting up Smart Rooms (bedrooms with a fax and sockets for computers) and a business centre.

◖ Open all year ⃠ Nearest tube station is Green Park (Piccadilly, Victoria and Jubilee lines). Private car park (£32 per night); on-street parking (metered) ⃫ 39 single, 83 'classic rooms' (twin/double), 99 'executive rooms' (twin/double), 39 suites; all with bathroom/WC; all with TV, room service, hair-dryer, mini-bar, direct-dial telephone; no tea/coffee-making facilities in rooms ⃠ 2 restaurants, bar, lounge; conferences (max 500 people incl up to 260 residential), functions; civil wedding licence; gym; early suppers for children ⃟ No wheelchair access ● No children in 1 restaurant eves; no dogs ▭ Amex, Delta, Diners, MasterCard, Switch, Visa ⃞ Single £247, single occupancy of twin/double £280, twin/double £329, suite from £423; deposit required. Continental B £13, cooked B £17; bar/bistro L £20, D £40; alc L £35, D £65. Special breaks available

---

Pelham Hotel

15 Cromwell Place, London SW7 2LA
TEL: 0171-589 8288   FAX: 0171-584 8444
EMAIL: pelham@firmdale.com
WEB SITE: www.firmdale.com/

Chic meets antique in this plush rendition of country-house living.

That the brochure for the Pelham Hotel – one of Tim and Kit Kemp's clutch of exquisitely designed small London hotels – has been put together by *The World of Interiors* speaks volumes. Within the nondescript Victorian block lies a panoply of gorgeous rooms that, through matching the boldest fabrics and eye-catching flower displays with graceful antiques and works of art, combine flamboyance with traditional English style. There are two extremely cosy, panelled sitting-rooms, one furnished in pine, the other (a former smoking room) in dark mahogany. Downstairs lies an enticing bar/dining-room, its boarded floor and fun, yellow-and-blue checks setting a more modern tone. The breakfast choices cover just about anything that you could want, while contemporary dishes, such as chargrilled tuna with couscous, appear on the dinner menus. The bedrooms are as dashing as the rest of the establishment: the walls may be papered with a

---

The Which? Hotel Guide *is one of many titles published by Which? Books. If you would like a full list, write to Which? Books, Castlemead, Gascoyne Way, Hertford X, SG14 1LH, or access our web site at www.which.net/.*

cord or bow motif, the curtains and beds are draped with oodles of fine fabric, and the bathrooms are slick, marble affairs. Note, however, that the cheaper rooms can be small, and that the noise from the busy street filters into the front-facing rooms, despite their double glazing. While the Kemps' Covent Garden Hotel (see entry) attracts limelight-seekers, the Pelham is popular with behind-the-scenes media and fashion types, along with well-heeled American tourists. South Kensington's big museums are a short walk away, and the Tube is across the road.

◑ Open all year; dining-room closed Sat eve ⃗ Nearest tube station is South Kensington (Piccadilly, District and Circle lines). On-street parking (metered); public car park nearby ⃗ 7 single, 15 twin, 22 double, 2 suites; family rooms available all with bathroom/WC; all with TV, 24-hour room service, hair-dryer, mini-bar, direct-dial telephone, radio; some with trouser press, personal safe; no tea/coffee-making facilities in rooms ⃝ Dining-room, bar, 2 sitting-rooms; functions (max 50 people residential), conferences; leisure facilities nearby (reduced rates for guests); early suppers for children; cots, babysitting ⃗ No wheelchair access ● No dogs ⃞ Amex, MasterCard, Visa ⃝£⃝ Single £171, single occupancy of twin/double £206 to £265, twin/double £206 to £265, family room £300, suite £412 to £647; deposit required. Continental B £13, cooked B £15; bar/bistro L, D £10; set L £14.50, D £17.50; alc L, D £24

Pembridge Court

34 Pembridge Gardens, London W2 4DX
TEL: 0171-229 9977 FAX: 0171-727 4982

A very comfortable Notting Hill base, far more cheerful and unpretentious than many of the capital's other smart little hotels.

The grand, nineteenth-century mansion, covered in classical mouldings, looks rather intimidatingly formal from the street, yet the fun-loving manager, Valerie Gilliat, who has worked here for 27 years, invests Pembridge Court with a thoroughly informal air. The simple basement bar, furnished with a plethora of caps and sporting memorabilia, has recently been named the 'Darling Bar', after Valerie's habit of saying to guests, 'See you in the bar, darling.' Like the adjacent restaurant, which offers a short, eclectic dinner menu (which can also be taken in the bedrooms) of anything from seafood pasta to chargrilled vegetables with couscous, it is intended for residents only. Dozens of framed fans, gloves and shawls act as substitutes for paintings elsewhere in the hotel, including the bedrooms. These vary significantly in size, and therefore also in price (three cheers for a London hotel that includes both VAT and English breakfast in its tariff), but all feature high-class reproduction furnishings. The larger ones are very spacious, and include a sitting area. If you're in a smaller room, you might want to use the appealing public sitting-room, which is well stocked with books and games, and where you might find the resident ginger cats, Spencer and Churchill, lounging on one of the squashy sofas.

◑ Open all year ⃗ Nearest tube station is Notting Hill Gate (Central, District and Circle lines). Limited parking in private car park (2 spaces) ⃗ 3 single, 3 twin, 13 double, 1 four-poster; family rooms available most with bathroom/WC, some with shower/WC; all with TV, room service, hair-dryer, trouser press, direct-dial telephone, air-conditioning; no tea/coffee-making facilities in rooms ⌀ Restaurant, bar, sitting-room; leisure facilities nearby (reduced rates for guests); early suppers for children; cots, high chairs, babysitting, baby-listening ⅙ No wheelchair access ● No dogs in public rooms ▭ Amex, Delta, Diners, MasterCard, Switch, Visa £ Single £115, single occupancy of twin/double £140 to £150, twin/double £140 to £180, four-poster £180, family room £180; deposit required. Alc D £20

The Portobello

22 Stanley Gardens, London W11 2NG
TEL: 0171-727 2777   FAX: 0171-792 9641

Fashionable and quirky, low-key hideaway, strewn with antiques in a leafy, residential part of Notting Hill.

A porter in jeans and sporting a ponytail sets the informal tone for this hip little hotel close to the equally trendy Portobello Road. The two tall, nineteenth-century houses, filled with a treasure-trove of idiosyncratic antique clutter and militaristic prints and paintings, evoke a colonial, Victorian atmosphere. The bedrooms, though wholly individual, could be classed in three types. The best are decked out in magnificent, chunky Victorian furniture, such as a half-tester bed and claw-foot, cast-iron bath. The mid-priced double rooms may feature exotic décor, perhaps in Moroccan or oriental style. The fun, tiny single rooms, called 'cabins' on account of their nautical feel, have their mod cons hidden away in old campaign cabinets. You might also be interested in a room with a bath in the bedroom, or one overlooking the lovely, secluded gardens (to which there is unfortunately no access) at the rear. Downstairs lie a rather grand, yet restful, Victorian drawing-room, and, in the basement, a marble-floored restaurant/bar, offering a 24-hour, short dining menu. Something akin to an up-market tea-room, this has tables dressed in lacy cloths, while the shell motif in its cornicing echoes the hotel's final, eccentric flourish: outside one window is a Victorian shell grotto.

◑ Closed 23 Dec to 2 Jan ☈ Nearest tube station is Notting Hill Gate (Central, District and Circle lines). On-street parking (metered), public car park nearby ⌸ 5 single, 2 twin, 12 double, 3 four-poster; most with shower/WC, some with bathroom/ shower/WC; all with TV, room service, hair-dryer, mini-bar, trouser press, direct-dial telephone ⌀ Restaurant/bar, drawing-room, drying-room; leisure facilities nearby (free for guests); cots, high chairs, babysitting ⅙ No wheelchair access ● Dogs by arrangement in some public rooms and bedrooms ▭ Amex, Delta, Diners, MasterCard, Switch, Visa £ Single £110, single occupancy of twin/double £120, twin/double/four-poster £150 to £250; deposit required. Cooked B £5; bar/bistro L £15, D £20; alc L £20, D £25

Sandringham Hotel

3 Holford Road, London NW3 1AD
TEL: 0171-435 1569   FAX: 0171-431 5932

The most conventional and comfortable but least personal accommodation of the Guide's three Hampstead choices.

The imposing Victorian house is perfectly situated on a quiet back-street, a few minutes' stroll from the Heath and tube. With its large, walled garden to the rear, a London base with less of an urban feel would be hard to find. Country-house-style furnishings reinforce the point. The breakfast room is refined, with swagged curtains and crisp tablecloths, while bedrooms feature complimentary sherry, a few antiques and good-quality reproduction furniture, along with smart, chrome-fitted bathrooms and maybe a fancy bed. Room 6's has an ostentatious canopy; this and the other bedrooms overlooking the garden are the more peaceful, but those at the front are hardly noisy.

Reports have been mixed this year. One couple, who booked the whole hotel for the night of their marriage, judged the staff to be extremely helpful, 'coping with all our crises cheerfully' and the rooms 'beautifully decorated and completely clean'. But another pair of correspondents were disappointed in housekeeping standards in their original room and found the promised '24-hour service' only reluctantly stretched to tea and sandwiches at 9pm. More reports, please.

○ Open all year ☒ Nearest tube station is Hampstead (Northern line). Private car park; on-street parking (metered) ⟻ 5 single, 1 twin, 5 double, 2 four-poster, 2 family rooms, 2 suites; all with bathroom/WC or shower/WC exc 2 family rooms with shared bathroom/WC; all with TV, room service, hair-dryer, direct-dial telephone; no tea/coffee-making facilities in rooms ✓ Breakfast room, lounge, garden; functions (max 35 people residential/non-residential), conferences ᴊ No wheelchair access ● No children under 8; no dogs; no smoking in bedrooms ▭ Amex, Delta, MasterCard, Switch, Visa £ Single £75 to £95, single occupancy of twin/double £95 to £100, twin/double £125 to £140, four-poster £140, family room £150, suite £150; deposit required. Continental B £6.50, cooked B £8.50

The Savoy

The Strand, London WC2R 0EU
TEL: 0171-836 4343   FAX: 0171-240 6040
EMAIL: info@the-savoy.co.uk.
WEB SITE: www.savoy-group.co.uk/

History, grandeur, luxury, fine cuisine... and prices to match: this is one of the world's great hotels.

'At that price it should have been good, and indeed it was,' was one verdict on a room at the Savoy, a double-edged sentiment probably echoed by most resident guests. This London landmark, founded in 1889, also attracts a welter of non-residents. For the cost of a champagne cocktail you can bask in screen-idol glory in the American Bar; for a few pounds more you can take afternoon tea in a foyer of ballroom proportions, amid pastoral murals and a piano tinkling away under a gazebo. Splash out on a full meal, and you really start to savour the atmosphere. Join politicians and captains of industry tackling weighty matters and English and Italian fare in the discreet Grill Room, or experience the palatial River Restaurant, where Thames views and a dance band which plays most nights serve as the backdrop for such classic dishes as chateaubriand. But to appreciate the hotel fully, of course, you need to stump up the cost of a room. All have specially made mattresses, linen sheets and fantastic, marble bathrooms, with sunflower-type shower heads. The most memorable have art-deco-style furnishings and/or river views; the latter come with a hefty mark-up (but note that you don't pay extra for rooms with partial river views). Service, summoned through a panel of buttons in the bedrooms, is as good as it gets: 'Nothing was too much trouble,' concludes one satisfied reporter.

◑ Open all year ⧉ Nearest tube stations are Charing Cross (Northern, Jubilee and Bakerloo lines) and Embankment (District and Circle lines). Private car park (£24 per day); on-street parking (metered) 🛏 55 single, 100 double, 52 suites; all with bathroom/WC; all with TV, room service, hair-dryer, mini-bar, direct-dial telephone, fax and modem points; no tea/coffee-making facilities in rooms ✧ 3 restaurants, bar, lounge; functions (max 500 people incl up to 359 residential), conferences; civil wedding licence; gym, sauna, heated indoor swimming-pool, beauty treatments, massage, leisure facilities nearby (free for guests); cots, high chairs, babysitting ♿ Wheelchair access to hotel and Grill Room (no WC in restaurant), lift to bedrooms, 3 rooms specially equipped for disabled people ⊖ No dogs ▭ Amex, Diners, MasterCard, Visa £ Single from £250, double from £295, 1-bedroom suite from £425, 2-bedroom suite from £790; deposit required. Continental B £15, cooked B £19; set L £28.50, D £39.50 to £43.50. Special breaks available

Searcy's Roof Garden Bedrooms

30 Pavilion Road, London SW1X 0HJ
TEL: 0171-584 4921 FAX: 0171-823 8694

Cosy and tranquil bedrooms, with a few idiosyncratic touches, in a hideaway Knightsbridge location.

Though seconds from Sloane Street's ritzy stores, Searcy's is not somewhere that you stumble across by accident. The tall, lemon-yellow, nineteenth-century building, though rather marred by a multi-storey car park opposite (charging affordable night-time rates, though punitive during the day), occupies a peaceful, back-street spot. The bedrooms (there are no public rooms whatsoever) lie above ground-floor function rooms, and are reached by means of a front door that opens directly, and mysteriously, into an old cage lift. With their lacy bedspreads and light, floral schemes on the walls and fabrics, they feel quite feminine, but in a graceful, rather than a flouncy, guest-housey, way; a few antiques add touches of sophistication. The bathrooms receive consistent praise, though in two rooms you'll find the bath in the bedroom. Room 5, a suite which has this arrangement, is made even more peculiar by having its twin beds hidden away under toothy, Gothic arches. Breakfast is of the continental variety only, and has to be taken in the bedrooms, but fresh orange juice and hot croissants are on offer. The roof garden (as in the B&B's title) is rather unprepossessing – since Searcy's is a no-smoking establishment, it seems to be used mainly by those in need of a ciggie.

◑ Closed 24 to 26 Dec ⧉ Nearest tube station is Knightsbridge (Piccadilly line). Public car park nearby 🛏 3 single, 4 twin, 4 double, 2 suites; family rooms available all with bathroom/WC; all with TV, hair-dryer, trouser press, direct-dial telephone ✧ Roof garden; functions (max 250 people non-residential, in private house), conferences; civil wedding licence ♿ No wheelchair access ⊖ No dogs; no smoking ⊟ Amex, MasterCard, Switch, Visa £ Single £82, single occupancy of twin/double £98, twin/double £112, family room £112, suite £140; deposit required. Continental B £6

The Stafford   NEW ENTRY

St James's Place, London SW1A 1NJ
TEL: 0171-493 0111   FAX: 0171-493 7121
EMAIL: info@thestaffordhotel.co.uk

Luxury and tradition in one of London's top small hotels; particularly popular with Americans.

The Stafford delivers service, comfort and a venerable English style, as well as prices, that can compete with the city's larger landmark hotels. Yet its relatively small size imbues it with a much more personal, even homely feel – that is, if you're used to chandeliers, stuccoed walls and fine antiques. On a cul-de-sac street in St James's, it enjoys a central yet utterly tranquil location; Green Park is just 75 yards away, reached via a passageway. The Stars and Stripes fly from its Victorian façade: two-thirds of guests come from across the Atlantic, and the hotel has strong historical links with the US. These are in evidence in the American Bar, a much-loved institution festooned with visitors' baseball caps, ties and signed celebrity photos. Americans love the hotel's quintessential Englishness, on display in the utterly refined drawing-room where afternoon tea is served, and in the grand but small-scale restaurant, the setting for accomplished, classic British and contemporary cuisine. A hotel cat who recently passed away has made it to heaven, painted on the ceiling's frescoed sky. Bedrooms, with old-fashioned radios and house plants, are paragons of understated tastefulness. Many of the best – lavish but decorated with a lightness of touch – can be found in the Carriage House, a converted stable block in the mews behind the main building.

◑ Open all year ☢ Nearest tube station is Green Park (Piccadilly, Jubilee and Victoria lines). On-street parking (metered); public car park nearby (£35 per day) ⊨ 11 single, 19 twin, 33 double, 4 four-poster, 14 suites; 13 in annexe; family rooms available; all with bathroom/WC; all with TV, room service, hair-dryer, direct-dial telephone, safe, voice mail, modem and fax points ✓ Restaurant, bar, lounge; functions (max 75 people residential/non-residential), conferences; civil wedding licence; early suppers for children by arrangement; cots, babysitting ⅋ No wheelchair access ● No dogs ⊟ Amex, Diners, MasterCard, Switch, Visa £ Single £234, single occupancy of twin/double £259, twin/double £288, four-poster £306, family room £306, suite £470; deposit required. Continental B £13.50, cooked B £15.50; bar meals £15, set L £20/£23.50, D £23.50/£27; alc L, D £45. Special breaks available

Thanet Hotel

8 Bedford Place, London WC1B 5JA
TEL: 0171-636 2869   FAX: 0171-323 6676

A very modest but well looked after B&B in a fine Georgian building.

As long as you're not expecting great luxury, this Bloomsbury B&B is unlikely to disappoint. Its location – part of a handsome Georgian terrace between two leafy squares and a short stroll from London's best free entertainment (namely the British Museum) – is enviable. The street, however, is a busy cut-through for traffic, so try to avoid front-facing bedrooms. The building has retained some period features, such as a fanlight behind the front door and an oval skylight over the stairs (the less able should note it's a long climb to the top floor). The young, keen, hands-on owners, Lynwen and Richard Orchard, have decorated the place sympathetically, for example putting historic prints of London on the stairs and in the handsomely proportioned breakfast room. (We have received consistently good reports about breakfasts, particularly their size.) Bedrooms benefit from high ceilings and are well maintained and cheerful, though you should also expect simple furnishings and shower-rooms that are small and old-fashioned. Evidence of the Orchards' caring approach comes in the rooms' exemplary information folders, with thorough details on sightseeing and restaurant recommendations.

◗ Open all year   ⧅ Nearest tube stations are Russell Square and Holborn (Piccadilly and Central lines). On-street parking (metered); public car park £16 per day
⇖ 4 single, 4 twin, 5 double, 3 family rooms; all with shower/WC; all with TV, hair-dryer, direct-dial telephone   ⊘ Breakfast room; cots, high chairs   ♿ No wheelchair access   ⬤ No dogs or smoking   ▭ Amex, Delta, MasterCard, Switch, Visa   £ Single £57, twin/double £75, family room £91; deposit required

---

Tophams Belgravia

28 Ebury Street, London SW1W 0LU
TEL: 0171-730 8147   FAX: 0171-823 5966
EMAIL: tophams_belgravia.compuserve.com

Snug and loveable family-run hotel in the heart of Victoria.

Tophams takes its name from the family that has run it for six decades. Its cosy atmosphere and personal service has won it many plaudits over the years and plenty of devoted guests – perhaps the most loyal is a Californian who has furnished the single room he regularly uses with his own paintings and books. The hotel discreetly occupies five interconnecting houses along busy Ebury Street, and behind the smart porticoed façades lies a warren of passages and dinky rooms. The hotel is undergoing a gradual but extensive refurbishment programme. When our inspector called, plans were afoot to revamp the rather formal little restaurant into a bar/brasserie, inserting parquet flooring and banquette seating, and to turn a meeting room into the breakfast room. The diminutive sitting-room, with wing-back armchairs and scattered newspapers, will disappear during 1999 but the basement Ebury Club bar (a 1960s throwback with lurid furnishings) is presently escaping unscathed. Change continues apace upstairs; the corridors' rather threadbare carpets have been thrown out, and more bedrooms have been given a complete overhaul. These bask in pretty, cottagey colour schemes and fabrics and the latest in shower technology; mod cons are often ingeniously hidden away in cupboards to maximise the frequently very limited space available. By contrast, the few rooms still in need of a face-lift are plain and dated. Rooms to the front have effective double glazing, while those to the rear are very tranquil.

◑ Closed Chr & New Year 🔁 Nearest tube station is Victoria (Victoria, District and Circle lines). On-street parking (metered); public car park nearby (£24 per day)
🛏 9 single, 9 twin, 13 double, 3 four-poster, 4 family rooms, 1 suite; most with shower/WC; all with TV, hair-dryer, direct-dial telephone; room service for some rooms ⌘ Bar/brasserie, breakfast room, bar; conferences (max 30 people residential/non-residential); early suppers for children; cots, toys, high chair, baby-listening
♿ Wheelchair access to hotel (3 steps) and restaurant (2 steps), 3 ground-floor bedrooms ● No dogs ▭ Amex, Delta, Diners, MasterCard, Switch, Visa
£ Single £75 to £110, single occupancy of twin/double £120 to £140, twin/double £120 to £140, four-poster £140 to £220, family room £160, suite £220 to £260; deposit required. Bar/bistro L, D £12.50; alc L, D £20. Special breaks available

---

The Wilbraham

1–5 Wilbraham Place, London SW1X 9AE
TEL: 0171-730 8296   FAX: 0171-730 6815

Bargain rates (for this location) in an enviably placed, old-fashioned hotel just yards from Sloane Square.

If you're looking for simple, but not too basic, accommodation in the Chelsea/Knightsbridge area, the Wilbraham Hotel may fit your needs. Its three interconnected, tall houses occupy part of a terrace across from a derelict church on a tranquil side-street just round the corner from Sloane Square. Cross the threshold, and it feels like stepping back decades in time, and nowhere more so than in the hotel's most atmospheric room: the dark-panelled, club-like Buttery Bar, where meals are served. Many of the dishes are as unfashionable as the surroundings in which they are served, and the exemplary breakfast choices run to porridge and grilled kippers, while the dinners feature prawn cocktail and cottage pie. A couple of massive, panelled bedrooms (the most expensive) adopt a similar style to the Buttery. Most, however, are far smaller, and are furnished in upbeat, fresh-looking yellow and green colour schemes. While the house-keeping standards are good, and all the bedrooms are *en suite*, the bathrooms are dated and offer few frills (expect a bar of unwrapped soap and towels only). The staff are personable and the service courteous.

◑ Open all year; restaurant/bar closed Sun and bank holidays 🔁 Nearest tube station is Sloane Square (District and Circle lines). On-street parking (metered); public car park nearby (£17.50 per day) 🛏 2 single, 21 twin, 17 double, 5 family rooms, 4 suites; most with bathroom/WC exc 2 singles with shower/WC; all with TV, room service, direct-dial telephone, some with hair-dryer; no tea/coffee-making facilities in rooms
⌘ Restaurant/bar, lounge, TV room; early suppers for children; cots, high chairs, babysitting ♿ No wheelchair access ● No dogs ▭ None accepted £ Single £80, twin/double £100 to £106, family room £120, suite £132. Continental B £4, cooked B £6; restaurant/bar L £5, D £8

 This denotes that you can get a twin or double room for £70 or less per night inclusive of breakfast.

Windermere Hotel

142–144 Warwick Way, London SW1V 4JE
TEL: 0171-834 5163   FAX: 0171-630 8831
EMAIL: 100773.1171@compuserve.com

As smart as Pimlico's many budget hotels get, in a somewhat noisy, but convenient, spot, under ten minutes' walk to Victoria station.

The Windermere's only real drawback is its location. The significant amount of traffic that passes its front door creates too much noise to be screened out totally by the double glazing, and across the street lie unsightly blocks of flats. But the hotel is so spruce that it is still well worth considering as an inexpensive base in central London. The owners, the Hambis, are obsessed with keeping up, and improving, appearances. The railings round the neoclassical façade are neatly painted gold and black, and the window boxes are full of daffodils. The public areas have been recently repainted: the elegant little sitting-room is now a mottled salmon pink, while the jolly basement restaurant (offering such simple dishes as pasta and steak, taken mostly by residents) has pillars and balustrades painted on its walls. Further evidence of a caringly run establishment are fresh flowers on the dining-room tables, and a daily weather forecast posted at the reception desk. All the bedrooms are cheerfully decorated, with matching colour schemes, but they vary considerably in size and comfort, from small rooms without *en suite* facilities to something like Room 15, which is fairly spacious, with elaborate bed drapes, stencilled walls and a smart bathroom.

① Open all year   ☑ Nearest tube station is Victoria (District, Circle and Victoria lines). Public car park nearby (£8.50 per day for guests)   🛏 4 single, 5 twin, 11 double, 3 family rooms; some with bathroom/WC, most with shower/WC; all with satellite TV, room service, hair-dryer, direct-dial telephone, safes, some with trouser press
✓ Restaurant, bar, sitting-room; early suppers for children; cots, high chairs, toys
🚫 No wheelchair access   ● No dogs; no smoking in public rooms   ▭ Amex, Delta, MasterCard, Switch, Visa   £ Single £59 to £77, single occupancy of twin/double £64 to £85, twin/double £69 to £99, family room £99; deposit required. Alc D £12

Woodville House

107 Ebury Street, London SW1W 9QU
TEL: 0171-730 1048   FAX: 0171-730 2574

Simple but good-value and enthusiastically run B&B near Victoria train and coach stations.

Rachel Joplin and Ian Berry's establishment has been featured in the *Guide* for eight consecutive years. One of the many cheap B&Bs on Ebury Street's long Georgian terraces, even its neat exterior suggests higher standards than its competitors'. Its style – notably the florid wallpaper throughout – is decidedly unfashionable, and you should not expect great luxury. Bedrooms are small (none has *en suite* facilities) and the shared bathrooms are simply done. Yet the jolly, hands-on owners go out of their way to fulfil their visitors' needs. For example, in the summer fans are provided in rooms without air-conditioning; and a menagerie of teddies awaits in the family room. In the guests' kitchen you can do some ironing, make hot drinks and help yourself to biscuits, and breakfast features home-made muesli and eggs any which way. Although there is no lounge, you're welcome to use the secluded courtyard garden if it's fine. When booking, ask for a bedroom at the rear, as front-facing ones are noisy. See also the entry for nearby Morgan House, under the same ownership.

◑ Open all year ⤴ Nearest tube station is Victoria (Victoria, District and Circle lines). On-street parking (metered); public car park nearby (£6 per day) ⇤ 4 single, 3 twin, 3 double, 2 family rooms; all with TV, hair-dryer, 3 doubles with air-conditioning; no tea/coffee-making facilities in rooms ⌂ Breakfast room, drying-room, library, garden; babysitting, toys, patio play area 🚫 No wheelchair access ⊖ No dogs; no smoking in public rooms ▭ Delta, MasterCard, Visa £ Single £39, single occupancy of twin/double £48, twin/double £58, family room £75 to £100; deposit required

'We came down for a pre-dinner drink and were surprised to see that the tables in the dining-room were not laid. It was only then that we were informed of the new scheme, i.e. that there would be no waitress service and that instead we were firstly to find a table and then go to the bar to place our order with the same inexperienced young men from the same menu that we had had at lunchtime (a menu that had the appearance of being filched from a hamburger joint). We were given a ridiculous plastic sunflower with a number on it and instructed to return to our table and await the food. This process was to be repeated for each course, and although we were hotel residents we were expected to join the queue with the casual diners.'

On a hotel in Hertfordshire

ENGLAND

CALLOW HALL

ASHBOURNE

The Elms

Stockton Road, Abberley, Worcester WR6 6AT
TEL: (01299) 896666   FAX: (01299) 896804

*Slickly run country-house hotel in an imposing Queen Anne
mansion.*

'Quite luxurious and extremely well managed', is the accurate summary of one
correspondent about this balustraded pile, overlooking sweeping lawns to the
front and formal gardens to the rear. The hands-on, debonair owner Marcel
Frichot originates from the Seychelles but was, until recently, based in colder
climes – at Knockinaam Lodge in Portpatrick, Scotland (see entry). The Scottish
hotel, he explains, 'was a labour of love, while this is more a business
proposition' – which is perhaps partly reflected by the fact that much of the trade
here comes from meetings and functions. Yet the hotel has a great deal with
which to woo the independent traveller, not least a full set of almost stately
public rooms, ennobled by extravagant flower displays, dramatic fireplaces and
high ceilings. Marcel appointed a new chef in spring 1998, but does not
anticipate any radical changes from the rich, high-quality dishes – such as foie
gras terrine and sea bream with a saffron risotto – that previously came out of the
kitchens; reports welcome, please. The bedrooms are furnished with top-of-
the-range country-house fabrics and antiques, and are either large 'standard'
rooms or enormous 'master' rooms (the biggest are Rooms 3 and 7). The
bathrooms are capacious, too, and have big sunflower-head showers.

○ Open all year   ⊿ On A443, 2 miles west of Great Witley (ignore Abberley turning).
Private car park   ⤙ 2 single, 8 twin/double, 1 four-poster, 5 suites; family rooms
available all with bathroom/WC; all with TV, room service, hair-dryer, mini-bar,
direct-dial telephone, some with trouser press; no tea/coffee-making facilities in
rooms   ✅ Restaurant, bar, lounge, drawing-room, garden; functions (max 80 people
incl up to 30 residential), conferences; civil wedding licence; tennis, croquet; early
suppers for children; cots, high chairs, baby-listening   ♿ No wheelchair access
● No dogs in public rooms; no smoking in restaurant   ▭ Amex, Delta, Diners,
MasterCard, Switch, Visa   £ Single £75, single occupancy of twin/double £90,
twin/double £110, four-poster £135, family room £145, suite £135; deposit required.
Set L £12.50/£15, alc D £29.50. Special breaks available

Uplands Hotel

Victoria Road, Aldeburgh IP15 5DX
TEL: (01728) 452420   FAX: (01728) 454872

*A quaint, seaside establishment, with some impressive period public
rooms, but simpler bedrooms.*

In the best tradition of 'We liked the product so much, we bought the company',
David and Jenny Evans were regular guests at the Uplands Hotel for ten years
before taking over this year. A fresh coat of white paint on the outside of the hotel

demonstrates their eager intention to spruce things up, though the understated charm and distinctive Georgian interiors remain. This was once the home of the eminent Victorian medic Elizabeth Garrett Anderson, but its history goes further back than that, and the couple has been slowly unearthing the secrets of the house, such as the wine cellar and smugglers' tunnel that connects it with the adjacent village church. Their plans also include restoring the two-hundred-year-old conservatory that looks out across the well-tended walled garden lined with small trees. The interior is more unassuming, though there's an unusual, round entrance hall and a grand dining-room with a plasterwork ceiling. The previous owners, Patricia Tidder and Nichola Winter, have now retired, but the continuity has not been lost, as many of the staff have stayed on, including the chef. One visitor told us that their meal was 'first class', as was the standard of service. The nicest rooms are in the main house; they are simply decorated and 'a lot larger than a lot of hotels we have stayed in'. However, the garden chalet rooms, built thirty years ago, are a bit musty and dated.

◗ Closed Chr & New Year   ☑ Opposite church on A1094 heading into Aldeburgh. Private car park   ⊨ 4 single, 9 twin, 5 double, 2 family rooms; some in annexe; all with bathroom/WC exc 3 singles with shower/WC; all with TV, direct-dial telephone   ⊘ Dining-room, bar, lounge, TV room, conservatory, garden; cots, high chairs   ♿ Wheelchair access to hotel (1 step) and dining-room, 8 ground-floor bedrooms, 1 room specially equipped for disabled people   ● Dogs in some bedrooms only, by arrangement; no smoking in some public rooms   ▭ Delta, MasterCard, Switch, Visa   £ Single £35 to £48, single occupancy of twin/double £48, twin/double £55 to £68, family room £80; deposit required. Set D £14.50; alc D £23. Special breaks available

---

ALDERMINSTER Warwickshire   map 5

Ettington Park

Alderminster, Stratford-upon-Avon CV37 8BU
TEL: (01789) 450123   FAX: (01789) 450472

Gargoyles galore at this ancient, aristocratic pile.

The place to start is the bar, which is Gothic on a Gormenghastic scale: the doorway is flanked by spires, the ceiling is plastered with stucco octagonals and, if you press the vast fireplace in the right spot, a secret door reveals steps down to a mile-long escape tunnel. Naturally, this claims to be the most haunted house in England – though who authenticates such things remains a mystery. The Victorian architect, Pritchard, who designed some of the additions, is rumoured to have killed himself after realising that he would never do better. Ettington Park was, since Norman times, the family seat of the Shirleys and, as loyal Catholics, they undoubtedly hatched many plots here. These days you are more likely to meet parties of bankers on strenuous leadership courses (do mountaineers do strenuous book-keeping courses?), or couples relaxing in the smallish pool before they begin their role-play evening (an unsolved mysterious murder perhaps) or enjoying a two-day break, including tickets to see some Shakespeare at Stratford. Ettington Park does not come cheap, but special weekend deals bring costs down considerably.

The bedrooms are either decorated in country-house style, with elegant chintzes and polished, dark-wood furniture, or else are themed rooms, such as Room 10 – the Downing Street room. The former are less pricey.

◗ Open all year ⚡ 5 miles south of Stratford-upon-Avon, off A3400 just outside Alderminster. Private car park 🛏 14 twin, 25 double, 2 four-poster, 5 family rooms, 2 suites; all with bathroom/WC; all with TV, room service, hair-dryer, trouser press, direct-dial telephone ⚑ Restaurant, bar, 2 lounges, library, conservatory, garden; functions (max 100 people incl up to 96 residential), conferences; fishing, gym, sauna, solarium, heated indoor swimming-pool, tennis, croquet, clay-pigeon shooting, archery early suppers for children; cots, high chairs, toys, babysitting, baby-listening ♿ Wheelchair access to hotel (ramp) and restaurant, WC (unisex), 10 ground-floor bedrooms, 1 room specially equipped for disabled people ● Dogs in bedrooms only, by arrangement; no smoking in restaurant ▭ Amex, Delta, Diners, MasterCard, Switch, Visa £ Single occupancy of twin/double £130, twin/double £190, four-poster £350, family room £270, suite £350; deposit required. Bar/bistro L £6; set L £15, D £31.50; alc L £17.50, D £36. Special breaks available

---

ALDWINCLE Northamptonshire   map 6

The Maltings

96 Main Street, Aldwincle, Oundle, Kettering NN14 3EP
TEL: (01832) 720233   FAX: (01832) 720326

A quiet rural location with sociable, friendly hosts.

The attractive, stone-built Elizabethan maltings and Margaret and Nigel Faulkner's farmhouse stretch down one side of the village lane, with a farm gate between. At the back of the yard – all lined with flowers in tubs – stands the converted granary with two bedrooms upstairs and a shared lounge below. The style is faultlessly charming: smart blue and cream fabrics, white walls, collections of old bottles, antique furniture, a torch 'for reading under the bedclothes', and lots of extras like biscuits and fresh milk on the tea tray downstairs. Breakfast is served over in the main house – a short walk through the garden, which is full of flowers even in winter. With windows on both sides, the house is bright and cheerful and has plenty of interesting pieces of furniture and collections of curios. There is a third bedroom here, which has the disadvantage of a bathroom down the hall but is otherwise very comfortable.

◗ Closed Chr to New Year's Day ⚡ Enter Aldwincle village from A605; Maltings is 150m past telephone box, on right. Private car park 🛏 3 twin; all with private bathroom/WC; all with hair-dryer; tea/coffee-making facilities in some rooms only ⚑ Dining-room, 2 lounges, drying-room, garden ♿ No wheelchair access ● No children under 10; no dogs or smoking ▭ Delta, MasterCard, Visa £ Single occupancy of twin/double £35 to £37, twin/double £49 to £51; deposit required. Special breaks available

---

The text of the entries is based on inspections carried out anonymously, backed up by unsolicited reports sent in by readers. The factual details under the text are from questionnaires the Guide sends to all hotels that feature in the book.

ALSTONEFIELD **Staffordshire**   map 5

Stanshope Hall

Stanshope, Ashbourne DE6 2AD
TEL: (01335) 310278   FAX: (01335) 310470

*Externally austere but internally exuberant stone house in good
walking country.*

Almost at the head of Dovedale, Nick Lourie and Naomi Chambers' establishment is perfectly situated for exploring the surrounding countryside on foot.
Externally, it is a rather austere-looking building, in grey stone with a double
frontage, but inside, the clever use of *trompe l'oeil* effects brightens things up
considerably: in the drawing-room, birds glide around the walls while clouds
float across the ceiling; in the dining-room, the ceiling is an artistic reflection of
the table and rug. The three-course dinners offer a fixed-price, limited choice:
perhaps an avocado and pine-nut salad, followed by roast pheasant with crispy
bacon, then a rhubarb and orange tart. One reader waxes lyrical about a treacle
tart with 'meltingly delicate pastry'. The bedrooms continue the playful style,
with a Moorish slant to the largest of them, Egyptian hieroglyphics and
bullrushes in the smallest, and a more traditional, Regency feel for the third –
though the artist has stocked the bathroom with a few fish, just for good measure.
'A marvellously relaxing place to stay', enthused one reader.

○ Closed 25 & 26 Dec; dining-room closed Wed & Thur eves   ⚡ From Ashbourne,
take A515 to Buxton; turn left to Thorpe, Ilam and Dovedale; at Ilam memorial turn right
(signposted Alstonefield); Stanshope is 3 miles from Ilam on road to Alstonefield.
Private car park   🛏 1 twin, 2 double; all with bathroom/WC; all with TV, hair-dryer,
direct-dial telephone   ⚸ Dining-room, drawing-room, garden; early suppers for
children; cots; high chairs   ♿ No wheelchair access   ● No children in dining-room
eves; no dogs; smoking in public rooms only, if other guests consent   ▭ Delta,
MasterCard, Switch, Visa   £ Single occupancy of twin/double £25 to £35,
twin/double £50 to £70; deposit required. Set D £18 (price valid till Easter 1999). Special
breaks available

ALTON **Staffordshire**   map 5

Alton Towers

Alton, Stoke-on-Trent ST10 4DB
TEL: (01538) 704600   FAX: (01538) 704657

Family hotel with themed rooms, in the grounds of Alton Towers.

Few hotels do quite as much to entertain their younger guests than Alton
Towers: the lifts have ghostly music and flashing lights, and the bedrooms are
themed along the lines of exploration and botany. Hence you might bump into
an eccentric plant-hunter, or discover the combined helicopter and pirate-
galleon contraption which rises up through the atrium. Gardening-theme
bedrooms might have trellised wallpaper and watering-can lamps, while the
explorer rooms have bunk-beds and skull-and-crossbone lamps (ask for the
latter – they are more fun).

Dining takes place in the Secret Garden restaurant; in the evenings you'll find burgers, stir-fries, roasts and pasta; breakfasts bring croissants, fresh fruit and traditional fry-ups. The Nemesis breakfast is the option for those taking up the offer of exclusive use of that ride for hotel guests.

The service at the Alton Towers Hotel has much to commend it, but one correspondent wrote to complain of noise late in the evening and of an unhelpful staff response.

◗ Closed 24 to 30 Dec   ⏩ From M1, exit at Junction 23A and take A50 to Uttoxeter, following signs to Alton Towers; from M6, exit at Junction 16 and take A500 or A50 to Alton Towers. Private car park   🛏 167 family rooms, 8 suites; all with bathroom/WC; all with TV, hair-dryer, direct-dial telephone, some with mini-bar; trouser press available on request   ⏰ Restaurant, 2 bars, lounge, TV room, 2 drying-rooms, games room, garden; functions (max 200 people residential/non-residential), conferences; sauna, solarium, heated indoor swimming-pool; early suppers for children; cots, high chairs, toys, playrooms, babysitting, baby-listening, outdoor play area   ♿ Wheelchair access to hotel and restaurant, 41 ground-floor bedrooms, 9 rooms specially equipped for disabled people   ● No dogs; no smoking in restaurant or bedrooms   ▭ Amex, Delta, MasterCard, Switch, Visa   £ Single occupancy of family room £99 to £125, family room £99 to £125, suite from £225; deposit required. Cooked B £5; bar/bistro L £5.50; alc D £15. (Prices valid till Mar 1999.) Special breaks available

---

AMBLESIDE Cumbria   map 8

Chapel House

Kirkstone Road, Ambleside LA22 9DZ
TEL: (015394) 33143 (AND FAX)

Cheerful, homely guesthouse, on a steep hill on the outskirts of Ambleside, popular with walkers.

These two terraced cottages date from the sixteenth century. The oldest part of the village stands around the Bridge House and spills up the hill on the road to Kirkstone Pass. Though situated directly on the road, the guesthouse is not too noisy, and parking is possible on the street outside. It's a short, but steep, walk into Ambleside from here – good practice for the fells. Sandra and Duncan Hamer run this place in an informal, no-frills style. The lounge contains books and guides on the local area, and even one of Duncan's proud early watercolours. There's a tiny bar near a stone fireplace full of antique gadgets, and beyond (in the next cottage) is the dining-room, where Duncan dishes up surprisingly ambitious dinners with a variety of sauces. The bedrooms feature decent-quality cream bedspreads and clock radios, but are mostly small. Indeed, all the rooms are modestly sized and furnished, while some bathrooms seem stuck in a 'sixties time warp'. It's not a place where you can expect a great deal of privacy, so prepare to rub along with your fellow guests and compare notes on hill-climbing.

◗ Closed Jan & Feb; limited opening in Nov & Dec   ⏩ From M6 (Junction 36) take A591 into Ambleside; turn right into Smithy Brow leading to Kirkstone Road. On-street parking   🛏 2 single, 2 twin, 6 double; family rooms available some with shower/WC; all with hair-dryer, clock radio   ⏰ Dining-room, bar, lounge, drying-room; leisure

facilities nearby (free for guests); early suppers for children; cots, high chairs
  ⬥ No wheelchair access ● No dogs; no smoking in dining-room and bedrooms
  ⬜ None accepted ⏣ Single £42 to £45, single occupancy of twin/double £50 to £56, twin/double £84 to £90, family room £115; deposit required. Set D £16. Special breaks available

Drunken Duck Inn

Barngates, Ambleside LA22 0NG
TEL: (015394) 36347 FAX: (015394) 36781
EMAIL: info@drunkenduckinn.demon.co.uk

Friendly, informal, Lakeland pub, with better-than-average food and accommodation.

Though it's in a rural location, this attractive old pub is rarely short of customers, and it can get a bit noisy on fine summer weekends. It's popular for several reasons: its strategic situation between Ambleside and Hawkshead (two of Cumbria's most popular centres); its characterful bars serving a wide range of very decent ales and good pub food; and its simple but pleasant hotel accommodation, with a separate dining-room for residents. So it caters for locals and holidaymakers alike, with cheerful, informal service and open fires in winter. The bar is a beamed room with simple, wooden furnishings and a medley of pictures, horse brasses, harnesses, tankards, fox masks and farming implements dangling from the walls and beams. Here, too, you can find out how the pub got its name, from a tall tale related near the fireplace. The residents' dining-room is a modern but traditionally furnished extension to the rear, with classy plasterwork. The inventive dinner menus might include Bury black pudding or Gressingham duck breast, and there are good malts and wines to be had by the glass. The upper storey includes a quiet landing area featuring cherry-red walls and leather wing armchairs. Older pieces mingle happily with practical, modern fittings. Some bedrooms are in a quieter annexe.

◑ Closed 24 & 25 Dec 🔲 Take B5286 from Ambleside towards Hawkshead for 2½ miles; turn right and follow signs to Drunken Duck Inn. Private car park 🛏 1 twin, 7 double, 1 four-poster; all with bathroom/WC; all with TV, hair-dryer, direct-dial telephone ⊘ 3 dining-rooms, bar, drying-room, library; fishing; early suppers for children; high chairs ⬥ Wheelchair access to hotel (1 step) and dining-rooms, WC (unisex), 1 ground-floor bedroom ● Dogs in bedrooms by arrangement; no smoking in dining-rooms and library ⬜ Amex, Delta, MasterCard, Switch, Visa ⏣ Single occupancy of twin/double £45 to £55, twin/double £65 to £75, four-poster £75 to £90; deposit required. Bar/bistro L £4.50; alc D £16.50. Special breaks available

Riverside Lodge NEW ENTRY

Rothay Bridge, Ambleside LA22 0EH
TEL: (015394) 34208

Charming riverside guesthouse within easy walking distance of the centre of Ambleside.

This creeper-clad house stands by the roadbridge across the River Rothay, a busy junction for holiday traffic, but is quietly secluded in its own mature grounds of award-winning shrubs, trees and lawns. The lush banks beside the house, which is approached by a separate footbridge, evoke a most peaceful scene. Riverside Lodge dates back to the early 1700s, and has quite a bit of history to it (was Bonnie Prince Charlie here?) – it's full of character inside. The cosily furnished lounge and dining-room lie just inside the main entrance from the car park, both cheerful, cottagey rooms with fringed sidelights, beams and exposed stonework. Ladderback chairs, plants and horse-brasses give it a welcoming feel, and open fires blaze when the weather's chilly. Bedrooms are similarly cosy, with simple and fairly conventional décor – honey pine, pastels and chintzes. One is on the ground floor. The Lodge makes a convenient base for touring, with easy parking in the grounds and access to Loughrigg Fell, popular with walkers.

● Closed Chr 🗲 Approaching Ambleside from south on A591, take left fork (A593), signposted Coniston; where road goes over Rothay Bridge follow signs for Riverside Lodge. Private car park ⌸ 1 twin, 3 double, 1 family room; all with bathroom/WC exc 1 double with shower/WC; all with TV, room service, hair-dryer ⌘ Dining-room, lounge, drying-room, garden; fishing ⌖ No wheelchair access ● No children under 10; no dogs; smoking in bedrooms only ▭ MasterCard, Visa £ Twin/double £46 to £62, family room £58 to £77; deposit required. Special breaks available

Rothay Manor

Rothay Bridge, Ambleside LA22 0EH
TEL: (015394) 33605   FAX: (015394) 33607
EMAIL: hotel@rothaym.demon.co.uk

Elegant Regency house, offering reassuring, well-practised hospitality and excellent food.

Most visitors to Ambleside spot the signs to this hotel while whirling round the one-way system in their cars, but within its secluded and established grounds the traffic noise is muted to a distant buzz. It's a quietly grand, listed house, dating from the early nineteenth century; a former prosperous merchant's home, it retains many gracious period features, including fine Regency cast-ironwork and acanthus-leaf mouldings. Under the same family ownership as a hotel for nearly thirty years, it has built up an enviable reputation for high-quality food, service and accommodation. Regular visitors return for reliable helpings of old-fashioned, well-mannered, country-house style and immaculate housekeeping. Two soothing lounges (one non-smoking) flank the entrance hall, decorated in cream and mulberry hues, with jugs of flowers and elegantly highlighted plasterwork. The restaurant is formally set with heavy, fluted wineglasses and, in the evenings, candles on gleaming mahogany tables. The individually decorated bedrooms feature easy chairs, fitted storage space and good bathrooms. Those with balconies have clever, double-glazed french windows, which open in Velux or casement style. Menus are mercifully straightforward, and afternoon teas are a legend. For all its elegance, it's a child-friendly hotel, offering 'scary monster pizzas' and boiled eggs with soldiers at high tea.

◑ Closed 3 Jan to 5 Feb 🗷 On A593, ¼ mile south-west of Ambleside, towards Coniston. Private car park 🛏 2 single, 3 twin, 5 double, 5 family rooms, 3 suites; some in annexe; all with bathroom/WC; all with TV, room service, hair-dryer, direct-dial telephone ✅ 2 restaurants, bar, 2 lounges, garden; functions (max 25 people residential/non-residential), conferences; croquet; leisure facilities nearby (free for guests); early suppers for children; cots, high chairs, baby-listening ♿ Wheelchair access to hotel (ramp) and restaurants, WC (unisex), 2 ground-floor bedrooms specially equipped for disabled people ● No children under 6 in restaurants eves; no dogs; no smoking in some public rooms 🗀 Amex, Delta, Diners, MasterCard, Switch, Visa £ Single £78, single occupancy of twin/double £98, twin/double £125, family room £125, suite £175; deposit required. Set L £14, D £25/£31; alc L £14. Special breaks available

---

Rowanfield   NEW ENTRY

Kirkstone Road, Ambleside LA22 9ET
TEL: (015394) 33686   FAX: (015394) 31569

Star guesthouse on the Kirkstone Pass road, stylish, welcoming and beautifully located. And they cook well.

Hidden behind a farm gate on a tricky bend leading up to the pass (approach it from the Ambleside end; the angle's too sharp to turn if you're heading downhill), Rowanfield is easily missed. But Philip and Jane Butcher have been here nine years now, and are well into their stride. This is a peach of a place, overlooking the slopes of Wansfell and a tracery of stone walls where sheep and Highland cattle roam. It's no longer a working farm, but the house is a typical Cumbrian farmhouse of about 1840, attractively proportioned and sympathetically renovated. Inside and out, it's in immaculate condition: the kind of place you could imagine photographed in some style magazine, but where you immediately feel at home. Two squarish ground-floor rooms house a relaxing lounge full of toning furnishings in comfortable groups by a wood-burning stove. The dining-room is in a more cottagey style with painted chairs and Laura Ashley-look wallpaper. It's stylish and pleasantly unfussy – just one or two pictures on each wall and half a dozen well-spaced tables. Set dinners (order in advance) prepared by Philip, a trained chef, are delicious and simple, though served rather early for guests who want to listen to The Archers – at 7pm; Rowanfield is unlicensed, so bring your own alcohol. For breakfast, you might have plum compote or American pancakes. Bedrooms, all individual, are decorated with terrific flair and a pleasure to behold, with lots of careful attention to detail. Room 8, at the top of the house, is one of the most charming, with sloping ceilings and a beautifully embroidered bed-quilt. Guests have use of a large fridge-freezer on the landing. Sadly for singles, hefty supplements weight costs towards shared occupancy.

◑ Closed mid-Nov to Mar (open Chr and New Year); restaurant closed Sun eve
🗷 Just north of village centre, turn right at signpost 'Kirkstone 3'; Rowanfield is ¾ mile along, on right-hand side. Private car park 🛏 2 twin, 5 double; 3 with bathroom/WC, 4 with shower/WC; all with TV, hair-dryer ✅ Dining-room, lounge, drying-room,

garden   No wheelchair access   No children under 8; no dogs; no smoking
Amex, Delta, MasterCard, Switch, Visa   Single occupancy of twin/double £49 to
£56; twin/double £58 to £72; deposit required. Set D £20. Special breaks available

Wateredge Hotel

Borrans Road, Waterhead Bay, Ambleside LA22 0EP
TEL: (015394) 32332   FAX: (015394) 31878

Restful, lakeside hotel, offering traditional comfort and picture-postcard views of Windermere.

Sandwiched between a busy road and the shores of Windermere, the hotel certainly has an appropriate name. Despite the passing traffic, these much-expanded, seventeenth-century fishing cottages manage to seem utterly peaceful inside. Typical clients are older visitors who enjoy peace and quiet, and relaxing in the three civilised lounge areas near the entrance. One such room admittedly has a discreetly concealed television, but most guests choose the upper lounge, where the morning papers lie and big picture windows frame much more entertaining scenes of the gardens and watercraft crossing the lake from the nearby Steamer Pier or the hotel's private jetty. Light lunches (soup and sandwiches) are served in this room. The oldest section of the building houses the snug bar (all beams and knick-knacks) and the twin-part dining-room off it, which is genteel with its fanned napkins and balloon-backed chairs; menus are also in a traditional vein. The bedrooms are clean, fresh and tidy, and are decorated in traditional country style with Laura Ashley wallpapers and slightly dated pastels. They vary greatly in shape and size (the quirky architecture causes some awkward arrangements), but are all attractive and well kept. The larger ground-floor rooms have balconies and patios and command the highest tariffs. All in all, a well-established favourite, managed with confidence and consideration.

Closed mid-Dec to mid-Jan   1 mile south of Ambleside on A591 at Waterhead, adjacent to Steamer Pier. Private car park   3 single, 3 twin, 6 double, 1 family room, 9 suites; all with bathroom/WC exc 2 singles with shower/WC; all with TV, room service, hair-dryer, direct-dial telephone;   Dining-room, bar, 4 lounges (1 with TV), drying-room, garden; rowing boat, leisure facilities nearby (free for guests); early suppers for children, by arrangement   No wheelchair access   No children under 7; dogs in bedrooms only, by arrangement; no smoking in dining-room and 2 lounges   Amex, Delta, MasterCard, Switch, Visa   Single £68 to £84, single occupancy of twin/double £79 to £115, twin/double £114 to £150, family room £164 to £196, suite £156 to £192 (rates incl dinner); deposit required. Bar/bistro L £10. Special breaks available

'I complained at one hotel that I had been woken three times in the middle of the night by drunken residents bellowing outside my door. "What a pity," said the owner with a laugh. "We sleep in another building, so I never heard a thing."'
On a hotel in Wales

APPLEBY-IN-WESTMORLAND Cumbria   map 10

Appleby Manor   [NEW ENTRY]

Roman Road, Appleby-in-Westmorland CA16 6JD
TEL: (017683) 51571   FAX: (017683) 52888
EMAIL: appleby.manor@btinternet.com
WEB SITE: www.btinternet.com/-appleby.manor

Friendly, well-managed hotel with extensive facilities in lovely Eden Valley setting.

First impressions may suggest that this large, portentous building of red sandstone is rather 'corporate' in style. A leisure club, conference wing and membership of the Best Western hotel consortium may not be quite what you're looking for on a touring holiday in the Lake District. At close quarters, though, this place reveals great individuality. It's completely unpretentious and has a genuinely personal touch – qualities engendered by its enthusiastic owner, Nick Swinscoe, and his well-trained staff. Judging by the letters we've received from contented visitors, they're getting things right at Appleby Manor, hence this year's upgrade from a round-up to a full entry. The atmosphere is upbeat and dynamic – improvements are in progress on all fronts, including extensions to the conservatory and continuous refurbishment of the accommodation. It caters unstuffily for a wide range of tastes: you can wallow in a hot jacuzzi, play snooker or Monopoly, stride off across the Pennines, or channel-hop through videos and satellite TV. Sustenance varies from hearty cream teas and a boggling choice of malts at the bar to ambitious cuisine by toqued chefs. There's plenty of well-furnished lounge and bar space to relax in, and bedrooms are well equipped and comfortably spacious. Disproportionately high bathroom ceilings are cunningly lowered by baffle lighting systems, and half-shade lights make for easier reading in bed. The best rooms have four-posters and panoramic views.

◑ Closed 24 to 26 Dec   🔁 From south, leave M6 at Junction 38, take B6260 to Appleby; drive through village to T-junction, turn left, then first right, follow road for ¾ mile. Private car park   🛏 8 twin, 12 double, 5 four-poster, 5 family rooms; 7 in annexe; all with bathroom/WC; all with TV, room service, hair-dryer, direct-dial telephone, fax point   ✓ Restaurant, bar, 2 lounges, 2 drying-rooms, conservatory, games room, leisure club, garden; conferences (max 34 people incl 30 residential), functions; sauna, solarium, heated indoor swimming-pool, steam room, pool table, snooker, croquet, table-tennis; early suppers for children; cots, high chairs, baby-listening   ♿ Wheelchair access to hotel and restaurant, 10 ground-floor bedrooms, 2 rooms with some modifications for disabled people   ● Dogs in annexe only; no smoking in restaurant and some bedrooms   🗀 Amex, Delta, Diners, MasterCard, Switch, Visa   £ Single occupancy of twin/double £60 to £67, twin/double £80 to £94, four-poster £90 to £114, family room £80 to £94; deposit required. Continental B £9, cooked B £9; bar/bistro L £6; alc L, D £22. Special breaks available

---

 This denotes that the hotel is in an exceptionally peaceful situation where you can be assured of a restful stay.

Underscar Manor

Applethwaite, Keswick CA12 4PH
TEL: (017687) 75000   FAX: (017687) 74904

Italianate manor in lovely grounds, with exceptional food and extravagant furnishings.

Underscar Manor has quite a history; built for a Wakefield cotton baron in the 1850s, it occupies a truly magnificent site at the base of Skiddaw, overlooking astonishing vistas of Derwentwater. The house itself is an eye-catcher – an Italian-style campanile over the main entrance frames an imposing lantern stairwell. Its grounds encompass velvety lawns and a fine collection of specimen conifers – home to a fair proportion of Cumbria's dwindling red-squirrel population (notices at the end of the drive warn motorists to watch out for them; they are less strong and swift than their pestilent grey cousins). If the house itself has an interesting past, so do its owners, Pauline and Derek Harrison, whose hardworking esprit de corps has contributed to Underscar Manor's present-day success. Of self-confessed 'humble' origins, they worked their way to successful restaurateurdom in Manchester, and then achieved their dream as Lakeland hotel-keepers. In the last eight years they have energetically transformed Underscar Manor into a distinctive and luxurious place, whose furnishings are as sybaritic as its architecture. Bedrooms are decked out in honeymoon style and crammed with extra comforts; bathrooms boast gilt fittings and floral basins; while public rooms are draped in expensive fabrics and swags of flowers and fruit. The conservatory-style restaurant is understandably a focal point, sparkling with crystal and floral centrepieces. Lucky diners might choose a lobster and king prawn hot-pot gateau, followed by saddle steak of local venison with potato cakes, wild mushrooms and port wine and redcurrant sauce. For all this, Underscar manages to be a homely and relaxing place, welcoming rather than daunting, with soft toys adding a winsome touch.

○ Open all year   ⚡ Leave M6 at Junction 40 and take A66 to Keswick for 17 miles; at large roundabout take third exit and turn immediately right to Underscar; entrance is ½ mile on right. Private car park   ⌸ 11 double; all with bathroom/WC; all with TV, room service, hair-dryer, direct-dial telephone; tea/coffee-making facilities on request ✧ 2 restaurants, 2 lounges, drying-room, conservatory, garden; functions (max 30 people incl up to 22 residential), conferences   ᨷ No wheelchair access   ● No children under 12; no dogs; no smoking in restaurants   ▭ Amex, Delta, MasterCard, Switch, Visa   £ Single occupancy of double £85 to £120, double £150 to £250 (rates incl dinner); deposit required. Set L £25; alc L £38. Special breaks available

Denotes somewhere you can rely on a good meal – either the hotel features in the 1999 edition of our sister publication, The Good Food Guide, *or our inspectors thought the cooking impressive, whether particularly competent home cooking or more lavish cuisine.*

APULDRAM West Sussex map 3

Crouchers Bottom

Birdham Road, Apuldram, Chichester PO20 7EH
TEL: (01243) 784995   FAX: (01243) 539797

Unpretentious, modern rooms in this hotel just outside the elegant cathedral city of Chichester.

Plenty of changes are afoot in the nether regions of the Croucher properties – Drew and Lesley Wilson are literally building on their past success, expanding the 'coach-house' to add more bedrooms and extending the bar and dining-room. The hotel's expansion is a testament to its winning combination of clean, simple rooms and friendly, relaxed service. As we went to press, all the building work was due to be completed by the start of summer 1998. The house is situated on the main A286 road south of Chichester, but it's not one of Britain's busiest highways, so don't worry about the noise. The public rooms in the main house are unstuffily decorated: the conservatory-style dining-room is bright and airy, while the lounge's exposed floorboards are covered with rugs and leather sofas. In the black, wooden coach-house across the courtyard, most of the bedrooms are on the ground floor and are cheerily decorated in plain colours. Some of the bathrooms are on the small side, but all are spotlessly clean and fresh. Culture vultures heading off to attend a performance at the Chichester Festival Theatre can enjoy a pre-theatre dinner, choosing from a three-course menu of home-cooked food. Everyone else can dine at leisure on the likes of beef carbonade or poussin served with wild mushrooms.

◑ Open all year ▨ 2 miles south of Chichester on A286, just after Black Horse pub, on opposite side of road. Private car park ⤙ 5 twin, 9 double, 1 four-poster, 1 family room; all in coach-house; all with bathroom/WC; all with TV, room service, hair-dryer, direct-dial telephone, some with mini-bar, trouser press ⊘ 2 dining-rooms, bar, lounge, garden; functions (max 45 people incl up to 38 residential), conferences; early suppers for children; cots, high chairs, baby-listening ♿ Wheelchair access to hotel (ramp) and restaurant, 12 ground-floor bedrooms, 2 specially equipped for disabled people ⬤ No children under 12 in dining-room eves; no dogs in public rooms; no smoking in bedrooms ▭ Amex, Diners, MasterCard, Visa £ Single occupancy of twin/double £45 to £55, twin/double £65 to £85, four-poster £75 to £95, family room £100 to £105; deposit required. Set D £19.50; alc D £25. Special breaks available

---

ARNCLIFFE North Yorkshire map 8

Amerdale House

Arncliffe, Littondale, Skipton BD23 5QE
TEL: (01756) 770250 (AND FAX)

An idyllic setting and excellent food are the main attractions at this small-scale, country-house hotel.

Littondale is arguably one of Yorkshire's most beautiful valleys, and the village of Arncliffe, home to Nigel and Paula Crapper's Victorian manor, is the sort of place where sheep have to be shooed off the cricket pitch before play can commence. This is ideal hiking territory, and you would be pushed to find another base with such a warm, accommodating style, elegant furnishings, beautifully kept gardens and, at the end of a day's walking or touring, reliably praiseworthy food to boot. The bedrooms are not aiming for any style awards, but are pleasantly decorated, with relaxing, light colour schemes and oak furniture made by a local carpenter – Littondale provides a superb panorama of its namesake. Welcoming nibbles will keep you going until the main event in the evening, when Nigel's cuisine takes centre-stage. Modern, imaginative dishes are combined with more traditional choices in generous portions to much acclaim; you might start with a salad of smoked chicken, sun dried tomatoes and Parmesan, slot in a second course of Tay smoked salmon, before moving on to monkfish with bacon and scallops, and then finishing with Yorkshire curd tart, or local Dales cheeses with home-made oatcakes.

◗ Closed mid-Nov to mid-Mar ⌇ On edge of village of Arncliffe; 7 miles north of Grassington. Private car park ⌇ 3 twin, 7 double, 1 four-poster; 1 in annexe; most with bathroom/WC, some with shower/WC; all with TV, room service, hair-dryer, some with trouser press ⌇ Dining-room, bar, lounge, library, garden; early suppers for children; cots, high chairs ⌇ No wheelchair access ● No dogs; no smoking in dining-room ⌇ Delta, MasterCard, Switch, Visa £ Single occupancy of twin/double £73, twin/double/four-poster £125 to £131 (rates incl dinner). Special breaks available

---

ARRATHORNE North Yorkshire map 9

Elmfield Country House

Arrathorne, Bedale DL8 1NE
TEL: (01677) 450558 FAX: (01677) 450557

Squeaky clean, modern guesthouse, in a tranquil, rural spot.

Elmfield Country House is clearly a labour of love for its owners, Edith and Jim Lillie, whose unceasing toils ensure that you won't find a speck of dust in their regularly redecorated and spruced-up house. The only fly in the ointment is the rather off-putting, brown, roughcast exterior that can cause you the odd twinge of misgiving as you draw near, driving along a track through the rolling fields, having paid due heed to the signs that warn you to look out for learner tank-drivers from Catterick. The pretty garden, which has koi carp swimming in its ponds and a burbling waterfall, helps to soften the edges, but, once inside, the genuine warmth of the Lillies' welcome will soon put the smile back on your face. The spacious and sprawling house offers enough room to allow families to do their own thing: children can play table football in the large, sunny conservatory, while their parents slump into the cane chairs, bolstered with bright and comfy floral cushions, to plan trips out to the local dales and moors. The bedrooms are all of a good size and spotlessly kept, and their individual décor includes patchwork quilts, lacy drapes, the odd brass bed and a locally made four-poster. Edith sticks to plain, homely English cooking in the evening, based on roasts, grills and home-made pies.

◑ Open all year ⚅ From Bedale, take A684 towards Leyburn; turn right at first crossroads after Patrick Brompton; Elmfield is 1½ miles on right. Private car park ⊫ 3 twin, 3 double, 1 four-poster, 2 family rooms; 4 with bathroom/WC, 5 with shower/WC; all with TV, limited room service, hair-dryer, direct-dial telephone; iron on request ⊘ Dining-room, bar, lounge, drying-room, conservatory, games room, garden; functions (max 50 people incl up to 20 residential), conferences; fishing, solarium; early suppers for children; cots, high chairs ⅍ Wheelchair access to hotel and dining-room, 2 ground-floor bedrooms specially equipped for disabled people ● No dogs; no smoking in some public rooms and some bedrooms ▭ MasterCard, Visa £ Single occupancy of twin/double £31, twin/double £44, four-poster £50, family room £52; deposit required. Set D £12

ASHBOURNE Derbyshire

map 5

Callow Hall

Mappleton Road, Ashbourne DE6 2AA
TEL: (01335) 343403   FAX: (01335) 343624

A secluded country-house hotel with a relaxing atmosphere.

What a wonderful gravy train Victorian law must have been! This great, grey manor house, with its bell-tower, mullions and acres of parkland, was built by a solicitor from Ashbourne in 1850 – only gradually to be run down into a dilapidated wreck by the time David Spencer and family came here 15 years ago. Their work in restoring the place to its former glory is into the stage of finishing touches now: rampant rhododendrons are being cut back to reveal Victorian woodland walks, and the spacious rooms are filled with interesting furniture and decorations – well-used leather chesterfields in the sitting-room, and old maps and gilt-framed paintings dotted throughout. David's obvious pleasure in getting the basics right is revealed in such things as the good, strong showers; as one reader remarked, 'comfort, cleanliness and care and atmosphere were all excellent', and another praised the good beds. This attention to detail also manifests itself in the food supplies, which include home-cured bacon, home-smoked salmon and home-made bread. Yet one correspondent complained that the menu was exactly the same for three nights running. Another criticised the choice for vegetarians. More positively, one visitor reported: 'Callow Hall has been excellent, especially the food'.

◑ Open all year ⚅ Follow A515 through Ashbourne towards Buxton; turn left at Bowling Green pub, then first right into Mappleton Road; entrance is on right after humpbacked bridge. Private car park ⊫ 3 twin, 10 double, 1 four-poster, 1 family room, 1 suite; all with bathroom/WC; all with TV, room service, hair-dryer, trouser press, direct-dial telephone ⊘ 3 restaurants, bar, sitting-room, garden; conferences (max 30 people incl up to 16 residential), functions; fishing; early suppers for children; cots, high chairs ⅍ Wheelchair access to hotel and restaurants, 1 ground-floor bedroom specially equipped for disabled people ● Children discouraged from restaurants eves; dogs in bedrooms only, by arrangement; no smoking in restaurants or bedrooms ▭ Amex, Diners, MasterCard, Switch, Visa £ Single occupancy of twin/double £75 to £95, twin/double £115 to £140, four-poster/family room £140, suite £170; deposit required. Set Sun L £18.50, D £37; alc D £32

ASHBURTON Devon   map 1

Holne Chase

Two Bridges Road, Ashburton, Newton Abbot TQ13 7NS
TEL: (01364) 631471   FAX: (01364) 631453
EMAIL: info@holne-chase.co.uk
WEB SITE: www.holne-chase.co.uk/

---

*Totally peaceful, grand country house in spectacular grounds, but
some quibbles about service and prices.*

When our inspector arrived, a pop video was being filmed in the grounds of
Holne Chase, and the grand country house was all-a-kilter. This jetsetting mob
just didn't fit with the quiet reserve of most of Philippa and Sebastian Hughes'
guests: people who want to escape fast living and come to where 'you can hear
the grass grow', who want to be able to walk around the vast wooded grounds (it
takes an hour and a half) and see no one else, who want to feel pampered in an
up-market, friendly way. A Devon moth-collector comes once a month to search
for rare species. The walled Victorian garden provides fresh flowers for the house
and vegetables for the table; if you're lucky you'll see red deer, buzzards and
herons from your bedroom window. The atmosphere inside is one of a
comfortable country house. There's no dress code for dinner, and the new chef
Ross Duncan's modern English menu features dishes such as fillet of red mullet
with tomato salsa, followed by tenderloin of pork with an apple and thyme
crumble. Bedrooms in the main house vary from the grandly baronial to the
glamorously intimate, with Vernford Brook being perhaps the nicest. Those in
the converted coach house have mezzanine levels.

   Prices and service in the restaurant have presented problems – one reader
complained about too many (high) supplements, high bar prices, and variable
service, especially at breakfast. More reports, please.

◑ Open all year   ⊋ Travelling south on A38, take second Ashburton exit (first if
travelling north); follow signs to Two Bridges for 3 miles; hotel is on right ¼ mile after
Holne bridge. Private car park   ⊨ 10 twin/double, 7 suites; 4 in annexe (suites);
family rooms available all with bathroom/WC; all with TV, room service, hair-dryer,
direct-dial telephone, some with mini-bar, trouser press   ⍋ 2 restaurants, bar, lounge,
drying-room, library; private sitting-rooms in suites; park and woodland, gardens;
conferences (max 75 people incl up to 17 residential), functions; fly fishing, putting
green, croquet; golf courses nearby (reduced rates for guests); shooting, riding nearby;
early suppers for children (high tea 6pm, booking required); cots and high chairs, baby-
listening   ⑤ Wheelchair access to hotel and restaurant (1 step, ramp available; WC), 1
ground-floor bedroom, 1 specially equipped for disabled people   ● No children under
10 at D; no dogs in public rooms, dogs £5 per night in bedrooms; no smoking in
restaurant   ▭ Amex, Delta, Diners, MasterCard, Switch, Visa   £ Single occupancy
of twin/double £75, twin/double £118 to £136, four-poster £158, family room £173,
suite £158; deposit required. Bar/bistro L £6.50; set L £20, D £25; alc L, D £29.50.
Special breaks available

---

*Many hotels offer special rates for stays of a few nights or more. It is
worth enquiring when you book.*

ASHTON KEYNES Wiltshire   map 2

Two Cove House

Ashton Keynes, Swindon SN6 6NS
TEL: (01285) 861221

Traditional family home, with plenty of history and well-kept gardens.

It seems fitting that the Hartlands settled in Two Cove House after their years of serving in the forces, as this house of pretty, Cotswold stone has plenty of military history of its own, including a Civil War fratricide. Today its peaceful situation at the heart of the village, and the secluded garden in which the Hartlands take so much pride, belies such turbulence. Inside, however, there are plenty of regimental reminders in the form of the major's collection of old swords and uniforms, and his strategic-planning skills come in extremely useful for visitors wondering how best to tackle the sights of the Cotswolds – the 'briefing room' includes a large, framed map, stacks of local information, including menus from pubs and restaurants, and even videos of the main attractions. The 'clean and comfortable' bedrooms are of a good size, are equipped with brass or wooden beds, and have cheerful colour schemes. Fresh milk is available in a fridge on the landing. Being heavily involved in village life, the Hartlands require at least 24 hours' notice if you would like to eat in, and will join you at the dinner table. A typical summer menu might start with chilled tomato and orange soup, go on to salmon mayonnaise, and finish with a pavlova, or chocolate mousse, and coffee. Otherwise, the major can provide you with a guide to good local inns and restaurants, including the pub just around the corner. 'The Hartlands were very welcoming,' reports one correspondent.

◑ Closed Chr; dining-room closed Sun eve ⬏ In Ashton Keynes, turn east at White Hart, and left 100 yards further on. Private car park 🛏 2 twin, 2 double; twins with bathroom/WC, 1 double with shower/WC; some with TV; hair-dryer on request
✓ Dining-room, lounge, drying-room, garden; early suppers for children; cot, baby-listening ⅙ No wheelchair access ● No children under 10 in dining-room eves; dogs in bedrooms only, by arrangement; no smoking in dining-room ☐ None accepted £ Single occupancy of twin/double £34, twin/double £50 to £54; deposit required. Set D £17.50. Special breaks available

ASHWATER Devon   map 1

Blagdon Manor

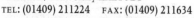

Ashwater, Beaworthy EX21 5DF
TEL: (01409) 211224   FAX: (01409) 211634
EMAIL: blagdon_manor@compuserve.com

High-quality accommodation in particularly cared-for country house.

Tim and Gill Casey spent 18 years in Hong Kong prior to taking over Blagdon Manor. They went out with a suitcase and returned with a 40-foot container, most of the contents of which now feature somewhere in the house. Tim was a flight engineer on jet planes, so his unruffled attitude is most conducive to hotel-keeping, while Gill is the creative genius behind the décor, curtains and flower arrangements. As a result the house has a particularly cherished atmosphere, and guests can expect to feel pampered and welcomed. From the outside, the hotel doesn't appear to live up to the grandeur of its title as a manor, although its history dates back to the Domesday Book. There's a date proclaiming '1683' in the dining-room and, as previous owners became more affluent, so they built more and more. It seems larger on the inside, perhaps because the outside is dwarfed by the fabulous aspect of the lawn, with its endless views, pond, parterre and kitchen garden. There are even outdoor heaters so that guests can enjoy a pre-dinner drink while watching the sunset, no matter how chilly the weather – or they can play snooker in the bar. The décor inside comprises a happy combination of English beams, sophisticated pastel colours and Far Eastern antiques. The set dinner is taken communally around a large table, and may consist of roasted English goats' cheese with a chicory, orange and walnut salad, followed by a suprême of guinea-fowl served on a bed of puy lentils with bacon and thyme. The bedrooms are of a high standard, with elegant, voluptuous fabrics and furnishings, and vanity lights around all the mirrors.

◗ Closed 25 & 26 Dec   ☑ Leave Launceston on A388 Holsworthy road; pass first sign to Ashwater; turn right at second sign then take first right signposted Blagdon; entrance is on right. Private car park   🅿 2 twin, 4 double, 1 four-poster; all with bathroom/WC; all with TV, hair-dryer, direct-dial telephone, some with trouser press   ⊘ Dining-room, bar, 2 lounges, library, games room, garden; conferences (max 14 people incl up to 7 residential); croquet   ♿ No wheelchair access   ● No children under 12; no dogs; smoking in bar and library only   ⊟ Amex, Delta, MasterCard, Switch, Visa   £ Single occupancy of twin/double £60 to £70, twin/double/four-poster £95 to £110; deposit required. Set D £19.50

ASKRIGG North Yorkshire   map 8

Helm   NEW ENTRY   No under 10s

Askrigg, Leyburn DL8 3JF
TEL: (01969) 650443   FAX: (01969) 650443 (daytime)
EMAIL: drewhelm@compuserve.com

Stylish cottage oozing with character and with unbeatable views over Wensleydale.

John and Barbara Drew's seventeenth-century cottage perched high above Wensleydale takes a bit of finding; once there, a pretty dovecot, whose snowy-white occupants roost on the slates and rough stones of the house, is the first sign that this is not the average twee cottage. Inside, there's bags of character, for example an underground dairy and a massive stone cheese press left over from the days when Wensleydale cheese was made here. Local cheeses still round off one of the enticingly ambitious evening meals that John and Barbara offer along with a surprisingly serious choice of wines. Expect the likes of venison with a cassis gravy, monkfish with a fresh herb crust, or guinea-fowl in red wine and wild mushrooms – even at breakfast you have a choice of half a dozen gourmet sausages. As a designer whose work you may see on the labels and logos of the local dairy, Barbara has an eye for style that has produced three delightful bedrooms, each with a distinct identity that combines antiques with modern touches: Askrigg has a walnut bed, mahogany wardrobe and dressing-table and Georgian fireplace with hob grates; Bainbridge is light and airy in blue and cream with stencilled wall friezes; while Whitfield has a lovely suite of Edwardian satinwood furniture and a claw-foot bath set against a warm orange and lemon-toned backdrop – you may wake to find a cow munching outside the bedside window!

◑ Closed mid-Nov to 2 Jan ⊿ From A684 take Askrigg turn at Bainbridge; turn right at T-junction to Askrigg; after 200 yards turn left at no-through-road sign. Go uphill, taking right fork; Helm is last house on right. Private car park ⤶ 1 twin, 2 double; all with shower/WC exc 1 double with bathroom/WC; all with TV, hair-dryer, direct-dial telephone ⊘ Dining-room, lounge, drying-room, garden ⑁ No wheelchair access ● No children under 10; no dogs or smoking ⊟ Delta, MasterCard, Visa £ Single occupancy of twin/double £48, twin/double £72; deposit required. Set D £16.50. Special breaks available

---

ASTON CLINTON Buckinghamshire
map 3

Bell Inn

Aston Clinton, Aylesbury HP22 5HP
TEL: (01296) 630252   FAX: (01296) 631250

Country-house comforts and French flamboyance combined in a traditional coaching-inn, made even more appealing by a policy of keeping room rates reasonable.

Think flagged floors, oak panelling, open fires... and then change tack and consider hand-painted four-posters, fireside rugs and plump armchairs. The Bell Inn combines the best of both these worlds. The former are to be found on the ground floor of this red-brick coaching-inn; the latter upstairs, and in the long-ago converted brewery across the side-road. The country-house comforts are the product of fifty years' experience and an abundance of quiet good taste (the Harris family is a pioneer of the English country-house hotel). The bedrooms in the inn itself creak characterfully underfoot, and may bend around doglegs or drop by a step or two; the two facing the busy road are protected with fairly effective double glazing. The courtyard rooms across the side-road overlook either a much complimented rose garden (blooming marvellously in July and August) or a walled garden draped in wistaria.

The Bell's restaurant may come as a surprise to the uninitiated after the smoky woodwork and polished flagstones: a gracefully curving corridor opens into a broad room, the walls painted vibrant green, with murals of seasonal foliage and feathered friends. Aylesbury duckling is the natural local speciality, while a curry-spiced codling, or chicken with a leek and crayfish mousseline, serve as examples of the chef's inventive approach to classical French cooking.

◑ Open all year ⤢ In Aston Clinton village, off A41 between Tring and Aylesbury. Private car park ⮎ 9 twin, 5 double, 2 four-poster, 4 suites; some in annexe; all with bathroom/WC; all with TV, room service, hair-dryer, direct-dial telephone, some with trouser press; no tea/coffee-making facilities in rooms ⌀ Restaurant, bar, drawing-room, smoking-room, garden; functions (max 85 people incl up to 40 residential), conferences; croquet; early suppers for children; cots, high chairs, babysitting, baby-listening ♿ Wheelchair access to hotel (ramp) and restaurant, WC (M, F), 7 ground-floor bedrooms ◒ No children under 12 in restaurant Sat eves; no dogs; no smoking in restaurant/some bedrooms ☐ Amex, Delta, MasterCard, Switch, Visa £ Single occupancy of twin/double £60 to £90, twin/double £60 to £90, four-poster £80 to £90, suite £90 to £130; deposit required. Continental B £6, cooked B £9.50; set L £12/£14.50; alc L, D £29.50. Special breaks available

---

ATHERSTONE Warwickshire   map 5

Chapel House   [NEW ENTRY]

Friar's Gate, Atherstone CV9 1EY
TEL: (01827) 718949   FAX: (01827) 717702

Quiet, town-house hotel, in a pretty, Warwickshire market town.

If Atherstone is a quiet corner of the Midlands well placed for Birmingham, Coventry and Leicester, then Chapel House is situated in a quiet corner that is well placed for the market town itself. Tucked down the side of St Mary's church, this eighteenth-century town house has an easy, relaxing atmosphere, with hints of French elegance – a mix that attracts both business people and couples on short breaks. The dining-room looks out on a walled garden, and, with its swagged curtains, warm colours and marble fireplace, manages to be both cosy and rather grand at the same time. The cooking is often French in flavour: a typical table d'hôte, five-course dinner might include pike mousseline, a pan-fried duck breast, goats' cheese with salad and, finally, poached pear with fresh figs, raspberries and liquorice ice-cream. The bedrooms have a simple, old-fashioned style; Room 5 is a particularly pleasant double, with its smart blue colour scheme and antique bed.

◑ Closed 25 & 26 Dec; dining-rooms closed Sun eve, bank hol Mon ⤢ From A5, follow signs into Atherstone town centre; turn right into Friar's Gate at Nationwide building society; hotel is to right of church. On-street parking (free) ⮎ 4 single, 3 twin, 6 double; some with bathroom/WC, most with shower/WC; all with TV, room service, direct-dial telephone, clock radio ⌀ 2 dining-rooms, lounge, conservatory, garden; functions (max 50 people incl up to 13 residential), conferences; early suppers for children; cots, babysitting, baby-listening ♿ No wheelchair access ◒ No children under 10 in dining-rooms eves; no dogs; no smoking in dining-rooms ☐ Amex, Delta, Diners, MasterCard, Switch, Visa £ Single £48 to £55, single occupancy of twin/double £53 to £62, twin/double £65 to £75; deposit required. Set L £12; alc L, D £22.50. (Prices valid till Jan 1999.) Special breaks available

---

Where we know an establishment accepts credit cards, we list them. There may be a surcharge if you pay by credit card. It is always best to check when booking whether the card you want to use is acceptable.

AYLESBURY Buckinghamshire   map 3

Hartwell House

Oxford Road, Aylesbury HP17 8NL
TEL: (01296) 747444   FAX: (01296) 747450
EMAIL: info@hartwell-house.com
WEB SITE: www.hartwell-house.com/

*Fantastically grand Jacobean stately home oozing with stories,
statues and staff.*

As you drive past the gates, you know you're in for a treat. Every inch of the
grounds, sculpted by a student of Capability Brown, signals opulence: by the
time you've passed the (private) church and the restored coach houses, looked
over the bridge (brought from Kew Gardens at the turn of the century) to the
lake, and crunched round the circular drive to the vast yellow house, you'll be
expecting erstwhile wigged aristocracy to meet you. But no – it will be one of the
more than hundred full-time staff who work in this most voluptuous of hotels.
Inside, the symbols of excess overwhelm the senses – eagles, Graeco-Roman
mythological figures, Doric columns and all manner of fruit form a fabulous
plasterwork concoction on the walls and ceiling of the massive reception hall,
while the Rococo landscaped ceiling in the morning room features the four
elements. These booming rooms are filled with period furniture, some of which
you can sit on, some of which you can't – little signs let you know. Hartwell's
most famous resident was the exiled Louis XVIII, who was in the panelled bar
(then a chapel) in 1814 when he heard he could return to France. There are two
dining-rooms to choose from: the Soane has lovely domed ceilings, and the Doric
is filled with the eponymous columns. On the suitably sophisticated menu
might be smoked salmon served with marinated tomatoes, caviar and
buckwheat blinis, followed by roast squab pigeon with pan-fried foie gras and a
Madeira sauce. Bedrooms range from the cavernous, fit-for-a-queen type suites,
with as much room and as many antiques as a small museum, to the simply
grand. Some bedrooms are up in the coach houses, where you'll also find the
indoor pool and fitness centre.

---

❶ Open all year   ⤢ In Aylesbury, take A418 towards Oxford; Hartwell House is 2 miles
along this road on right-hand side. Private car park   ⤺ 5 single, 23 twin/double, 5
four-poster, 13 suites; 16 in annexe; all with bathroom/WC; all with TV, room service,
hair-dryer, trouser press, direct-dial telephone   ⌁ 2 dining-rooms, bar, 4
drawing-rooms, 2 drying-rooms, library, spa, garden; conferences (max 60 people incl
up to 40 residential); fishing, gym, sauna, solarium, heated indoor swimming-pool,
tennis, croquet, free membership of nearby leisure facilities; early suppers for children,
by room service   ♿ Wheelchair access to hotel (2 steps, ramp) and restaurant, WC
(unisex), 10 ground-floor bedrooms, 1 specially equipped for disabled people
● No children under 8; no dogs in public rooms and some bedrooms; no smoking in
some public rooms and some bedrooms   ▭ Delta, MasterCard, Switch, Visa
£ Single £125, single occupancy of twin/double £155, twin/double £195, four-poster
£280, suite from £280; deposit required. Continental B £11, cooked B £15; bar/bistro L
£4; set L £20/£27.50, D £42; alc D £42. Special breaks available

The Barns   NEW ENTRY

Morton Farm, Babworth, Retford DN22 8HA
TEL: (01777) 706336   FAX: (01777) 709773
EMAIL: thebarns@btinternet.com

Good-value B&B, with smart, well-kept rooms.

This handsome barn conversion, built in the mellow, red brick of north
Nottinghamshire, stands a few minutes away from the A1. Over the last 14 years,
Rosalie Brammer has developed the business into a smooth-running operation –
almost like a small hotel in atmosphere rather than a B&B – which is popular
with overseas visitors. Downstairs, there is a country-cottage-style sitting-room,
with stripped-pine furniture and a log fire on chilly evenings. The complimentary sherry and whisky – and not those tight-fisted measures that some
hotels put in their rooms – are indicative of the thoughtful, informal atmosphere
at the Barns. 'Good breakfasts' are served in a large dining-room, with plenty of
space around the tables if you don't fancy chit-chat with your neighbours. The
bedrooms have been carefully planned to make the most of some fine old beams;
knick-knacks, piles of magazines and books add to the cosiness, and make up for
the rather ordinary décor. Room 5, in particular, with its two double beds, is
excellent family value. All the rooms have nice, thoughtful touches, like
bone-china crockery on the tea tray, a large bottle of shower gel in the
immaculate shower, and a clock radio by the bed.

◑ Open all year   ⊿ 2 miles east of A1 on B6420, south-west of Babworth. Private car
park   1 twin, 3 double, 1 four-poster, 1 family room; 3 with bathroom/WC, 3 with
shower/WC; all with TV, hair-dryer, clock radio   Dining-room, sitting-room, garden;
cots, high chairs   No wheelchair access   No dogs; no smoking   Amex,
Delta, MasterCard, Visa   Single occupancy of twin/double from £32, twin/double
from £45, four-poster from £55, family room £55; deposit required

Haigs

273 Kenilworth Road, Balsall Common CV7 7EL
TEL: (01676) 533004   FAX: (01676) 535132

*Cheerful and hospitable owners lift this roadside hotel – convenient
for the NEC.*

This business-oriented hotel was going through big changes when our inspector
called – summer being the quiet time, as the NEC season is over. Alan and Hester
Harris are determined to have a hotel that looks like a hotel rather than a 1920s
house, so a new façade is planned, plus four more bedrooms – Hester's particular
project is to update the faded, 'sixties-style bar with cane chairs and colourful
fabrics; 'Everyone's good at something and I'm good at curtains!' What will not
change is the poppy-themed restaurant, a spacious, prettily decorated area
offering imaginative à la carte dinners or a three-course table d'hôte menu,
which mixes old favourites with more adventurous dishes: grilled duck and

apricot sausage with a red-wine and celeriac sauce to start, perhaps, followed by roast beef and Yorkshire pudding.

The bedrooms, which have already been altered as part of the changes, are a distinct improvement, with bold, contemporary colour schemes and stylish bathrooms. Double glazing helps keep the traffic noise down for those at the front of the hotel.

◑ Closed 25 Dec to 4 Jan; restaurant closed Sun eve ⏏ On A452, 6 miles south of Junction 4 of M6, 4 miles north of Kenilworth. Private car park ⏏ 5 single, 10 twin, 8 double; most with bathroom/WC, some with shower/WC; all with TV, room service, hair-dryer, trouser press, direct-dial telephone ✅ Restaurant, bar, lounge, garden; functions (max 100 people incl up to 41 residential), conferences; leisure facilities nearby (reduced rates for guests); early suppers for children; high chairs ♿ Wheelchair access to hotel and restaurant, WC (unisex), 5 ground-floor bedrooms, 2 rooms specially equipped for disabled people ● Dogs in bedrooms only, by arrangement ▭ Amex, Delta, MasterCard, Switch, Visa £ Single £50 to £55, single occupancy of twin/double £60 to £65, twin/double £65 to £73; deposit required. Set L £14.50, D £20; alc D £28.50

BANTHAM Devon   map 1

Sloop Inn

Bantham, Kingsbridge TQ7 3AJ
TEL: (01548) 560489   FAX: (01548) 561940

Characterful old hostelry with simple bedrooms, in pretty Devon village.

South Devon villages don't come much more picture-postcard than this thatched affair, or better situated – it's just a few hundred yards to the undeveloped, dune-backed Hope Cove. The Sloop Inn fits in perfectly in a rather nautical way, with its panelled walls, hefty beams and brass portholes – very fitting for a sixteenth-century hostelry that has seen more than its fair share of smuggled goods. The place is now packed with locals and visitors, propping up the bar and sampling the above-average pub fare – as would be expected, the long menu is strong on seafood. You could start with hot potted shrimps, followed by sea bass with a Pernod and pink-peppercorn sauce. Unfortunately, the atmosphere and character of downstairs are not continued in the bedrooms, which remain adequately functional. The sprigged wallpaper and bedcovers brighten things up a bit, but this is not the place for those who like to laze around in their rooms all day – it suits walkers, surfers or drinkers who like value for their money.

◑ Closed Chr & New Year ⏏ From mini-roundabout on A379 near Churchstow take Bantham road for 3 miles. Private car park ⏏ 3 double, 2 family rooms; all with bathroom/WC; all with TV, hair-dryer ✅ Dining-room, bar; cots; high chairs ♿ No wheelchair access ● No pipes or cigars ▭ Delta, Switch £ Single occupancy of double £36, double £64, family room £80; deposit required. Bar/bistro L £4.50, D £6.50; alc L £12.50, D £16. Special breaks available

---

Please let us know if an establishment has changed hands.

map 2

Little Barwick House

Barwick, Yeovil BA22 9TD
TEL: (01935) 423902   FAX: (01935) 420908

Agreeable restaurant-with-rooms, set amid verdant parkland near Yeovil.

Emerge from the foliage-draped, narrow sandstone cutting that bores into the little village of Barwick, and you really will feel that you've found the light at the end of the tunnel. Christopher and Veronica Colley's Georgian country house, a gleaming, white edifice bordering a delightful woodland garden, is a sight to gladden the jaded heart. Indoors, the feel is more homely than the façade and extensive grounds might lead you to expect. A hat-stand bearing a panama and other titfers adds a jaunty air to the hallway, while a David Hockney print adds a bright splash to a traditional drawing-room. The restaurant, which overflows into a second section, enjoys splendid garden views. Here, at the heart of the enterprise, you can feast on dishes from Veronica's much-praised repertoire, which might include a warm salad of quail's eggs and smoked bacon with spinach, followed by fillets of sole baked with a tarragon-cream sauce, and finally a chilled damson soufflé. The bedrooms team pretty wallcoverings and fabrics with good, old furniture. As we went to press the house was on the market.

◗ Closed Chr & New Year   ⊠ Take A37 south from Yeovil; after 1 mile, turn left at roundabout; hotel is ¼ mile further on, on left. Private car park   ⊏⊐ 2 twin, 4 double; all with bathroom/WC exc 2 double with shower/WC; all with TV, room service, hair-dryer, direct-dial telephone   ⊘ Restaurant, bar, drawing-room, garden; early suppers for children   ⑁ No wheelchair access   ⊖ No dogs in public rooms; no smoking in restaurant or bedrooms   ▭ Amex, MasterCard, Switch, Visa   £ Single occupancy of twin/double £55, twin/double £89 (1998 prices); deposit required. Set D £21/£28. Special breaks available

                                   map 8

Fischer's Baslow Hall

Calver Road, Baslow, Bakewell DE45 1RR
TEL: (01246) 583259   FAX: (01246) 583818

Top-notch cooking and stylish rooms, on the outskirts of Baslow.

The stone mullions and tall chimneys of Fischer's Baslow Hall suggest an older vintage, but it is, in fact, Edwardian, and remained a family home until 1988, when Susan and Max Fischer came here. The front door leads directly into a small sitting-room, where guests take pre-dinner drinks – in front of the log fire on chilly evenings; despite the stained glass, gargoyles and high ceilings, the atmosphere is cosy and intimate. There are three dining-rooms – food is an important element of any stay here – with residents usually taking dinner in the elegant front room. Max's cooking is of the highest order, and is based very much around the seasons – he's a keen gardener, and was busy in the herb garden when we inspected. A three-course dinner might start with roasted scallops, then move on to breast of duckling with braised chicory and a Shiraz sauce; dessert could be a rich chocolate marquise, or perhaps a raspberry soufflé. Café Max offers a less formal menu at lunch-times and on midweek evenings. The bedrooms are impeccably stylish and well designed, with smart bathrooms.

○ Closed 25, 26 Dec & 1st week in Jan ⊿ Fischer's Baslow Hall is on right as you leave Baslow village on A623 Stockport road. Private car park ⌁ 1 twin, 3 double, 1 four-poster, 1 suite; all with bathroom/WC; all with TV, room service, hair-dryer, direct-dial telephone; no tea/coffee-making facilities in rooms ⊘ 3 dining-rooms, sitting-room/bar, garden; functions (max 40 people incl up to 6 residential), conferences; civil wedding licence; early suppers for children; cots, high chairs, baby-listening ♿ No wheelchair access ● No children in main dining-room after 7pm; no dogs; no smoking in dining-rooms ☐ Amex, Delta, Diners, MasterCard, Switch, Visa £ Single occupancy of twin/double £80 to £95, twin/double £95 to £130, four-poster/suite £130; deposit required. Cooked B £8.50; bar/bistro L £5 to £14, D £25; set L £20/£24, D £42. Special breaks available

---

BASSENTHWAITE Cumbria   map 10

Willow Cottage   NEW ENTRY

Bassenthwaite, Keswick CA12 4QP
TEL: (01768) 776440

A poppet of a B&B, on the edge of an untouristy village, offering great charm and a friendly welcome.

Bassenthwaite is a pleasant, mercifully untourist-ridden, little place on the north-eastern edge of the eponymous lake, and Chris and Roy Beaty's quaint, terracotta-coloured cottage stands on a quiet corner near the village green. Beyond the colourful gardens, visitors find themselves in the 'garden hall', an imaginative entrance filled with all kinds of garden and farm implements, rag dolls, potpourri, etc. The breakfast area – just two simple tables in the lounge-cum-breakfast room – is furnished with the same charm as the rest of the house. There are no other public rooms, just two of the sweetest little bedrooms imaginable – the sort that make you want to check in straight away. Crooked timbering, brass-and-iron bedsteads with antique linen and patchwork quilts, rustic, painted furniture, dried flowers and skilful stencils on the plain, but uneven, walls characterise these charming rooms. Both have pretty bathrooms. The rooms recently starred in a *Country Living* article, so Willow Cottage is getting its name on the map. Chris is a down-to-earth, but extremely creative, hostess, who is always ready to snap up and renovate unconsidered trifles; as she says: 'Nothing in my house is valuable – just pretty.' Breakfasts are healthy feasts of fresh fruit, yoghurt and home-laid eggs. There's a decent pub in the village for evening meals.

○ Closed mid-Dec to 29 Dec ⊿ At Keswick on A66, take A591 north at roundabout, signposted Carlisle; after 6½ miles turn right into Bassenthwaite village. Through village, cottage is on far right-hand corner before little bridge. Off-road parking ⌁ 1 twin, 1 double; both with bathroom/WC; both with hair-dryer ⊘ Lounge/breakfast room, garden   🚫 No wheelchair access   ● No children; no dogs; no smoking   ⬠ None accepted   💷 Single occupancy of twin/double £30 (low season only), twin/double £40 to £43; deposit required.

BASSENTHWAITE LAKE Cumbria   map 10

The Pheasant

Bassenthwaite Lake, Cockermouth CA13 9YE
TEL: (017687) 76234   FAX: (017687) 76002

A fine location and plenty of old-world character keep this traditional English inn well patronised.

The quiet loop road to Wythop Mill gets surprisingly busy from time to time, as locals and holidaymakers beat a well-trodden path to this rambling, white-painted Cumbrian inn, with black-rimmed windows, just off the A66. The surroundings are lovely: beyond the hotel's charming, dingly-dell-type gardens, steep banks of woodland rise towards grand fells. This ever-popular country pub gets high marks for its exceptional amount of convivial public space, which is just as well, for there are no distracting televisions or telephones in any of the rooms. The quaint, original bar, in gleaming oak and painted ox-blood colour, is the best sort of English pub, though only a handful of people at a time can enjoy it. The three light, relaxing lounges offer much more guest space, and open fires in winter. The restaurant is a simple, pleasantly proportioned room, with plain walls and dark beams, though the central tables seem uncomfortably cramped. The food has been criticised this year, and the two timed sittings for dinner suggest that attention is paid to passing trade at the expense of residents. Breakfasts, however, offer an impressive range of fare, including cold ham and kedgeree, green figs and oatmeal porridge (but cream and brown sugar would have been nice, too). The bedrooms are cosy and traditional, with plain walls and cane and pine furnishings. Some bathrooms, however, show unacceptable signs of wear. This applies to other areas of the Pheasant as well, where some of the traditional furnishings, once comfortably worn, are now looking over-tired and due for replacement before long.

◗ Closed 24 & 25 Dec   🚗 7 miles west of Keswick, just off A66; follow signs for Wythop Mill. Private car park   🛏 5 single, 7 twin, 7 double, 1 four-poster; some in annexe; all with bathroom/WC exc 2 singles with shower/WC; all with hair-dryer; no tea/coffee-making facilities in rooms   ⊘ Restaurant, bar, 3 lounges, drying-room, garden; fishing; early suppers for children; cots, high chairs   🚫 No wheelchair access   ● No babies or young children in restaurant eves; no dogs in bedrooms   ⬠ MasterCard, Switch, Visa   💷 Single £59 to £66, single occupancy of twin/double £69 to £76, twin/double £90 to £98, four-poster £96 to £104; deposit required. Bar/bistro L £5; set L £13, D £22. Special breaks available

---

The text of entries is based on unsolicited reports sent in by readers and backed up by inspections. The factual details are from questionnaires the Guide *sends to all hotels that feature in the book.*

Riggs Cottage

Routenbeck, Bassenthwaite Lake, Cockermouth CA13 9YN
TEL: (017687) 76580 (AND FAX)

Rural bliss in a tiny, old-world cottage near Bassenthwaite.

If you follow the directions carefully, Riggs Cottage isn't too difficult to find, but it's not accustomed to passing trade. Beyond the village of Wythop Mill, a rough track leads down to a couple of quaint cottages nestling in a fold among the fells. Parts of Riggs Cottage date back four hundred years, and it certainly looks antique, with its low ceilings and uneven floors. Hazel and Fred Wilkinson moved here after running a guesthouse in Keswick for some years, and they have a natural ease of manner and ready welcome for unexpected strangers, with a cup of tea on offer and an instant willingness to share their much-loved family home. The gardens ramble around the house apparently much as nature intended, but they are actually very productive, providing Hazel with cherries, damsons, apples and plums for cakes and preserves, while the honey comes from their own bees. Besides looking after the house, garden and guests, she finds time to bake bread, make jam, paint on china and do decoupage work, too. The beamed lounge-cum-dining-room downstairs is warm and cheerful, with china, plants and log fires. From here, a narrow staircase winds up to three small, cosy bedrooms, with simple furnishings but masses of character. Guests eat around one large table, and breakfasts may include fish and local sausage, fresh fruit salad and unusual, home-made breads and preserves – how about rhubarb and ginger jam on caraway and pecan bread?. Dinners feature lots of local produce, too, and the Wilkinsons lay on barbecues from time to time on warm summer evenings.

◑ Open all year ▨ From A66 Keswick to Cockermouth road, follow signs to Wythop Mill; cottage is signposted on right, 1 mile after Pheasant Inn. Private car park
⊭ 1 twin, 1 double, 1 family room; family room with shower/WC; ⊘ Lounge/dining-room, drying-room, garden; babysitting ⅙ No wheelchair access
● No children under 5; no dogs; no smoking ▭ MasterCard, Switch, Visa
£ Single occupancy of twin/double £30, twin/double/family room £40 to £50; deposit required. Set D £13. Special breaks available

---

BATH Bath & N. E. Somerset   map 2

Cheriton House

9 Upper Oldfield Park, Bath BA2 3JX
TEL: (01225) 429862   FAX: (01225) 428403
EMAIL: cheriton@which.net

Fresh and well-maintained B&B on hillside overlooking town.

If you choose to take the ten-minute walk from the centre of Bath to the Cheriton, your uphill efforts will be rewarded by the stunning views down over the city's honey-coloured Georgian buildings. Cheriton House, on a tree-lined residential street with a sprinkling of guesthouses, is less spectacular than the views, but is a perfectly pleasant and well cared-for Victorian house. The three large windows at the front make the most of the views and bring lots of light into the smart, cream-painted breakfast room. For anyone tired of staring at the real thing, framed prints and old maps of Bath decorate the walls. Service at breakfast is friendly and unobtrusive, and the atmosphere is relaxed – you can help yourself from the jugs of orange juice and filter coffee. Although they do not serve evening meals, Iris Wroe-Parker and John Chiles are happy to help you find a good place to eat and have compiled two files full of menus from local restaurants – you can leaf through these in comfort in the guests' lounge, which faces the attractive back garden. Bedrooms are all newly decorated, and some retain their original Victorian features, such as marble fireplaces and moulded ceilings.

○ Open all year ☑ ½ mile south of Bath, just off A367 Wells Road. Private car park ⮑ 2 twin, 6 double, 1 four-poster; all with shower/WC exc 1 twin, 1 double with bathroom/WC; all with TV, hair-dryer, direct-dial telephone, clock radio; ✓ Breakfast room, lounge, drying-room, garden; functions (max 15 people residential/non-residential), conferences; ♿ No wheelchair access ● No children under 12; no dogs; smoking in lounge and some bedrooms only ⊟ Amex, Delta, Diners, MasterCard, Switch, Visa £ Single occupancy of twin/double £42 to £48, twin/double £58 to £72, four-poster £72; deposit required. Special breaks available

Fountain House

9–11 Fountain Buildings, Lansdown Road, Bath BA1 5DV
TEL: (01225) 338622   FAX: (01225) 445855
EMAIL: fountain@gic-net.com
WEB SITE: www.gic-net.com/fh/

Top-notch, serviced apartments, in a prime, town-centre location.

If you hanker after greater anonymity than is generally available in a conventional town-house hotel, then Fountain House may offer the solution. New arrivals at the centrally located house, in one of Bath's characteristic, stone terraces, find themselves admitted by intercom to a hallway, then whisked by lift to the accommodation. This comes in one-, two- and three-bedroomed options, each offering a lounge/dining-room and kitchen complete with dishwasher. It's here that you'll find the wicker basket full of light refreshments that is augmented daily by the discreet delivery of a hamper containing all the cereals, yoghurts, fresh bread and pastries that you'll need to prepare yourself a substantial breakfast. The staff are effective, but professionally invisible. This sort of discretion carries a hefty price tag, and the rooms are furnished and decorated to an appropriately high standard. We particularly liked the light and airy feel of the one-bedroomed, front-facing Room 10, and also the smart, split-level Huntington Suite. Be sure to enquire about parking at the time of booking, as there's garaging for only one car, plus one dedicated parking space – and parking in Bath is notoriously difficult.

○ Open all year ☑ Leave M4 at Junction 18, turn right, and, at second major set of traffic lights, turn right again into Lansdown Road; Fountain House is 50 yards on right. Private car park (£15 per day); on-street parking (metered); public car park nearby (£5 per day) ⮑ 13 suites; one with garden; all with kitchen and bathroom/WC; all with satellite TV, hair-dryer, mini-bar, direct-dial telephone, ironing facilities

⚡ Drying-room; cots, high chairs, babysitting   ♿ No wheelchair access
◒ None 🖩 Amex, Diners, MasterCard, Switch, Visa £ Single occupancy of suite £127 to £176, suite £154 to £320; deposit required.

Haydon House

9 Bloomfield Park, Bath BA2 2BY
TEL: (01225) 444919/427351 (BOTH ALSO FAX)
EMAIL: haydon.bath@btinternet.com

Charming, Edwardian guesthouse, offering the warmest of welcomes.

The typically flower-bedecked, Edwardian exterior sets the tone for the welcome that awaits guests arriving at Haydon House – Magdalene Ashman-Marr and her husband, Gordon, really are superbly attentive hosts. The large, pink lounge, with its ample supply of magazines and scores of celebrity and family prints, is supremely comfortable, while in the exquisite garden the mind-boggling array of plants and flowers creates a beautiful picture, not to mention a heady scent! The five bedrooms are decorated to a high standard, and the attention paid to guests' comfort is impressive – fluffy, white bathrobes and potpourri sachets in the wardrobes are but two of the thoughtful touches. The 'Bloomfield breakfast', which is a relaxed and chatty affair, is served in the pleasant breakfast room, where guests dine together at one table. Try the porridge with Scotch, or golden rum, and Muscavado sugar – it's made to an old family recipe and is simply delicious.

◑ Open all year ↗ From Bath centre, follow signs for A367 towards Exeter and up Wells road for ½ mile; at end of a short dual carriageway, fork right into Bloomfield Road and second right into Bloomfield Park. On-street parking (free) ↤ 1 twin, 2 double, 1 four-poster, 1 family room; all with bathroom/WC exc doubles with shower/WC; all with TV, hair-dryer, direct-dial telephone; trouser press on request ⚡ Dining-room, lounge, library, garden; cots, high chairs ♿ No wheelchair access ◒ Children by arrangement only; no dogs; no smoking 🖩 Amex, Delta, MasterCard, Visa
£ Single occupancy of twin/double £45 to £55, twin/double £65 to £85, four-poster £85 to £90, family room £85 to £110; deposit required. Special breaks available

Holly Lodge

8 Upper Oldfield Park, Bath BA2 3JZ
TEL: (01225) 424042   FAX: (01225) 481138
WEB SITE: www.bath.org/hotel/hollyl/

Well-established B&B, on the south side of Bath, continuing to offer high standards.

This spacious, Victorian villa, with a terraced garden dotted with statuettes, a gazebo and well-used garden furniture, has views north over the city. Plush furnishings in the lounge – swagged curtains, chandeliers and a smattering of china ornaments – give a formal feel to the house, but the welcome is friendly. The ultimate appeal lies in the breakfast: served in the conservatory, it's a memorable affair – scrambled egg and smoked salmon, strawberries and warm croissants are the norm – or you can go for the full English version. There's also a choice of teas and good coffee. Upstairs, the excellent bedrooms have good fabrics, magazines and a soft toy to keep you company. The bathrooms are modern and immaculate.

◖ Open all year ⬛ ½ mile south-west of city centre, off A367 Wells Road. Private car park �ⱼ 1 single, 2 twin, 2 double, 2 four-poster; all with bathroom/WC exc single with shower/WC; all with TV, hair-dryer, trouser press, direct-dial telephone, clock radio ⊘ Dining-room, lounge, conservatory, garden; cots, high chairs, baby-listening ⅋ No wheelchair access ⬤ No dogs; no smoking ▭ Amex, Delta, Diners, MasterCard, Switch, Visa £ Single £48, single occupancy of twin/double £55, twin/double £75 to £85, four-poster £89; deposit required

---

Queensberry Hotel

Russel Street, Bath BA1 2QF
TEL: (01225) 447928   FAX: (01225) 446065
EMAIL: queensbury@dial.pipex.com

Smart and dignified hotel, with renowned restaurant, in centre of Bath.

The Queensberry Hotel occupies four grand, Bath-stone houses, distinguishable from the rest of the terrace only by the polished-brass name plaque and stained-glass lettering above the porch. This feeling of understated luxury continues throughout the hotel, and the polite, helpful staff add to the overall sense of a smoothly run establishment. In the front drawing-room, muted shades of cream and green create an atmosphere of elegance and calm; guests can relax here, amongst the antiques and fresh flowers, or in the snug, well-stocked bar at the back of the hotel. In summer, drinks and snacks are served in the walled courtyard garden. The bedrooms are simply and tastefully decorated, and have an original Bush radio in each one. The ceilings are very low in the top-floor rooms, while the original drawing-rooms on the ground floor (Rooms 7 and 8) benefit from high ceilings and huge, floor-to-ceiling windows. Room 4 is similarly well proportioned, newly refurbished and with a four-poster bed. The hotel's popular Olive Tree Restaurant is light and bright, despite its basement setting. With its well-worn, oriental rugs and crisp, white tablecloths, the atmosphere is relaxed but professional, and chef Matthew Prowse's menu offers a good choice of contemporary cooking. Dishes include roast loin of lamb with spinach, tomato and balsamic vinegar, and vegetarian sweet-potato and caramelised-onion gâteau, with roast-black-olive and tomato chutney.

◖ Closed Chr ⬛ In centre of Bath, just north of Assembly Rooms. On-street parking (free nearby) ⟷ 13 twin, 15 double, 1 four-poster; all with bathroom/WC exc 1 double with shower/WC; all with TV, room service, hair-dryer, direct-dial telephone; no tea/coffee-making facilities in rooms ⊘ Restaurant, bar, 2 drawing-rooms, garden; conferences (max 29 people residential/non-residential), functions; early suppers for children; cots, high chairs, babysitting, baby-listening ⅋ No wheelchair access ⬤ No dogs ▭ Delta, MasterCard, Switch, Visa £ Single occupancy of twin/double from £80, twin/double from £100, four-poster £195; deposit required. Continental B £3.50 (free if served in room), cooked B £7.50; set L £13.50, D £21; alc L, D £28

Royal Crescent

16 Royal Crescent, Bath BA1 2LS
TEL: (01225) 823333   FAX: (01225) 339401

Discreet and luxurious hotel literally at the heart of the city.

Built between 1767 and 1775, John Wood's Royal Crescent is a remarkable piece of architecture, and the equally remarkable, eponymous hotel can be found at number 16. The hotel is as luxurious as you would expect, and the public rooms ooze with rich, yet tasteful, colours, chandeliers and gilt. The food served in the Pimpernel Restaurant also aims for the top in terms of its ingredients and style – a tempura of langoustines, then a sauté of scallops with crab beignets, all rounded off with an *assiette* of pineapple, might be one dinner choice from the three-course menu. The bedrooms, complete with a selection of Jane Austen novels in each, are divided between the Dower House, the Garden Villa and the main building. The Bath House (due to open in September 1998) will provide a range of leisure facilities for guests and club members, and on our inspection a Japanese tea-house was planned for the garden. Unusually, this hotel is aiming to become more child-friendly – toy boxes, children's videos and a babysitting service are now available. The staff are very professional, yet also extremely personable and friendly.

◑ Open all year ⓩ In city centre. Private car park. ⊨ 14 twin, 12 double, 2 family rooms, 14 suites; some in annexe; all with bathroom/WC; all with TV, room service, hair-dryer, mini-bar, direct-dial telephone, CD player, video, air-conditioning, fax, voice mail; no tea/coffee-making facilities in rooms ⊘ 2 restaurants, bar, lounge, library, garden; functions (max 100 people incl up to 84 residential), conferences; civil wedding licence; sauna, heated indoor/outdoor swimming-pool, croquet, leisure facilities nearby (free for guests); early suppers for children; cots, high chairs, toys, babysitting
♿ Wheelchair access to hotel (ramp) and restaurants, 3 ground-floor bedrooms
● No dogs in public rooms; no smoking in public rooms and some bedrooms
▭ Amex, Delta, Diners, MasterCard, Switch, Visa £ Single occupancy of twin/double £170 to £260, twin/double £170 to £260, family room from £295, suite from £370; deposit required. Continental B £12, cooked B £14.50; set L £19.50, D £31; alc L, D £33

Sydney Gardens

Sydney Road, Bath BA2 6NT
TEL: (01225) 464818   FAX: (01225) 484347

A cosy B&B, set in attractive, mature gardens.

This magnificent, Italianate, Victorian house, complete with tower and spire, is located on the fringe of Bath's historic city centre, overlooking a landscaped park. It's run by husband and wife Peter and Geraldine Beaven, who have carefully refurbished it in keeping with its nineteenth-century origins. A relaxed and unhurried atmosphere is palpable, and guests can come and go as they please during their stay – a walk through the back-garden gate and park will have you in the town centre before you know it. Both the dining-room and lounge are tastefully decorated with good-quality fittings; the high, Victorian ceilings and garden views give them an airy and spacious feel. The six bedrooms are all individually decorated, and have good-sized bathrooms. The attic room, with its blue colour scheme and ceiling beams, is especially peaceful and full of character; its popularity means that priority is given to guests who book for two nights at the weekend.

○ Closed 24 Dec to 1 Feb ⤢ On A36 ring road in Bath, off Sydney Place. Private car park ⤒ 2 twin, 3 double, 1 family room; all with bathroom/WC; all with TV, hair-dryer, direct-dial telephone ✓ Dining-room, lounge, garden ♿ No wheelchair access ● No children under 4; dogs in bedrooms only, by arrangement; no smoking ▭ Amex, Delta, MasterCard, Switch, Visa £ Single occupancy of twin/double £49 to £59, twin/double £59 to £75, family room £75 to £90; deposit required

---

BATHFORD Bath & N.E. Somerset map 2

Eagle House

Church Street, Bathford, Bath BA1 7RS
TEL: (01225) 859946 (AND FAX)
EMAIL: jonap@psionworld.net

Discreet, Georgian house, where friendly hosts offer B&B in an elegant setting.

Bath's Georgian splendour is a wonder to behold, and the world and his wife knows it. There's more architectural aplomb to be admired in the nearby conservation village of Bathford – all that's missing are the crowds that blight the spa town. A high wall masks much of the glory of Eagle House (named for the sculpted predator that looms, wings outstretched, astride the house's bay-fronted, rear façade). Wander here, and you can appreciate the mathematical symmetry and perfection of John Napier's grand home (and it's fitting that such precision should be enjoyed by a man who shares his name with the inventor of logarithms). Within a formally elegant space, John and his wife Rosamund have fashioned a wonderfully unstuffy and relaxing home. Both the splendid drawing-room and breakfast room enjoy views over a fine, terraced garden, which subsides into a lovely valley. The bedrooms, named after trees, are attractively and appropriately furnished, and each has special character. Those in search of greater privacy might prefer to rent the two-bedroomed cottage that stands within a tranquil, walled garden.

○ Closed 20 Dec to 3 Jan ⤢ Turn on to A363 to Bradford-on-Avon from A4; after 150 yards, fork left up Bathford Hill; turn first right into Church Street; Eagle House is on right. Private car park ⤒ 1 single, 2 twin, 2 double, 2 family rooms, 1 suite; some in annexe; all with bathroom/WC exc single with shower/WC; all with TV, room service, hair-dryer, direct-dial telephone ✓ Breakfast room, drawing-room, drying-room, garden; functions (max 18 people incl up to 12 residential); tennis, croquet; early suppers for children; cots, high chairs, toys, babysitting, baby-listening ♿ No wheelchair access ● None ▭ Delta, MasterCard, Visa £ Single £36 to £48, twin/double £46 to £74, family room £56 to £74, suite £75 to £98; deposit required. Cooked B £3.50. Special breaks available

Fox Hole Farm   NEW ENTRY

Kane Hythe Road, Battle TN33 9QU
TEL: (01424) 772053   FAX: (01424) 773771

A restored country cottage, providing the perfect place to relax and unwind in cosy comfort.

About three miles from the seething hordes tramping the field at Battle – nowadays just camera-carrying tourists rather than weapon-wielding soldiers – is a haven of rural tranquillity. Paul and Pauline Collins have left Brighton beach behind and have moved inland to restore this cosy, eighteenth-century woodcutter's cottage. At the end of a long, bumpy farm track, and surrounded by acres of rolling fields and forests, this spot is as quiet as quiet can be. There are gardens at the back and a stream flowing down beside the hen-field, where thirty hens are kept busy providing accompaniments to the morning bacon. The dining/sitting-room is authentically rustic, with a beamed ceiling, pine dresser, log fire and a table made from a Spanish ox-cart wheel. One of the three bedrooms is on the ground floor, with views of the newly planted orchard of apple, plum, pear and cherry trees. The bedroom above has such seriously sloping floors that huge blocks are placed under one side of the bed to make it level! All the rooms are tastefully decorated and beautifully furnished, high-lighting the cottage's best features. Pauline is happy to cook an evening meal, given notice, and, in the summer, breakfast can be taken on the south-facing patio.

◑ Open all year   ▨ Go west from Battle on A271. Take first right (B2096). Fox Hole is ¾ mile on right. Private car park   ▃ 3 double; all with bathroom/WC; all with TV, room service, hair-dryer   ⊘ Sitting-room/dining-room, garden   ⅗ No wheelchair access   ● No children under 10; no dogs in bedrooms; no smoking   ▭ MasterCard, Visa   £ Single occupancy of double £39, double £49; deposit required. Special breaks available

PowderMills

Powdermill Lane, Battle TN33 0SP
TEL: (01424) 775511   FAX: (01424) 774540
EMAIL: powdc@aol.com

Spacious country-house hotel, with elegant grounds, a mile or so from the famous battlefield.

For such a peaceful, pleasant spot, PowderMills has an alarmingly explosive history: until 1876, gunpowder was manufactured here for the British forces – during the Crimean War, 1,300 barrels of local gunpowder were used. The present building dates from 1796, an explosion at the works having destroyed the original, 120-year-old Powdermill House that year. The airy restaurant – the most spacious of the public rooms – looks as if it's been transported from a tropical colonial outpost, with its wicker chairs, potted plants, tiled floor and cool, white walls. It's a most relaxing place in which to sit back and enjoy the cuisine, which one reader described as 'excellent, innovative, but not taken to extremes', though another complained of tough fillet of beef. Duck-liver parfait with kumquat preserve, and baked fillet of chicken with a mushroom and shallot ragoût might be on the menu. The house is decorated in traditional style, with a fair smattering of antiques and intriguing nick-nacks. Of the impressive bedrooms in the main house, the Wellington suite, where the general himself once stayed, is the biggest and best, though the double-aspect Room 11 is bright and sunny. Less inviting are Garden Rooms 1 and 2, both much less luxurious in their furnishings and rather dark – one reader complained of damp and mildew. The rooms across the gravel drive in the new Pavilion are more modern, and have balconies. A couple of readers have noted a rather off-hand and charmless approach to customer service. More reports, please.

○ Open all year ⚏ Powdermill Lane leads off A21, opposite Battle railway station. Private car park ⤶ 7 twin, 17 double, 5 four-poster, 6 suites; some in annexe; family rooms available; all with bathroom/WC; all with TV, room service, hair-dryer, trouser press, direct-dial telephone, some with tea/coffee-making facilities ✓ Restaurant, bar, lounge, TV room, library, garden; functions (max 300 people incl up to 35 residential), conferences; civil wedding licence; fishing, unheated outdoor swimming-pool; early suppers for children; cots, high chairs, baby-listening ♿ Wheelchair access to hotel (1 step) and restaurant, 5 ground-floor bedrooms, 1 room specially equipped for disabled people ● No children under 10 in restaurant eves; no dogs in restaurant ▭ Amex, Diners, MasterCard, Switch, Visa £ Single occupancy of twin/double £70, twin/double £90 to £125, four-poster £95 to £150, suite £150 to £185; deposit required. Bar/bistro L £5; set L £15.50, D £20; alc D £26. Special breaks available

---

BEAMINSTER Dorset   map 2

Bridge House

3 Prout Bridge, Beaminster DT8 3AY
TEL: (01308) 862200   FAX: (01308) 863700

Characterful public areas and pretty bedrooms in a small hotel, with a good reputation for food, at the heart of Hardy country.

Venerable flagstones and a cavernous, inglenook fireplace offer clues to the vintage of this part-thirteenth-century, sometime priest's house deep in Hardy's Wessex. Approach at nightfall, and the pools of light that flood from the ranks of the gently arched windows lining the façade of the low-slung, rough-stoned building hold out the promise of the warm welcome that Peter Pinkster's well-drilled staff emphatically achieve. 'A very pleasant place to be! Civilised and restful,' reported one correspondent. The interior décor in the public rooms cleverly counterpoints the old and new, with the heavy beams and occasionally skew-whiff walls being offset by modish plaid upholstery and bright, modern prints and paintings in the bar and sitting-room. Rattan-backed chairs also help to span the centuries in the peachy-pink, Georgian-panelled dining-room, where guests might dine on a filo parcel of goats' cheese and sun-dried tomatoes, followed by a confit of duck with raspberry-vinegar sauce, and finally a honey roulade with walnut cream. It's a more formal dining area than the adjacent conservatory or the breakfast room, both of which feature rather incongruous (green plastic) garden furniture. The bedrooms are attractively decorated in cheerful colours, and feature good, old or modern, pine furniture. The cheaper rooms in the coach-house conversion are more cottagey.

◑ Open all year 🔃 In centre of Beaminster; down hill from town square. Private car park � 1 single, 4 twin, 8 double, 1 family room; some in annexe; all with bathroom/WC exc single with shower/WC; all with TV, room service, hair-dryer, direct-dial telephone ✅ Dining-room, breakfast room, bar, sitting-room, drying-room, conservatory, garden; conferences (max 14 people residential/non-residential); early suppers for children; cots ♿ No wheelchair access ⬤ Dogs in bedrooms only, by arrangement; no smoking in dining-room, discouraged in bedrooms 💳 Amex, Delta, Diners, MasterCard, Switch, Visa 💷 Single £61, single occupancy of twin/double £64 to £80, twin/double £88 to £112, family room £108; deposit required. Bar/bistro L £5 to £8.50; set L £11.50, D £21.50. Special breaks available

---

BEAULIEU Hampshire   map 2

Montagu Arms

Palace Lane, Beaulieu, Brockenhurst SO42 7ZL
TEL: (01590) 612324   FAX: (01590) 612188
EMAIL: enquiries@montagu-arms.co.uk

Sophisticated inn, with a good restaurant, in honey-pot village.

There has been a roadside inn on this site since the sixteenth century, but the present building dates from the eighteenth century, with more recent additions here and there. Named after the local landowning family, it's a long, low, red-brick building, with creepers growing up the front and hanging baskets around the door. The Beaulieu River winds behind the hotel – and there are good walks along its banks. Inside, the smell of wood smoke and the ticking of a grandfather clock create a relaxing and welcoming atmosphere in a chintzy lounge with an open fire, exposed beams and cream panelling. A tiled conservatory opens out on to a pretty, terraced garden with white, wrought-iron tables and chairs – used for cream teas in summer. The bedrooms are named after trees – such as Apple, Chestnut, Hornbeam or Walnut – and the lavishly draped curtains, matching bedspreads and cushions are in co-ordinating floral fabrics. The refurbished bar, now renamed Monty's, offers snacks; there's also a more formal restaurant, which serves well-presented, traditional dishes. Although there are no tea- or coffee-making facilities in the rooms, a particularly enjoyable aspect of a stay at the Montagu Arms is the early-morning tea and home-baked biscuits that are delivered to your bedroom.

◑ Open all year 🔃 In Beaulieu village. Private car park 🚗 4 single, 3 twin, 8 double, 1 four-poster, 5 family rooms, 3 suites; all with bathroom/WC; all with TV, room service, hair-dryer, trouser press, direct-dial telephone; no tea/coffee-making facilities in rooms ✅ Restaurant, bar, lounge, conservatory, garden; functions (max 110 people incl up to 44 residential), conferences; civil wedding licence; leisure facilities nearby (free for guests); early suppers for children; cots, high chairs, baby-listening ♿ No wheelchair access ⬤ No children in restaurant eves; no dogs; no smoking in restaurant 💳 Amex, Delta, Diners, MasterCard, Switch, Visa 💷 Single £69, single occupancy of twin/double £109, twin/double £129, four-poster £159, family room £159 + £15 per child, suite £185 to £195; deposit required. Set D £26; alc L £16, D £31.50. Special breaks available

---

BEERCROCOMBE Somerset   map 2

Frog Street Farm

Beercrocombe, Taunton TA3 6AF
TEL: (01823) 480430 (AND FAX)

Friendly hosts, and championship bloodstock, at a peaceful, working farm within easy reach of Taunton.

Veronica and Henry Cole's delightful, fifteenth-century farmhouse may not be the easiest place in the world to find, but it's worth persevering in order to experience not only the warmth of the Coles' genuine, country hospitality and the secluded setting of their home, but also the thrill of an encounter with their famous racehorses. Last year we reported that 1994's Gold Cup runner-up, Dubacilla, was just about to foal, and at the time of this year's inspection her week-old second foal was nuzzling up to its proud mum in the paddock. There's lots of equine memorabilia of Dubacilla's triumphs, as well as those of Just So, the Coles' Grand National runner-up, scattered around the rustic dining-room and the memorable, Jacobean, panelled room – one of three comfortable lounges. The Coles are happy to talk horses and racing with even the least expert visitor, but a more unassuming couple it's difficult to imagine. Veronica looks thoroughly at home in her farmhouse kitchen, and uses organic produce – home-grown or locally sourced – to create hearty dinners featuring old favourites like watercress soup, tenderloin of pork, sticky toffee pudding or home-made ice-cream. The three pleasant bedrooms feature chintzy, cottagey décor and good, chunky, pine furniture. 'Almost impossible to fault... Can't wait to go again,' reported one satisfied visitor.

◑ Closed Nov to Feb   🔁 Leave M5 at Junction 25 and take A358 towards Chard; leave at Hatch Beauchamp, and by Hatch Inn take Station Road for 1 mile. Private car park   🛏 1 twin, 2 double; all with bathroom/WC; all with hair-dryer   ⌀ Dining-room, 3 lounges, TV room, drying-room, garden; fishing   ♿ No wheelchair access
◗ No children under 11; no dogs; no smoking   ▭ None accepted   £ Single occupancy of twin/double £30, twin/double £50 to £60. Set D £10 to £16

BELSTONE Devon   map 1

Tor Down House   [NEW ENTRY]

Belstone, Okehampton EX20 1QY
TEL: 01837 840731 (AND FAX)

Warm and thoughtful hospitality in a Dartmoor longhouse dating back to the fourteenth century.

Tor Down House seems to contradict its setting. In a landscape of raw, inhospitable beauty, at times bleak and windswept, its three-foot thick walls and thatched roof make it the warmest of havens, and inside the atmosphere is cosy: comfy chairs, books to dip into, a roaring fire and two curled-up cats. Maureen and John Pakenham are an interesting, well-travelled couple, and their home is full of fascinating artifacts reflecting their interests – photographs taken by John and paintings by Maureen. During the week the couple cook dinner (if requested in advance) for guests who dine together at a long wooden table – bring your own wine, as John and Maureen are not licensed to provide it. There are three rooms, all with four-poster beds (two have *en suite* bathrooms), and breakfast is a sumptuous affair: we were spoilt with poached duck eggs – not to mention chocolate Easter eggs! Maureen and John are naturally hospitable hosts who go out of their way to make your stay relaxed and welcome, and they are full of suggestions for walks and restaurants. Their attention to detail is touching; as we headed off to the local pub one evening, John equipped us with a torch – precious indeed when we were confronted by a pair of red eyes glowing in the darkness (a cow wandering down the country lane that gave us the fright of our life)!

◖ Closed Chr to New Year ⤷ From A30, 2 miles east of Okehampton, take Okehampton/Belstone turn-off by BP garage. Immediately past garage, opposite layby on left, take first right turn to Priestacott (don't take second right to Belstone). Follow lane for a mile and turn left at T-junction; house is 50 yards along on right before cattle grid. Private car park ⤷ 3 four-poster; 1 with bathroom/WC, 1 with shower/WC, 1 with private shower/WC (not *en suite*); all with TV, hair-dryer ✓ Dining-room, lounge, garden ♿ No wheelchair access ● No children under 14; no dogs or smoking ▭ MasterCard, Visa £ Single occupancy of four-poster £40; four-poster £60; deposit required. Set D £22.50

BEPTON West Sussex   map 3

Park House

Bepton, Midhurst GU29 0JB
TEL: (01730) 812880   FAX: (01730) 815643
WEB SITE: www.freepages.co.uk/parkhouse_hotel/

Informal country-house hotel complete with immaculate gardens and cheery hosts.

The first of May is a momentous date in many calendars, recalling images of men with bells on their legs prancing around poles, Soviet tanks in Red Square and the last Labour election victory. For the O'Briens, it's the day the family took over this homely hotel over half a century ago. Since then they have played host to all and sundry, as shown by the 'Rogue's Gallery' in the bar, where the walls are lined with famous faces – from the Queen presenting polo trophies at nearby Cowdray Park to signed photos of June Whitfield, Peter Ustinov and Trevor McDonald. Sitting alongside a sleepy byway south of Midhurst, the house is rather unprepossessing from the outside, but the inside is elegantly decorated without being stuffy or intimidating. The comfy sofas and log fire of the drawing-room are surrounded by pale yellow walls with niches and alcoves filled with books and china. The slightly more formal dining-room has deep-red walls and a fine selection of antique tables, where a traditional home-cooked dinner is served. There's no set menu, but there's always a choice at each course, and vegetarians can be catered for if you let the O'Briens know. Bedrooms are brightly decorated in smart stripes, pretty floral prints or just plain pastels, with simple but clean bathrooms.

○ Open all year   ⊿ 2 miles south of Midhurst on B2226. Private car park 🛏1 single, 6 twin, 6 double, 1 family room; 4 in annexes; all with bathroom/WC; all with TV, room service, hair-dryer, trouser press, direct-dial telephone, radio   ⊘ Dining-room, bar, drawing-room, TV room, garden; functions (max 70 people incl up to 28 residential), conferences; outdoor heated swimming-pool, tennis, putting green, pitch & putt, croquet; early suppers for children; cots, high chairs, toys, babysitting, baby-listening   ċ Wheelchair access to hotel (1 step) and restaurant, 3 ground-floor bedrooms, 1 specially equipped for disabled people   ● No dogs in some public rooms and some bedrooms; no smoking in dining-room and some bedrooms   ▭ Amex, Delta, Diners, MasterCard, Switch, Visa   £ Single £50 to £70, single occupancy of twin/double £50 to £90, twin/double £90 to £130, family room £110 to £150. Set L £12.50/£19, D £17.50/£24. Special breaks available

---

BERRYNARBOR Devon   map 1

Bessemer Thatch   NEW ENTRY

Berrynarbor, Combe Martin, Ilfracombe EX34 9SE
TEL: (01271) 882296 (AND FAX)

Cosy little (unthatched) hotel, with exceptionally friendly owners, in heart of 'best-kept village'.

Bessemer Thatch is down at the bottom of the valley, by the church and the pub. It's in the oldest part of the village, but don't look for any thatched roofs, as all the houses burnt down in 1930 and now they're tiled and slated. However, the hotel retains its thirteenth-century character – inside all is cottagey and low-ceilinged (whilst from the walled garden, its beamed exterior looks very Tudor). One previous resident, a tall rector, had floors lowered and ceilings raised to accommodate his height. Lacy tablecloths, a red-patterned carpet and a heavy dresser lend the small dining-room a homely feel; the lounge is even more cosy, with chairs, thickly strewn with cushions and throws, facing into a con-versation-inducing circle. Hosts Colin Applegate and Wendy Burchell say that the best part of their job is socialising with their guests, so don't be surprised if the evening meal is rounded off with a trip to the local pub together! Wendy creates the standard, traditional favourites, with some more unusual dishes thrown in for good measure – you could try ratatouille tartlets with Parmesan slivers, followed by steak and kidney hotpot with herby, crusted dumplings. Three of the chintzy, pretty bedrooms are in the house, and three are in the 'cottage suite' in the garden; Room 3 is the pick of the bunch, with its four-poster and views across the hills.

○ Open all year   ⊿ Turn left off coast road to Ilfracombe, ¾ mile west of Combe Martin. Hotel is in centre of village, opposite church. On-street parking (free) 🛏 1 twin, 2 double, 2 four-poster, 1 suite; some in annexe; all with bathroom/WC exc 1 four-poster with shower/WC; all with TV, room service, hair-dryer, direct-dial telephone   ⊘ Dining-room, lounge, garden; leisure facilities nearby (reduced rates for guests)　 ♿ No wheelchair access　◯ No children under 16; no dogs; smoking in lounge only　☐ MasterCard, Switch, Visa　£ Twin/double/four-poster £33 to £66, suite £38 to £76; deposit required. Alc D £15. Special breaks available

---

BETHERSDEN Kent　　　　　　　　　　　　　　　　　　　　　　　map 3

Little Hodgeham

Smarden Road, Bethersden, Ashford TN26 3HE
TEL: (01233) 850323

Fairy-tale cottage in rose-bowered garden, run on genteel house-party lines.

If you are seeking out inglenooks, beams and diamond-paned windows, look no further – Erica Wallace's 500-year-old Tudor cottage will suit you perfectly. It is a half-timbered building set in rambling rose gardens and surrounded by wooded farmland. Lilies, clematis and jasmine scent the garden and a creeping vine threatens to engulf the ancient façade. The floral theme continues in the handful of cosy bedrooms. The spacious double, which also serves as a family room, has flowery wallpaper, a half-canopied bed, an *en suite* shower-room and lovely views of the duck pond, sunken patio and fountain. The four-poster room, decorated in pink, also has twin beds on an upstairs, split-level area. Although Erica offers her guests 'simple' communal suppers by arrangement, she admits that she finds it difficult to produce anything less than elaborate dinner parties: starters might be a mango, shrimp and avocado salad or a warm tart of tomato and anchovy followed by a lavish fish course and a seasonal dessert such as summer pudding. Erica is happy to provide guests with plenty of information about local sights, but if they prefer to spend the day enjoying her swimming-pool or relaxing in her lounge, that's fine by her.

◒ Closed Sept to mid-Mar　⊞ 10 miles west of Ashford on A28 Bethersden road, turn right at Bull pub and go towards Smarden for 2 miles; cottage is on right. Private car park　↳ 1 twin, 1 double, 1 four-poster + twin; family room available; 2 with bathroom/WC, double with shower/WC; all with room service, hair-dryer　⍓ Dining-room, lounge, TV room/library, conservatory, garden; unheated outdoor swimming-pool　♿ No wheelchair access　◯ Children by arrangement; no dogs　☐ None accepted　£ Single occupancy of twin/double £40, twin/double/four-poster £67 to £73, family room (rates on application); deposit required. Set D £15. Special breaks available

---

'Although we had booked several months earlier, two of our sons were accommodated in the proprietor's own bedroom, as the room which we had been told over the phone was available, and which was next to ours, was occupied. This was not particularly satisfactory, as the proprietor's room was arranged so you had to walk through the bathroom to get to the main part of the room, so if one occupant of the room wanted to use the bathroom in privacy, the other was trapped either in or out of the room.'
On a hotel in Stirlingshire

Bibury Court

Bibury, Cirencester GL7 5NT
TEL: (01285) 740337   FAX: (01285) 740660
EMAIL: andrew@biburycourt.co.uk
WEB SITE: www.biburycourt.co.uk

Grand, but unmodish and relatively affordable, country-house hotel, in a memorable spot.

Bibury Court offers an opportunity to stay in one of the most imposing of the Cotswolds' many country-house hotels – and in one of the loveliest settings – without having to consult the bank manager first. Spanning 300 years, from Tudor through to Edwardian, the mansion stands ensconced in six acres of delectable grounds that encompass a wild orchard and a large sweep of daisy-flecked lawns alongside the River Coln. Provided that your stay doesn't coincide with a function, this is a wonderfully peaceful bolt-hole, far from the madding Bibury crowds. Flagstones in the hall, a moose's head over the stairs and oak panelling in the bar and drawing-room firmly establish the requisite country-house atmosphere. In the often vast bedrooms, chunky antiques intermingle with more prosaic furniture, and the bathrooms, some of which lie across corridors, may feature original Edwardian fittings. The housekeeping, however, can be less than faultless, and likewise in the traditional-style restaurant – which in summer extends into a smart conservatory overlooking the orchard – there can be slips in the service and quality of the cuisine.

○ Closed 22 to 30 Dec   ⊿ Behind church in Bibury, next to river. Private car park
⊭ 2 single, 2 twin, 7 double, 5 four-poster, 2 family rooms, 1 suite; most with bathroom/WC, 1 four-poster with shower/WC; all with TV, room service, hair-dryer, direct-dial telephone, some with ironing facilities   ✓ Restaurant, conservatory, bar, drawing-room, TV room, drying-room, library, games room, garden; functions (max 110 people incl up to 38 residential), conferences; fishing, snooker, pitch & putt, croquet, leisure facilities nearby (reduced rates for guests); early suppers for children; cots, high chairs, baby-listening   ♿ No wheelchair access   ● No dogs in some public rooms
▭ Amex, Diners, MasterCard, Switch, Visa   £ Single £64, single occupancy of twin/double £75, twin/double/four-poster £95, family room £115, suite £125; deposit required. Cooked B £4.50 to £7; bar/bistro L £3 to £8.50; alc D £24. (Prices valid till Mar 1999.) Special breaks available

The Swan

Bibury, Cirencester GL7 5NW
TEL: (01285) 740695   FAX: (01285) 740473
EMAIL: swanhot1@swanhotel-cotswolds.co.uk
WEB SITE: www.swanhotel.co.uk

Luxury and style, without country-house-hotel preciousness, in a honey-pot, Cotswolds village.

William Morris famously called Bibury 'the most beautiful village in England'; whether he would come to the same conclusion now, if he visited on a sunny summer's day when the place is heaving with day-trippers, is debatable. Many make for the Swan, a much-photographed, creeper-covered, old building, in a prime spot overlooking the River Coln. Its bold interior soon confounds your first impressions of a classic inn: hitting all sorts of notes, it ranges from flamboyant in the draped, chandeliered and stuccoed Signet Room restaurant, to modernist chic in Jankowski's Brasserie and the adjacent bar, where a large mural of members of staff who have made a significant contribution to the hotel dominates the proceedings. The brasserie offers uncomplicated fare – pastas, grills, scampi and chips, plus children's staples – to cater for its wide-ranging clientele, while the Signet Room works from a table d'hôte menu of more adventurous dishes. Striking antiques make the bedrooms as stylish as the rest of the establishment. Their bathrooms are particularly indulgent, the best having big, whirlpool tubs and walk-in, multi-jet showers. Most rooms face the front, benefiting from the river views but enduring some traffic noise.

◑ Closed 20 to 28 Dec　▨ By river in Bibury, on B4425 between Burford and Cirencester. Private car park.　⬆ 5 twin, 9 double, 3 four-poster, 1 family room; 16 with bathroom/WC, 2 with shower/WC; all with TV, room service, hair-dryer, direct-dial telephone; no tea/coffee-making facilities in rooms　⌀ 2 restaurants, bar, 2 lounges, garden; functions, conferences; civil wedding licence; fishing; early suppers for children; cots, high chairs, babysitting, baby-listening　⅖ No wheelchair access ● No dogs; smoking in some public rooms, discouraged in bedrooms　▭ Amex, MasterCard, Switch, Visa　£ Single occupancy of twin/double £99, twin/double £150, four-poster from £205, family room £250; deposit required. Bar/bistro L £9.50, D £15; set D £26.50. Special breaks available

---

BIGBURY-ON-SEA Devon　　　　　　　　　　　　　map 1

Burgh Island

Bigbury-on-Sea, Kingsbridge TQ7 4BG
TEL: (01548) 810514　FAX: (01548) 810243

Step back in time in this outrageously authentic monument to art deco.

When the tide is high, Burgh Island is cut off; you have to get across the sandbar on a 'sea tractor' (like a gigantic Dinky toy), and so begins the fun. The minute you step through the portals, hold on to your hats (and feather boas and cigarette-holders), ladies and gentlemen, and prepare to shimmy! From the music coming from radiograms to the pale décor, Beatrice and Tony Porter have created a Great Gatsby world of glamour and style. The huge ballroom (used as a restaurant) just makes you want to dance cheek to cheek, the Ganges Restaurant (which has a bit of a ship welded on to the side of it) is reminiscent of all those glamorous cruises, and the cocktail bar (complete with fountain and peacock ceiling) is just the place for pre-dinner socialising, darling. The menu is no less adventurous – maybe a trio of breaded West Country cheeses with a salad of red cabbage and hazelnuts, followed by poached brill with mussel and parsley fricassee.

Bedrooms follow the art deco theme: all straight lines and curves, with mirrors and period three-piece suites. One slightly disappointed guest said that, although the room was decked out with original furniture, some of it was 'quite tatty', and the bed 'creaked badly'. TVs in all the bedrooms are one concession to the modern world. Outside, behind the hotel, is the magical, enticing, natural 'Mermaid pool', with a little bathing platform amid the red rocks.

◐ Closed Jan and weekdays in Feb ⤢ Follow signs to Bigbury-on-Sea. At St Ann's Chapel, call hotel from phone box. Do not drive across beach to island. Private car park (on mainland) ⬑ 15 suites, incl 18 bedrooms; some in annexe; family rooms available all with bathroom/WC exc 1 with shower/WC; all with private sitting-room, sea views, TV, limited room service, hair-dryer, direct-dial telephone; tea/coffee-making facilities on request ⊘ 2 restaurants, palm court/bar, sun lounge, drying-room, conservatory, games room, garden; functions (max 60 people incl up to 36 residential), conferences; civil wedding licence; fishing, gym, sauna, unheated outdoor swimming-pool, tennis, snooker, table tennis, shop, helicopter pad; early suppers for children; cots, high chairs, baby-listening ♿ No wheelchair access ● No children under 7 at D; no dogs ☐ Amex, Delta, Diners, MasterCard, Switch, Visa £ Suite £104 to 129 (rates incl dinner); deposit required.

Aug 2001: £110pp → £136. Dinner! £90

BILLINGSHURST West Sussex   map 3

Old Wharf

Newbridge, Wisborough Green, Billingshurst RH14 0JG
TEL: (01403) 784096 (AND FAX)

Intriguingly different B&B in a converted, canal-side warehouse.

David and Moira Mitchell have definitely made the most of restoring their unique home. Not only that, but they have a singular approach to their 'business': 'We don't like being too commercial,' says David, 'but prefer to spend time getting to know our guests and letting them linger over their breakfasts.' And those breakfasts include home-made muesli, and, in the summer, a barbecue outside. The warm welcome is made complete by their two Border collies, Max and Merlin, who add to the idyllically rustic feel.

In days of yore, this was a bustling hive of activity: built in 1839, it was the warehouse for all the local produce, which was then shipped down the Arun Canal to Pulborough. It's now over a hundred years since the warehouse was last used as it was originally intended, and for the past eleven of those the Mitchells have been converting it into a fine B&B. The most striking feature is the huge hoist wheel over the stairwell, and less obvious aspects are the underfloor heating (no radiators here) and the trapezoidal design, which gives the rooms their beautiful angles. Primrose is the best of the three, with its own little sitting-room and lovely views of the canal and gardens. Peach and Bluebell are two cosy twins with stencilled walls and peaceful outlooks.

◐ Closed 2 weeks Chr & New Year ⤢ Head west from Billingshurst on A272 for 2 miles; house is on left-hand side, by banks of canal, just after river bridge. Private car park ⬑ 2 twin, 1 suite; all with bathroom/WC; all with TV, hair-dryer, suite with modem point; cordless phones available ⊘ Dining-room, sitting-room, garden;

fishing, heated outdoor swimming-pool, tennis   ⛴ No wheelchair access
● No children under 12; no dogs; no smoking   💳 Amex, MasterCard, Visa
£ Single occupancy of twin £40, twin £55, suite £70; deposit required

---

BIRCH VALE Derbyshire   map 8

Waltzing Weasel Inn

New Mills Road, Birch Vale, Stockport SK22 1BT
TEL: (01663) 743402 (AND FAX)

*Real ale, up-market cooking and good rooms combine to make a
superior pub close to Kinder Scout.*

Somehow Linda and Michael Atkinson's pub manages to achieve that elusive
goal of being a fine drinking house combined with good rooms and restaurant.
The bar is exactly as it should be: real ale served from hand pumps,
spoke-backed chairs, the occasional rickety table and plenty of polished wood
and brass. Through the door and down the stairs is the restaurant, a cosy, homely
room, with a tapestry on the wall behind the sideboard – laden with fruit and
cheeses – and views across to Bleaklow. Our inspection lunch of celery and
Stilton soup followed by crayfish tails was out of the top drawer; puddings tend
to be traditional – bread-and-butter pudding, treacle tart or fruit crumbles. The
bedrooms are decorated in a smart, farmhouse style, and some have views of the
surrounding countryside.

◐ Open all year   🗺 ½ mile west of Hayfield on A6015. Private car park   🛏 1 single,
2 twin, 5 double; all with bathroom/WC exc single with shower/WC; all with TV,
hair-dryer, trouser press, some with direct-dial telephone   ✓ Restaurant, bar,
drying-room, garden; functions (max 30 people incl up to 15 residential), conferences;
early suppers for children   ⛴ No wheelchair access   ● No children under 5 in
restaurant eves   💳 Amex, Delta, MasterCard, Switch, Visa   £ Single £38, single
occupancy of twin/double £58 to £78, twin/double £65 to £95; deposit required.
Bar/bistro L £8.50; set D £21.50/£25.50. Special breaks available

---

BIRMINGHAM West Midlands   map 5

The Burlington

6 Burlington Arcade, 126 New Street, Birmingham B2 4JQ
TEL: 0121-643 9191, 0121-643 5075   FAX: 0121-628 5005
EMAIL: mail@burlingtonhotel.com
WEB SITE: www.burlingtonhotel.com

Swish, business-oriented hotel, with touches of period elegance.

If the exact centre of Birmingham could be decided upon, then the Burlington
would have a strong claim to be within a minute's walk of it. In fact, it is so
central that arriving by car becomes something of a liability: drop off your cases
in a loading bay in Stephenson Street, then drive 100 yards to the NCP car park
and walk back – it's much simpler to arrive at New Street Station instead.

In Victorian times the establishment was the Midland Hotel, and vestiges of
its former grandeur remain, for example, in the marble columns and

stained-glass windows. Some senior members of staff can recall the days of lords and ladies in their finery attending grand balls in the 'fifties, but these days the Burlington is more likely to host business conferences, and the old ballroom has become a smart, split-level restaurant. The service here is friendly and unhurried, and provides good, tasty food – though portions are not over-generous. An inspection meal started with an excellent ravioli of mussels, went on to a smoked medallion of pork, and finished with a passion-fruit mousse. In contrast, the buffet breakfast served in the same room the next morning was far less impressive, featuring heated-up scrambled eggs on soggy toast and catering sachets of butter.

The bedrooms are smart, comfortable and characterless, with useful additions like a television-sound relay to the bathroom and a trouser press tucked away behind a mirror.

● Closed 25 Dec ⤷ In city centre, close to New Street Station. Public car park nearby (£2 per day to hotel guests) ⤷ 34 single, 18 twin, 47 double, 2 four-poster, 6 family rooms, 5 suites; all with bathroom/WC; all with satellite TV, room service, hair-dryer, trouser press, direct-dial telephone, voice mail ✅ Restaurant, dining-room, bar, lounge; functions (max 400 people incl up to 197 residential), conferences; gym, sauna, solarium; cots, high chairs ♿ No wheelchair access ● No children under 3; dogs in bedrooms only, by arrangement; no smoking in some bedrooms ▭ Amex, Delta, Diners, MasterCard, Switch, Visa £ Single £105, single occupancy of twin/double £115, twin/double £115, four-poster £180, family room £140, suite £225 (prices valid till Oct 1998); deposit required. Continental B £8.50, cooked B £11.50; bar meals £8; set L, D £19; alc L, D £25. Special breaks available

---

Copperfield House

ℒℒ

60 Upland Road, Selly Park, Birmingham B29 7JS
TEL: 0121-472 8344   FAX: 0121-415 5655

Small, family-run hotel, in quiet spot – handy for central Birmingham.

This leafy, suburban street is probably as quiet as you could hope for close to central Birmingham – just ten minutes' walk from the cricket ground, for example, or the Pebble Mill television studios. John and Jenny Bodycote's house is red-brick Victorian, with the choicest bedrooms, Rooms 3 and 4, on the ground floor. Each bedroom is pleasantly furnished, and some have the added luxury of a video and a collection of classic films; the attic rooms are quieter and plainer, but are a steep climb away. The dining-room has smart, bentwood chairs and Impressionist prints. The chef is John and Jenny's daughter Louise, who trained at the Prue Leith College of Food and Wine; she produces well-priced, straightforward dishes, such as carrot and orange soup, rack of lamb with a herb mousse, and desserts like cheesecakes and fruit crumbles. For after-dinner coffee or drinks, there is a sitting-room (stocked with newspapers) with an honesty bar.

● Open all year; dining-room closed Sun eve ⤷ Situated midway between A38 (south) and A441, hotel is on south side of Birmingham, approximately 3 miles from M6 (Junction 6) and 4 miles from M42 (Junction 2). Private car park ⤷ 5 single, 4 twin, 7 double, 1 family room; most with bathroom/WC, some with shower/WC; all with TV,

room service, hair-dryer, direct-dial telephone, some with trouser press, video
⍋ Dining-room, bar, sitting-room, garden; conferences (max 15 people residential);
early suppers for children; cots, high chairs   ♿ No wheelchair access   ● No dogs in
public rooms; smoking in sitting-room and bedrooms only   ▭ Amex, Delta,
MasterCard, Switch, Visa   £ Single £55, single occupancy of twin/double £55,
twin/double £65, family room £75; deposit required. Set D £15 to £17. Special breaks
available

Swallow Hotel

12 Hagley Road, Five Ways, Birmingham B16 8SJ
TEL: 0121-452 1144 FAX: 0121-456 3442

Expensive, but luxurious, hotel, with good facilities and courteous staff.

The Five Ways roundabout in Birmingham is not the most exotic of locations,
but if any hotel can convince you that such a mundane traffic island is a million
miles away then it's the swish and luxurious Swallow Hotel. There's the
Egyptian-themed swimming-pool, for a start – it used to be a car park – and then
there are the bellboys, who appear to have walked off the set of the 1930s
Hollywood movie *Grand Hotel*, and the yards of marble and neo-Edwardian
elegance. More practically, there is sound insulation from the road outside. The
bedrooms keep up the stylish atmosphere with their spaciousness, marbled
bathrooms, air-conditioning, satellite televisions, modem lines and mini-bars.
Dining is either in the ultra-swanky Edward Elgar Restaurant, where you will
find all the lobster, foie gras and delicate desserts you might ever want, or in the
less formal Langtry's, which is a conservatory-style room serving more traditional English fare.

◑ Open all year ⤢ Near centre of Birmingham at Five Ways, where A456 crosses
A4540. Private car park ⊨ 14 single, 38 twin, 42 double, 4 suites; all with
bathroom/WC; all with satellite TV, room service, hair-dryer, mini-bar, trouser press,
direct-dial telephone, ironing facilities, air-conditioning ⍋ 2 restaurants, bar, lounge,
library; conferences (max 20 people residential/non-residential); gym, solarium, heated
indoor swimming-pool, leisure facilities nearby (free for guests); cots, high chairs, baby-
listening ♿ Wheelchair access to hotel (lift) and restaurants, WC (unisex), lift to
bedrooms, 1 room specially equipped for disabled people ● No dogs in public
rooms; no smoking in some bedrooms ▭ Amex, Delta, Diners, MasterCard, Switch,
Visa £ Single £160, twin/double £180, suite £325; deposit required. Bar/bistro L, D
£28; set L £21.50, D £27; alc L, D £38. Special breaks available

---

BISHOP'S TAWTON Devon map 1

Halmpstone Manor

Bishop's Tawton, Barnstaple EX32 0EA
TEL: (01271) 830321 FAX: (01271) 830826

*Immaculately kept farmhouse that thinks it's a country-house hotel,
with fun hosts.*

This is the kind of place which satisfies on every level. The food is good, the bedrooms are good, the welcome is good. The secret lies in the fact that the Stanburys 'try and keep it as a home, rather than a hotel'; they are very skilled at doing just that, largely because it *has* been Charles' home for a long time – he was born here. He also runs the adjacent farm, but the only sight that guests get of any agricultural note is a glimpse of the (rather ugly) slurry tank, just beyond the pretty, lawned garden. Other than that, the large, brownstone manor seems completely isolated, lost among the soft, rolling hills of north Devon. Inside, the Stanburys have created an elegant, unfussy home, using the grand proportions of the house to best advantage. Jane takes pride in her flowers, so you can expect some classy arrangements, both in the peachy, spruce lounge and in the fabulously panelled restaurant. Plaudits abound for her five-course dinners, too; a cheese soufflé might be followed by fillet of sea bass in a buttery orange sauce and broccoli cream, and then best end of local lamb with a herb and brioche crust and a port sauce.

The bedrooms are splendid and luxurious, with all manner of extras – fluffy bathrobes, chocolates, sherry, fruit and home-made biscuits. Jane provides complimentary tea and cakes on arrival, and the orange juice is freshly squeezed every morning.

◑ Closed Nov and Jan ⤴ South of Bishop's Tawton, take turning opposite BP petrol station; follow road for 2 miles, ignoring Hannaford turn, then turn right at Halmpstone Manor sign. Private car park ⤶ 3 double, 2 four-poster; 1 in annexe; all with bathroom/WC exc 2 doubles with shower/WC; all with TV, room service, hair-dryer, trouser press, direct-dial telephone ✧ Restaurant, bar, lounge, garden; functions (max 30 people incl up to 10 residential), conferences ꜔ No wheelchair access ● No children under 12; no dogs or smoking in bedrooms ▭ Amex, Diners, MasterCard, Switch, Visa 💷 Single occupancy of double £70, double £100, four-poster £140; deposit required. Set D £25.

BLACKWELL Warwickshire   map 5

Blackwell Grange

Blackwell, Shipston-on-Stour CV36 4PF
TEL: (01608) 682357 (AND FAX)

Up-market, peaceful B&B, in beautiful, rural location.

The first thing you notice on turning into Liz Vernon Miller's drive is not the attractive, stone-built house, but the thatched, seventeenth-century barn which, in spring, is used for lambing. Beyond this lie a secluded garden, various outbuildings and the creeper-clad house, whose atmosphere is surprisingly genteel considering that it is actually a working farm with a flock of over two hundred ewes. The sitting-room is particularly pleasant, with mullioned windows on three sides, oil paintings in gilt frames and plenty of books to peruse in front of a log fire. Dinners are provided by arrangement, perhaps carrot soup, followed by roast pheasant and then a lemon soufflé. 'The food was simple yet superb,' wrote one correspondent. You can breakfast on freshly laid eggs from the farm's pedigree poultry.

The two upper bedrooms are nicely furnished in country-house style, with beautiful old furniture and hunting prints on the walls; their creaky floors add to the ambience. Downstairs, there is a third room with a larger bathroom that is suitable for guests in wheelchairs, while the fourth is mostly used as a self-catering cottage.

◑ Closed Chr & Jan; dining-room closed Sun eve　🔁 Take A3400 towards Oxford from Stratford-upon-Avon; after 5 miles, turn right by church in Newbold-on-Stour; in Blackwell, fork right. Private car park　↳ 1 single, 2 twin, 1 double; 1 in annexe; 3 with bathroom/WC, single with shower/WC; some with TV, hair-dryer on request ✓ Dining-room, sitting-room, garden　& Wheelchair access to hotel (1 step) and dining-room, 1 ground-floor bedroom specially equipped for disabled people ● No children under 12; no dogs; no smoking　▭ Amex, Delta, MasterCard, Visa £ Single £28, single occupancy of twin/double £35, twin/double £60; deposit required. Set D £12.50 to £17.50

BLAKENEY Norfolk　　　　　　　　　　　　　　　　　　　map 6

White Horse

4 High Street, Blakeney, Holt NR25 7AL
TEL: (01263) 740574　FAX: (01263) 741303

Excellent food at this popular, village pub with tidy bedrooms.

You feel very much at the wild and windy edge of England when standing on Blakeney quay looking out over the saltmarsh, so it's comforting to know that only a few steps away, huddled in the high street, is the comforting interior of this homely pub and hotel. On most nights you can be assured that the bar and restaurant will both be busy. The bar is particularly attractive, with its dark-green carpets and curtains lit up by small lamps giving it an extremely cosy feel. Dishes of the day are marked on the blackboard, or you can choose from a very solid selection of pies and other pub favourites. The restaurant is rather dowdy in comparison, with pub-style, dark-wood tables and simple place-settings. The food, however, cooked by Chris Hyde, is sure to put you in a good mood. A typical meal is likely to include locally caught seafood, such as in the crab and salt-cod salad, which may be followed by loin of lamb served on creamed leeks with a sherry-vinegar sauce, and then poached pineapple with vanilla ice-cream and a fudge sauce. Presentation is not a strong point, but the taste of the food is thankfully always excellent. There's also an attractive courtyard conservatory for dining, with pine tables and a tiled floor, although it wasn't being used on our visit. For guests, there is also an enticing lounge, with lush, deep-blue sofas and green cane chairs, and typical Norfolk coastal scenes decorating the walls. The bedrooms can be on the small side, and only the Harbour Room has sea views; nevertheless, they all have well-fitted bathrooms and sturdy, pine furniture.

◑ Open all year; restaurant closed Sun & Mon eves　🔁 On the High Street in Blakeney. Private car park　↳ 2 single, 1 twin, 4 double, 2 family rooms, 1 suite; one in annexe; all with bathroom/WC exc single with shower/WC; all with TV, hair-dryer, direct-dial telephone, clock radio　✓ Restaurant, bar, lounge, conservatory, garden; early suppers for children; high chairs, baby-listening　& No wheelchair access ● No dogs　▭ Amex, Delta, MasterCard, Switch, Visa　£ Single £25 to £35, single occupancy of twin/double £40 to £50, twin/double £50 to £70, family room £80 to £90, suite £60 to £80; deposit required. Bar/bistro L, D £11; alc D £17.50

Lord Crewe Arms

Blanchland, Consett DH8 9SP
TEL: (01434) 675251   FAX: (01434) 675337

A former monastery oozing history, at the heart of a lovely, north-eastern village.

Blanchland village is something of an oddity, laid out in the 1750s along the foundation lines of monastic buildings erected in the twelfth century by the order of White Canons. In a laudable recycling exercise, lowly monks' residences became private houses, while the abbot's guesthouse became first a manor house, then later the Lord Crewe Arms. Not surprisingly, history and flagstones lie thick on the ground in the vaulted Crypt Bar and the Hilyard Room, where a gigantic inglenook hides a priest-hole. If thoughts of the supernatural won't disturb your slumbers, the shadow of Dorothy Forster, heroine of the 1715 Jacobite rebellion, is reputed to haunt an area beyond a massive door made from the original inn sign, and her portrait looks down on diners in the pine-panelled restaurant. Four-course dinners offer plenty of unambitious, but competently prepared, food for all tastes; otherwise you could go for a wild-boar and pheasant pie salad in the Crypt Bar. The bedrooms in the main building are full of creaky, squeaky antique character, like the Bamburgh Room (Dorothy Forster's favourite haunt), with its mullioned windows and views of the walled garden, or the oak-beamed Radcliffe in the crenellated tower. They cost the same as such spacious, atmospheric options as September and February in the Angel Inn, a former pub across the square.

◖ Open all year   ⊿ On B6306, 10 miles south of Hexham. On-street parking (free)   🛏 4 twin, 13 double, 1 four-poster, 2 family rooms; all with bathroom/WC; all with TV, room service, hair-dryer, trouser press, direct-dial telephone, ironing board   ⦸ Restaurant, bar, lounge, drying-room, garden; functions (max 65 people incl up to 20 residential), conferences; civil wedding licence; early suppers for children; cots, high chairs, babysitting, baby-listening   ♿ No wheelchair access   ● No dogs in public rooms   ⊟ Amex, Delta, Diners, MasterCard, Switch, Visa   £ Single occupancy of twin/double £80, twin/double/four-poster/family room £110; deposit required. Bar/bistro L £7, D £10; set Sun L £15; alc D £28. Special breaks available

Appletree Holme

Blawith, Ulverston LA12 8EL
TEL: (01229) 885618

Warm hospitality and wonderful food, in an idyllic location far from all madding crowds.

When Roy and Shirley Carlsen moved to this isolated, stone fell-farm twenty years ago, they planned to take things easy after busy careers running a much larger hotel-restaurant. But enough visitors trek down the bewildering farm tracks (note directions carefully!) to keep them fully occupied, and though they do not offer hotel facilities their brand of hospitality is by no means a part-time job. Over the years they have expended lavish amounts of energy and imagination in restoring the place to the high standards of craftsmanship that they both appreciate, and the result is a delightful, individual home. 'Roy likes bathrooms,' says Shirley when she shows people round. And certainly the sybaritic plumbing is very striking, especially if you're put in the Blue Room, which has a huge, circular whirlpool, and also in the Rose Room, with its semi-sunken bath. Orchard has a palatial shower compartment in the bedroom, while the bathroom in Down House (in a separate building) takes up an entire floor. There are plenty of other things to remember about Down House, including the fell views (tremendous from every aspect of the house), which extend grandly beyond the nearby gardens and orchards; the local area is a haven for wildlife – Appletree Holme is now completely surrounded by a site of special scientific interest. Roy's cooking is another source of satisfaction. If you arrive after 5pm you'll catch him in the kitchen, apron donned, rustling up a delicious feast of traditional local and home-grown fare, subtly spiced with Mediterranean ideas. Breakfasts are equally indulgent.

◗ Open all year   🔌 Turn into lane opposite Blawith church, pass through farm, and take first right and then first left turning at the sign. Private car park   🛏️ 1 twin, 3 double; 1 in annexe; all with bathroom/WC exc twin with shower/WC; all with TV, room service, hair-dryer, radio, telephone (not direct-dial);   ⌀ Dining-room, lounge, drying-room, library, garden   ♿ No wheelchair access   ● No dogs; no smoking   ▭ MasterCard, Visa   £ Single occupancy of twin/double £69 to £73, twin/double £123 to £131; deposit required. Set D £23.50

BOLTON ABBEY North Yorkshire   map 8

Devonshire Arms

Bolton Abbey, Skipton BD23 6AJ
TEL: (01756) 710441   FAX: (01756) 710564

Luxurious country-house hotel, with characterfully themed rooms, and paintings and furniture on loan from Chatsworth House.

The serried ranks of green wellies and trout-fishing rods lined up at the main entrance porch of the Devonshire Arms give off a slightly misleading, county-set image. The aristocratic pedigree is certainly all present and correct, however: the Duke of Devonshire's family has owned the Bolton Abbey estate for a couple of centuries, and has liberally sprinkled the former coaching-house with oils and antiques from Chatsworth House. True to form, a log fire sighs in the flagstone-floored reception hall, overlooked by the requisite antlers and ancestral representations, and the Burlington restaurant is just the place for a formal evening blow-out amid gold-swagged opulence. So the contrast to the recently restyled, ultra-modern, fun and funkily chic Devonshire Brasserie and Bar is all the greater; loud plaid furniture, electric-blue wooden wall-cladding and retina-taxing modern art all clamour for attention. Head chef Andrew Nicholson has a reputation for serving a blend of classical and modern cuisine that suits both culinary venues equally well. You might try sea bass with an olive crust served with a red-pepper salsa, or a more weighty offering, like beef fillet accompanied by foie gras sausage and polenta. One couple, who preferred 'simpler dishes, such as poached turbot or salmon with new potatoes and vegetables', were also amiably catered for. The modern Wharfedale Wing's crisp and fresh bedrooms all have dale views, but are more standardised than those in the Old Wing, which feature fun themes and Chatsworth heirlooms. Park Top (the name of one of the duke's winning racehorses) has Lester Piggott's boots tethered to the door, while anglers can rehearse their tall tales among the piscine paraphernalia of Fisherman.

◐ Open all year ⬕ At junction of A59 and B6160, 5 miles north-west of Ilkley. Private car park ⊨ 18 twin, 13 double, 7 four-poster, 3 suites; all with bathroom/WC; all with TV, room service, hair-dryer, trouser press, direct-dial telephone, iron ⊘ 2 restaurants, 2 bars, 4 lounges, garden; conferences (max 110 people incl up to 41 residential), functions; civil wedding licence; fishing, gym, sauna, solarium, heated indoor swimming-pool, tennis, leisure facilities nearby (free for guests); early suppers for children; cots, high chairs, babysitting, baby-listening ♿ Wheelchair access to hotel and restaurants, WC (unisex), 15 ground-floor bedrooms, 2 rooms specially equipped for disabled people ● No dogs or smoking in restaurants ▭ Amex, Delta, Diners, MasterCard, Switch, Visa £ Single occupancy of twin/double £110, twin/double £155 to £175, four-poster £195, suite £275; deposit required. Bar L £10, D £15; set L £20, D £38. Special breaks available

---

BOMERE HEATH Shropshire   map 7

Fitz Manor

Bomere Heath, Shrewsbury SY4 3AS
TEL: (01743) 850295 (AND FAX)

Historic and well-worn family home, hidden away in the depths of the rolling Shropshire countryside; excellent value.

Dawn and Neil Baly's gorgeous fifteenth-century house has been in their family for four generations. A night or two here may appeal to those who fancy a radical change from the often impersonal experience of staying in a hotel. It will not, however, appeal to shrinking violets: the Balys share their home with guests, even eating with them *en famille*. The manor's black-and-white timbered façade is in need of attention, but its gabled and harled rear face overlooks a lovely garden with pergola, croquet lawn and secluded outdoor swimming-pool. Inside, polished wooden floors run through many of the rooms, which are furnished with family photos, fine antiques and gently fraying soft furnishings. Candlelit dinners, taken round a single table, concentrate on traditional English home cooking: maybe prawn cocktail, a roast and trifle – bring your own wine. The three bedrooms have much character, with rugs on blackened floorboards, battered antiques and loose-covered armchairs; the best is the palatial Green Room. They all share an old-fashioned bathroom and a separate loo.

◐ Open all year ⬕ Going west out of Shrewsbury, take B4380 to Montford Bridge, then to Forton, Mytton and Fitz; turn right after 1 mile; the manor's drive is a mile further on, straight ahead. Private car park ⊨ 1 single, 2 twin; some with trouser press; hair-dryer on request ⊘ Dining-room, TV room, games room, garden; fishing, outdoor heated swimming-pool, snooker, croquet; early suppers for children; cots, high chairs, toys   ♿ No wheelchair access   ● Dogs and smoking by agreement   ☐ None accepted   £ Single £25, single occupancy of twin £25, twin £50; deposit required. Set D £12.50

BONCHURCH Isle of Wight   map 2

Peacock Vane   NEW ENTRY

Bonchurch, Ventnor PO38 1RJ
TEL: (01983) 852019   FAX: (01983) 854796

Luxurious country house, with a choice of restaurants and a fantastic piano bar.

Whether they are here for a weekend away or just for a meal, all guests will enjoy the sumptuous surroundings and the sheer indulgence of a visit to the Peacock Vane. The young, enthusiastic owner, Lawrence Allen, and his wife Mandy, are keen to make their hotel more than just somewhere to eat or rest your head. Guests can eat in the conservatory, or in the bistro-style back room, as well as in the main restaurant, with its impressive, marble fireplace. After dinner, the upstairs bar, liberally stocked with interesting bottles, entices you to stay up; surrounded by plush sofas, chandeliers and a piano – played professionally at the weekends – you will feel like a guest at an exclusive, country-house party. Patio doors lead on to a balcony with views over the secluded gardens. The bedrooms are a delight, furnished as they are with antiques and decorated in bold patterns, in a mixture of the traditional and the contemporary. Each room is different – some have sea views; some, like Dolphin, have a four-poster bed; while others, such as Eyebright and Mercury, have huge, luxurious bathrooms.

◐ Open all year; restaurants closed Sun eve (except residents)   ⛒ Bonchurch is first village going south on A3055 from Shanklin. Hotel is in centre of village beside duck pond. Private car park   ↳ 1 single, 2 twin, 5 double, 2 four-poster, 1 family room, 2 suites (one with private garden); all with bathroom/WC; all with TV, room service, hair-dryer, trouser press, direct-dial telephone; no tea/coffee-making facilities in rooms   ⚼ 2 restaurants, 2 bars, lounge, drying-room, library, conservatory, garden; functions (max 60 people incl up to 25 residential), conferences; fishing, golf, gym, heated outdoor swimming-pool, tennis, boating, horse-riding; early suppers for children; cots, high chairs, baby-listening, baby pool   ♿ No wheelchair access   ● No children aged between 2 and 6; dogs in 1 suite only, by arrangement   ☐ Delta, MasterCard, Switch, Visa   £ Single £65, single occupancy of twin/double £65, twin/double £105, four-poster/family room/suite £125; deposit required. Alc D £20

'The fish of the day, as told to us, was "Salmon with blackcurrant sauce". We then heard the next table being told it was "salmon with blackcurrant hollandaise sauce". Finally we overheard a third table being told it was "salmon with raspberry hollandaise". None of the three permutations sounded particularly appealing...'
On a hotel in the Peak District

Leathes Head

Borrowdale, Keswick CA12 5UY
TEL: (017687) 77247   FAX: (017687) 77363
EMAIL: eng@leatheshead.co.uk
WEB SITE: www.leatheshead.co.uk

Quality furnishings, super food and attention to detail mark out this turn-of-the-century hotel in a prime Lake District location.

The newish arrivals at the Leathes Head, which first appeared as a new entry in the *Guide* last year, seem to have very steady hands on the tiller. Perhaps a nautical metaphor isn't out of place for a house built for a Liverpool shipping magnate and a hotelier who used to work in shipping? At any rate, Patricia Brady and Mark Payne, both exiles from City life, give the impression of being people who like to see things moving (check out those framed, decorative, transport-stock certificates on the stairway). Their well-thought-out renovations of this fine, Edwardian property are reaping dividends: it's now an exceptionally smart and comfortable place. Sensibly, they've gone for a stylish mix of well-designed contemporary furnishings and antiques rather than fake rusticity or olde-worlde quaintness. A sun lounge with attractive wicker seating supplements the lounge, bar and dining-room space in the converted reception rooms off the hallway. Warmth and personality come across with the masses of games, books you might actually want to read, open fires and well-chosen, carefully arranged pictures (local watercolours, geese drawings by indigenous Canadians, cartoons). The original features of the house (fireplaces, plasterwork and stained glass) have been retained, and its large windows survey an idyllic slice of brilliant Lakeland scenery. The bedrooms are equally streamlined and well equipped. And then, of course, there's the food, which is alone sufficient reason to stay here; an appetising, five-course menu includes several choices at each course, and a good cheeseboard. 'From arrival to departure, we felt here was a perfect balance struck between attentiveness to all our needs and friendly informality,' concluded one reader.

◑ Closed Nov and Jan to mid-Feb   ⤴ 3½ miles south of Keswick on B5289. Private car park ⤴ 2 twin, 7 double, 2 family rooms; most with bathroom/WC, some with shower/WC; all with TV, limited room service, hair-dryer, direct-dial telephone, clock radio, some with trouser press   ⊘ Dining-room, bar, 2 lounges, drying-room, conservatory, garden; conferences (max 50 people incl up to 11 residential); croquet, leisure facilities nearby (reduced rates for guests); early suppers for children; cots, high chairs, toys   ♿ Wheelchair access to hotel (ramp) and dining-room, 2 ground-floor bedrooms, 1 room with some modifications for disabled people   ● No dogs; no smoking in bedrooms   ▭ Delta, MasterCard, Switch, Visa   £ Single occupancy of twin/double £40 to £79, twin/double £59 to £109, family room £69 to £119; deposit required. Set D £19. Special breaks available

---

If you have a small appetite, or just aren't feeling hungry, check if you can be given a reduction if you don't want the full menu. At some hotels you could easily end up paying £30 for one course and a coffee.

BOSHAM West Sussex map 3

The Millstream

Bosham Lane, Bosham, Chichester PO18 8HL
TEL: (01243) 573234   FAX: (01243) 573459

Jolly nice staff, comfortable rooms and a picturesque spot all meet in this popular getaway.

'We had an excellent stay – very friendly staff and an extremely welcoming atmosphere.' So wrote another satisfied customer of the Millstream, and it's easy to see why such plaudits come in. Bosham, where Canute allegedly tried to turn back the tide, is one of those typically English villages, complete with a name designed to confuse unsuspecting visitors (it's pronounced 'Bozzam'). Bang in the middle is the capacious cottage, dating back to 1701, which forms the heart of the Millstream. It has been much extended over the intervening years, most recently last year, but has always successfully managed to integrate the new with the old. Pleasant gardens run between the hotel and its stream – a delightful spot for a summer-afternoon tea. The public rooms are equally fresh: the lemony walls of the bar and long lounge are offset by fresh flowers and comfy armchairs, while the restaurant has an unfussy, summery feel to it. The 'excellent food', served by 'attentive, friendly and competent staff', could include deep-fried Brie with a golden plum compote, succeeded by venison, pigeon breast and stuffed quail with a black-cherry and brandy sauce. The 'superior' rooms are just that, with limed-oak or cherrywood furniture, pleasing colour schemes and smart, marble bathrooms; Room 14A has a double aspect overlooking the garden at the back. Other rooms vary in size and have rather more traditional, functional bathrooms, but all are tastefully decked out.

◑ Open all year ⬚ From Chichester, take A259 to Bosham; turn left at Bosham roundabout and follow signs to Bosham church/quay. Private car park ⌸ 5 single, 9 twin, 15 double, 1 four-poster, 2 family rooms, 1 suite; all with bathroom/WC; all with TV, room service, hair-dryer, trouser press, direct-dial telephone, some with air-conditioning ✇ Restaurant, bar, lounge, garden; functions (max 24 people residential incl up to 14 non-residential), conferences; civil wedding licence; early suppers for children; cots, high chairs, babysitting, baby-listening ♿ Wheelchair access to hotel and restaurant, WC (unisex), 7 ground-floor bedrooms, 1 room specially equipped for disabled people ● No dogs in public rooms; no smoking in restaurant and some bedrooms ▭ Amex, Delta, Diners, MasterCard, Switch, Visa £ Single £69, single occupancy of twin/double £85, twin/double/four-poster/family room £109 to £116, suite £139; deposit required. Bar/bistro L £10.50, D £20; set L £13.50, D £20. Special breaks available

---

BOTALLACK Cornwall map 1

Manor Farm

Botallack, St Just, Penzance TR19 7QG
TEL: (01736) 788525

Superb B&B with great welcome, in windswept location.

If this seventeenth-century, granite farmhouse were any further west, it would fall off the cliffs into the sea. Despite being on the outskirts of a tiny village, it feels distinctly remote and windswept – no doubt this is why it was chosen as the location for 'Nampara' in the television series 'Poldark'. The possibilities for walks are myriad, with cliffs and moorlands – embellished with the occasional, decorative tin mine – stretching endlessly in either direction. You may not wish to venture too far, however, as the charms of this welcoming B&B may tempt you to stay within its walls (at one of which, incidentally, John Wesley stood and preached, despite being pelted by the angry villagers of Botallack). Mrs Joyce Cargeeg is the quintessential hostess, greeting you on first-name terms as you arrive, showing you round her home with evident delight, and warning you of the steps and hazards of the low-beamed, solidly furnished house – 'We're up and down here.' The hallway, breakfast room and tiny 'reading room' are boldly decorated in deep reds, and are furnished with family pictures and chunky dressers and tables in polished, dark wood. The bedrooms are equally confidently furnished, one with a fabulous four-poster, another with a half-tester. Although not all are *en suite*, they each have a private shower-room. Breakfast is a real event, catering for healthy eaters as well as for those who prefer a traditional fry-up, with a simply delicious fruit salad to start with and plenty of home-made, wholemeal bread. No evening meal is available (Joyce blames her age, although her energy is undiminished), but there is a pub nearby.

◑ Open all year   ▣ Follow B3306 to north of St Just and fork left towards coast; pass Queen's Arms on right; Manor Farm is straight ahead at next junction. Private car park ▱┳ 1 twin, 1 double, 1 four-poster; 1 with bathroom/WC, 2 with shower/WC; all with TV, hair-dryer   ⊘ Breakfast room, lounge, study, garden   ₺ No wheelchair access ● No dogs; no smoking; smoking in study only   ▭ None accepted   £ Twin/double/four-poster from £46; deposit required

---

Eastwell Manor

Eastwell Park, Boughton Lees, Ashford TN25 4HR
TEL: (01233) 219955   FAX: (01233) 635530

Grand, family-owned hotel in 62 acres of land offering good sporting facilities and fine cuisine.

As you approach, the view is breathtaking: a creeper-clad Jacobean-style mansion with carved, brick chimneys and turreted roofs. Manicured lawns, topiaried hedges and a scallop-shell fountain help create a formal setting around which the hotel's extensive estate fans out. Although much of the building dates from this century, the site is mentioned in the Domesday book and old stonework has been used for newer additions. Even now the house is evolving – 19 two-bedroom apartments are due to be completed in the stable-yard mews house by summer 1999. Standards are high, and you can expect large, well-equipped bedrooms, furnished with comfortable sofas, oak cupboards and bedcovers in pastel colours; the spacious bathrooms come with dressing tables and parquet floors. The hotel's public rooms are no less impressive: the dining-room has high-backed chairs, white tablecloths, a vast stone fireplace and a wood-panelled ceiling. The lounge offers red chesterfields, a roaring fire – and the hotel cat. Food is taken seriously at Eastwell: the à la carte dinner menu might offer roast sea bass, braised rabbit or guinea-fowl with pancetta, followed by unusual fruit puddings like Cox's Apple soup or strawberry spring rolls.

◑ Open all year ⤧ Just off A251 in Boughton Aluph village. Private car park ⤙ 6 twin, 15 double, 1 four-poster, 2 family rooms, 3 suites; all with bathroom/WC; all with TV, room service, hair-dryer, trouser press, direct-dial telephone ✓ Dining-room, bar, lounge, games room, gardens; functions (max 100 people non-residential, 50 residential), conferences; civil wedding licence; tennis, croquet, snooker; early suppers for children; cots, high chairs, baby-listening ᣑ Wheelchair access to hotel (2 steps, ramp) and restaurant, 3 ground-floor bedrooms, 1 specially equipped for disabled people, lift ● No smoking in dining-room and some bedrooms; no dogs in dining-room ▭ Amex, Delta, Diners, MasterCard, Switch, Visa £ Single occupancy of twin/double £130, twin/double £170, four-poster £190, family room £390, suite £240 to £330; deposit required. Set L £16.50; alc L, D £36

BOUGHTON MONCHELSEA Kent map 3

Tanyard Hotel

Wierton Hill, Boughton Monchelsea, Maidstone ME17 4JT
TEL: (01622) 744705   FAX: (01622) 741998

Fourteenth-century house in Kent heartland with hospitable hosts.

One look at this wonky medieval house with its picturesque half-timbered frontage, jutting out at first-floor level, and it's easy to understand its appeal. Set in a valley, it has a small stream flowing into a lily pond and a lush garden with well-tended lawns and flowerbeds. Jan Davies runs it both as a hotel and as a 28-cover restaurant, open to non-residents. She does the cooking herself and serves her mouthwatering concoctions in a candlelit dining-room (the oldest part of the house), where gleaming cutlery and crisp tablecloths are set off by rough walls, beamed ceiling and stone floor. There are usually four choices per course, with house specialities such as twice-baked cheese soufflé, breast of duck with bitter orange sauce and sticky toffee pudding. Service is efficient and attentive. The rooms are as atmospheric and charming as you'd expect, often with slanting floors and peach or cream colour schemes. Woods of Windsor toiletries are set out in the immaculate bathrooms, which may come with a semi-circular bath. Jan is particularly attentive to details, providing delicious-smelling bubble bath, chunky towelling robes and chocolates.

◑ Closed late Dec & early Jan ⤧ From B2163 at Boughton Monchelsea turn down Park Lane, opposite Cock pub; take first right down Wierton Lane and bear right; hotel is on left at bottom of hill. Private car park ⤙ 1 single, 2 twin, 2 double, 1 suite; most with bathroom/WC, 1 twin with shower/WC; all with TV, hair-dryer, direct-dial telephone ✓ Dining-room, bar, lounge, garden; functions (max 28 people non-residential, 11 residential); early suppers for children, by arrangement ᣑ No wheelchair access ● No children under 6; no dogs; no smoking in dining-room ▭ Amex, Delta, Diners, MasterCard, Switch, Visa £ Single £65, single occupancy of twin/double £80 to £85, twin/double £105 to £115, suite £150; deposit required. Set Sun L £25, D £29

BOURNE Lincolnshire   map 6

Bourne Eau House

30 South Street, Bourne PE10 9LY
TEL: (01778) 423621

Tastefully elegant, family house, with kind, civilised hosts.

This handsome house in the centre of Bourne is tucked between two branches of the River Eau, with a well-kept garden and gravel drive between it and the road. Various parts of the house were built during various centuries, and the owners, George and Dawn Bishop, have carefully preserved the character of each period in the appropriate rooms. The sixteenth-century part of the house is represented downstairs by the music room, with its piano and tapestries. In the drawing-room next to it, where guests take sherry before dining, can be found the elegance of seventeenth-century France. The oldest part, the dining-room, is cave-like in its wood and stone, with high-backed chairs standing around a long, single table. Guests dine together; should conversation flag, there is always something of interest in the house itself to set things off again. George Bishop, having travelled extensively for the United Nations, and having written books on all kinds of subjects (the latest being a six-volume history of science), is an interesting host. The bedrooms are carefully furnished, and have extras like fruit, sweets and fresh milk for the tea tray. Of the three, the Jacobean room is possibly the best, on account of its antique bed and stone fireplace; the stairs up to the bathroom might not suit everyone, though.

○ Closed Chr & Easter; dining-room closed Sun eve   ↗ In Bourne town centre, opposite the cenotaph. Private car park   ⬅ 2 twin, 1 double; all with bathroom/WC exc 1 twin with shower/WC; all with TV, room service, hair-dryer, direct-dial telephone   ⌖ Dining-room, drawing-room, music room; early suppers for children; cots, high chairs, toys, playroom, babysitting, baby-listening, outdoor play area   ⅚ No wheelchair access   ● No dogs; no smoking in bedrooms, discouraged in public rooms   ⊟ None accepted   £ Single occupancy of twin/double £35, twin/double £70. Set D £22.50

BOURNEMOUTH Dorset   map 2

Carlton Hotel

East Overcliff, Bournemouth BH1 3DN
TEL: (01202) 552011   FAX: (01202) 299573

Exemplary service at a seaside grand hotel, with good leisure facilities.

With its flowing, art-deco lines and coffee-and-cream-striped 'decks', Bournemouth's Carlton Hotel looks like a liner ready to slip its moorings and glide from its clifftop position into the sea below. There's a nautical theme, too, in the part-panelled cocktail bar, and it's easy to imagine that you're cruising in some style. Sketches of eminent military men and politicians (the hotel is a popular billet for senior politicos at party conference time) add gravitas and something of the air of a gentlemen's club. The split-level dining-room has a bright, spacious feel, and its globe lamps and brass rails reiterate the art-deco look; some tables here have a sea view, but for many this is largely obscured by the high, greenery-clad wall that surrounds the swimming-pool area. The friendly, unfailingly helpful staff rather managed to distract our inspector's attention from a disappointing meal of salade niçoise followed by chicken with pasta, sun-dried tomatoes and oyster mushrooms. Things picked up with a delightful passion-fruit tart, but the food was less distinguished than the setting, service, or tariff would lead you to expect. One correspondent also wrote to register the perceived shortcomings of the food, describing a chicken main dish as 'uninspired'. The bedrooms are well proportioned and freshly, if somewhat blandly, decorated in a rather impersonal, corporate style.

◑ Open all year ⤓ In Bournemouth, follow signs to East Cliff. Private car park. ⌸ 3 single, 25 twin, 30 double, 10 family rooms, 6 suites; all with bathroom/WC; all with satellite TV, room service, hair-dryer, trouser press, direct-dial telephone; mini-bar on request ⊘ Dining-room, bar, 3 lounges, library, conservatory, games room, garden; functions (max 150 people residential/non-residential), conferences; civil wedding licence; gym, sauna, solarium, indoor and outdoor heated swimming-pools; early suppers for children; cots, high chairs, toys, playrooms, babysitting, baby-listening ᕕ Wheelchair access to hotel (5 steps, porters will assist) and dining-room, 5 ground-floor bedrooms; lift ● Children discouraged from dining-room; no dogs in public rooms; no smoking in some bedrooms ▭ Amex, Delta, Diners, MasterCard, Switch, Visa ⌹ Single £115 to £135, single occupancy of twin/double £145 to £165, twin/double/family room £180 to £200, suite £230 to £250; deposit required. Bar/bistro L £9, D £12; set L £16.50, D £23; alc L £20, D £25. Special breaks available

---

Langtry Manor

Derby Road, East Cliff, Bournemouth BH1 3QB
TEL: (01202) 553887 FAX: (01202) 290115
EMAIL: lillie@langtrymanor.com
WEB SITE: www.langtrymanor.com/

Memories of royal rumpy-pumpy at a cheerful, family-run hotel, ideal for a romantic break with just a hint of naughtiness.

The plaque erected on this mock-Tudor building by the local town council is admirably circumspect: 'Built 1877 as The Red House for the Socialite, Beauty and Actress Lillie Langtry. Edward, Prince of Wales (later King Edward VII) provided the residence, to which he was a regular visitor.' The hotel's brochure is rather more forthcoming when it comes to explaining why a man destined to reign over an empire on which the sun never set should wish to spend time in a spacious and comfortable, though hardly palatial, house in a suburban street: 'love nest', it trills; 'favourite mistress', it gasps. The hotel fairly revels in its former role as the backdrop for illicit princely passion, with the staff being eager to point out enduring evidence of the couple's trysts, such as the pane of glass etched with intertwined initials, and the 'king's peep hole' from which Edward would survey the assembled dinner guests before deciding whether or not they would provide amusing company. There's also the defiantly *Je ne regrette rien* motto – 'They Say. What say they? Let them say' – inscribed below the minstrels' gallery of the large dining hall. It's here that a six-course, Edwardian banquet is served on Saturday nights by girls in mobcaps and period dress. Food on non-banquet nights is appropriately traditional: perhaps tomato and orange soup, followed by roast leg of English pork, and finally 'Lillie Swans' – a meringue, fresh-fruit and cream confection.

Pamela Hamilton Howard, while clearly enjoying her role as custodian of a little part of the nation's history, makes sure that her staff get the basics right, too. So new arrivals are ushered into the comfortable lounge for a welcoming glass of sherry or pot of tea before being shown to the pretty, and generally spacious, bedrooms with names like the dandyish Disraeli Suite, or the Langtry Suite, whose four-poster is rakishly large and looms over a heart-shaped bath complete with tied-back modesty drapes.

◖ Open all year 🅿 Turn off A338 at railway station, continue over next roundabout, then turn left into Knyveton Road. Hotel is at end, at junction with Derby Road. Private car park 🛏 7 twin, 7 double, 9 four-poster, 1 family room, 2 suites; some in annexe; all with bathroom/WC exc 1 double with shower/WC; all with TV, room service, hair-dryer, mini-bar, direct-dial telephone ✇ Dining hall, bar, lounge, conservatory, garden; functions (max 100 people incl up to 50 residential), conferences; civil wedding licence; early suppers for children; cots, high chairs ♿ Wheelchair access to hotel (ramp) and dining hall, 4 ground-floor bedrooms ⊜ No children under 7 in dining hall eves; no dogs in public rooms; no smoking in dining hall and some bedrooms ▭ Amex, Diners, MasterCard, Switch, Visa 💷 Single occupancy of twin/double from £70, twin/double from £90, four-poster from £100, suite from £130, family room (price on application); deposit required. Set D £20. Special breaks available

---

Dial House

The Chestnuts, High Street, Bourton-on-the-Water,
Cheltenham GL54 2AN
TEL: (01451) 822244   FAX: (01451) 810126

A curate's egg of a hotel, in the centre of the most trippery of all the Cotswolds' villages.

This lovely, seventeenth-century house suggests a civilised respite from all the tacky souvenir shops nearby. In fact, it does and it doesn't. Some rooms – notably the best, antique-rich bedrooms in the main house and the flagstone-floored restaurant, with its inglenook fireplace – live up to the building's promise. And where the hotel really excels is in its food: dinners comprise beautifully presented dishes that are fairly imaginative in their starters and main courses, though they revert to the traditional in their substantial puddings; while breakfasts run the gamut of everything from croissants to kippers. On the down side, the bedrooms in a newer wing at the rear of the building may be small, while those in the annexe may exhibit distressingly busy design schemes, with little coherence or style. Our inspector also found evidence of poor room maintenance: the seal round a bath was broken and a chair collapsed when he sat on it. Staff are friendly and competent; however, even though the owner was present during our stay, he showed no inclination to communicate with us at any stage.

◐ Open all year ⚄ In centre of Bourton-on-the-Water, off A429. Private car park
🛏 1 single, 4 twin, 6 double, 3 four-poster; some in annexe; most with bathroom/WC,
some with shower/WC; all with TV, room service, hair-dryer, direct-dial telephone
✓ Restaurant, bar, 2 lounges, drying-room, conservatory, garden; functions (max 32
people incl up to 27 residential), conferences; croquet ♿ No wheelchair access
⬤ No children under 10; no dogs; no smoking in some bedrooms ▭ Amex, Delta,
MasterCard, Switch, Visa £ Single £48, single occupancy of twin/double £58,
twin/double £96, four-poster £116; deposit required. Set L £10.50; alc D £20

BOVEY TRACEY Devon   map 1

Edgemoor Hotel

Haytor Road, Bovey Tracey, Newton Abbot TQ13 9LE
TEL: (01626) 832466 FAX: (01626) 834760

*Delightfully airy and spacious hotel run with personal care, handy
for walks on Dartmoor.*

It's hard to believe this was built in the 1870s as a school for poor boys – it seems
so grand now. But the windows in what is now the drawing-room, and was then
the assembly room, give the game away; they are huge, designed to let in as
much natural light as possible so as to save on lighting costs! This is not the only
room that benefits from the light and airy proportions: so does the formal,
pastel-coloured restaurant, with fresh flowers and lacy tablecloths, and the
whole place maintains an elegant yet unstuffy atmosphere. Most of the public
rooms are well co-ordinated in floral style, while the bar is distinctly informal,
with a clinker-built bar, roaring fire and traditional pub settles. On the extensive
menu (there are three chefs) might be warm avocado in a Dijon mustard sauce
topped with grated Parmesan, followed by sirloin steak flamed in brandy,
finished with a cracked black peppercorn sauce. Some of the bedrooms are in a
newly built annexe; although they are plush and comfortable, they lack the
character of those in the main house. All are done out in smart country style, with
sprigged walls, new pine furniture and good bathrooms – and those essential
extras, a teddy bear and two plastic ducks.

◐ Closed 6 days from New Year ⚄ Turn off A38 on to A382 Bovey Tracey road; turn
left at second roundabout towards Widecombe; after ½ mile fork left and hotel is ½ mile
along this road, on right. Private car park 🛏 3 single, 3 twin, 7 double, 2 four-poster,
2 family rooms; 5 in annexe; most with bathroom/WC, 3 with shower/WC; all with TV,
room service, hair-dryer, trouser press, direct-dial telephone ✓ Restaurant, 2 bars,
lounge, garden; conferences (max 50 people incl up to 17 residential), functions; early
suppers for children; cots, high chairs, baby-listening ♿ No wheelchair access
⬤ No children under 8 at dinner; no dogs or smoking in restaurant ▭ Amex, Delta,
Diners, MasterCard, Switch, Visa £ Single £49 to £53, single occupancy of
twin/double £60 to £65, twin/double £80 to £90, four-poster £90 to £100, family room
£94 to £104; deposit required. Bar/bistro L, D £6; set L £16, D £22.50. Special breaks
available

---

*Don't expect to turn up at a small hotel assuming that a room will be
available. It's always best to telephone in advance.*

Lindeth Fell

Lyth Valley Road, Bowness-on-Windermere,
Windermere LA23 3JP
TEL: (015394) 43286　FAX: (015394) 47455

*Well-established, older-style hotel, in magnificent grounds, offering
a great welcome.*

This is one of several palatial Edwardian villas above the shores of Windermere
that have been converted into country-house hotels, but it is one of the best, not
just for its setting – in marvellous, show-piece gardens (mature rhododendrons,
shrubs and bulbs) – but also for its genuinely warm, family welcome. It's
popular with older visitors, and caters for conservative tastes in terms of its décor
and food. The panelled entrance hall, so often an inviting feature in these fine
houses, acts as an additional, cosy lounge; log fires blaze in a prettily tiled
fireplace, and a stained-glass window catches the eye by the staircase. Off it lie
two lounges (blue and pink) – light, serene rooms, full of comfortable, matching
armchairs and sofas and featuring plenty of tasteful bits and bobs on walls and
mantelpieces. The restaurant is in two sections, one enjoying stunning,
picture-window views (plans are in hand to expand this area). Menus are
heartily English, and Sunday lunch is a popular affair. The spacious, light and
agreeable bedrooms ring the changes in traditional styles. Windermere (the
master bedroom) cuts a dash in sunshine yellow, and sports flouncy coronet
drapes that are echoed in the pelmets and valances; others are more restrained.
The charming Kennedy family is on hand overseeing things, and the staff are
notably friendly. Rather than hike up the tariff with optional frills, the owners
emphasise solid good value; Lindeth Fell is less pricey than some of its obvious
rivals.

◖ Closed Jan to mid-Feb　　On A5074, 1 mile south of Bowness-on-Windermere.
Private car park　　2 single, 4 twin, 6 double, 2 family rooms, 1 suite; most with
bathroom/WC, 2 with shower/WC; all with TV, room service, hair-dryer, direct-dial
telephone, some with trouser press　　2 restaurants, 3 lounges, drying-room, bar
service, garden; conferences (max 40 people incl up to 15 residential); fishing, tennis,
putting green, pitch & putt, croquet; early suppers for children　　Wheelchair access
to hotel (ramp) and restaurants, 1 ground-floor bedroom specially equipped for
disabled people　●　No children under 7; no dogs; smoking in one lounge and
bedrooms only　　MasterCard, Visa　　Single £40 to £53, single occupancy of
twin/double £55 to £67, twin/double £80 to £150, family room £93 to £118, suite £100
to £150; deposit required. Bar/bistro L £7.50; set Sun L £12, D £19. Special breaks
available

---

*'On sitting down to some work at the desk, I found that the only socket to
plug my laptop and printer into was attached to the lighting circuit. I
could have lights, laptop or printer, but no two at any one time. I
eventually managed to balance the computer on top of the minibar and
the printer on top of the luggage stand and work without the benefit of
light.'*
On a hotel in Brighton

Linthwaite House

Crook Road, Bowness-on-Windermere,
Windermere LA23 3JA
TEL: (015394) 88600   FAX: (015394) 88601
EMAIL: admin@linthwaite.com
WEB SITE: www.linthwaite.com/

A superb setting and an air of colonial elegance enhance this splendid Edwardian country house.

At Linthwaite House you're only a few minutes' drive from the holiday bustle of Windermere, but, cocooned in such opulent grounds, you could be in the depths of the countryside. Fifteen acres of mature woodlands and immaculate gardens surround this palatial villa, with its timbered gables and wide verandah. From smooth croquet lawns and paved terraces there's a magnificent panorama of the lake and wooded fells beyond; strolls through the grounds lead to a private tarn stocked with fish. Inside, the handsome rooms evoke an air of leisured indulgence; travelling trunks and leather suitcases make a talking point in the entrance hall, while wicker chairs and ceiling fans in the extensive public rooms suggest warmer climes. Sporting equipment and decoy ducks deck walls and shelves, and an amazing collection of artifacts from bygone times invites your curiosity on a plate rail round the restaurant (ginger-beer casks, spice jars, hatboxes, old bottles). The theme continues in the lavishly furnished bedrooms, which are full of sumptuous extras. The best enjoy the lake views, but even those without are blissful havens. The whole house feels luxuriously relaxing, stylish and beautifully kept. Food is a strong point too: elegant, professional cooking, perfectly presented. Smart enough to attract high-ranking statesmen from halfway round the world for a recuperative treat, Linthwaite House is no budget option, but short-break rates are worth inspecting.

◑ Open all year ⬀ On B5284, 1 mile west of Windermere Golf Club, ¾ mile south of Bowness. Private car park ⬅ 1 single, 4 twin, 12 double, 1 suite; all with bathroom/WC; all with satellite TV, room service, hair-dryer, trouser press, direct-dial telephone ⟡ Restaurant, bar, lounge, drying-room, conservatory, garden; functions (max 47 people incl up to 36 residential); civil wedding licence; fishing, putting green, croquet, leisure facilities nearby (free for guests); early suppers for children; cots, high chairs, babysitting ♿ Wheelchair access to hotel (1 step) and restaurant, 5 ground-floor bedrooms ● No children under 7 in restaurant eves; no dogs; no smoking in restaurant and some bedrooms ▭ Amex, Delta, MasterCard, Switch, Visa £ Single £75 to £95, twin/double £90 to £180, suite £210 to £230; deposit required. Bar/bistro L from £6; set D £33.50. Special breaks available

---

BRACKNELL Berkshire   map 3

Coppid Beech Hotel   **NEW ENTRY**

John Nike Way, Bracknell RG12 8TF
TEL: (01344) 303333   FAX: (01344) 301200

Business hotel, with idiosyncratic touches and an eye on the weekend market.

You could be forgiven for thinking that you have spent too long on the piste when spotting this Alpine chalet among the bewildering bypasses and roundabouts of outer Bracknell. The steep, snow-repellent gables, wooden balconies and clock-tower turret sit incongruously atop a slickly-run hotel serving the corporate needs of the M4-corridor industries. If you are here on business, you'll find all the accoutrements necessary for an efficient, overnight pit-stop between appointments, but several clever touches also set this place apart as one that you might find appealing enough to while away a weekend in – provided you compromise on some rather prosaic immediate surroundings in order to enjoy the accessibility of numerous local attractions, like Windsor, Henley or Legoland.

Colour-coded fish in triangular tanks are used to steer guests via the appropriate corridors to smart and functional, if fairly bland, bedrooms offering all the usual facilities, plus modems and mini-bars, nail-files and cleansing lotions. Toning and torture are provided in a leisure club equipped with exercise machines, a sauna and sunbeds. Different dining tastes are catered for either by the steaks-and-pasta approach of a German bierkeller, or within the more refined surroundings – indoor trellises and pergolas – of Rowan's Restaurant. And if the Alpine architecture has put you in the mood, you'll find a dry ski slope, toboggan run and ice rink at the leisure centre across the road.

○ Open all year ⚡ Leave M4 at Junction 10; turn left into Bracknell exit; follow A329(M) to the Coppid Beech roundabout; take first exit (B3408), signposted Binfield; hotel is 300 metres along on right, at mini-roundabout. Private car park ⏗ 44 single, 98 twin, 38 double, 6 family rooms, 19 suites; all with bathroom/WC; all with TV, room service, modem point, hair-dryer, mini-bar, trouser press, direct-dial telephone ⚒ 2 restaurants, 2 bars, lounge; conferences (max 350 people incl up to 205 residential), functions; civil wedding licence; gym, sauna, solarium, heated indoor swimming-pool, leisure facilities nearby (reduced rates for guests); early suppers for children; cots, high chairs, babysitting ♿ Wheelchair access to hotel (ramp) and restaurants, WC (unisex), 12 ground-floor bedrooms, 2 rooms specially equipped for disabled people ● No dogs in public rooms ⊟ Amex, Delta, Diners, MasterCard, Switch, Visa £ Single £135, single occupancy of twin/double £165, twin/double/family room £165, suite £205 (1998 prices); deposit required. Bar/bistro L £5 to £20, D £20; set L £20, D £25; alc L, D £35. Special breaks available

Bradford Old Windmill

4 Masons Lane, Bradford-on-Avon BA15 1QN
TEL: (01225) 866842   FAX: (01225) 866648

Interesting, ethnic food and lots of fun close to the centre of this popular Wiltshire town.

The cult success of the television series 'Jonathan Creek' has re-introduced the great British public to the romance of living in a windmill. If you've ever been intrigued by what life must be like 'in the round', you can satisfy your curiosity with a stay at Peter and Priscilla Roberts' unusual home, situated within an easy walk of the antique shops at the commercial heart of Bradford-on-Avon. The characteristically rotund shape of the creeper-clad, hillside dwelling offers a clue as to its former role (the sails have long gone), and the small, dramatically sloping gardens add to the general air of fun and intrigue. Once indoors, the generally plain décor provides a suitable canvas for antique agricultural artifacts like the impressive scythe that hangs menacingly next to the stone fireplace, apparently silently breathing memento mori. Priscilla serves imaginative, vegetarian, ethnic dishes from the four corners of the world, and guests eat around a communal table. The bedrooms have all the charm and off-beat character that you might expect, with exposed beams, a hanging-basket chair and king-sized, circular bed setting the tone in Great Spur, while Damsel boasts a whirlpool bath, waterbed and windchimes.

◑ Closed Jan & Feb; dining-room closed Tue, Wed, Fri & Sun eves ☑ Entering Bradford-on-Avon from north on A363, find Castle pub; go down hill towards town centre; after 50 yards turn left into a gravelled private drive immediately before first roadside house (no sign on road). Private car park 🛏 2 double, 1 suite; all with bathroom/WC exc 1 double with shower/WC; all with TV, hair-dryer, radio ⌀ Dining-room, lounge, drying-room, garden ♿ No wheelchair access ● No children under 6; no dogs; no smoking ▭ Amex, MasterCard, Visa £ Single occupancy of double £59 to £69, double £69 to £89, suite £89 to £99; deposit required. Set D £18

Priory Steps

Newtown, Bradford-on-Avon BA15 1NQ
TEL: (01225) 862230 FAX: (01225) 866248

Agreeable conversion of a terrace of weavers' cottages, now offering comfortable accommodation under the Wolsey Lodge banner.

Priory Steps' central, hillside location means that the accommodation in the mellow-stoned, seventeenth-century structure is arranged in topsy-turvy fashion. The public rooms are two levels below the street entrance, making the whole distinctly Tardis-like in its dimensions. The hotel is owned and run by Carey Chapman and his wife Diana; Carey's father was a barrister, and there's just a touch of the Rumpoles about the civilised library, with its burgundy walls, well-laden shelves and amusing collection of legal figurines. Diana plans and cooks the food, which is provided in the jauntily yellow, beamed dining-room, and is served in traditional Wolsey Lodge, house-party style at one long table. Guests can stroll from the public rooms to the secluded, south-facing, terraced gardens. There are five comfortable, tastefully decorated bedrooms, most of which offer sweeping views of the town. On a clear day, you can look forward to being able to see the famous White Horse on Salisbury Plain.

◑ Open all year ☑ From A363 signposted to Bath, turn left at sign to Turleigh, 200 yards north of town centre. Private car park 🛏 2 twin, 3 double; suite available; all with bathroom/WC; all with TV, hair-dryer ⌀ Dining-room, lounge, library, garden ♿ No wheelchair access ● No dogs; smoking in 1 public room only ▭ MasterCard, Visa £ Single occupancy of twin/double £50, twin/double/suite £66. Set D £18

Woolley Grange

Woolley Green, Bradford-on-Avon BA15 1TX
TEL: (01225) 864705   FAX: (01225) 864059
EMAIL: woolley@luxury-hotel.demon.co.uk

A wealth of activities for children leaves adults free to enjoy the serenity of a Jacobean country house.

As you approach Woolley Grange, it is the powerful cocktail of aromas from the herb and kitchen gardens that makes the strongest impression on the senses – even more so than the grand aspect of the Jacobean residence, built in mellow, Bath stone and clad in ivy. As you lean on the balustrade overlooking a large fish pond teeming with lily pads, or admire the views of the rolling countryside from the outdoor heated swimming-pool, the serenity of the locale cannot fail to affect you. The age and magnificence of the establishment don't make for snooty staff, however. Despite the ubiquity of antique (mainly period) furniture, the hotel is specifically aimed at families: children are welcome, and stay free on z-beds in their parents' rooms. Those of eight and over will find an exciting array of games in the Hen House, while tots will be well looked after by the all-day nannies in the crèche – the Woolley Bears' Den.

At dinner, the smart restaurant, whose menu is based on produce from the garden and the local farming community, provides a respite for child-weary parents – those who wish to eat with their families are seated in the Victorian conservatory. There are several rooms available for sitting in, including the airy and light drawing-room, complete with leather sofas and real fire, just off the reception. The individually decorated bedrooms have period double beds and décors to match. The attic room, West Gable, reached by a narrow, twisting staircase just inside the door, is delightfully quirky, and has a memorable bathroom with a free-standing bath and parlour palms.

◑ Open all year   ⃞ On B3105, 1 mile north-east of Bradford-on-Avon. Private car park   ⌁ 1 single, 3 twin, 8 double, 8 family rooms, 3 suites; some in annexe; most with bathroom/WC, some with shower/WC; all with TV, room service, hair-dryer, direct-dial telephone; no tea/coffee-making facilities in rooms   ⊘ 2 restaurants, 2 drawing-rooms, TV room, library, conservatory, games room, garden; functions (max 70 people incl up to 46 residential), conferences; heated outdoor swimming-pool, tennis, badminton, croquet; early suppers for children; cots, high chairs, toys, nursery, babysitting, baby-listening, outdoor play area   ঙ No wheelchair access   ● No dogs in public rooms; no smoking in restaurants   ⃞ Diners, MasterCard, Switch, Visa   £ Single £90, single occupancy of twin/double from £90, twin/double from £99, family room from £125, suite from £170; deposit required. Bar/bistro L, D £8.50; set L £15, D £34.50. Special breaks available

---

'We ordered a bottle of Australian Shiraz, to which the wine waiter replied, "A good choice, though I would have gone for the Italian myself," as he walked off. To add insult to injury, the wine didn't arrive until halfway through the first course.'
On a hotel in the Peak District

BRAMPTON Cumbria

map 10

Farlam Hall

Brampton CA8 2NG
TEL: (016977) 46234   FAX: (016977) 46683
EMAIL: farlamhall@dial.pipex.com

Traditional, country-house comfort and outstanding food, in a peaceful, Eden Valley setting.

Just outside the little town of Brampton, in quiet grounds with bulb-strewn lawns and a grand cedar tree, this fine hotel offers convenient access to the Pennines, Carlisle and the M6. It's a rambling, much-extended – but mainly Victorian – building, creeper-covered in parts; some sections date back to the fifteenth century, when it was a fortified farmhouse. The interior is traditionally furnished: plants, pictures and antiques leave no awkward gaps in the handsome rooms. Softly ticking clocks break up the silences, while such unusual features as old dolls and stuffed birds add to the nineteenth-century ambience. The restaurant, with its strapwork ceiling and big windows, is decorated in blue and gold. The bedrooms are light and spacious, with antiques, well-co-ordinated décor and good bathrooms; many have lovely views over the grounds and fields which surround the house. Food is an important side of the business, and the style of service is quite formal. Four-course, fixed-price dinners might include asparagus with vinaigrette, fillet of turbot with buttered cabbage and a prawn sauce, and a choice of rich puddings and cheeses. For all its considerable grandeur, Farlam Hall feels a friendly house, and the management is down-to-earth.

◗ Closed 25 to 30 Dec   ⤧ On A689 Brampton to Alston road, *not* in Farlam village. Private car park   ⤧ 5 twin, 6 double, 1 four-poster; one in annexe; all with bathroom/WC; all with TV, room service, hair-dryer, trouser press, direct-dial telephone, some with tea/coffee-making facilities   ⦿ Restaurant, 2 lounges, garden; functions (max 40 people incl up to 24 residential), conferences; croquet   ₺ No wheelchair access   ◗ No children under 5   ▭ MasterCard, Switch, Visa   £ Single occupancy of twin/double £120, twin/double £220, four-poster £240 (rates incl dinner). Special breaks available

---

BRANSCOMBE Devon

map 2

The Bulstone

Higher Bulstone, Branscombe, Seaton EX12 3BL
TEL: (01297) 680446 (AND FAX)

A cheerful hotel designed specially for the under-5s and their parents.

It's not surprising that Kevin Monaghan has made a success of his 'Hotel For Families With Young Children' – he's the kind of genial man who's good with youngsters, yet won't let them get out of hand. After all, as he says, 'It's not what we do for the kids, it's what we do for the parents.' The whole idea is to make life easier for mum and dad (and grandparents too), so children's tea is at 5pm, leaving time to get them down before adults eat later on. Of course the place is full of baby-minders, high chairs and bottle-sterilisers, but toys are confined to the bright playroom, and children are not allowed in the lounge. The décor is not inspiring, but Kevin says, 'We've kept it functional so we can clean up jammy fingerprints,' and, seeing as most of the clientele is under five, it's understandable. The grounds have a climbing frame and swings, and plenty of room to play, and a donkey sanctuary is close by. Family units are furnished with new pine, and clean sheets are provided (with a smile) at all hours. These are the sorts of things that make parents feel at ease. On the simple dinner menu might be home-made chicken-and-sweetcorn soup, followed by lamb pie with onion, apple and potato.

○ Open all year   ↗ On A3052 at Branscombe Cross, take left turning for the Bulstone, 1 mile away; ignore all other Branscombe turnings. Private car park ⇤→ 1 twin, 1 double, 10 family rooms; 6 family rooms with bathroom/WC; all with hair-dryer ⊘ Dining-room, bar, lounge, TV room, drying-room, conservatory, playroom and guest kitchen, garden; functions (max 24 people residential); early suppers for children; babysitting, cots, high chairs, toys, outdoor play area, baby-listening   ⛿ No wheelchair access ● No children over 9 months in restaurant eves; no dogs; no smoking ⊟ Delta, MasterCard, Switch, Visa £ Single occupancy of twin/double £30, twin/double £42, family room £47 to £75; deposit required. Set D £15. Special breaks available

Masons Arms   **NEW ENTRY**

Branscombe, Seaton EX12 3DJ
TEL: (01297) 680300   FAX: (01297) 680500

Up-market hostelry in remote village, serving good food; stay in the annexe rooms, not in the pub itself.

Most of Branscombe straggles along the side of a valley, but it has a pretty centre and the Masons Arms is in the thick of things. The proprietor, Murray Inglis, must be on to a good thing – so far he has acquired a gorgeous row of thatched cottages on the hill above the pub to use as bedrooms, as well as a couple of houses across the road. The best room is The Linney, in a fabulous, converted barn, but the rooms in the cottages have views across the hills to the sea, characterfully bulging walls, and include one four-poster. Avoid the rooms at the back of the pub – Murray is in the process of upgrading them, and at the moment they need it. The ones at the front are fine – simple and spruce, with antique furniture and floral covers. Downstairs, the main bar has lots of beams and inglenooks; a spit roast turns over the open fire on Sundays, and the service is excellent. You can eat here or in the cosy dining-room, from a menu that might include saffron shellfish linguini with prawns, crab and chilli, and a herbed roast rump of pork, served with garlic mash and a balsamic- and olive-oil dressing. There's a welcome no-smoking bar and a small guests' sitting-room, too.

○ Open all year   ↗ 3 miles south of A3052, between Sidford and Colyford. Private car park ⇤→ 3 single, 5 twin, 12 double, 1 four-poster; some in annexe; most with bathroom/WC; all with TV, room service, direct-dial telephone, some with trouser press ⊘ Dining-room, 2 bars, sitting-room, garden; functions (max 60 people incl up to 30 residential), conferences; early suppers for children; high chairs, baby-listening ⟨wheelchair icon⟩ Wheelchair access to hotel and dining-room, 3 ground-floor bedrooms ⬤ No smoking in some public rooms ▭ Delta, MasterCard, Switch, Visa £ Single £15 to £22, single occupancy of twin/double £28 to £42, twin/double £30 to £60, four-poster £50 to £72; deposit required. Bar/bistro L £7, D £12; set D £21

BRAY Berkshire   map 3

Monkey Island Hotel

Bray, Maidenhead SL6 2EE
TEL: (01628) 623400   FAX: (01628) 784732

Handsome style and seclusion in Georgian pavilions hidden away on a private island on the Thames.

A pub called the Fish and a local estate agent named Pike help to set the tone for a stay in Bray. The Thames gurgles past this hotel on all sides, ruffling the tips of the weeping willows and delivering drifting ducks and swans hither and yon. Cars are left behind on the north bank, and the two cream-coloured, Regency pavilions are approached via a narrow footbridge and a guard of honour formed by cohabiting peacocks and Canada geese. Corporate deals and discussions are conducted beyond the pergolas and statuary, but with seemingly little infringement on those taking tea and planning lazy days beside the river.

The bizarre frescoes of anthropomorphised apes in the vaulted Monkey Room in the Lodge might suggest the reason for the island's peculiar name – though the more likely explanation is that the land was once occupied by monks. Following aperitifs taken beneath the simian fishermen, or in the adjoining woody terrace bar, dinner among foliage follows in the restaurant, perched on the prow of the island. The duck, served with wild berries and a lemon and honey *jus*, or the mussels accompanying leeks and saffron in a soup, could conceivably have come from local waters; the tiger prawns (served with scallops and a vegetable tagliatelle) and ostrich steak must have come from further afield.

All the bedrooms are to be found in the Temple, a hundred yards across the lawn from the Lodge. Permutations on the theme of plush fabrics and period wallpapers lend each of the elegant, if often smallish, rooms an individual appeal, and all overlook stretches of lawn or water, or both.

◑ Closed after Chr lunch till mid-Jan ⟐ Hotel is signposted in Bray village. Private car park ⟕ 2 single, 9 twin, 14 double, 1 suite; all with bathroom/WC; all with TV, room service, hair-dryer, mini-bar, trouser press, direct-dial telephone ⟨restaurant icon⟩ Restaurant, bar, lounge, garden; conferences (max 150 people incl up to 26 residential); functions; civil wedding licence; fishing, gym, croquet, archery, laser clay-pigeon shooting; early suppers for children; cots, high chairs ⟨wheelchair icon⟩ No wheelchair access ⬤ No dogs ▭ Amex, Delta, Diners, MasterCard, Switch, Visa £ Single £100, single occupancy of twin/double £110, twin/double £125, suite £180; deposit required. Continental B £8.50, cooked B £12; bar/bistro L £15, D £28; set L £21, D £28; alc L, D £32. (Prices valid till Apr 1999.) Special breaks available

---

The Guide *is totally independent, accepts no free hospitality, and survives on the number of copies sold each year.*

Roebuck Inn   [NEW ENTRY]

Brimfield, Ludlow SY8 4NE
TEL: (01584) 711230   FAX: (01584) 711654

Unpretentious, traditional village pub, run by young and friendly new owners.

Under its previous owner, the Roebuck Inn was famous for its highly accomplished, British country cooking. Since arriving in the summer of 1997, David Willson-Lloyd, one of the chefs, and his wife Susan, who runs things behind the bar, have brought the pub more down to earth: food prices have been reduced, one menu operates throughout the establishment and a casual, cheerful atmosphere pervades the place. Locals tend to hang out in the simply furnished snug bar. A more appealing place in which to eat is the rear lounge/bar, amid dark-wood panelling and black beams festooned with hops, or in the jolly dining-room, which is decked out in orange and gold tones and wicker chairs. The food is above-average pub fare, typified by such dishes as a substantial fish pie or a cappuccino brûlée. But there are also more ambitious options – maybe quail stuffed with apricots, raisins and pine-nuts, or duck breast in a ginger and kumquat compote. The three very habitable, good-sized bedrooms sport grey-and-blue colour schemes and smart, limed-oak furniture. Traffic disturbance is minimal: the main roads bypass this nondescript village.

○ Open all year   ⚑ In Brimfield village, just off A49 between Ludlow and Leominster. Private car park   ⊨ 1 twin, 2 double; twin with bathroom/WC, doubles with shower/WC; all with TV, room service, hair-dryer, trouser press, direct-dial telephone   ✧ Dining-room, bar, 2 lounge bars, drying-room, terrace; functions (max 70 people incl up to 6 residential), conferences; early suppers for children; cots, high chairs, baby-listening   ♿ No wheelchair access   ● No dogs in eating areas; £5 cleaning charge for dogs in bedrooms; no smoking in dining-room   ▭ Delta, MasterCard, Switch, Visa   £ Single occupancy of twin/double £45, twin/double £60; deposit required. Bar/bistro L £10, D £12.50; alc L £15, D £20. Special breaks available

Berkeley Square Hotel

15 Berkeley Square, Clifton, Bristol BS8 1HB
TEL: 0117-925 4000   FAX: 0117-925 2970

Reliable base for both tourists and business folk, in the nicest part of Bristol.

Name the hotel and you've defined the location – a dignified sprawl along most of one side of an impressive Georgian square. A more modern look prevails in the smart interior, where the public rooms have a pronounced, business-like crispness. There's a definite buzz to the basement bar (as popular as a local watering-hole as it is with visitors), but things take a more sedate turn in the elegant restaurant, called, inevitably, Nightingales. The bedrooms – many of which are single, reflecting the needs of the enterprise's business clientele – are named after distinguished Bristolians, so you might be bowled over by W G Grace, or enjoy discovering John Cabot – just two of the roll call of individuals who first saw the light of day here. Another room pays tribute to Archie Leach, the city's best-known twentieth-century son – but he's remembered in his later incarnation as the impeccably suave Cary Grant. You can expect all the usual bells and whistles of a well-run business hotel, plus such extras as fresh fruit and decanters of sherry.

◑ Open all year 🔁 Turn left at top of Park Street into Berkeley Avenue leading into Berkeley Square. Private car park (£3 per day) 🛏→ 23 single, 6 twin, 10 double, 1 suite; all with bathroom/WC; all with TV, room service, hair-dryer, trouser press, direct-dial telephone 𝄈 Restaurant, bar, lounge; conferences (max 40 people residential/non-residential), functions; cots, high chairs, baby-listening 🔦 No wheelchair access ● No dogs in public rooms ▭ Amex, Delta, Diners, MasterCard, Switch, Visa £ Single £86, single occupancy of twin/double £91, twin/double £107, suite £125; deposit required. Bar/bistro L, D £6; set L, D £19; alc L, D £20. Special breaks available

---

BROAD CAMPDEN Gloucestershire map 5

Malt House

Broad Campden, Chipping Campden GL55 6UU
TEL: (01386) 840295   FAX: (01386) 841334

It's hard to find fault with this dreamy, cottagey hotel in an off-the-beaten-track Cotswold village.

Jean and Nick Brown's little hotel is an escapist haven in the centre of a sleepy village just a mile from touristy Chipping Campden but far removed in atmosphere. It looks absurdly picturesque: a row of old golden-stone cottages, wistaria clambering round peekaboo windows that spy on a gorgeous garden with a babbling brook, croquet lawn and daffodil-spattered cherry orchard. The interior looks just as sublime. Open fires, beautiful flower displays and fine paintings invest public rooms with real warmth. Meals take place at antique oak tables in a low-beamed dining-room, while two bijou sitting-rooms invite you to put your feet up. Bedrooms all look over the garden; antiques, murals and bold colour schemes complement their intrinsic character – Room 5, a large attic room, is a good choice, not least for its superb bathroom.

Inventive dinners, produced by the Browns' son Julian and offered on short table d'hôte menus, are modern British and may include dishes such as lambs' kidneys with a pancetta and parsley dressing, and poached strawberries with green peppercorn ice-cream.

◑ Closed 23 to 26 Dec; restaurant closed Tue eve 🔁 1 mile south-west of Chipping Campden, signposted from B4081; on left, 250 yards beyond Bakers Arms pub. Private car park 🛏→ 3 twin, 3 double, 1 four-poster, 1 family room; all with bathroom/WC; all with TV, hair-dryer, some with trouser press; radios 𝄈 Dining-room, bar/lounge, drying-room, garden; conferences (max 20 people incl up to 8 residential); croquet, free membership of nearby leisure facilities; early suppers for children by arrangement; cots, high chairs, toys, baby-listening 🔦 No wheelchair access ● No dogs or smoking in

public rooms ☐ Amex, Delta, MasterCard, Switch, Visa £ Single occupancy of
twin/double £55 to £80, twin/double/four-poster £75 to £98, family room £93 to £105;
deposit required. Set D £25.50 to £27. Special breaks available

---

BROADWAY Worcestershire   map 5

Barn House   NEW ENTRY

152 High Street, Broadway WR12 7AJ
TEL: (01386) 858633 (AND FAX)

---

*Superior B&B, with a number of alluring features, in an ancient
house on the high street of this famous Cotswolds village.*

The Ricketts' fascinating, rambling, mellow-stone house dates from medieval
through to Victorian times. Guests have the run of a beamed dining-room, where
breakfast is served round a single table; an elegant sitting-room, with a
help-yourself bar; and, most memorably, the giant, vaulted Barn Room – a
second sitting-room furnished with pikes and muskets, and stocked with games
for evening entertainment. Residents can also explore the 16 acres of paddocks,
orchards and gardens (open to the public in summer through the National
Gardens Scheme), and may use a large, if not particularly smart, heated indoor
swimming-pool. The bedrooms come in all sizes and styles. Of the three in the
main house, the largest, with old, pine panelling and antiques, is Big Double;
however, its bath is of the tub variety – ask for The Office if you want a
full-length bath. Also on offer is the Garden Suite – a very roomy, modern-
designed, outhouse conversion, with a sitting-room and kitchen – and, when it's
not let for self-catering, a nattily furnished cottage just up the road.

◑ Open all year   ⬚ Situated in upper High Street of Broadway (now a cul-de-sac).
Private car park   ⬚ 2 twin, 2 double, 2 suites; some in annexe; 3 with bathroom/WC;
all with TV, hair-dryer, some with trouser press   ⬚ 2 sitting-rooms, dining-room,
library, conservatory, garden; heated indoor swimming-pool, croquet; cots, high
chairs   ⬚ No wheelchair access   ⬚ Dogs in some bedrooms only; smoking in 1
sitting-room only   ☐ None accepted   £ Single occupancy of twin/double £25 to
£65, twin/double £48 to £75, suite £65 to £75; deposit required.

Collin House

Collin Lane, Broadway WR12 7PB
TEL: (01386) 858354   FAX: (01386) 858697

---

*The opportunity to stay in a lovely Cotswold country house without
breaking the bank.*

This sixteenth-century wool merchant's house, a mile from Broadway, has
appeared in the *Guide* since 1991. In December 1997 the new, keen owners Keith
and Tricia Ferguson took over; staff, including the chef, have stayed on,
however. The Fergusons intend to maintain the atmosphere of a small,
unpretentious country-house hotel, but are going a bit more mainstream. TVs
have appeared in bedrooms, and, to woo more local trade, coffees, teas and bar
meals are much promoted. What have not altered, of course, are the hotel's

period features – the flagstoned hall, the beamed, mullion-windowed restaurant, the large bar where settles, sofas and dining tables are accommodated in front of an imposing inglenook fireplace. The chintzy bedrooms, especially Barley and Wild Rose up under the black-beamed eaves, are nearly as characterful; old-fashioned bathrooms could, however, do with updating. Recommended, largely traditional English fare (perhaps venison steak in a gin-and-blackberry sauce, and bread-and-butter pudding) is served as inexpensive 'Cotswold suppers' in the bar, and as full three-course dinners in the restaurant. The new Broadway bypass, which will run close to the hotel's two acres of grounds, hadn't quite opened when we visited. Reports, please, on its effect, as well as on how the new owners are getting on.

◖ Closed 24 to 28 Dec   ⤢ 1 mile west of Broadway, turn right off A44, signposted to Willersey. Collin House is a short way along Collin Lane on right. Private car park ⤸ 1 single, 3 twin, 1 double, 2 four-poster; most with bathroom/WC, 1 twin with shower/WC, single with shower only; all with TV, room service, hair-dryer   ⊘ Restaurant, bar, lounge, garden; functions (max 50 people incl up to 13 residential); croquet; early suppers for children; cots   ♿ No wheelchair access   ● No children under 6 in restaurant eves; no dogs; no smoking in restaurant   ▭ Delta, MasterCard, Switch, Visa   £ Single £46, single occupancy of twin/double £68, twin/double from £88, four-poster £98; deposit required. Bar/bistro L £15, D £18; alc L £16.50, D £22. Special breaks available

---

Dormy House

Willersey Hill, Broadway WR12 7LF
TEL: (01386) 852711   FAX: (01386) 858636
EMAIL: reservations@dormyhouse.co.uk

High standards, and prices, in a multi-purpose hotel on a hill above Broadway.

Dormy House is part of Group 4, the company that hit the headlines a few years ago for losing prisoners in its care. Those entrusted with keys are better looked after: service in the hotel, overseen by a long-standing Danish manager, is deferential and speedy. This sizeable complex has evolved around a seventeenth-century farmhouse, spilling out into converted cottages, outbuildings and new extensions. The clientele is evenly split between the business and leisure markets, and the hotel is large enough, and well enough run, to meet the needs of both fully. The atmospheric public rooms, characterised by exposed-stone walls, flagstone floors and inglenook fireplaces, are clustered in the farmhouse. The smartest of these, the restaurant, is divided between intimate dens within the house and a large, open conservatory. Its wide-ranging menus offer cuisine of consistently top-notch quality, praised for its choice ingredients and interesting ideas. The bar is also deservedly popular with locals, for simpler meals. The bedrooms are fairly luxurious, though perhaps not quite enough to justify fully their hefty price tags. They are dotted all round the hotel: those in the cottages are a good choice, since they have vaulted ceilings and direct access to the semi-private gardens.

◑ Closed 24 to 26 Dec ⬀ From Broadway, go towards Oxford for 1½ miles on A44.
At top of Fish Hill, take left turn signposted Saintbury/picnic area; after ½ mile fork left:
Dormy House is on left. Private car park ⬅ 6 single, 24 twin, 12 double, 4
four-poster, 3 suites; some in annexe; all with bathroom/WC exc singles with
shower/WC; all with TV, room service, hair-dryer, trouser press, direct-dial telephone
 ✅ Restaurant, 3 bars, 2 lounges, games room, garden; functions (max 170 people incl
up to 74 residential), conferences; civil wedding licence; gym, sauna, putting green,
croquet; early suppers for children; cots, high chairs, babysitting, baby-listening
 ♿ No wheelchair access   ● Dogs in some bedrooms only, by arrangement (£5)
 ▭ Amex, Delta, Diners, MasterCard, Switch, Visa   £ Single £71, single occupancy of
twin/double £95, twin/double £142, four-poster £170, suite £182; deposit required.
Bar/bistro L, D £13; set Sun L £19.50, D £30.50; alc L £19, D £37. Special breaks
available

BROADWAY Worcestershire   map 5

Lygon Arms

Broadway WR12 7DU
TEL: (01386) 852255   FAX: (01386) 858611
EMAIL: info@the-lygon-arms.co.uk
WEB SITE: www.savoy-group.co.uk

It costs a small fortune to enjoy the history, luxury and fine cuisine of arguably the UK's most famous inn and the Cotswolds' best-known hotel.

Lording it over the high street of this much-visited, picturesque village, the Lygon Arms has been receiving guests since at least as long ago as 1532. Everyone from monarchs (Charles I was a notable early visitor) to dogs (who are provided with a special pack of goodies) are treated to a royal welcome. The staff are what you would expect from a hotel of this calibre (it's owned by the Savoy Group): well trained, extremely helpful and fairly formal.

The large, busy complex incorporates a series of intimate sitting-room areas, with flagged and wooden floors, exposed stone walls and fires, a magnificent, barrel-vaulted restaurant, a wine bar, a snazzy health club – even an art gallery. The highly rated restaurant serves both traditional British fare and accomplished, sophisticated modern dishes. The bedrooms in the old building benefit, as you'd imagine, from a plethora of creaks and beams, as well as a welter of period furniture that includes wonderful, carved beds. Apparently Americans prefer rooms in the modern wings on account of their king-size beds; ground-floor rooms here have direct access to terraces, which can be used for breakfast. For all this history and these facilities, don't expect to escape paying under £300 a night for dinner, bed and breakfast for two on the rack-rates. Prices drop a little on special breaks.

◑ Open all year ⬀ In the centre of Broadway, on A44 near Evesham. Private car
park ⬅ 2 single, 8 twin, 44 double, 5 four-poster, 6 suites; family rooms available all
with bathroom/WC; all with TV, room service, hair-dryer, trouser press, direct-dial
telephone; no tea/coffee-making facilities in rooms   ✅ Restaurant, bar, 6
sitting-rooms, games room, garden; functions (max 130 people incl up to 100
residential), conferences; civil wedding licence; gym, sauna, solarium, heated indoor

swimming-pool, croquet; early suppers for children in bedroom; cots, high chairs, babysitting, baby-listening &. Wheelchair access to hotel and restaurant, WC (unisex), 5 ground-floor bedrooms, 2 rooms specially equipped for disabled people ● No children under 8 in restaurant eves; no dogs or smoking in restaurant ▭ Amex, Delta, Diners, MasterCard, Switch, Visa ▭£ Single £124, single occupancy of twin/double £159, twin/double from £194, four-poster/suite from £259, family room from £306; deposit required. Cooked B £9.50; bar/bistro L, D £15; set L £24.50, D £36; alc L £35, D £50. (1998 prices.) Special breaks available

Mill Hay House

Snowshill Road, Broadway WR12 7JS
TEL: (01386) 852498   FAX: (01386) 858038
EMAIL: broadway-tower@clara.net
WEB SITE: www.broadway-cotswolds.co.uk

B&B in a grand family home, where you can play at being lord of the manor.

'Exclusive accommodation', says the sign at the gate of this large, elegant, red-brick and mellow-stone Queen Anne house, on a back road outside Broadway (expect just a little traffic noise). The owners of Mill Hay House have been offering B&B for 25 years and Annette and Dominic Gorton, the young couple who now manage the business, live in one of the house's wings, so guests staying in the three bedrooms are afforded considerable privacy and are left to their own devices. Guests have the run of the three acres of landscaped gardens that encompass tiered lawns, a rose garden and a trout-stocked lake and, inside, of the flagstoned hall and panelled lounge, both hung with stern family portraits and gory hunting still lifes. Breakfast is a leisurely affair, taken at separate tables at any reasonable time. The bedrooms are extremely tasteful and comfortable. The best, the Garden Suite, has a four-poster bed, while the Rose Garden Room comes with a fine, deep bath in its swanky bathroom, and the Balcony Room, as expected, has a balcony overlooking the rear garden. However, given the high rates, a better selection of tea things and fresh milk in the rooms' fridges would not go amiss; our inspector also felt that the 35p-per-minute phone charge was exorbitant for a B&B.

● Open all year ⊿ Turn off Broadway High Street by Main Green and head towards Snowshill. Mill Hay House is 1 mile on right. Private car park ⊨ 1 twin, 1 double, 1 four-poster; all with bathroom/WC exc double with shower/WC; all with TV, direct-dial telephone, kitchenette, safe; hair-dryer on request ⊘ Lounge, TV room, garden &. No wheelchair access ● No children under 12; no dogs; no smoking ▭ MasterCard, Visa ▭£ Twin/double £70 to £80, four-poster £100; deposit required. Special breaks available

'When announcing "Continental breakfast is off", the waitress said nothing more till asked what was proposed instead, and then "thought" there might be a possible substitute.'
On a hotel in the Peak District

College House

Chapel Street, Broadwell, Moreton-in-Marsh GL56 0TW
TEL: (01451) 832351

Extremely tasteful, outstanding-value guesthouse, in a venerable, Cotswolds village home.

Though the rates suggest that College House (once owned by Oxford University) might be a run-of-the-mill B&B, it is, in fact, a lovely, seventeenth-century house, furnished with considerable style and comfort. Standing on the edge of a peaceful village with a handsome green, the house has no sign indicating that accommodation is offered, as the bubbly Sybil Gisby has no trouble in filling her sensational bedrooms. These offer superb, massive bedrooms, with high-quality bed linen and antiques; one has a Victorian slipper bath, while another features a priest-hole that has been prettily stencilled by the local farmer's wife. Much of downstairs is an open-plan space, rigged out with flagstone floors and canary-yellow walls. Meals are served here, round a long, pine table that stands over the former village well (from which, at certain times of the year, baby frogs can appear under the skirting boards). Sybil, who used to own a local restaurant, says that in the evening many guests eat in – 'especially if they've already experienced my cooking!' A typical set meal might be mushrooms in a Stilton sauce, chicken stuffed with Parma ham and mozzarella and served with pasta, and a citron tart; bring your own wine.

◑ Closed Chr; dining-room closed Sun eve   ⊿ North of Stow-on-the-Wold, turn off A429 to Broadwell; at village green follow signposts to Evenlode until you reach College House on Chapel Street. Private car park   ⊨⇥ 3 double; all with bathroom/WC; all with TV, hair-dryer   ⊘ Dining-room, lounge;   ₺ No wheelchair access   ● No children under 16; no dogs; no smoking in bedrooms   ⊡ None accepted   £ Single occupancy of double £50 to £63, double £55 to £68; deposit required. Set D £17.50

Grove House

Bromsberrow Heath, Ledbury HR8 1PE
TEL: (01531) 650584

A thoroughly appealing private home, offering peace, good food and more than interesting surroundings.

Grove House belongs to one of those 'difficult to categorise' types of accommodation: not a hotel, not a guesthouse, but a private home belonging to the Wolsey Lodge consortium, where guests may stay, and dine, in considerable style. As in all such places, particular social skills may be required; on the other hand, if things are quiet, you may be left entirely to your own devices. But this is no hardship: there is plenty to read, and the cooking is excellent. Grove House lies just a couple of minutes' drive from the M50, a motorway spur linking the M5 with Ross-on-Wye, but it is so secluded amid its orchards and farmland, that you would never guess. The house is Grade-II-listed, partly fifteenth century, though most of its outer casing dates from 1750. The first-floor drawing-room is elegant and spacious, full of books, pictures, antiques, magazines and memorabilia signalling a family of some background. The panelled dining-room contains a single long table in house-party style, and a dresser loaded with china. The bedrooms are equally interesting – some have four-posters – and all offer character and masses of extras (such as home-made biscuits, mineral water, fruit bowls and books). There's a hard tennis court in the gardens, and although you can no longer ride the Ross family's horses (due to insurance difficulties), riding can be arranged locally.

◑ Closed 25 & 31 Dec ⤤ In Bromsberrow Heath, turn right by post office and go up hill; Grove House is on right. Private car park ⌁ 1 twin, 2 four-poster; all with bathroom/WC; all with TV, hair-dryer ⟡ Dining-room, drawing-room, garden; ⟁ No wheelchair access ● Children discouraged from dining-room eves; no dogs; smoking in drawing-room only ▭ None accepted £ Single occupancy of twin £49, twin/four-poster £68. Set D £22

BROMSGROVE **Worcestershire**   map 5

Grafton Manor

Grafton Lane, Bromsgrove B61 7HA
TEL: (01527) 579007   FAX: (01527) 575221
EMAIL: steven@grafman.u-net.com
WEB SITE: www.hotelnet.co.uk/hotelnet/pride/pb11/home

Grandeur, family hospitality and good food in a long-established country-house hotel.

Both the imposing, red-brick manor and its associations with the present owners have considerable pedigree: though revamped after a fire in 1710, the house has pre-Norman origins, while the Morris family has been here for much of this century, and has been welcoming paying guests since 1980. In addition to the warmth of the hospitality, the appeal of staying here lies in the six lovely acres of grounds that take in a lake, a water garden and chapel, and in the ornate – evolved rather than overly designed – interior of the manor, full of carved ceilings and antiques. Although in the garden the hum of traffic on the nearby M5 intermingles with the birdsong, the rich and heavy furnishings largely preclude any noise within the house. The bedrooms are spacious and traditionally furnished, featuring solid, old furniture, coronet beds and often William Morris patterns. But perhaps a night or two at Grafton Manor is most often remembered for one of Simon Morris's dinners. His modern, English cuisine is affected by Mediterranean influences, and makes much use of herbs, vegetables and fruit grown in the hotel's garden. Examples of his dishes might include fillets of crispy salmon served with baby squid and basil bouillabaisse, or confit of duck on a parsnip and ginger purée with cassis sauce.

◑ Open all year ⤤ 1½ miles south of Bromsgrove centre, off B4091. Private car park ⌁ 1 single, 2 twin, 3 double, 1 four-poster, 2 suites; all with bathroom/WC; all with TV, room service, hair-dryer, trouser press, direct-dial telephone, radio; no tea/coffee-making facilities in rooms ⟡ 2 dining-rooms, lounge, garden; functions (max

40 people incl up to 17 residential), conferences; civil wedding licence; early suppers for children; cots, high chairs ⟂ No wheelchair access ● No dogs; no smoking in dining-rooms ▭ Amex, Diners, MasterCard, Switch, Visa £⟩ Single £85, single occupancy of twin/double £95, twin/double £105, four-poster £125, suite £150; deposit required. Set L £20.50, D £29/£31.50. Special breaks available

---

BROUGHAM Cumbria   map 10

Hornby Hall   NEW ENTRY

Brougham, Penrith CA10 2AR
TEL: (01768) 891114 (AND FAX)

Tranquil manor farm, offering quiet value and good home cooking with a touch of class.

As its name suggests, Hornby Hall is no common-or-garden farm, but a former manor house dating back to the sixteenth century. The resident hosts, Allan and Ros Sanders, can scarcely believe their good fortune at living here, though it isn't actually their own home: the house and peaceful farmland all around belong to friends. Hornby Hall is a long, low-slung building in russet-coloured, Penrith sandstone, which glows warm and welcoming in the setting sun as guests return down the long drive in anticipation of a satisfying, home-cooked dinner. Give some notice if you want an evening meal – you may be treated to a bit of estate-raised pheasant or venison. The antique dining-room in the oldest part of the house is an imposing place, with a stone inglenook, Jacobean panelling and sandstone flagstones; guests share a single, long table in house-party style. Sometimes private groups bag the whole house, but at other times individual guests soon feel at ease in the light, serene sitting-room. The bedrooms all differ in shape and size (one of the most interesting is reached by a quaint, spiral staircase). They are simply furnished, showing the same restrained, good taste and quality as are evident in the rest of the house, and have excellent views.

◐ Closed Chr to New Year; dining-room closed Sun eve ⟐ Leave M6 at Junction 40; head east on A66 for 4 miles; turn left just past telephone box, signposted Hornby Hall. Private car park ⟻ 1 single, 3 twin, 2 double, 1 family room; most with bathroom/WC, some with shower/WC (not *en suite*); all with hair-dryer, some with TV ⟡ Dining-room, sitting-room, drying-room, garden; functions (max 60 people incl up to 14 residential), conferences; fishing, game shooting; early suppers for children; cots, high chairs, baby-listening ⟂ No wheelchair access ● No dogs in bedrooms; smoking in sitting-room only ▭ Delta, MasterCard, Switch, Visa £⟩ Single £26, single occupancy of twin/double £45, twin/double £46 to £63, family room £73 (1998 prices); deposit required. Set D £18. Special breaks available

---

'We asked for a bottle of still water. The water came in a jug and tasted like flat fizzy water. I asked the waitress and she assured me that it was still water. I called the proprietor and was finally told that it was flat fizzy water from the night before. The waitress had understood that we had asked for such a thing.'
On a hotel in Kent

BROXTED Essex map 3

Whitehall

Church End, Broxted, Dunmow CM6 2BZ
TEL: (01279) 850603   FAX: (01279) 850385

*A converted Elizabethan house that combines an attractive rural
location with good facilities for both business and leisure guests.*

While its location just ten minutes from Stansted Airport makes this hotel
popular with business clientele, there's enough individual character here to
satisfy most types of visitor. This sprawling Elizabethan manor house might be
on the occasional flightpath, but the location is usually surprisingly peaceful,
close to the local flintstone church of St Mary's with views across a gentle
landscape of fields and farms. Inside, the décor makes the most of the original
600-year-old exposed beams in the public rooms, with a new, harlequin-style
carpet adding a brighter touch. The restaurant is probably the most attractive –
it's based around the old medieval hall and has a high-pitched roof, wonky
floors and leaded windows. Bedrooms are divided between the main house and
the new extension that leads to the conference facilities. In the main house the
best rooms are probably those that look out to the garden, with its luxuriant
lawn and trimmed yew trees – the Garden Room, for example, has oak panelling
around a stone fireplace and a good-sized bathroom.

◑ Closed 26 to 31 Dec   ⊿ Leave M11 at Junction 8 and follow signs to Stansted
airport and then Broxted. Private car park   ⊨→ 4 twin, 18 double, 3 family rooms, 1
suite; all with bathroom/WC; all with TV, room service, hair-dryer, trouser press,
direct-dial telephone   ⟡ 2 restaurants, bar, 2 lounges, garden; functions (max 120
people non-residential, 52 residential), conferences; civil wedding licence; unheated
outdoor swimming-pool, croquet; early suppers for children; cots, high chairs
⅙ Wheelchair access to hotel (1 step) and restaurant, WC (M, F), 6 ground-floor
bedrooms ● No dogs ⊟ Amex, Delta, Diners, MasterCard, Switch, Visa
£ Single occupancy of twin/double £80, twin/double £110 to £140, family room £155,
suite £220. Continental B £6.50, cooked B £9.50; set L £19.50, D £22; alc D £37.50

BROXTON Cheshire map 7

Broxton Hall

Whitchurch Road, Broxton, Chester CH3 9JS
TEL: (01829) 782321   FAX: (01829) 782330

*Small country-house hotel filled with antique furnishings not far
from Chester.*

Broxton Hall makes a striking first impression as you pull up in front of it. The
large black-and-white half-timbered building looks Tudor, but in fact only the
central core dates from that time, as the two wings were added later. Inside, the
cluttered reception area leads into a sitting-room dominated by a huge fireplace
and furnished with a sofa and comfy chairs invariably inhabited by a cat or two
(look out for Bobby, an unashamed attention-stealer). The nearby lounge,
stuffed with furniture and antiques (as are the upstairs corridors), features yet

another grand fireplace. Despite the down-to-earth jumble and lived-in feel, a hushed atmosphere sometimes prevails, and you might have to fight the urge to whisper! The elegant dining-room with deep pink walls looks to the pretty, south-facing garden and is the setting for sampling culinary delights such as mussels in herb and garlic butter and a white wine sauce, followed by braised lamb shank cooked with tomato and Mediterranean vegetables.

Bedrooms vary in size and all are perfectly comfortable, although rooms with newer bathrooms have the edge over the others. One of the most popular rooms seems to be the one housing an elaborately carved four-poster bed – in which the judge who sentenced Charles I to death is said to have slept soundly.

○ Closed 25 & 26 Dec　☑ 8 miles from Chester on A41 towards Whitchurch. Situated at Broxton roundabout, on left. Private car park　⊨↦ 1 single, 3 twin, 5 double, 1 four-poster; all with bathroom/WC; all with TV, room service, hair-dryer, direct-dial telephone, some with trouser press　⊘ 2 dining-rooms, bar, lounge, drying-room, conservatory, garden; conferences (max 60 people incl up to 10 residential), functions; leisure facilities nearby (reduced rates for guests); early suppers for children; cots, high chairs, baby-listening　ᘗ No wheelchair access　◖ None　▭ Amex, Diners, MasterCard, Switch, Visa　⊡ Single £60, single occupancy of twin/double £65, twin/double £70 to £80, four-poster £105; deposit required. Bar/bistro L £10; set L £16, D £25.50. Special breaks available

Frogg Manor

Nantwich Road, Fullers Moor, Broxton, Chester CH3 9JH
TEL: (01829) 782629　FAX: (01829) 782459

Delightfully eccentric country-house hotel with an excellent restaurant and an irrepressible owner.

Owner John Sykes has firmly stamped his mark on Frogg Manor, as indeed have the eponymous frogs. From the driveway sign urging you to 'drive carefully, frogs crossing' to the abundance of frogs of every shape, size and form dotted throughout the public rooms (but mostly congregating in the first-floor lounge) you can't fail to notice the frog references, which apparently stem from a girlfriend nicknamed 'Froggy'.

The small restaurant is a stylish room with green walls and carpets, formally laid tables and views from the attached conservatory area to the well-tended garden. This sets the scene for a high-calibre dinner, the menu for which might incorporate poached pear and Roquefort or toad-*not*-in-the-hole as a starter, followed by roast rack of lamb or Paraguayan chicken pancake. The lounge and bar area is more homely, with comfy sofas and antique furniture.

Bedrooms are all immaculate and decorated to a very high standard. Churchill, with its blue colour scheme and views to the garden, has one of the biggest bathrooms, which is inordinately well stocked (as they all are) with everything you could possibly want: tights, new toothbrush and toothpaste, deodorant, plasters and aspirins to name a few. Of the smaller rooms, Sherlock Holmes is an attractive choice, full of pine furniture, with a low ceiling and lots of books, while the *pièce de résistance* is the very comfortable Wellington Suite. For a small extra supplement you can upgrade from the standard cotton sheets to Irish linen.

❍ Open all year 🚗 From Chester head south on A41; turn left on to A534 towards Nantwich. Frogg Manor is approx 1 mile down on right. Private car park 🛏 5 double, 1 four-poster; most with bathroom/WC, 2 with shower/WC; all with TV, hair-dryer, trouser press, direct-dial telephone, radio ⊘ Dining-room, bar, lounge, conservatory, garden; functions (max 55 people incl up to 12 residential), conferences; civil wedding licence; tennis ⅋ No wheelchair access ● No dogs in public rooms or most bedrooms; no smoking in part of dining-room ⊟ Amex, Delta, Diners, MasterCard, Switch, Visa £ Single occupancy of twin/double £50 to £95, twin/double £70 to £130, four-poster £120. Continental B £8.50, cooked B £10; alc L £17, D £27.50. Special breaks available

---

BUCKLAND Gloucestershire map 5

Buckland Manor

Buckland, Broadway WR12 7LY
TEL: (01386) 852626 FAX: (01386) 853557
EMAIL: buckland-manor-uk@msn.com

Truly luxurious, exclusive, country-house hotel – as good as any in the Cotswolds.

This gorgeous, multi-gabled house, dating largely from the thirteenth century, pitches itself at individual travellers with deep pockets. What you're paying for is the utmost privacy: the hotel is situated far from the crowds of Cotswolds tourists, standing alongside a cul-de-sac hamlet and surrounded by many acres of lawns, tiers of flowerbeds and daffodil-spattered grassy banks. While accommodating fewer than 30 guests (there being just 14 bedrooms), the house itself is huge; functions and conferences rarely happen, and children under 12 are banned. The cost of staying here is also justified by the pampering, formal service: for example, drinks are served, since there is no bar, and morning tea (included in the rates) is brought to your room. The grander bedrooms, such as the panelled Oak Room, are rigged out with splendid antiques, though the standard rooms can seem somewhat over-priced. All, however, come with lavish bathrooms, and some have real fires. The public rooms, ennobled by lavish flower displays and individually lit, gilt-framed, oil paintings (plus, in the sitting-room, a photo of Queen Mary visiting the house in 1944), aspire to the heights of gracious country living. The hotel's character is equally well reflected in its highly lauded, innovative dinners (served with much palaver, and for which jackets and ties are required). Typical main courses might be sauté loin of venison on Parmesan and grain-mustard polenta with a port-wine sauce, or pan-fried John Dory with honey- and basil-pickled aubergines and a raw tomato sauce.

❍ Open all year 🚗 From Broadway, take B4632 towards Cheltenham; after 1½ miles, turn left into Buckland; hotel is on right in village. Private car park 🛏 4 twin, 5 double, 3 four-poster, 1 suite; family rooms available; all with bathroom/WC; all with TV, room service, hair-dryer, direct-dial telephone; no tea/coffee-making facilities in rooms ⊘ Restaurant, bar, sitting-room, library, garden; functions (max 34 people residential/non-residential); heated outdoor swimming-pool, tennis, croquet, putting green ⅋ No wheelchair access ● No children under 12; no dogs ⊟ Amex, Delta,

Diners, MasterCard, Switch, Visa £ Single occupancy of twin/double £178 to £325, twin/double £188 to £335, four-poster £295, suite £325; deposit required. Bar/bistro L £6; set L £29.50; alc L, D £40

BUCKLAND MONACHORUM Devon map 1

Store Cottage

The Village, Buckland Monachorum, Yelverton PL20 7NA
TEL: (01822) 853117 (AND FAX)

Cute, terraced cottage in village centre, providing top-class B&B accommodation – but mind your head on the low beams!

Annabel and John Foulston have only two bedrooms in their tiny stone cottage, but it's as much as they want. They say that they find the B&B business 'heartening', which is a good sign, an indication of their natures as well as those of the guests that they attract. Store Cottage is a wholesome kind of place, situated at the centre of the pretty village of Buckland Monachorum. The mossy, tiled roof and the miniature patio at the front (a sun trap in summer) look well established – the house itself is around three hundred years old – and there are plenty of flowers here, along with a little bench that you can sit on if you want to catch the sun. Inside, low beams, a cavernous fireplace and pink sofas provide a refined backdrop. Breakfast is eaten communally around a long table, and is served on chunky blue plates made by a local pottery. There's lots of variety offered at this morning feast: oatcakes, muffins and a change of special each day – perhaps kidneys and bacon, or scrambled eggs and smoked salmon, or else a hearty veggie option. The two bedrooms are decorated in bold colours, old pine furniture, and have high, inviting-looking beds. The bathroom in the double room is of a better size than the shower-room belonging to the twin.

◑ Closed Chr to 2 Jan ⧗ From A386, follow signs to Buckland Monachorum; Store Cottage is on main street, just past church. Private car park ⬅ 1 twin, 1 double; double with bathroom/WC, twin with shower/WC; all with TV, hair-dryer, radio ✓ Lounge, drying-room, garden ⅙ No wheelchair access ● No children under 12; no smoking ⬜ None accepted £ Single occupancy of twin/double £30, twin/double £45

BUCKNELL Shropshire map 7

Bucknell House

Bucknell SY7 0AD
TEL: (01547) 530248

Enjoyably old-fashioned B&B with a thoroughly homely atmosphere.

In these remote parts, the whole family can end up offering B&B: Brenda Davies, the owner of this former vicarage, is the sister of Jocelyn Williams at Llanfair Waterdine's Monaughty Poeth (see entry). Guests have been coming down the tree-lined drive to stay in this handsome Georgian house for two decades. There is much to enjoy here – from the well-proportioned dining-room and sitting-room, stuffed full of antiques and silverware as well as plenty of domestic clutter and family photos, to the lovely views from the rear of the house across the Teme Valley's water meadows. Bedrooms are refreshingly undesigned and unco-ordinated. The best, the large Rose Room, is the only one to enjoy the valley view; the other two have more utilitarian modern furniture. All share a simple bathroom, plus a second downstairs loo. Brenda enjoys a chat and is keen to pass on her extensive knowledge of the area. The array of sightseeing leaflets in a corner of the sitting-room, along with a folder of more information covering suggested drives, restaurants and so forth, puts many a tourist office to shame.

◗ Closed Dec & Jan   ⚡ From A4113 Ludlow to Knighton road, take B4367 towards Craven Arms; house is just past 30mph limit. Private car park   ⬆ 1 twin, 2 double; all with TV, hair-dryer   ✅ Dining-room, sitting-room, garden; fishing, tennis   ♿ No wheelchair access   ● No children under 12; dogs in bedrooms only   🚭 None accepted   £ Single occupancy of twin/double £25, twin/double £40; deposit required. Special breaks available

---

BURFORD Oxfordshire   map 5

Burford House

99 High Street, Burford OX18 4QA
TEL: (01993) 823151   FAX: (01993) 823240
EMAIL: burfordhouse@cotswolds.com
WEB SITE: www.cotswolds.com/cotswolds/hotels/burford.html

Very smart bedrooms in an old town house full of character, as well as good lunches and teas.

Jane and Simon Henty have been here for two years now, and are proof of the pudding that up-market B&Bs can corner a fair slice of the market. They run the B&B in conjunction with a smart restaurant, which is open only for lunches and other kinds of puddings and slices (of the cake variety) for tea. When we inspected, a mouthwatering smell was wafting from the kitchen – 'chocolate fudge cake', said Jane from the depths – while several delicious-looking confections were laid out in the dining-room. Nevertheless, as Simon is keen to point out, it's their overnight guests who have priority in the house. The half-timbered, half-stone building dates back to 1600, and the Hentys have decorated and furnished the interior to appeal to those who enjoy plush, luxurious accommodation. A deep-blue carpet downstairs sets off the highly polished antique furniture and mullioned windows to great effect, and there are plenty of fresh flowers and a good choice of books in all the rooms. The Garden Room, which looks out to the pretty, walled patio and is filled with two huge, squashy sofas and a ticking grandfather clock, is a particularly conducive place for unwinding. Upstairs, on the landing, you are greeted by the first of many smart bears; the bedrooms all have very good beds (three have four-posters) and friendly looking teddies – not to mention antique chests, flowers, mineral water, claw-foot baths, characterful, sloping ceilings and all manner of pampering extras. Don't forget that dinner is not served, but Burford has plenty of good eateries.

◗ Open all year ☑ Halfway along Burford High Street. On-street parking (free); public car park nearby ⇖ 1 twin, 3 double, 3 four-poster; family rooms available all with bathroom/WC; all with TV, room service, hair-dryer, direct-dial telephone; no tea/coffee-making facilities in rooms ✓ Dining-room, 2 lounges, drying-room, garden; early suppers for children; cots, high chairs, babysitting, baby-listening ₺ No wheelchair access ● No dogs; no smoking in bedrooms ▭ Amex, Delta, MasterCard, Switch, Visa £ Single occupancy of twin/double £75, twin/double £80, four-poster from £90; family room from £95; deposit required. Bar/bistro L from £4. Special breaks available

Lamb Inn

Sheep Street, Burford OX18 4LR
TEL: (01993) 823155   FAX: (01993) 822228

The comforts of a country house within a mellow-stone inn at the centre of a picturesque Cotswolds village.

All the ingredients necessary for enjoying a quintessential English country sojourn are to be found here: an idyllic, honey-pot village of higgledy-piggledy houses, thick with tea-shops and antiques; rolling meadows contained within high hedgerows; and 'ye olde' country inn to hole up in among plump sofas, roaring fires and the accumulated china and copper of past centuries. The flagstones and timbers of the Lamb Inn date back to medieval times, while the present ambience sits squarely in the timeless, country-house tradition, with cottagey-style bedrooms bedecked with attractive fabrics and choice antiques, oriental rugs softening the lounge bar, and parquet, candles and white damask in the dining-room. The menu similarly reflects the manner of the manor, with roasts, game and fine seafood basking in ragoûts, bathed in *jus*, or popped into paupiettes.

Richard de Wolf, the owner for over a dozen years now, is a highly particular proprietor, and his meticulousness has obviously been absorbed by the staff – though one correspondent found the constant plumping and straightening of fixtures and furnishings to be more of an irritation than an inspiring example of efficient housekeeping. Certainly, disturbing a guest's packing – as happened to our dissatisfied correspondent – in order to make up a room before it has even been vacated seems rather like jumping the gun. He also found the breakfast 'inferior'. More reports would be welcome.

◗ Closed 25 & 26 Dec ☑ Sheep Street is on the left as you descend Burford High Street. Private car park ⇖ 3 twin, 11 double, 1 four-poster; all with bathroom/WC exc 1 double with shower/WC; all with TV, room service, hair-dryer, direct-dial telephone; no tea/coffee-making facilities in rooms ✓ Dining-room, bar, 2 lounges, garden; early suppers for children; cots, high chairs, baby-listening ₺ No wheelchair access ● No smoking in dining-room; dogs £5 per night in bedrooms ▭ Delta, MasterCard, Switch, Visa £ Single occupancy of twin/double £58 to £75, twin/double/four-poster £100 to £110; deposit required. Bar/bistro L £6 to £8; set Sun L £17.50, D £24. Special breaks available

Hoste Arms

The Green, Burnham Market, Kings Lynn PE31 8HD
TEL: (01328) 738777   FAX: (01328) 730103
EMAIL: thehostearms@compuserve.com
WEB SITE: www.greatinns.co.uk

A historic coaching inn brought right up to date by its energetic owners, with some stylish new rooms added this year.

The great popularity of the Hoste Arms does not seem to diminish the enthusiasm of its owners, Paul and Jeanne Whittome, to ring the changes. And their approach seems to win more and more approval, judging by the crowds of visitors who arrive every lunch-time. People mainly congregate in the airy, stone-tiled conservatory during the day, but in the evenings they drift into the cosier restaurant rooms, with their creaky, stripped floorboards and comfortable, informal settings, with padded bench seating. Despite the emphasis on food, Paul, ever casual in polo shirt and slacks, has converted one of these rooms into a lounge for the hotel guests, something he says he should have done long ago. The bedrooms are impressively individual, with a varied use of high-quality fabrics to create different styles and moods. Some have private patios that overlook the newly laid, formal walled garden. Sadly, while one guest told us that they found the atmosphere convivial, they were not as impressed with their dinner.

The Whittomes have also opened the Railway Inn, six small bedrooms and a sitting-room in the restored Burnham Market railway station, five minutes' walk away, which they offer as an overspill. Breakfast is served at the main hotel.

◑ Open all year   ◪ Hotel overlooks Burnham Market's village green, 2 miles from A149. Private car park   ⌁ 4 single, 4 twin, 7 double, 4 four-poster, 1 family room; all with bathroom/WC exc singles with shower/WC; all with TV, room service, hair-dryer, direct-dial telephone   ⊘ Restaurant, bar, lounge, conservatory, garden; functions (max 150 people incl up to 37 residential), conferences; early suppers for children; cots, baby-listening   ♿ No wheelchair access   ● None   ▭ MasterCard, Switch, Visa   £ Single £50 to £60, single occupancy of twin/double £50 to £60, twin/double £60 to £86, four-poster £70 to £98, family room £85 to £101; deposit required. Bar/bistro L £6, D £15; alc L £17.50, D £22.50. Special breaks available

---

Ounce House

Northgate Street, Bury St Edmunds IP33 1HP
TEL: (01284) 761779   FAX: (01284) 768315
EMAIL: pott@globalnet.co.uk

A perfectly presented, yet relaxed, period home reasonably close to the city centre.

It might detract from the aesthetic appeal, but the car park at the front of this imposing Victorian merchant's house is a very welcome bonus for guests staying at Ounce House. They have the benefits of a central location, just a short walk from the Abbey, but also the chance to relax in the large, wild and wooded garden that lies at the back of the house. Simon and Jenny Pott have done full justice to the elegant proportions of their home by filling it with antique furnishings, oil paintings and plenty of personal touches and mementoes. The bay-fronted living-room has long drapes and is teeming with arty objects to enjoy and admire. This leads through to an equally attractive dining-room, where guests breakfast round a splendid long table. For less formal relaxing there is also a pocket-sized, cosy TV room with green leather armchairs and bookcases. Bedrooms upstairs all have ample room and pleasant furnishings – Barclay, at the back of the house, overlooks the garden.

○ Open all year; restaurant closed Sun & Mon eves ⏌ Leave A14 at second Bury St Edmunds exit; head towards town centre; turn left at next roundabout into Northgate Street. Ounce House is on right. Private car park ⏌ 1 single, 1 twin, 2 double; family rooms available; all with bathroom/WC exc 1 single with shower/WC; all with TV, hair-dryer, trouser press, direct-dial telephone, radio alarm clock ⊘ Dining-room, bar/TV room/library, living-room, gardens; meetings (max 12 people incl up to 4 residential); early suppers for children; cots, high chairs, toys, babysitting, baby-listening ♿ No wheelchair access ● No dogs; smoking in bar/TV room/library only ☐ Amex, MasterCard, Switch, Visa £ Single £45 to £50, single occupancy of twin/double £50 to £55, twin/double £70 to £80; deposit required. Set D £22 to £26. Special breaks available

Ravenwood Hall

Rougham Green, Bury St Edmunds IP30 9JA
TEL: (01359) 270345 FAX: (01359) 270788

A country house dating back to the sixteenth century, with plenty of eccentric and personal touches.

The long drive, lawns and mature trees might lead you to expect a conventional country-house hotel, but all is not as it appears. Firstly there is the fenced-off section of the grounds that contains a herd of goats and a Shetland pony kept as pets by the owner, Craig Jarvis. Then once inside, the informal décor gives things a personable, light-hearted feel. The mix of old and new includes rich red wallpaper and tartan fabrics in the lounge, which has an ancient fireplace, a stuffed fish and a quirky collection of paintings, prints and cartoons. In the bar, blackboards propped up in every spare space have the day's meals chalked up, and a warm cosy atmosphere is created by the use of candles on the bar surface. In the beamed restaurant the age of the house really shines through: one end is dominated by an all-encompassing medieval fireplace, while the other has deep-varnished wood panelling. The informality is again emphasised by the array of pre- and post-prandial drinks displayed on a central table. Bedrooms are all individually designed in bold colours and snazzy borders. St Edmunds Room in the main house has a four-poster bed and a teddy-bear theme; the mews bedrooms are neat and tidy, but smaller.

○ Open all year ⏌ Take A14 east out of Bury St Edmunds; turn right to Rougham, left at Blackthorpe Barn; hotel is signposted soon afterwards on right-hand side. Private car park ⏌ 2 twin, 11 double, 1 four-poster; 7 in annexe all with bathroom/WC; all with TV, room service, hair-dryer, direct-dial telephone ⊘ Restaurant, bar, lounge, garden;

functions (max 150 people incl up to 28 residential); civil wedding licence; heated outdoor swimming-pool, croquet, clay-pigeon shooting, shooting nearby, free membership of nearby leisure facilities; early suppers for children; cots, high chairs, baby-listening   ♿ Wheelchair access to hotel, restaurant, WC (unisex), 5 ground-floor bedrooms, 2 specially equipped for disabled people ● No smoking in bedrooms or restaurant ▭ Amex, Delta, Diners, MasterCard, Switch, Visa £ Single occupancy of twin/double £63 to £73, twin/double £83 to £93, four-poster £115, family room £115 (prices valid till June 1999); deposit required. Bar/bistro L, D £2.50 to £15; set L, D £19; alc L, D £25. Special breaks available

Twelve Angel Hill

12 Angel Hill, Bury St Edmunds IP33 1UZ
TEL: (01284) 704088   FAX: (01284) 725549

Fine Georgian town house providing ample bedrooms and elegant public rooms.

It's five years since Bernie and John Clarke came to this classy city-centre address, but year by year they continue to make noticeable improvements to this top-of-the-range bed and breakfast. This year sound-proofing has been added to prevent the sounds of Angel Hill, one of the busiest parts of the town, from disturbing the agreeable atmosphere inside. There's also lush new red wallpaper in the front lounge. However, the quieter cosy bar area – part of the original Tudor house predating the Georgian façade – remains. Behind it is the patio garden, which gives access through a gate to a handy and invaluable car park. Upstairs the six bedrooms, named after wines, are thoughtfully decorated and have bright, fresh bathrooms. The spacious Chablis room, with its plump double bed, is probably the best, enhanced by the addition of large armchairs and antique furniture. Service is very friendly but unobtrusive.

◑ Closed Chr & Jan ⊠ Follow A14 to Bury St Edmunds ring road, and take second exit (Bury St Edmunds central). Follow road to next roundabout and take left exit (Northgate Street). Turn right after ½ mile into Looms Lane; after 50 yds, turn left under archway. Private car park; public car park nearby (50p per day) ⇤ 1 single, 1 twin, 2 double, 1 four-poster, 1 suite; 2 with bathroom/WC, most with shower/WC; all with TV, hair-dryer, trouser press, direct-dial telephone, radio alarm ✓ Breakfast room, bar, lounge, patio garden   ♿ No wheelchair access ● No children under 16; no dogs; no smoking ▭ Amex, Delta, Diners, MasterCard, Visa £ Single £50, single occupancy of twin/double £55 to £60, twin/double £75, four-poster £80, suite £80 (1998 prices); deposit required.

BUTTERMERE Cumbria   map 10

Bridge Hotel

Buttermere, Cockermouth CA13 9UZ
TEL: (01768) 770252   FAX: (01768) 770215

Popular pub-hotel, in a wonderful location between Buttermere and Crummock Water.

The Bridge Hotel's picturesque setting, on the daisy chain of westerly lakes near Buttermere, ensures that it's never short of daytime visitors; in fact, it's quite a problem keeping enough car-parking space for bona fide guests. Speckled hens and stray sheep occasionally find their way here, too, adding to the pastoral scene. The hotel's main entrance is restricted strictly to residents, so if all you want is a bar snack, head towards the back of the building, where tables spill out on to a stream-side beer garden in fine weather. The stone bar areas are full of quaint photos and mementoes relating to the pub's history (look for the sign for the old pack-horse bridge from which the pub takes its name), or to Cumbrian rural life. The menus spring few surprises, offering hungry walkers well-tried favourites like jacket potatoes and Yorkshire pudding. The residential section is gradually getting a makeover, and now has an exceptionally smart and attractive lounge, and a surprisingly elegant dining-room painted in sunshine yellow. Upstairs, the bedrooms vary considerably: some older-style rooms are a bit lacklustre, but the wave of refurbishment is steadily washing through, and the newly refurbished rooms are stylish and smart, if a bit short on personality. Four-poster rooms, like Thomas Carlyle, fall into this latter category. Self-catering apartments have recently been opened in a pleasantly designed annexe.

◑ Open all year   ⓩ Off B5289, in Buttermere village. Private car park   ⊫ 2 single, 6 twin, 11 double, 3 four-poster; all with bathroom/WC; all with room service, direct-dial telephone, some with hair-dryer   ⊘ Dining-room, 2 bars, 2 lounges, drying-room, patio, garden; functions (max 60 people incl up to 42 residential), conferences; early suppers for children; cots, high chairs, baby-listening   ♿ No wheelchair access   ● Dogs in bedrooms only, by arrangement (£3.20 per day); smoking in some bedrooms only   ▭ MasterCard, Switch, Visa   £ Single £56 to £64, single occupancy of twin/double £84 to £96, twin/double £112 to £128, four-poster £124 to £140 (rates incl dinner); deposit required. Bar/bistro L from £4, D from £5.50; set D £21. (Prices valid till Apr 1999.) Special breaks available

---

Wood House   [NEW ENTRY]

Buttermere, Cockermouth CA13 9XA
TEL: (017687) 70208

Secluded National Trust property, with gorgeous views of Crummock Water.

Mike and Judy McKenzie moved to this picturesque location from their lighting business in Carlisle, and struck a deal with the National Trust to restore and run the inside of the property as a guesthouse while the NT undertook the maintenance of the exterior. It's been a labour of love on both sides, and a very expensive project. The house is a fine specimen of whitewashed, Lakeland-stone and slate architecture from the seventeenth century. It stands in three-and-a-half acres of woodland and gardens, with a splendid panorama of the lake beyond. It's only half a mile from the honey-pot village of Buttermere, but within the gated grounds you could be miles from anywhere. Mike and Judy have a free hand over the interior, and, as you might expect of National Trust tenants, they both have excellent taste and a keen sense of what goes with the house. The furnishings and décor are serene and beautiful, though completely unpretentious. Guests have the use of a civilised, airy sitting-room, decorated in blues with plain walls; the dining-room is in warmer, peachy tones, and guests sit round a single, polished, oval table. Good, plain cooking (pre-booked) is served at 7.30pm. Judy skilfully makes her own soft furnishings, and both she and Mike obviously have an eagle eye for pictures and antiques. The bedrooms reach similarly high standards and enjoy lovely views. Self-catering accommodation is available in an outlying building.

◑ Closed mid-Nov to mid-Feb ⤢ Leave M6 at Junction 40; take A66 west and leave at Portinscale, then follow signs for Buttermere. Private car park ⬅ 2 twin, 1 double; twins with bathroom/WC, double with shower/WC; all with hair-dryer ⌁ Dining-room, sitting-room, garden; fishing ♿ No wheelchair access ⬤ No children under 16; no dogs; no smoking ▭ None accepted £ Single occupancy of twin/double £37, twin/double £58. Set D £18

BUXTON **Derbyshire**   map 9

Brookfield on Longhill

Brookfield Hall, Longhill, Buxton SK17 6SU
TEL: (01298) 24151   FAX: (01298) 72231

A fine, country-house hotel, with stylish rooms and good views of the Peak District.

Situated 1,400 feet above sea level, and looking south towards Buxton, Roger Handley's late-Victorian house has commanding views – as well as good sledging most winters. The double-gabled, grey-stone house has been beautifully restored by the Handleys over the past 14 years – their care and attention to detail really pays off in the first-floor bedrooms, where the Blue Room has a superb, Victorian bathroom and the Yellow Room has a large four-poster with barley-twist legs. It is worth paying the small supplement for these rooms rather than going for those on the second floor, though all show the same sense of style and good taste. Downstairs, there are two sitting-rooms and two dining-rooms; one of these, leading on to the conservatory, has smart, Lloyd Loom chairs. The à la carte menu offers a good selection of typical, country-house fare: leek and potato soup, perhaps, followed by grilled breast of duckling served on a plum sauce and, for dessert, sticky toffee pudding or 'Eton mess' – crushed meringue, chopped strawberries, cream and Grand Marnier.

◑ Open all year ⤢ 1½ miles north-west of Buxton on A5004. Private car park ⬅ 2 twin, 5 double, 1 four-poster; family rooms available; all with bathroom/WC; all with TV, room service, hair-dryer, direct-dial telephone, some with trouser press; no tea/coffee-making facilities in rooms ⌁ 2 dining-rooms, bar, 2 sitting-rooms, drying-room, library, conservatory, garden; functions (max 30 people incl up to 8 residential), conferences; civil wedding licence; early suppers for children; cots, high chairs, toys, baby-listening, outdoor play area ♿ No wheelchair access ⬤ Dogs in public rooms if other guests consent ▭ Delta, MasterCard, Visa £ Single occupancy of twin/double £55, twin/double/four-poster £80, family room £85. Set L £15, D £20; alc D £23. (Prices valid till Jan 1999.) Special breaks available

---

Reports are welcome on any hotel, whether or not it is in the Guide.

Chilvester Hill House

Calne SN11 0LP
TEL: (01249) 813981/815785   FAX: (01249) 814217

Self-assured country home run as a Wolsey Lodge by marvellous hosts.

Gill and John Dilley have taken a large and inherently grand house (with substantial grounds, including five acres set aside for Gill's beef cattle) and made it instantly relaxing and cosy. Somehow, they've managed to create a warm, kick-your-shoes-off atmosphere in a place they plainly love, without ever compromising the restrained splendour. The drawing-room and dining-room have the antiques, gracious proportions and tasteful demeanour you'd expect in such a fine home. The latter even has a drawing by Howard Carter (of Tutankhamen fame). The family sitting-room is a treasure trove of the heart, an endlessly fascinating clutter of artifacts that mean something to the Dilleys, the walls bedecked with maps of the Ottoman Empire (the couple lived for many years in the Middle East where John was an occupational physician). Local maps and guides abound and the Dilleys are well-informed about the area, and happily share their knowledge.

Gill's dinners capitalise on home-grown and local produce, and what's in season. On the night we inspected she was offering mushrooms à la grecque with baguettine, followed by breast of chicken flambé with wine and cream sauce, pineapple and strawberry salad, and cheese. Guests dine together round the same table, as at many Wolsey Lodges. As well as hosting three airy, comfortable and endearingly old-fashioned guest bedrooms, the upper floor displays more family treasures, including an extensive collection of Huntly & Palmer biscuit tins.

◑ Closed one week in spring or autumn   ⊿ 1 mile from Calne on A4 towards Chippenham, turn right signposted Bremhill and Ratford and immediately turn right again through gateposts. Private car park   ⌐⟋ 3 twin/double; family rooms available; all with bathroom/WC; all with TV, clock radio; hair-dryers available   ⊘ Dining-room, drawing-room, sitting-room (TV), garden; bar service; functions (max 50 people incl 6 residential), conferences; high chair, baby-listening   ⅙ No wheelchair access   ● No children under 12 exc babes in arms; no dogs   ▭ Amex, Diners, MasterCard, Visa   £ Single occupancy of twin/double £45 to £55; twin/double £70 to £85, family room £90 to £105; deposit required. Set D £18 to £25

'They supplied a toothbrush when I discovered I had lost mine. They couldn't dry socks overnight because the tumble dryer was on the blink, but the willingness to make me feel that any request would be dealt with promptly and sympathetically was impressive. The proprietor even apologised, as I was paying before leaving, for the amateurish fax with spelling mistakes that he had just discovered a junior member of staff sent me concerning the reservation. I felt well looked after.'
On a hotel in the Lake District

CALSTOCK Cornwall map 1

Danescombe Valley Hotel

Lower Kelly, Calstock PL18 9RY
TEL: (01822) 832414 FAX: (01822) 832446
EMAIL: danescombe@aol.com
WEB SITE: www.inforamp.net/~lower/dvi

Wonderfully atmospheric hotel in riverside spot, with fantastic views from the bedrooms and good food.

The Danescombe Valley Hotel would not look out of place in a steamy, Deep South movie starring Paul Newman and Elizabeth Taylor, such is its colonial look, complete with verandah, latticework balustrading and shutters, and its fabulous position on a sweeping bend of the River Tamar. The view is splendid, too: of a magnificent viaduct straddling the river, plenty of bird life and sunsets to set the heart aflame. The Tamar Valley was once the heart of the Cornish flower industry (the climate is so mild) and daffodils, no longer harvested, grow wild. Lloyd Loom chairs on the terrace continue the plantation theme, but that's where it ends – inside, the hotel is perfectly English, in a distinctly cosmopolitan, arty way: paintings by local artists grace the bright walls, Nepalese *tanquas* enliven the flagged bar and fresh flowers are everywhere. Dinner is now served only on Friday and Saturday, in the small, mulberry-coloured dining-room, so make sure you time it right in order to experience the intimate, yet flamboyant, 'dinner-party experience'. The no-choice, mouthwatering menu is deceptively simple – a Harbourne blue goats' cheese soufflé might be followed by Tamar salmon served with orange-flavoured couscous, and then topped off with an almond cake with plums poached in port. The bedrooms are filled with heavy, beautifully carved, antique furniture, pretty fabrics and more pictures, and, of course, have that great view. Rooms 1 and 5 have free-standing baths in the centre of their bathrooms. As we went to press, the hotel was up for sale.

◗ Closed Apr to Oct; dining-room closed Sun, Mon, Tue, Wed & Thur eves
◳ ½ mile west of Calstock village along river road; turn right after viaduct. Private car park ⊷ 2 twin, 3 double; all with bathroom/WC; all with hair-dryer; no tea/coffee-making facilities in rooms ⌂ Dining-room, bar, lounge, drying-room, garden
♿ No wheelchair access ● No children under 12; no dogs; no smoking in dining-room ▭ Amex, Delta, Diners, MasterCard, Switch, Visa £ Twin/double £100 to £125; deposit required. Set D £30

CAMPSEA ASHE Suffolk map 6

Old Rectory

Campsea Ashe, Woodbridge IP13 0PU
TEL: (01728) 746524 (AND FAX)

A secluded, Georgian house, with a quirky style and well-regarded food.

Informality is a buzzword at the Old Rectory, and visitors are always appreciative: as one regular recounted, 'To us it sums up what is special about the place.' Stewart Bassett, who has run the hotel for 14 years, is now resigned to the tag of eccentricity that he is so often labelled with, but it seems to strike the right note with his guests. Another special feature of the hotel is its peaceful location, hidden from the road by rhododendron bushes, and close to the village church, with the amusing spectacle of rabbits feeding voraciously on the lawn every morning. Dinner is a no-choice, three-course affair prepared by Stewart, and often decided upon after a quick chat with his guests. In summer, it is served in the conservatory overlooking the garden, and in winter in the old-style dining-room, with guests huddled around the log fire. A typical meal might start with a smoked-salmon and spinach tart with a lightly dressed salad, followed by chicken breast with a cream-cheese, lemon, tarragon and butter topping, finally ending with a hot ginger and pear upside-down pudding. This year, the pine four-poster room, with its enormous bathroom, won particular praise, especially the desk, at which one guest enthusiastically told us you could 'sit and write a novel'. Meanwhile, another reporter felt that the Attic Room in the eaves was well worth the climb.

◗ Closed Chr; dining-room closed Sun eve　🔄 Next to church in Campsea Ashe village. Private car park　🛏 1 single, 2 twin, 5 double, 1 four-poster; one in annexe; all with bathroom/WC; 1 with TV　⊘ 2 dining-rooms, bar, lounge, library, conservatory, garden; conferences (max 40 people incl up to 9 residential); croquet　🚫 No wheelchair access　◖ Dogs in some bedrooms only, by arrangement; no smoking　▭ Amex, Diners, MasterCard, Visa　£ Single £40, single occupancy of twin/double £48, twin/double £65, four-poster £80; deposit required. Set D £18

CANNINGTON Somerset　　　　　　　　　　　　　　　　　map 2

Blackmore Farm　NEW ENTRY

Blackmore Lane, Cannington, Bridgwater TA5 2NE
TEL: (01278) 653442　FAX: (01278) 653427
EMAIL: dyerfarm@aol.com

Glorious, fourteenth-century manor house, offering great-value B&B on a working farm.

There are dozens of country-house hotels that would kill for a façade half as lovely as that of the mellow-stoned, creeper-clad Blackmore Farm. Not only is Anne and Ian's wonderful, family home a perfect essay in medieval Englishness, but it also offers accommodation, in rooms bursting with character, for less than most country-house hotels charge for dinner!

The Dyers have a young family, so despite the house's antiquity there's no sense of stuffy grandeur about it – the riot of beams, rough stone walls and leaded windows notwithstanding. Breakfast is served on a long, intricately carved, sixteenth-century table in the magnificent Great Hall, beneath the steely gaze of a stag's head. By contrast, the sitting-room is small and cosy, with a television, a selection of board games and lots of local guides and information. The bedrooms in the main house range in style and size, from the grand West Bedroom, with its fine, antique furniture, Gothic arches and splendid four-poster, to the split-level Gallery, a panelled affair with a separate sitting area, and the simpler Solar, which has three single beds. Across the courtyard, the Stable is a bright barn conversion that has been adapted to meet the needs of guests with disabilities; it has been assessed as being at level 2 of the English Tourist Board's Accessible Scheme, making it suitable for use by guests with disabilities and their travelling companions. 'The hospitality is fantastic and it's excellent value for money. I would commend it to anybody,' concluded one rave report.

◐ Open all year   🖪 From Bridgwater, take A39 for Minehead; after 3 miles, turn left at Tincknells (just before village of Cannington) into Blackmore Lane; follow lane for 1 mile; Blackmore Farm is first on left after Maltshovel pub. Private car park   🛏 2 double, 1 four-poster, 1 family room; one in annexe; all with bathroom/WC exc family room with shower/WC; all with TV, hair-dryer   ⊘ Dining-room, sitting-room, garden; functions (max 25 people incl up to 8 residential), conferences; fishing; cots, high chairs, babysitting, outdoor play area   ⅔ Wheelchair access to hotel (ramp) and dining-room, 1 ground-floor bedroom specially equipped for disabled people ● No dogs; no smoking   ▭ MasterCard, Visa   £ Single occupancy of double £25 to £30, double £40 to £46, four-poster £46, family room £50; deposit required.. Special breaks available

---

CANTERBURY Kent

map 3

Canterbury Hotel   NEW ENTRY

71 New Dover Road, Canterbury CT1 3DZ
TEL: (01227) 450551   FAX: (01227) 780145
EMAIL: canterbury.hotel@btinternet.com

A touch of France in the heart of Kent – but stick to the superior rooms.

This stretch of the A2 is lined with hotels vying for customers, many of whom might stop off here for a meal in the restaurant, clutching their copy of *The Good Food Guide*. You'd be equally well advised to make it your base for a stay in Canterbury – the city centre is about ten minutes away on foot. The attractive Georgian house is set back from the road, the red brick offset by the deep-green awnings and bright-white window frames and columned porch. The star attraction is the sunflower-yellow restaurant, La Bonne Cuisine, where the emphasis is on the visual quality of the food as much as the taste. Textures, colours and fabulous presentation add to the appreciation of the delicious ingredients; French onion soup, followed by pan-fried monkfish with leeks and cream, all rounded off with tarte Tatin, might comprise a typical meal. Upstairs, things are rather dowdy and basic on the first floor, with small and unappealing standard rooms. It's worth every single penny to pay the extra and move up in the world to the second-floor superior rooms. The difference is astounding – bright, sunny décor, very smart bathrooms, bold, attractive fabrics – even a four-poster in one room. Service on inspection was efficient but friendly, with everyone welcoming and eager to please.

◐ Open all year ⧖ On A2, south-east of city centre; follow road round city walls, turning off at Dover exit. Private car park ⧖ 4 single, 11 twin, 8 double, 1 four-poster, 1 family room; most with bathroom/WC, some with shower/WC; all with TV, room service, hair-dryer, direct-dial telephone ⊘ Restaurant, bar, lounge, garden; functions (max 25 people residential/non-residential), conferences; cots, high chairs ⅙ No wheelchair access ⊖ No dogs in public rooms ⊟ Amex, Delta, Diners, MasterCard, Switch, Visa £ Single £45 to £48, single occupancy of twin/double £50 to £53, twin/double £60 to £65, four-poster £80 to £85, family room £72 to £77; deposit required. Bar/bistro L £7.50; set L £11.50 to £15.50, D £15.50; alc L, D £24. Special breaks available

---

Falstaff Hotel [NEW ENTRY]

St Dunstan's Street, Canterbury CT2 8AF
TEL: (01227) 462138 FAX: (01227) 463525

Olde worlde charm and character a short walk from the city centre and the cathedral.

High above the heads of passers-by hangs a huge sign fashioned from curly, black wrought-iron, boldly stating 'Est. 1403'. Looking at the building beneath it, it seems a justifiable statement – the black beams sag a little, the leaded bow windows reach almost down to the pavement and the whole building shouts 'I'm old' at you. Nigh on 600 years since it opened, the Falstaff may have changed names (until 1783 it was known as the White Hart) but it still serves its purpose well – feeding and sheltering passing pilgrims, though these days they are more likely to be from Kentucky than Kent. Inside, the atmospheric lounge has a grand fireplace beneath the beamed ceiling, and the restaurant, though a new extension, is still in keeping with the rest of the building. A typical dinner here might consist of saffron risotto with roasted calamaris, roast wood-pigeon with wild mushrooms, and pineapple and mango tuile basket. As you might expect for an old coaching inn beside the city's West Gate, a main road runs outside the door, so those bedrooms facing the front suffer from traffic noise, especially on the ground floor, where the windows look out directly on to the street. All are agreeably furnished and decorated, and often come with creaking floors and black beams. Room 9, one of the four-posters, is particularly pleasant and more peaceful, being at the back. The old pub has just closed and will soon become more bedrooms.

◐ Open all year ⧖ 6 single, 3 twin, 11 double, 2 four-poster, 1 family room, 1 suite; all with bathroom/WC exc 2 singles with shower/WC; all with TV, room service, hair-dryer, trouser press, direct-dial telephone ⊘ Restaurant, bar, lounge, garden; cots, high chairs, baby-listening ⅙ Wheelchair access to hotel and restaurant (1 step), WC (unisex), 6 ground-floor bedrooms ⊖ No smoking in restaurant and some bedrooms; only small dogs in bedrooms ⊟ Amex, Delta, Diners, MasterCard, Switch, Visa £ Single £75, single occupancy of twin/double £85, twin/double £85, four-poster/family room/suite £95; deposit required. Continental B £6.50, cooked B £9.50; bar/bistro L, D £6; set L £5, D £15; alc D £25. Special breaks available

---

Many hotels put up their tariffs in the spring. You are advised to confirm prices when you book.

Magnolia House | NEW ENTRY |

36 St Dunstan's Terrace, Canterbury CT2 8AX
TEL: (01227) 765121 (AND FAX)
WEB SITE: www.smoothound.co.uk/hotels/magnoli.html/

Friendly, unassuming B&B, in a quiet spot ten minutes' walk from the city centre.

St Dunstan's Terrace, a peaceful little back street around the corner from the city's West Gate, is a curious mix of old and new. On one side is a stretch of detached, modern houses, on the other a beautiful, Regency terrace of white façades with black, wrought-iron balconies – and, at one end, an elegant, Georgian house. Magnolia may be singled out in the name, but the whole house is a riot of colour and blooms: in spring, wistaria trails around one corner, tulips cover the doorstep and flowers hang from every windowsill. It is no surprise, then, to discover that Magnolia House received first prize for a floral display in the 'Canterbury in Bloom' contest. The floral theme continues indoors, where each room has a posy on its door and much of the décor involves flowery motifs. The bedrooms are comfortable, with a homely, welcoming feel; there is a four-poster room on the ground floor, with a grand bathroom featuring a corner bath. Those rooms at the back have views of the pretty, walled garden, as does the cheerful breakfast room. Ann and John Davies are genial hosts, who will make you feel right at home.

◖ Open all year; dinner Nov to Feb only (by arrangement)   ⬀ Approaching Canterbury from west on A2, turn left at first roundabout, signposted to university; St Dunstan's Terrace is third turning on right. Private car park.   ⇤ 1 single, 2 twin, 3 double, 1 four-poster; 3 with bathroom/WC, 4 with shower/WC; all with TV, hair-dryer, some with trouser press   ✧ Lounge, breakfast room, drying-room, garden   ⇘ No wheelchair access   ● No children under 12; no dogs; no smoking   ▭ Amex, Delta, Diners, MasterCard, Switch, Visa   £ Single £36 to £45, single occupancy of twin/double £45 to £55, twin/double £68 to £70, four-poster £95; deposit required. Set D from £18

CARBIS BAY Cornwall   map 1

Boskerris Hotel

Boskerris Road, Carbis Bay, St Ives TR26 2NQ
TEL: (01736) 795295   FAX: (01736) 798632

Family, seaside hotel, with friendly staff.

The young, but friendly and chatty, staff help to make a stay at Marie and Spencer Monk's traditional, seaside hotel a real pleasure. The hotel's location – a short walk from Carbis Bay's station – makes it the ideal base for exploring St Ives without having to cope with the arty resort's legendary traffic problems. Most of the rooms in the between-the-wars building are built into the hillside and have sea views, and the facilities available in the grounds that slope gently towards the sea include a heated outdoor swimming-pool. This, as well as a programme that encompasses early suppers for children, make it an ideal choice for families. Grown-ups gather for pre- and post-dinner drinks in a small and pleasant bar, but there are also plenty of comfy sofas in the well-furnished lounges for those who choose to abstain. The views from the smart but simple dining-room are splendid, and the fare is reliable, if short on culinary fireworks; a typical menu might include minestrone, followed by crevettes à l'américaine, roast loin of pork Normandy and then a fresh fruit salad. The bedrooms are generally of a good size, and are well equipped and pleasantly, if unremarkably, furnished.

◑ Closed Nov to Easter   ⤢ Leave A30 at St Ives exit (A3074); Boskerris Road is third turning on right (after petrol station) in Carbis Bay. Private car park ⤶ 5 twin, 8 double, 6 family rooms; all with bathroom/WC; all with TV, room service, hair-dryer, direct-dial telephone   ⌾ Dining-room, bar, 3 lounges, TV room, drying-room, garden; functions; heated outdoor swimming-pool, putting green; leisure facilities nearby (free for guests); early suppers for children; cots, high chairs, toys, babysitting, baby-listening ⅙ No wheelchair access ● No dogs in public rooms ▭ Amex, Delta, Diners, MasterCard, Switch, Visa £ Twin/double £77 to £92, family room (rates on application); deposit required. Bar/bistro L £4; set D £18.50. Special breaks available

---

CARLISLE Cumbria   map 10

The Beeches

Wood Street, Carlisle CA1 2SF   *L*
TEL: (01228) 511962

Roses round the door and village charm, just five minutes off the M6.

The village of Botcherby has long been incorporated into the outskirts of Carlisle, but a small enclave around the quiet cul-de-sac of Wood Street still retains its pretty cottages. So a brief drive from Junction 43 of the M6, past the petrol stations, off-licences and Chinese take-aways of modern suburbia, takes you to this delightful, pink-washed, Georgian building dating from 1767. It makes a marvellous stopover for motorway users on the way to Scotland, and is a good touring base for the northern Lakes or Hadrian's Wall. Heather and Bill Kilpatrick make visitors extremely welcome in their much-loved home, however long the drive takes to get there, and the Beeches is thoroughly well kept, warm and comfortable. There are just three bedrooms to let, without locks, numbers or names: two twins and a double with a canopied bed – all are charming and well co-ordinated, offering books, rosebud china and comfy seating. Heather works for Laura Ashley, so the fabrics and wall-coverings may look familiar. All the rooms share a single, Victorian-style bathroom, made pretty and personal with ornaments and plants, and including a few nods to Victorian sentiment in the shape of 'kind thoughts' and pictures of roses. There's no guest lounge, but the breakfast room is as beautifully kept as the bedrooms; guests share a single table. The Kilpatricks will happily pass on their local knowledge about places to visit and restaurants for dinner. Pre-booked evening meals are available on request.

Prices are quoted per room *rather than* per person.

◑ Open all year ⊿ Leave M6 at Junction 43 for A69 to Carlisle; after ½ mile, turn left into Victoria Road (with Esso petrol station to your right); at top of hill turn sharp left into Wood Street. Private car park ⊨ 2 twin, 1 double; all with TV, hair-dryer, some with trouser press ✅ Breakfast room, garden ♿ No wheelchair access ⬤ No dogs or smoking in breakfast room ☐ None accepted £ Single occupancy of twin/double £20 to £30, twin/double £37 to £40; deposit required

Number Thirty One

31 Howard Place, Carlisle CA1 1HR
TEL: (01228) 597080 (AND FAX)

Style and imagination reign supreme in this super, Victorian guesthouse.

Since arriving in this attractive, terraced town house on a quiet, tree-lined side-street not far from the city centre, Philip and Judith Parker have made a terrific success of their new life-style – and have attracted a wave of positive reader reports. After working in the hotel industry for over twenty years, they decided to turn their combined experience to good use and to have a shot at setting up their own business. Now Number Thirty One is a showcase of imaginative design, full of individuality and taste. Scarcely an inch of the place can have escaped the Parkers' keen scrutiny: cupboards and bathrooms have been cleverly inserted; unusual paint finishes and stencils applied, even to the insides of wardrobes; and all kinds of details thoughtfully considered. So the bath towels are extra large, the showers work effectively, and every room contains well-chosen books, pictures and fascinating objects from the Parkers' considerable travels. Sticky fingers are not a problem, as the Parkers do not allow children under 18. There are three bedrooms: Yellow (described by one reader as 'the best hotel room I have ever stayed in') has a half-tester; Blue has a walk-in wardrobe; and Green, the oriental room, a flamboyant bedhead dragon designed by Philip. The front reception room is now a charming guest lounge, where the items on the walls and mantelpiece could keep you amused for quite a while, even without tackling all the books and games. But the most interest focuses on the adjacent dining-room, where Philip's inspired dinners cause quite a stir. Even reading his entertaining, computer-generated menus will have you salivating, but don't expect much advance notice of what's on offer, because dinner is based on what's freshest in the market that day (guests' tastes and dislikes are obviously taken into account). A class act!

◑ Closed 1 Dec to 1 Mar ⊿ From M6 Junction 43 take the Warwick road towards Carlisle. Howard Place is first road on right after sixth set of traffic lights. On-street parking (free) ⊨ 1 twin, 2 double; all with bathroom/WC; all with TV, room service, hair-dryer, trouser press ✅ Dining-room, lounge, library, garden; conferences (max 10 people incl up to 3 residential) ♿ No wheelchair access ⬤ No children under 18; no dogs; no smoking ☐ Amex, Delta, Diners, MasterCard, Switch, Visa £ Single occupancy of twin/double £40 to £55; twin/double £60 to £80; deposit required. Set D £18

Foresters Arms

Carlton-in-Coverdale, Leyburn DL8 4BB
TEL: (01969) 640272 (AND FAX)

A village local in the depths of the Dales, with a culinary whizz at the helm turning out serious gastronomic creations.

The Foresters Arms has everything you would expect from an outing to a classic, seventeenth-century, village pub. The journey there could take you the length of Coverdale, through wild and brilliant scenery, if you take the road from Kettlewell – then, at journey's end, flagstone floors, oak-beamed ceilings and real fires accompany a pint of hand-pulled ale. Chef-cum-landlord Barrie Higginbotham is one of a growing breed who take the country-inn experience a step or two further, with ambitious and accomplished cooking in place of the traditional cheese sandwich and meat pie, and the option of accommodation at the end of the day in order to do full justice to the gastronomic experience. The choice is vast, from roast black pudding with Dijon vinaigrette, or wild-boar sausage and liver with garlic mash, to such veggie-fodder as leek and blue-cheese strudel with chargrilled vegetables. The range of fish dishes alone is mind-boggling and merits special attention, as do puddings like bitter-chocolate terrine or baked mango soufflé. The bedrooms are bright and cottagey, with an easy-going décor of pine furniture and light hues; thoughtful extras like bathrobes, fruit and flowers add a touch of luxury that raises them above the level of normal pub accommodation. The rear-facing rooms have the bonus of a green-field and moorland vista beyond a Viking burial mound.

❶ Closed Jan; restaurant closed Sun & Mon eves;   ⏱ Off A684, 5 miles south-west of Leyburn. Private car park   ⨀ 1 twin, 2 double; twin with bathroom/WC (not *en suite*), doubles with shower/WC; all with TV, hair-dryer   ✓ Restaurant, bar, lounge, drying-room; functions; early suppers for children; high chairs   ♿ No wheelchair access ⊖ No children under 12 in restaurant eves; dogs in bar/1 bedroom only; no smoking in lounge ⬜ Delta, MasterCard, Switch, Visa   £ Twin/double £60; deposit required. Alc L £18, D £24

Aynsome Manor

Cartmel, Grange-over-Sands LA11 6HH
TEL: (015395) 36653   FAX: (015395) 36016

Comfortable, traditionally furnished, historic manor house in lovely setting.

The pastoral scenery of the south Lakes is especially lush around Cartmel, and its twelfth-century priory attracts many visitors. Aynsome Manor is a smallish, rather plain house on the edge of the village, which once housed descendants of the Earl of Pembroke (the priory's founder). It commands fine views of the Vale of Cartmel, a mix of woods, pastureland and open fells; Morecambe Bay is within easy reach. All around the house lie its established gardens, with trim conifers, lawns and rockeries. Many of the eighteenth-century features are still intact, including panelling, plasterwork and massive walls. The furnishings are heartily traditional, with a good sprinkling of genuinely old pieces and plenty of personality. The emphasis, however, is on comfort, service and food rather than designer elegance. The menu echoes this, offering no-nonsense dishes like roast sirloin of beef served with Yorkshire pudding and horseradish sauce, alongside more recherché offerings such as Flookburgh shrimps or Holker Hall venison. The cooking is accomplished enough to win high praise in food guides, and Sunday lunch-times are always busy.

◗ Closed 2 to 29 Jan ☑ Leave M6 at Junction 36 and follow A560 towards Barrow-in-Furness; leave dual carriageway at signs for Cartmel. Hotel is on right, ½ mile north of Cartmel village. Private car park ⬅ 5 twin, 6 double, 1 four-poster; some in annexe; family rooms available; all with bathroom/WC exc 1 twin with shower/WC; all with TV, limited room service, direct-dial telephone; hair-dryer on request ✅ Dining-room, bar, 2 lounges, drying-room, garden; functions (max 32 people incl up to 24 residential); early suppers for children; ♿ No wheelchair access ⬤ No children under 5; dogs in bedrooms only (75p per day); no smoking in dining-room ☐ Amex, Delta, MasterCard, Switch, Visa £ Single occupancy of twin/double £55 to £62, twin/double/four-poster/family room £93 to £109 (rates incl dinner); deposit required. Set L £12. Special breaks available

---

Uplands

Haggs Lane, Cartmel, Grange-over-Sands LA11 6HD
TEL: (015395) 36248   FAX: (015395) 36848
EMAIL: uplands@kencomp.net

Views, food and decorative panache in southern Lakeland.

The history of this appealing country-house hotel is linked with the Lake District's culinary impresario, John Tovey, who bought it as a joint venture over a decade ago with Di and Tom Peter, who both worked at Miller Howe. Uplands is now under the ownership of the capable Peters duo since John's recent retirement to warmer climes. Needless to say, food is an important part of its attractions. Tom is the chef, regularly featuring in the food guides for his delicious and inventive cooking. What about a hot sole soufflé stuffed with mushroom duxelles and served with watercress sauce, or (more simply) a roast leg of lamb with apple and mint sauce? Imaginatively prepared vegetables and toothsome puddings are strong points; so is the affordable wine list. The setting for these delights is exceptionally attractive: a contemporary, but relaxing, style imbues the lemon and cream lounge and dining-room with interest and serenity. Large, modern prints from the Metropolitan Museum of Art enliven plain walls, and tall windows overlook a gorgeous view – zoom in on it with thoughtfully provided binoculars. The bedrooms are no less appealing: light, airy and tasteful schemes and plenty of personal touches characterise the five individually designed rooms.

● Closed Jan & Feb; dining-room closed Mon eve 🔀 Turn up Haggs Lane opposite Pig and Whistle pub in Cartmel village; hotel is 1 mile down this road. Private car park 🛏 3 twin, 2 double; 2 with bathroom/WC, 3 with shower/WC; all with TV, room service, hair-dryer, telephone (not direct-dial); no tea/coffee-making facilities in rooms ⌀ Dining-room, lounge, drying-room, garden; functions (max 28 people incl up to 10 residential); early suppers for children 🦽 No wheelchair access ● No children under 8; no dogs in public rooms; no smoking in dining-room ▭ Amex, MasterCard, Visa £ Single occupancy of twin/double £43 to £53, twin/double £66 to £86. Set L £15.50, D £27. Special breaks available

---

CARTMEL FELL Cumbria map 8

Lightwood

Cartmel Fell, Grange-over-Sands LA11 6NP
TEL: (01539) 531454 (AND FAX)

Rolling, southern Lakeland countryside surrounds an old Cumbrian farmhouse of real character.

Many visitors hammer along the A-roads for their first glimpse of Lake Windermere; in doing so, however, they miss an extraordinarily pretty and peaceful pocket of countryside. The bucolic, sweeping fells on Windermere's south-eastern flank are well worth exploring – but make sure you have time to get thoroughly lost. Lightwood (now more a country guesthouse than a working farm) lies deep in the heart of a maze of rural lanes. Enough discover it, though, to make booking ahead advisable, for Lightwood's four charming bedrooms are very popular. Evelyn and her Italian husband Fideo Cervetti have been offering a well-tried formula of super-value accommodation for quite a while now. Well-cooked dinners (sometimes with Italian flavours) are provided if pre-booked. A generous amount of Evelyn's family house – all beamed and cosy, with many fascinating, original features – is available for visitors to use. The main sitting-room contains an authentic, cherrywood 'bachelor's chest' (a sort of built-in bureau), and the window seats give some idea of the thickness of the walls. There's even a conservatory, whose expansion is planned this year, and guests are welcome to patrol the extensive, landscaped gardens. The bedrooms are snug and comfortable, with simple pine or oak furnishings, displaying the beams and uneven floors of the seventeenth century. All have their own bathrooms or shower-rooms.

● Closed Chr, Jan & Feb 🔀 Leave M6 at Junction 36 and follow A590 to Newby Bridge. Follow A592 for 1 mile. Take steep turn to right signposted Bowland Bridge and Cartmel Fell. Continue 2½ miles to Lightwood. Private car park 🛏 1 twin, 2 double, 1 family room; all with bathroom/WC; all with room service, some with TV; hair-dryer available on request ⌀ Dining-room, sitting-room, TV room, drying-room, conservatory, garden; cots, high chairs 🦽 No wheelchair access ● No dogs; smoking in sitting-room only ▭ MasterCard, Switch, Visa £ Single occupancy of twin/double £30 to £33, twin/double £48 to £52, family room £60 to £65; deposit required. Set D £14. Special breaks available

---

Please let us know if an establishment has changed hands.

CASTLE ASHBY **Northamptonshire** map 5

The Falcon

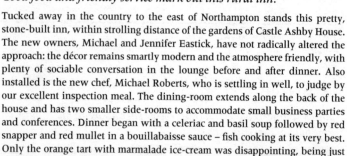

Castle Ashby, Northampton NN7 1LF
TEL: (01604) 696200   FAX: (01604) 696673
EMAIL: falcon@castleashby.co.uk

Good food and friendly service mark out this rural inn.

Tucked away in the country to the east of Northampton stands this pretty, stone-built inn, within strolling distance of the gardens of Castle Ashby House. The new owners, Michael and Jennifer Eastick, have not radically altered the approach: the décor remains smartly modern and the atmosphere friendly, with plenty of sociable conversation in the lounge before and after dinner. Also installed is the new chef, Michael Roberts, who is settling in well, to judge by our excellent inspection meal. The dining-room extends along the back of the house and has two smaller side-rooms to accommodate small business parties and conferences. Dinner began with a celeriac and basil soup followed by red snapper and red mullet in a bouillabaisse sauce – fish cooking at its very best. Only the orange tart with marmalade ice-cream was disappointing, being just too tart for its own good. The service was impeccably attentive without ever being overpowering. The bedrooms are spacious and pleasant with bright, modern bathrooms.

◑ Open all year   ☒ Leave A428 Northampton to Bedford road at signpost to Castle Ashby. Private car park   ⚑ 3 single, 4 twin, 9 double; some in annexe; all with bathroom/WC exc 1 single with shower/WC; all with TV, room service, hair-dryer, trouser press, direct-dial telephone   ✅ Dining-room, 2 bars, 2 lounges, TV room, drying-room, garden; functions (max 200 people incl up to 29 residential), conferences; civil wedding licence; fishing, golf; early suppers for children; cots, high chairs   ♿ Wheelchair access to hotel and restaurant, WC (unisex), 4 ground-floor bedrooms, 1 specially equipped for disabled people   ● None   ▭ Amex, Delta, MasterCard, Switch, Visa   £ Single £78, single occupancy of twin/double £83, twin/double £93; deposit required. Bar/bistro L, D £6 to £9.50; set L £15 to £19, D £22; alc L, D £27. Special breaks available

---

CASTLE COMBE **Wiltshire** map 2

Manor House

Castle Combe, Chippenham SN14 7HR
TEL: (01249) 782206   FAX: (01249) 782159
EMAIL: enquiries@manor-house.co.uk
WEB SITE: www.manor-house.co.uk

Picture-postcard, English manor house, with excellent leisure facilities.

The southern Cotswolds and its fringes embody the essence of England's green and pleasant land, with deep valleys and rolling hills peppered with golden villages. Castle Combe is one of those villages whose name pops up at dinner-party debates over England's prettiest hamlet, and its manor does more than its bit to hold up the side. Its extensive grounds set the creeper-clad, fourteenth-century house slightly apart from things, and its dignified gates, parted to reveal a sweeping driveway, heighten the sense of anticipation. The high-pitched roofs and soaring chimneys lead the eye upwards, and somehow serve to emphasise the tranquillity of the location, set amid swards of parkland that meander down to the trout-rich River Bybrook. Dark, Jacobean panelling and a stone fireplace emblazoned with heraldic devices confer an aristocratic air on the imposing front hall. Two agreeable sitting-rooms and a conservatory provide alternative places in which to linger with a post-prandial drink, or to wrestle with the Sunday supplements. The bedrooms in the main house adopt a grander manner and more period features than the cottagey style that prevails in the annexes that line the drive. The cooking, with a French slant but with fine British cheeses, is assured.

◖ Open all year ⤵ From Chippenham, take A420 towards Bristol; fork left on to B4039 to Castle Combe; pass through village and over bridge and take immediate right-hand turning into hotel grounds. Private car park 🛏 10 twin/double, 23 double, 9 four-poster, 1 cottage suite; some in annexe; family rooms available; all with bathroom/WC; all with TV, room service, hair-dryer, direct-dial telephone, some with tea/coffee-making facilities ⊘ Restaurant, bar, 4 sitting-rooms, library, conservatory, garden; functions (max 90 people residential/non-residential), conferences; civil wedding licence; fishing, golf, heated outdoor swimming-pool, tennis, croquet; early suppers for children; babysitting ⟐ No wheelchair access ⬤ No dogs; no smoking in bedrooms ⊟ Amex, Delta, Diners, MasterCard, Switch, Visa £ Single occupancy of twin/double £115 to £145, twin/double £120 to £145, four-poster/family room £285, suite £205 to £265; deposit required. Continental B £10, cooked B £13; bar/bistro L £6; set L £17/£19, D £35; alc D £48. Special breaks available

---

Grey Gables

Norwich Road, Cawston, Norwich NR10 4EY
TEL: (01603) 871259 (AND FAX)

An unfussy, secluded, family home and restaurant, in attractive, open countryside, with attentive, friendly owners.

It's about 20 years since James and Rosalind Snaith first began welcoming guests to their Victorian, red-brick home, which was formerly the local rectory. Grey Gables is set behind tall hedges, in tranquil countryside, and there is little doubt that you will have an undisturbed stay here. There's a simple, family style to the furnishings of the house: photos are placed on top of the small marble fireplace in the sitting-room, where you can sit on the soft, pale-blue sofas and look through the bay-fronted window to the lawns and tidy flowerbeds of the garden. The candlelit dining-room is altogether larger and longer, with dark-wood tables and plain, straw-mat place-settings. Rosalind – often seen in her apron – does the cooking, and you can enjoy a fairly unchanging menu, including, for instance, a mushroom-filled, filo-parcel starter with gazpacho sauce, followed by fresh salmon, served warm with a prawn and white-wine sauce. The self-effacing James is master of the wine cellar, from which he produces an impressive selection of bottles, listed by year. The bedrooms are plain and simple, with a modicum of furnishings, but are none the less good value. Room 1 is a spacious double that has good views of the front lawns, while Room 8 is set apart from the others, with a stand-alone bath.

◑ Closed 25 & 26 Dec ⬚ 1 mile south of Cawston village, near Eastgate. Private car park ⬚ 2 single, 1 twin, 5 double, 1 family room; 5 with bathroom/WC, 1 with shower/WC; all with TV, room service, hair-dryer, direct-dial telephone ⬚ 2 dining-rooms, sitting-room, garden; functions (max 30 people incl up to 16 residential), conferences; tennis ⬚ No wheelchair access ● No children under 5 in dining-rooms eves; no dogs in public rooms; no smoking in dining-rooms ⬚ MasterCard, Visa ⬚ Single £21, single occupancy of twin/double £30 to £40, twin/double £44 to £60, family room £48 to £68; deposit required. Bistro D £9; set L £14; alc D £17. Special breaks available

---

CHADLINGTON Oxfordshire   map 5

Chadlington House   **NEW ENTRY**

Chapel Road, Chadlington, Chipping Norton OX7 3LZ
TEL: (01608) 676437 (AND FAX)

Newly refurbished hotel in pretty rural village, with plush, colourful rooms.

When Jane Turner left her computer business and bought Chadlington House, she became only the eighth owner of this 350-year-old gabled and beamed house. Having, as she says, always had 'an interest in doing things right', she set about creating a tasteful, well-thought-out hotel, where guests get value for money in a friendly, stylish environment. So she gutted the place, right back to the colonnaded stone arches, stained-glass windows and wooden floors, and then set about refurbishing. The cosy drawing-room has yellow walls, tapestried round-back chairs and swagged curtains; there are plenty of bright colours and plants in the hallways; and the Garden Room restaurant is freshly done out with exposed brick walls, a slanting glass roof, marble tables and Lloyd Loom-style chairs. For outdoor dining, doors open out on to a patio, from where steps lead up to an acre of walled garden. The good-value menu features plenty of French and Spanish influences – you might try melon and papaya with Serrano ham, followed by Andalucian-style Dover sole, prepared with black olives and tomatoes. The seven bedrooms are named after the villages they face (which gives a good idea of the splendid views from the house): Charlbury has a four-poster decorated with feminine twists of lace, and Wychwood is colourful and bright. All are large, with good-quality reproduction furniture and smart bathrooms.

◑ Open all year; restaurant closed Sun & Mon eves (exc residents) ⬚ In centre of Chadlington, 200 yards from village hall. Private car park ⬚ 1 single, 2 twin, 3 double, 1 four-poster suite; family rooms available; 3 with bathroom/WC, 4 with shower/WC; all with TV, room service, hair-dryer, direct-dial telephone ⬚ 1 restaurant, 1 dining-room/function room, bar, drawing-room, drying-room, meeting room, garden; functions (max 120 people non-residential, 18 residential), conferences; civil wedding licence; croquet; early suppers for children; cots, high chairs, baby-listening ⬚ No wheelchair access ● No children under 12; no dogs; no smoking

Delta, MasterCard, Switch, Visa £ Single £65, single occupancy of twin/double £75, twin/double £78, family room £86, four-poster suite £91; deposit required. Set L (by arrangement) £7.50 to £14.50, D £19.50 (prices valid till Jan 1999). Special breaks available

---

CHAGFORD Devon map 1

Mill End

Sandy Park, Chagford, Newton Abbot TQ13 8JN
TEL: (01647) 432282   FAX: (01647) 433106

Enthusiastically run small hotel with functioning millwheel, close to Dartmoor.

Trudy is the head of PR at Mill End; so enthusiastic is her welcome that she once spent the night in bed with a guest, and received a letter of appreciation for her trouble. Trudy is, of course, a dog – a King Charles spaniel to be exact – whose tail-wagging and good spirits are unceasing. She will show you around the grounds of the hotel, leading you past the sculpture of a lady and bird by the river, over the little tributary flowing under the house, to the revolving millwheel which is her owner's pride and joy. Julian Peck (together with partner Jill Day) took over the hotel just over a year ago; the full restoration of the wheel was his first 'little project', and soon the hotel should be able to generate its own electricity. Julian is hardly less exuberant than Trudy, and the hotel is filled with his and Jill's 'little treasures' – family furniture, photos and pictures are interspersed with more formal armchairs and sofas. The restaurant has a view to the river and fresh flowers on the tables; on the menu might be a salad of Parma ham with quail's eggs and asparagus, followed by roasted tail of monkfish, and finishing off with a terrine of three chocolate mousses. The good-sized bedrooms are decorated in warm, pastel colours and again feature fresh flowers. Those on the ground floor have private patios. One satisfied guest proclaimed the 'service first class, the hotel elegant'.

◑ Open all year ⏩ On A382, 5 miles north of Moretonhampstead. Private car park
🛏 15 double, 2 family rooms; all with bathroom/WC; all with TV, room service, hair-dryer, trouser press, direct-dial telephone, ironing facilities ⌦ Restaurant, bar, lounge, TV room, drying-room, garden; functions (max 40 people incl up to 34 residential), conferences; fishing, croquet, boules, quoits; early suppers for children; cots, high chairs, baby-listening ♿ Wheelchair access to hotel and restaurant, 3 ground-floor bedrooms ◒ No children under 5 in restaurant eves; no dogs in public rooms; smoking in TV room and some bedrooms only ▭ Amex, Delta, MasterCard, Switch, Visa £ Single occupancy of double £50, double £70, family room £89; deposit required. Set L £15, D £25; alc D £25. Special breaks available

---

'The final straw when I was leaving the hotel was seeing porters sweeping litter and broken bottles under a car parked outside the front of the hotel. "Out of sight out of mind" seems to sum up the running of this hotel during my stay.'
On a hotel in North Yorkshire

Charingworth Manor

Charingworth, Chipping Campden GL55 6NS
TEL: (01386) 593555   FAX: (01386) 593353

Medieval manor house much expanded into a fairly convincing country-house hotel.

Around the original house, which dates from the fourteenth century, has grown a large, rambling, mellow-stone hotel complex with a warren of flagstone corridors. It surveys extensive gardens and a 54-acre estate and includes good leisure facilities (see below), but it is the character of the rooms in the old manor that, above all, makes the place recommendable. Here, the pair of restful and elegant sitting-rooms feature leaded windows and log fires, while the restaurant, divided into four intimate, interconnecting dining-rooms, is a romantic place to dine. The beamed, mullion-windowed bedrooms in the old house are romantic places to sleep, particularly those with the view and the two with antique four-posters. All rooms are rigged out with antiques, armchairs and pleasing bathrooms with cheerily-coloured tiles, but those in the heavily converted outbuildings come a distant second in the charm stakes. The hotel's biggest drawback is that, being part of a small chain, it has a less personal feel than many Cotswold country houses. A recent guest felt that the young staff, while enthusiastic and helpful, could have done with more direction, and, partly as a consequence of this, a number of small things could have been improved – disappointing at these prices. More reports please.

○ Open all year ⊅ Turn off A429 on to B4035 towards Chipping Campden. Hotel is 3 miles further on, on right. Private car park ⊨ 18 twin, 3 double, 2 four-poster, 3 suites; all with bathroom/WC; all with TV, room service, hair-dryer, trouser press, direct-dial telephone; no tea/coffee-making facilities in rooms ⊘ Restaurant, 3 sitting-rooms, games room, garden; functions (max 50 people residential/non-residential), conferences; civil wedding licence; sauna, solarium, indoor heated swimming-pool, tennis; early suppers for children; cots, high chairs, baby-listening ⅊ No wheelchair access ● No children in restaurant after 6:30pm; no dogs ⊟ Amex, Delta, Diners, MasterCard, Switch, Visa   £ Single occupancy of twin/double £105, twin/double from £140, four-poster £240, suite £260; deposit required. Set L £17.50, D £37.50; alc D from £47.50. Special breaks available

Thatch Lodge Hotel   NEW ENTRY

The Street, Charmouth, Bridport DT6 6PQ
TEL: (01297) 560407 (AND FAX)

Spick-and-span small hotel on a busy road a short drive from Lyme Regis.

The name gives the game away: Christopher and Andrea Worsfold's small hotel, clearly their pride and joy, sports a neatly trimmed barnet, jauntily offsetting the pink-rendered walls of the venerable house. In an area famous for fossils, Thatch

Lodge is itself no spring chicken, dating back to 1320 and coming complete with all the heavy beams and inglenooks you might expect. The small conservatory even boasts a 200-year-old vine, from which Andrea selects dessert grapes to serve to diners from the end of August through to November. It's a useful addition to the impeccably neat and tastefully arranged sitting-room. There's a rustic feel to the heavily beamed restaurant, where floral drapes, wheelback chairs and an inglenook fireplace set the tone. Andrea's dinners (cooked by arrangement) are interesting: perhaps cream of carrot, ginger and orange soup, followed by lemon and lime sorbet, roast breast of chicken filled with ricotta and sun-dried tomatoes, wrapped in bacon and served with a herb-butter sauce, and hot vanilla soufflé with a hot strawberry and Cointreau filling.

The bedrooms, some a tad on the small size, are pleasantly furnished with good, old – often antique – furniture, and simply decorated with cheerful borders and classy fabrics.

◗ Closed mid-Jan to March ⊠ Leave A35 at sign to Charmouth, 2 miles east of Lyme Regis. Private car park ⌸ 1 twin, 4 double, 2 four-poster; some with bathroom/WC, most with shower/WC; all with TV, hair-dryer, some with trouser press ⊘ Restaurant, sitting-room, drying-room, conservatory, garden ⅋ No wheelchair access ● No children; no dogs; no smoking ▭ Delta, MasterCard, Switch, Visa £ Twin/double £70 to £80, four-poster £90; deposit required. Set D £23. Special breaks available

---

CHARTHAM **Kent**   map 3

Thruxted Oast

Mystole, Chartham, Canterbury CT4 7BX
TEL: (01227) 730080   FAX: (01227) 730056

The oast with the most: hospitable hosts, blissful bedrooms and serene surroundings.

Tim and Hilary Derouet's herculean efforts to restore their home from its former, near-derelict state have not gone unnoticed: not only have we received consistent praise from readers, but the renovation also featured in *Ideal Home* magazine. It's not until you see the before-and-after photographs in the kitchen that you truly realise how extensive the year-long work was – and not just indoors: the now-beautiful gardens were, back in 1986, a muddy mess. 'By the time we moved in, it was me that needed complete renovation' – Hilary's words say it all. The five oast-houses today make a very plush, characterful place in which to stay, and the Derouets make you feel quite at home. Breakfast is taken around the huge, scrubbed table in the kitchen, and includes a variety of home-made jams and marmalades. The bedrooms themselves are decked out in a fresh, country style, with patchwork bedspreads and hand-made hot-water-bottle covers; bathrobes are on hand in the snug, *en suite* shower-rooms. The whole house is strewn with knick-knacks of varying shapes and sizes, from jars to an old wooden cart once used to take children to the hop fields. Don't go without paying a visit to the smallest room – the wooden loo seat has a (tongue-in-cheek) four-crown classification from the ETB!

ENGLAND

◗ Closed Chr ⤢ From Canterbury, take A28 towards Ashford; after crossing bypass, turn left into St Nicholas Road and then right; after 2 miles go straight over crossroads; house is near bottom of hill, on right. Private car park ⤚ 3 twin; all with shower/WC; all with TV, hair-dryer, direct-dial telephone ⌀ Lounge, drying-room, garden; croquet ♿ No wheelchair access ● No children under 5; no dogs; no smoking in bedrooms ▭ Amex, MasterCard, Visa £ Single occupancy of twin £68, twin £78; deposit required.

CHEDDLETON Staffordshire
map 5

Choir Cottage & Choir House

Ostlers Lane, Cheddleton, Leek ST13 7HS
TEL: (01538) 360561

Pleasant B&B with rooms in a cottage in the small garden.

Approaching Choir Cottage up the deep, tree-lined Ostler's Lane, it comes as a surprise to find William and Elaine Sutcliffe's house is actually on the edge of a housing estate. But no matter, the sense of quiet and peace is never really troubled because of it, and there are a couple of pubs within walking distance for an evening meal. The cottage is deceptive: from the outside you see a stone-built, pretty two-up-two-down, but inside there are two four-poster rooms with *en suite* shower-rooms attached. With their patchwork covers, framed samplers and knick-knacks, the rooms tread a fine line between twee and cosy. The Sutcliffes are thoughtful hosts, showing guests where things are on arrival and serving an excellent breakfast in the main house in the morning (it's only a few steps across the garden). A few biscuits and fresh milk in the room would round off this smart, good-value B&B perfectly.

◗ Closed Chr and New Year ⤢ 3 miles south of Leek; in Cheddleton turn off A520 opposite Red Lion Inn into Hollow Lane; left (200 yards after church) into Ostlers Lane; cottage on right halfway up hill. Private car park ⤚ 1 four-poster, 1 suite; both in annexe; suite with bathroom/WC, four-poster with shower/WC; TV, room service, hair-dryer, direct-dial telephone; some with trouser press ⌀ Dining-room, lounge, conservatory, garden; ♿ No wheelchair access ● No children under 5; no dogs or smoking ▭ None accepted £ Single occupancy of twin/double £35 to £38, four-poster £57 to £58, family room £76 to £80, suite £57 to £58; deposit required.

CHELTENHAM Gloucestershire
map 5

Hotel on the Park

Evesham Road, Cheltenham GL52 2AH
TEL: (01242) 518898   FAX: (01242) 511526
EMAIL: hotel@epinet.co.uk
WEB SITE: www.i2i.net/hotelonthepark.htm

Snazzy, small, town-house hotel that is a Regency wonderland.

The handsome, Regency mansion lies across the road from Pittville Park, in an exclusive, residential area built in the 1820s and 1830s. Inside, every room is a highly designed, contemporary rendition of that period; most striking is the

170

small-scale restaurant, a study in grey and white in its striped walls and long window drapes, tablecloths, and even its plates. Two outsize teddy bears sitting at one table suggest that the hotel doesn't take itself too seriously, as do a saxophone lampstand in the elegantly proportioned bar/sitting area, and a bowl of lollipops at the reception.

As well as being rich and challenging in its combinations of ingredients and flavours, the food is as decorative as the surroundings. The limited-choice *menu du jour* is good value, while there is also a pricier table d'hôte menu offering more options. The service is extremely obliging – the staff are used to meeting the challenging demands of Americans, with whom the hotel is very popular – and owner Darryl Gregory, who is much in evidence, ensures that the ambience is less formal than the surroundings might suggest. Furnished with apposite antiques and long, swagged curtains – and with bathrooms offering such indulgent features as a phone, and maybe a Victorian tub bath – the bedrooms are photogenic and fairly luxurious. However, the traffic noise from the busy A-road that passes right by the hotel does impinge on them, even though the front-facing bedrooms are double-glazed.

◖ Open all year ⤧ From the town-centre one-way system, follow signs for Evesham. Hotel is ½ mile out of town, on left, opposite park. Private car park; on-street parking (free) ⤶ 4 twin, 6 double, 1 four-poster, 1 suite; family rooms available all with bathroom/WC; all with TV, room service, hair-dryer, direct-dial telephone, radio ⍟ Restaurant, bar, library, garden; functions (max 34 people incl up to 24 residential), conferences ♿ No wheelchair access ⬤ No children under 8; no dogs in public rooms; smoking in 1 public room only, discouraged in bedrooms ▭ Amex, Diners, MasterCard, Switch, Visa £ Single occupancy of twin/double £78, twin/double from £95, four-poster £165, family room from £115, suite £125; deposit required. Continental B £6.50, cooked B £9; bar/bistro L £10; set D £22.50; alc L £20, D £28. Special breaks available

---

Lypiatt House

Lypiatt Road, Cheltenham GL50 2QW
TEL: (01242) 224994   FAX: (01242) 224996

Roomy, up-market B&B in the salubrious Montpellier district of Cheltenham.

This imposing, cream-coloured, Victorian mansion – 10 to 15 minutes on foot from the town centre – is as well proportioned inside as out, with its sweeping staircase and high-ceilinged rooms. But the atmosphere is not in the least bit intimidating. After a friendly greeting from the Medforths and their golden retriever, you can make yourself at home in a smart sitting-room enlivened by bold flower displays, or you can help yourself to a drink from an honesty bar set up in the fetching, black-and-white-tiled conservatory. You may not see your unobtrusive hosts again until breakfast, which includes home-made muesli and is taken in a basement room that is prettified by birds and fruit trees stencilled on the walls. The bedrooms, furnished in dark, reproduction wood or modern pine, are generally spacious affairs, though the cheapest are cosy attic arrangements. The beds, some of which feature patchwork quilts, are turned down in the evening. Our only quibble with staying here is that the A40 runs right past the side of the building.

◑ Open all year ⯐ On A40 in Montpellier district of Cheltenham, 3 miles west of M5 (Junction 11). Private car park ⛟ 2 single, 3 twin, 5 double; all with bathroom/WC; all with TV, room service, hair-dryer, direct-dial telephone, radio ⟡ Dining-room, conservatory/bar, sitting-room, drying-room, garden; functions (max 30 people incl up to 18 residential) ♿ No wheelchair access ● Children by arrangement; no dogs ▭ Amex, Delta, MasterCard, Switch, Visa £ Single £50 to £56, single occupancy of twin/double £56, twin/double £60 to £75; deposit required.. Special breaks available

Milton House

12 Royal Parade, Bayshill Road, Cheltenham GL50 3AY
TEL: (01242) 582601   FAX: (01242) 222326

Top-notch, town-house B&B in the centre of Cheltenham, offering an excellent welcome and some fun touches.

Milton House delivers that magical combination of high standards and very competitive rates. The service, provided by Alex Gamez, a jolly and efficient Anglicised Mexican, is admirable. The location – a two-minute walk to the shops and restaurants on Montpellier Walk and The Promenade via the B&B's pretty back garden – could hardly be bettered. The house (part of a handsome, Regency terrace) has considerable elegance, particularly in its graceful sitting-room, which is decked out in period style, with a pink ceiling and striped wallpaper; big, squashy sofas, complimentary sherry and piles of newspapers and magazines ensure that the room is much used. Though the breakfast room is a little more guesthousey, breakfast itself is a cut above the average, with hot milk for coffee and croissants for those eschewing the cooked dishes. The bedrooms mainly feature simple, pine furniture, but are more memorable for their baskets of big, fluffy towels and flurries of animals correlating to their names. Duck, for example, has a duck door wedge, a furry duck and pictures of ducks in the bedroom, as well as a rubber duck in sunglasses in the shower-room. Penchants for frogs, hedgehogs and sheep can also be satisfied.

◑ Closed Chr & New Year ⯐ In town centre, close to Montpellier Street roundabout on A40. Private car park ⛟ 2 single, 1 twin, 2 double, 1 four-poster, 2 family rooms; half with bathroom/WC, half with shower/WC; all with TV, room service, hair-dryer, direct-dial telephone ⟡ Breakfast room, sitting-room, conservatory/bar (with TV), garden; ♿ No wheelchair access ● No children under 8; no dogs in public rooms; smoking in conservatory/bar only ▭ Amex, Delta, Diners, MasterCard, Switch, Visa £ Single £40, single occupancy of twin/double £45 to £55, twin/double £55 to £68, four-poster £68, family room £78; deposit required. Special breaks available

 This denotes that you can get a twin or double room for £70 or less per night inclusive of breakfast.

Use the index at the back of the book if you know the name of a hotel but are unsure about its precise location.

Castle House

23 Castle Street, Chester CH1 2DS
TEL: (01244) 350354 (AND FAX)

City-centre, small B&B, in a historical house, convenient for sightseeing.

Castle House looks like a smart, Georgian town house; it is evidently well loved by its amiable owners, Cathy and Coyle Marl. Once inside this conveniently located B&B, however, head off up the lovely, highly polished, wooden staircase and you soon realise that the house is older than it looks. In the warm, upstairs breakfast room, a fine Elizabethan coat of arms above the fireplace helps to date the house to the sixteenth century. The bedrooms are named rather than numbered – 'The room with the funny wall' is particularly popular with American guests because of the glass panel which displays the ancient wattle and daub that formed part of the old, exterior wall; it has a small *en suite* shower-room. High standards are shown in all the shiny new shower-rooms – most have a double shower tray, so the showers themselves are very roomy. If you long for a soak in the tub, however, there is one in the bathroom along the corridor which is shared by the two small, but neat, single rooms, but which is available for any guest. The only potential drawback to Castle House may be the shortage of parking spaces.

◑ Open all year   ⬈ Next to police headquarters and racecourse in Chester. Public car park nearby (free); on-street parking   ⇱ 2 single, 1 twin, 1 double, 1 family room; 3 with shower/WC; all with TV, some with hair-dryer   ⧉ Breakfast room, lounge, drying-room, garden; cots, high chairs, toys, baby-listening   ⬤ No wheelchair access   ⬤ None   ▭ MasterCard, Visa   £ Single £23, single occupancy of twin/double £35, twin/double £45, family room £55; deposit required.

Green Bough Hotel

60 Hoole Road, Chester CH2 3NL
TEL: (01244) 326241   FAX: (01244) 326265

Comfortable bedrooms, spread between two buildings, on the outskirts of Chester.

The Green Bough Hotel is not in the most picturesque part of Chester, sitting as it does on a busy main road dominated by B&Bs, small hotels and a few pubs and restaurants. The location isn't all bad, however, as it is very close to the city centre, as well as being convenient for the motorway if you're using Chester as a staging post.

The hotel is divided between a large, red-brick, Victorian house and half of the adjacent building, and in the couple of years that owners Janice and Philip Martin have been ensconced here, they have been progressing with a slow, steady programme of refurbishment. The bedrooms, although varied in size, are now very inviting, featuring smart fabrics and stylish furnishings. Several rooms have lovely brass or wrought-iron beds; many of the *en suite* bathrooms are also newly done out in smart, Victorian-style fittings. The public rooms have been undergoing a similar refit, although the carved oak fireplace (parts of which date from the 1780s) in the lounge will definitely stay put. The heavy, gold, swagged curtains and red wallpaper can make the small Fleur de Lys restaurant seem a little dark, but it is still a good spot in which to enjoy such dishes as poached River Dee salmon or fillet of pork with an apple and cider sauce. The Martins are making a huge effort – we would welcome more readers' reports on their progress.

◑ Open all year; restaurant closed Sun eve   ⊉ Leave M53 at Junction 12 and follow A56 to Chester; hotel is 1 mile from motorway on right-hand side. Private car park ⌸ 1 twin, 16 double, 1 four-poster, 2 family rooms; some in annexe; all with bathroom/WC; all with TV, room service, hair-dryer, direct-dial telephone, some with trouser press   ⊘ Restaurant, bar, lounge; functions (max 60 people incl up to 40 residential); early suppers for children   ⅙ Wheelchair access to hotel (2 steps), 6 ground-floor bedrooms   ● No dogs; no smoking   ▭ Amex, Delta, Diners, MasterCard, Switch, Visa   £ Single occupancy of twin/double £40 to £45, twin/double £50 to £65, four-poster £65, family room £75; deposit required. Bar/bistro L, D £5; set L £10, D £15. Special breaks available

---

Redland Hotel

64 Hough Green, Chester CH4 8JY
TEL: (01244) 671024   FAX: (01244) 681309

Irresistible B&B, with luxurious rooms and bags of character, a mile from the city centre.

Stepping into the Redland Hotel is a bit like stepping into Dr Who's Tardis: from the outside it looks like any other traditional, red-brick, Victorian house, but walk through the studded wooden front door and you're transported into the delightful world of Teresa and Bill White. The house is filled with curiosities and unusual objects – all of which have a story behind them, which Teresa willingly recounts. The knights in shining armour? They were rescued from the BBC after it had finished filming the 'Blackadder' TV series. The elaborately carved four-poster bed in the Jacobean Room? It dates from 1718, and once had pride of place in Perth Castle. The latest acquisition is a shiny brass binnacle from an old tugboat, which now sits in the wood-panelled hallway.

It seems a shame that only B&B, and not evening meals, are offered at the Redland, as the grand, panelled dining-room would make a perfect setting for dinner. The lounge, with its Wedgwood-blue-and-white corniced ceiling and selection of chairs and sofas, is where you may find fellow guests enjoying a drink from the honesty bar in the evenings.

The bedrooms vary in size, but all are immaculate and furnished to a very high standard, and several have corner baths. Unexpected bonuses come in the forms of a sauna, sunbed and laundry room in the basement.

◑ Closed 24 & 25 Dec   ⊉ On A5104, 1 mile from city centre. Private car park ⌸ 3 single, 1 twin, 5 double, 4 four-poster; family rooms available most with bathroom/WC, some with shower/WC; all with TV, hair-dryer, trouser press, direct-dial telephone   ⊘ Drawing-room, dining-room, laundry room; sauna, solarium; cots, high chairs   ♿ No wheelchair access   ● No dogs; no smoking in some bedrooms   ▢ None accepted   ⓔ Single £45, single occupancy of twin/double £50, twin/double £65, four-poster £75 to £80, family room £75.

CHESTER-LE-STREET Co Durham   map 10

Lumley Castle

Chester-le-Street DH3 4NX
TEL: 0191-389 1111   FAX: 0191-387 1437

A luxurious hotel in a fourteenth-century castle, run with a strong Elizabethan theme.

If you have ever wanted to step back a few centuries, Lumley Castle could be just the job. The imposing, turreted pile looks down from a hilltop outside Chester-le-Street, promising an out-of-the-ordinary stay, which it delivers by and large, thanks to a maze of flagstoned corridors and a pronounced Elizabethan flavour – staff even dress in period costume. It's a large and busy place, so be prepared for the company of others, particularly when Elizabethan banquets are held in the Baron's Hall to the accompaniment of troubadours in the Minstrels' Gallery, or on such themed evenings as 'Murder by Candlelight'. Those shy of a potential Renaissance pastiche could opt for a quieter time surrounded by stone columns and statues under the vaulted roof in the main restaurant. As is often the case, the more pricey bedrooms are the most characterful; rooms in the courtyard, some with heavy, oak beams, are the cheapest option – they are plush, elegantly furnished and hung with rich fabrics – but for a more memorable stay, dig deeper into the wallet and go for those in the castle itself, which are mostly spacious, oak-panelled and furnished with handsome antiques. Feature rooms offer something further, perhaps a free-standing bath in the bedroom or a pedigree Queen Anne four-poster.

● Closed 25, 26 Dec & 1 Jan   🔁 Leave A1(M) at exit for Chester-le-Street and follow A167 south for 3 miles to Junction 67. Private car park   🛏 4 single, 7 twin, 41 double, 7 four-poster, 2 family rooms, 1 suite; 38 rooms in annexe; all with bathroom/WC; all with TV, room service, trouser press, direct-dial telephone, some with hair-dryer   ⌀ 2 restaurants, 3 bars, lounge, games room, garden; functions (max 200 people incl up to 115 residential), conferences; leisure facilities nearby (reduced rates for guests); early suppers for children; cots, high chairs, babysitting, baby-listening   ♿ No wheelchair access   ● No dogs   ▢ Amex, Delta, Diners, MasterCard, Switch, Visa   ⓔ Single £72, single occupancy of twin/double £90, twin/double/family room £120, four-poster £165, suite £200; deposit required. Continental B £6.50, cooked B £7.50; set L £13.50, D £24.50; alc L, D £27.50

CHILGROVE West Sussex   map 3

Forge Cottage

Chilgrove, Chichester PO18 9HX
TEL: (01243) 535333   FAX: (01243) 535363

Smarter-than-average B&B, with stupendous breakfasts.

It's not often that you get a top-notch chef creating a culinary morning masterpiece at an Aga beside your table – but you do here. Neil Rusbridger, a modest and attentive host (and chef at the White Horse next door), rustles up a gourmet feast for his bleary-eyed guests as they sit around the big breakfast table enjoying the enticing smells and freshly squeezed orange juice. As for the bedrooms, they're just as intimate and sumptuous, though the ones upstairs are a little difficult to get to for anyone with mobility problems. Each room is beautifully decorated, playing on the natural assets of sloping floors, exposed beams, low ceilings and oodles of atmosphere. On the ground floor, Wildham even comes with an old brick bread oven. The cottage's past life as the village blacksmith's home can be seen from a sneaky peek at the wattle-and-daub walls in the hall: part of the exposed wall has been covered in glass so that you can see the sixteenth-century workmanship. Much more hi-tech are the keyless door locks, which appear to be straight out of 'Star Trek' – although terrestrial television hasn't yet reached these parts (only satellite channels are available). As there isn't a shop for miles, a nice little extra is being able to buy such forgotten essentials as M&S ladies' underwear, emery boards and even condoms.

◗ Closed last week Oct & 2 weeks Jan or Feb; restaurant closed Sun & Mon eves
☑ On B2141 between Chichester and Petersfield, next to White Horse Inn. Private car park ⮕ 1 single, 3 twin, 1 double; all with bathroom/WC exc single with shower/WC; all with satellite TV, room service, hair-dryer, direct-dial telephone; tea/coffee-making facilities on request ✓ Restaurant, bar, garden; functions (max 25 people incl up to 9 residential), conferences; croquet ♿ Wheelchair access to hotel (1 step) and restaurant, 2 ground-floor bedrooms, 1 room specially equipped for disabled people ● No children under 14; no dogs in some bedrooms; no smoking in bedrooms
▭ Amex, Delta, Diners, MasterCard, Switch, Visa £ Single £30 to £35, single occupancy of twin/double £40 to £79, twin/double £60 to £89; deposit required. Bar/bistro L £12, D £15; set L £17.50, D £23.50; alc L £17.50, D £23.50. Special breaks available

---

CHILLATON Devon   map 1

Quither Mill   [NEW ENTRY]

Quither, Chillaton, Tavistock PL19 0PZ
TEL: (01822) 860160

Perfect rural retreat in an old mill, handy for Dartmoor.

The road ends at Quither, so there's no need to worry about passing traffic at this beautiful old stone-built mill. There are a few houses around, but the main view from the hotel is of woods and pastures extending to the horizon. The huge mill-wheel dominates the front of the house, almost dwarfing the not insubstantial front door. Inside, the atmosphere is one of understated elegance in a family setting, with highly polished flags, solid antique furniture and beamed ceilings. One satisfied guest told us: 'The whole place exuded welcome, and the food was really something... The innovative way Mrs Wright prepares vegetables was memorable (at least I hope my wife can remember how!).' Misty, the old, grey, purring cat will show you around: the dining-room, where guests eat communally from a single huge table (you might have Quither Smokie – smoked haddock in a cheese sauce – followed by baked breast of turkey stuffed with rosemary and apricots); the lounge, with its great wood-burner and family pictures; and the breakfast room, where you can see the goings-on at the Aga through a hatch. Two of the bedrooms are in the house (the Pink Room is particularly nice, with toys adorning the low beams, to stop you banging your head) and one is in Owl Cottage, just outside. All are cottagey and comfortable, with luxurious extras such as heated towel-rails and good shower-rooms.

◑ Open all year　☑ From Tavistock (Bedford Square) follow Chillaton sign, forking left after 2 miles; after 3 miles, turn right for Quither. Private car park　🛏 1 twin, 2 double; one in annexe; all with bathroom/WC exc 1 twin with shower/WC; all with TV, hairdryer　✅ Dining-room, breakfast room, bar, lounge, garden　♿ No wheelchair access　● No children under 7; no dogs in public rooms; no smoking　▢ MasterCard, Visa　£ Single occupancy of twin/double £40, twin/double £60 to £70; deposit required. Set D £17.50

Tor Cottage　| NEW ENTRY |

Chillaton, Tavistock PL16 0JE
TEL: (01822) 860248　FAX: (01822) 860126
EMAIL: info@torcottage.demon.co.uk
WEB SITE: www.torcottage.demon.co.uk

Dreamy cottage in a lost valley, with surprisingly sumptuous rooms and plenty of extras.

This year we received many reports from readers praising 'an ideal location for a getaway luxury and pampered break' that had recently been opened by Maureen Rowlatt – it sounded so good, we had to go and investigate. About a year ago, Maureen decided that it was time to allow guests to experience the little haven that is Tor Cottage. So she set to work embellishing her dream home with splendid, private garden rooms, an outdoor pool, and every extra that you could possibly imagine in the bedrooms. A small stream flows through the bottom of the valley, from which the hills stretch upwards, covered in wild flowers, with 18 acres of bluebell woods, home to badgers, buzzards, ponies, deer and foxes. The garden is lit at night, and has a wild, lost feel to it – there's a frog pond, bamboo groves, and a hammock for total escapism. The cottage itself houses the foliage-filled conservatory, where guests take breakfast and, twice a week, supper – 'this is a place for people who care about what they eat', commends one reader. Maureen specialises in vegetarian cookery, but will happily cater for meat eaters. On the days when she doesn't conjure up a full dinner, a light tray supper is provided in your room. One of the bedrooms is up in the cottage's eaves – a sprigged, country-style room, with a good power shower and heated towel rails in the bathroom. Outside, in the converted outbuildings, the pick of the rooms is the sumptuous Garden Room, with its coir carpet, high, beamed ceiling, fully functional wood burner and fabulous blue sofa. The other rooms are no less plush: each has its own private garden (some less established than others), a fridge to store your booze in (it's a long way to the pub and the hotel is not licensed), fluffy bathrobes, a CD player, good linen, a torch, brolly, and a citronella candle with which to ward off insects on balmy nights. On top of all this is the 'Tor Cottage trug', which guests receive on arrival, containing bubbly, exotic fruit and home-made fudge. There's even a jacuzzi in the cottage for guests' use. As Maureen says, 'pampering is the order of the day here'.

◑ Closed 20 Dec to 4 Jan 🅿 In Chillaton, with pub and post office on left, drive up hill towards Tavistock; after 300 yards, take right turning signposted 'Bridlepath, No Public Vehicular Access'; hotel is ½ mile further, through second gate. Private car park
🛏 1 twin, 3 double; some in annexe; suites available; 2 with bathroom/WC, 2 with shower/WC; all with TV, room service, hair-dryer, CD player, fridge ⊘ Dining-room, 2 lounges, drying-room, conservatory, garden; fishing, heated outdoor swimming-pool
♿ No wheelchair access ● No children under 16; no dogs; no smoking ▭
MasterCard, Switch, Visa £ Single occupancy of twin/double £38, twin/double/suite £76; deposit required. Light suppers £7.50; set D (twice a week) £25. Special breaks available

---

CHIPPING CAMPDEN Gloucestershire   map 5

Cotswold House

The Square, Chipping Campden GL55 6AN
TEL: (01386) 840330 FAX: (01386) 840310
EMAIL: reception@cotswold-house.demon.co.uk
WEB SITE: www.cotswold-house.demon.co.uk

Imaginatively furnished town-house hotel, bang in the centre of arguably the finest Cotswolds town.

A stay in this wonderful, seventeenth-century, wool-merchant's house on the high street of this honey-pot, honey-stone town offers, as its name perhaps suggests, an intense Cotswolds experience. The traffic and crowds, and the sightseers in the hallway gawping at the splendid spiral staircase, may make you wish that you'd chosen somewhere more secluded. But then again, the large, immaculate walled garden, with its tulip-filled borders, and the refined drawing-room serve as effective bolt-holes from the hoi polloi, and the bedrooms facing the garden are peaceful. Most bedrooms are highly stylised: a very feminine one has bows and ribbons on the walls, another adopts a masculine, military theme, while a further room has Indian overtones in the minarets carved into the bedhead and the tigers painted on to the bathroom tiles. A new chef has taken over in the kitchen: reports, please, on his cooking. Dining options are the Garden Room Restaurant, where the food appears as elaborate as the stuccoed ceiling, and the less formal, voguishly rustic Forbes Brasserie (the hotel's hands-on owner is called Christopher Forbes) for grills, pastas, salads and tea-room fare.

◑ Closed Chr 🅿 From A44 between Moreton-in-Marsh and Broadway, 2 miles north on B4081. Private car park 🛏 3 single, 5 twin, 6 double, 1 four-poster; all with bathroom/WC exc 1 single with shower/WC; all with TV, room service, hair-dryer, trouser press, direct-dial telephone; no tea/coffee-making facilities in rooms
⊘ 2 restaurants, bar, 2 drawing-rooms, garden; conferences (max 30 people incl up to 15 residential), functions; croquet, golf nearby (reduced rates for guests); early suppers for children ♿ No wheelchair access ● No children under 7; no dogs; smoking in drawing-rooms only ▭ Amex, Delta, Diners, MasterCard, Switch, Visa £ Single

£55 to £75, single occupancy of twin/double £95 to £110, twin/double £120 to £150, four-poster £160; deposit required. Bar/bistro L £10, D £12; set Sun L £16.50, D £21.50; alc D £29.50. Special breaks available

---

CHITTLEHAMHOLT Devon

map 1

Highbullen

Chittlehamholt, Umberleigh EX37 9HD
TEL: (01769) 540561   FAX: (01769) 540492

Fine country-house hotel with some unusual features and excellent facilities, including an 18-hole golf course.

If you stay at Highbullen and don't participate in some sporting activity, whether it's golf, tennis (indoor or outdoor), squash, fishing, snooker, swimming, or simply walking in the beautiful parkland, you will definitely feel a bit left out. There are gentler pursuits available, such as croquet and indoor putting, but action is the order of the day. There's even an essential endeavour to be made inside the hotel, in the form of climbing up the viewing tower high above the splendid, Victorian-Gothic house, from where you are lord of all you survey. You can see the home farm and its outbuildings, as well as two other houses, Whitehall and Rowcliffes, all of which contain several bedrooms, and are surrounded by pretty gardens. The main house is an intriguing combination of traditional exterior, country-house-type ground-floor public rooms and bedrooms, and Swiss-chalet-style restaurant and bar. There is no formal reception – and service is informal and hands-off. A whole room is given over to the billiards table; the lounge has a most impressive picture window with views over the golf course, and is filled with comfy sofas and a sprinkling of antiques. Downstairs, in what were originally the cellars, is the Alpine-style bar, where pine furniture nestles in lots of subterranean nooks and alcoves. A spring dinner menu offered plenty of choice – perhaps smoked-haddock creams wrapped in smoked salmon, followed by loin of pork Perdita, cooked with apple juice and brandy, and served with crisp crackling and apple sauce. The bedrooms are spacious and elegant, with antique beds and good bathrooms.

◑ Open all year   ◲ Turn off B3226 (from South Molton) to Chittlehamholt; hotel is ½ mile beyond village, on right. Private car park   ↳ 1 single, 32 double; some in annexe; all with bathroom/WC; all with TV, hair-dryer, direct-dial telephone, room service in some parts of hotel   ✅ Restaurant, bar, lounge, drying-room, library, conservatory, games room, garden; conferences; fishing, golf, sauna, solarium, heated indoor swimming-pool, tennis, squash, croquet, billiards   ♿ No wheelchair access   ◗ No children under 8; no dogs   ⊟ Delta, Switch   £ Single £65 to £80, double £115 to £180 (rates incl dinner). Cooked B £3; bar/bistro L £5. Special breaks available

---

The text of the entries is based on inspections carried out anonymously, backed up by unsolicited reports sent in by readers. The factual details under the text are from questionnaires the Guide sends to all hotels that feature in the book.

Plough at Clanfield

Bourton Road, Clanfield, Bampton OX18 2RB
TEL: (01367) 810222   FAX: (01367) 810596

Extremely civilised accommodation in impossibly quaint, old house.

At the edge of the village of Clanfield sits the Plough, built in 1560, with blowsy roses and ivy climbing over its leaded windows, flower baskets hanging from its drunken gables, and eaves leaning this way and that. It used to be the local pub, as the name suggests – the eponymous plough lurks behind a hedge outside – but now it is a very English, very civilised, country hotel. Cream teas are taken in a garden which looks very much like a village green – the perfect place from which to admire the Plough's handsome, Elizabethan architecture. Inside, the mulberry-coloured carpets and beamed rooms create a formal atmosphere, although the arrangement of high-backed chairs in circles around shiny, antique, coffee tables in the lounge bar encourages conversation. Floral cushions and curtains complement the dried- and fresh-flower arrangements. There are cushioned window seats in the Tapestry dining-room, as well as plenty of well-spaced, round tables and the occasional decorative plate or brandy keg on the walls. Featuring on the fairly traditional, five-course dinner menu might be a light lobster bisque with white-truffle oil, followed by home-made granita, and then roast chump of English lamb with a pesto glaze and Madeira *jus*.

Plans are afoot for an extension housing seven more bedrooms; at present, the simpler bedrooms are better value than the four-posters, as smaller bedrooms do not necessarily mean smaller bathrooms. All are named after flowers and appropriately done out – Bluebell has a cute, patchwork quilt, and Primrose is yellow, with a solid four-poster.

◖ Closed 25 to 30 Dec   ▧ At junction of A4095 and A4020 at edge of Clanfield. Private car park ⬚⬚ 4 double, 1 four-poster, 1 four-poster suite; all with bathroom/WC; all with TV, room service, hair-dryer, trouser press, direct-dial telephone   ⬚ Dining-room, lounge/bar, drying-room, garden; functions (max 10 people incl up to 6 residential), conferences;   ⬚ No wheelchair access ● No children under 12; no dogs in bedrooms   ⬚ Amex, Delta, Diners, MasterCard, Switch, Visa   ⬚ Single occupancy of double £65 to £95, double £95, four-poster £110, suite £125; deposit required. Set L £17, D £32.50. Special breaks available

Grey Friar Lodge

Clappersgate, Ambleside LA22 9NE
TEL: (015394) 33158 (AND FAX)
EMAIL: gflodge@aol.com

A warm welcome awaits – as they say in some other guides. It's certainly true at this peaceful, homely, Victorian house near Ambleside.

Grey Friar Lodge has a number of pre-ordained advantages. The first is its setting, amid fine, well-kept grounds overlooking toothsome views of the Brathay Valley and conveniently located for exploring the central Lakes. The second is the handsome, period feel of the house – a capacious Victorian dwelling, dating from 1869, of classic Lakeland stone. The third, and most important, is the personalities of its owners, Sheila and Tony Sutton, who are unfailingly kind and friendly to their guests. Their enthusiasm for their home is infectious, and as they show you round you'll note all manner of personal touches. An eclectic jumble of antique weaponry, jugs, barometers and china in the hallway sets an appropriate tone for a house of this period, and the rest of the rooms are furnished in a pleasantly old-fashioned manner, with lots of ornaments and pictures, and antiques here and there. Several rooms have lovely views; all are comfortable and personalised with good facilities, and one has a four-poster. The hearty, no-choice dinners accompanied by pre-selected wines are a winning formula, too, with Sheila's home-made chocolates presenting a final flourish. The tariff is very reasonable for such attentive, unpretentious hospitality.

◑ Closed Nov to Feb, weekdays Feb to Easter ▱ On A593, 1½ miles west of Ambleside. Private car park ⊨ 2 twin, 5 double, 1 four-poster; all with bathroom/WC exc 2 doubles with shower/WC; all with TV, hair-dryer ⌀ Dining-room, 2 lounges, drying-room, garden; ⅃ No wheelchair access ● No children under 10; no dogs; no smoking in bedrooms; smoking in 1 lounge only ☐ None accepted £ Single occupancy of twin/double £34 to £37, twin/double £57 to £63, four-poster £61 to £67; deposit required. Set D £17.50. Special breaks available

Nanny Brow [NEW ENTRY]

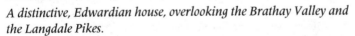

Clappersgate, Ambleside LA22 9NF
TEL: (015394) 32036   FAX: (015934) 32450

A distinctive, Edwardian house, overlooking the Brathay Valley and the Langdale Pikes.

Situated in a lush, wooded valley a mile or two from Ambleside, this country-house hotel occupies a sizeable plot of sloping, mature gardens, reached by a sharply angled drive (take care as you emerge on to the main road). It's a fine example of Edwardian building, designed at the turn of the century as an architect's residence; inside and out, the elegance of that gracious age shines through in the generous, domesticated proportions. The Edwardian style suits many country-house hotels very well, and Nanny Brow is no exception. The instantly welcoming entrance hall ushers visitors into a tranquil drawing-room, whose beautiful plasterwork was sadly damaged by 1998's New-Year storms and is now due for an expensive renovation. The restaurant opposite is in similar, period style, while a small, but stylishly contemporary, bar towards the rear of the building adds a limited amount of extra seating for pre- and post-dinner drinks. The bedrooms vary considerably, from spacious, ornate suites to modern and more standard rooms. They have been described as pedestrian – more reports, please.

○ Open all year ⊿ On A593 1½ miles west of Ambleside, towards Coniston/ Langdale. Private car park ⊫ 7 twin, 2 four-poster, 3 family rooms, 6 suites; all with bathroom/WC; all with TV, room service, hair-dryer, trouser press, direct-dial telephone; no tea/coffee-making facilities in rooms ⦸ Restaurant, bar, drawing-room, drying-room, garden; functions (max 75 people incl up to 36 residential), conferences; fishing, solarium, croquet, leisure facilities nearby (free for guests); early suppers for children; cots, high chairs, babysitting, baby-listening ⅙ No wheelchair access ● No children under 12 in restaurant eves; no dogs in public rooms; no smoking in restaurant and some bedrooms ⊟ Amex, Delta, Diners, MasterCard, Switch, Visa ⊡ Single occupancy of twin £55, twin £110, four-poster £130, family room/suite £120; deposit required. Set D £20.50/£27.50. Special breaks available

---

CLEARWELL Gloucestershire   map 2

Tudor Farmhouse

Clearwell, Coleford GL16 8JS
TEL: (01594) 833046   FAX: (01594) 837093
EMAIL: reservations@tudorfarmhse.u-net.com

Snug hotel in a splendid, old building on the edge of the Forest of Dean.

This pinkish-stone, former farmhouse, in the centre of a pretty village with a Gothic castle, is as characterful as its name suggests. Owners Deborah and Richard Fletcher, a youngish, enthusiastic team, have allowed the building's antiquity – expressed in plentiful oak panelling, black beams, latch doors and a spiral, wooden staircase – to set the tone. A stay here is a fairly intimate experience, since the restaurant and sitting-room are dainty and compact. The candlelit dinners, offered on a wide-ranging table d'hôte menu that is supplemented by a separately priced grills menu, are hearty, mainstream, country-house fare: maybe Brie fried in breadcrumbs and crushed almonds, baked lamb in a herb pastry and treacle tart. The bedrooms in the main house can be small and quite simple, but are enormously characterful. More comfortable accommodation is available in the smartly converted cottages and stables out at the back. Of these, good choices are the Cottage Suite, which spreads over two floors and has a mini-kitchen, and the Cottage Room, a vaulted affair with an ecclesiastical feel. Since Deborah gave birth to twins, the Fletchers claim to be more child-friendly, and will arrange babysitting and special early meals.

○ Closed 23 to 30 Dec; restaurant closed Sun eve ⊿ 3 miles off A466 between Chepstow and Monmouth. Private car park ⊫ 2 single, 6 double, 2 four-poster, 3 suites; some in annexe; family rooms available; 7 with bathroom/WC, 6 with shower/WC; all with TV, hair-dryer, direct-dial telephone ⦸ Restaurant, bar, sitting-room, drying-room, conservatory, garden; early suppers for children; cots, high chairs, babysitting ⅙ No wheelchair access ● No children in restaurant after 6.30pm; dogs in some bedrooms only, by arrangement; no smoking in restaurant and some bedrooms ⊟ Amex, Delta, MasterCard, Switch, Visa ⊡ Single £49, single occupancy of double £49, double £58, four-poster £68, family room from £78, suite £80 to £90 (prices valid till Feb 1999); deposit required. Set D £19; alc D £22.50. Special breaks available

Cleeve Hill Hotel

Cleeve Hill, Cheltenham GL52 3PR
TEL: (01242) 672052   FAX: (01242) 679969

Comfortable and thoroughly tasteful B&B, offering fine views and breakfasts.

The hillside position of this gabled, Edwardian house compensates for some traffic noise from the B-road that passes by it and its distance – a ten-minute drive – from Cheltenham. It luxuriates in long views across the valley to the Malvern Hills to the front, while the grassy Cleeve Common rises directly behind it, crossed by the Cotswolds Way. John Enstone, once a BA pilot, and his wife Marian offer refined but unpretentious accommodation (their house is not really a hotel but a B&B). An open-plan airiness pervades the downstairs, where a conservatory breakfast room with a tent-effect ceiling lies off a roomy, L-shaped sitting-room-cum-bar. The substantial breakfasts feature eggs and mushrooms from local farms, plus a cornucopia of choices that even extends to milk of varying creaminess. The bedrooms – typically large and spotless – sport smart, co-ordinated fabrics, dark, reproduction furniture and a pile of fluffy towels; most overlook the valley (including Room 8, a good choice on account of its big, bay window). An otherwise positive report points out that the flight of steps leading up from the car park makes the establishment unsuitable for those with restricted mobility.

◗ Closed Chr ⤢ Between Prestbury and Winchcombe on B4632, 2½ miles from Cheltenham. Private car park ⤶ 1 single, 2 twin, 5 double, 1 family room; all with bathroom/WC; all with TV, hair-dryer, direct-dial telephone; trouser press on request ⬧ Breakfast room, sitting-room/bar, garden ♿ No wheelchair access ◐ No children under 8; no dogs; no smoking ▭ MasterCard, Visa ⬰ Single £50, single occupancy of twin/double £55 to £65, twin/double £65 to £80, family room £90; deposit required.

Plough Inn

Abingdon Road, Clifton Hampden, Abingdon OX14 3EG
TEL: (01865) 407811   FAX: (01865) 407136

Historical inn, bursting with character and good bedrooms.

The front portion of this delightful pub may be Georgian, but the rest of it, judging by the chunky, low, oak beams and the thatched roof, is much older, possibly dating back to Plantagenet times. One satisfied guest reports that he stayed in the large, ground-floor room in the 'new' (AD *circa* 1500) cottage annexe – which shows the historical context – and found the place 'a great success'. The Plough Inn is popular with locals and visitors alike: despite the no-smoking policy, you'll see them propping up the bar, engaging in conversation, or simply soaking up the cosy atmosphere around the roaring fire in the (hopefully not aptly named) Hangover Bar. They are in fascinating company:

Hampden Room is so named because John Hampden, cousin of Oliver Cromwell and instigator of the Civil War, is reputed to have visited the Plough Inn and to have rested in this little parlour. Compliments abound about the food: 'outstanding', said one replete diner. Dinner is a romantic occasion, with candles and a pretty view over the patio and garden; on the tasty, traditional menu might be smoked trout, followed by grilled fillet of beef with a wild-mushroom and port sauce, and then, if you've room, a sticky toffee pudding. All the eight four-poster bedrooms are done out extremely stylishly and with much charm. 'Staff brilliant,' concludes our reporter, who also enthused about the big bathroom and fresh milk.

◑ Open all year ⤢ In village centre, on A415. Private car park ⤺ 2 double, 8 four-poster, 1 family room; some in annexe; 7 with shower/WC; 4 with bathroom/WC; all with TV, room service, hair-dryer, trouser press, direct-dial telephone, some with mini-bar ✧ 2 restaurants, bar, lounge, TV room, garden; functions (max 400 people incl up to 22 residential), conferences; early suppers for children; cots, high chairs, babysitting, baby-listening ⬇ Wheelchair access to hotel and restaurants, WC (unisex), 5 ground-floor bedrooms, 1 room specially equipped for disabled people ⬤ No dogs; no smoking; ▭ Delta, MasterCard, Switch, Visa ⌂ Single occupancy of double/four-poster £55, double/four-poster £75, family room £95; deposit required. Bar/bistro L £6, D £13; alc L £21

Bailiffscourt

Climping, Littlehampton BN17 5RW
TEL: (01903) 723511   FAX: (01903) 723107

Seeing is believing at this impressively realistic, and luxurious, medieval manor house.

Prepare to enter the land of make believe, where nothing is as it appears. Approaching this golden-stone building, with its leaded windows and low roof, you'd be forgiven for thinking that you were entering a medieval manor house. In fact, all this (with the exception of the Norman chapel) was built in the 'thirties, albeit from authentic materials retrieved from derelict buildings across England. Inside, the illusion is even better, with rough-hewn walls, richly embroidered tapestries, low doorways and stone-flagged floors. A series of cosy, intimate rooms serves as a lounge and, at the end of one authentically echoing corridor, a hefty, studded door leads to the beamed restaurant, where fricasee of lobster cooked with tomato and basil might be followed by fillet of beef under a horseradish crust, with a white-wine and shallot sauce. Each of the bedrooms (all named after serfs who worked the land many moons ago) is individually and stylishly decorated, with almost a little too much panache. Many have four-poster beds, and six their own open fireplaces. Baylies, with its cavernous, beamed ceiling and twin baths, remains a firm favourite. More rooms are in the outer buildings, with Thatch House linked to the main house by an underground passage. One couple was 'dismayed' to find themselves in the midst of a corporate pigeon shoot, when they had looked forward to peace and indulgence, and found the management dismissive of their complaints. At these prices, one would expect perfection.

◑ Open all year ⛽ In Climping, just off A259, 4 miles south of Arundel. Private car park 🛏 1 single, 1 twin, 15 double, 13 four-poster, 1 family room, 1 four-poster suite; some in annexe; all with bathroom/WC; all with TV, room service, hair-dryer, direct-dial telephone, some with trouser press ✅ Restaurant, bar, 3 lounges, drying-room, games room, garden; functions (max 40 people incl up to 15 residential), conferences; civil wedding licence; heated outdoor swimming-pool, tennis, snooker, shooting; early suppers for children; cots, high chairs, baby-listening ♿ No wheelchair access ⬤ No smoking in restaurant; no dogs in bedrooms ▭ Amex, Delta, Diners, MasterCard, Switch, Visa £ Single £120, single occupancy of twin/double £120, twin/double £135, four-poster £220, family room £175, suite £300; deposit required. Bar/bistro L £6; set L £19.50, D £33.50; alc D £40. Special breaks available

---

CLUN Shropshire   map 7

Birches Mill

Clun, Craven Arms SY7 8NL
TEL: (01588) 640409 (AND FAX)

Inexpensive, hideaway guesthouse in a seventeenth-century Welsh Marches mill.

Gill Della Casa and Andrew Farmer emigrated from London to this extremely tranquil spot about three miles from Clun some five years ago. It's easy to see how they were seduced by the old mill with its deeply pitched slate roof and three acres of meadows and gardens and gurgling stream. Space is at a premium in the dinky, beamy interior, so the dining-room, with inglenook fire and flagstone floor, doubles as the sitting-room. The three pretty bedrooms share one communal bathroom; they do, however, come with pleasing pine furniture and maybe brass beds or patchwork quilts, as well as basins and a basket of Body Shop goodies. Breakfast includes freshly squeezed orange juice, home-made muesli and a vast array of home-made jams, while for dinner (by arrangement) you might have local asparagus, then barbecued chicken with tabbouleh, and home-made ice-cream; bring your own booze.

◑ Closed Nov to Mar ⛽ Leave Clun on A488 to Bishops Castle; take first left signposted to Bicton, then second left (signposted Mainstone). Birches Mill is first right after Llanhedric Farm. Private car park 🛏 1 twin, 2 double; no tea/coffee-making facilities in rooms ✅ Dining-room/sitting-room, drying-room, garden; ♿ No wheelchair access ⬤ No children under 8; no dogs or smoking ▭ None accepted £ Single occupancy of twin/double £28, twin/double £42; deposit required. Set D £16

 This denotes that the hotel is in an exceptionally peaceful situation where you can be assured of a restful stay.

Where we say 'Deposit required', a hotel may instead ask for your credit card details when taking your booking.

COCKERMOUTH Cumbria   map 10

Low Hall   **NEW ENTRY**

Brandlingill, Cockermouth CA13 0RE
TEL: (01900) 826654
EMAIL: ludd@msn.com

*Friendly B&B accommodation in a seventeenth-century farmhouse,
with good cooking and quiet, pastoral surroundings.*

A drive across farmland from one of the minor roads near Lorton Vale takes you
to this charming and inviting place owned by Enid Davies and her husband
Hugh (an anaesthetist). Well-behaved dogs may greet new arrivals; after that,
you'll probably find Enid at home, and within minutes you'll feel at ease in this
peaceful house. Two acres of paddocks and tidy gardens with a stream running
through them surround Low Hall, and in fine weather you may be able to enjoy
tea outside. The house is well furnished and smartly decorated throughout, and
includes plenty of objects of personal interest: family photos deck the
sitting-room furniture, and a Noah's Ark menagerie made from Ambleside
pottery makes a talking point on the windowsill. The three thoughtfully
equipped bedrooms have fresh, floral décor and some older-style furnishings, as
well as good bathrooms. Food is an important part of Low Hall's hospitality. No
dinners are served, but breakfast is a substantial feast of porridge, home-made
muesli and oatcakes, compotes and croissants, and over 20 kinds of tea, as well
as such hot dishes as Turkish eggs or bacon butties. Vegetarians are generously
catered for, too. Plenty of books and maps point out local places to explore.

◑ Open all year (exc owners' holidays)   ⊿ From A66 at Cockermouth, take A5086
towards Egremont; after 1 mile, turn left by school towards Lorton; take second right
(signposted Low Hall) and follow lane to hotel. Private car park   ⤶ 1 twin, 2 double;
twin with bathroom/WC, doubles with shower/WC; some with TV; hair-dryer on
request   ⊘ Dining-room, sitting-room, TV room, garden   ⅚ No wheelchair access
◓ No children under 10; well behaved dogs welcome but must sleep in cars; no
smoking   ▭ MasterCard, Visa   £ Single occupancy of twin/double £25, twin/double
£50 to £60

Toddell Cottage   **NEW ENTRY**

Brandlingill, Cockermouth CA13 0RB
TEL: (01900) 828696 (AND FAX)

Friendly, family-run, cottage accommodation, with designer flair.

Mike and Janet Wright recently exchanged the flight paths near Heathrow for a
dream cottage tucked away in the deep-green countryside south of Cockermouth. Small wonder, then, that they exude contentment at every turn.
Turning Mike's professional design skills to good use, the Wrights have
converted this 300-year-old, listed Cumbrian longhouse, with black-edged
windows, into an unexpectedly stylish B&B. It's a new way of life, but
hospitality comes naturally to them, particularly at mealtimes. Dinners comprise
three-course, set menus, featuring appetising-sounding dishes like smoked-fish

pie and sticky toffee pudding, while breakfasts offer a generous range of fare, from Mike's Irish porridge to apple pancakes or omelettes Arnold Bennett. Janet combines inventive cooking with a sideline in reflexology and aromatherapy, so aching muscles can be soothed, too. The small dining-room and lounge are simple, but charming, rooms, with corkscrew beams and stone fireplaces. Stencilled decorations adorn the landing and bedroom walls. The cosy bedrooms have modern pine fittings and sparkling bathrooms, with unusual ceramic basins made by a local potter; one has a Japanese-style half-bath. Cottage gardens to the back of the house lead towards woods and a stream, which Sid, the cat, no doubt regards as happy hunting grounds.

◑ Open all year ⤇ From A66 at Cockermouth, take A5086 towards Egremont; after 1 mile turn left at crossroads by school, then first right signposted Brandlingill. Cottage is 1 mile along, on right. Private car park ⬫ 1 single/bunk-bedded (let to children), 1 double, 1 family room; 2 with shower/WC; all with TV, hair-dryer ⟡ Dining-room, lounge, drying-room, garden ⟁ No wheelchair access ● No children under 5; no dogs; no smoking ▭ None accepted £ Single (children only: 5–9 £10, 10–16 £15), double £37 to £40, family room £52 to £57; deposit required. Set D £13.50. (Prices valid till Jan 1999.) Special breaks available

---

COGGESHALL **Essex**   map 3

White Hart

Market End, Coggeshall, Colchester CO6 1NH
TEL: (01376) 561654   FAX: (01376) 561789

An Italian influence to the food amid comfortable traditional English country-inn surroundings.

The White Hart is one of the grandest and most historic buildings in this sleepy, but picturesque, East Anglian village, but it also has an unexpected cosmopolitan touch. For many years it's had an exclusively Italian menu in the restaurant and, although ownership has changed in the last year, this tradition continues; several of the staff are Italian, too. Otherwise the hotel, including the decoration, is quintessentially English. Behind the front windows is as traditional a pub as you could find, supported by solid oak beams and, at the furthest and presumably warmest end, a huge brick fireplace. At the back of the hotel is the long restaurant, with low, beamed ceilings and small windows that look on to a courtyard. Upstairs, the residents' lounge is well worth a look – part of the old hall is set around a huge fireplace with well-used but comfortable sofas and armchairs. The bedrooms feature strong patterns, bold colour and well-appointed bathrooms.

◑ Open all year; restaurant closed Sun eve ⤇ From A12 follow signs through Kelvedon, then take B1024 to Coggeshall. Private car park ⬫ 2 single, 3 twin, 13 double; all with bathroom/WC; all with TV, hair-dryer, trouser press, direct-dial telephone ⟡ Restaurant, bar, lounge, garden; functions (max 20 people incl up to 18 residential), conferences; cots ⟁ No wheelchair access ▭ Amex, MasterCard, Switch, Visa £ Single £62, single occupancy of twin/double £67, twin/double £97; deposit required. Bar/bistro L, D £15; set L, D £15; alc L, D £18.50

COLCHESTER **Essex** map 3

Hockley Place

Rectory Road, Frating, Colchester CO7 7HG
TEL: (01206) 251703 (AND FAX)

A sumptuous house, in delightful grounds, run by its helpful owner as a Wolsey Lodge.

Aficionados of English architecture will appreciate the clean lines and cool, high-ceilinged interiors of this Lutyens-style house. While this is still Helen Bowles' family home, it has all the trappings of a country-house hotel. You approach it down a rhododendron walk – at its best in May and June – and there is a heated swimming-pool, a gymnasium equipped with a multi-gym, and a croquet lawn for those who like to enjoy sport with a large gin and tonic to hand. The spacious public rooms have been attentively decorated, and original features, such as the exposed, oak beams in the dining-room and the broad, Austrian-oak staircase, make the house enormously individualistic. The set evening meal might include mackerel in an orange sauce, followed by poussin stuffed with garlic cream cheese, grapes and brandy, and then rhubarb brûlée. Helen can also cater for special diets, such as gluten-free and kosher. The bedrooms all have a high standard of decoration, with matching curtains and bedspreads, while two of the rooms have extra-long beds for tall guests.

◑ Open all year ◪ From Colchester take A133 towards Clacton-on-Sea; turn off at B1029 signposted Brightlingsea; turn first right into Rectory Road. Private car park 🛏 2 twin, 1 double, 1 family room; all with bathroom/WC exc 1 twin with shower/WC; all with TV, hair-dryer, trouser press ⌀ Dining-room, lounge, TV room, library, garden; gym, heated outdoor swimming-pool, croquet; early suppers for children ᵹ No wheelchair access ● No children under 12; no dogs; no smoking ▭ Amex, Delta, Diners, MasterCard, Switch, Visa £ Single occupancy of twin/double £40, twin/double £60, family room £80; deposit required. Set D £20

COLERNE **Wiltshire** map 2

Lucknam Park

Colerne, Chippenham SN14 8AZ
TEL: (01225) 742777 FAX: (01225) 743536
EMAIL: 106312,3342@compuserve.com

Top-notch country house, with magnificent grounds and impressive leisure facilities.

The mature beech trees which proudly flank the mile-long avenue that winds up to the Palladian elegance of this fine house hold the promise of something special. And the house lives up to its name: Lucknam Park's restrained eighteenth-century façade is surrounded by 280 acres of parkland, and, as you explore, you'll discover sweeping lawns, stately terraces, an exquisite courtyard and lovely walled garden. Architecturally, the house, though large, is quietly dignified rather than off-puttingly grand. Once within, there's a plethora of places in which to unwind, from the civilised, panelled library, where architectural prints complement the interesting selection of old books that lines the shelves, to the bow-fronted drawing-room, where a confidently sunny colour scheme highlights the intricacies of the cornicing and provides a more modern counterpoint to the richly traditional furnishings and drapes. A concerto of chimes from a notable collection of clocks hails the hour. If you like to lace your relaxation with rather more activity, there's a swimming-pool and gym area where you can work up an appetite.

Dinner is served beneath crystal chandeliers and a painted ceiling in the former ballroom. The food comes with a hefty price tag: perhaps cannelloni of lobster, tomato and basil, followed by roast Trelough duck with beetroot sauce and savoyard potatoes, then apple charlotte. The bedrooms, which are split between the main house and a courtyard block, are tastefully furnished and decorated in a variety of modish styles. The bathrooms are luxurious.

○ Open all year ⊉ 6 miles north-east of Bath; ¼ mile from crossroads for Colerne. Private car park ⊫ 1 single, 11 double, 18 twin/double, 3 twin/double suites, 8 four-poster suites; some in annexe; family rooms available; all with bathroom/WC; all with TV, room service, hair-dryer, direct-dial telephone ⊘ 2 restaurants, bar (at leisure spa), drawing-room, library, games room, garden; functions (max 120 people incl up to 80 residential), conferences; civil wedding licence; gym, sauna, solarium, heated indoor swimming-pool, tennis, clay-pigeon shooting, croquet, equestrian centre, beauty salon, whirlpool spa; early suppers for children; cots, high chairs, babysitting ⅋ Wheelchair access to hotel (1 step) and restaurants, WC (unisex), some ground-floor bedrooms ● No children under 12 in restaurants eves; no dogs; no smoking in restaurants ⊟ Amex, Delta, Diners, MasterCard, Switch, Visa ⊡ Single £130, single occupancy of twin/double £160, twin/double £160 to £265, suites (incl four-poster) £355 to £625, family rooms: room rate + £25 per child; deposit required. Continental B £11, cooked B £18; bar/bistro L £24; set D £40; alc D £57. Special breaks available

COLN ST ALDWYNS Gloucestershire   map 2

New Inn

Coln St Aldwyns, Cirencester GL7 5AN
TEL: (01285) 750651   FAX: (01285) 750657
EMAIL: stay@new-inn.co.uk
WEB SITE: www.new-inn.co.uk/

Up-market inn, with designer bedrooms and interesting food.

This establishment's name is a misnomer if there ever was one – the creeper-clad, Elizabethan inn fits seamlessly into this somnolent, Cotswolds village that is close geographically to Bibury but far removed in atmosphere. Throughout the compact establishment – whether in the traditional bar, with its red-tiled floor, black beams and hops hanging from the ceiling, or in the dainty restaurant and petite, flagstoned sitting-room – the ambience is one of understated civility. The professional, uniformed staff meet the demands of a largely smart, Gloucestershire-set clientele. While the table d'hôte restaurant menu is pithy and sophisticated, the eclectic bar menu delivers such pub staples as fish and chips, along with more fancy options like chargrilled smoked salmon with a pineapple salsa and pickled ginger. The interior-designing skills of Sandra-Anne Evans, one of the owners, are much in evidence in the high-quality, bijou bedrooms.

Worth considering are the multi-beamed Winson, with its offbeat, vaulted bathroom, and, in an outbuilding, Windrush, the only room with a king-sized bed and its own patio.

◑ Open all year ⊉ Between Bibury (B4425) and Fairford (A417), 8 miles east of Cirencester. Private car park ⤙ 1 single, 2 twin, 6 double, 1 four-poster, 1 family room, 3 suites; some in annexe; most with bathroom/WC, some with shower/WC; all with TV, room service, hair-dryer, direct-dial telephone, some with trouser press ⌸ Restaurant, bar, sitting-room; conferences (max 12 people incl up to 10 residential); early suppers for children ⅙ Wheelchair access to hotel and restaurant, WC (unisex), 1 ground-floor bedroom ● No children under 10 in restaurant eves; dogs in bar only; no smoking in restaurant or bedrooms ▭ Amex, Delta, MasterCard, Switch, Visa £ Single £65, single occupancy of twin/double £78, twin/double/four-poster £93, family room £111, suite £110; deposit required. Bar/bistro L, D £8 to £12.50; set L £15.50 (Sun), £26.50, D £26.50. Special breaks available

---

COLYFORD Devon
map 2

Swallows Eaves

Colyford, Colyton EX13 6QJ
TEL: (01297) 553184   FAX: (01297) 553574

Spruce, well-kept hotel in quiet village, run with enthusiasm and charm.

They knew how to build houses in those days: the well-proportioned rooms at this hotel make the best of the sunlight, and the interior has a calm, composed feel about it. Those days were the late 'twenties, so the house has had plenty of time to establish itself, as has the wistaria, which climbs up the pebble-dashed walls to the gables and eaves. Unfortunately, the hotel is set near the road, but the gardens are simple and smart, with manicured lawns and blowsy roses. Inside, pastels and subdued colours predominate, which makes room for the ebullient personality of Jane Beck, who, together with her husband Jon, makes Swallows Eaves a very pleasant, friendly place in which to stay. The chairs in the small lounge are placed in a circle, so guests 'have to talk to each other', and dinner is served in the best room in the house – it is airy, with a stripped wooden floor, and a separate sitting area for pre-dinner drinks. On the (limited-choice) menu might be fresh asparagus spears with butter, followed by fillet of beef prepared with grain mustard and white wine, and then an orange and brandy syllabub. Upstairs, the bedrooms are well turned-out, with quality fabrics and perfectly formed bathrooms. Look out for the rabbits in the back yard!

◑ Closed Dec to Feb ⊉ On A3052 Lyme Regis to Sidmouth road; in centre of village. Private car park ⤙ 4 twin, 4 double; all with bathroom/WC, exc 2 doubles with shower/WC; all with TV, room service, hair-dryer ⌸ Dining-room, lounge, garden; leisure facilities nearby (free for guests), sauna, solarium at small extra charge ⅙ No wheelchair access ● No children under 14; no dogs; no smoking ▭ Delta, Switch, Visa £ Single occupancy of twin/double £50 to £58, twin/double £70 to £78. Set D £21. Special breaks available

Trengilly Wartha   NEW ENTRY

Nancenoy, Constantine, Falmouth TR11 5RP
TEL: (01326) 340332 (AND FAX)
EMAIL: trengilly@compuserve.com

Straightforward country inn, serving up excellent food in back-of-beyond location.

Trengilly Wartha really is lost in a tangle of narrow lanes and hidden valleys in deepest, darkest Cornwall. Its name means 'settlement above the trees' – *in* the trees would be more appropriate, as it clings on to the wooded hillside and has steeply banked gardens. The eighteenth-century farmhouse now serves as a hostelry for locals, as well as a good eatery and place to stay for those exploring the region. There are real ales and ciders aplenty, along with lots of wines by the glass or bottle (a huge sign by the wine display proclaims 'Drink here or take away'). You can eat in the low-beamed, friendly bar, or in the more formal, French-style restaurant, where an innovative menu might offer a twice-baked soufflé of Devon blue cheese served on a red-pepper coulis, followed by roast guinea-fowl on a bed of roasted root vegetables with a beetroot sauce. Coffee and home-made petits fours are taken in the welcoming guests' lounge, which is well stocked with old pine dressers full of books and games, and is sprucely done out in dark pinks. The bedrooms, while well decorated, tend to be on the small size, and have functional, but not stylish, bathrooms, making this a place for a good meal and overnight stop rather than a long stay.

◐ Open all year; restaurant closed 25 Dec   ☑ Follow signs to Constantine; take Gweek road out of village by Spar shop. Hotel is signposted off that road, 1 mile out of village. Private car park   🛏 2 twin, 4 double, 2 family rooms; some in annexe; 6 with bathroom/WC, 1 with shower/WC; all with TV, direct-dial telephone   ⌀ Restaurant, bar, lounge, drying-room, games room, conservatory, garden; functions (max 28 people incl up to 18 residential), conferences; early suppers for children; cots, high chairs, toys, baby-listening   ♿ No wheelchair access   ● Dogs £1 per day in bedrooms; no smoking in some public rooms and some bedrooms   ▭ Amex, Delta, Diners, MasterCard, Switch, Visa   £ Single occupancy of twin/double £34 to £44, twin/double £48 to £80, family room £80 to £90; deposit required. Bar/bistro L £8, D £12; set D £17.50/£21.50. Special breaks available

Inn on the Green   NEW ENTRY

The Old Cricket Common, Cookham Dean SL6 9NZ
TEL: (01628) 482638   FAX: (01628) 487474

Great combination of modern styling and traditional materials in a village hideaway.

Heaven knows how one would play cricket on Cookham Dean's common – better just to head for the far boundary of the expanse of deep divots and rough grass, where this reinvented hostelry stands. The mock-Tudor timbering, multiple gables and creeper cladding appear suitably traditional for this quiet village, which is tucked away in the woody heights within a wide turn of the Thames. Yet inside you'll find scrubbed-pine, art-deco statuettes and a shelf of fine Armagnacs to complement the woodwormed timbers, beer jugs and real ale. You can dine off white damask under a brass chandelier, or in the more informal surroundings of wooden planking and brick fireplaces. The food, too, springs appealing surprises, with foie gras appearing pan-fried on top of brioche, wild boar roasted in a honey and soy-sauce glaze, and old culinary chestnuts like Black Forest gâteau converted into cherry ice-cream with a kirsch-soaked chocolate sponge. The bedrooms are divided between the inn itself (fairly plain at the time of our spring inspection, but spacious), a bungalow in the courtyard (featuring lots of antique pine and lacy, white linen) and a convincingly reconstructed outbuilding (full of characterful timbers, more antique pine and stylish bathrooms contrasting grey slate and white porcelain). The new ideas work well with the traditional materials, and Neil Grice and his chief of staff, Jane Godsalve, run a smooth operation with polished informality.

○ Open all year ⤢ Entering Cookham Dean from Marlow, follow road past Chequers pub on left and Hendersons Coachworks ¼ mile further on; take next right turn into Hills Lane and follow lane; turn right at memorial cross; hotel is at end of road. Private car park ⤒ 1 single, 3 twin, 3 double, 1 four-poster; some in annexe; family rooms available; all with bathroom/WC; all with TV, room service, some with hair-dryer ✓ Restaurant, bar, lounge, conservatory, function room, garden; functions (max 100 people incl up to 15 residential), conferences; civil wedding licence; early suppers for children; cots, high chairs, outdoor play area ⅙ No wheelchair access ● No dogs ▭ Amex, Delta, MasterCard, Switch, Visa £ Single £50, single occupancy of twin/double £55 to £70, twin/double/family room £70 to £90, four-poster £80; deposit required. Bar/bistro L £7; set L, D £16/£21; alc L, D £25

COPTHORNE West Sussex map 3

The Copthorne NEW ENTRY

Copthorne Way, Copthorne, Crawley RH10 3PG
TEL: (01342) 714971   FAX: (01342) 717375
EMAIL: sales.coplgw@mill-cop.com
WEB SITE: www.mill-cop.com/

Surprisingly amiable business hotel, with great facilities, near Gatwick and the M23.

This is a rarity in the world of business hotels: somewhere that manages to deliver the goods with regard to efficiency and comfort without becoming sterile and faceless. Most of the hotel was built in the early 'seventies, around a sixteenth-century house which still survives as the White Swan pub. Timbers from demolished farm outbuildings were used, so the new parts blend with the old quite successfully, giving the rooms more character than you'd expect. Of the two restaurants, the Lion D'Or is infinitely better than the Brasserie, and the menu might include roasted-tomato and red-pepper soup, followed by grilled scallops with marinated vegetables. The standard bedrooms come in two guises: classic or superior, both fitted with all the expected facilities. The décor tends to be on the masculine side – lots of burgundy, green and brown is in evidence –

and the odd rustic beam makes an appearance. The newer, connoisseur rooms are a cut above the rest, with their corner whirlpool baths (complete with a family of rubber ducks), modem points, king-sized beds, ironing boards and late check-out time (4pm) as standard; some even have four-posters. There is also a fully equipped leisure complex and extensive grounds for guests' use, plus a shuttle bus to the airport between 6am and midnight. The service is efficient without being impersonal, and there's always someone around to help first-timers who might get lost in the seemingly labyrinthine series of corridors.

◑ Open all year; Lion D'Or restaurant closed Sun eve ⤧ From M25, take Junction 8 on to M23 towards Brighton; then Junction 10 on to A264 towards East Grinstead; after 1 mile, take third exit on first roundabout, signposted Copthorne Hotel. Private car park (short-term, free), long-term secure parking, off-site (£3.35 per day) ⤙ 5 single, 66 twin, 144 double, 4 family rooms, 8 suites (6 with four-poster); all with bathroom/WC; all with satellite TV, room service, hair-dryer, mini-bar, trouser press, direct-dial telephone, some with modem point, ironing facilities ⌖ 2 restaurants, 2 bars, lounge/conservatory, 13 meeting/banqueting rooms, garden; conferences (max 110 people residential/non-residential), functions; civil wedding licence; gym, sauna, solarium, heated indoor swimming-pool, tennis, putting green, croquet, jogging trail, squash, ricochet; early suppers for children; cots, high chairs, babysitting, outdoor play area ♿ Wheelchair access to hotel (ramp) and restaurants, WC (unisex), 134 ground-floor bedrooms, 1 room specially equipped for disabled people ● No dogs in public rooms; no smoking in some bedrooms ▭ Amex, Delta, Diners, MasterCard, Switch, Visa £ Single £115, single occupancy of twin/double £115, twin/double £125, family room £155, suite £155 to £225; deposit required. Continental B £9.50, cooked B £12; bar/bistro L, D £16; set L, D £17; alc L, D £30. (Prices valid till Sept 1998.) Special breaks available

---

Corndene

Coreley, Ludlow SY8 3AW
TEL: (01584) 890324 FAX: (01584) 890324

Simple but comfortable B&B in the lovely south Shropshire hills, with excellent facilities for disabled guests.

Clare and David Currant's rambling, creeper-covered, Georgian-with-Victorian-additions home is an unusual example of how a B&B can offer considerable comfort in plainly furnished surroundings. Though bedrooms are decked out in unfussy, modern pine, woodchip walls and rather dowdy carpet tiles, they are extremely practical. All three are on the ground floor and have full wheelchair access and specially adapted bathrooms with giant showers. About half the Currants' bookings come from disabled people, but their consideration extends equally to all visitors, with offers of fresh milk and ironing facilities and a useful, fully equipped guests' kitchen. Evening meals are no longer available, but breakfasts, served in a little gingham-clothed dining-room, are carefully prepared and ample. French windows in two bedrooms and the sunny sitting-room lead on to Corndene's lovely, bosky grounds that incorporate a pond, meadow, small wood and two life-size, equine statues made of willow twigs. The surrounding hilly countryside, criss-crossed by a maze of high-sided lanes that feel more Devonian than Salopian, is one of the loveliest parts of the county.

● Closed Dec to Feb ⊿ 1 mile south and 1 mile east of B4214, across Clee Hill Common. Private car park ⌂ 3 twin; all with shower/WC; all with TV; hair-dryer on request ⊘ Dining-room, lounge, garden; kitchen for guests' use; cots, high chairs, babysitting ⅙ Wheelchair access to hotel, 3 ground-floor bedrooms specially equipped for disabled people ● No dogs in public rooms; no smoking ⊡ None accepted £ Single occupancy of twin £25, twin £44; deposit required. Special breaks available

---

CORSE LAWN Gloucestershire   map 5

Corse Lawn House

Corse Lawn, Gloucester GL19 4LZ
TEL: (01452) 780771   FAX: (01452) 780840

Long-established, unstuffy, family-run, country-house hotel – a classic of its kind.

There is no shortage of spruce, country-house hotels in Gloucestershire. Yet the Hine family, which has been at the helm here for twenty years, regards such ingredients as a relaxed atmosphere, friendly but efficient service and good food as being more important than any smart, 'designed' look. That said, the Hines accept that parts of their fine Queen Anne house (with its sympathetic newer extensions) do look a little shabby, and refurbishment plans are mooted. Perhaps the fact that, as well as positive feedback, we have received a negative comment about how the hotel is 'tired and becoming scruffy' will spur them on. There is a range of places in which to relax and eat, from a fairly formal lounge and Regency-styled restaurant to a rather lacklustre bar-cum-bistro (due for a revamp). Baba Hine has presided for many years over the kitchen, supervising the production of reliably good Anglo-French cuisine for both the restaurant and bistro. Dishes run the full gamut of sophistication, from roast, boned quail with a wild-mushroom risotto to old favourites like sponge puddings and crème brûlée. Breakfasts, including kippers, croissants and home-made yoghurt and jams, are judged to be excellent, too. The bedrooms major on comfort, most sporting bed drapes, a sofa and good bathrooms, with mop-head showers. Additional likeable touches include upholstered chests in place of luggage racks, and tea trays stocked with fresh milk, proper coffee and leaf tea.

● Open all year ⊿ 5 miles south-west of Tewkesbury on B4211. Private car park ⌂ 7 twin, 8 double, 2 four-poster, 2 suites; all with bathroom/WC; all with TV, room service, hair-dryer, trouser press, direct-dial telephone ⊘ 4 restaurants, bar, 2 lounges, garden; functions (max 80 people incl up to 38 residential), conferences; heated outdoor swimming-pool, tennis, croquet, badminton; early suppers for children; cots, high chairs, baby-listening ⅙ Wheelchair access to hotel and restaurant, WC (M,F), 5 ground-floor bedrooms ● No dogs or smoking in restaurant ⊡ Amex, Delta, Diners, MasterCard, Switch, Visa £ Single occupancy of twin/double £65 to £70, twin/double £100, four-poster £120, suite £135; deposit required. Bar/bistro L, D £10 to £15; set L £15 to £17, D £25; alc L, D £30. Special breaks available

Crest Guesthouse

39 Friars Road, Coventry CV1 2LJ
TEL: (01203) 227822   FAX: (01203) 227244

Well-maintained, good-value B&B, close to the station and shops.

This neat, red-brick villa close to Coventry's city centre is something of a find –
especially after negotiating the inner ring-road. Peggy Harvey's smart, blue-
and-white painted house is a welcome sight, and Peggy is a cheerful, friendly
person, who does her best to make her guests feel at home. The four bedrooms
are nicely decorated with lace curtains, flowery duvet covers and pine furniture;
the two twins have modern, white-tiled shower units, while the two singles
share a bathroom and separate lavatory. Breakfasts are served in the lounge/
dining-room, which has plenty of soft chairs around the television, fresh flowers
and patio doors opening out to the rear garden.

◑ Closed 25 & 26 Dec   🖈 Turn off inner ring-road at Junction 5 and follow signs for
city centre; turn left immediately after first set of traffic lights. Private car park
🛏 2 single, 2 twin; twins with shower/WC; all with TV, hair-dryer   ⊘
Lounge/dining-room, garden;   ♿ No wheelchair access   ● Dogs in bedrooms only,
by arrangement; no smoking   ▭ None accepted   £ Single £25, single occupancy of
twin £35, twin £45 to £50; deposit required.

Hipping Hall

Cowan Bridge, Kirkby Lonsdale, Carnforth LA6 2JJ
TEL: (015242) 71187   FAX: (015242) 72452
WEB SITE: www.dedicate.co.uk/hipping-hall

*A hospitable stay in a handsome, country home, with a sumptuous
dining experience.*

Ian and Jocelyn (better known as 'Jos') are a hospitable couple who take great
pleasure in entertaining their guests in their elegant country home. Guests are
invited to help themselves to drinks from the hospitality bar in the conservatory
– a bright and cheerful room, with plants and chirping lovebirds. Dinner is a
ceremonious affair in the Great Hall – a wonderfully spacious barn conversion
that is handsomely furnished with selected antiques bought at auction. It's a
sociable occasion, at which guests enjoy a sumptuous, five-course dinner around
a long, oak table. Ian takes a particular interest in wine, and serves three
different sorts throughout the meal. A typical menu may feature celery and
lovage soup, followed by fillet of salmon with wilted spinach and lemon and
chive sauce; dessert might be a raspberry torte with raspberry coulis. Coffee is
taken in the lounge, and sometimes Ian and Jos join their guests for an
after-dinner glass of wine and a chat. Guests have then only to stagger to the
immaculate bedrooms with their smart, *en suite* bathrooms. In the morning, they
can ease themselves into the day behind newspapers at individual tables in the

breakfast room, and may help themselves to fruit, cereal and juices followed by a cooked English breakfast, according to taste.

◑ Closed Dec to Feb ⊠ On A65, 8½ miles east of M6 (Junction 36), 2 miles east of Kirkby Lonsdale. Private car park ⤙ 2 twin, 3 double, 2 suites; some in annexe; all with bathroom/WC; all with TV, hair-dryer, direct-dial telephone, radio ⊘ Dining-room, breakfast room, lounge, bar/conservatory, garden; conferences (max 7 people residential); croquet; early suppers for children ♿ No wheelchair access ⬤ No children under 12; no dogs in public rooms; no smoking in bedrooms □ Amex, MasterCard, Switch, Visa £ Single occupancy of twin/double £72, twin/double £88, suite £102 (1998 prices); deposit required. Set D £17 to £24. Special breaks available

---

CRACKINGTON HAVEN Cornwall   map 1

Manor Farm

Crackington Haven, Bude EX23 0JU
TEL: (01840) 230304

A house-party welcome and total rural seclusion in this Domesday-listed farmhouse.

There's a dinner party every night at Manor Farm. At 6.30pm guests meet for drinks and are introduced to one another by Paul Knight. He then takes them through to the dining-room, where the place-settings are named and much mingling begins. One satisfied guest enthused about the 'superb, beautifully presented cooking' and the 'top-notch, very reasonably priced wines'. For starters Muriel Knight may provide savoury puddings with mushrooms, garlic, bacon and cheese, followed by roast cod in a green pepper crust with a lime vinaigrette. Pudding might be banana and meringue glace with clotted cream and apricot sauce, and of course cheese and biscuits. After all this good home cooking, depending on the season, guests may sit around the Swedish wood-burner in the beamed 'winter lounge' or watch the sun set through the mullioned windows of the 'summer lounge'. After coffee, the spruce, homely bedrooms will beckon.

The grounds of this lovely old farm are as splendid as the suppers – beautifully manicured sloping lawns, immaculately kept flower beds, fancy topiary – but the buildings themselves are welcomingly higgledy-piggledy and low-slung. An old waterwheel and the amazing mullioned windows lend historical character, supporting a reader's verdict that Manor Farm is 'a real "bolt hole" from modern stresses and strains'!

◑ Closed 25 Dec ⊠ From A39 take B3263 towards Crackington Haven. At seafront, turn inland, ignoring High Cliff Road; after 1 mile turn left into Church Park Road, then take first right into lane. Private car park ⤙ 1 twin, 3 double; all with bathroom/WC exc 2 doubles with shower/WC; no tea/coffee-making facilities in rooms ⊘ Breakfast room, dining-room, bar, 2 lounges, TV room, drying-room, garden; conferences (max 10 people incl up to 4 residential); ♿ No wheelchair access ⬤ No children; no dogs or smoking □ None accepted £ Single occupancy of twin/double £35 to £40, twin/double £60; deposit required. Set D £15

map 3

Kennel Holt Hotel **NEW ENTRY**

Goudhurst Road, Cranbrook TN17 2PT
TEL: (01580) 712032   FAX: (01580) 715495

Old-world, country-house luxury, with luscious gardens and superb food.

The Kennel Holt Hotel is a bit of a find – a lovely, old house in a secluded setting, just around the corner from Sissinghurst Gardens. With Sally and Neil Chalmers as hosts, staying here is more like staying with friends (albeit wealthy ones!) than being in a hotel. A warm, relaxed atmosphere pervades the house, typified by the wood-panelled sitting-room at the back: after helping yourself from the honesty bar, choose a CD to listen to, then kick off your shoes and curl up on a squishy sofa in front of a roaring log fire and wind down. There are plenty of books to keep you amused, including some delightful old children's tomes, or else the Chalmers' dog, Clovis, might be at hand for a shaggy story. The menu will tax even the most decisive diner; our inspector eventually plumped for a salad of Parma ham, mushrooms and sun-dried tomatoes, followed by roast turbot with grilled fennel, peppers and onions, all rounded off with a crème brûlée with rhubarb compote. The restaurant is actually three intimate, interlinked rooms, with big beams and crisp, white napery. It's smart without being intimidating, and the service is spot-on. Every bedroom is sympathetically decorated in keeping with the Elizabethan origins of the house – and named accordingly. Sir Francis Drake is a fine, four-poster room, while King Henry VIII is a huge double, with creaking floors, a brick fireplace and views of the well-manicured gardens.

◑ Closed 2 weeks mid-Jan; restaurant closed Mon eve   ⊠ On the A262, 3 miles from Goudhurst, heading towards Cranbrook and A229. Private car park   ⤶ 2 single, 2 twin, 4 double, 2 four-poster; most with bathroom/WC, 3 with shower/WC; all with TV, room service, hair-dryer, direct-dial telephone; no tea/coffee-making facilities in rooms   ⊘ Restaurant, bar, 2 sitting-rooms, drying-room, garden; functions (max 20 people incl up to 18 residential), conferences; croquet, putting green; early suppers for children; cots, high chairs, baby-listening   ♿ No wheelchair access   ● No children under 10 in restaurant eves; no dogs; no smoking in restaurant, discouraged in bedrooms   ▭ Amex, Delta, MasterCard, Switch, Visa   £ Single £90, single occupancy of twin/double £125, twin/double/four-poster £138 to £180; deposit required. Set L, D £27.50 to £32.50. Special breaks available

---

Old Cloth Hall

Cranbrook TN17 3NR
TEL: (01580) 712220 (AND FAX)

Wolsey Lodge manor, offering warm hospitality in a wonderfully peaceful spot.

Katherine Morgan's enthusiasm for her house and guests is the key to her success. She runs a stunning, fifteenth-century manor house, set in rhododendron- and azalea-filled gardens, in a remote corner of Kent. The building's half-timbered façade is crooked with both age and pretty, mullioned windows, while the back is of old, red brick, clad with creepers and climbers. Flagstoned floors, wood-panelled walls and leaded windows make the inside as appealing as the outside. Guests take pre-dinner sherry in an oak-beamed drawing-room warmed by a roaring fire burning in a vast fireplace. Dinners are served at one long, mahogany table in the parquet-floored dining-room, and Katherine joins her guests (unless they are honeymooners or with friends). She relies on her one-acre vegetable garden for home-made soups and seasonal produce, while main courses might be chicken with asparagus sauce, or local lamb or pork prepared with orange juice and mustard. Puddings are fruity: crumbles, tarts or home-made ice-cream. The three bedrooms have lots of character, with their sloping floors and beamed ceilings; their colour schemes are orange, peach and pink. There's a particularly large four-poster, with a big *en suite* bathroom. Katherine is happy to let her guests make full use of the swimming-pool and the old tennis court.

◑ Closed Chr ☑ 1 mile east of Cranbrook on Tenterden road; turn right just before cemetery. Private car park ⤙ 1 twin, 1 double, 1 four-poster; all with bathroom/WC; all with TV, hair-dryer, direct-dial cordless telephone, some with trouser press ⊘ Dining-room, drawing-room, garden; unheated outdoor swimming-pool, croquet, tennis; early suppers for children ⅄ No wheelchair access ● Children by arrangement; no dogs; no smoking in bedrooms ▭ None accepted £ Single occupancy of twin/double £45 to £55, twin/double £90, four-poster £95. Set D £21

CRANFORD ST ANDREW **Northamptonshire** map 6

Dairy Farm

Cranford St Andrew, Kettering NN14 4AQ
TEL: (01536) 330273

Traditional country hospitality in a delightful seventeenth-century manor house.

Looking out of the mullioned windows of Audrey and John Clarke's farmhouse sitting-room, you see a scene little changed in two hundred years: the circular stone-built dovecot to the right, sheep grazing in the meadow, and the Norman church partly hidden by aged horse-chestnut trees. John has retired from full-time farming now (despite the name, the Dairy was an arable farm) but is still a mine of interesting information, pointing out the style of thatching used on his roof, the wartime history of the area and how to get your rhubarb cropping in mid-winter.

The bedrooms are old-fashioned and uncluttered, with uneven floors and big baths (no showers). There are also two rooms out in the bothy, which are fine for a family or small group. The walls are plain tongue-and-groove panelled with dozens of historical pictures and photographs to admire. The dining-room has an inglenook fireplace and solid old furniture. Audrey does traditional cooking: three-course set menus with home-grown vegetables. Particular likes and dislikes of guests are sorted out when booking.

❶ Open all year ⤢ From Cranford High Street take Grafton road; after 700 yards take first right into St Andrew's Lane. Dairy Farm is at end. Private car park 🛏 2 twin, 2 double, 1 four-poster; some in annexe; family rooms available; 3 with bathroom/WC; all with TV, hair-dryer ⊘ Sitting-room, dining-room, garden; functions (max 12 people residential/non-residential); croquet; early suppers for children; cots, high chairs, toys, babysitting, baby-listening ♿ No wheelchair access ⬤ Dogs in annexe bedrooms only, by arrangement; no smoking ▭ None accepted £ Single occupancy of twin/double £22 to £25, twin/double £36 to £50, four-poster £58, family room £56 to £63. Set D £12.50

CREED Cornwall — map 1

Creed House

Creed, Grampound, Truro TR2 4SL
TEL: (01872) 530372

Wonderful family atmosphere in gracious Georgian rectory, with greatly loved garden.

The Croggon family have lived in this rambling, rural retreat for the past 25 years, so the place has a real sense of being a family home. In that time the family has rediscovered the 'lost gardens of Creed', and has restored the original, Georgian garden plan, although Mrs Croggon says that they 'manage' the gardens rather than control them – indeed, the many visitors who come here in summer (the grounds are opened to the public to raise money for charity) tend to disappear in the thick foliage. She also says that she wants to create an 'old-fashioned, house-party atmosphere', treating people as guests of the family. The public rooms are very gracious, with bright walls and plenty of spruce rugs. Breakfast is taken communally round a large table in the dining-room, under the watchful oil portraits of various handsome ancestors, and the big, country-style sitting-room offers lots of 'sink-into-me' sofas around the open fire, in which you can recline and meet your fellow residents. The three bedrooms are all of a good size, and are furnished with heavy, antique furniture; you either get a room-with-a-view or a room-with-a-loo (two have private bathrooms, the other is *en suite*). Mrs Croggon does not serve an evening meal, but is very helpful with advice on local pubs, as well as on beaches.

---

❶ Closed Chr & New Year ⤢ From Grampound, follow Creed Lane for 1 mile, then turn left opposite Creed church; hotel is on left. Private car park 🛏 3 twin/double; all with bathroom/WC (only 1 *en suite*); some with hair-dryer ⊘ Dining-room, sitting-room, TV room, study, garden; tennis ♿ No wheelchair access ⬤ No children under 8; no dogs; no smoking ▭ None accepted £ Single occupancy of twin/double £35, twin/double £55 to £65.

'The restaurant staff were very friendly; however, I was ignored twice by different staff around the hotel. They apologised, "I didn't know you were a resident". There won't be a next time, but if there were I would have to remember to wear Versace and not my M&S.'
On a hotel in the Cotswolds

CREWKERNE Somerset map 2

Broadview Gardens

East Crewkerne, Crewkerne TA18 7AG
TEL: (01460) 73424 (AND FAX)
EMAIL: broadgdn@eurobell.co.uk
WEB SITE: www.broadgdn.eurobell.co.uk

Delightful landscaped gardens place this well-run guesthouse more than a cut above the opposition.

Robert and Gillian Swann's colonial-style 'twenties bungalow looks as if it's been transported from an Indian hill station in the last days of the Raj. You almost expect it to be populated by characters from a Paul Scott novel, busily arranging tiffin or discussing yesterday's chukka. Instead, you'll find Gillian and Robert, a cheerfully unpretentious couple who enjoy devoting their energies to looking after their guests and keeping their wonderful landscaped garden in tiptop condition. Inside the house, you'll discover spick-and-span, but essentially homely, accommodation, liberally sprinkled with the Swanns' assorted collections. An array of plates, paintings and figurines gives a distinctive look to a guest sitting-room, which is flooded with light from a glass cupola, as well as picture windows. Guests eat around a highly polished single table, enjoying good English fare like mushroom soup, roast loin of pork, and orange and cherry upside-down cake with cream. The bedrooms feature good, solid furniture and chintzy, teetering on fussy, décor.

◑ Open all year　🚠 From A303 take A356 to Crewkerne; when in Crewkerne, take first left turning after petrol station into Ashlands Road, then turn right at T-junction; hotel is 300 yards on right. Private car park　🛏 1 twin, 2 double; 2 with bathroom/WC, 1 double with shower/WC; all with TV, hair-dryer, fridge　✅ Dining-room, sitting-room, conservatory, garden; high chairs　♿ No wheelchair access　● Dogs in bedrooms only, by arrangement; no smoking　▭ Delta, MasterCard, Visa　£ Single occupancy of twin/double £35 to £46, twin/double £50 to £56; deposit required. Set D £14

CROOK Cumbria map 8

Birksey Brow　| NEW ENTRY |

Crook, Kendal LA8 8LQ
TEL: (01539) 443380

Cheerful and personal, farmhouse accommodation, in peaceful rural setting.

A short drive from the village of Crook, between Kendal and Windermere, takes you to this working farm of Lakeland stone, set high on a hillside and surrounded by sheltered gardens. Friendly dogs and potbellied pigs may greet you as you arrive. Robin and Dany Brown raise Highland cattle on their 35-acre holding, but Dany also finds time to run a successful B&B, as well as an aromatherapy and beauty-treatment business at home (book a massage if your muscles ache after fell-walking). The house is beautifully kept, too, and is full of books, photos, pretty silver and antiques, with a lounge filled with plump upholstery and a handsome, terracotta-coloured dining-room. An animal theme runs through much of the décor, while a shepherd's crook stands in the hall. At some point, you'll probably glimpse Mrs Brown's palatial kitchen. By prior arrangement, guests can enjoy some super cooking using farm produce – though squeamish souls may balk at munching beef derived from those patrician beasts roaming the fields outside. Bring your own wine if you like. Look out for damson compotes at breakfast time (a local speciality), and home-made jams and jellies. The three bedrooms all have good views, plenty of light and good-quality furnishings, as well as lots of personality. All have their own bathrooms (though one is not *en suite*).

◐ Closed Chr & New Year   ⊿ From A591 from Kendal, take B5284 to Crook; travel past Sun Inn on right and up hill; pass village hall and church on left; farm is ½ mile further, on right. Private car park   ⊫ 2 twin, 1 double; family rooms available; double with bathroom/WC, 1 twin with shower/WC; all with TV, hair-dryer, some with trouser press   ⊘ Dining-room, lounge, TV room, garden; babysitting   ♿ No wheelchair access   ● No children under 8; no dogs; no smoking   ▭ None accepted
£ Single occupancy of twin/double £50, twin/double £50 to £66, family room £70; deposit required. Set D £17.50 to £20

CROOKHAM Northumberland   map 10

Coach House

Crookham, Cornhill-on-Tweed TD12 4TD
TEL: (01890) 820293   FAX: (01890) 820284

Converted farmhouse-courtyard complex with caring and friendly owner.

Lynne Anderson has run the Coach House at Crookham for 20 years with an admirable enthusiasm for her guests' happiness, and a well-thought-out, practical approach to travellers' needs – several of the rooms are particularly suitable for wheelchair users. The old farm buildings form a courtyard that sits alongside the A697, but it's not a busy road, and the pleasantly rural setting and damson orchard at the rear (whose bounty finds its way into Lynne's cuisine) make it easy to turn a blind eye to this minor quibble. The big, barn-like lounge, with its high roof beams, is a great spot in which to enjoy afternoon tea or a tipple from the well-stocked honesty bar, or you could ensconce yourself in the small TV room and enjoy the tantalising smells wafting in from the kitchen next door. The bedrooms in the Dower House have the most character, courtesy of the massive, exposed A-beams, panelled, stripped-pine doors and collections of straw hats and wooden ducks. The Coach House bedrooms, by contrast, are altogether more plain and practical, but no less comfy, and feature rustic bedspreads, Impressionist prints on the walls and a fresh, uncluttered style. Lynne's cooking is described as 'good, wholesome food', including the likes of pâtés and soups to start, followed by roasts – maybe pheasant or turkey with all the trimmings. Good, solid breakfasts of porridge made from proper pinhead oatmeal, or Scottish smoked bacon, local sausages and free-range eggs, will set you up for the day ahead.

◗ Closed Nov to Easter ⊐ On A697, 3½ miles south of Cornhill-on-Tweed. Private car park ⊨ 5 twin, 4 double; most with bathroom/WC; all with TV, direct-dial telephone, some with fridge, electric blanket ⊘ 2 dining-rooms, lounge, TV room, garden; cots, high chairs ⅄ Wheelchair access to hotel and dining-room, WC (unisex), 6 ground-floor bedrooms, 3 rooms specially equipped for disabled people ● No dogs in public rooms; no smoking in dining-room ⊟ MasterCard, Visa £ Single occupancy of twin/double £23 to £36, twin/double £46 to £72; deposit required. Set D £16.50

CROSTHWAITE Cumbria   map 8

Crosthwaite House

Crosthwaite, Kendal LA8 8BP
TEL: (01539) 568264
EMAIL: crosthwaite.house@kencomp.net

Handsome, period-style, budget accommodation in the heart of damson country.

This fine, cream-painted, Georgian house is easily spotted near the church on the edge of Crosthwaite village, commanding a swathe of luscious Lyth Valley views. (Adjacent buildings have been converted into self-catering accommodation.) Gardens rise behind the house towards orchards behind, where damsons grow in profusion. The Dawsons are a friendly, unassuming couple, with previous experience of Lakeland hotel-keeping. They have lovingly restored this house to its present good condition, and it now feels thoroughly like a family home. A stripped-pine floor graces the dining-room, where the décor is pleasantly restrained, with light, plain walls. Plants, ornaments and china add plenty of personal touches, though the furnishings throughout break no moulds. The bedrooms vary in size and style, but are light and pleasant; the front rooms trade magnificent views for a little daytime traffic noise. Shower-rooms have been incorporated into all of them, though the architecture of the house means that some are very compact. Good, simple dinners featuring local produce are available by prior arrangement, and there are plenty of games for wet days. Resident dogs and cats provide additional interest.

◗ Closed Dec and Jan ⊐ Leave M6 at Junction 36 and take A590 (signposted Barrow); turn right on to A5074 (signposted Bowness and Windermere); turn right after passing Lyth Valley Hotel; continue to T-junction, turn left; hotel is on right. Private car park ⊨ 1 single, 2 twin, 3 double; all with shower/WC; all with TV ⊘ Dining-room, lounge; early suppers for children; cots, high chairs, baby-listening ⅄ No wheelchair access ● No dogs or smoking in public rooms ⊟ None accepted £ Single £20 to £22, single occupancy of twin/double £20 to £22, twin/double £40 to £44. Set D £12

If you make a booking using a credit card and find after cancelling that the full amount has been charged to your card, raise the matter with your credit card company. It will ask the hotelier to confirm whether the room was re-let, and to justify the charge made.

Brakes Coppice Farm

Forewood Lane, Crowhurst, Battle TN33 0SJ
TEL: (01424) 830347 (AND FAX)

Homely B&B, on a working farm set in 70 acres of meadowland.

'Brakes' is derived from 'bracken', which once covered the area, and 'coppice' refers to the avenue of silver-birch and fir trees which lines the long, twisting lane leading to this welcoming establishment. Fay and Michael Ramsden's whitewashed farmhouse is only five minutes away from the historic town of Battle, and a footpath through the fields is said loosely to follow the route which soldiers took to the Battle of Hastings in 1066. They could probably have done with one of Fay's breakfasts on the way – a hearty feast of as much bacon, eggs, mushrooms and tomatoes as you like, or haddock, if you prefer. She serves it up on bone-china plates set on crisp, white tablecloths. The bedrooms themselves are a little cramped, with small, *en suite* bathrooms and, although they are homely, they lack much character. Their shortcomings are overridden, however, by the stunning views that you enjoy from all three bedrooms, over rolling hills to the sea; there are also great views from the farm of the South Downs and Beachy Head. The lounge is large and comfy, warmed by a real fire, with a video for guests to use if they wish. Fay does not provide evening meals, but is happy to recommend good places in which to eat nearby.

◗ Closed 21 Dec to 5 Jan   ⌧ Take turning to Crowhurst off A2100 just south of Battle; farm is 1 mile on left. Private car park   ⊨ 1 single, 1 twin, 1 double; single with bathroom/WC, others with shower/WC; all with TV, hair-dryer, trouser press, direct-dial telephone, ironing facilities   ⌀ Breakfast room, lounge, garden;   ᕳ No wheelchair access   ● No children under 12; no dogs; no smoking   ▭ None accepted
£ Single £30, single occupancy of twin/double £35, twin/double £55. Special breaks available

Croyde Bay House

Moor Lane, Croyde EX33 1PA
TEL: (01271) 890270

Snug and welcoming hotel, in breathtaking spot right by the sea.

This hotel is about as close as it can get to the sea without having to be a boat. On a high tide at full moon, the surfers pass close enough to the windows to be able to share your pre-dinner G&T (well almost), and apparently the sun lounge is the place to be in a storm in order to appreciate the full effect of the waves lashing the building – but rest assured, this does not happen too often. Regular guests recommend the view over the rock pools, the vast, golden expanse of Croyde Bay, and the warm welcome that they receive from Jennifer Penny and her staff. 'We shall certainly visit the hotel again,' enthused one reader, who praised 'the quality of the meals' and the hosts, Jennifer and Alex, who 'combine organising ability with friendliness'. Inside, the hotel makes no concessions to modernity, preferring solid, old-fashioned furniture and décor, with dark-wood panels and beams; there's a fine, carved bar in the reception, and plenty of cosy chairs in the lounge. The five-course dinners, served in a bright dining-room with a corner aspect to the sea, follow an equally reassuring, traditional pattern, with perhaps a melon and strawberry cocktail to start, followed by Ardennes pâté and toast, and then venison steak, pan-fried with a peppery cream sauce. Guests make requests for their favourite bedrooms – Room 7, above the sun lounge, is popular, but all have views to the sea and a pretty, floral style. Room 3 has an original, huge bath ('you can swim in it'), and there is access to Room 10 from the car park – handy for less mobile guests.

◖ Closed mid-Nov to 1 Mar   ⊿ Take B3231 to Croyde; turn left in village centre, then left again into Moor Lane. Hotel is by slipway. Private car park   ⤶ 2 twin, 3 double, 2 family rooms; 5 with bathroom/WC, 2 with shower/WC; all with TV, hair-dryer, trouser press   ⊘ Dining-room, bar, 2 lounges, drying-room, conservatory, garden; croquet; early suppers for children; cots, high chairs   ᴋ Wheelchair access to hotel (1 step) and dining-room, WC (F), 1 ground-floor bedroom   ● No dogs in public rooms; no smoking in some public rooms   ⊟ Amex, Delta, MasterCard, Switch, Visa   £ Single occupancy of twin/double £43 to £46, twin/double £66 to £72, family room £83 to £90; deposit required. Set D £19.50. (Prices valid till Mar 1999.) Special breaks available

---

CRUDWELL Wiltshire   map 2

Crudwell Court

Crudwell, Malmesbury SN16 9EP
TEL: (01666) 577194   FAX: (01666) 577853
EMAIL: crudwellcrt@compuserve.com

Unflashy country house, with a certain well-worn charm.

The extensive grounds and lovely, formal walled garden point to something rather grander than this creeper-clad seventeenth-century former rectory, but help to make it a little different from the average country-house hotel. Once indoors, you'll encounter a dignified house of fine proportions, furnished and decorated in a fashion that elevates comfort over style, with a spacious drawing-room and an attractively high-ceilinged reading room offering pleasant places in which to sit and relax with a paper or while perusing the menu. Dinner is served in an elegant, airy and well-lit restaurant, which overlooks both a delightful lily pond and the church where the rector once tended to the spiritual needs of his flock. Nick Bristow's staff have won a good reputation for menus offering such dishes as breast of pigeon served on rösti potatoes with a wild-mushroom sauce, baked fillet of sea bass served on a lemon and dill sauce with savoury rice, and dark-chocolate and ginger torte on a Cointreau sauce.

The bedrooms are generally well proportioned and comfortable, if fairly simple. One correspondent found the furnishings and décor of their standard bedroom disappointing, complaining in particular of chipped paintwork and a run-down bathroom. More reports, please.

○ Open all year ⊿ Leave M4 at Junction 17 and take A429 Malmesbury to Cirencester road; hotel is 3 miles north of Malmesbury, set back from road on right, next to church. Private car park ⊨ 1 single, 14 twin; family rooms available all with bathroom/WC; all with TV, room service, hair-dryer, direct-dial telephone, some with trouser press ⊘ Restaurant, 2 lounges, conservatory, garden; functions (max 90 people incl up to 29 residential), conferences; civil wedding licence; heated outdoor swimming-pool; early suppers for children; cots, high chairs, babysitting, baby-listening ⅙ No wheelchair access ● No dogs in public rooms ▭ Amex, Delta, Diners, MasterCard, Switch, Visa ⌷ Single £45, single occupancy of twin £50, twin £88, family room £98; deposit required. Alc L £7.50, D £19.50 to £25. Special breaks available

---

CUCKFIELD West Sussex   map 3

Ockenden Manor

Ockenden Lane, Cuckfield RH17 5LD
TEL: (01444) 416111 FAX: (01444) 415549

Oodles of atmosphere, winningly combined with luxurious lodgings and attentive service.

The history of this splendid house reads like a centuries-spanning soap opera, with all the pre-requisite elements of drama, passion, intrigue and tragedy: the house burning down in 1608, two of Timothy Burrell's three wives dying, will-changing to cut out disfavoured relatives, politics, high finance, a Jewish boys' school and troop-billeting during World War II. Things are a touch quieter these days. Ockenden sits in manorial splendour surrounded by the quaint village of Cuckfield and, with its imposing mixture of golden-stone and half-timbered buildings set amid manicured gardens, visually lives up to its role. Inside, the public rooms, from the cosily cluttered bar to the elegant sitting-room, are all adorned with fresh flower arrangements that fill the air with their sweet-smelling scent. The wood-panelled restaurant is the venue for an atmospheric evening meal – perhaps carrot and tomato soup, followed by roast Southdown lamb with a creamed-garlic sauce, rounded off with an iced raspberry parfait.

Every bedroom is different from the next, but all are resplendently furnished and each is named after a member of the owners' family, which, given the number of rooms, brings the Waltons to mind! Alice has lovely downland views, David a claw-legged, free-standing bath, and Master its own little sitting-room. Those in the oldest part of the house, such as the split-level Merrick, with its four-poster bed, are all the more characterful for their odd shapes and uneven floors.

○ Open all year ⊿ In centre of Cuckfield, at end of Ockenden Lane. Private car park ⊨ 1 single, 4 twin, 12 double, 2 four-poster, 3 suites; family rooms available; all with bathroom/WC; all with TV, room service, hair-dryer, trouser press, direct-dial telephone, clock radio ⊘ Restaurant, bar, sitting-room, 2 drying-rooms, conservatory, garden; functions (max 75 people incl up to 45 residential), conferences; civil wedding licence; croquet; early suppers for children from 6.30pm; cots, high chairs, babysitting, baby-listening ⅙ No wheelchair access ● No dogs; no smoking in restaurant ▭ Amex, Delta, Diners, MasterCard, Switch, Visa ⌷ Single

£105, single occupancy of twin/double £105 to £160, twin/double £125 to £185, four-poster £220 to £260, family room £220 + £20 per child, suite £260; deposit required. Cooked B £6.50; set L £20, D £32.50; alc L, D £42

DARTMOUTH Devon map 1

Ford House **NEW ENTRY**

44 Victoria Road, Dartmouth TQ6 9DX
TEL: (01803) 834047 (AND FAX)

Small, friendly establishment, run with great good humour by an amiable Australian couple.

Ford House is about 500 yards up from the quay, in a quiet enough street. The leat flowing right next to the detached, ivy-clad house gives it a rural feel, but, as proprietors Jayne and Richard Turner will tell you, there are 24 restaurants and 14 pubs within walking distance. Not that you'll feel the need to stray far, as the Turners are keen gastronomes who specialise in dinner-party weekends. The set menu, planned in advance in consultation with guests, might consist of carrot mousse with a clam sauce, followed by fillet of kangaroo with a Madeira and maraschino demi glaze, while pudding could be an apricot focaccia with Beenleigh blue cheese. Dinner is taken communally, around a large, oval table. Jayne and Richard, good-humoured folk, hail from Australia (and spend their winters there), but have definitely made Ford House their home and encourage guests to do the same: you bring your own wine, 'just like in Australia', and there's a Pianola in the sitting-room for after-dinner hilarity. Games, magazines, fresh flowers and lots of pictures and photos (some by local artists, some taken by Richard) make for a relaxed atmosphere. The bedrooms are on the small side, but have inviting beds, pretty fabrics and good bathrooms.

◗ Closed Nov to Mar ⊠ Entering Dartmouth on A3122, take right-hand feeder road into Townstal Road leading to Victoria Road. Private car park ⨳ 2 twin, 2 double; 3 with bathroom/WC; all with TV, room service, hair-dryer, mini-bar, direct-dial telephone ⌀ Dining-room, sitting-room, garden; early suppers for children; cots, babysitting ♿ No wheelchair access ● None ▭ MasterCard, Visa £
Twin/double £45 to £70; deposit required. Set D £25. Special breaks available

---

DAWLISH Devon map 1

Oak Cottage **NEW ENTRY**

Luscombe Hill, Dawlish EX7 0PX
TEL: (01626) 863120

Wonderfully theatrical and welcoming house, brimming with character, with very friendly owners.

It's hard to believe that Oak Cottage was converted from four estate-workers' cottages, so grand are its fixtures and fittings, but the nearby castle was built by Nash, so the outbuildings had to live up to the splendour of the stately home. As a result, Oak Cottage has no real front door, but what it does have are splendid, mullioned windows, a pitched roof, heavy doors with carved frames, wonderful wood panelling, deep window seats and a huge garden. On top of this, Tony and Liz Williams have filled it to the brim with rich colours and fabrics, heavy, antique furniture and about a thousand framed pictures. As they say, 'People seem to come in and just enjoy being here,' but this hotel will not appeal to the minimalist. Guests (a maximum of four at any one time – there are only two bedrooms) can choose between the small lounge, with its cosy, wood fire, or the main lounge, with its more grand, sculpted, stone fireplace. The dining-room is done out in reds, with one heavy table. Liz says that 'feeding people is very much part of the deal here', and she uses local produce and cheeses; you may find home-made mushroom soup, followed by spiced lamb with apricots, on the menu. The two bedrooms – which are in separate parts of the house, so guests have total privacy – are large and boldly decorated in theatrical colours; they have excellent bathrooms.

◗ Closed Chr & New Year; dining-room closed Mon eve ⊿ From end of M5 at Exeter, take A38, then A380 (left-hand lane) to Torquay; after 2 miles, take B3192 to Teignmouth, then second left to Dawlish; after 1½ miles, cottage is third house on left. Private car park ⌐ 1 twin, 1 double; both with bathroom/WC; both with TV, hair-dryer ✓ Dining-room, 2 lounges, garden ♿ No wheelchair access ● No children under 15; no dogs; no smoking in bedrooms ⊟ None accepted £ Single occupancy of twin/double £38, twin/double £56; deposit required. Set D £17.50

DEDHAM Essex

map 6

Dedham Hall

Brook Street, Dedham, Colchester CO7 6AD
TEL: (01206) 323027   FAX: (01206) 323293

An inspirational location for lovers of Constable country in a historic home with an impressive restaurant.

Strictly speaking, this slumbering fifteenth-century house is part of the pretty village of Dedham, yet its location is wonderfully rural. It stands in its own grounds complete with a large pond, home to ducks and geese, and is only a short walk from the River Stour and some of the memorable views familiar to all lovers of the artist John Constable. In fact homage is paid to him almost daily at the house by the groups of artists who stay at the hall to take part in the painting courses that run throughout most of the year. The Hall itself is actually a cottage and a larger house joined together, creating a haphazard mix of rooms and corridors. There is a small lounge and bar, in addition to the restaurant and breakfast room, yet it all still feels very much like the home of owners Wendy and Jim Sarton. There are no keys to the bedrooms as the Sartons want people to feel free to come and go as if it were their own house. The rooms reflect the owners' desire to keep things relaxed and informal, with simple furnishings collected together over time, including lots of stripped pine. Wendy is the cook as well. A typical fixed-price dinner might include fresh dressed crab followed by pan-fried skate with capers.

◑ Open all year; restaurant closed Sun eve   ⧉ Take Dedham/Stratford St Mary exit off A12; follow signs to Dedham; hotel is at end of High Street on left. Private car park ⯆ 1 single, 2 twin, 2 double, 1 family room; 4 with bathroom/WC, 2 with shower/WC; all with TV, hair-dryer; extra 10 annexe rooms for painting holidays   ⍋ restaurant, breakfast room, 2 bars, 2 lounges, garden; functions (max 50 people incl up to 20 residential); early suppers for children; cots, high chairs   ⟁ No wheelchair access ● No dogs; smoking in some public rooms only   ⬜ Delta, MasterCard, Switch, Visa ⒠ Single £45, single occupancy of twin/double £45, twin/double £65, family room £75. Set L £18.50, D £19.50 (D £15 for guests)

Maison Talbooth

Stratford Road, Dedham, Colchester CO7 6HN
TEL: (01206) 322367   FAX: (01206) 322752

Ornate bedrooms and lavish bathrooms in a comfortable house with country views.

The striking pink washed façade and the fountain with 12 plumes in the centre of the circular driveway set the tone of this fine country house. From here you get an uninterrupted rural view across the Stour valley towards Stratford St Mary in the distance. The sense of uninhibited space continues inside – each of the ten bedrooms is lavishly decorated to the point of decadence. Shakespeare, a principal room, has an over-the-top boudoir feel that would have made Napoleon feel at home; as well as an enormous bed, there's a bed-sized sunken bath flanked by basins on either side. A standard room, such as Brooke, has a more intimate feel, in blues and golds, with a free-standing bath. The hotel lists all its rooms as 'suites'; one has a private sitting-room and two have private terraces, but only one has an additional bedroom.

Guests can congregate in the large, classically styled drawing-room, with french windows leading to the lawn. The restaurant is in an old, half-timbered weaver's cottage close to the river, a minute's drive away by courtesy car. The restaurant is well known locally for its rotating daily lunch-time roast. Alternatively, the à la carte menu might include offerings such as scallops in the shell with spinach and champagne sauce and medallions of venison with roasted vegetables, cranberry-filled apple and green peppercorn sauce.

◑ Open all year; restaurant closed Sun eves in winter   ⧉ From A12 take exit to Dedham; turn right over A12 flyover; hotel is 600 yards on right. Private car park ⯆ 1 twin, 8 double, 1 suite; family rooms available; all with bathroom/WC; all with TV, room service, hair-dryer, direct-dial telephone, some with mini-bar; trouser press and tea/coffee-making facilities on request   ⍋ Bar, drawing-room, lounge, drying-room, gardens; restaurant nearby (courtesy car); functions (max 70 people incl up to 22 residential), conferences; civil wedding licence; croquet, outside chess; tennis nearby (free for guests), golf nearby (reduced rates for guests); early suppers for children; cots, high chairs, toys, baby-listening   ⟁ No wheelchair access ● No dogs; no smoking in some bedrooms   ⬜ Amex, Diners, MasterCard, Switch, Visa   ⒠ Single occupancy of twin/double £95 to £130, twin/double £115 to £175, family room £195, suite £195; deposit required. Cooked B £7.50; set L £16/£18.50, D £20/£23.50; alc L, D £30. Special breaks available

DENT Cumbria   map 8

Stone Close

Main Street, Dent, Sedbergh LA10 5QL
TEL: (01539) 625231   FAX: (01539) 726567
EMAIL: p.rushton@kencomp.net

Charming Dales tea-shop-cum-B&B in a picturesque, rural village.

Dent isn't really that far from the main roads and motorways, but, after a chase across the sheep-strewn, single-track lanes of these Pennine foothills, it feels like the back of beyond. It's a delightful village, full of whitewashed cottages and cobblestones – the sort that visitors like to find at the end of a hard day's hill-walking, or a leisurely driving tour. So the teas and crafts on offer go down pretty well with day-trippers, as well as with those who decide to take advantage of the three quaint, pretty bedrooms upstairs, or those in Dolly's Cottage next door. Lift up the latches, Red-Riding-Hood-style, and you'll find simple, rustic charm, original fireplaces and wash-basins in the rooms (none is *en suite*). Stone Close is under new ownership this year, but Kay and Peter Rushton seem to be keeping this thriving little business in much the same way as their predecessors. So its character remains in the tea-shop occupying two slate-floored rooms downstairs, where old-fashioned meat hooks hang from the seventeenth-century beams and cast-iron ranges buttress the end walls. Typical specialities from across the Pennine divide are on offer throughout the day – Yorkshire curd tart, perhaps, or Wensleydale beef crumble. The imaginative breakfasts with a wholefood slant will set you up for a day's march.

◖ Closed 4 to 31 Jan   ⊠ On cobbled Main Street, next to car park. Public car park nearby   ⊨⇀ 2 single, 3 double, 1 family room; some in annexe; 1 double with bathroom/WC; all with TV, some with trouser press, direct-dial telephone   ⊘ Dining-room, garden; early suppers for children; cot, high chairs, baby-listening   ⅋ No wheelchair access   ● No smoking   ▭ Delta, MasterCard, Switch, Visa   £ Single £19, single occupancy of double £25, double £33 to £50, family room £38 (1998 prices); deposit required. Bar/bistro L £6, D £8; alc D £10. Special breaks available

---

DIDDLEBURY Shropshire   map 5

Delbury Hall

Diddlebury, Craven Arms SY7 9DH
TEL: (01584) 841267   FAX: (01584) 841441
EMAIL: wrigley@delbury.demon.co.uk

Stately Georgian mansion with a laid-back family atmosphere, set in extensive grounds.

'Delbury is probably the most beautiful Georgian house in Shropshire,' boldly claims the brochure. Lording it over 80 acres of grounds that encompass a lake, trout fishery and nursery, and reached via a bumpy track through a field, it must certainly be one of the grandest. You enter a handsome hall with a sweeping oak staircase and galleried landing. Off it lie two expansive sitting-rooms with fine cornices and roaring fires, and a dining-room where meals are taken round an antique table amid silver candelabra. Yet, despite such impressiveness, Lucinda and Patrick Wrigley's home is far from being a stuffy country house. Dogs, cats and children are much in evidence, and you may be invited into the kitchen to taste mum's home-made flapjacks, or dad's home-cured prosciutto. Patrick is co-owner of a local inn and takes his cooking seriously. A set dinner might entail a goats' cheese mousse, followed by duck breast in a raspberry vinaigrette and mini chocolate soufflés; the house is licensed, with an honesty bar and wine list. Antique beds and lovely rural views distinguish the bedrooms. Only one – the four-poster room – is *en suite*, but the others are never let without a bathroom of their own except to families.

◑ Closed Chr ⤢ In Diddlebury, follow signs to Delbury Hall Fishery, then signs to Hall. Private car park ⤙ 2 twin, 1 double, 1 four-poster; all with bathroom/WC (not all *en suite*); all with TV, hair-dryer, direct-dial telephone ⬥ Dining-room, drawing-room, lounge, drying-room, games room, garden; functions; civil wedding licence; fishing, tennis, snooker; early suppers for children; cots, high chairs, playrooms, babysitting, outdoor play area ♿ No wheelchair access ⬤ No dogs in hotel (kennels available); no smoking in bedrooms ▭ MasterCard, Switch, Visa £ Single occupancy of twin/double £50, twin/double £80, four-poster £90; deposit required. Set D £28

DISS Norfolk   map 6

Salisbury House

Victoria Road, Diss IP22 3JG
TEL: (01379) 644738 (AND FAX)

A large, Victorian town house that hides a trendy, bistro restaurant and ornately decorated bedrooms.

Despite the substantial-looking Victorian frontage of this hotel, it is far smaller and more intimate than you might expect. Indeed, much of the public space inside is given over to two restaurants, one formal and one a bistro, both of which attract a sizeable amount of local business, thanks to the culinary skills of the owner, Barry Davies, helped by his wife, Sue. The formal restaurant at the front of the house is decorated fairly simply, but has two attractive bay windows that look out to the garden lawns. In comparison, the bistro is a riot of colour, with bright-yellow walls picked out with blue plates, and a stripped-pine floor. The menus for the two are pretty similar. Our inspector started with a light and tasty baked avocado and cream with tomato and Parmesan shavings, followed by leg of guinea-fowl stuffed with white sausage and served on a bed of potato rösti with a smoked-chicken *jus* that was well presented and full of flavour. Dessert was a decent nougat parfait with honey crème anglaise. Each of the three bedrooms shows plenty of individual design touches, with antique beds and exciting colour schemes. Room 4, in the garden courtyard annexe, has an impressive four-poster that dominates the room and is extremely comfortable.

◑ Closed 2 weeks summer; restaurant & bistro closed Sun & Mon eves ⓩ ¼ mile from town centre, on A1066 heading east. Private car park ⌁ 2 double, 1 four-poster; 1 in annexe; 2 with bathroom/WC; all with TV, room service, hair-dryer, mini-bar ⍢ 2 restaurants, 2 lounges, conservatory, garden; functions (max 60 people incl up to 6 residential), conferences; croquet; early suppers for children; baby-listening ⅙ No wheelchair access ● No dogs; no smoking in restaurants, discouraged in bedrooms ▭ MasterCard, Visa £ Single occupancy of double £45 to £58, double £70 to £82, four-poster £78; deposit required. Cooked B £4.50; bar/bistro L, D £9; set L, D £25.

DODDISCOMBSLEIGH Devon   map 1

Nobody Inn

Doddiscombsleigh, Exeter EX6 7PS
TEL: (01647) 252394   FAX: (01647) 252978
EMAIL: inn.nobody@virgin.net
WEB SITE: www.intellect-net.com/west/country/hotels/devon/nobody/htm

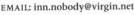

Fantastic old hostelry in remote village serving up very good food.

It's highly unlikely that there'll be nobody in at the Nobody Inn. People come from miles around to eat, buy wine and stay in the huge rooms at Town Barton, the house across the field. This is English hospitality at its best, with locals propping up the bar, an extensive wine and food menu, and a classic low-beamed pub complete with roaring fire, heavy wood settles and chunky tables. Our inspector's lunch of blue-cheese soup with a mixed salad, followed by ginger-and-rhubarb crumble, was very good. The restaurant menu features main dishes such as braised lamb sweetbreads cooked in a creamy white-wine sauce with mushrooms and parsley, or sliced fillet of beef served with a rich tarragon sauce. Nick Borst-Smith has 800 wines in his cellar, as well 245 whiskies and 40 Devon cheeses, so you won't want for spoiling. There are perfectly good bedrooms in the pub, but the calm restraint of Town Barton is a real welcome; huge rooms with straightforward décor in a house dating back to 1241 provide the antidote to any excesses you may have indulged in. Torches are provided for the 150-metre walk to the inn for supper, but you don't need to move in the morning unless you want a full cooked breakfast – tea, fresh milk, cereals and toast-making equipment are provided in the rooms.

◑ Closed 25 Dec, 26 Dec (eve); restaurant closed Sun & Mon eves ⓩ Leave A38 at Devon & Exeter racecourse (signposted Dunchideock); follow signs to Nobody Inn for 3 miles. Private car park ⌁ 2 twin, 5 double; some in annexe; 4 with bathroom/WC, 1 with shower (no WC); all with direct-dial telephone, some with TV ⍢ Restaurant, bar; ⅙ No wheelchair access ● No children under 14; no dogs; no smoking in restaurant ▭ Delta, MasterCard, Switch, Visa £ Single occupancy of twin/double £33 to £38, twin/double £52 to £64; deposit required. Cooked B £3; bar/bistro L, D £5; alc D £15

The Guide *office can quickly spot when a hotelier is encouraging customers to write a letter recommending inclusion. Such reports do not further a hotel's cause.*

DONNINGTON Berkshire

map 2

Donnington Valley Hotel |NEW ENTRY|

Old Oxford Road, Donnington, Newbury RG14 3AG
TEL: (01635) 551199   FAX: (01635) 551123
EMAIL: 106543.3217@compuserve.com

Modern and traditional approaches combined in a hotel for both business and country-house guests.

This polished operation appeals on several levels: the conference suites and surrounding golf course hold an obvious allure for those on business and entertaining; a fine restaurant and celebrity-sprinkled calendar of recitals and literary soirées draw an appreciative, local audience; and the immaculately decorated bedrooms provide a comfortable base should you be exploring the Newbury area at your leisure. Considerable thought has gone into the hotel's strategy – the numbers of corporate clients are restricted to avoid the prevailing air of calm being overwhelmed by the cut and thrust of commerce in full flow. The hotel is handily placed – between Newbury and an M4 junction – and may initially look unpromisingly akin to a new housing development. Hold firm, though, and you are rewarded with a modern interpretation of a traditional, Edwardian lobby, complete with tropical parlour plants, a mezzanine piano-bar and a gallery restaurant beneath a high, pine-clad, pitched ceiling. The mellifluous tones of the proprietor's own radio station, Classic FM, are piped throughout.

Chef Kelvin Johnson's menus favour a distinctly Mediterranean influence – for instance, mushroom polenta served with noisettes of lamb, or fillets of sea bass dressed with sun-dried tomato pickle.

○ Open all year ☒ From M4, Junction 13, take A34 south; take Donnington exit. Hotel is 1 mile further. Private car park ⊨ 15 twin, 38 double, 5 suites; family rooms available; all with bathroom/WC; all with TV, room service, hair-dryer, trouser press, direct-dial telephone ⊘ Restaurant, bar, lounge, function suites, garden; functions (max 140 people incl up to 120 residential), conferences; civil wedding licence; golf; leisure facilities nearby (reduced rates for guests); early suppers for children; high chairs, baby-listening ⅙ Wheelchair access to hotel and restaurant (ramps/lift), WC (M, F), 12 ground-floor bedrooms, 3 rooms specially equipped for disabled people ● No dogs in public rooms ▭ Amex, Diners, MasterCard, Visa £ Single occupancy of twin/double £110, twin/double £110, family room £130, suite £200; deposit required. Continental B £7.50, cooked B £11.50; bar/bistro L £7.50, D £10.50; set L £19.50, D £21.50; alc L, D £35

DORCHESTER Dorset

map 2

Casterbridge Hotel

49 High East Street, Dorchester DT1 1HU
TEL: (01305) 264043   FAX: (01305) 260884

Comfortable, well-equipped rooms in a carefully managed town-house hotel set on the high street of a historic market town.

Wives whose husbands are past the first flush of their ardour, or in their cups, might think twice about pernoctating in Dorchester, the model for Hardy's Casterbridge. Those who can overcome the fear of finding themselves being sold may discover agreeable quarters at Rita and Stuart Turner's small hotel, a Georgian town house usefully situated on Dorchester's main street. The Turners' enterprise is run with care and imagination, and would be an equally good choice whether you found yourself in the town on business or were simply enjoying the lovely Dorset countryside. This is an elegant, yet unpretentious, sort of place, with a small, impeccably neat sitting-room furnished with chairs and a sofa in smart blues and clarets, tied-back floral drapes and striking classical paintings. The adjacent bar, with its rugs on boards, rattan chairs and gold-and-red fleurs-de-lys wallpaper, has a clubbier feel, and displays a good range of local books and tourist information. Generous breakfasts are served in an airy conservatory area towards the rear. The bedrooms vary in size and are individually decorated and furnished in a variety of bright, cheerful styles. They're uniformly well equipped, and the Turners have recently introduced such innovations as power showers to keep them up to the mark.

◗ Closed 25 & 26 Dec   ⊿ In centre of Dorchester, 100 yards east of town clock. Private car park; on-street parking (free)   ⊨ 5 single, 3 twin, 5 double, 1 four-poster, 1 family room; some in annexe; most with bathroom/WC, some with shower/WC; all with TV, room service, hair-dryer, direct-dial telephone, some with trouser press   ⊘ Breakfast room/conservatory, bar/library, sitting-room, garden; cots, high chairs, toys, baby-listening   ♿ Wheelchair access to hotel and breakfast room (ramp); 3 ground-floor bedrooms   ● No dogs; no smoking in some public rooms and some bedrooms   ▭ Amex, Delta, Diners, MasterCard, Switch, Visa   £ Single £38 to £40, single occupancy of twin/double £45 to £48, twin/double £64 to £68, four-poster £75 to £80, family room £70 to £80; deposit required. Special breaks available

---

DORCHESTER Oxfordshire   map 2

George Hotel

25 High Street, Dorchester, Wallingford OX10 7HH
TEL: (01865) 340404   FAX: (01865) 341620

Traditional, very comfortable hotel, brimming with historical features.

The George Hotel has pride of place in the centre of Dorchester-on-Thames, right opposite the abbey amidst other picture-postcard buildings with Tudor overhangs and climbing roses. Indeed, some guests have been known to complain about this close proximity to the bells of the abbey, which ring out resonantly on Tuesdays and Sundays. The roads around are named Rotten Row and Queen Street and, with the presence of the gaily painted carriage outside the George, you half expect a mail coach pulled by galloping, steaming horses to arrive to allow its occupants to partake of refreshments at the hotel. Meals can be taken in the bar, which is definitely a sitting-down rather than a propping-up kind of place, with its carved, oak tables and roaring fire – here you could try a saladette of citrus chicken, or pan-fried brill in a baby-girolle sauce. In the wonderful, high-beamed restaurant, which used to be the banqueting hall in days gone by, the menu keeps up with the latest trends with such dishes as saffron lasagne or sauté scallops with a lime and coriander salsa, followed by pan-fried halibut steak with crispy pancetta bacon, grain-mustard mash and barigoule sauce. The two modern parts of the hotel achieve varying degrees of success: the lounge, with its brick walls and inviting sofas, is cosy and characterful, while the motel-like annexe housing several of the bedrooms is much less attractive. Go for the rooms in the main house, which have beamed and sloping ceilings, and are restfully done out in greens and peachy tones, with plenty of antiques.

◑ Open all year 🔲 On High Street. Private car park ⛟ 3 single, 2 twin, 10 double, 2 four-poster, 1 family room; some in annexe; all with bathroom/WC; all with TV, room service, hair-dryer, direct-dial telephone, some with trouser press ⚇ Restaurant, bar, lounge, garden; functions (max 350 people incl up to 32 residential); conferences; corporate entertainment, e.g. quad bikes, assault courses; early suppers for children; cots, high chairs, baby-listening ♿ Wheelchair access to hotel and restaurant (ramp), 6 ground-floor bedrooms ● No dogs in public rooms; no smoking in restaurant and some bedrooms ▭ Amex, Delta, MasterCard, Switch, Visa £ Single £63, single occupancy of twin/double £70, twin/double £80, four-poster £93, family room £100; deposit required. Cooked B £3.50; bar/bistro L, D £4 to £14; alc L, D £23. Special breaks available

---

DOVER Kent

map 3

Old Vicarage

Chilverton Elms, Hougham, Dover CT15 7AS
TEL: (01304) 210668   FAX: (01304) 225118

Exemplary elegance, charming hosts, peaceful location: perfect for the night before a ferry-crossing.

The welcome awaiting guests is much more down-to-earth and relaxed than might be anticipated, given the rather formal appearance of this delightful B&B – even more so if Jake and Dino, the Evisons' two boisterous labradors, are involved. Tea and home-made fruit cake appear very soon after you do, and can be enjoyed in the garden if the weather permits. Built in 1870, this old vicarage has been lovingly restored by Judy and Bryan Evison. The sitting-room is brimful of art, antiques, and family photos – as is the dining-room, which is just as formal, if not more so. Both have verdant garden views. The sizeable bedrooms are plush and elegant, with thick, soft carpets and subtle, relaxing colour schemes. Only one is *en suite,* though the other two both have their own private bathrooms. Dinner can be rustled up if you book in advance, or the Evisons have a wealth of local suggestions, as well as handy maps in case you get lost. All this deep amongst green fields and pretty woods, only a couple of miles from the hustle of Dover.

◑ Closed 1 week over Chr 🔲 Leave Dover on B2011; turn right after Priory railway station, signposted Hougham; keep right at fork after 1 mile; Old Vicarage is about 200 yards on right. Private car park ⛟ 1 twin, 1 double, 1 family room; all with bathroom/WC (only double *en suite*); all with TV, hair-dryer ⚇ Dining-room, sitting-room, games room; early suppers for children, by arrangement; cots, high chairs, toys, playroom, garden, baby-listening ⅊ No wheelchair access ● No dogs; no smoking ▭ MasterCard, Visa £ Twin/double £55 to £60, family room £65 to £70; deposit required. Set D £20 to £22.50

DREWSTEIGNTON Devon map 1

Hunts Tor   NEW ENTRY

Drewsteignton, Exeter EX6 6QW
TEL: (01647) 281228 (AND FAX)

Classy sustenance and good bedrooms in a peaceful, Devon village.

Tucked away in the corner of a square in a sleepy village in the north-eastern corner of Dartmoor, this tiny place looks more like a pretty retirement cottage than a smart, little hotel with an acclaimed restaurant. A sweet, cheerful garden and a tiny canopy outside the front door belie the fairly formal, muted interior. Sue and Chris Harrison have made the best use of the wooden fittings of their part 300-year-old, part 100-year-old, house to create a stylish, sophisticated feel, with mulberry-hued walls, striped sofas and colourful tiles around the fireplaces. Guests dine either in the official dining-room, which is filled with pretty plants and wooden sideboards, or in the fantastically cosy and welcoming 'little dining-room', around a huge, country-kitchen table and under dried flowers twisting from the chunky beams overhead. Be sure to order your meal 24 hours in advance. Sue's set menus feature such mouthwatering delicacies as buckwheat blinis with smoked salmon, dill and crème fraîche, followed by breast of duck with lentils and roast shallots in a ginger and coriander sauce, and then perhaps a lemon tart. After supper, coffee is taken in the lounge, which has a distinctly 'twenties feel to it. The three bedrooms are much grander than you would expect in such a diminutive establishment – they have separate sitting areas, with capacious, squashy sofas, as well as good-sized beds and smartly decorated walls.

◑ Closed end Oct to early Mar ◪ On village square, at opposite end to church. Private car park; on-street parking (free) ⊨ 1 twin, 1 double, 1 suite; all with bathroom/WC; all with TV, room service, hair-dryer ⊘ 2 dining-rooms, bar, lounge ⅊ No wheelchair access ● No children under 10; no dogs in public rooms; no smoking in dining-rooms ▭ None accepted £ Single occupancy of twin/double £40, twin/double £62 to £68, suite £75; deposit required. Set D £20 to £23 (must give 24 hours' notice)

DULVERTON Somerset map 1

Ashwick House

Dulverton TA22 9QD
TEL: (01398) 323868 (AND FAX)

Marvellous Exmoor country house in idyllic setting, run with flair, care and a twinkle in the eye.

The road to Ashwick House meanders gracefully over sweeping hillocks and clanking cattle-grids, taking in a palm tree or two on the way. It all augurs well for visitors to Richard Sherwood's Edwardian house, an ostensibly plain leviathan which occupies a glorious position amid six acres of inviting grounds above the valley of the River Barle. The hotel's character asserts itself the second you enter the door, when you find yourself in a flagstoned baronial-style hallway, with a sweeping staircase leading up to a delightful gallery. It's hard to believe that the sedate drawing-room, with its inset Chinese panels and dramatic, newly fitted pink-and-purple swag-and-tail drapes, was requisitioned during the war as a workshop for the manufacture of camouflage nets, but there's a photograph to prove it. It's equally hard to believe that anything so redolent of conflict has ever shattered the peace of the restful fabric-panelled library, where today's guests can wrestle with a three-dimensional jigsaw of the Houses of Parliament, distracted from their task only by the clock that chimes the hours in a burst of birdsong.

In the traditional restaurant, guests might choose from the handwritten menu such dishes as celery and walnut soup, a no-choice entrée like Somerset pork fillet with fresh sorrel stuffing, and then a rich chocolate rum torte. The spacious bedrooms are tastefully decorated and handsomely furnished. Extras range from the whimsical (Donald Duck hair-dryers and teddy bears), through the fortifying (complimentary sherry or vermouth) to the just plain thoughtful (Scrabble for a rainy day). Richard has now placed binoculars in all the rooms to help guests get a better view of the birds, and other wildlife, that swoop around the water garden and majestic grounds – there's even a tape to help with identification of birdsong.

◑ Open all year   🅿 At post office in Dulverton, take B3223 signposted Exford and Lynton; drive over moor; cross 2 cattle-grids and take a left turn to Ashwick House. Private car park   🛏 2 twin, 4 double; all with bathroom/WC; all with TV, room service, hair-dryer, trouser press, direct-dial telephone, clock radio, some with mini-bar; no tea/coffee-making facilities in rooms   ⎷ Restaurant, 2 drawing-rooms, drying-room, library, garden; functions (max 60 people incl up to 12 residential), conferences; solarium; early suppers for children   ♿ No wheelchair access   ● No children under 8; no dogs; no smoking in restaurant and some bedrooms   ⬚ None accepted
£ Single occupancy of twin/double £48 to £60, twin/double £96 to £104; deposit required. Set L £15, D £22. Special breaks available

---

DUNSLEY North Yorkshire   map 9

Dunsley Hall   NEW ENTRY

Dunsley, Whitby YO21 3TL
TEL: (01947) 893437   FAX: (01947) 893505

Clubby country house, with plush, newly refurbished bedrooms and restrained, grown-up style.

Dunsley Hall started life at the turn of the century as a residence for a Newcastle fishing magnate. You can certainly see why he chose this spot, perched on high ground at the edge of the North York Moors National Park, which drops away dramatically to give superb views along the coast. The outstanding feature of the interior is oak – acres of glowing golden panels that exude a warm sheen of luxury in all the classy public rooms. The Oak Lounge, an excellent venue for sinking into creaky leather sofas, is embellished with stained-glass windows and ornate plaster friezes, while in the equally oaky restaurant, elegant chairs, white linen, gleaming cutlery and huge balloon wineglasses set the tone. The ambitious modern menu takes its influences from the Mediterranean to the Far East. The service, which is polite with an edge of formality, is supervised by owner Bill Ward, a hands-on, no-nonsense sort of chap who likes to see that his guests are happy. This aim would certainly be achieved in the newly refurbished bedrooms: they are all spick and span and kitted out in a tastefully opulent style with a fair sprinkling of antique furniture, and have stone-mullioned leaded windows, sea views and luxurious bathrooms. Room 18, a mini-suite, is a real treat, with excellent coastal views and a magnificent Regency walnut half-tester bed with matching walnut furniture.

◑ Open all year ⭐ Signposted from A171 Whitby road. Private car park 🅿 2 single, 3 twin, 7 double, 2 four-poster, 1 family room, 2 suites; most with bathroom/WC, 2 with shower/WC; all with TV, room service, hair-dryer, trouser press, direct-dial telephone ✐ 2 restaurants, bar, lounge, drying-room, garden; functions (max 200 people incl up to 33 residential), conferences; civil wedding licence; golf, gym, sauna, solarium, heated indoor swimming-pool, tennis, putting green, croquet; leisure facilities nearby (free for guests); early suppers for children; cots, high chairs, baby-listening ♿ Wheelchair access to hotel (ramp) and restaurants, WC (unisex), 2 ground-floor bedrooms ⬤ No children under 4 in main restaurant eves; no dogs; no smoking in some bedrooms ▭ Amex, Delta, MasterCard, Switch, Visa £ Single £58, single occupancy of twin/double £67, twin/double £95, four-poster £110, family room £115, suite £149; deposit required. Bistro D £20; set D (restaurant) £24 Special breaks available

---

DUNSTER Somerset   map 1

Exmoor House Hotel [NEW ENTRY]

West Street, Dunster, Minehead TA24 6SN
TEL: (01643) 821268   FAX: (01643) 821267

Small hotel, recently refurbished by new owners, in lovely village with National Trust castle.

The striking, pristine, lemon-stucco façade, set off by rows of colour-cascading window boxes, gives just a hint of what David and Karan Howell have set out to do since taking over the helm of this Georgian town house at the heart of a bustling, touristy village. Both the neatness and the passion for bright, bold colours are mirrored in an interior that sometimes seems to owe more to the Mediterranean than to the mid-west of England. This effect is at its most startling in the front-facing, bright bar/sitting-room area, where a gloriously sunny effect has been achieved by tempering yellow with a spot of red rag-rolling; Lindsay-tartan chairs, and fabrics and upholstery in modish plaids and stripes, give the room a smart, vibrant feel. By comparison, the bright yellow of the residents' drawing-room seems almost muted, suffering, perhaps, from the lack of natural light. The Garden Room restaurant is more upbeat, prettily mixing lemon and blue elements in a simple, but elegant, room, which leads out to a small terrace where diners might enjoy a sundowner on a fine summer evening. The short menu offers one or more alternatives at all but the soup stage, and may perhaps include smoked-salmon and prawn whirls, followed by leek and potato soup, then chicken breast prepared with apple and cider, before finally dessert and coffee.

The six bedrooms are individually decorated and furnished with flair and imagination, from the delicate blue of the pretty Delphine's Room to the flowing lines of The Sleigh and the mock-medievalism of The Gothic. All feature classy fabrics and the same sure touch with colour that is a hallmark of the place, though some are a bit on the small side.

◑ Open all year   ⤢ From A39, 2 miles outside Minehead, take A396 signposted Dunster; follow road down high street and through traffic lights; hotel is on right. On-street parking (free)   ⤙ 2 twin, 4 double; 1 double with bathroom/WC, most with shower/WC; all with TV, room service, hair-dryer, trouser press, direct-dial telephone   ✓ Dining-room, bar/sitting-room, drawing-room; functions (max 50 people incl up to 12 residential);   ♿ No wheelchair access   ● No children under 12; no dogs; smoking in bar only   ▭ Amex, Delta, MasterCard, Switch, Visa   £ Single occupancy of twin/double £35 to £50, twin/double £55 to £90; deposit required. Set D £24.50. Special breaks available

---

DURHAM Co Durham   map 10

Georgian Town House

10–11 Crossgate, Durham DH1 4PS
TEL: 0191-386 8070 (AND FAX)

Comfy B&B with quirky modern décor right in Durham's centre.

You could hardly ask for a better location when visiting Durham. The Georgian Town House sits at the top of a cobbled street just a few minutes' stroll from the railway and bus stations, and a short walk across the River Wear will bring you to an ample choice of restaurants and pubs, not to mention the Norman castle and cathedral – visible from some of the rooms, and particularly attractive when floodlit. Fruit trees stencilled on the white façade of the house let you know what the interior has in store. Staying at Jane Weil's B&B is rather reminiscent of watching one of those popular programmes where interior designers make over an otherwise plain house with liberal use of stencils and brightly coloured paints and fabrics. The result is undeniably bright, cheerful and fun: pillars, ivy, fleurs-de-lys, sun, moon and stars are all used to good effect – particularly in diverting your attention from the less-than-generous proportions of the rooms, which are a riot of bright and breezy colour-washed walls, bold fabrics and simple furniture given the stencils-and-gilt-paint treatment. The small conservatory makes a pleasant breakfast room, and, even if seating is a little tight, treats like scrambled egg with smoked salmon should get the day off on the right note.

All entries in the Guide *are rewritten every year, not least because standards fluctuate. Don't trust an out-of-date edition.*

◗ Open all year ⊅ From A1(M), Junction 62, take A690 to Durham; follow signs to Crook and Newcastle; at 3rd roundabout turn left. On-street parking (free) ⌨ 1 twin, 5 double, 1 family room; all with bathroom/WC; all with TV; hair-dryer on request
∅ Lounge, breakfast room/conservatory, garden ⅚ No wheelchair access
● No dogs; no smoking in bedrooms ☐ None accepted £ Single occupancy of twin/double £40, twin/double £50 to £55, family room £75 to £85; deposit required.

EAST BARKWITH Lincolnshire   map 9

Bodkin Lodge

Grange Farm, Torrington Lane, East Barkwith,
Market Rasen LN8 5RY
TEL: (01673) 858249

Classic elegance and welcoming hospitality distinguish this rural retreat.

As you approach, the driveway to Anne and Richard Stamp's bungalow gives you few clues to the real nature of the place. There are flowers in tubs and a slightly Mediterranean-looking porch, but it is only when you enter Bodkin Lodge, and walk through the beech-floored hall into the sitting-room, that the full flavour of the establishment comes across. With its elegant white drapes, touches of gilt and subdued, natural colours, 'bungalow' seems a far too tight-fisted description for such a spacious villa.

There are only two guest rooms, of which the corner double is preferable for its views over the fields and hedgerows of the land that is still farmed by a younger generation of Stamps. Each room has a small lobby, giving it extra privacy, and a smart, well-equipped bathroom that offers both a bath and a separate shower. Don't be surprised if there is a large sheet of wallpaper stuck to the wall – Anne often tests her guests' opinion on any changes that she makes to the décor. Visitors are offered a complimentary sherry in the sitting-room (but bring your own wine, as the Stamps have no licence) before wandering through to the cosy dining-room. Dinner is taken with other guests, and sometimes with the Stamps, too. Anne might typically serve a cucumber mousse, followed by pheasant breast cooked in a redcurrant and orange sauce, then a choice of desserts and local cheeses with biscuits to finish. Next day you might raise an appetite for breakfast by exploring the farm walk that meanders along the hedgerows, taking in the field where Cromwell reputedly once asked for directions.

◗ Closed Chr & New Year ⊅ Turn off A157 by war memorial in East Barkwith into Torrington Lane; hotel is at end, on right. Private car park ⌨ 1 twin, 1 double; both with bathroom/WC; all with TV, hair-dryer, clock radio ∅ Dining-room, sitting-room, drying-room, garden; fishing; early suppers for children ⅚ No wheelchair access
● No children under 10; no dogs; no smoking ☐ None accepted £ Single occupancy of twin/double £25 to £30, twin/double £43 to £50; deposit required. Set D £14; alc D £7

Use the maps in the central section of the Guide *to pinpoint hotels in a particular area.*

EAST BUCKLAND Devon   map 1

Lower Pitt

East Buckland, Barnstaple EX32 0TD
TEL: (01598) 760243 (AND FAX)
WEB SITE: www.castlelink.co.uk/perl/

*Reliable restaurant-with-rooms in characterful old Devon
longhouse, well off the beaten track.*

Everything about Lower Pitt is well established. The village must be one of the
sleepiest in north Devon; the house is a sixteenth-century longhouse with a
pretty cherry tree out front; Suzanne and Jerome have been here for two decades;
and for the last several years we have consistently received complimentary
reports on Suzanne's cooking: 'every bit as excellent as you described' concurred
one reader. Her extensive menu features classics such as suprême of guinea fowl
with a mushroom, Madeira and tarragon sauce, but she's also a dab hand at
creating exotic dishes like Moroccan lamb tajine, or a prawn, mango and
cashew-nut salad with a Thai-style shrimp dressing. It's fun to dine in the cosy,
low-ceilinged part of the restaurant (originally the dairy – note the tiny windows
and shutters) with its pew-like room dividers, or, if you prefer more space, you
can opt for the conservatory section, which is surrounded by an exuberant little
garden. Diners and residents can sit around the huge open grate in the tiny bar,
or take coffee in the peaceful lounge, but the real character of the house comes
through upstairs, where bulging walls and drunken floors would make the most
devout teetotaller stagger. Mind your head on all the low doorways. The
bedrooms are on the small side, but are prettily done out in cottagey style.

◑ Closed 24 & 25 Dec ▨ 3 miles north of A361, signposted East and West Buckland;
hotel is around corner from church. Private car park 🛏 1 twin, 2 double; twin with
bathroom/WC, doubles with shower/WC; all with TV, hair-dryer ⊘ restaurant, bar,
lounge, garden; ♿ No wheelchair access ⬤ No children under 12; no children in
restaurant after 9pm; no dogs; smoking in bar only ▭ Amex, MasterCard, Switch,
Visa £ Single occupancy of twin/double £40, twin/double £60; deposit required. Alc
D £25. Special breaks available

EAST GRINSTEAD West Sussex   map 3

Gravetye Manor

Vowels Lane, East Grinstead RH19 4LJ
TEL: (01342) 810567   FAX: (01342) 810080
EMAIL: gravetye@relaischateaux.fr

*Glorious gardens, sumptuous repasts and plush rooms, but all at a
hefty price.*

Gravetye celebrated a big anniversary year in 1998, marking four hundred years
since Richard Infield built the manor for his wife, Katherine, and forty years
since Peter Herbert created a country-house hotel within it. In true keeping with
the hotel's style and demeanour, any commemorations were discreet and

understated, two watchwords of a stay here. It's luxurious, yet unpretentious, elegant, yet unintimidating. The open-plan reception, with its acres of polished wood and roaring log fire, leads on to the equally inviting sitting-room. Both have impressive, moulded-plaster ceilings, installed in 1906 and still standing the test of time, despite the occasional overflowing bath. As you sit down for dinner, surrounded by crisp linen and gleaming glasses, remember that the chairs were made exclusively for Gravetye and the blueprint then destroyed. Mark Raffan's cuisine continues to excel: Roquefort soufflé, grilled calf's liver with bacon and red-wine sauce, and caramelised lemon tart might be your choice. Every bedroom is harmoniously furnished and immaculately presented, and many, such as Bay and Holly, have views of William Robinson's famous natural English gardens. Even Larch, the single, is spacious and smart, with a *trompe l'oeil* window in the jazzy bathroom. All come with a supply of Gravetye's own spring water, while the kitchen garden provides fruit, herbs, eggs and vegetables.

◑ Open all year ⤭ Leave M23 at Junction 10 on to A264 towards East Grinstead; at second roundabout take third exit (B2028). After Turners Hill village, turn left (Selsfield Road), then first left into Vowels Lane. Private car park ⤶ 1 single, 9 twin/double, 7 double, 1 four-poster; most with bathroom/WC; all with TV, room service, hair-dryer, trouser press, direct-dial telephone, radio, safe; no tea/coffee-making facilities in rooms ⊘ Restaurant, bar, 2 sitting-rooms, garden; functions (max 16 people residential/non-residential), conferences; fishing, croquet; cots, babysitting, baby-listening ♿ No wheelchair access ● No children under 7 except babes in arms; no dogs; no smoking in restaurant ▭ Delta, MasterCard, Switch, Visa £ Single £100 to £130, single occupancy of twin/double £171, twin/double £136 to £259, four-poster £212 to £259. Continental B £12, cooked B £14.50; set L £30, D £38; alc L, D £59

EAST KNOYLE Wiltshire

map 2

Milton Farm

East Knoyle, Salisbury SP3 6BG
TEL: (01747) 830247

The unusual bonus of a swimming-pool at a picture-postcard farmhouse B&B in a stunning location.

It's not so much *Paradise Lost* as East Knoyle's Elysian fields at Janice Hyde's Milton Farm, a glorious Queen Anne house set at the foot of a densely wooded hill and overlooking undulating downs. The Hydes have held the stewardship of this working farm for generations, so there's a definite lived-in family quality to the house, whose original features are counterpointed by those of a more contemporary life. A certain grandeur is established at the gate, where stone lions on high pedestals guard the property against invaders. Those guests who are undaunted by the leonine sentinels will find themselves welcomed in the house's one public area, a dining-room boasting exposed-stone walls and a notable fireplace. Breakfast is served here, on striking Portuguese ceramics which Janice also sells from a gallery set up in an outbuilding in the grounds. The two guest bedrooms are simply, but solidly, furnished in a comfortable, if not exactly stylish, way. Summer-season guests are most likely to make optimum use of the garden, and in particular of the huge outdoor swimming-pool, a welcome bonus on a sultry day.

◑ Closed Dec to Feb **↗** ¼ mile off A350 north-west of East Knoyle, signposted Milton. Private car park **↤** 1 twin, 1 double; twin with shower/WC, double with bathroom/WC; both with TV **✓** Dining-room, garden; heated outdoor swimming-pool; high chairs **હ** No wheelchair access **●** Dogs by arrangement only **☐** None accepted **£** Twin/double £50.

EASTON GREY **Wiltshire**   map 2

Whatley Manor

Easton Grey, Malmesbury SN16 0RB
TEL: (01666) 822888   FAX: (01666) 826120

Extensive leisure facilities at a seventeenth-century manor house on the edge of the Cotswolds.

Easton Grey sounds like the protagonist of a Jane Austen novel, and indeed Whatley Manor, a fine edifice of golden Cotswold stone, was well into its second century by the time Miss Austen got around to weaving her devilishly insightful tales of social observation amongst the landed gentry. It's an easy drive to Bath, a favourite Austen location, but guests, whether on business or at leisure, may find the diversions on offer at the hotel offer stiff competition to the famous spa town. The original house was extended (sprouting new wings) by a wealthy sports-minded owner in the 1920s, and more recent expansion has seen an additional 11 bedrooms installed in a Court House annexe, bringing the total number up to 29. The extensive gardens and a swathe of paddocks running down to the River Avon are big enough to absorb the additional development without compromising the essential peace or seclusion of the place.

There's a clubby feel to the rather intimate, book-lined bar which offers an alternative meeting place to the traditionally oak-panelled drawing-room or the lighter, thoughtfully lit and inviting hall lounge. The dining-room is a graceful, tasteful affair with a light peaches-and-cream colour scheme. It's a suitably elegant spot to enjoy dinner: perhaps mushroom and tarragon soup, followed by Dover sole meunière and summer pudding. The bedrooms go for a traditional, play-safe look. You'll get a better view of the grounds from the main house rooms than from the smaller offerings in the Court House, which are cheaper.

◑ Open all year **↗** On B4040, 3 miles west of Malmesbury. Private car park **↤** 12 twin, 14 double, 1 four-poster, 2 family rooms; some in annexe; all with bathroom/WC; all with TV, hair-dryer, direct-dial telephone, some with room service **✓** Dining-room, bar, 2 lounges, library, 2 games rooms, garden; functions (max 80 people non-residential, 60 residential), conferences; civil wedding licence; fishing, sauna, solarium, heated outdoor swimming-pool, tennis, croquet, snooker, clay-pigeon shooting; early suppers for children; cots, high chairs, babysitting, baby-listening **હ** No wheelchair access **●** No dogs in public rooms **☐** Amex, Diners, MasterCard, Visa **£** Single occupancy of twin/double £78 to £88, twin/double/family room £92 to £126, four-poster £126; deposit required. Set L £15.50, D £30. Special breaks available

Tree Tops

The Village Green, East Ord, Berwick-upon-Tweed TD15 2NS
TEL: (01289) 330679

Exceptionally caring hosts in a homely guesthouse with a delightful garden.

In their simple but pretty 1920s bungalow that occupies a peaceful spot set back from East Ord's village green, John and Elizabeth Nicholls set a standard of genuine warmth and hospitality that guesthouse visitors can usually only dream of. The name seems a touch baffling until John takes you on a walk down the magical garden that boasts two summerhouses and extends deceptively beyond the immaculate croquet lawn, shrubbery and fruit orchard to a wild woodland glade of mature beech, aspen and cherry trees. There's no better way to get acquainted with its secrets than by taking afternoon tea and home-made scones in the primrose-yellow revolving summerhouse christened 'Poets Corner'. Back indoors, the house turns out to be unexpectedly large, and the simple, fresh décor complements the care and thought that John and Elizabeth have put in to guarantee a special stay; you'll find parking discs, timetables, bathrobes, local biscuits and a host of useful extras in the cheerful, uncluttered rooms, and the comfy sitting-room contains painstakingly in-depth information about the area, with hints and tips that only local people would know. At meal-times, fresh local produce and organic fruit and vegetables from the garden are much in evidence. Candlelit evening meals are served on Wednesdays, and on Saturday's special 'Border Nights', which offer a unique way to taste regional Northumbrian and Scottish specialities, John's Scottish roots and clan regalia are proudly displayed.

◖ Closed 1 Nov to 31 Mar; dining-room open Wed & Sat eve only ⬚ At East Ord green, turn right at mini-crossroads; take second right into hotel. Private car park ⌂ 1 twin, 1 double; double with bathroom/WC, twin with shower/WC; all with TV, limited room service, hair-dryer, clock radio; iron on request ⬦ Dining-room, sitting-room, drying-room, 2 summerhouses, garden; croquet ⛬ No wheelchair access ◓ No children under 15; no dogs or smoking ⬚ None accepted ⬚ Single occupancy of twin/double from £33, twin/double from £46; deposit required. Set D £15. Special breaks available

---

Gara Rock

East Portlemouth, Salcombe TQ8 8PH
TEL: (01548) 842342 FAX: (01548) 843033

A warm welcome, and oodles of entertainment for children and adults at this clifftop hotel.

Gara Rock started life as a killjoy sort of place – its bird's-eye spot, high on the clifftop above a gorgeous, secluded, sandy beach, made it ideal as a lookout station, from which the coastguards would pounce on smugglers. But all that stopped in 1909 when it became a hotel, and now it is firmly dedicated to bringing joy to people of all ages. Children are warmly welcomed here; entertainments are laid on in the form of clown shows, barbecues and parties for the youngsters, and weekly discos and tennis tournaments for the adults. The focus on sunny days is, of course, the beach – a few minutes' scramble down the hill, with a wreck to explore past the point and no traffic for miles around. While the charm of the original coastguards' cottages has been lost in the sprawl of extensions (which house self-contained, family apartments), the main house has comfortable and bright public rooms. Stripped floors and panelled walls lend them character, and in the bar you can honk a horn if 'in need of urgent lubrication'. There's plenty of choice on the menu – bistro-type dishes like lasagne and pizza are available all day, and in the evening you can go for something a bit more up-market, such as chorizo-sausage hors d'oeuvre with a selection of salads, followed by skate wing with roasted-red-pepper butter. The bedrooms in the main house have recently been refurbished, so stay in these rather than in the faded self-catering units outside.

◑ Closed Nov to Jan　⊅ From Kingsbridge, head towards Dartmouth on A379 for 4 miles; at Frogmore turn right over bridge; follow signs to East Portlemouth and Gara Rock. Private car park　⌁ 42 rooms, which can be let as twin/double/family rooms; some in annexe; suites available; most with bathroom/WC, some with shower/WC; all with TV, direct-dial telephone, radio, some with trouser press　⊘ 2 restaurants, bar, lounge, drying-room, games room, garden; functions (max 150 people incl up to 100 residential), conferences; heated outdoor swimming-pool, tennis; leisure facilities nearby (reduced rates for guests); early suppers for children; cots, high chairs, babysitting, baby-listening, mini-club, children's entertainment in high season; ⅋ No wheelchair access　● No smoking in public rooms; dogs £10 per day ▭ Delta, MasterCard, Switch, Visa　£ Single occupancy of twin/double £38 to £70, twin/double £54 to £100, family rooms and apartments (prices on application); deposit required. Cooked B £8.50; bar/bistro L £4.50; set D £16. Special breaks available

---

EAST WITTON　North Yorkshire　　　　　　　　map 9

Blue Lion

East Witton, Leyburn DL8 4SN
TEL: (01969) 624273　FAX: (01969) 624189

Classy and characterful country inn, with renowned food.

The Blue Lion may look like a pub in a tranquil estate village, but once you're through the door that notion is soon dispelled. Gone are its days as a simple coaching-inn catering to drovers passing through Wensleydale – its latest incarnation is as a decidedly up-market inn, focused firmly on the ambitious cuisine served in the classic bar and inviting restaurant. The well-heeled clientele could hardly be further from the bluff, cloth-capped Yorkshireman of legend; conversation in the hugely atmospheric main bar – a traditional assemblage of flagstones, hissing log fire and oak pews with a pubby patina – is likely to centre on racehorse breeding or the slopes at Verbier. Guests can sink a pint of hand-pulled ale, which tilts the neck to the appropriate angle to facilitate a lengthy study of the blackboard menus that take up a good chunk of the walls, before selecting crab and ginger tagliatelle with toasted Gruyère, perhaps, followed by chargrilled venison steak with blueberries and shallots. For pudding, fresh figs with Christmas-pudding ice-cream and cinnamon and Madeira syrup takes some beating. Although the wine list is peppered with serious names, it is refreshing to be able to choose from around eight good wines offered by the glass. The popularity of the bar can make the atmosphere somewhat hectic, so the intimate restaurant, with its wooden floor and log fire, offers sanctuary. The bedrooms take a back seat to the Blue Lion's culinary endeavours, and are nothing to get excited about. Their décor is simple and well co-ordinated; some rooms have Victorian furniture to add a touch of interest.

○ Open all year; restaurants closed Sun & Mon eves (bar menu available) ⤢ On A6108 Masham to Leyburn road. Private car park ⤶ 2 twin, 9 double, 1 family room; some in annexe; all with bathroom/WC exc 2 doubles with shower/WC; all with TV, direct-dial telephone; hair-dryer on request ⊘ 2 restaurants, 2 bars, garden; functions (max 100 people incl up to 24 residential), conferences; tennis; early suppers for children; high chairs, babysitting, baby-listening ♿ Wheelchair access to hotel (1 step) and restaurants, WC (unisex), 4 ground-floor bedrooms ● No dogs in restaurants ▭ MasterCard, Switch, Visa £ Single occupancy of twin/double £48 to £65, twin/double £75 to £85, family room £85. Bar/bistro L £6; alc D £25. Special breaks available

---

EATON BISHOP Herefordshire   map 5

Ancient Camp Inn   NEW ENTRY

Ruckhall, Eaton Bishop, Hereford HR2 9QX
TEL: (01981) 250449   FAX: (01981) 251581

Friendly, peaceful, country pub, offering strikingly good food and magnificent views of the River Wye.

An Iron Age hill-fort gives this pleasant country inn its name. Tracking it down among the winding lanes and hidden villages west of Hereford takes perseverance, but success is rewarded by a breathtaking, grandstand vista of the River Wye, a flower-filled terrace and excellent food, served in pleasantly unpretentious surroundings. Three years into their new life at the Ancient Camp Inn, Pauline and Ewart McKie have now had enough time to acclimatise following their lengthy, expatriate sojourn managing hotels in the Caribbean. They seem to have taken to the cooler climes of the Herefordshire countryside like ducks to water, and are thoroughly at home behind the bar and in the kitchen: after teething troubles with chefs, Ewart rolled up his sleeves and now does the cooking himself, with very successful results, while the cheerfully efficient Pauline stays mainly front-of-house. Fresh, high-quality produce emerges in clearly recognisable guises after imaginative, but unfussy, treatment behind the scenes. The unevenly flagstoned bar areas are simply furnished with a mix of rough-hewn, wooden trestles and small, round tables modestly skirted with Laura Ashley fabrics. Fresh flowers, piped musical classics and contemporary prints and drawings add civilised, up-market touches. The bedrooms are light, modern and well equipped. The better-than-average breakfasts give you another chance to enjoy the view if you choose your table carefully.

O Closed 1 to 22 Jan   **⊿** From Hereford take A465 to south-west; turn right 200 yards after Belmont roundabout signposted Belmont Abbey and Ruckhall. Inn is 2½ miles further, in hamlet of Ruckhall. Private car park   **⊨** 1 twin, 2 double, 2 suites; 2 with bathroom/WC, 3 with shower/WC; all with TV, direct-dial telephone; ironing facilities and hair-dryer available   **⊘** Restaurant, bar, lounge, garden; functions (max 70 people incl up to 10 residential); fishing; golf nearby   **⅄** No wheelchair access   **●** No children under 14; no dogs; smoking in bar and lounge only   **▭** Delta, MasterCard, Switch, Visa   **£** Single occupancy of twin/double £45, twin/double £50, suite £60; deposit required. Bar/bistro L £8; alc D £25

EDITH WESTON Rutland

map 6

Normanton Park

Rutland Water South Shore, Edith Weston, Oakham LE15 8RP
TEL: (01780) 720315   FAX: (01780) 721086

Lakeside hotel with friendly staff, appealing to both business people and weekenders.

Normanton Park stands close by the south shore of Rutland Water, and is the former coaching stables to some long-gone stately home. It is quite a grand building itself: a single-storey, stone-built block with clock tower and neo-classical flourishes that looks into what was once the stableyard, now a car park. Unfortunately this means most bedrooms do not look out over the lake – those that do are worth the supplement. Room 23, for example, is a bright double in country-house style, with half-tester and sofa; as in all the rooms, there is a cafetière with real coffee, and home-made biscuits, on the tray. Other rooms open directly from the car park and, in contrast, seem dark and slightly dated in style. Much brighter and more attractive is the Orangery restaurant that looks out over the lake and caters for a mixed clientele of business people, yachties, fishermen and weekenders. For less formal dining there is also the Sailing Bar, a split-level restaurant offering anything from salads or sandwiches to local trout steamed with prawns, apricot and vegetable julienne. Afterwards coffee is served in the very cosy cocktail-bar-cum-lounge, its walls decorated with historical pictures of the stables and the house.

O Open all year; restaurant closed Sun eve   **⊿** Take turning off A606 signposted Edith Weston/Rutland Water. Private car park   **⊨** 1 single, 5 twin, 10 double, 2 four-poster, 5 family rooms; all with bathroom/WC exc 2 twins with shower/WC; all with TV, room service, hair-dryer, trouser press, direct-dial telephone; ironing facilities   **⊘** Restaurant, bar, lounge, garden; functions (max 120 people incl up to 50 residential), conferences; civil wedding licence; fishing; cots, high chairs, babysitting, baby-listening   **⅄** Wheelchair access to hotel (1 step) and restaurant, 8 ground-floor bedrooms, 2 rooms partially equipped for disabled people   **●** Dogs £10 per stay   **▭** Amex, Delta, MasterCard, Switch, Visa   **£** Single £58 to £65, single occupancy of twin/double £58 to £65, twin/double/four-poster £75 to £85, family room £85; deposit required. Bar/bistro L, D £7 to £15; alc L, D £22.50. Special breaks available

---

Don't forget that other hotels worth considering are listed in our Round-ups near the back of the Guide.

Great Fosters   NEW ENTRY

Stroude Road, Egham TW20 9UR
TEL: (01784) 433822   FAX: (01784) 472455
EMAIL: greatfosters@compuserve.com

Luxury, at a price, in a Tudor Royal hunting lodge, handy for Heathrow and the M25.

Dating back to 1550, Great Fosters has a history that is almost tangible, and the miles of polished wood reek of it. Doing the dusting and polishing here is rather like painting the Forth Bridge, with so many panelled walls, creaking floorboards and carved banisters to keep pristine. After stooping to fit through the tiny wicket door within the front door, the first of these wooden wonders you glimpse is the huge panelled reception. From then on, it's all mullioned windows, hanging tapestries, grand fireplaces and beamed ceilings. Top of the range are the feature rooms, from the overtly opulent Italian Bedroom to Panel II with its open fireplace. The more affordable rooms are still atmospheric, with smartly pleasant décor. The smallest room (no, not that one) is Curtain – a cute little single with an unbelievably bijou bath – not one for a long soak. The past guest list is almost as illustrious as the woodwork: Elizabeth Taylor, Julie Andrews and Bing Crosby, to name a few. Charlie Chaplin apparently made daily use of the secret passage between Tapestry and Nursery rooms to wish his children goodnight. If you're not dashing off to the airport, a stroll in the pretty gardens is well worth it, especially in the Topiary Garden, modelled on the design of a Persian carpet. 'Friendly service and excellent food,' was one reader's verdict. The table d'hôte menu might offer slivers of melon with marinated berries, julienne of duck with mango and cucumber sauce, and orange bavarois.

◑ Open all year   🔁 Leave M25 at Junction 13 towards Egham; at end of slip road turn left at large roundabout into avenue; turn left at mini-roundabout, cross railway and continue to end; turn right at mini-roundabout; bear left at next roundabout towards Virginia Water; hotel is on left, on B389. Private car park   🛏 21 single, 4 twin, 16 double, 1 four-poster, 2 suites; some in annexe; most with bathroom/WC, some with shower/WC; all with TV, hair-dryer, trouser press, direct-dial telephone, some with room service   ⌘ Restaurant, bar, lounge, TV room, games room, garden; conferences (max 250 people incl up to 26 residential), functions; civil wedding licence; tennis, croquet; early suppers for children; cots, high chairs, babysitting, baby-listening   ⟐ Wheelchair access to hotel (2 steps) and restaurant, WC (unisex), 2 ground-floor bedrooms, 1 specially equipped for disabled people   ● No dogs   ▭ Amex, Diners, MasterCard, Switch, Visa   £ Single from £95, single occupancy of twin/double from £98, twin/double from £105, four-poster/family room from £170, suite from £195; deposit required. Set L £15.50, D £25; alc L, D £30. Special breaks available

Where we say 'Deposit required', a hotel may instead ask for your credit card details when taking your booking.

ELTERWATER Cumbria

map 8

Britannia Inn

Elterwater, Ambleside LA22 9HP
TEL: (015394) 37210   FAX: (015394) 37311

Popular walkers' pub in the depths of Langdale.

This straightforward, Cumbrian inn on the village green puts on no airs and graces, but it does have some history and plenty of character. Its location, in one of the most popular centres of the gorgeous Langdale Valley, means that it is never short of visitors, and it's an obvious focal point of village life. Named after a sailing ship, the SS *Britannia*, the inn dates back some four hundred years, and though it has inevitably been adapted to suit its modern, catering role, it's still a 'proper' English pub. The simply furnished bar contains dining areas, though residents' dinners take priority during the evenings. Among the plain, wooden tables and ubiquitous wheelback chairs, you may spot a fine, carved sideboard and some interesting naval bric-a-brac. Log fires tempt customers inside on chilly days. Bar food includes such well-tried staples as jacket potatoes, steaks, and cream teas, as well as full meals like Cumberland pie or poached salmon. Even the simplest cheese roll is a generously superior crusty snack, and service is willing and pleasant. The bedrooms are small and quaintly dimensioned, though the furnishings (florals and routine, modern veneers) lack much charm, but as they're booked up six weeks ahead at weekends, there's little incentive for improvement. Overspill rooms lie in a beamed annexe over the village shop opposite – these may be quieter at closing time.

○ Closed 25 & 26 Dec ⊞ From Ambleside, take A593 to Coniston; turn right at Skelwith Bridge Hotel on to B5343. Private car park ⊫ 1 single, 3 twin, 9 double; some in annexe; 1 double with bathroom/WC, most with shower/WC; all with TV, hair-dryer, direct-dial telephone ✓ Bar/dining-room, lounge, drying-room; cots, high chairs ♿ No wheelchair access ● No smoking or dogs in dining-room area ▭ Amex, Delta, MasterCard, Switch, Visa £ Single £20 to £24, single occupancy of twin/double £34 to £56, twin/double £40 to £62; deposit required. Bar/bistro L £6, D £6.50; alc L £12, D £13. Special breaks available

ELY Cambridgeshire

map 6

Black Hostelry

Cathedral Close, The College, Ely CB7 4DL
TEL: (01353) 662612   FAX: (01353) 665658

A small, atmospheric B&B with ancient, monastic origins, near the cathedral.

This is as close to medieval living as you are likely to get nowadays: the Black Hostelry is situated within the environs of Ely Cathedral, and once belonged to the black-robed monks of the town's Benedictine monastery. For almost 20 years it has been the private home of Mr and Mrs Green, who have wisely tampered as little as possible with their historic surroundings, which include original, Norman arches and a medieval undercroft. The two bedrooms are comfortably furnished; the nicest overlooks an attractive, walled garden, and has a sitting-room and a small bathroom. The other room is of a good size and has a private bathroom next door, but its toilet is downstairs, off the hallway. If you stay in this room, you can breakfast at an ancient dean-and-chapter table in the vaulted undercroft, which is stained with the ink and sealing wax from old documents signed at ecclesiastical meetings.

◑ Closed Chr   🔼 In centre of Ely, on south side of cathedral. Private car park
🛏 1 family room, 1 suite; both with bathroom/WC (family room WC not *en suite*); both with TV   ⊘ Garden   ᕁ No wheelchair access   ● No smoking   ▭ None accepted   £ Single occupancy of family room/suite £49, family room/suite £57; deposit required

---

ETCHINGHAM East Sussex map 3

King John's Lodge

Sheepstreet Lane, Etchingham TN19 7AZ
TEL: (01580) 819232   FAX: (01580) 819562

A historic country house, with a warm, family atmosphere and gorgeous gardens.

Architectural devotees would love King John's Lodge: although it's mainly built of seventeenth-century, Jacobean stone, there are older, Elizabethan bits, as well as more recent, Victorian and Edwardian additions. The hotchpotch of styles blends into a wonderfully rambling country house, with diamond-shaped windows and a soft-orange tiled roof. Jill and Richard Cunningham decided to run their house as a B&B after their four children grew up, but it still has the atmosphere of a family home, and photos are displayed in the sitting-room, where pine furniture, china and fresh flowers give a fresh, airy feel. The dining-room is more formal, with a grand fireplace, burnt-sienna walls, sombre portraits and a heavily beamed ceiling. There are four bedrooms, including the Blue Room (a roomy double), Elizabethan (a pine-furnished, family room) and Jacobean (a large room, with a grandstand view of the garden). Jill is the gardener, and has cultivated the land into distinct areas: formal, woodland, wild and – the most popular with guests – a secret garden with a pretty waterfall. Her work has been featured in garden magazines, and she opens the garden regularly to the public. Evening meals are served only by arrangement, and might consist of asparagus, followed by coq au vin and then strawberries.

◑ Closed Chr & New year   🔼 Turn off A21 at Flimwell and follow A2087 to Ticehurst; turn left past church and first left again; house is 1 mile on left. Private car park
🛏 2 twin, 2 double; family suite available; 3 with bathroom/WC, 1 with shower/WC
⊘ Dining-room, sitting-room, TV room, garden; heated outdoor swimming-pool, tennis, croquet   ᕁ No wheelchair access   ● No children under 7; no dogs; smoking in 1 public room only   ▭ None accepted   £ Single occupancy of twin/double £40 to £45, twin/double £65 to £70, family suite £80 to £85; deposit required. Set D £25

Prices are quoted per room *rather than* per person.

EVERSHOT Dorset   map 2

Summer Lodge

Summer Lane, Evershot, Dorchester DT2 0JR
TEL: (01935) 83424   FAX: (01935) 83005
EMAIL: sumlodge@sumlodge.demon.co.uk
WEB SITE: www.integra.fr/relaischateaux/summer

Quite simply superb – a hotel for all seasons set in a quintessentially English landscape.

Hotel inspectors get to see and stay in an awful lot of hotels. Just occasionally, we come across one that really makes the heart soar so much that we just long to return. Summer Lodge is such a place. From the hydrangeas that blaze with colour as you sweep into the driveway, to the staff who appear, apparently unbidden, to carry your bags, everything at this Georgian former dower house of the earls of Ilchester seems designed to accord the most genuine of (properly English and restrained) welcomes. The creamy, creeper-clad façades, hanging baskets, delightful terraces and manicured croquet lawn all conspire to conjure up an image of a dreamy, idealised summer of long ago. The interior, a collection of light, airy rooms, is no less special, not least the drawing-room designed by a certain Mr Thomas Hardy before he decided to give up the day job.

Bright, modern art (echoed in the watercolours that distinguish the rather grand menus) adds vigour to a pretty dining-room, where guests might dine on rillettes of salmon, followed by creamy courgette soup, roasted breast of guinea-fowl with ceps, and then apricot and almond tart with an apricot and muscat sorbet. The bedrooms, which overlook the gardens or village, are individually decorated in an agreeable style which manages to team flamboyant colours with daintily elegant furniture. Each has its characteristic cheesecover – part of a collection that is gradually taking over the hotel.

❍ Open all year ⊿ 1 mile west of A37, midway between Dorchester and Yeovil; entrance to hotel is in Summer Lane. Private car park ↵ 3 single, 13 twin, 1 suite; some in annexe; all with bathroom/WC; all with TV, room service, hair-dryer, direct-dial telephone, radio ⌀ Dining-room, bar, 2 drawing-rooms, garden; functions (max 20 people incl up to 17 residential), conferences; civil wedding licence; heated outdoor swimming-pool, tennis, croquet; early suppers for children; cots, high chairs, babysitting, baby-listening ♿ Wheelchair access to hotel (ramp) and dining-room, WC (M, F), 3 ground-floor bedrooms, 1 room specially equipped for disabled people ● No children under 7 in dining-room eves; no dogs in public rooms ▭ Amex, Delta, Diners, MasterCard, Switch, Visa £ Single £125, single occupancy of twin £165, twin £165 to £235, suite £275 (prices valid till Apr 1999); deposit required. Set L £13/£17.50, D £36; alc L £25, D £40. Special breaks available

---

'At breakfast we asked, "Do you have any jam instead of marmalade?" "No", came the reply. "We make our own jam – this year it's marmalade." I think it was my wife's guffaw of incredulity which extracted a dish of damson jam from the owner's private store.'
On a hotel in Northamptonshire

Evesham Hotel

Coopers Lane, Off Waterside, Evesham WR11 6DA
TEL: (01386) 765566   FAX: (01386) 765443

A tirade of jollity, plus real consideration for all guests' needs, in one of the country's best hotels for families.

The tone may be unremittingly light-hearted – the brochure takes the form of a cartoon strip, a dinner-menu heading reads 'un-mucked-about food – not everyone wants to be saucy the whole time' – but John Jenkinson and his devoted, dynamic staff take the task of pleasing their guests extremely seriously. Most of the hotel's many plaudits have come from the way in which children and parents are treated. Expect teddy-bear key fobs, more teddies, rubber ducks and games in the bedrooms, a toy-stocked playroom, swings and a trampoline in the large garden, a fun indoor pool (the antithesis of most hotels' showy pools) – even a step to help little boys use the gents' urinal. Also on offer are proper children's meals and a bedroom baby-listening service while parents eat. But don't typecast the hotel as a playschool: on a typical weekend evening there are normally no more than half a dozen families with children staying. People of all ages enjoy not only the wit, but also the good food and drink displayed on the voluminous menus and wine list; vegetarians are particularly well catered for but, in typically eccentric fashion, lovers of French and German wines not at all. Furnishings throughout the largely Georgian building (with a Tudor core and modern additions) concentrate more on comfort than style. A stroll along the river, 150 yards away, should clear your head of all the puns and jokes.

◐ Closed 25 & 26 Dec   ⬀ Coopers Lane is off Waterside (A44), which runs along River Avon in Evesham. Private car park   ⬔ 5 single, 10 twin, 23 double, 2 family rooms; all with bathroom/WC exc 2 singles with shower/WC; all with TV, room service, hair-dryer, direct-dial telephone, ironing facilities   ✣ Restaurant, bar, lounge, drying-room, garden; conferences (max 12 people residential/non-residential); heated indoor swimming-pool, putting green, croquet, leisure facilities nearby (free for guests); early suppers for children; cots, high chairs, toys, playroom, babysitting, baby-listening, outdoor play area   ♿ No wheelchair access   ● No dogs in public rooms; no smoking in restaurant and some bedrooms   ▭ Amex, Delta, Diners, MasterCard, Switch, Visa   £ Single £58, single occupancy of twin/double £64, twin/double £88, family room £120; deposit required. Bar/bistro L, D £7; alc L, D £20. Special breaks available

Southgate Hotel

Southernhay East, Exeter EX1 1QF
TEL: (01392) 412812   FAX: (01392) 413549

Smart, highly polished, business hotel, with more character than most.

'A very good babysitting service here,' declared a satisfied father to all and sundry when our inspector arrived at the reception desk – not the usual kind of recommendation for a business hotel, but it shows why the Southgate prides itself on being more than just a place to have meetings and late nights. Most of the guests are indeed business folk, but the hotel also offers good-value weekend breaks for those visiting Exeter. From the outside, the original part of the building is lost among new extensions and roundabouts, but the huge, classical doorway sets the tone for the smart interior. Immaculate, colourful furnishings are crammed into the interconnecting public rooms, with sprinklings of antique vases, glamorous lampstands and plants. The Cloisters Restaurant is very formal, with green, striped walls, and big, bentwood chairs set around square tables. On the menu might be seared scallops served on a bed of mixed leaves with aubergine crisps, followed by rack of lamb with a red-wine and rosemary sauce. The bedrooms are as luxurious (and standardised) as you would expect in this type of establishment, and are done out in interesting, checked patterns, with bright walls and reproduction furniture.

◑ Open all year 🅩 In city centre. Private car park �│🚃 46 twin, 53 double, 6 family rooms, 5 suites; all with bathroom/WC; all with TV, room service, hair-dryer, mini-bar, trouser press, direct-dial telephone ◈ Restaurant, bar, 3 lounges; conferences (max 100 people residential/non-residential), functions; gym, sauna, solarium, heated indoor swimming-pool; early suppers for children; cots, high chairs, babysitting, baby-listening 🔥 Wheelchair access to hotel (ramp) and restaurant, 12 ground-floor bedrooms, 3 rooms specially equipped for disabled people ◐ No dogs or smoking in public rooms ▭ Amex, Delta, Diners, MasterCard, Switch, Visa ₤ Single occupancy of twin/double £99, twin/double/family room £99, suite £125 to £130; deposit required. Continental B £8, cooked B £11; set L £12.50, D £19.50; alc D £27.50. Special breaks available

---

EYTON Herefordshire   map 5

Marsh Country Hotel

Eyton, Leominster HR6 0AG
TEL: (01568) 613952
EMAIL: meg@themarsh.kc3ltd.co.uk

Magnificent restoration of a manor house dating from the fourteenth century, turned into a sensational rural bolt-hole.

Small country-house hotels don't come much better than this. Hidden away down deep country lanes in the Welsh Marches, both the house and its setting are dreamy. A beautiful garden, open every so often through the National Gardens Scheme, surrounds the creamy-plastered, grey-beamed building and has everything from a willow hanging over a lily pond to a reed-cultivation area. Jacqueline and Martin Gilleland have complemented the smart, beam-rich interior with striking colour schemes: orange in the glorious vaulted and flagstoned medieval hall that serves as the sitting-room, various shades of yellow in the intimate, sunny dining-room. Jacqueline's creative dinners are much praised – though there is a limited choice if you're staying on special-break rates: quite a disadvantage at this level, felt one reader. Many of the vegetables, fruit and herbs come from the garden. Since the restaurant receives few non-residents, and there are only four bedrooms, this is a supremely peaceful place to stay. The bedrooms, sporting coronets over beds, and with high-quality bathrooms (bathrobes provided), are both pretty and seductive. They are all priced the same, so it's worth asking for one of the larger ones, such as Kingfisher or Owl. As we went to press, the hotel was up for sale.

○ Closed 3 weeks in Jan ⚡ 2 miles north-west of Leominster; turn right on to B4361 towards Richards Castle; turn left after 1 mile (signposted Eyton and Lucton) and continue to common. Private car park ⬅ 1 twin, 3 double; all with bathroom/WC; all with TV, room service, hair-dryer, direct-dial telephone; no tea/coffee-making facilities in rooms ✅ Dining-room, bar, sitting-room, garden; croquet ♿ No wheelchair access ● No children under 12; no dogs; no smoking in bedrooms or restaurant ▭ Amex, Diners, MasterCard, Switch, Visa £ Single occupancy of twin/double £85, twin/double £120 to £130; deposit required. Set L £20, D £25. Special breaks available

---

 map 1

Penmere Manor

Mongleath Road, Falmouth TR11 4PN
TEL: (01326) 211411   FAX: (01326) 317588
EMAIL: reservations@penmere.demon.co.uk

Reassuringly efficient Best Western hotel, with excellent leisure facilities in quiet grounds.

This is the kind of hotel in which reliability of standards and quality are the order of the day. You know that an efficient welcome, a warm room and a good swim await you, and that nothing much will go wrong – equally, however, nothing much will be wonderfully exciting. The off-white Georgian manor is relaxed yet imposing, surrounded by park-like grounds with tall evergreens and croquet lawns, with an extension to one side housing the excellent pool complex, where you can restore yourself with a swim, a bubble in the jacuzzi, or a sweat in the sauna.

The interior of the house is open-plan, with interconnecting rooms, pastel hued and inoffensive, with a hushed atmosphere. The pianist who plays during dinner takes requests – you fill in a card left for the purpose on your table. Your meal might start with fettucine, bound with a smoked haddock, saffron and lemon-sole sauce, followed by braised beef served in a tomato and red-wine sauce, topped with fried onions. Our inspector's glass of white wine came none too chilled, however. The bedrooms are standard affairs, done out in Best Western livery, with rather small bathrooms. Some offer good views over the gardens to the sea.

○ Closed 24 to 27 Dec ⚡ Take A39 towards Falmouth; turn right at Hillhead roundabout; turn left after 1 mile into Mongleath Road. Private car park ⬅ 10 single, 8 twin, 5 double, 14 family rooms; most with bathroom/WC, some with shower/WC; all with TV, room service, hair-dryer, direct-dial telephone, some with mini-bar, trouser press ✅ Restaurant, 2 bars, lounge, library, 2 games rooms, garden; functions (max 66 people residential), conferences; civil wedding licence; gym, sauna, solarium, heated indoor and outdoor swimming-pools, croquet, fitness trails, bowls, table tennis, snooker; leisure facilities nearby (reduced rates for guests); early suppers for children; cots, high chairs, toys, playrooms, babysitting, baby-listening, outdoor play area ⟨⟩ No wheelchair access ⬤ No dogs in public rooms; no smoking in some bedrooms ▭ Amex, Delta, Diners, MasterCard, Switch, Visa £ Single £59, single occupancy of twin/double £70, twin/double/family room £90; deposit required. Bar/bistro L £5.50; set D £22

FAREHAM **Hampshire** map 2

Solent Hotel [NEW ENTRY]

Rookery Avenue, Whiteley, Fareham PO15 7AJ
TEL: (01489) 880000 FAX: (01489) 880007
EMAIL: solent@shireinns.co.uk

Corporate hospitality and great facilities at a business hotel that makes an effort to be more personal than most.

Far enough away from the M27 for it to be unobtrusive, but near enough to be ideally located for Southampton, Portsmouth and the ferries, this is a marked step up from most business hotels. From the outside, it might look like a cross between an overgrown Swiss chalet and your local superstore, but inside it's much more appealing. The octagonal, galleried reception area has cherry-wood panelling, comfy sofas and a fireplace, while the open-plan bar is a touch more inviting than expected. The bedrooms themselves are more businesslike, with a masculine, corporate feel to them, but they're all spacious. Even the standard (known as 'executive') rooms have a separate seating area – well appointed and just the ticket if you don't require lashings of atmosphere. There's a phone in the bathroom, for when some calls are more urgent than others, and fresh milk in the fridge. If you've had a hard day, there's plenty of opportunity to work off your worries in the pool, gym, squash court, sauna or solarium. After all that activity, your worked-up appetite can be sated in the restaurant, with peppered tuna on wilted spinach and roasted peppers, followed by chocolate and banana torte with toffee sauce. The staff are informal, attentive and friendly – and every first-time guest is greeted by the manager and shown around. One quirk is that floors are numbered American-style so that the ground floor is first, the first is second, and so on.

◑ Open all year ▤ Leave M27 at Junction 9; follow sign for Whiteley, then sign for hotel. Private car park ↳ 21 twin, 47 double, 6 four-poster, 9 family rooms, 7 suites; all with bathroom/WC; all with satellite TV, room service, hair-dryer, trouser press, direct-dial telephone, some with mini-bar ✣ Restaurant, bar, 2 lounges, conservatory, games room, private dining-rooms, dining terrace, garden; conferences (max 120 people incl up to 80 residential), functions; civil wedding licence; gym, sauna, solarium, steam rooms, heated indoor swimming-pool, tennis, snooker, squash; early suppers for children; cots, high chairs, babysitting ⟨⟩ Wheelchair access to hotel and restaurant (ramp), WC (unisex), 16 ground-floor bedrooms, 2 specially equipped for disabled people ⬤ No dogs in public rooms, dogs in bedrooms £5 per night; no smoking in some public rooms and some bedrooms ▭ Amex, Delta, Diners, MasterCard, Switch, Visa £ Single occupancy of twin/double £112, twin/double £140, four-poster £160, suite £160; family room (weekday) £125 plus £5 per child over

5), (weekend) £57 per parent plus same supplements for children; under-16s in own room £16 per child; deposit required. Bar/bistro L, D £6; set L, D £22; alc L, D £25 (1998 prices). Special breaks available

---

FARNHAM Dorset map 2

Museum Hotel

Farnham, Blandford Forum DT11 8DE
TEL: (01725) 516261 FAX: (01725) 516255

Traditional village pub with a reputation for themed nights – and smart, comfortable bedrooms to retire to.

The notice board at the Museum hotel always seems to promise something going on: in January it's Burns Night, February is for Valentines and March St Patrick's Day. It's not that the people of Farnham are more Celtic (or more romantic) than their brethren in the rest of England's midwestern counties, just that mein host John Barnes is a gregarious soul who likes to bring a spot of jolliness into the long, dark winter nights. The same affable approach characterises the way in which John and his spouse Lizzie run the hotel side, with a dash of good-humoured marital banter and a ready wit that's always ready to test the mettle of any new faces spotted at the bar or restaurant tables. Cooper's Bar, a traditional rustic pub which dates back to Cromwellian times, has all the beams, horse brasses and wall-mounted plates you could wish for. It's the heart of the enterprise, and a more inviting place than the more basic Woodlands Bar where the locals gather for a spot of billiards or a game of dominoes. Food is served in the bar or beneath a glass canopy in a bright, modern, conservatory-style extension to the rear. There's also a more traditional dining area, complete with wheelback chairs, floral drapes and a good old pine dresser. The menu is big on fish and seafood: perhaps baked garlic mussels, followed by red mullet on ratatouille, then Grand Marnier pancakes.

The bedrooms, housed in a converted stable block, are more sophisticated than you might expect, and include a four-poster. They team pastel colour schemes with good, specially commissioned, pine furniture. And the name? It commemorates the fact that the building once housed the museum of the local Pitt Rivers Estate.

◑ Closed 25 Dec; restaurant closed 25 and 26 Dec   ⃟ Off A354, 18 miles west of Salisbury. Private car park   ⊨ 2 twin/double, 1 double, 1 four-poster; all in annexe; all with bathroom/WC; all with TV, mini-bar, direct-dial telephone   ⊘ 2 restaurants, 2 bars, conservatory, games room, garden; functions (max 12 people incl up to 4 residential), conferences   ᕷ Wheelchair access to hotel (1 step) and restaurant, 4 ground-floor bedrooms   ⬤ No dogs; no smoking   ⊟ Delta, MasterCard, Switch, Visa   £ Single £45, single occupancy of twin/double £45, twin/double/four-poster £65; deposit required. Bar/bistro L £12, D £18

It is always worth enquiring about the availability of special breaks or weekend prices. The prices we quote are the standard rates for one night – most hotels offer reduced rates for longer stays.

Strenneth

Airfield Road, Fersfield, Diss IP22 2BP
TEL: (01379) 688182   FAX: (01379) 688260
EMAIL: ken@mainline.co.uk

Lots of individual design touches by the owners make this a well-run and comfortable B&B.

The mustard-coloured façade of a small cottage confronts you as you pull up in the tarmac driveway; however, from the other side, this house looks very different, and has a fine, tall, brick frontage overlooking the lawned gardens. Just as the house is a curious amalgamation of styles, so is its name, Strenneth – a mix of the names of the family that own it: Kenneth and Brenda Webb and their daughter Stephanie. This is very much a family business, and Brenda also runs a hairdressing salon (next to Room 7), which Stephanie will soon join as a beauty therapist. Downstairs, the public rooms are fairly small and typically have a lot of furnishings – many of them antiques – under the low, beamed ceilings. Each of the seven bedrooms has had alterations made by Ken himself, and plenty of frills and flounces give them an individual style; Room 6 has a four-poster and a 'Pharaoh' bath. The four rooms in the courtyard wing have less character, but probably a superior standard of fittings, including Room 2, with its antique French brass bed.

◖ Open all year   ⊞ Off A1066 near South Lopham, continue through Fersfield until you see hotel sign. Private car park   ⊨ 1 single, 2 twin, 3 double, 1 four-poster; family rooms available; 4 with bathroom/WC, 3 with shower/WC; all with TV
⊘ Breakfast room, 2 lounges, garden; cots, high chairs   ⅋ No wheelchair access
◗ No dogs in public rooms; no smoking in public rooms and some bedrooms
⊟ MasterCard, Visa   ⅊ Single £27, single occupancy of twin/double £30, twin/double £45, four-poster £60, family room £55; deposit required. Special breaks available

Downcliffe House

6 The Beach, Filey YO14 9LA
TEL: (01723) 513310   FAX: (01723) 513773

Welcoming beach-front hotel, with uncomplicated, family appeal.

This hotel has a great location: smack on Filey's seafront, overlooking miles of sandy beach. A small, flowery terrace in front of the handsome, double-fronted, Victorian house provides a great spot in which to breathe the sea air and take in the wonderful vista towards the huge cliffs that extend from Filey Brigg to the tip of Flamborough Head. Filey is a no-nonsense sort of place that is all about fish and chips and sandcastles; in this setting, Downcliffe House excels at what it aims for – achieving a smooth blend of down-to-earth friendliness and hotel-class comfort. The new owners, Paul and Angela Manners, keep an immaculately decorated hotel, with an unpretentious, homely style in the bedrooms. The sea views enjoyed by all are certainly a plus – indeed, Room 10, on the top floor, has a large corner bath from which you can see pretty well all around the bay. The restaurant, which is decorated in pink and pastel green and has a deep-burgundy carpet, and the convivial bar, which can get quite lively in the evenings, both share in the bounty of the seafront panorama. The menu offers plenty of traditional, seaside staples, with modern tweaks keeping it lively; you might start with Norwegian prawns with ginger and spring onions, follow that with oven-baked salmon with a coriander crust, and end with something sticky, like banoffi pie, from the choice of puddings.

◖ Closed Jan ⤢ On seafront in Filey. Private car park. ⊨ 1 single, 1 twin, 8 double; 8 with bathroom/WC, 2 with shower/WC; all with TV, limited room service, hair-dryer ✅ Restaurant, bar, lounge; functions (max 60 people incl up to 19 residential); early suppers for children; cots, high chairs ♿ No wheelchair access ● Dogs in bedrooms only, by arrangement; no smoking in restaurant ▭ Amex, Delta, MasterCard, Switch, Visa £ Single £32, twin/double £60; deposit required. Alc L £7, D £14. Special breaks available

---

FLAMBOROUGH East Riding of Yorkshire   map 9

Manor House

No under 8's

Flamborough, Bridlington YO15 1PD
TEL: (01262) 850943 (AND FAX)

Antique furniture and traditional jumpers in a stylish Georgian house handy for spectacular coastal scenery.

Lesley Berry is an energetic lady who has several strings to her bow. As well as running her gorgeously furnished Georgian guesthouse, she deals in antiques and sells traditional 'ganseys' – intricately patterned fishermen's sweaters – from a craft shop in front of the house. The nearby cliffs at Flamborough Head are just one of the many reasons that might bring you to this historic stretch of coast, where twitchers flock in search of rare sightings, while beneath the waves, local divers have discovered the wreck of John Paul Jones' flagship *Bonhomme Richard*, sunk in 1779. Lesley's interest in antiques has filled the Manor House with character and wonderful treasures: the sitting-room has warm wooden floors and rank upon rank of books, courtesy of her partner Geoffrey, an author and avid reader, while the two bedrooms are a treat after a bracing walk along the coast – the larger of the two has an incredible seventeenth-century Portuguese bed in rosewood and walnut, and the smaller has a brass bed and a Victorian claw-foot bath with ancient brass taps. It's at meal-times that you really feel a guest in a lovely private house; you eat Wolsey-Lodge-fashion around a shared table – and where better to enjoy the freshest fish, crab and seafood from local fishing villages such as Robin Hood's Bay or Staithes? Guests are invited to bring their own wine.

◖ Closed Chr ⤢ From Bridlington B1255 to Flamborough; pass church on right; house is on next corner (Lighthouse Road/Tower Street). Private car park ⊨ 1 double, 1 four-poster/family room; both with bathroom/WC; both with TV, hair-dryer ✅ Dining-room, sitting-room, library, garden; croquet; early suppers for children ♿ No wheelchair access ● No children under 8; no dogs; no smoking in bedrooms,

smoking in public rooms if other guests consent ⊟ Amex, Delta, MasterCard, Visa
£ Single occupancy of double £38, double £60, four-poster £70 (£86 if used as family
room); deposit required. Set D £21 (by arrangement)

FLETCHING East Sussex map 3

Griffin Inn

Fletching, Uckfield TN22 3SS
TEL: (01825) 722890   FAX: (01825) 722810

Outstanding food in lively, welcoming pub with rooms above.

At the heart of this picturesque village stands the white-painted inn which has
been quenching thirsts for four hundred years. Its pulling power reaches beyond
the ale pumps – its top-notch food is justly renowned. Making your mind up
from the choice on the inventive menus in the beamed restaurant could be a
lengthy business: grilled fresh sardines with coriander or roasted tomato and
tarragon soup to start; Thai green vegetable curry or chargrilled suprême of
guinea-fowl on sweet potato mash to follow, and topped off with chocolate
marquise with blackcurrant coulis or prune and almond flan. The wood-
panelled bar has a huge log fire, or in summer there's a garden and terrace with
Downland views. This is very much a pub-with-rooms, and you do have to go
behind-the-scenes to get upstairs. Big is best here, with the spacious Fletching
room definitely worth the extra money – it has a huge brick fireplace, impressive
four-poster and wonderfully creaky floor. The other three rooms in the inn,
while pleasant enough, are smaller and a bit more basic, with the loo tucked
away in a cupboard and the shower opening directly into the bedroom. Four
new *en suite* doubles are due to appear in the old converted barn by the end of
August 1998.

◑ Closed 25 Dec; restaurant closed Sun eve   ⤤ Take A22 south from East Grinstead;
at Nutley turn right to Fletching; inn is in village. Private car park   ⊨ 2 twin, 6
four-poster; some in annexe; family rooms available; all with shower/WC exc 3 four-
posters with bathroom/WC; all with TV, limited room service, hair-dryer   ✧
Restaurant, bar, games room, garden; functions (max 150 people non-residential),
conferences (limited); early suppers for children; high chairs, babysitting   ♿
Wheelchair access to inn and restaurant (2 steps), WC (M,F), 2 ground-floor
bedrooms   ● No dogs or smoking in bedrooms   ⊟ Amex, Delta, Diners,
MasterCard, Switch, Visa   £ Single occupancy of twin/double £45 to £55,
twin/double £55, four-poster £65 to £85, family room £75 to £85; deposit required.
Bar/bistro L, D £8; alc L, D £21. Special breaks available

FORD Wiltshire map 2

White Hart

Ford, Chippenham SN14 8RP
TEL: (01249) 782213   FAX: (01249) 783075

---

*Hearty, sixteenth-century, Cotswolds pub with a prime, riverside
position.*

The Cotswolds area isn't exactly short on nice, old, country pubs; what elevates Chris and Jenny Phillip's sixteenth-century coaching-inn above the opposition is its delightful position – by a bridge over a trout stream of the River Bybrook. The inn has grown rather haphazardly down the years, and elements of it now sprawl over both sides of the road. The central focus remains the open-plan bar and restaurant facilities, which spread through three rooms of the main building. With its beamed ceiling, wheel-back chairs, landscape prints, wall-mounted muskets and bristling antlers, there's a definitely rustic feel to the restaurant, where guests might dine on tomato soup, followed by suprême of salmon with a herb crust and a piquant provençale salsa. The stable block houses the most up-to-date and attractive bedrooms, some with sloping ceilings up in the eaves, like Rooms 4 and 8. There are also three rooms in the main building.

○ Open all year ▨ Between Bath and Chippenham on A420. Private car park ⊨ 1 twin, 5 double, 4 four-poster, 1 family room; some in annexe; most with bathroom/WC, 3 with shower/WC; all with TV, direct-dial telephone, some with hair-dryer, trouser press ✓ Restaurant, bar, games room, garden; conferences (max 14 people incl up to 11 residential); heated outdoor swimming-pool ⊸ Wheelchair access to hotel and restaurant (1 step), 4 ground-floor bedrooms ● Dogs in bar and bedrooms only; no smoking in bedrooms ▭ Amex, Delta, Diners, MasterCard, Switch, Visa £ Single occupancy of twin/double £50, twin/double/four-poster £75, family room £90; deposit required. Bar/bistro L £10; alc L, D £18. Special breaks available

---

FOWEY Cornwall map 1

Marina Hotel

Esplanade, Fowey PL23 1HY
TEL: (01726) 833315   FAX: (01726) 832779
EMAIL: marina.hotel@dial.pipex.com
WEB SITE: www.cornwall-online.co.uk/marina_hotel

Cosy hotel, with great view over the estuary in attractive town.

Despite the desperately narrow streets and confounding one-way system, Fowey is an almost impossibly picturesque town. It tumbles down a fairly steep hill to the estuary, where boats bob and the view is magnificent: across to Polruan and out to sea. If you play your cards right, you can take one of the boats out for a sail – two of them belong to the owner of the Marina Hotel, and are available for guests to use. After your nautical exploits, restore yourself in the wood-panelled, homely bar (or on the sun terrace right by the water's edge, if the evening is balmy), and then repair to the intimate, but smart, restaurant, with its pretty place-settings, pine dressers and farmhouse chairs. Here the menu might include asparagus spears rolled in bread and butter and baked with Parmesan cheese, followed by grilled devilled halibut steak served with a spicy tomato and spring-onion sauce. The bedrooms vary in outlook and noise levels. The best have a view of the sea and the village of Bodinnick across the estuary, others face the road behind. All are colourfully and comfortably decorated.

◗ Closed 20 Dec to 28 Feb   ⤇ Near bottom of main road into town, turn right on to esplanade; hotel is 50 yards along on left. Public car park nearby (£2 per day, May to Sept)   ⤇ 4 twin, 7 double; all with bathroom/WC exc 2 doubles with shower/WC; all with TV, room service, direct-dial telephone   ⌖ Restaurant, bar, lounge, garden; baby-listening   ♿ No wheelchair access   ● No dogs; no smoking in restaurant   ⊟ Amex, Delta, MasterCard, Switch, Visa   £ Twin/double £60 to £98; deposit required. Set D £18; alc D £25. Special breaks available

---

FRAMPTON Dorset   map 2

Hyde Farm House

Dorchester Road, Frampton, Dorchester DT2 9NG
TEL: (01300) 320272

Outstanding accommodation, with glorious gardens, in a rural location an easy drive from Dorchester.

The designation 'farm house' may lead you to expect something altogether less sophisticated than John Saunders' and Jan Faye-Schjoll's delightful country house, which is surrounded by seven acres of attractive woodland, paddocks and terraced gardens, which slope gently down to the River Frome. The face that the house presents to the world on the approach along its private road is not its best, and its fairly anonymous, red-brick exterior fails to prepare visitors for either the splendours of the garden or the engaging collection of art, artifacts and interesting furniture to be found inside. John is an affable host and encourages guests to get to know each other; the drawing-room – a spacious, airy affair – makes the ideal setting for doing this, with its collections of, among other things, Clarice Cliff pieces, Staffordshire figures and ceramic cats, which provide enough talking points to break down the barriers of natural reserve. A chaise longue adds a dash of decadence to a tantalisingly turquoise room, replete with interesting art and china and modestly described as a television room. An attractive conservatory provides an alternative bolt-hole, and is the ideal venue for pre-dinner drinks on a fine night. John improvises his menu to suit the tastes and requirements of his guests, so, on a spring Sunday night, he was planning to defer to tradition and serve avocado with apple and prawns, followed by roast pork and then a whisky and cream torte. The cuisine is generally Anglo-French in style.

The staircase leading to the bedrooms is flanked by more Staffordshire figures, with Gladstone and Queen Victoria having pride of place on the rise, while Napoleon glowers from the landing opposite. The spacious bedrooms are tastefully decorated in various pastels and florals, and are furnished with handsome, antique beds.

◗ Closed Chr & New Year   ⤇ On A356 in Frampton, pass church on right and village hall on left, then two small houses on left; hotel is 500 metres further on, on left (turn before small sign). Private car park   ⤇ 2 twin, 1 double; all with bathroom/WC; all with hair-dryer   ⌖ Dining-room/conservatory, drawing-room, TV room, drying-room, garden; fishing   ♿ No wheelchair access   ● No children under 12; no dogs; no smoking   ⊟ None accepted   £ Single occupancy of twin/double £30, twin/double £60. Set D £15

Maypool Park Hotel   NEW ENTRY

Maypool, Galmpton, Brixham TQ5 0ET
TEL: (01803) 842442   FAX: (01803) 845782

Straightforward hospitality, good bedrooms and a fabulous location in Agatha Christie country.

The gardens of the Agatha Christie estate, which lies behind the hotel, are open three times a year, each time for one day only, so you may have to time your visit carefully! But the view from the glorious terrace, over the wooded slopes down to the River Dart far below, is reason enough to come here. One satisfied guest called the hotel 'quite a find', while another commented on the 'relaxing atmosphere and beautiful views'. Gill and Peter Bennion have been here for less than a year, and are still making their mark, but Gill's parents ran a hotel, so it must be in the blood. The Bennions are sensible enough to make the best use of the view, so, on clement days, guests have lunch, drinks and supper on the glowing local stone of the terrace, by the fountain or amid the hydrangeas. The house was converted from Victorian cottages and has a light, fresh character inside, though an old-fashioned swirly carpet still extends throughout the ground floor. The restaurant is spacious, with old pine dressers and peachy tablecloths; on the menu might be Italian avocado and Scottish smoked salmon with crème fraîche and dressed salad leaves, followed by roast loin of Devon lamb served on a potato and celeriac rösti with a rosemary *jus*. You could round that off with a chilled lemon soufflé and tuile biscuit. The bedrooms are tranquil, done out in muted pinks, greys and whites; seven of the ten bedrooms have very good new bathrooms, three still await the same treatment.

◗ Closed Chr & New Year   ⤢ Turn south-west off A3022, signed Greenway Quay and Maypool, into Manor Vale Road. Follow signs to Maypool for 1½ miles. Private car park   ⤙ 2 single, 4 twin, 3 double, 1 suite; all with bathroom/WC; all with TV, hair-dryer, direct-dial telephone   ⧸ Breakfast room, restaurant, bar, lounge, garden; functions (max 50 people incl up to 20 residential), conferences   ⅀ No wheelchair access   ● No children under 12; no dogs; no smoking   ⊟ Amex, Delta, MasterCard, Switch, Visa   £⋅ Single £42, single occupancy of twin/double £48 to £58, twin/double £68 to £78, suite £90; deposit required. Set Sun L £17.50, D £18.50. Special breaks available

---

Eslington Villa

8 Station Road, Low Fell, Gateshead NE9 6DR
TEL: (0191) 487 6017   FAX: (0191) 420 0667

Friendly Edwardian hotel with a good reputation for food in a quiet suburb of Gateshead.

If you're a business traveller in the Newcastle area looking for a relaxed hideaway with good cuisine and a cheerful welcome, Eslington Villa is just the ticket. Although it sits just above the Team Valley industrial estate, an acre of landscaped gardens – where birdsong is dominant rather than the normal background of traffic noise – provides an agreeable buffer from the less lovely environs of Gateshead. The conservatory restaurant, with an onyx-tiled fireplace and fresh flowers on the tables, looks down the steeply sloping garden and makes a pleasant setting in which to dig into the extensive choice of modern English cooking. Table d'hôte and à la carte menus offer sturdy dishes such as wild boar sausage with olive-oil mash and rack of lamb with rosemary and garlic. Leave space for puddings, which are enticing variations of old favourites – for example bread and butter pudding with pecans and cinnamon-scented custard. The lounge and restaurant alike have Edwardian fireplaces and plaster mouldings, while in the bedrooms a simple, uncluttered style revolves around dark reproduction furniture and good-quality bathrooms.

◗ Closed 25 & 26 Dec and bank hols; restaurant closed Sun eve ⬧ Leave A1(M) at Team Valley Trading Estate and approach Gateshead along Team Valley; at top of Eastern Avenue, turn left into Station Road. Private car park ⬧ 1 single, 2 twin, 7 double, 2 four-poster; some in annexe; family rooms available; all with bathroom/WC, exc 1 single with shower/WC; all with TV, room service, trouser press, direct-dial telephone ⬧ Restaurant, bar, lounge, conservatory, garden; functions (max 55 people incl up to 23 residential), conferences; early suppers for children, by arrangement; cots, high chairs ⬧ Wheelchair access to hotel (2 steps), restaurant, WC (M, F), 3 ground-floor bedrooms ⬧ No dogs; no smoking in dining-room ⬧ Amex, Delta, MasterCard, Switch, Visa £ Single £45, single occupancy of twin/double £60, twin/double £70, four-poster £70, family room £75. Set L £16, D £23; alc L, D £27. Special breaks available

---

GILLAN Cornwall   map 1

Tregildry Hotel

Gillan, Manaccan, Helston TR12 6HG
TEL: (01326) 231378   FAX: (01326) 231561
EMAIL: trgildry@globalnet.co.uk

Fantastic views and relaxed elegance at this small country hotel.

It seems that Huw and Lynne Phillips have now established themselves fully at this small hotel – after only two seasons in residence, business is brisk. The reasons for this are obvious: from the hotel's superb, seductive location in the depths of the Lizard Peninsula, to the delightful way in which Lynne has stamped her personality on the interior. Caribbean colours jostle with Indonesian rattan furniture, photographs of local wrecks look down over inviting squashy sofas, and the views from the huge picture windows are stunning. Room 3 includes the best of the lot, as well as striking décor and special touches like fresh milk and fruit in the fridge outside in the corridor, but Room 1 looks out over Gillan Creek to the sea. Downstairs, the Herra Restaurant serves three-course dinners, adopting a modern approach to traditional dishes – perhaps green-lentil soup garnished with chopped mushrooms, followed by lamb shank braised with root vegetables and accompanied by chickpeas served with couscous, and fruit pavlova or sticky toffee pudding to finish.

◗ Closed Nov to Feb ⊿ From B3293 head for Manaccan and then follow signs for Gillan. Private car park ⬛ 3 twin, 7 double; all with bathroom/WC exc 1 twin with shower/WC; all with TV, room service, hair-dryer, direct-dial telephone ⌀ Restaurant, bar, 2 lounges, garden; functions (max 30 people incl up to 20 residential), conferences ♿ No wheelchair access ● No children under 8; no dogs in public rooms; smoking in some public rooms only ▭ Delta, MasterCard, Switch, Visa £ Twin/double £110 to £130 (rates incl dinner); deposit required. Special breaks available

---

GILLINGHAM Dorset   map 2

Stock Hill

Stock Hill, Gillingham SP8 5NR
TEL: (01747) 823626   FAX: (01747) 825628
EMAIL: reception@stockhill.net
WEB SITE: www.stockhill.net

Acclaimed service at a serene country house with a gourmet reputation.

As you sweep into the beech tree-lined drive, it's easy to imagine what it must have been like a century ago to approach this fine, creeper-clad, Victorian house in a horse-drawn carriage. The level and manner of service that you can expect from Nita and Peter Hauser and their hand-picked crew is certainly redolent of an earlier, and more leisured, age, if the evidence of our postbag is anything to go by. One correspondent wrote to praise the good balance of 'informality and professionalism', as well as Nita's discreet, but evidently effective, management style (the Hausers have been at the helm here for over a dozen years). The comfortable, and tastefully decorated, public rooms are ennobled by their interesting collections of oriental china and glass bonsai trees, which help to reinforce the welcoming, 'private house' feel that prevails.

The food, served in an elegant restaurant, is both inventive and superbly well executed; a typical menu might include nuggets of sea bass in a beer batter with a spiced-tomato and sweet-red-pepper confit, followed by hedgerow rabbit casseroled with fresh ginger and coconut milk and served with lemon grass and polenta. When it comes to dessert, Peter gives free rein to the influence of his Austrian homeland with a repertoire of tortes and other creations that would look thoroughly at home in the smart coffee-houses of Vienna's Kohlmarkt. One correspondent commended the waiting staff: 'There is a sense of occasion because the service is splendidly competent without being stiff.'

The bedrooms display the same sense of style and individuality as the public rooms, whether it be in a carved Irish church door recycled as a bedhead, or a four-poster bedecked with gilded cherubs. Rooms in the converted stable block are light, airy and furnished in a more contemporary style.

◗ Open all year ⊿ On B3081, 1½ miles west of Gillingham, 3 miles south of A303. Private car park ⬛ 1 single, 5 twin, 3 double, 1 four-poster; some in annexe; all with bathroom/WC; all with TV, room service, hair-dryer, trouser press, direct-dial telephone; no tea/coffee-making facilities in rooms ⌀ 2 restaurants, 2 lounges, garden; conferences (max 12 people incl up to 10 residential); sauna, tennis, putting green, croquet; early suppers for children ♿ No wheelchair access ● No children

under 7; no dogs; smoking discouraged in bedrooms   ▭ MasterCard, Switch, Visa
£ Single £110 to £145, single occupancy of twin/double £145 to £165, twin/double
£240 to £280, four-poster £270 (rates incl dinner); deposit required. Set L £21. Special
breaks available

GISLINGHAM Suffolk   map 6

Old Guildhall

Mill Street, Gislingham, Eye IP23 8JT
TEL: (01379) 783361

*A large, and surprisingly spacious, medieval, thatched cottage, with
charming, mild-mannered hosts.*

It might look effortless, but a lot of hard work has gone into creating this
picture-perfect, pink-washed, English cottage. Not a thatch appears out of place
on its tall, sloping roof, while the lawns that surround the house on three sides
are immaculately tended. Inside, all is spacious and light, not at all cramped as
you might expect. Ray and Ethel Tranter have created a large, open-plan interior
on the ground floor, while still retaining the oak frames. Everything about the
place looks comfortable and well loved, with a brick fireplace as the centrepiece
and the couple's dogs slumbering in the corners. Ethel serves her traditional
home cooking through a serving hatch in the small, simple dining-room.
Upstairs, the bedrooms are off a corridor known as the Gallery (where there is a
writing desk), which gives you views down into the garden and beyond, to the
open countryside. The rooms are of a decent size, with good bathrooms – and
some of the lowest ceilings that our inspector has ever encountered.

◑ Closed Jan   ↗ In the centre of Gislingham, opposite village school. Private car
park   ⟻ 3 twin, 1 double; all with bathroom/WC; all with TV, hair-dryer   ✥
Dining-room, bar, 2 lounges, garden; functions (max 20 people incl up to 8 residential);
early suppers for children; cots, high chairs   ♿ No wheelchair access   ● Dogs in
bedrooms only, by arrangement; no smoking   ▭ None accepted   £ Single
occupancy of twin/double £28, twin/double £56; deposit required. Set D £12.50 (price
valid till Feb 1999). Special breaks available

GLEWSTONE Herefordshire   map 5

Glewstone Court

Glewstone, Ross-on-Wye HR9 6AW
TEL: (01989) 770367   FAX: (01989) 770282

A laid-back country-house hotel, full of interesting bric-a-brac.

Christine and William Reeve-Tucker's enterprise makes a welcome change from
the typical country-house hotel, where the atmosphere can often be rather stiff
and the look can be one of formulaic smartness. Here, William, who may greet
you in well-worn jeans, prefers to be on first-name terms with his guests, which
may include both children and dogs. His Georgian house, sandwiched between
Victorian additions, is stuffed to the gunnels with curios – a wooden pig and
ceramic frogs here, a doll's house and Chinese screens there – which imbue the

place with a thoroughly relaxed, lived-in feel. Perhaps the most enjoyable room is the large, panelled bar- cum-lounge, whose french windows open on to the garden where you can eat and drink in summer. For dinner, you can opt either for the bistro menu (though the bistro room itself is a bit glum), or go the full, three-course hog in the restaurant, whose walls are prettily stencilled by Christine's own hand. The menu is fairly conventional, offering such dishes as rack of lamb and bread-and-butter pudding. More stencilling and patchwork quilts make the bedrooms attractive, too, and the fun teapots and occasional rakish nude prints add amusing, individual touches. Victoria is huge, with floor-to-ceiling windows overlooking the fruit orchards that surround the hotel's grounds.

◖ Closed 25 to 27 Dec   ⬚ Off A40, between Ross-on-Wye and Monmouth. Private car park   ⊨ 1 single, 4 double, 2 four-poster; all with bathroom/WC exc 2 doubles with shower/WC; all with TV, room service, hair-dryer, direct-dial telephone   ⊘ 3 restaurants, bar, lounge, garden; conferences (max 60 people incl up to 7 residential), functions; croquet; early suppers for children; cots, high chairs, baby-listening   ♿ No wheelchair access   ⬤ None   ⊟ Amex, Delta, MasterCard, Switch, Visa   £ Single £45, single occupancy of double £55, double £86, four-poster £100 (prices valid till Mar 1999); deposit required. Bar/bistro L £8 to £15, D £10 to £17; set Sun L £14, D £25. Special breaks available

---

GLOSSOP Derbyshire   map 8

Wind in the Willows

Derbyshire Level, Glossop SK13 7PT
TEL: (01457) 868001   FAX: (01457) 853354
EMAIL: twitwh@aol.com

A small country-house hotel with charming bedrooms and friendly hosts.

As a young man, Peter Marsh wanted to be a hotelier but ended up in the motor trade; his brother, who wanted to be in the motor trade, became a hotelier. Nowadays they have the matter sorted to their mutual satisfaction and are both hoteliers, Peter running this smart and affable establishment on the outskirts of Glossop. The house was built in the 1830s for a mill-owner, and is a solid, sandstone building which has been furnished to retain the period atmosphere, featuring plenty of polished wood, chintz and antimacassars. The bedrooms are named after characters from the Kenneth Grahame classic, though the theme only gives a flavour to each room and is never over the top. Otter, then, is bright and spriggy, with stripped-pine furniture and a shower-room; Mole is a cosy room, with a four-poster, leather armchairs and books; while Toad is the grandest, with a half-tester bed and views of the sheep-dotted hillside from the bay window.

Dinners are served at a fixed time, with four choices at each of the three courses, local lamb from Kinder Scout being a firm favourite for a main course, preceded, perhaps, by a cheese and spinach tart, and followed with a brandy and chocolate torte.

◗ Closed Chr   ⤢ 1 mile east of Glossop centre on A57, turn down road opposite Royal Oak pub; hotel is 400 yards along on right. Private car park   ⇌ 3 twin, 8 double, 1 four-poster; some with bathroom/WC, some with shower/WC; all with TV, room service, hair-dryer, trouser press, direct-dial telephone   ⊘ Restaurant, bar, lounge, study, conservatory, garden; functions (max 40 people incl up to 12 residential), conferences; leisure facilities nearby (reduced rates for guests)   ⟐ No wheelchair access   ⊖ No children under 10; no dogs or smoking in public rooms   ▭ Amex, Delta, Diners, MasterCard, Switch, Visa   ⟦£⟧ Single occupancy of twin/double £70 to £88, twin/double £85 to £110, four-poster £110; deposit required. Set D £21

GOATHLAND North Yorkshire   map 9

Mallyan Spout Hotel

Goathland, Whitby YO22 5AN
TEL: (01947) 896486   FAX: (01947) 896327
EMAIL: peter_heslop@msn.com

A traditional hotel in the thick of the tourist action of the North York Moors National Park.

A short walk will deliver you to the waterfall, sometimes issuing forth a proud gush, at others a mere trickle, that gave the hotel its odd-sounding name. In recent years the limelight has shone on the village of Goathland, known under its TV alias as Aidenfield, and in need of no introduction to fans of 'Heartbeat'. Although the series has undeniably boosted tourist numbers to the area, the Mallyan Spout's owners, Peter and Judith Heslop, have no intention of letting the village's fame and fortune go to their heads. The place is resolutely old-fashioned, from the portrait of Winston Churchill in the main lounge through to the hunting pictures that adorn the walls in the bar. In the sustenance department, the adjectives 'home-made' and 'local' appear frequently enough on the menu of the formal restaurant to reassure diners on freshness and quality. Main courses run a bewildering gamut of over 20 tried-and-tested dishes with a strong bias towards freshly caught fish from the quay at Whitby, just a short drive away. The newest bedrooms are the best – Rooms 11 and 23, spacious affairs with king-sized beds and glorious views through picture windows; otherwise, the cheaper options are generally plainly and sensibly decorated and offer a huge variety of sizes and levels of comfort.

◗ Closed 25 Dec   ⤢ Off A169 Pickering to Whitby road. Private car park; on-street parking (free)   ⇌ 2 single, 6 twin, 5 twin/double, 10 double, 1 four-poster, 2 family rooms; some in annexe; all with bathroom/WC; all with TV, room service, hair-dryer, direct-dial telephone, radio, some with trouser press; no tea/coffee-making facilities in rooms   ⊘ Restaurant, 2 bars, 3 lounges, drying-room, garden; functions (max 80 people incl up to 55 residential), conferences; early suppers for children; cot   ⟐ Wheelchair access to hotel (1 step) and restaurant; 2 ground-floor bedrooms in annexe (1 step)   ⊖ No children in restaurant eves; no dogs in some public rooms, dogs in bedrooms £2.50 per night   ▭ Amex, Delta, MasterCard, Switch, Visa   ⟦£⟧ Single £50, single occupancy of twin/double £55, twin/double £75 to £130, four-poster £80, family room £90; deposit required. Bar/bistro L £2.50 to £10, D £2.50 to £15; set L £13.50, D £19.50/£23. Special breaks available

GOLCAR West Yorkshire map 9

Weavers Shed NEW ENTRY

86–88 Knowl Road, Golcar, Huddersfield HD7 4AN
TEL: (01484) 654284   FAX: (01484) 650980
EMAIL: souffle@globalnet.co.uk

Acclaimed modern British cuisine draws a steady stream of devotees to this restaurant-with-rooms.

The Weavers Shed is still first and foremost a restaurant-with-rooms, but that's not to say that the five bedrooms are merely a half-hearted appendage to the culinary endeavours. Brook has a modern pine four-poster and a snazzy, plaid carpet, Drake features original mouldings and a fireplace – in fact, except for Hoyle, each exudes distinct character on a fresh and simple theme, with contemporary design touches and a mix of modern and antique pine. The heart of the enterprise, the restaurant, is decorated in rustic chic – all bare beams and rich, Sardinian flagstones, framed, big-name menus on the walls and eye-popping tableware. You can take it as read that the food's ingredients are fresh, seasonal and largely organic (the restaurant has its own family farm). The dinner menu might feature red mullet with a Moroccan lemon salad, chargrilled loin of Worsbrough red deer with rösti and a blackcurrant *jus*, rounded off with an old favourite like sticky toffee pudding. The annual calendar of events features foodie treats on themed evenings, and guest-chef visits from the likes of Frances Bissell, Alastair Little and Rowley Leigh.

◗ Closed Sun & Mon 🚗 Leave M62 at Junction 24; follow A640 (Rochdale road) at roundabout; at second roundabout, continue on A640 through Outlane into New Hey Road, which bears right; after 2 miles take first left after Lower Royal George pub into Rochdale Road; keep straight on to Golcar; road bears round to right (Town End), left (Church Street), then Knowl Road. Weavers Shed is on left. Private car park
🛏 1 twin, 3 double, 1 four-poster; all with bathroom/WC; all with TV, hair-dryer, mini-bar, direct-dial telephone ✓ Restaurant, bar, lounge, function room, garden; conferences (max 50 people incl up to 5 residential); high chairs ♿ Wheelchair access to hotel (ramp) and restaurant, WC (unisex), 2 ground-floor bedrooms
● No dogs 💳 Amex, Delta, MasterCard, Switch, Visa 💷 Single occupancy of twin/double £30 to £45, twin/double/four-poster £50 to £65; deposit required. Set L £14; alc L, D £35. Special breaks available

GOUDHURST Kent map 3

Star & Eagle

High Street, Goudhurst, Cranbrook TN17 1AL
TEL: (01580) 211512   FAX: (01580) 211416

Half-timbered, village pub, offering no-frills accommodation and traditional fare.

Goudhurst is a pretty village in the Kentish Weald, surrounded by orchards and hop fields, and the pub lies at its heart. Its chequered history includes a spell as a monastery, as well as the headquarters of an eighteenth-century smuggling outfit called the Hawkhurst Gang. The vaulted stonework in parts of the building dates back to medieval times. Nowadays, it's a no-nonsense, typically English pub, featuring copper pans, pewter tankards, solid, leather chairs and a vast, brick-built, inglenook fireplace. The bedrooms are plainly furnished and smell of polish; you are likely to find simple, pine furniture, floral bedspreads and basic bathrooms. Last year we reported that Rooms 1 and 4 were due for refurbishment, and as we went to press this year this was still the case. However, the 'tired hallway' that we noted last year has now been transformed by cream-coloured paintwork and bright, yellow-gold wallpaper. Room 5 is the room to choose if you want a four-poster bed; it has a wood-panelled ceiling, two easy chairs and views of the churchyard and high street. The good-value food includes such starters as home-made soup or pâté, and main courses like fisherman's pie or salmon fillets.

◑ Closed 25 Dec ☒ On A262, 2 miles off A21. Private car park ⇤ 1 single, 4 twin, 4 double, 2 four-poster; family rooms available; most with bathroom/WC; all with TV, hair-dryer, trouser press, direct-dial telephone ⊘ Restaurant, bar, garden; functions (max 100 people incl up to 21 residential), conferences; cots, high chairs, toys, baby-listening ⅙ No wheelchair access ● No dogs ▭ Delta, MasterCard, Switch, Visa £ Single £40, single occupancy of twin/double £40, twin/double £45 to £55, four-poster/family room £70; deposit required. Bar/bistro L, D £6; set Sun L £15; alc L £16

Borrowdale Gates

Grange-in-Borrowdale, Keswick CA12 5UQ
TEL: (01768) 777204   FAX: (01768) 777254

Peaceful, traditional, family-run hotel, in picturesque Lakeland location.

Borrowdale is one of the most beautiful of all Cumbria's valleys, and Grange-in-Borrowdale, in the middle of it, is an idyllic village. The Borrowdale Gates takes full advantage of its setting, in pastoral, sheep-grazing land with Words-worthian crags all around. The core of the hotel is a Victorian house in classic, Lakeland stone and whitewash, but, as the business has successfully expanded, newer wings have been sympathetically added to the sides and rear, so the public rooms ramble in interconnecting spaces through modern, picture-windowed extensions, partially divided by stone-faced or ironwork screens. Plants, coffee tables and plenty of books and magazines help to make them more personal. The bedrooms are well furnished and very comfortable, though few are especially memorable in terms of their décor or furnishings. Ten are on the ground floor – handy for visitors with limited mobility. The housekeeping and facilities are excellent: the friendly Parkinsons, who own the hotel, adopt a hands-on approach, and employ very pleasant staff. Chef Michael Heathcote produces à la carte lunches and four-course table d'hôte meals using much local fare accompanied by interesting sauces. Sunday lunches, rain or shine, feature roast beef with Yorkshire pudding. Sandwiches are also available.

◑ Closed Jan ⤴ From Keswick, follow B5289 with Derwentwater on right. After 4 miles, turn right over double-humpback bridge into Grange village. Hotel is ½ mile through village, on right. Private car park ⤴ 3 single, 12 twin, 11 double, 2 family rooms; most with bathroom/WC, 2 with shower/WC; all with TV, hair-dryer, trouser press, direct-dial telephone, some with limited room service ⦸ Restaurant, bar, 4 lounges, drying-room, garden; functions (max 60 people incl up to 55 residential); early suppers for children; cots, high chairs, baby-listening, outdoor play area ♿ Wheelchair access to hotel and restaurant, WC (M, F), 10 ground-floor bedrooms (1 step up from public rooms) ⬤ No children under 5 in restaurant eves; no dogs; no smoking in restaurant ⊟ Amex, Delta, MasterCard, Switch, Visa £ Single £58 to £87, single occupancy of twin/double £73 to £115, twin/double £105 to £168, family room (rates on application); all rates incl dinner; deposit required. Bar/bistro L (Mon to Sat) £6.50; set Sun L £14.50; alc L £11.50, D £32.50. Special breaks available

---

GRASMERE Cumbria   map 8

Michael's Nook   NEW ENTRY

Grasmere, Ambleside LA22 9RP
TEL: (015394) 35496   FAX: (015394) 35645

Rambling, early Victorian country-house hotel overlooking the vale of Grasmere, renowned for outstanding food.

A secluded hillside setting in 13 acres of woods and established gardens makes a good first impression. Though close by the Lake District's most trampled Wordsworthian thoroughfares, this hotel feels completely private. The name, of course, is a reference to one of the Lakeland Bard's lyric poems. Built in local grey stone, partly creeper-covered, the house dates from 1869. It first opened as a hotel, under its present ownership, exactly a century later. For years it was the family home of Reg Gifford a genial and canny hotelier who also owns the businesslike Wordsworth Hotel in central Grasmere. The Giffords no longer live on site, but keep a firmly 'hands-on' approach to the running of the place (you may find Mr Gifford answering the door to greet visitors in person). The house is grandly but personally furnished (Reg used to be an antique dealer), so rooms bristle with china, clocks, handsome mahogany wardrobes, and all manner of collectable objects and pictures amid forests of fresh flowers and the smarter sort of magazine. The drawing-room boasts a grand piano and well-stuffed sofas, while the bar is a cosier room full of trophies, tankards, brasses and dog pictures (Great Danes and cats form part of the friendly entourage). The restaurant is a refined but intimate place of polished mahogany and cherry-coloured walls, scintillating in crystal and silver, but enhanced most of all by William Drabble's exquisite cooking. The bedrooms, all different and constantly changing under the Giffords' restless urge to refurbish whenever they get tired of looking at the wallpaper, are as comfortable and elegant as the rest of the house suggests.

◑ Open all year ⤴ Turn off A591 north of Grasmere village, between Swan hotel and its car park; bear left at fork; hotel is 400 yards on right. Private car park ⤴ 1 twin, 6 twin/double, 4 double, 1 four-poster, 2 suites; all with bathroom/WC; all with TV, room service, hair-dryer, direct-dial telephone, some with trouser press ⦸ Restaurant, bar, drawing-room, drying-room, garden; functions (max 40 people incl up to 28 residential), conferences; civil wedding licence; croquet; leisure facilities nearby (free for guests);

early suppers for children   ♿ No wheelchair access   ● No children under 7 in restaurant eves; no dogs; no smoking in restaurant   ▭ Amex, Delta, Diners, MasterCard, Switch, Visa   £ Single occupancy of twin/double from £135, twin/double from £176, four-poster £270, suite from £320 (rates incl dinner); deposit required. Set L £34.50. Special breaks available

White Moss House

Rydal Water, Grasmere, Ambleside LA22 9SE
TEL: (015394) 35295   FAX: (015394) 35516

Small country-house hotel with Wordsworthian associations and wonderful food.

White Moss House is one of numerous Wordsworthian properties in the Lake District: built in 1730, it was bought for William's son. By all accounts, the Wordsworths weren't great foodies, but if they could revisit their old family house today they'd discover some much better cooking than they used to dish up at Dove Cottage. Shielded from the nearby busy road by established gardens, White Moss House directs its gaze at picturesque Rydal Water beyond. Despite the centrality of food in this hotel, the dining-room is a small place – low-ceilinged, cottagey and domesticated in scale, it seats fewer than 20 people. Peter Dixon's exquisite cuisine moderne – though it's heartily English – receives a regular round of gongs from the major food guides. It's a five-course affair, served at 8pm (choiceless until the puddings), and is memorable enough to bring back salivating regulars for decades. If you've any room left, the breakfasts are good, too. Before, and after, dinner, guests repair to an elegant, tall-ceilinged lounge, decorated in smart chintz. A multi-fuel stove keeps the chill off, and the window seat makes a good vantage point for the sloping gardens. The bedrooms have stacks of character, and are all different; Rooms 6 and 7 have their own lounge and strikingly pretty décor.

◐ Closed Dec to Feb; dining-room closed Sun eve   ◪ On A591, at northern end of Rydal Water, halfway between Ambleside and Grasmere. Private car park   ⮞ 3 twin, 2 twin/double, 3 double, 1 four-poster; some in annexe; all with bathroom/WC; all with TV, room service, hair-dryer, direct-dial telephone, some with trouser press; no tea/coffee-making facilities in rooms   ✓ Dining-room, 2 lounges, drying-room, garden; fishing; leisure facilities nearby (free for guests)   ♿ No wheelchair access ● Children by arrangement; no dogs   ▭ MasterCard, Switch, Visa   £ Single occupancy of twin/double £89, twin/double/four-poster £144 to £178. Set D £28. Special breaks available

---

GRASSINGTON North Yorkshire   map 8

Ashfield House

Summers Fold, Grassington, Skipton BD23 5AE
TEL: (01756) 752584 (AND FAX)

An exceptionally friendly guesthouse, in an archetypally pretty Wharfedale village.

Grassington is one of those villages that you would love to have to yourself for a while, but the throngs of day-trippers in the tea-shops just won't play along. Perhaps the nearest you can get is by staying at Linda and Keith Harrison's classy, seventeenth-century guesthouse, taking in the charm of the winding lanes and cobbled square in the evening, when everyone else has left. Situated just off the main square, Ashfield House is a reassuringly rustic, ivy-swathed stone house, made up of three joined-up former miners' cottages. Inside, a stylish mix of modern interior-design tricks, such as stencilling and sponge-finished walls, combine with colourful, contemporary sofas, dark beams and bare, stone walls to great effect. The house backs on to a large, walled garden, and is far enough away from the square to ensure a sound night's sleep in any of the cosy bedrooms; there's not much room to run around in, but they're kitted out with pine furniture in a pleasing, cottagey style that steers clear of fussiness. Room 4 is the only room without its own, modern shower, but instead has a lovely, private, blue bathroom just along the corridor. Keith's traditional dinners are created from fresh local produce, and foster an air of conviviality to help guests get to know one another.

◑ Closed Chr & Jan; dining-room closed Sat eve, and Wed in summer ⤴ Turn off B6265 into Grassington village square; after 300 yards turn left along Summers Fold. Private car park ⤷ 3 twin, 4 double; all with shower/WC exc 1 double with private bathroom/WC (not *en suite*); all with TV, hair-dryer, clock radio ✧ Dining-room, bar, 2 lounges, drying-room, garden; leisure facilities nearby (free for guests) ⅃ No wheelchair access ● No children under 5; no dogs; no smoking ▭ MasterCard, Visa ⓔ Single occupancy of twin/double £30 to £45, twin/double £60 to £64; deposit required. Set D £17.50. Special breaks available

---

GREAT DUNMOW Essex   map 3

The Starr

Market Place, Great Dunmow, CM6 1AX
TEL: (01371) 874321   FAX: (01371) 876337
WEB SITE: www.zynet.co.uk/menu/starr

A welcoming restaurant where diners can stay in tidy, well-fitted rooms in the converted stable block.

It might be the 'delicious dinners' – as one guest described them – that draw people to this friendly restaurant with rooms, but those who stay have also commented on the helpful service and comfortable bedrooms as well. At the heart of this authentic Essex village lies the dignified Georgian frontage of the Starr; inside, though, it has a neat, unfussy feel, with bench seats and a large brick fireplace in the small front bar. You pass the bar to reach the restaurant at the back, and here regular visitors will notice an immediate difference this year: owner Brian Jones has just completed a conservatory extension, and this adds an immeasurable amount of space and light to the main dining area, which, like many medieval rooms, has small windows and low ceilings. A typical meal might start with pear and dolcelatte tart with prosciutto and fresh fig salad, followed by curry-dusted roast cod on puy lentils with salsa verde. All the bedrooms are across a courtyard in the converted stable block. They are none too large, but have good, straightforward furnishings and smart, bright bathrooms worthy of special mention. One otherwise satisfied visitor felt that the bath towels could be bigger and found the lighting at the dressing table 'inadequate' for putting on make-up, but 'neither of these points would stop me returning'.

◐ Closed Sun evening and 1st week of Jan   🔁 Off A120 in centre of Great Dunmow. Private car park   🛏 1 twin, 6 double, 1 four-poster; all with bathroom/WC; all with TV, direct-dial telephone   ✓ Restaurant, bar, conservatory, meeting/private rooms; functions (max 36 people incl up to 16 residential), conferences; early suppers for children; cots, high chairs, babysitting, baby-listening   ⅙ No wheelchair access ● Dogs in bedrooms only, by arrangement; smoking in bar only   ▭ Amex, Delta, Diners, MasterCard, Switch, Visa   £ Single occupancy of twin/double £69, twin/double £105, four-poster £121; deposit required. Bar/bistro L £11 to £22.50, D £22 to £35

GREAT HUCKLOW Derbyshire   map 9

Hucklow Hall

Great Hucklow, Tideswell, Buxton SK17 8RG
TEL: (01298) 871175   FAX: (01298) 873801

Good books, food and conversation at this delightful, country manor house.

Set in beautiful countryside, John and Angela Whatley's 300-year-old manor house is a tremendously atmospheric place to use as a base while exploring the Peak District. John is a woodcarver, and examples of his art are dotted around the house, adding to the attractive, rustic look of the rooms. Dining takes place around a single table, with guests chatting sociably – this is the sort of place where television is frowned upon. Angela's cooking is homely, and relies on old favourites like pies and roasts, with traditional puddings. Dinner needs to be ordered in advance, when booking your room. Afterwards, most guests prefer to head to the lounge for coffee, where there is a log burner and plenty of books to leaf through. Another option on summer evenings is also the pretty, English country garden. The bedrooms are large, with an authentically ancient character – right down to the shared bathrooms.

◐ Closed Dec & Jan   🔁 Great Hucklow is signposted from A623 Stockport to Chesterfield road; hotel is at east end of village. Private car park   🛏 1 single, 1 twin, 1 double   ✓ Dining-room, lounge, drying-room, garden   ⅙ No wheelchair access ● No children under 5; no dogs; no smoking   ▭ None accepted   £ Single £21, twin/double £42; deposit required. Set D £16

'The whole eating experience took less than one hour. In this time tables were being frantically laid and we were aware of the "turnover". When we complained we were told that Saturdays are always busy and that we should have requested to eat more slowly.'
On a hotel in East Anglia

Croft Country House

Great Longstone, Bakewell DE45 1TF
TEL: (01629) 640278

*Friendly hosts and quiet, village location for this unpretentious,
country-house hotel.*

With the Longstone Ridge curling around the village, there is something of a
'hidden valley' appeal about Great Longstone. Allan and Lynne Macaskill's
hotel is right at the heart of the village – the sort of place where you can forget
about the car and simply walk everywhere. Over three acres of gardens surround
the largely Victorian house, which has pleasant verandahs on two sides and
long-established wistaria climbing up the ironwork. The central feature of the
building is a large atrium-cum-sitting-room, with a gallery and clerestory above
– the type of space that one associates with Victorian libraries or museums rather
than with private houses. It's quite fitting, then, that Allan uses these walls to
display his large collection of late-nineteenth-century watercolours – they add
considerable charm, both to this room and to the bedrooms. Of these, the
prettiest are the two at the front of the house; Chatsworth is a pleasant, corner
room with a Victorian brass bed and period furniture. Those with pine furniture
are less successful – sometimes rather plain – but all are well equipped and
comfortable. As this is a small hotel, dinner is served at a fixed time (7.30pm),
and there is a table d'hôte menu with no choice of main course: 'It's better to do
one main course and have it fresh,' says Lynne; 'If I did four or five alternatives,
everyone would know it couldn't all be fresh.' A typical meal might begin with
baked pears and Stilton, be followed by a courgette and cream-cheese soup, then
roast beef in a red-wine sauce and, finally, a tropical-fruit meringue roulade.

◗ Closed 2 Jan to 11 Feb ⬈ From Bakewell, take A6 Buxton road and turn right on to
A6020; after approx 1 mile, turn left towards Great Longstone; hotel entrance is on right
in village. Private car park 🛏 1 single, 2 twin, 6 double; 5 with bathroom/WC, 4 with
shower/WC; all with TV, room service ⬧ Restaurant, bar, 2 sitting-rooms,
drying-room, garden; conferences (max 30 people incl up to 9 residential); early
suppers for children; cots, high chairs 🦽 Wheelchair access to hotel and restaurant,
WC (unisex), lift to bedrooms ◖ No dogs; no smoking in restaurant ▭ MasterCard,
Switch, Visa £ Single £60, single occupancy of twin/double £70, twin/double £98;
deposit required. Set D £23.50. Special breaks available

Red Gate

32 Avenue Road, Great Malvern WR14 3BJ
TEL: (01684) 565013 (AND FAX)

*B&B run by caring hosts in a prettily furnished, late-Victorian
house on the outskirts of this well-known spa town.*

One of a number of large, red-brick houses on a fairly dull residential street
about a ten-minute walk from the town centre, Red Gate doesn't look much from

the outside, yet it fully deserves inclusion in the *Guide* for the keen stewardship provided by its owners, Barbara and Richard Rowan, who have been giving guests an effusive welcome since 1985. Their home is furnished in fetching guesthouse style. The sitting-room is redolent of a Victorian parlour, full of flower displays and books (some repeat guests apparently use the B&B like a library, taking books away and returning them when they next stay). The red-and-pink dining-room is the venue for breakfast – for which there are ample choices – and maybe light evening meals, if you twist the Rowans' arm. The dainty bedrooms are decorated with busy floral schemes or a lighter stencilling effect. Ask for one looking over the good-sized garden at the rear and the Malvern Hills beyond – perhaps Room 3, which has a half-tester bed and bay sitting area.

◑ Closed Chr & New Year   ⊿ Close to Great Malvern railway station. Private car park   🚗 1 single, 2 twin, 3 double; 3 with bathroom/WC, 3 with shower/WC; all with TV, room service, hair-dryer, clock radio   ⌀ Dining-room, sitting-room, drying-room, garden   ♿ No wheelchair access   ● No children under 8; no dogs; smoking in sitting-room only   ⬚ Diners, MasterCard, Visa   £ Single £28 to £30, single occupancy of twin/double £33 to £36, twin/double £50 to £52 (prices valid till Easter 1999); deposit required

---

GREAT MILTON Oxfordshire   map 2

Le Manoir aux Quat' Saisons

Church Road, Great Milton, Oxford OX44 7PD
TEL: (01844) 278881   FAX: (01844) 278847
EMAIL: lemanoir@oxfordshire.co.uk

The closest you can come to a French château in the English countryside; a hymn to the senses.

Raymond Blanc is obsessed: obsessed with simultaneously rousing the palate, soothing the retina and pampering the flesh. The lord of the Manoir is much in evidence about his estate, assessing this, tweaking that, and generally inspiring his legion of finely tuned staff to greater heights of polished performance. Sensory therapy at this anglicised château may involve extensive plastic surgery on your gold card, but the operation is performed by some of the most skilful hands in the business, and the cost is in line with the hospitality supplied at this rarefied level.

Le Manoir – excepting the stones of the fifteenth-century, mullioned manor – is distinctly M. Blanc's own creation, from initiating reworked Jacobean boudoirs or space-age oriental suites, to the culinary techniques that refresh the lardons and paint ripe curlicues in the crème anglaise. At the time of our spring inspection, Le Manoir was completing the more visibly disruptive elements of an expansive renaissance, with a new bedroom block in matching Cotswold stone having materialised, the kitchens having been extended and topped off with a new turret, and an interior designers' velvet revolution having quietly replaced the country-house classics of shiny chintz and plumped settees with clean lines and uplifting colours. The Conservatory restaurant is now all blond wood and thick, cream linen, while the main lounge whispers uncluttered elegance. Yet if ostentation is more your *tasse de Darjeeling*, plenty remains throughout the bedrooms, most notably in the pale-pink bedroom of the Dovecote, beneath a canopy held aloft by hovering doves, or in the voluptuously frescoed bathroom of Mermaid Rose, where you can work up an imperial lather in unison, reclining in twin roll-top tubs. Equally engaging features are to be found in each of the highly individual bedrooms. While the eight-course *menu gourmand* of M. Blanc's culinary dexterity may be the initial attraction of Le Manoir, the lasting impression will be the sum of many impeccable parts.

◑ Open all year   ⤢ Off A329, signposted 'Great Milton Manor'. Private car park ⤶ 18 double, 3 four-poster, 7 suites; some in annexe; family rooms available; all with bathroom/WC; all with TV, room service, hair-dryer, trouser press, direct-dial telephone; no tea/coffee-making facilities in rooms   ⌛ 3 restaurants, bar, 2 lounges, conservatory, garden; functions (max 30 people incl up to 28 residential), conferences; civil wedding licence; croquet; early suppers for children, by arrangement; cots, high chairs, baby-listening   ♿ Wheelchair access to hotel and restaurants, WC (unisex), 5 ground-floor bedrooms, 1 room specially equipped for disabled people   ● No dogs; no smoking in restaurants   ▭ Amex, Delta, Diners, MasterCard, Switch, Visa £ Single occupancy of double £210 to £310, double/four-poster/family room £210 to £310, suite £370 to £435; deposit required. Continental B £9.50, cooked B £14.50; set L £32, D £72; alc L, D £80. Special breaks available

---

GREAT SNORING Norfolk   map 6

Old Rectory

Barsham Road, Great Snoring, Fakenham NR21 0HP
TEL: (01328) 820597   FAX: (01328) 820048

A fascinating, ancient house, in a perfect, English-country-village setting – if a little expensive.

To say that Great Snoring is a sleepy village is pretty close to the truth: nothing appears to have disturbed the calm of this part of rural England for centuries, and the Old Rectory is testament to the ageless quality of English country houses. It was a manor house before it was a rectory, which goes some way to explaining the unlikely proportions and extraordinary, hexagonal turrets of Rosamund and William Scoles' house. In summer, you will approach it past lawns bathed in sunlight and mature trees filled with birdsong; just across the drive from the house is a small gate in the wall leading to the village churchyard. Inside, it's a rambling house, with Norfolk scenes liberally decorating the walls. The sizeable lounge has a luxurious wallpaper of deep-red flowers, as well as oriental carpets and relaxing armchairs, and the ticking of clocks punctuates the quiet – there's also a copy of *The Oldie* for you to peruse. Rosamund is proud to call her home 'a bit of old England', and lays out the family silver for dinner, which she cooks herself; the ostrich Stroganov is one of her more popular dishes. Upstairs, the comfortable bedrooms have tasteful antiques, high ceilings and good, solid beds, which you might need to take a running leap at to clamber into.

◑ Closed 24 to 27 Dec 🔁 Hotel is behind church on Barsham Road in Great Snoring. Private car park 🛏 3 twin, 3 double; all with bathroom/WC; all with TV, room service, hair-dryer, direct-dial telephone; no tea/coffee-making facilities in rooms ⊗ Dining-room, lounge, garden; conferences (max 12 people incl up to 6 residential); early suppers for children ♿ No wheelchair access ● Children by arrangement only; no dogs; no smoking in dining-room ☐ Amex, Delta, MasterCard, Switch, Visa £ Single occupancy of twin/double £70, twin/double £93; deposit required. Set D £22

GRIMSTON Norfolk   map 6

Congham Hall

Lynn Road, Grimston, King's Lynn PE32 1AH
TEL: (01485) 600250   FAX: (01485) 601191

A classic, English, country-house hotel, in gorgeous grounds and with high levels of service.

This elegant, pale-cream, Georgian villa has just about everything you might need to pursue a traditional, country-house weekend: it has its own swimming-pool, tennis court and croquet lawn, and there is even a village cricket pitch. However, as the owners Christine and Trevor Forecast proudly remark, 'For your weekend break we organise nothing,' as they are happiest when their guests are completely relaxed. The soothing smells of the potpourri dotted around the house should certainly help you do that; these are created by Christine from some 700 varieties of herbs grown in the hall's renowned herb garden. The herbs are also important ingredients in the dishes served up in the stylish Orangery Restaurant. A typical meal might start with a gratin of King's Lynn brown shrimps with Parmesan biscuit layers, followed by boned quail with streaky-bacon stuffing and a bay-leaf sauce, and end with vanilla mascarpone and sesame dentelle layers with oven-dried fruits. In the bedrooms, fresh flowers abound; the best rooms have bold, coloured designs and coronet beds or a four-poster to match the spacious setting.

◑ Open all year 🔁 North-east of King's Lynn, turn off A148 at sign for Grimston; hotel is 2½ miles on left. Private car park 🛏 1 single, 10 twin/double, 1 four-poster, 2 suites; all with bathroom/WC exc single with shower/WC; all with TV, room service, hair-dryer, direct-dial telephone, radio, some with trouser press; tea/coffee-making facilities on request ⊗ Restaurant, bar, lounge, drying-room, garden; functions (max 50 people incl up to 27 residential), conferences; civil wedding licence; heated outdoor swimming-pool, tennis, putting green, croquet ♿ No wheelchair access ● No children under 12; no dogs; smoking discouraged in bedrooms ☐ Amex, Delta, Diners, MasterCard, Switch, Visa £ Single £80, single occupancy of twin/double from £90, twin/double from £120, four-poster £155, suite £195; deposit required. Bar/bistro L £5; set L £9.50/£13.50, D £32; alc L £20. Special breaks available

---

  This denotes that the hotel is in an exceptionally peaceful situation where you can be assured of a restful stay.

Church House

Grittleton, Chippenham SN14 6AP
TEL: (01249) 782562   FAX: (01249) 782546

House-party-style hospitality at a listed, Georgian rectory in a delightful, Cotswolds village.

High hedges screen the dignified, Georgian walls of Michael and Anna Moore's sturdy former rectory. These, and the sweeping, gravel driveway that curls around the well-kept lawn, instantly convey the message that you've stumbled upon a place with more than just a touch of class. There are 11 acres of grounds, some of which are given over to a walled garden, and some to Anna's strutting Javanese peafowl and the free-range hens that lay your breakfast eggs. Indoors, the splendid staircase that rises above the flagstoned hallway characterises a fine interior that is humanised by family mementoes. These include a number of sketches and oils by Michael's artistic mother, which are proudly displayed in the pale-yellow drawing-room.

Given notice, Anna is happy to provide dinner, using home-grown, organic fruit and vegetables and locally sourced ingredients, such as Dorset air-dried ham and regional cheeses. Served at a stately, William IV dining table, it is usually something of an occasion.

To avoid compromising the proportions of the guest bedrooms, the Moores have opted to have the *en suite* facilities screened from view rather than shoehorned into plasterboard bathrooms. Room 4 boasts a sunken bath, a blue colour scheme and, like the others, a superb view.

◑ Open all year　🔲 In Grittleton village, between church and pub. Private car park　🛏 2 twin, 1 double, 1 family room; 2 with bathroom/WC, 2 with shower/WC; all with TV, hair-dryer　⊘ Dining-room, drawing-room, garden; conferences (max 20 people incl up to 4 residential); heated outdoor swimming-pool, croquet　♿ No wheelchair access　● No children under 12 exc babes in arms; no dogs; no smoking in dining-room　▭ None accepted　£ Single occupancy of twin/double £33, twin/double £57, family room £77; deposit required. Set D £17. Special breaks available

---

Angel Hotel

91 High Street, Guildford GU1 3DP
TEL: (01483) 564555   FAX: (01483) 533770

Ancient coaching-inn turned sophisticated hotel in the centre of town.

Overlooking Guildford's cobbled High Street, the whitewashed exterior of the Angel Hotel looks as inviting now as it must have looked to tired fifteenth-century travellers on their way from London to Portsmouth. Doors, windows and arched gateway are strikingly edged in black, and large upper-case letters advertise its former use as 'posting house' and 'livery stables'. The hotel name is picked out in gold letters above the door and a wrought-iron terrace on the first floor is decorated with flowers. Inside, the atmosphere is maze-like, with intimate corners where residents and non-residents enjoy morning coffee and a chat, escaping from the frenetic shopping rush outside. Antiques, old wood doors and oak panelling create a relaxing atmosphere. A cosy, galleried lounge has a beamed Jacobean fireplace and a large, wall-mounted parliament clock dating from 1688. Spiral stairs lead down into the thirteenth-century crypt, now called No 1 Angel Gate, and used as a restaurant, with stone vaulting and flagstone floors. Upstairs, the bedrooms are as comfortable as you might expect: half-tester beds, rich carpets, sumptuous easy chairs and spacious bathrooms; slippers are now provided in the rooms. Service is efficient and courteous.

❍ Open all year ⊿ Halfway up High Street (closed to vehicles 11am to 4pm Mon to Fri & Sun; 9am to 5.30pm Sat). On-street parking (free eves); public car park nearby (£15.50 per day) ⊨ 5 twin, 6 double, 10 suites; all with bathroom/WC; all with satellite TV, 24-hour room service, hair-dryer, direct-dial telephone; no tea/coffee-making facilities in rooms ⊘ Restaurant, bar, 2 lounges; functions (max 70 people incl up to 28 residential), conferences; cots, high chairs, babysitting, baby-listening ⟐ Wheelchair access to hotel, lift to bedrooms, 1 specially equipped for disabled people ⬤ None ⊟ Amex, Diners, MasterCard, Switch, Visa £ Single occupancy of twin/double £135, twin/double £135, suite £150 to £200; deposit required. Continental B £7.50, cooked B £9.50; bar/bistro L £15, set L £18.50, D £21.50; alc L, D £25. Special breaks available

---

HADLEY WOOD Hertfordshire
map 3

West Lodge Park

Cockfosters Road, Hadley Wood, Barnet EN4 0PY
TEL: 0181-440 8311   FAX: 0181-449 3698

Attention to detail to the fore at this comfortable country house with landscaped grounds in London's green belt.

While the urban accoutrements of Greater London have managed to engulf much of the green belt, this sturdy-looking whitewashed Georgian villa has managed to preserve enough acres of shrubbery and grassy expanses to reduce the roar of passing traffic to a distant thrum. Several delightful Regency touches, like the plaster garlands and mouldings around the cheerful reception lounges and staircase, have stood the test of time. Meanwhile, much new development was afoot at the time of our spring inspection, with the builders about to move in and extensively expand the incongruous brick-and-timber bar and restaurant areas. The Beale family have passed their golden anniversary in charge, and remain much involved – from overseeing the extensions to selecting the tasselled canopies and pleated pelmets in the bedrooms.

By and large, bedrooms border on the compact side of comfortable but come with numerous welcoming trimmings, like fresh flowers, bath ducks and teddy bears. Rose, a four-poster room, is particularly splendid, in muted yellow, with a Victorian bathroom and a view over the arboretum. 'Modern British' neatly summarises the style of fine dining on offer: a more detailed inspection of an appealing Connoisseur's Choice menu might reveal scallops with mint couscous, lemon sorbet, monkfish tails on a pea purée and banana tarte Tatin.

◗ Open all year 🆉 Leave M25 at Junction 24; follow signs to Cockfosters; hotel is first turning on left, ½ mile down road. Private car park 🏃 13 single, 9 twin, 29 double, 4 four-poster; family rooms and suites available all with bathroom/WC; all with TV, room service, hair-dryer, trouser press, direct-dial telephone, some with mini-bar ✅ Restaurant, bar, 2 lounges, conservatory, garden; conferences (max 80 people incl up to 55 residential), functions; civil wedding licence; putting green, clay-pigeon shooting, croquet; leisure facilities nearby (free for guests); early suppers for children; cots, high chairs, babysitting, outdoor play area ♿ Wheelchair access to hotel (ramp) and restaurant, 7 ground-floor bedrooms, 1 specially equipped for disabled people ◖ No dogs; no smoking in restaurant and 20 bedrooms ☐ Amex, Delta, MasterCard, Switch, Visa 💷 Single £93, single occupancy of twin/double £112, twin/double £130 to £155, four-poster £198, family room £225, suite £250; deposit required. Continental B £9, cooked B £11; set L £23, D £26. Special breaks available

---

HALIFAX West Yorkshire   map 8

Holdsworth House

Holdsworth, Halifax HX2 9TG
TEL: (01422) 240024   FAX: (01422) 245174

Period charm and good cuisine in a lovely Jacobean manor house.

Holdsworth House can hardly undo several centuries of encroachment by less than lovely neighbours, so its location is best glossed over – although the owners have recently completed projects to improve the approach and entry to the hotel. Once you're inside and looking at the world through mullioned windows, the classic period detail that surrounds you in the public rooms is beyond reproach: lounges come with wooden floors, old settles and comfy armchairs, and the dining-room, all dark panelling and gilt-framed portraits beneath a beamed roof, is a pleasure. Cuisine is modern and French-oriented, with starters like glazed scallops, then Normandy onion soup with Calvados and cider before a rich main course of veal and foie gras sausage on olive mash. The bedrooms are a real mixed bag, as one might expect from a hotel whose clientele ranges from business clients to honeymooners; they vary from standard plain and functional affairs to superior efforts with brass, four-poster or half-tester beds and heavy antiques – choose the latter if you're staying for pleasure.

◗ Closed 1 week at Chr 🆉 From Halifax, take A629 towards Keighley; after 1½ miles turn right into Shay Lane, signposted Holmfield; hotel is 1 mile on right. Private car park 🏃 16 single, 4 twin, 14 double, 1 four-poster, 5 suites; family rooms available all with bathroom/WC exc 2 single with shower/WC; all with TV, room service, hair-dryer, direct-dial telephone, some with mini-bar ✅ Dining-room, 2 bars, lounge, garden; 3 private dining-rooms functions (max 150 people incl up to 44 residential), conferences; civil wedding licence; leisure facilities nearby (free for guests); early suppers for children; cots, high chairs, babysitting, baby-listening ♿ Wheelchair access to hotel (1 step) and restaurant, 21 ground-floor bedrooms, 2 specially equipped for disabled people ◖ No dogs in public rooms; no smoking in public rooms and some bedrooms ☐ Amex, Delta, Diners, MasterCard, Switch, Visa 💷 Single £58 to £80, single occupancy of twin/double £58 to £80, twin/double/four-poster £60 to £115, family room £70 to £125, suite £85 to £125; deposit required. Cooked B £7.50; alc L, D £25

HAMBLETON **Rutland** map 6

Hambleton Hall

Hambleton, Oakham LE15 8TH
TEL: (01572) 756991   FAX: (01572) 724721

*A stylish and sophisticated country-house hotel, with excellent food
and hideway location.*

The flooding in the late 'seventies of Rutland Water could hardly have worked
out better for Tim and Stefa Hart's Victorian shooting lodge: not only do many of
the rooms have views of it, but the lake has slotted itself so neatly into the
environment that it's hard to imagine that it was not always there. Reached by a
narrow spit of land and a tree-lined sweep of driveway, the hall was the scene of
riotous nineteenth-century parties – hence the motto over the entrance: 'Do as
you please'. An intimate, but rather grand, reception area sets the tone, leading
on into an elegant, chintzy drawing-room, whose doors open out to a patio and
lake views – perfect for early evening drinks. Next to this is the restaurant – again
quite grand, but on a small scale. The à la carte menu is extensive and priced well
above the set menu: a typical sample of the latter would be pan-fried red mullet,
followed by a salad of fillet of roasted lamb with new potatoes and asparagus,
and finally a hot passion-fruit soufflé.

The bedrooms are all individually styled – some, such as Qazvin, with great
panache (seventeenth-century Persian painted panels and a wardrobe in the
shape of a mughal's tent); others are more subdued, decorated in classic
country-house chintzes, with views over Rutland Water. Chota, meaning 'small'
in Urdu, is the smallest room, but that is purely relative.

◑ Open all year   ⤢ Off A606, 3 miles east of Oakham, on a peninsula which juts out
into Rutland Water. Private car park   ⇥ 11 twin, 3 double, 1 four-poster; family
rooms available all with bathroom/WC; all with TV, room service, hair-dryer, direct-dial
telephone; no tea/coffee-making facilities in rooms   ⊘ 3 restaurants, bar,
drawing-room, drying-room; functions (max 60 people incl up to 30 residential),
conferences; civil wedding licence; heated outdoor swimming-pool, tennis; early
suppers for children; cots, babysitting, baby-listening   ♿ Wheelchair access to hotel
(2 steps, ramp) and restaurant, WC (M, F), lift to bedrooms   ● No babies in restaurant;
dogs in bedrooms only, by arrangement   ▭ Delta, MasterCard, Switch, Visa
£ Single occupancy of twin/double £125 to £145, twin/double £145 to £295,
four-poster £165 to £195, family room £190 to £220; deposit required. Cooked B £12;
set L £19.50, D £35; alc L, D £52.50

HAMPTON COURT **Surrey** map 3

Carlton Mitre

Hampton Court Road, Hampton Court, East Molesey KT8 9BN
TEL: 0181-979 9988   FAX: 0181-979 9777
EMAIL: mitre@carltonhotels.co.uk
WEB SITE: www.carltonhotels.co.uk

Smart, riverside hotel, with fine views of the palace.

There have been a few changes at the Mitre over the last year, of which the most notable is the recent overhaul of the brasserie – now known as 'The Landings', because it overlooks riverside mooring stages. The theme, as you might expect, has a nautical flavour, and there is now waiter service at the tables. The Minstrel's Bar has also opened as a snug, book-lined retreat, which is popular for pre-dinner drinks. The bedroom corridors have not escaped attention, either – their paintwork has been superseded by pink and green wallpaper. The superior bedrooms (rooms are classed according to their view, the quieter ones overlooking the courtyard or river) have also been redecorated, and are of a high standard, with built-in wardrobes and spacious bathrooms. Such improvements have enhanced what is a very comfortable, up-market hotel, catering for business people as well as for holidaymakers visiting Hampton Court. The hotel lies opposite the palace, and was originally built in 1665 on the orders of Charles II to accommodate guests of the royal household; portraits of historical figures on the walls serve as a reminder of its past. It has no garden, but the attractive, riverside terrace, brightened by tubs of flowers, is a good place for a drink. The rotunda-shaped restaurant serves traditional, tasty dishes, including a variety of vegetarian offerings. Ask for a window seat – the views are stunning.

◑ Open all year ☑ On intersection of Hampton Court Way and A308 Hampton Court Road, opposite Hampton Court Palace, next to bridge. Private car park ⬛ 21 twin, 14 double, 1 suite; family rooms available; all with bathroom/WC; all with TV, room service, hair-dryer, mini-bar, trouser press, direct-dial telephone ⊘ 2 restaurants, bar, lounge, library functions (max 175 people incl up to 72 residential), conferences; early suppers for children, served in bedroom; cots, high chairs, babysitting, baby-listening ♿ No wheelchair access ● None ▭ Amex, Delta, Diners, MasterCard, Switch, Visa £ Single occupancy of twin/double £125 to £135, twin/double £150 to £170, family room £150, suite £195; deposit required. Continental B £7, cooked B £9; bar/bistro L, D £10; set L, D £20; alc L, D £27.50. Special breaks available

---

HAMSTERLEY FOREST Co Durham   map 10

Grove House

Hamsterley Forest, Bishop Auckland DL13 3NL
TEL: (01388) 488203   FAX: (01388) 488174
EMAIL: xov47@dial.pipex.com

Superb hospitality in a family home embraced by the depths of Hamsterley Forest.

Wrapped in five thousand acres of sylvan seclusion, yet a mere 20 minutes from Durham city centre, Helene and Russell Close's home has an enviable location. Red squirrels, roe deer and woodpeckers roam in the man-made Forestry Commission forest, a paradise for walkers and would-be Hansels and Gretels. After a long day's strolling around forest, cathedral or castle, you can rest your feet by an open fire in the long, beamed lounge whose grandeur gives away the building's origins as an aristocratic Regency shooting lodge. The feel is very much that of a relaxed family home, with school photos and trophies for golfing, riding and rally-driving on display. The dining-room sets a more imposing tone for Helene's set dinners – traditional English with a Germanic hint, due to her family's origins (her father bought the house after escaping from Germany before the Second World War). She is a Cordon Bleu cook: a typical menu might feature goats' cheese and leek tartlets, rack of lamb with herbs and beetroot and red onion relish, and apple pancakes with maple sauce for pudding. There are three bedrooms, all with restful, modern colour schemes and leafy views; sybarites should try to bag the one with a capacious sunken bath.

◐ Closed Chr & New Year　⤴ North of West Auckland turn off A68 and follow signs to Hamsterley Forest; turn right in Hamsterley village; at Bedburn, fork left; hotel is 3 miles inside the forest on a tarmac road. Private car park　⇱ 1 twin, 2 double; doubles with bathroom/WC, twin with shower/WC; all with hair-dryer　✔ Dining-room, 2 lounges, garden　♿ No wheelchair access　● No children under 8; no dogs or smoking　▭ None accepted　£ Single occupancy of twin/double £24 to £27, twin/double £48 to £53; deposit required. Set D £16.50

HANLEY CASTLE **Worcestershire**　　　　map 5

Old Parsonage Farm

Hanley Castle, Worcester WR8 0BU
TEL: (01684) 310124
EMAIL: opwines@aol.com

Convivial guesthouse where the focus is on eating and drinking.

Situated next to a B-road, but with open fields behind, Tony and Ann Addison's unassuming, red-brick, eighteenth-century farmhouse is no longer part of a farm, but is now a civilised family home, which is fairly choosy about the guests that it receives. In order to fit in, you should be willing to interact with your fellow guests, perhaps over a glass or two of Chablis. Socialising takes place in the two drawing-rooms, one of which has a TV (there being none in the bedrooms) and a good selection of maps and local literature. Guests eat at individual tables in the beamed, yellow dining-room. Ann's dinners – which give no choice except for puddings – offer the likes of baked scallops, duck breast in a honey and lemon sauce and then chocolate and brandy mousse, plus cheese, coffees and mints. Since Tony is a wine importer, equal emphasis is placed on what to drink: the wine list is interesting, substantial and keenly priced. There are just three refreshingly unfrilly bedrooms; the best two are very spacious and have large *en suite* bathrooms, while the third is smaller, and has a bathroom down the corridor.

◐ Closed mid-Dec to mid-Jan　⤴ Take B4211 out of Upton-upon-Severn for 2 miles towards Worcester; turn left on to B4209; farm is 150 yards on right. Private car park ⇱ 3 double; all with bathroom/WC (1 not *en suite*); no tea/coffee-making facilities in rooms　✔ Dining-room, bar, 2 drawing-rooms (one with TV), drying-room, garden; ♿ No wheelchair access　● No children under 12; dogs in utility room only (kennels available); smoking in 1 drawing-room only　▭ None accepted　£ Single occupancy of double £28 to £30, double £39 to £52; deposit required. Set D £16. Special breaks available

Pheasant Hotel

No under 10s

Harome, York YO6 5JG
TEL: (01439) 771241

A relaxed country house in a tranquil but undistinguished village near the North York Moors National Park.

Set in gently folded countryside that lacks the drama of the Yorkshire Dales or the bleak appeal of the Moors, the goal of the Pheasant appears to be to soothe its guests, rather than to excite or surprise them. Two cottages and the village smithy and shop have been fused into an orderly little set-up with an attractive flagstoned terrace overlooking the village pond – a busy lunch-time in the pubby wood-beamed Sinnington bar clasping a pint of Theakstons by the open fire is about as loud as things get. The spacious lounge was once the blacksmith's cottage and offers comfy floral sofas into which you can sink to read a book or watch the ducks gliding across the pond and generally taking over the village in large numbers. The bedrooms are a decent size and have a light, cottagey décor – nothing exceptional, but they are spotlessly kept, and extra touches, like turned-down sheets in the evening and bathrobes, make you feel more at home. Culinary fly-by-nights have no place on the traditional menu, which sticks firmly to tried and tested favourites, starting with soup, pâté or perhaps a smoked chicken salad, moving on to roast beef or Scarborough sole and finishing with sticky toffee meringue or local cheeses.

◗ Closed Dec, Jan & Feb   From Helmsley take A170 towards Scarborough; after ¼ mile, turn right for Harome; hotel is in village near church. Private car park   2 single, 6 twin, 4 double, 2 suites; suites in annexe all with bathroom/WC; all with TV, direct-dial telephone; hair-dryer available on request   Dining-room, bar, lounge, drying-room, garden; indoor heated swimming-pool; golf club nearby (reduced rates for guests); early suppers for children   Wheelchair access to hotel and restaurant, WC (M, F), 1 ground-floor bedroom specially equipped for disabled people   ● No children under 10; dogs in bedrooms only, by arrangement; no smoking in dining-room   Delta, MasterCard, Switch, Visa   Single £62, twin/double £124, suite £130 (rates incl dinner); deposit required. Bar/bistro L £7

White House

? unfriendly

10 Park Parade, Harrogate HG1 5AH
TEL: (01423) 501388   FAX: (01423) 527973
EMAIL: info@whitehouse-hotel.demon.co.uk
WEB SITE: www.whitehouse-hotel.demon.co.uk

Elegant, Venetian-inspired villa, with an enviable location overlooking Harrogate's splendid common.

As long as Harrogate's reputation as a town of genteel charm endures, visitors will continue to seek out the White House for its elegant reminder of a more gracious age. It faces 'the Stray', an oasis of greenery in a town plagued by traffic congestion, and the Italianate façade, added for a former mayor of the town and a doctor of water cures, singles it out from the streets of look-alike stone terraces. The interior also keeps Jennie Forster's hotel ahead of the opposition in the style department: the generously proportioned rooms, with period fireplaces and high ceilings festooned with ornate plasterwork, are further gentrified by the spoils of Jennie's career as an interior designer – graceful antiques, gilt mirrors, fresh flowers and family photos round off a scene that is both stylish and relaxing. The individually furnished bedrooms feature more antiques, swagged curtains, plush fabrics and fluffy creatures to put outside the door as 'do not disturb' messages; go for one of the front-facing rooms, like Munroe or Harriet, for the extra light and views across the Stray. Cuisine with a modern twist is served in the 1836 restaurant, where wedding-cake-style plaster friezes, incorporating the original owner's initials, and port-wine-coloured walls hung with paintings set a romantic scene. Our inspector's meal of baby haggis, salmon with a couscous and coriander crust, followed by a sticky ginger parkin was competently prepared, but one reader was disappointed with a meal of soup and 'luxury' sausages. Others found that the clothes' storage space in their room was inadequate, and also felt that the rather curt notice informing guests that they would be charged £25 for bringing food into the bedrooms was hardly welcoming.

◑ Open all year; restaurant closed Sun eve ⤢ Telephone for directions. On-street parking (free) ⤴ 2 single, 4 twin, 3 double, 1 four-poster suite; 8 with bathroom/WC, 2 with shower/WC; all with TV, hair-dryer, direct-dial telephone; limited room service ⟡ Restaurant, lounge, library, garden; functions (max 150 people incl up to 19 residential); civil wedding licence; leisure facilities nearby (reduced rates for guests); early suppers for children; cots, high chairs, toys, babysitting, baby-listening ♿ No wheelchair access ⬤ No dogs; no smoking in restaurant or bedrooms ▭ Amex, Delta, MasterCard, Switch, Visa £ Single £65 to £92, single occupancy of twin/double £75 to £120, twin/double £95 to £125, four-poster suite £110 to £135; deposit required. Set L £15.50, D £13; alc L, D £25. Special breaks available

---

HARTFIELD East Sussex   map 3

Bolebroke Mill

Edenbridge Road, Hartfield TN7 4JP
TEL: (01892) 770425 (AND FAX)

Hugely charismatic rooms in a Domesday watermill with a picture-book setting.

Even in these parts, where oasthouses and cute cottages are commonplace, B&Bs don't come much more atmospheric and characterful than this. An old converted watermill, with all its innards still in place, Bolebroke is in an idyllic location, complete with ducklings on a pond and a gaggle of geese in the garden – all the more appealing after the rather bumpy ride down the track from the main road. It hasn't been a working mill for over fifty years, and the white clapboard structure now houses a spacious lounge with two charming bedrooms above, each accessed by its own, rather steep, stairway. Bathrooms are ingeniously hidden in old grain-storage chambers, which could make a trip to the loo an adventure for those unsteady on their pins. Further exploration is required to reach the main house for breakfast – it's through the trapdoor and past the stone wheels. However, the effort is repaid by a repast as unusual as the rooms: beefsteak mushrooms topped with cheese and bacon, or caviare on poached eggs, rather than the usual fry-up. Across the yard in the black winnowing barn are three other, equally intriguing, bedrooms: two with four-posters. Again it's a game of hunt the bathroom – all the time remembering to duck beneath the beams, some of which the seven dwarves would find too low. Bolebroke Mill is strictly non-smoking throughout.

◗ Closed Chr & Jan ⤵ Take A264 from East Grinstead towards Tunbridge Wells for 6 miles; at crossroads turn right to Hartfield on B2026; after 1 mile turn left into an unmade lane just past Perryhill Nursery; follow signs down lane. Private car park ⤒ 1 twin, 2 double, 2 four-poster; all with bathroom/WC; all with TV, hair-dryer, clock radio ⌅ 2 dining-rooms, 2 lounges, garden; babysitting in evening, by arrangement ♿ No wheelchair access ◓ No children under 7; no dogs or smoking ▭ Amex, MasterCard, Visa £ Single occupancy of twin/double £54, twin/double £59, four-poster £76; deposit required

---

HARVINGTON Worcestershire   map 5

Mill at Harvington

Anchor Lane, Harvington, Evesham WR11 5NR
TEL: (01386) 870688 (AND FAX)

Keenly run, riverside hotel, whose location has recently proved more of a curse than a blessing.

The severe flooding in the Vale of Evesham in spring 1998 wreaked terrible damage on Simon and Jane Greenhalgh's Georgian house and mill: when our inspector called, the high-tide mark was clearly visible some way up the walls of the ground-floor rooms. Needless to say, all had to be completely gutted, and the hotel was closed for much of 1998 (when we went to press, it was intending to reopen in August 1998). We eagerly anticipate its return to the fray. Its large garden, bordering a long, tranquil tranche of the River Avon (fishing and mooring are possible), plus its heated outdoor pool, make this a particularly enjoyable place in which to stay in fine weather. All the bedrooms have river views, including six extremely spacious and tasteful garden rooms in a new, purpose-built block. The lack of pretension that pervades the whole enterprise is reflected in its good-quality, country cooking, whose choices are offered on menus that are paragons of readable simplicity. Breakfasts have also been judged good and substantial. One correspondent eulogises about the hotel: 'An idyllic setting, charming house, old-world courtesy... Everything cooked to a turn... These people have got it right: please applaud them accordingly.' Bouquets, then, to the Greenhalghs – long may they carry on their good work.

◗ Closed 24 to 29 Dec ⤵ Turn south off B439 opposite Harvington village, down Anchor Lane; hotel driveway is 600 yards on left. Private car park ⤒ 5 twin, 16 double; some in annexe; all with bathroom/WC; all with TV, room service, hair-dryer, direct-dial telephone ⌅ 2 restaurants, bar, lounge, garden; functions (max 42 people residential/non-residential), conferences; fishing, heated outdoor swimming-pool, tennis, croquet; early suppers for children   🚫 No wheelchair access   ⊖ No children under 10; no dogs; no smoking in restaurants   ▭ Amex, Delta, Diners, MasterCard, Switch, Visa   £ Single occupancy of twin/double £62 to £66, twin/double £85 to £115; deposit required. Bar/bistro L £7; set L £15, D £21; alc D £24. Special breaks available

---

HARWICH Essex   map 6

The Pier at Harwich

The Quay, Harwich CO12 3HH
TEL: (01255) 241212   FAX: (01255) 551922

Seafront hotel that's a good stopover for ferry travellers and has two nice seafood restaurants.

You could not have a greater contrast between the view from this hotel and that of its sister establishment, Maison Talbooth, situated a short distance away along the River Stour. While the latter looks out across acres of green fields divided by hedgerows, the Pier has views of giant slabs of sea and sky, punctuated by the odd, grimy fishing boat and derricks and dockyards. Nevertheless, the hotel itself has a jaunty look, with its seaside Victorian style, and there is a comfortable, easy-going feel inside. The Pier is partly popular because of its reputation for good food. There's a choice between the Ha'penny Pier, which serves a variety of fish, steak and pasta, but steadfastly resists the temptation to serve its haddock and cod with chips, and the more formal Pier Restaurant, which is decorated in a breezy pale blue, where you could have a starter of lobster bisque with cream and brandy, followed by pan-fried baby Dover soles with nut-brown butter and lemon, and then a dessert of rum and dark-chocolate torte served on a white-chocolate sauce. The bedrooms tend more towards the pastel, with the best being Room 3, which also has a bracing sea view.

◑ Closed 24 to 26 Dec   ↗ On quay in Harwich. Private car park   ⇤ 2 twin/double, 4 double; family rooms available; all with bathroom/WC; all with TV, direct-dial telephone   ✥ 2 restaurants, bar; conferences (max 70 people incl up to 6 residential), functions; cots, high chairs   🚫 No wheelchair access   ⊖ No dogs   ▭ Amex, Delta, Diners, MasterCard, Switch, Visa   £ Single occupancy of double £55 to £70, twin/double £75 to £90, family room £85 to £100. Cooked B £4; bar/bistro L, D £12; set L £17.50; alc L, D £25

HASSOP Derbyshire   map 9

Hassop Hall

Hassop, Bakewell DE45 1NS
TEL: (01629) 640488   FAX: (01629) 640577
EMAIL: hassophallhotel@btinternet.com

Large stately home, set in quiet countryside, popular with wedding parties.

First impressions can be deceptive, and Tom Chapman's country pile looks overwhelmingly grand as you walk towards its neoclassical façade; in fact, the building is a curious amalgamation of periods, to which the Chapmans add a light touch. The front of the house contains a series of ornate and elegant rooms, which look out over an unspoilt, rural panorama of sheep-cropped grass and parkland trees. With their capacity to accommodate large groups, these rooms are popular for weddings and conferences – important elements of Hassop Hall's business. The bar, with its low ceiling painted with coats of arms, is more intimate. The bedrooms can be extremely spacious: Room 17 has a series of fluted columns and arches running across it, plus an original, Victorian bath. Yet these high-ceilinged rooms are so large that they can seem a little bare and in need of some sizeable paintings or tapestries to go with the homely furnishings. Breakfast is served in the bedrooms, which is pleasant on a sunny morning if you have a room at the front. 'Delightfully eccentric stately home,' wrote one correspondent. 'Massive rooms with numerous faults that make you feel you are at home rather than in a hotel. All is forgiven because you feel as though it's your house for the weekend.'

○ Closed Chr; restaurants closed Sun eve 🖾 2 miles north of Bakewell on B6001. Private car park 🛏 2 twin, 2 twin/double, 5 double, 2 four-poster, 2 family rooms; all with bathroom/WC; all with TV, room service, hair-dryer, direct-dial telephone, radio ✧ 3 restaurants, bar, lounge, garden; functions (max 120 people incl up to 30 residential), conferences; civil wedding licence; tennis; early suppers for children; cots, high chairs, babysitting 🦽 Wheelchair access to hotel (ramp) and restaurants, WC (M), lift to bedrooms and WC (F) ◔ Dogs in bedrooms by arrangement only; no smoking in some public rooms ⬜ Amex, Delta, Diners, MasterCard, Switch, Visa £ Single occupancy of twin/double £79 to £129, twin/double/four-poster £79 to £129, family room £109; deposit required. Continental B £7, cooked B £10; set L £16 to £20, D £27 to £32.50 (1998 prices). Special breaks available

---

HATCH BEAUCHAMP Somerset   map 2

Farthings

Village Road, Hatch Beauchamp, Taunton TA3 6SG
TEL: (01823) 480664 FAX (01823) 481118

Georgian house with smart restaurant and pleasant bedrooms at a reasonable price.

Though only a short drive from the M5, Hatch Beauchamp seems a typically sleepy Somerset village, and the ultra-smart-looking Farthings, with its pristine Georgian façade and contrasting black balcony, seems at first a tad incongruous. Indoors, the town-house look continues, with Oxford-striped sofas and chairs in the neat sitting-room, and a faintly colonial club look in the bar, where guests peruse the menu in basket-weave chairs beneath jolly, Victorian-style prints. Things move up a further gear in the smart, airy restaurant, where swag-and-tail drapes, green-and-white table linen, stylish seaside prints and modern retro-style chairs create a classy impression. The food is generally traditional with the odd twist – perhaps smoked fillet of trout with a horseradish cream, followed by minted lamb cutlets, and then baked custard with bananas and dark rum.

The house has been extended over the years, and the recently refurbished bedrooms in the older part have retained some fine old walnut furniture, as well as some clever reproduction pieces. Modish décor and lovely garden views give some of the rooms in the newer section, such as Beech, a decent stab at competing with the greater character of the original rooms.

◑ Open all year; restaurant closed Sun eve 🔟 Off A358, 5 miles south of Taunton. Private car park 🛏 4 twin, 5 double; family rooms available; all with bathroom/WC; all with TV, room service, hair-dryer, direct-dial telephone ✅ Restaurant, bar, sitting-room, drying-room, garden; functions (max 140 people incl up to 18 residential), conferences; civil wedding licence; croquet; leisure facilities nearby (reduced rates for guests); early suppers for children; cots, high chairs, toys, baby-listening, outdoor play area ♿ No wheelchair access ● No children under 14 in restaurants eves; no dogs; no smoking 💳 Amex, Delta, MasterCard, Switch, Visa £ Single occupancy of twin/double £55, twin/double £80, family room £90; deposit required. Set D £19. Special breaks available

---

HATHERSAGE Derbyshire

map 9

Highlow Hall

Hathersage, Hope Valley S32 1AX
TEL: (01433) 650393 (AND FAX)

Isolated manor house with good views; well placed for walks.

Built by a certain Robert Eyre in the sixteenth century, this stone manor house can appear bleakly forbidding in the wrong sort of weather: the dark, crenellated skyline and stone archways send a shiver through the imagination – as they are supposed to have done for Charlotte Brontë after her stay here, ensuring the lasting, literary fame of the Eyre name. Inside, the stone-flagged floors, oak doors and huge, inglenook fireplace of the banqueting hall continue the style, but owners Penny and Barrie Walker have added modern comforts like central heating and carpets, too. The bedrooms are spacious and, though rather functional in appearance, are certainly comfortable. Those with views across the surrounding moors are worth asking for, with Room 3 enjoying a corner position. The breakfasts are designed to keep you going all day, with smoked salmon, scrambled eggs or kippers on offer. Evening meals are available on request.

◑ Closed Dec 🔟 From Hathersage, take B6001 towards Grindleford; turn off at sign to Abney and continue 1 mile to Highlow Hall. Private car park 🛏 1 twin, 1 double, 1 four-poster; family rooms available; four-poster with bathroom/WC, 2 with shower/WC; all with hair-dryer ✅ Dining-room, lounge, library, garden; functions (max 6 people residential); fishing ♿ No wheelchair access ● No children under 12; no dogs; no smoking in bedrooms 💳 MasterCard, Visa £ Single occupancy of twin/double £38, twin/double £58, four-poster £63, family room £68; deposit required. Set D £17. Special breaks available

---

 This denotes that you can get a twin or double room for £70 or less per night inclusive of breakfast.

Northleigh House

Five Ways Road, Hatton, Warwick CV35 7HZ
TEL: (01926) 484203 FAX (01926) 484006

Cheerfully relaxing B&B in rural Warwickshire.

First appearances can be deceptive: Sylvia Fenwick's large house, in open countryside, is a fairly anonymous building, and the moss in the car park could do with clearing. But once you're inside, the bedrooms are meticulously co-ordinated and comfortable: Gold has gold taps and a gold-patterned duvet, Chinese has bamboo headboards and oriental pictures, but Blue is perhaps the best, with its king-sized bed and extra sitting area. All have neatly hidden fridges and good bathrooms or shower-rooms. Not that our correspondents were all impressed, however: 'Comfort was adequate,' wrote one, adding that a discarded spray can under the table seemed to suggest a certain laxity.

Sylvia does evening meals on request – you can choose to eat together with other guests, or separately. Alternatively, there are plenty of local dining possibilities. More reports, please.

◖ Closed mid-Dec to end Jan   ⤢ 5 miles north-west of Warwick on A4177; from Five Ways roundabout take Shrewley turning for ½ mile. Private car park   🛏 1 single, 1 twin, 5 double; all with bathroom/WC exc 3 doubles with shower/WC; all with TV, hair-dryer, fridge   ⊘ Dining-room, lounge, drying-room, garden   ⅋ No wheelchair access   ◖ No dogs in public rooms; no smoking   ▭ MasterCard, Visa   £ Single £33, single occupancy of twin/double £33 to £40, twin/double £46 to £58. Set D £16.50

Simonstone Hall   `NEW ENTRY`

Hawes DL8 3LY
TEL: (01969) 667255   FAX: (01969) 667741
EMAIL: @simonstonehall.demon.co.uk

Stone country house with sumptuously furnished rooms and magnificent Wensleydale views.

Simonstone Hall started life as a hunting lodge in the eighteenth century, and in spite of its new life as an opulent but distinctly user-friendly and informal hotel, it still reverts to its former function when the owner descends several times each year with shooting parties. Starting at the chesterfields in the flagstoned reception, the place is chock-full of antiques, gilt-framed mirrors, oil paintings and huntin' shootin' fishin' paraphernalia. You could pull on your green wellies and set off to join the sheep in the magnificent, green patchwork panorama, or simply take in the Daleside vistas from a decidedly more recumbent position peering from the depths of a squashy green damask sofa in the residents' lounge, where panelled walls have been painted to lighten the effect of sombre oils and a magnificent carved fireplace. The bedrooms show that no expense has been spared in converting the old lodge to a hotel: sleigh beds, four-posters, chaises longues, claw-foot baths, and rich, heavy fabrics draped around windows and beds, all contribute luxury touches. Some rooms are in converted cottages that form the newer section of the complex, but these are kitted out in the same opulent style. Dining could either be the full monty in one of the elegant dining-rooms, choosing from a robust menu of game, meats and rich sauces with a few fish and veggie options, or a more casual affair in the lively and pubby Game Tavern.

◑ Open all year ⊠ At Leyburn end of Hawes, take road signposted to Muker and Butter Tubs; turn left at T-junction, then first right signposted Simonstone, Butter Tubs and Muker; hotel is on this road. Private car park ⬓ 1 single, 4 twin, 8 double, 6 four-poster; some in annexe; family rooms available; all with bathroom/WC; all with TV, hair-dryer, direct-dial telephone ✅ Dining-room, bar, lounge, drying-room, private dining-room, garden; functions (max 54 people, or max 200 in marquee, incl up to 36 residential), conferences; civil wedding licence; fishing; shooting by arrangement; early suppers for children; cot, high chair, baby-listening ⅙ No wheelchair access
● No children under 15 in restaurant eves; no dogs in restaurant, dogs in some bedrooms only (£4 per night); no smoking in restaurant or bedrooms ▱ Delta, Diners, MasterCard, Switch, Visa £ Single £38 to £55, single occupancy of twin/double £50 to £70, twin/double £75 to £110, four-poster £110 to £140, family room £120 to £170, suite £120 to £160; deposit required. Bar/bistro L £10.50, D £12.50; alc L, D £22.50. Special breaks available

---

HAWKRIDGE Somerset

map 1

Tarr Steps

Hawkridge, Dulverton TA22 9PY
TEL: (01643) 851293   FAX: (01643) 851218

Friendly, unstuffy Exmoor hotel, popular with walkers.

This hotel's eyrie-like position, in the midst of an ancient broadleaf forest, high above the 17 gritstone slabs that make up the famous clapper bridge over the River Barle, is not the least of its advantages. Shaun and Sue Blackmore's large hybrid-Georgian/Edwardian house, overlooking what is reputedly the devil's favourite sunbathing spot, is everything you'd want an Exmoor country hotel to be: remote, comfortable and indulgent of the needs of visitors with outdoor interests, from walkers to bird-watchers. When you come in, possibly damp and stiff from a day on the moor, there's a cosy half-panelled bar, with a wood-burning fire, spindle-back chairs and a menagerie of wildlife heads to unwind among. The light, airy sitting-room is smarter, with bronzes on the Adam-style fireplace and enough books, life-style magazines and board games to while away a rainy afternoon in a space that avoids the deadening stiffness of so many country-house lounges. A traditional feel prevails in the two-sectioned dining-room, where guests might dine on hearty fare like creamy potato soup sprinkled with chives and lardons of bacon, followed by roast tenderloin of pork with garlic potatoes and a ginger sauce, rounded off with sticky toffee pudding with a warm caramel sauce. The bedrooms are something of a mixed bag, homelier than the public areas, and teeming with nice antiques and bamboo and basket-weave items; their views are tremendous. Like the public areas, they're television-free zones.

◗ Closed first 2 weeks in Feb ⤤ From B3222, on entering Dulverton follow signs to Hawkridge (not to Tarr Steps). Go through village following signs to hotel. Private car park ⇤ 2 single, 3 twin, 4 double, 2 four-poster; most with bathroom/WC; all with direct-dial telephone ⌁ 2 dining-rooms, bar, sitting-room, drying-room, garden; functions (max 20 people residential/non-residential), conferences; fishing, clay-pigeon and rough shooting; early suppers for children; cots, high chairs, baby-listening, outdoor play area ⚲ Wheelchair access to hotel and dining-rooms, WC (M), 1 ground-floor bedroom ● Children discouraged from dining-rooms eves; dogs in bar and bedrooms only (£3.50 per day); smoking discouraged in bedrooms ⊟ Delta, MasterCard, Switch, Visa £ Single £58 to £65, single occupancy of twin/double £75 to £100, twin/double/four-poster £116 to £130 (rates incl dinner) (1998 prices); deposit required. Bar/bistro L £5; set L £15. Special breaks available

---

HAWKSHEAD Cumbria map 8

Highfield House

Hawkshead Hill, Hawkshead, Ambleside LA22 0PN
TEL: (015394) 36344   FAX: (015394) 36793
EMAIL: highfield.hawkshead@btinternet.com

Beautifully located, family-run hotel, with a homely, reassuring atmosphere.

The bucolic landscapes around the show-piece village of Hawkshead attract many visitors, and roads leading towards the picturesque Tarn Hows can get fairly busy on fine, summer days. Highfield House, however, cushioned by a sizeable chunk of well-established gardens, seems light years away from traffic jams; set on rising land, well back from the road, it enjoys marvellous, uninterrupted views of the distant fells. A solid, seemly house in typical Victorian-Lakeland style, it's been a family hotel for over fifty years. The furnishings are traditional and undauntingly old-fashioned (busy carpets and Sanderson's William Morris patterns are favoured), but everything is very well kept and obviously cared for. Tall windows make the most of the light and the views. The bedrooms are mostly large and comfortable, though few spring any decorative surprises. Those at the top have more character, with their sloping ceilings, quirky shapes and exposed beams. Tempting set dinners using much local produce, followed by satisfying English puddings, please a satisfied band of regular stayers. Breakfast includes fresh fruit and yoghurt and smoked fish, as well as traditional Cumbrian fry-ups – 'unbelievable', raved one happy reader.

◗ Closed Jan ⤤ ¾ mile north-west of Hawkshead, on B5285 to Coniston. Private car park ⇤ 2 single, 3 twin, 6 double; family rooms available all with bathroom/WC exc 1 double with shower/WC; all with TV, room service, hair-dryer, direct-dial telephone ⌁ Dining-room, bar, lounge, drying-room, garden; leisure facilities nearby (free for guests); early suppers for children; cots, high chairs, baby-listening ⚲ No wheelchair access ● No dogs in public rooms; no smoking in dining-room and 1 bedroom ⊟ Delta, MasterCard, Switch, Visa £ Single £39 to £41, single occupancy of twin/double £49 to £51, twin/double £73 to £76, family room £95 to £100; deposit required. Bar/bistro L £6; set D £17.50

Ivy House

Main Street, Hawkshead, Ambleside LA22 0NS
TEL: (01539) 436204

Georgian guesthouse in show-piece village, offering friendly, family-run accommodation.

This handsome, period residence (ivy coloured, if not ivy clad) stands near the middle of one of the Lake District's most popular tourist centres. It dates from 1770 (so Wordsworth would have known it while he was at school in Hawkshead), and though listed and full of character, it's a friendly and informal place where visitors will soon feel at home and children are welcome. A lounge rather too full of chintzy seating gets folk talking, and there's plenty to look at on the walls – a collection of Wedgwood US bicentenary plaques, for instance, and some paintings donated by guests (though not, we understand, in lieu of the bill). The dining-room gives more of a sense of space, and is decorated in green with lots of china on display. Sample menus consist of traditional fare (soups, roasts and lots of rib-sticking puddings). The bedrooms are simple and agreeable, with plain walls offsetting smart, dark-blue quilts and pine or wicker furnishings. The annexe rooms next to the main house are more modern in style, having warmer colour schemes and neat bathrooms. Prospective guests will be relieved to hear that there's somewhere to park (Hawkshead clobbers its motoring visitors with hefty charges).

◑ Closed Nov to mid-Mar ⊅ In centre of Hawkshead village. Private car park ⊯ 2 twin, 7 double, 2 family rooms; some in annexe; most with bathroom/WC, some with shower/WC; all with TV, hair-dryer ⊘ Dining-room, lounge, drying-room; fishing; cots, high chairs ⅍ No wheelchair access ● Dogs in bedrooms only; no smoking in dining-room ⊟ None accepted £ Single occupancy of twin/double £30 to £32, twin/double £60 to £64, family room £70 to £81 (prices valid till Nov 1998). Set D £13

Queen's Head

Main Street, Hawkshead, Ambleside LA22 0NS
TEL: (015394) 36271   FAX: (015394) 36722

Prime-site Elizabethan inn specialising in fish dishes in the heart of Hawkshead.

Tourists flock to the well-kept Cumbrian village of Hawkshead, and a fair proportion of them, undeterred by a glum inn-sign featuring the Virgin Queen, spill from the car park into the nearest pub. By good fortune (for all concerned) that just happens to be this attractive half-timbered Tudor building on the main street. A notice propped outside at meal-times makes some of them do a double-take ('Extensive fish menu', it says – which some read as 'Expensive'). But the Queen's Head is far from expensive; in fact it's remarkably good value for the fresh and varied selection of fish that comes all the way from Lowestoft. Understandably, it's busy at lunch-times, both in its cosy, traditional bars crammed with toby jugs and horse brasses, and in the more genteel lace-clothed restaurant to one side. A dozen or so bedrooms ramble creakily across upper floors, varying in size and shape (many are rather small) but all appealingly furnished with thoughtful touches, such as the robes provided for the rooms with separate bathrooms (all have their own facilities). Landings, stairways and all public spaces are kept as neat as a pin.

○ Open all year ⚡ In centre of Hawkshead. Public car park nearby (free) ⛟ 9 double, 2 four-poster, 1 family room, 1 suite; 3 in annexe; 3 with bathroom/WC, most with shower/WC; all with TV, hair-dryer, direct-dial telephone ✓ Restaurant, bar; functions (max 60 people incl up to 30 residential); cots, high chairs ♿ No wheelchair access ⊖ No dogs; no smoking in bedrooms ▭ Delta, MasterCard, Switch, Visa £ Single occupancy of twin/double £45, twin/double £30 to £34, four-poster £36 to £38, family room £34, suite £36, annexe room £28 to £30; deposit required. Bar/bistro L £3.50 to £10.50, D £6 to £15. Special breaks available

---

HAWORTH West Yorkshire   map 8

Hole Farm

Dimples Lane, Haworth, Keighley BD22 8QT
TEL: (01535) 644755 (AND FAX)

Great-value farmhouse B&B, with bubbly hostess and animals galore.

Haworth will never want for visitors: they come in hordes on the trail of the former home of the Brontë sisters, but in the peace and tranquillity of Hole Farm, with its menagerie of horses, pigs, a peacock named Percy and a turkey named Gilbert, you would never know that all the hustle and bustle is just a ten-minute walk away. Janet Milner's 300-year-old, stone farmhouse sits high above Haworth – a location that can be particularly appreciated at breakfast time in the former dairy, now a combined sitting-room and breakfast room, whose french windows let you take in the lovely, moorland views whilst tucking into a real farmhouse breakfast of home-cured bacon and free-range eggs from the farm. Janet loves to chat with her guests, so this is the time to plan your day's activities in the characterful surroundings, featuring beamed ceilings and panelled walls. Self-catering cottages form the core of Janet's business, but don't think that the B&B accommodation is a mere afterthought: the two bedrooms come with the sort of extras – fresh flowers, fruit and biscuits – that you might expect in a rather more pricey hotel. One is decorated in summery blue and yellow, with tulips liberally painted all around, the other in Laura Ashley vein, with a charming, hand-stitched bedspread.

○ Closed Chr ⚡ In Haworth, follow signs for Brontë Museum; take first left past Sun pub and turn immediately left again; then follow signs to farm. Private car park ⛟ 1 twin, 1 double; both with shower/WC; both with TV, hair-dryer ✓ Sitting-room/breakfast room, garden ♿ No wheelchair access ⊖ No children under 12; no dogs; no smoking ▭ None accepted £ Single occupancy of twin/double £25, twin/double £40

Many hotels offer special rates for stays of a few nights or more. It is worth enquiring when you book.

Weavers

15 West Lane, Haworth, Keighley BD22 8DU
TEL: (01535) 643822   FAX: (01535) 644832

Top-notch Yorkshire cooking in a characterful restaurant-with-rooms.

Colin and Jane Rushworth have entered their third decade at the helm of Weavers, serving unpretentious, Yorkshire food at the heart of Brontë country. If it is the literary sisters that have brought you to Haworth, you couldn't be much closer to the former family parsonage, at the top of the cobbled high street, that threatens to turn the town into a Brontë visitors' park. Weavers is a conversion of three weavers' cottages, with a Victorian-style restaurant and a more characterful bar, liberally hung with bobbins and sundry tools of the trade in an interesting assemblage of clutter. Don't be misled by the 'honest northern' tag attached to Colin and Jane's cooking – it is certainly on a higher plane than the stark simplicity of such menu entries as Pennine meat-and-potato pie might suggest. Everything from bread to ice-cream is prepared in-house from the freshest, local produce, and the menu features so many old favourites with light, modern twists that you will be spoilt for choice: Lancashire-cheese fritters, for example, come with apple and grape chutney, and calf's liver with a gin and lime sauce. Puddings are comforting and rich – expect chocolate and marshmallow brownies or sticky toffee pudding. In the homely bedrooms, which are decorated with restraint, antique beds and interesting fittings, like a wooden chandelier, combine with views over the village, the Brontë parsonage and the moors.

◖ Closed 25 Dec to 10 Jan & 1 week late June; restaurant closed Sun & Mon eves
▧ Follow signs to Brontë Parsonage Museum in Haworth. Public car park nearby (£1.50 per day) ⊨ 2 single, 1 twin, 1 double; all with bathroom/WC; all with TV, room service, hair-dryer, trouser press, direct-dial telephone ⌗ Restaurant, bar, lounge; functions (max 45 people incl up to 6 residential); early suppers for children
♿ No wheelchair access ⬤ No dogs; no smoking in restaurant ▭ Amex, Delta, Diners, MasterCard, Switch, Visa ▤ Single £50, single occupancy of twin/double £60, twin/double £75; deposit required. Set D £13.50; alc D £20

HENLEY-ON-THAMES Oxfordshire   map 2

Red Lion

Hart Street, Henley-on-Thames RG9 2AR
TEL: (01491) 572161   FAX: (01491) 410039

Refined and traditional Georgian inn beside the Thames and close to the centre of town.

The lucky few with long-standing reservations for Regatta week can watch the winning boats cross the finishing line from the front windows of this historic coaching-inn. Consolation for the rest of the year comes from an uninterrupted view of the broad reach of the Thames and the balustraded (and busy) stone bridge carrying London-bound traffic a few strides away, and a short walk past a square-towered church and half-timbered houses to the town centre. The present Georgian-fronted building comes outwardly wrapped in aged wistaria and internally panelled in pale, mellow oak. The flagged and glazed corners closest to the bridge are given over to an intimate bar and a cheerful dining-room painted sunny yellow between the aged timbers. The more formal Regatta Restaurant provides an unfussily elegant space facing the water, with imaginative treatments of traditional English staples on offer, such as asparagus chargrilled and topped with Parmesan, or fillet of beef with peppered parsnips and pancetta.

Most bedrooms overlook the river (the only downside being the busy road junction below) and, bearing in mind the sixteenth-century origins of the building, are generally comfortable for space. The combination of period pieces and appropriate reproductions is perfectly agreeable, while the remains of Charles I's crest in the plaster elevates four-poster Room 108 to the 'memorable' category.

◑ Open all year ▨ Hotel is beside Henley Bridge. Private car park 🛏 3 single, 9 twin, 11 double, 2 four-poster, 1 family room; all with bathroom/WC; all with TV, room service, hair-dryer, trouser press, direct-dial telephone, no tea/coffee-making facilities in rooms ✓ Restaurants, bar; functions (max 80 people incl up to 51 residential), conferences; early suppers for children; cots, high chairs, babysitting, baby-listening ♿ No wheelchair access ⊖ No dogs ▭ Amex, Delta, MasterCard, Switch, Visa £ Single £85, single occupancy of twin/double £105, twin/double £115, four-poster £135, family room £140; deposit required. Continental B £8, cooked B £11; bar/bistro L £6, D £5; alc L, D £25

HERTFORD Hertfordshire map 3

Hall House

𝓛

Broad Oak End, Off Bramfield Road, Hertford SG14 2JA
TEL: (01992) 582807

Quiet, country setting for this pristine, modern, family house with a surprising history.

Olive and Tom Whiting's pristine country house is something of a rural bolt-hole, situated within minutes of the commercial trappings of Hertford. To find the primrose-stuccoed villa, you leave town by a leafy B-road, turn into a private, unpaved lane, and breach the enclosing brick wall into an immaculately trimmed garden of orderly conifers and lawns that a Gleneagles greenkeeper would be proud of. Such orderliness is not confined to the outdoors, for there is a display cabinet of glassware to admire in the drawing-room, and a distinctly colonial air, lent by cane chairs and bamboo prints, in the small conservatory. Two of the bedrooms are found in a garden chalet, while the third – a large room, with a spacious private bathroom – is upstairs in the main house. Scan the shelves, or pop open the drawers, and you will find fresh flowers, potpourri, Alka Seltzer tablets, Horlicks sachets... if Olive hasn't thought of something, you will probably never need it.

A fresh-fruit platter of mangoes, kiwis, strawberries and pineapples greets guests at breakfast-time in the timber-beamed dining-room. Olive will produce dinners, if required, according both to guests' preferences and the availability of fresh produce at the butcher's or fishmonger's. A study of the black-and-white photographs on the wall reveals that the house, though only 13 years old, was actually built around fifteenth-century timbers that were transported here from the site of the original Hall House.

◗ Closed Chr & New Year   ⚡ On A119 Hertford to Stevenage road, pass Hertford North station; turn left into Bramfield Road. After ½ mile, turn right into Broad Oak End, via a private lane between Broad Oak Manor nursing-home signs. Private car park ⌂→ 3 double; some in annexe; 1 with bathroom WC (not *en suite*), 2 with shower/WC; all with TV, hair-dryer, trouser press   ⚘ Dining-room, drawing-room, conservatory ♿ No wheelchair access   ⬤ No children under 14; no dogs; no smoking ⬚ MasterCard, Visa   £ Single occupancy of double £49, double £67; deposit required. Set D £22

HEXHAM Northumberland
map 10

Dene House   **NEW ENTRY**

Juniper, Hexham NE46 1SJ
TEL: (01434) 673413 (AND FAX)

Simple, cottage B&B, with exceptionally friendly welcome, in a peaceful, Northumberland village.

Dene House is a mellow, yellow, sandstone cottage that takes some beating as a relaxed and tranquil base in Hadrian's Wall country. Margaret Massey, 'a most organised, friendly and welcoming hostess', according to one reader, will make you feel at home with tea or coffee as soon as you arrive and begin to unwind in the lovely sun lounge that looks on to a garden of flowers and home-grown vegetables. If you want to walk off any surplus energy, the resident springer spaniel may accompany you around the nine acres of grassy pastures adjoining the house. That this is Margaret and John's family home is immediately clear: sheaves of dried flowers hang from the stair rails and form pretty arrangements around the house, photos of the family are dotted here and there, while aircraft and RAF memorabilia in the double bedroom tip the wink that their son is a pilot. The other two guest bedrooms are decorated in a similar, cottagey style – simple and fresh, with patchwork quilts, books on shelves and the odd teddy. You're welcome to bring your own wine for evening meals, arranged in advance with Margaret, who sets out the silver in the dining-room where there is a cosy, wood-burning stove and baskets of logs in the hearth. Breakfasts, cooked on the Aga in the farmhouse kitchen, are served around a lovely, pine table.

◗ Closed 24 & 25 Dec   ⚡ Take B6306 from Hexham; take first right fork then first left, both signposted Dye House; follow road for 3½ miles; Dene House is 100 yards past Juniper sign. Private car park   ⌂→ 1 single, 1 twin, 1 double; double with bathroom/WC, twin with shower/WC; all with hair-dryer   ⚘ Dining-room, lounge, sun lounge, drying-room, garden; cots, high chairs   ♿ No wheelchair access ⬤ No dogs in public rooms; no smoking   ⬚ None accepted   £ Single £20, single occupancy of twin/double £24, twin/double £40; deposit required. Set D £12

East Peterel Field Farm

Yarridge Road, Hexham NE46 2JT
TEL: (01434) 607209   FAX: (01434) 601753
EMAIL: bookings@petfield.demon.co.uk
WEB SITE: www.com.england/eastpeterelfieldfarm

Elegant B&B accommodation with wonderful food in a stylish family home on a stud farm.

Don't mistake this farm for the working variety where life revolves around tractors and livestock – although a Land Rover wouldn't come amiss for tackling the rutted track leading to this remote spot. When our inspector visited, expensive German cars were lined up in the courtyard, and ladies-who-lunch from the environs of Hexham were enjoying a cookery demonstration by a celebrity cook (if fortune favours you, some of the resulting creations might turn up on your dinner table). Inside, Sue and David Carr's heavily reworked seventeenth-century farmhouse is designed to let you soak up south-facing views in well-proportioned rooms that wouldn't look out of place in an interiors magazine. Staying here you have to accept the slight lack of privacy that comes from sharing a family home, but there's enough room to find a corner to yourself in the elegant sitting-room. The magnificent kitchen is enormous and has an attached refectory where breakfast, much praised by visitors, is served. Bedrooms have a feminine touch, with lacy canopies and great views – some have brass beds, although one reader reported that the mattress was rather like a hammock (and that the wardrobe was out in the hall).

◖ Closed Chr & New Year; restaurant closed Sun eve   ▨ From Hexham take B6306 south. Take first right to Whitley Chapel up to top of hill. Go over the crossroads, into dip, then turn right by tree with sign to farm. Private car park   ⊨ 1 twin, 2 double, 1 suite; all with bathroom/WC exc 1 double with shower/WC; all with TV, hair-dryer, some with trouser press   ⟡ Refectory, sitting-room/TV room, drying-room, library, garden; early suppers for children   ⅄ No wheelchair access   ● No dogs; no smoking in bedrooms   ⊟ None accepted   £ Single occupancy of twin/double/suite £37 to £39, twin/double £54, suite £58. Set D £18.50

Langley Castle   **NEW ENTRY**

Langley-on-Tyne, Hexham NE47 5LU
TEL: (01434) 688888   FAX: (01434) 684019

Pocket-sized medieval castle, turned into a hotel with sumptuous rooms, a rooftop chapel and wonderful Gothic character.

On first sight, the pint-sized Langley Castle has the too-perfect air of a Victorian folly, which might make you doubt that it is an authentic Gothic castle. Rest assured – it's the real McCoy, built in the fourteenth century by Sir Thomas de Lucy from his French-bashing booty earned at the Battle of Crécy. It lasted barely half a century before being gutted by fire, and was left as a shell for the next 500 years until a certain Cadwallader Bates, a Victorian gentleman-historian, set about rebuilding the ruin in true style. What makes it worth forking out pretty serious money for a stay here is the baronial splendour of the eight rooms in the castle proper, which are buffered from the modern world by seven-foot-thick walls – so thick that each room has a window seat set into them. Gothic-arched windows and doorways, stained glass, tapestries, richly canopied four-poster beds, and bathrooms with sauna or spa baths that are the last word in luxury, invest sumptuous rooms like Derwentwater and Cadwallader with a Gothic chic that hints at what the castle could have been like centuries ago – and you can bet that our modern standards of plumbing, heating and housekeeping leave our ancestors in the Dark Ages. Although stylish enough, the Castleview rooms, in a former coaching-inn annexe, can't compete. One down side of the castle's popularity as a venue for weddings and functions is that after dining on the rich, modern-influenced cuisine, you might find the snoozy peacefulness of the magnificent drawing-room, full of tapestries and lit by a Gothic window, shattered by gaggles of revellers.

◑ Open all year 🔁 Leave Hexham towards west on A69; turn left on to A686 signposted Langley Castle and follow road; hotel is signposted on right. Private car park ⤶ 1 twin, 9 double, 4 four-poster, 4 family rooms; some in annexe; all with bathroom/WC; all with TV, room service, hair-dryer, direct-dial telephone, some with mini-bar ⌁ Restaurant, bar, drawing-room, function suite and bar, garden; functions (max 160 people incl up to 40 residential), conferences; civil wedding licence; leisure facilities nearby (reduced rates for guests); early suppers for children; cots, high chairs, baby-listening 🦽 No wheelchair access ● No dogs in public rooms; no smoking in restaurant ▭ Amex, Delta, Diners, MasterCard, Switch, Visa £ Single occupancy of twin/double from £80, twin/double £99, four-poster £145; family room £129; deposit required. Bar/bistro L £6.50; set L £14.50, D £24.50. Special breaks available

---

HIGH BUSTON Northumberland   map 10

High Buston Hall

High Buston, Alnmouth, Alnwick NE66 3QH
TEL: (01665) 830341 (AND FAX)

Elegant, listed Georgian house, a stone's throw from the Northumberland coast.

As a base for exploring the coastline of Northumbria, High Buston Hall takes some beating; a further plus – a superb beach sheltered by dunes – lies just a short walk away. With the panache that one would expect from an English Heritage architect, owner John Edwards has worked his way through the main hall and three estate cottages to bring off a stylish conversion. The interior of the main hall uses chandeliers and oil paintings to good effect in setting off such period details as a grand, open staircase, but there is nothing intimidating about the ambience – the guests' lounge has plenty of local information and magazines to foster a relaxed feel. The spacious bedrooms have the odd antique wardrobe or chest of drawers, pine and wicker pieces and patchwork quilts; the four-poster room has rugs on its wooden floorboards and, along with the neighbouring double, distant sea views. Oak-smoked kippers from Craster make an appearance at breakfast, which is served at a communal table. Make sure that you order evening meals when you book; otherwise there's a good choice of eating options in Warkworth, just three miles away.

◗ Closed Dec; dining-room closed Sun eve 🔁 Just off A1068, between Warkworth and Alnmouth. Private car park 🛏 2 double, 1 four-poster; 2 with bathroom/WC, 1 with shower/WC (not *en suite*); all with TV; hair-dryer available ⌀ Dining-room, lounge, drying-room, garden; conferences (max 12 people incl up to 3 residential); early suppers for children; cots, high chairs, toys ♿ No wheelchair access ● No dogs; no smoking ▭ None accepted £ Single occupancy of double £40, double/four-poster £65; deposit required. Set D £25. Special breaks available

---

HIGHER BURWARDSLEY Cheshire map 7

Pheasant Inn

Higher Burwardsley, Tattenhall, Chester CH3 9PF
TEL: (01829) 770434 FAX: (01829) 771097
EMAIL: dave1pheas@aol.com
WEB SITE: home.aol.com.dave/pheas

Relaxed and welcoming pub in superbly isolated, hill-top setting.

The breathtaking view of the surrounding countryside from the terrace of the Pheasant Inn has been turning heads for years – it even prompted a proposal of marriage from one guest to his companion! On a summer's evening, space at the tables out here may well be at a premium, driving you inside the sandstone and half-timbered building. This is not too great a loss, however: the main bar, with its low, beamed ceiling, large open fire and resident parrot, or the cosy Highland Room, featuring tartan carpets and rosettes awarded to prize-winning Highland cattle (an obsession of the owner, David Greenhaugh, who has a nearby field full of the beasties), are both good spots in which to enjoy a bar meal. The menu and blackboard chalked up with daily specials offer such dishes as pancakes filled with mixed seafood and prawn bisque or chicken chasseur, and a selection of traditional, but comforting, desserts like chocolate fudge cake or bread-and-butter pudding. The large, flagstone-floored conservatory is popular for family meals – it even has a box of toys in one corner.

Most of the bedrooms are divided between two converted barns, while the tidy and well-kept Eaton Room is above the bar. The rooms in the barns have a more modern feel to them, and tend to be a little smaller, but they are still neat and comfortable, and offer yet more fabulous views from the narrow windows.

◗ Open all year 🔁 From A41 follow signs to Tattenhall, then Burwardsley; bear left at post office. Inn is at top of hill on left. Private car park 🛏 2 twin, 6 double, 1 four-poster, 1 family room; some in annexe; all with bathroom/WC; all with TV, hair-dryer, direct-dial telephone, radio, some with trouser press ⌀ Restaurant, bar, lounge, conservatory, garden; functions (max 40 people incl up to 20 residential), conferences; early suppers for children; cots, high chairs, toys, baby-listening ♿ No wheelchair access ● Dogs in bedrooms only (£2.50 per day); no smoking in some bedrooms ▭ Amex, Diners, MasterCard, Switch, Visa £ Single occupancy of twin/double £45, twin/double £70, four-poster £80, family room £90; deposit required. Bar/bistro L £12, D £15. Special breaks available

---

See page 6 for a brief explanation of how to use the Guide.

Hintlesham Hall

Hintlesham, Ipswich IP8 3NS
TEL: (01473) 652268   FAX: (01473) 652463

A stately residence with a vast array of public rooms and plenty of leisure facilities.

As befits a country house set in 175 acres of grounds, there are few facilities that this hotel can't offer; you could try a round on the 18-hole championship golf course, a visit to the spa, with its steam room and sauna, or a dip in the outdoor swimming-pool. Even if you don't sample any of these activities, a stay at Hintlesham Hall will probably satisfy any urges that you might have to imagine yourself living the life of a country squire. This pale-peachy-brown, Georgian home seems to have a succession of drawing-rooms, one following another as you proceed through its wings; each is done out in lush fabrics, with an individual colour tone in every room. The most attractive is the library, with its red walls and books in cabinets behind grilles. The ballroom-sized dining-room is positively over the top in its decoration, with the eye settling first on the pinks and lilacs around the ornate, plasterwork mirrors and fireplaces, and then on the green tablecloths, red chairs and blue carpet. Hintlesham's restaurant, after long years of praise, has received mixed reports lately; our own inspector gave a disappointed verdict of 'good in presentation, but sadly lacking in taste'. The bedrooms are all individually decorated, with high standards evident in the choice of fabrics and some antique furnishings.

◑ Open all year ◪ 5 miles west of Ipswich, on A1071 towards Sudbury. Private car park ⌂ 27 double, 2 four-poster, 4 suites; some in annexe; all with bathroom/WC; all with TV, room service, hair-dryer, mini-bar, direct-dial telephone; no tea/coffee-making facilities in rooms ✦ 3 dining-rooms, bar, 4 drawing-rooms, library, games room, garden; functions (max 100 people incl up to 66 residential), conferences; civil wedding licence; golf, gym, heated outdoor swimming-pool, sauna, steam room, tennis, putting green, snooker, clay-pigeon shooting, croquet; leisure facilities nearby (free for guests); cots, high chairs, babysitting, baby-listening ♿ Wheelchair access to hotel (1 step) and dining-rooms, WC (unisex), 9 ground-floor bedrooms ● No children under 10 in dining-rooms eves; no dogs in public rooms; no smoking in dining-rooms ▭ Amex, Diners, MasterCard, Switch, Visa £ Single occupancy of double £89 to £105, double £115 to £220, four-poster £220, suite £235 to £300. Cooked B £7.50; set L £19.50, D £26; alc L, D £35. Special breaks available

---

Homewood Park

Hinton Charterhouse, Bath BA3 6BB
TEL: (01225) 723731   FAX: (01225) 723820

Intimate and informal country house with fine gardens.

With grounds that run to ten acres, and overlooking the Limpley Stoke Valley, Homewood Park, just six miles from Bath, has all the credentials to make a good base for discovering the delights of the spa town, while providing a welcome refuge from its endless bustle and tourist hordes. Frank and Sara Gueuning have striven to make this creeper-draped, multi-gabled, mainly Georgian, part-Victorian house with a recent bedroom extension a discreetly elegant, distinctly pampering, sort of place. On arrival, guests are ushered through the stone arched doorway to a sunny, gracious drawing-room where tea, accompanied by delicious, straight-from-the-oven biscuits, is served. A vast bay window, mullioned panes and cheerful décor set a tone that is continued in the elegant restaurant, lined with oil paintings. The food – perhaps ravioli of Parmesan risotto with herbs and bacon, followed by poached turbot in a saffron and garlic bouillon, and tiramisù with espresso sauce and chocolate spaghetti – has won many plaudits.

The bedrooms, priced according to size and view, are attractively furnished and enlivened by bold colours and classy fabrics.

As we went to press, this hotel was up for sale.

○ Open all year ▨ 6 miles south-east of Bath on A36 to Warminster. Private car park ⌂ 9 twin/double, 7 double, 1 four-poster, 2 suites; family rooms available all with bathroom/WC; all with TV, room service, hair-dryer, direct-dial telephone; no tea/coffee-making facilities in rooms ⌀ Restaurant, bar, drawing-room, study, garden; functions (max 85 people incl up to 38 residential), conferences; heated outdoor swimming-pool, tennis, croquet; early suppers for children; cots, high chairs, babysitting, baby-listening ♿ Wheelchair access to hotel and restaurant, WC (unisex), 2 ground-floor bedrooms ● No dogs ▭ Amex, Delta, Diners, MasterCard, Switch, Visa £ Single occupancy of twin/double £105, twin/double £135, four-poster £200, suite £245; deposit required. Set L £22; alc D £47.50

HOLMESFIELD Derbyshire map 9

Horsleygate Hall

Horsleygate Lane, Holmesfield, Dronfield S18 7WD
TEL: (01142) 890333

Rural B&B, in a comfortable, family home, with good gardens and friendly hosts.

On the eastern edge of the Peak District, close to the urban centres of Chesterfield and Sheffield, Margaret and Robert Ford have managed to create something of a rural idyll – not least because of the warm, friendly welcome that they give their guests. Their stone farmhouse stands in a wonderful, sprawling, two-acre garden, where the dry-stone walls are covered in flowers, and chickens wander through carpets of daffodils watched by horses in the paddock. The house is done out in a country-farmhouse style, with rugs on the stone flags, pine doors and some interesting antiques. The bedrooms are creatively decorated with rich fabrics and a good mix of furniture to give a homely, comfortable look. All have views out across the garden towards the Peak District.

Eggs for breakfast come from the Fords' own, free-range chickens; also on offer might be Derbyshire oatcakes and soft fruits. Evening meals can be had at a number of local pubs.

◑ Closed Chr 🚗 Off B6051, north-west of Chesterfield. Private car park 🛏 1 twin, 1 double, 1 family room; double with bathroom/WC; hair-dryer available ⊘ Dining-room, lounge, garden ♿ No wheelchair access ● No children under 5; no dogs; no smoking 🚭 None accepted £ Single occupancy of twin/double £25, twin/double £40 to £45, family room £48; deposit required

---

HOPESAY Shropshire   map 7

Old Rectory

Hopesay, Craven Arms SY7 8HD
TEL: (01588) 660245   FAX: 01588 660502

Graceful family home with a lovely garden, where it feels more like staying with friends than in a hotel.

Michael and Roma Villar's largely Georgian, four-storey house stands in a captivating spot next to a fine Norman church, surveying the mature copper beeches and sweeping lawns of its own large garden and the National Trust's wooded Hopesay Hill beyond. A stay here offers the chance to experience the best of English country living in the Wolsey Lodge tradition. In the drawing-room, with its Adam fireplace and piles of *Country Life*, you can help yourself to drinks from a trolley and take them out to the garden terrace, where afternoon tea, including biscuits and cakes, is served when it's fine. Dinner is a formal, communal affair served at an antique oak refectory table. Roma's no-choice Aga-cooked dinner-party fare is praised, and often includes herbs, vegetables and fruit from the garden. As much thought goes into breakfasts, which feature home-made yoghurt and fruit compote and home-baked breads. Big, comfortable beds – made the old-fashioned way with sheets and blankets – and antiques, fresh flowers and expansive *en suite* bathrooms characterise the bedrooms.

◑ Closed Chr & New Year 🚗 Leave A49 at Craven Arms; take B4368 signposted to Clun; at Aston-on-Clun turn right over hump-backed bridge; house is 1 mile on, on left by church. Private car park 🛏 2 double, 1 suite; all with bathroom/WC; all with TV, hair-dryer, radio, electric blankets ⊘ Dining-room, drawing-room, drying-room, garden ♿ No wheelchair access ● No children; no dogs; no smoking 🚭 None accepted £ Double £70, suite £70; deposit required. Set D £20

HORLEY Surrey   map 3

Langshott Manor

Langshott, Horley RH6 9LN
TEL: (01293) 786680   FAX: (01293) 783905
EMAIL: admin@langshottmanor.com

New owners but still bursting with old-world charm and delicious, unpretentious food.

The modern world has inexorably marched on just a few miles from this most splendid Grade II-listed manor. Having left behind the aerial hurly-burly of

Gatwick and negotiated the tangled web of roads, you drive down a little lane which gets increasingly rural by the yard. By the time you reach the hotel sign, you feel as if you're deep in the heart of the countryside. The heavy chimneys and half-timbered walls, so redolent of the Elizabethan era, are surrounded by beautifully landscaped gardens and flowering bushes, while leaded windows peek out from the deep red tiles that extend down to the ground floor. The interior is as elegant as it is atmospheric. Nothing detracts from the beamed ceilings, heavy wooden staircases, sloping floors and warm fireplaces. Each bedroom is individually and luxuriantly furnished, and personal touches are not ignored either – guests get a personalised, handwritten note in their room welcoming them to the hotel. In both the bedrooms and public areas armfuls of fresh flowers fill the air with a fragrant aroma, surpassed only by the exquisite aromas from the dining-rooms, where a medley-of-fish soup could precede chicken breast wrapped in leeks with a julienne of vegetables, and finally a banana tarte Tatin with toffee-apple ice-cream. A word to the wise – the candles, both on the tables and the banisters, are filled with oil, not made of wax.

◗ Open all year ◪ From A23 at Horley Chequers roundabout, take Ladbroke Road to Langshott; manor is 1 mile on right. Private car park (1 week free parking at Courtlands for guests flying via Gatwick) ⟝ 2 twin, 9 double, 2 four-poster, 2 suites; some in annexe; all with bathroom/WC; all with TV, room service, hair-dryer, direct-dial telephone, some with mini-bar; no tea/coffee-making facilities in rooms ✧ 2 dining-rooms, bar, 2 lounges, garden; early suppers for children; cots, high chairs, baby-listening ㊓ No wheelchair access ● No dogs; no smoking in bedrooms ▭ Amex, Delta, Diners, MasterCard, Switch, Visa £ Single occupancy of twin/double £115 to £165, twin/double £145 to £195, four-poster £175, suite £195; deposit required. Set L £19/£24, D £35. Special breaks available

---

Bell Inn & Hill House

High Road, Horndon on the Hill, Stanford Le Hope SS17 8LD
TEL: (01375) 642463   FAX: (01375) 361611

A Tudor coaching-inn and a Georgian house with imaginative bedrooms and a welcoming, village atmosphere.

Two generations of the family owners of the splendid, fifteenth-century Bell Inn have been providing hospitality for more than 50 years – but not as long as some of the hot cross buns nailed to the beams of the pub have been there. This curious tradition (instituted when one landlord began his tenure on Good Friday 90 years ago) is one of the many stories that surround the inn. Some of the bedrooms, as well as the restaurant and, of course, the bar, are here, while Hill House – two doors along – has further rooms. The best rooms are in the Bell, and all have received the stylish attention of Christine Vereker. Each is named after a famous mistress, and the most notable is Lady Hamilton, which has a life-size model of her lover, Lord Nelson, in the corner. The bedrooms in Hill House are less extravagant, but cheaper. The menu offers a wide range of dishes, with plenty of old favourites as well. A typical menu might include confit of duck with onion marmalade and cassis sauce, or calf's liver, spring-onion mash, mushrooms and bacon.

◗ Open all year 🖪 From M25, Junction 30, follow A13 to Grays and then B1007 to Horndon on the Hill. Private car park 🛏 3 twin, 6 double, 1 four-poster, 1 family room, 4 suites; some in annexe; most with bathroom/WC, 3 with shower/WC; all with TV, room service, hair-dryer, trouser press, direct-dial telephone ⊘ Restaurant, bar, drying-room functions (max 200 people incl up to 31 residential), conferences; cots, high chairs ♿ No wheelchair access ● No dogs in public rooms and some bedrooms; no smoking in some bedrooms 🗖 Amex, Delta, MasterCard, Switch, Visa £ Single occupancy of twin/double £50, twin/double/four-poster £55, family room/suite £65; deposit required. Continental B £4, cooked B £6.50; bar/bistro L, D £7 to £12; alc L, D £21

HOVINGHAM North Yorkshire   map 9

Worsley Arms

Hovingham, York YO62 4LA
TEL: (01653) 628234   FAX: (01653) 628130

Good-value hotel, with cuisine to be reckoned with since moving on from being a simple coaching-inn.

The Worsley Arms has ticked over comfortably since it was built in 1841 by the Duchess of Kent's family, the Worsleys, whose grand family seat, Hovingham Hall, lies just up the road. Last century's original plan to turn Hovingham into a spa fizzled out, but a couple of years ago acclaim came somewhat belatedly to the village when Euan Rodger exchanged his manager's hat for that of proprietor, and brought in head chef Andrew Jones to propel the venture into the pages of the food guides. Situated firmly in the bosom of well-heeled North Yorkshire, the hotel has long had aspirations to soar higher than country-inn status, and exudes the smartly aloof air of a gentleman's retreat. The village pub is now a snazzy, cricket-themed bistro that acts as an informal alternative to the restaurant proper, and serves such sophisticated fare as Scottish mussels and scallops with ginger and garlic butter to 'open the innings', moving on to roast pigeon with garlic lentils and a red-wine sauce, and finishing with a blueberry crème brûlée and home-made shortbread. The restaurant offers game from the Hovingham estate and a superb choice of fish dishes. The bedrooms have also gone up-market, and are divided between the main building and the more cosy cottages across the unfortunately busy B-road that mars some of place's appeal.

◗ Open all year 🖪 On B1257 in central Hovingham, opposite village green. Private car park 🛏 1 single, 8 double, 9 twin/double; some in annexe; all with bathroom/WC; all with TV, room service, direct-dial telephone, clock radio ⊘ 2 restaurants, bar, 3 lounges, garden; functions (max 60 people incl up to 30 residential), conferences; tennis, shooting, squash; early suppers for children; cots, high chairs, babysitting, baby-listening ♿ Wheelchair access to hotel (ramp) and restaurants, WC (M, F), 4 ground-floor bedrooms ● No dogs in public rooms; no smoking in bedrooms 🗖 Amex, Delta, Diners, MasterCard, Switch, Visa £ Single £60 to £70, single occupancy of twin/double £60 to £70, twin/double £80 to £90; deposit required. Bar/bistro L, D £18; set L £16, D £26. Special breaks available

Lodge Hotel

48 Birkby Lodge Road, Birkby, Huddersfield HD2 2BG
TEL: (01484) 431001　FAX: (01484) 421590

Stylish Victorian house with a good culinary reputation in a quiet suburb handy for M62.

The discoloured exterior of this stone house, set in a walled garden, gives no clue to what lies inside until you approach the front door. Excellent stained-glass and pewter panels open into a relaxed lounge with a wealth of art-nouveau features that will delight fans of the style; comfy sofas provide a suitable vantage point to take in the lovely green and cream ceiling, panelled walls inlaid with chevron detail, and inspirational motto above a handsome fireplace. This work by the Mancunian architect Edgar Wood, originally undertaken for a Victorian gentleman's residence, now stands as a quirky setting for a rather less starchy enterprise. Garry and Kevin Birley run a welcoming and off-beat house with chef Richard Hanson at the culinary helm, producing adventurous modern dishes to great acclaim in an intimate red-and-gold restaurant: mustard and garlic fettucine with rabbit livers, then guinea-fowl with bubble and squeak could be rounded off with tarte Tatin and Calvados ice- cream. The bedrooms, although agreeable enough in a cottagey, pine-and-floral-print vein, have none of the flamboyance of the public rooms. Room 8 has a newer, more modern décor, and the lovely garden view makes it a good option; otherwise, go for broke with the posh Joseph Turner suite.

◑ Closed 26 Dec and bank hol Mons; restaurant closed Sun eve　⤢ Leave M62 at Junction 24; take A629 to Huddersfield; at first set of traffic lights turn left down Birkby Road; turn first right into Birkby Lodge Road; hotel is 100 yards on left. Private car park　🛏 5 single, 3 twin, 4 double, 1 four-poster; family rooms available; all with bathroom/WC exc 2 singles with shower/WC; all with TV, room service, hair-dryer, direct-dial telephone　🍽 Restaurant, bar, lounge, drying-room, library, 3 private dining-rooms, garden; functions (max 84 people incl up to 21 residential), conferences; golf, clay-pigeon shooting, hot-air ballooning; early suppers for children; cots, high chair, toys, baby-listening, outdoor play area　♿ Wheelchair access to hotel and restaurant (1 step), WC (unisex), 3 ground-floor bedrooms　● Dogs in ground-floor bedrooms only; no smoking in restaurant or bedrooms　▭ Amex, Delta, Diners, MasterCard, Visa　£ Single £60, single occupancy of twin/double £60, twin/double £70, four-poster £80, family room £95; deposit required. Set L £11/£14, D £24

Marshgate Cottage

Marsh Lane, Hungerford RG17 0QX
TEL: (01488) 682307　FAX: (01488) 685475

Attractive and functional modern cottage, in an idyllic, canalside setting.

Marshgate Cottage has insinuated itself almost seamlessly into the tranquil pastures surrounding Hungerford. Beside a whitewashed thatched cottage, Mike Walker's attractive and functional hotel has evolved unobtrusively into a low-rise ring of red-brick and glass buildings around an enclosed courtyard. A handful of detached neighbouring houses and a few squabbling ducks share the view over the knobbly pastures to the Kennet and Avon Canal. Cream walls, new pine furnishings and much varnished woodwork is the consistent theme throughout the bedrooms. Space is at a premium, and the rooms are compact but versatile, with Mike being happy to add a futon or two to accommodate family needs. Room 8 is more fancy, having a pine four-poster, while Room 5 has a small private patio area on the canal side. Beer jugs and teddy bears perched in the rafters of the tiny residents' lounge add a personal touch, though it would be standing room only if every guest decided to partake of the Monopoly, puzzles or playing cards at the same time. The Scandinavian-style conservatory breakfast room is more spacious, with Mike being inventive with the menu where possible, for instance when supplementing the traditional cereals and full English breakfast with feta, olives and figs for some guests from the Middle East.

● Open all year　🚉 From Hungerford High Street, turn at railway bridge into Church Street; after 1/2 mile, cross over stream and turn immediately right into Marsh Lane; hotel is at end, on right. Private car park　🛏 1 single, 1 twin, 4 double, 1 four-poster, 2 family rooms; 1 double with bathroom/WC, most with shower/WC; all with TV, hair-dryer, trouser press, direct-dial telephone　✓ Breakfast room, bar, lounge, drying-room, library, garden; functions (max 30 people incl up to 19 residential), conferences; cots, high chairs, toys, outdoor play area　♿ No wheelchair access ● No dogs or smoking in public rooms and some bedrooms　▭ MasterCard, Visa £ Single £36, single occupancy of twin/double £36, twin/double £49, four-poster £55, family room £56

HUNSTRETE **Bath & N.E. Somerset**　　　　　　　　　map 2

Hunstrete House

Hunstrete, Pensford, Bristol BS39 4NS
TEL: (01761) 490490　FAX: (01761) 490732
EMAIL: haydn@hunstretehouse.co.uk
WEB SITE: www.hunstretehouse.co.uk

A bull's-eye for this classic country house on the edge of the Mendips.

There aren't too many hotels in the *Guide* where toxophilites can indulge in their sport. Archers, like those who prefer to smash clay pigeons to smithereens, or to tap mallets on croquet balls, can get their eye in at Hunstrete House, where the 92-acre grounds provide lots of scope for indulging in leisure interests. Not that this fine Georgian house lacks reasons for staying indoors. There's a wide choice of public rooms in which you can always find a corner to curl up in with the paper or a good book, from a fairly casual bar to the restful library, with its plump sofas, and lounges with all the antiques, oil paintings and crystal chandeliers that you could want. One bright, cheerful dining-room overlooks the Italianate courtyard. Chef Clive Dixon's food is Anglo-French in style and crisply confident in execution. Offerings might include seared tuna niçoise, followed by Trelough duckling in a honey and vanilla sauce, and poached figs in red wine with cinnamon ice-cream. The bedrooms are smart, comfortable and tastefully furnished in an apposite style. The bathrooms are bright and fresh.

◗ Open all year 🆋 Leave Bath on A368 for Weston-super-Mare; after 7 miles turn off to Hunstrete; hotel is 30 yards on left. Private car park 🛏 1 single, 12 twin, 7 double, 1 four-poster, 2 suites; all with bathroom/WC; all with TV, room service, hair-dryer, trouser press, direct-dial telephone; no tea/coffee-making facilities in rooms
✓ 3 dining-rooms, bar, 3 lounges, library, garden; functions (max 200 people incl up to 45 residential), conferences; civil wedding licence; heated outdoor swimming-pool, tennis, croquet, archery, clay-pigeon shooting; early suppers for children; cots, high chairs, babysitting, baby-listening ♿ No wheelchair access ⬤ No dogs; no smoking in some public rooms and some bedrooms ▭ Amex, Delta, Diners, MasterCard, Switch, Visa £ Single £120, single occupancy of twin/double £120, twin/double £120 to £180, four-poster £170, suite £260; deposit required. Set L £20, D £55; alc L, D £40. Special breaks available

---

HUNTSHAM Devon   map 1

Huntsham Court

Huntsham, Bampton, Tiverton EX16 7NA
TEL: (01398) 361365   FAX: (01398) 361456

Fabulous Victorian pile, run more in the manner of a continuous house party than a sedate hotel.

Andrea Bolwig calls Huntsham Court 'the hotel that isn't a hotel'. What she means is that you make it your home for your stay – if you want to bring your friends, you can; if you want to stay up all night dancing, you can; if you want to eat all your meals in bed, you can, but your fellow guests may join you! The brochure declares that 'the country-house party is alive and kicking at Huntsham', so anything might happen, or else a lot of nothing – simply relaxing and eating. Don't expect to find TVs in every room or wall-to-wall carpets; instead, you'll encounter pianos, wonderful, wooden floors and panelling, mullioned windows and grand, log fires. Books, games, walks, tennis, a huge record collection and the friendly staff will entertain you between Andrea's five-course dinners, the contents of which are decided in consultation with guests – you are sent a sample list of the dishes that she likes creating, and you take it from there. You might start with a fresh tomato coulis soup, followed by smoked salmon with lemon herb quenelle, then a roast haunch of venison, and, finally, a raspberry almond torte. The bedrooms are idiosyncratic, in line with the whole place; some have half-testers, Beethoven has twin Victorian cast-iron baths, and most of them have a piano for your pre-breakfast scales, should the mood take you.

◗ Open all year 🆋 In Huntsham village. Private car park 🛏 2 twin, 2 twin/double, 7 double, 3 family rooms; all with bathroom/WC; all with hair-dryer, radio; no tea/coffee-making facilities in rooms ✓ Dining-room, bar, 2 lounges, drying-room, library, games room, garden; functions (max 50 people incl up to 20 residential), conferences; civil wedding licence; sauna, solarium, tennis, croquet; early suppers for children; cots, high chairs, babysitting ♿ No wheelchair access ⬤ No children in dining-room

eves; dogs by arrangement; smoking in dining-room with other guests' consent
▭ Amex, MasterCard, Switch, Visa   £ Single occupancy of twin/double £85,
twin/double £125, family room £150; deposit required. Set D £35

HURLEY Berkshire   map 3

Ye Olde Bell

High Street, Hurley, Maidenhead SL6 5LX
TEL: (01628) 825881   FAX: (01628) 825871

---

*Peaceful, rural feel, with character that survives corporate
ownership.*

This old inn has a quiet village setting on a minor road that comes to a dead end at
the nearby River Thames; it is also handy for the motorways that pass through
this affluent corner of rural England. The original building began life as a
twelfth-century guesthouse for a nearby monastery, and it's this lineage that
gives it a claim to the contested 'oldest inn in England' title.

The bedrooms are divided between the inn and a converted barn, next to the
car park located just across the road. The rooms in the annexe are smart and
businesslike, decorated with cream walls and chintzy fabrics. In 'superior' form,
they have enough extra space for a sofa, and come with treats like a fruit bowl,
mineral water and fluffy white bathrobes. The rooms in the main inn have less
space but more atmosphere. The old building is also home to the snug,
country-pub style bar, with lovely old wooden furniture and low beams. There's
no real ale to go with the real bar though, despite the Brakspear brewery being
just up the road in Henley. There are no such obvious oversights in the
restaurant, however, where formal English cooking is served in an intimate
wood-panelled dining-room. Pan-fried scallops followed by roast duck made
for a very well-presented inspection meal, with the duck being served from a
beautiful chrome-domed trolley.

The weekday room rates might dim the enthusiasm of self-financing customers, but the hotel is more than worthy competition for the Heathrow
mega-motels only 17 miles away.

◐ Open all year   ⊿ Take A4130 towards Henley; turn right into Hurley village; hotel is
½ mile on right. Private car park   ⊯ 3 single, 1 twin, 31 double, 2 four-poster, 4 family
rooms, 1 suite; some in annexe; all with bathroom/WC; all with TV, room service,
hair-dryer, trouser press, direct-dial telephone; mini-bar on request   ✓ Restaurant,
bar, lounge, garden; functions (max 120 people incl up to 77 residential), conferences;
civil wedding licence; croquet; early suppers for children; cots, high chairs   ↳ No
wheelchair access   ● No dogs in public rooms   ▭ Amex, Delta, Diners, MasterCard,
Switch, Visa   £ Single £119, single occupancy of twin/double £119, twin/double
£139, four-poster £155, family room £145, suite £170; deposit required. Continental B
£7.50, cooked B £9.50; bar/bistro L £10, D £12; set L £18, D £23.50; alc L, D £30.
Special breaks available

---

*'The bathroom shelf was scuffed and scraped and the toilet squashed into
a corner so that one could only sit on it with one's knees under one's chin.'*
On a hotel in the Lake District

HURSTBOURNE TARRANT Hampshire map 2

Esseborne Manor

Hurstbourne Tarrant, Andover SP11 0ER
TEL: (01264) 736444 FAX: (01264) 736725
EMAIL: admin@pride.u-net.com
WEB SITE: www.hotelnet.co.uk/pride/

Comfortable and traditional country house, with a keen eye to the future.

Ian Hamilton is a man with expansion on his mind: at the time of our spring inspection the builders were about their work, discreetly raising a new function room and relocating the kitchens to more extensive premises. The chunky, late-Victorian villa should absorb the changes well, with room enough still to spare among the acres of mature beeches and pine trees of this rolling countryside, which is close to the attractive, flint-and-thatch village of Hurstbourne. Changes are planned, too, for the agreeable home-from-home comforts of the residents' lounge and bar, though the abundance of deep sofas and air of informal contemplation is unlikely to be disturbed. The bedrooms revel in some luxurious touches, like coronet-topped beds, fluffy bathrobes and ruched curtains. Madingley has a silk-draped four-poster, Ferndown a spa bath, and even Arundel – the smallest room – has space enough in which to swing the proverbial pussy. For more reclusive surroundings, you could try one of the flint cottages in the grounds, which are simply decorated with cream walls and new pine furniture.

Sensible pricing options broaden the appeal of the menus, and you might find lemon sole or toad-in-the-hole on the table d'hôte, or sea bass with a niçoise *jus* or beef, wild mushrooms and garlic mash on the speciality menu.

Open all year · On A343, halfway between Newbury and Andover. Private car park · 6 twin, 8 double, 1 four-poster; some in annexe; all with bathroom/WC; all with TV, room service, hair-dryer, trouser press, direct-dial telephone · Restaurant, bar, lounge, garden; functions (max 50 people incl up to 30 residential), conferences; civil wedding licence; tennis, croquet; early suppers for children · Wheelchair access to hotel and restaurant, WC (unisex), 6 ground-floor bedrooms, 1 room specially equipped for disabled people · No dogs in public rooms · Amex, Delta, Diners, MasterCard, Switch, Visa · Single occupancy of twin/double £88, twin/double £95 to £112, four-poster £135; deposit required. Bar/bistro L, D £10, set L, D £17; alc L, D £25. Special breaks available

HUXLEY Cheshire map 7

Higher Huxley Hall

Red Lane, Huxley, Chester CH3 9BZ
TEL: (01829) 781484 FAX: (01829) 781142
EMAIL: info@huxleyhall.co.uk

An attractive, welcoming family home in a quiet and rural setting, with the bonus of a heated indoor swimming-pool.

With a name like Higher Huxley Hall you expect to find a grand ancestral home at the end of the long drive – rather than a semicircle of stone farm buildings with a large whitewashed house to one side. Despite this, however, and despite the fact that Jeremy and Pauline are only the second generation of the Marks family to live here, the name and the image it conjures up are still spot on. Once inside you realise that the antique-furnished house is much older than it appears: a beautiful wooden Elizabethan staircase dominates the comfortable lounge hall, where a roaring log fire positively begs you to sit and relax a while; or you could opt for the more formal lounge. The dining-room, with its family portraits on the walls, is the scene for a sociable five-course dinner (with wine available, as the Hall is licensed). As this is a Wolsey Lodge the emphasis is on all guests dining together around one long table, and the dinner usually consists of traditional fare, such as parsley soup and chicken in herb sauce followed by apple pie. The Marks make a huge effort, and food is tasty and very well presented with formal cutlery and silverware. Breakfast is similarly pleasurable, with good company and a wide selection of cereals, yoghurt, fruit and a cooked breakfast to start the day.

As you go up the stairs to your bedroom don't miss the old black-and-white family photos which line the walls, keeping an eye out for one of Jeremy's great-grandfather with Edward VIII. The bedrooms are comfortable and well furnished and look out over the neat garden. Characterful oak beams prevail in the rooms, but remember to duck when getting out of the bath if you have the double room, as the ancient beam above it is very low!

◑ Open all year (exc owners' holiday); restaurant usually open (meals must be booked 24 hours ahead) 🔁 Leave M6 at Junction 16; take A500 to Nantwich, then A51 towards Chester; after Tilstone Fearnall turn left on to A49; after 1 mile turn right to Huxley; take second left past Farmers Arms pub to T-junction; turn left and immediately right. Private car park ⇱ 1 twin, 1 double, 1 family room; all with shower/WC exc double with bathroom/WC; all with TV, hair-dryer, direct-dial telephone; iron available ⊘ Dining-room, lounge, conservatory, garden; coarse fishing, heated indoor swimming-pool, croquet; cots, high chairs, toys, baby-listening, outdoor play area ♿ No wheelchair access ● Children by arrangement; no dogs in hotel (outside kennels available); no smoking ☐ MasterCard, Visa £ Single occupancy of twin/double £38 to £45, twin/double £68 to £70, family room £75 to £80; deposit required. Set D £20 to £23. Special breaks available

---

INGLEBY GREENHOW North Yorkshire   map 9

Manor House Farm   *No under 12s*

Ingleby Greenhow, Great Ayton, Middlesbrough TS9 6RB
TEL: (01642) 722384
EMAIL: mbloom@globalnet.co.uk

Chatty hosts in a rural guesthouse on the edge of the Yorkshire moors.

Encounters with the animal kingdom are unavoidable on Margaret and Martin Bloom's farm: their eccentric menagerie encompasses a rare sheep collection, peacocks, rheas, assorted exotic waterfowl on the 300-year-old pond – even a wallaby bouncing around. You could set off directly for walks on the moors, or go deer- and bird-spotting in ten acres of woodland. The Blooms insist that guests in their unagricultural home – the farm side of things is managed – stay on a dinner, bed and breakfast basis, so there is a convivial ambience in the evenings when they join their guests after dinner in the sitting-room, where a wood-burning stove and heaps of books add to the feeling of relaxation. White-painted walls enhance the feeling of space in the bedrooms, which are immaculately kept and feature such quaint touches as china ducks and lacy curtains. Only one has *en suite* facilities, although the other two each have a private bathroom along the corridor, with a sunken or corner bath to add a touch of luxury.

◑ Closed Dec ⚡ In Great Broughton, turn at village hall and take road to Ingleby Greenhow; entrance is opposite church. Private car park ⬅ 2 twin, 1 double; all with bathroom/WC (twins not *en suite*); all with radio ⊘ Dining-room, sitting-room, library, garden; fishing ⟨ No wheelchair access ● No children under 12; no dogs; no smoking ▭ Delta, MasterCard, Switch, Visa £ Single occupancy of twin/double from £51, twin/double from £82 (rates incl dinner); deposit required

---

IPSWICH Suffolk   map 6

Belstead Brook Hotel

Belstead Road, Ipswich IP2 9HB
TEL: (01473) 684241   FAX: (01473) 681249

A slickly run business hotel with good leisure facilities and unexpectedly leafy setting.

Don't let the approach to the hotel through 'Brookside'-style housing estates put you off. The manor house retains its serenity, with some attractive grounds and the continued presence of the burbling Belstead brook along one side. It's a slight surprise to find that the entrance is not through the old creeper-clad façade of the manor, but via a new extension into a stately proportioned reception area. The restaurant, in the original part of the building, has more historical character, with fine wood panelling, red padded chairs and heavy drapes. Bedrooms in the main house are equipped to uniform business standards of style and comfort, in pastel shades with shiny bathrooms; 12 newly refurbished rooms in the garden extension are smaller, but brighter and airier. Rooms 310 and 302 are suitable for guests with disabilities.

◑ Open all year ⚡ At the main A12/A14 interchange roundabout take Ipswich West exit with Tesco store on left, then follow brown signs to hotel. Private car park ⬅ 16 single, 16 twin, 52 double, 2 family rooms, 2 suites; some in annexe; all with bathroom/WC exc 8 single with shower/WC; all with satellite TV, room service, hair-dryer, mini-bar, trouser press, direct-dial telephone ⊘ Restaurant, bar, 2 lounges, gardens; functions (max 180 people residential/non-residential), conferences; civil wedding licence; gym, sauna, solarium, heated indoor swimming-pool, croquet; leisure facilities nearby (free for guests); early suppers for children; cots, high chairs, baby-listening ⟨ Wheelchair access to hotel (ramp) and restaurant (5 steps, chairlift), WC (unisex), 35 ground-floor bedrooms, 2 specially equipped for disabled people, lift ● No dogs in public rooms, small dogs in bedrooms by arrangement; smoking in bar and some bedrooms only ▭ Amex, Delta, Diners, MasterCard, Switch, Visa

£ Single £76, single occupancy of twin/double £86 to £132, twin/double £92 to £102, family room £102, suite £138; deposit required. Bar/bistro L £12.50, D £15; set L, D £19.50; alc L, D £30. Special breaks available

Marlborough Hotel

Henley Road, Ipswich IP1 3SP
TEL: (01473) 257677   FAX: (01473) 226927

A business-oriented hotel in a large, Victorian, suburban house with a striking, modern interior.

The slightly unprepossessing façade of the Marlborough Hotel is thankfully no guide to the style that you will find through the front door. There have been plenty of changes to the hotel in the last couple of years, and they are all for the better. Situated in one of the formerly grand, but much altered, Victorian houses in this leafy suburb of Ipswich, the hotel is likely to appeal more to business travellers than to those looking to escape for the weekend. Nevertheless, the standard of fittings goes beyond what weary suit-wearers might expect. This is immediately apparent in the plush lounge next to the reception area, where the choice of bold colours has paid off with a striking array of curly-armed, blue sofas, replete with red and gold cushions. This stylish feel is also reflected in the brightly lit cocktail bar, which has a nautical theme. At the back of the hotel, the large, rectangular restaurant has windows overlooking the small but pretty garden, where guests can also take afternoon tea. The new look has not yet made it to all the bedrooms, however, but those that have been given the treatment, such as Rooms 15 and 42, have antique furnishings and bathrooms with attractive, marble tops. The best rooms face the road, but the views are nicer over the garden.

○ Open all year   From A12, take A1214; carry on to two sets of traffic lights; take second left on to Yarmouth Road; go straight across double mini-roundabouts; at traffic lights, turn righ; hotel is 500 yards further on, on right. Private car park   4 single, 5 twin, 12 double, 1 suite; all with bathroom/WC; all with TV, room service, hair-dryer, trouser press, direct-dial telephone   Restaurant, bar, lounge, study, garden; functions (max 85 people incl up to 40 residential), conferences; civil wedding licence; early suppers for children; cots, high chairs, babysitting, baby-listening   Wheelchair access to hotel (ramp) and restaurant, 8 ground-floor bedrooms   ● No dogs in public rooms; no smoking in restaurant   Amex, Delta, Diners, MasterCard, Switch, Visa   £ Single from £68, twin/double from £72, suite £90 (1998 prices); deposit required. Continental B £7.50, cooked B £10.50; bar/bistro L, D £7; set L £13.50, D £20; alc L, D £28. Special breaks available

'We ordered a room service lunch of sandwiches and salad, which was almost eaten when I discovered a small slug on a lettuce leaf. Feeling quite queasy I asked for the food to be returned to the kitchen. The waiter proffered the explanation that the lettuce was "organic".'
On a hotel in East Sussex

Library House

11 Severn Bank, Ironbridge, Telford TF8 7AN
TEL: (01952) 432299   FAX: (01952) 433967
EMAIL: libhouse@enta.net

Zestfully run and beautifully maintained B&B in the centre of Ironbridge.

'Having tried several places to stay in Ironbridge, I managed to get a few days in Library House, and now book well in advance to make sure I don't have to go anywhere else. Having a couple of days unwell in bed, I found Chris and George Maddocks to be caring – well past their duties as hosts – and the food delicious and the accommodation luxurious.' This reader's encomium is fully endorsed by our inspections. The B&B couldn't be better placed: yards from the famous bridge, yet set apart from the trippery tea-rooms and shops, up an alley. After you've dropped off your bags, the Maddocks will drive your car to a nearby car park, where they can arrange free parking. Within the Georgian building, the former local library is now the guests' sitting-room, hung, appropriately, with Lowry prints; there is an honesty bar here, but you'll be offered a glass of wine or beer, gratis, on arrival anyway. Across the hall lies a gorgeous breakfast room, in country-kitchen style with terracotta tiles and antique pine tables. Bedrooms, whose bird names appear on teddy-bear sweaters, are prettily if fussily decorated, with ruched curtains, loo rolls in flouncy holders, fresh flowers and a plethora of knick-knacks. Some are small; Wren has direct access to a terrace in the rear garden.

◐ Closed 24 to 26 Dec   ▨ In Ironbridge town centre; 60 yards from bridge. On-street parking (free); public car park nearby (free for guests)   ⊨ 4 twin; family room available; 2 with bathroom/WC, 2 with shower/WC; all with TV, hair-dryer   ✧ Breakfast room, sitting-room/library, TV room, drying-room, garden; cots, high chairs, toys   ♿ No wheelchair access   ● No dogs in public rooms; no smoking   ▭ None accepted   ⌷ Single occupancy of twin £40, twin £50, family room £65; deposit required

---

Severn Lodge

New Road, Ironbridge, Telford TF8 7AS
TEL: (01952) 432148 (AND FAX)

Classy B&B that is convenient for, but aloof from, the bustle of Ironbridge.

There is real value for money to be had from staying in Nita and Alan Reed's tastefully furnished B&B. Its three bedrooms are furnished in a style, and to a level of comfort, that would grace many a country-house hotel – where they would probably command a three-figure price tag. The red-brick, Georgian house is also ideally situated: off a peaceful, residential back street above the main road, but a mere three-minute walk to shops, eateries and the famous bridge, via a path. And from its elevated position it enjoys lovely views across the thickly wooded gorge. The rest of the set-up is as alluring as the bedrooms. You can relax in the large town garden, with its tiers of lawns, neat rockeries and ornamental pond, or browse through the pile of local literature in the smart guests' sitting-room. Good breakfasts are served round a single, antique, walnut table in an elegant little dining-room.

○ Closed 24 Dec to 1 Jan   ⬛ With bridge on your left, turn right immediately before Malthouse restaurant into New Road. Private car park   ⬅ 1 twin, 2 double; doubles with bathroom/WC, twin with shower/WC; all with TV, room service, hair-dryer ⬥ 2 dining-rooms, sitting-room, TV room, drying-room, garden   ⬥ No wheelchair access   ● No children under 12; no dogs; no smoking   ▭ None accepted £ Single occupancy of twin/double £40, twin/double £53; deposit required

---

KEMERTON Worcestershire   map 5

Upper Court

Kemerton, Tewkesbury GL20 7HY
TEL: (01386) 725351   FAX: (01386) 725472
EMAIL: uppercourt@compuserve.com
WEB SITE: www.cotswold.co.uk/cotswold/uppercourt.htm

Not a hotel as such, but an imposing family home in lovely grounds.

Diana and Bill Herford's Cotswold-stone Georgian manor, in the quiet heart of a picturesque village, is one of the more laid-back examples of a Wolsey Lodge (fine family homes that welcome paying guests and where some socialising is *de rigueur*). Both in its atmosphere and in its undesigned, gently fading, well-worn yet elegant style, the house bears little resemblance to a hotel. Antiques abound, and much of the furniture is stock from the Herfords' antique business. The bedrooms in the main house are pretty, characterful and comfortable, while further accommodation is provided in apartments (which can also be let as self-catering) in the adjacent converted stables and coach-house. Four-course candlelit evening meals, in the form of substantial dinner-party fare, with fresh vegetables from the garden, are eaten either communally with other guests, or at separate tables. Breakfast in bed is on offer at no extra charge. Upper Court is particularly enjoyable when the weather is fine, as it has 15 acres of grounds that encompass an old watermill, a lake rich in trout and wildfowl, and a croquet lawn.

○ Closed Chr   ⬛ In Kemerton, turn off the main road at the war memorial; Upper Court is 200 yards down road, behind parish (not RC) church. Private car park ⬅ 1 twin, 1 twin/double, 3 four-poster, 1 suite, 4 coach-house suites; family rooms available; all with bathroom/WC; all with TV, coach-house suites with telephone ⬥ Dining-room, drawing-room, drying-room, games room, garden; tennis, croquet, table tennis   ⬥ No wheelchair access   ● No children under 12 in main house; no dogs; no smoking   ▭ Amex, MasterCard, Visa   £ Single occupancy of twin/double £65, twin/double £75, four-poster £95, suite £110, family rooms from £95 + £10 per child; deposit required. Set D £30 (by arrangement)

Reports are welcome on any hotel, whether or not it is in the Guide.

KENDAL Cumbria map 8

Holmfield   NEW ENTRY

41 Kendal Green, Kendal LA9 5PP
TEL: (01539) 720790 (AND FAX)

Tranquil, cared-for accommodation in a comfortable Edwardian house on the fringes of Lakeland.

Despite its secluded location in a quiet residential cul-de-sac on the northern edges of town, news of this unusually designed Edwardian house is steadily spreading among aficionados of quality B&Bs. The blue-and-white 'Dutch barn' look makes it instantly memorable; inside, too, you'll find a place of some distinction. If you're interested, Eileen and Brian Kettle will proudly show you photos of their family home and its fine established gardens, where a croquet lawn and heated swimming-pool provide additional attractions after a dazzling display of early spring bulbs and rampant clematis. Beyond the gardens, Kendal Castle and the fells of south-east Lakeland are enticingly visible from this elevated position. Inside, the house is beautifully kept and thoroughly comfortable. A single large, light, ground-floor reception room offers lounge space and a breakfast area with a classic inglenook fireplace. The atmosphere is relaxing and civilised; guests share bathrooms and breakfast table, but there's plenty of elbow room. Three letting bedrooms, all different but well-kept and agreeable, feature a pleasant mix of unfussy florals and pastels with plenty of personal touches, such as period-look radios and lots of books. Breakfast may include treats like cheese and apple toasties or home-grown rhubarb; special diets can be handled on request. Kendal's eating places lie within reasonable walking distance, or a moment's drive.

◑ Open all year ↗ From A5284 Windermere road, follow signs to Kendal Green; at top of green take private road and follow sign to Holmfield. Private car park
⨦ 1 twin, 1 double, 1 four-poster; 2 private bathrooms; all with TV, hair-dryer
✅ Breakfast room/lounge, drying-room, garden; heated outdoor swimming-pool, croquet ♿ No wheelchair access ◆ No children under 12; no dogs or smoking
▭ None accepted £ Single occupancy of twin/double £23 to £30, twin/double £42 to £44, four-poster £44 to £48; deposit required. Special breaks available

---

KENILWORTH Warwickshire map 5

Castle Laurels

22 Castle Road, Kenilworth CV8 1NG
TEL: (01926) 856179   FAX: (01926) 854954

Friendly owners are steadily improving this small hotel opposite Kenilworth Castle.

'I've nothing against woodchip,' says Nicholas Moore, 'but not everywhere.' He and his wife Patricia have been steadily removing and replacing the offending wallpaper, bringing in smarter colours and styles that fit well with the Victorian features of their small hotel. Downstairs there is a comfortable lounge with music from the CD player drifting out into the panelled hall, then a stylish dining-room in blue and gold, complementing the dark polished furniture. Although most guests choose to walk out into Kenilworth for a restaurant meal, Nicholas does cook good-value traditional three-course dinners: home-made soup followed by chicken kiev and fruit crumble perhaps.

Some of the bedrooms have benefited from the Moore's renovations, with subdued colours and well-chosen pieces of period furniture. Room 2 is a pleasant double on the corner of the house with *en suite* shower-room.

◑ Closed Chr ⚡ On A452, almost opposite Kenilworth Castle. Private car park ⤶ 3 single, 3 twin, 4 double, 1 family room; all with shower/WC; all with TV, room service, hair-dryer, direct-dial telephone ⚥ Dining-room, lounge, garden; functions (max 21 people residential/non-residential); leisure facilities nearby (free for guests) ♿ No wheelchair access ● No dogs; no smoking ▭ Amex, Delta, Diners, MasterCard, Switch, Visa £ Single £33, single occupancy of twin/double £40, twin/double £53, family room £68 (prices valid till Feb 1999). Set D £11 to £13

KESWICK **Cumbria** map 10

Craglands

Penrith Road, Keswick CA12 4LJ
TEL: (01768) 774406

Well-kept guesthouse on the edge of town, offering high-quality but home-like accommodation and imaginative cooking at reasonable rates.

If you're arriving by car (as most people do), you may find yourself whirling past this Victorian semi-detached house a time or two. Access (and egress) via the hilly exit road take a bit of practice and plenty of care, but there is some parking to one side of the building. Once inside, relax and enjoy the views of Keswick's outlying fells in comfort. Though neither location nor architecture distinguish Craglands especially from many similar stone guesthouses in this popular Cumbrian tourist town, its advantages soon make themselves apparent; hence the showers of accolades it regularly receives from many quarters. Public rooms occupy two typically proportioned reception rooms on the ground floor: the light, well-furnished lounge at the front, and the dining-room, in a deep green mood, to the rear of the house. Upstairs lie five spotless bedrooms in fresh, spring colours. All give some inkling of the enticing countryside beyond the fairly busy road and neighbouring residential suburbs, and for those anxious to get their boots on, Wainwright awaits in the lounge. Typical dinners, changed daily, feature distinctly appetising set menus of local produce topped and tailed with complimentary sherry, irresistible puddings and petits fours. Guests are welcome to bring their own wine.

◑ Part time opening Dec to Feb; closed Chr ⚡ Going into Keswick (from Penrith or Windermere), Penrith Road is at foot of Chestnut Hill, on right. Private car park ⤶ 1 twin, 3 double; all with shower/WC exc twin with bathroom/WC all with TV, hair-dryer ⚥ Dining-room, lounge, drying-room ♿ No wheelchair access ● No children under 8; no dogs or smoking ▭ None accepted £ Single occupancy of twin/double £30, twin/double £50; deposit required. Set D £20

Dale Head Hall

Lake Thirlmere, Keswick CA12 4TN
TEL: (017687) 72478   FAX: (017687) 71070
EMAIL: enquiry@dale-head-hall.co.uk
WEB SITE: www.dale-head-hall.co.uk

Lake-shore hotel, with friendly hosts and many interesting features.

A busy road runs past just 100 yards away, at the top of the drive, but you'd never guess it in this secluded spot. It's a large, and rather curious-looking, house. As you approach from the driveway, the oldest section of the building, dating from Tudor times, seems barely to open its eyes at you, preferring to keep out draughts and intruders with small, fortress-like windows. In later, and less hostile, centuries, the house was reconfigured to take advantage of the spectacular view of Thirlmere, which lies directly below the immaculate, terraced gardens. The main reception rooms face the lake, as do some of the best bedrooms. Throughout, it's a house of great personality, matching that of its hosts, Caroline (chef) and Hans Bonkenburg (who is Dutch born). It's clearly a family business – children and in-laws all have a hand in the running of the place – which gives it a friendly, accessible air. Hans points out with great pride the period features of his home: the exposed stone wall in the hallway, the uneven floors, head-banging lintels, secret doors, and alcoves in which to put the baby. The Elizabethan dining-room, with beams and a huge inglenook fireplace, has the charm of the cottage that it originally was. Critics may carp that not all the furnishings and decorative touches seem entirely harmonious, but the overall effect is comfortable and characterful. Food and wine are serious elements in Dale Head Hall's attractions. Caroline's creative, five-course dinners may set your taste-buds agog – what about a duo of duck and pheasant breasts in puff pastry with a juniper and gin sauce and a kumquat and lemon compote, or an Armagnac and date pudding with citrus and butterscotch sauce and marmalade ice-cream?

◐ Closed Jan   ⊠ Halfway between Keswick and Grasmere on A591, at end of long private drive. Private car park   ⊫ 2 twin, 5 double, 1 four-poster, 1 suite; family rooms available; all with bathroom/WC exc four-poster with shower/WC; all with room service, hair-dryer, direct-dial telephone   ✧ Dining-room, bar, lounge, drying-room, garden; fishing; early suppers for children; cots, baby-listening   ⅏ No wheelchair access   ● No dogs; no smoking in some public rooms and bedrooms   ▭ Amex, Delta, MasterCard, Switch, Visa   £ Single occupancy of twin/double £55 to £65, twin/double £60 to £80, four-poster £70 to £100, family room £70 to £90, suite £75 to £110; deposit required. Set D £27.50. Special breaks available

The Grange

Manor Brow, Keswick CA12 4BA
TEL: (01768) 772500

Capably managed and welcoming small hotel on the outskirts of Keswick.

Keswick is full of humdrum guesthouse-hotels, but this immaculately kept place off the Windermere exit road has steadily earned itself top billing in the decade since Jane and Duncan Miller moved in. It's a substantial, mid-Victorian, detached house in quiet, hilly grounds, its site carefully chosen to maximise the vistas of gardens, town and fells. The spacious reception rooms include a traditionally furnished lounge, with an imposing marble fireplace; a dining-room decorated in shades of pink, with carefully dressed windows; and a residents-only bar of pubby, wooden tables and chairs – slightly incongruous in this domestic interior. An eye for detail will spot period features: fine door cases and plasterwork, for instance, which hint at a distinguished architectural pedigree. The bedrooms – in pinks, greens and creams – are light and have a mix of traditional and modern furnishings, from handsome, mahogany pieces and a half-tester in the best (Room 5) to more routine fittings. Shower-rooms have been shoe-horned into older dimensions with varying success. The traditional set menus receive much praise, and the emphasis is firmly on pleasing resident guests, though non-residents are welcome if there's room. As the bulging reservations book indicates, the Millers are clearly getting things right here. Many guests are regular visitors who appreciate the reliable standards and peaceful, welcoming air of this successful business.

◑ Closed mid-Nov to mid-Mar   ⬈ Take A591 from Keswick towards Windermere for ½ mile. Take first right-hand turning; hotel is 200 yards on right. Private car park ⇨ 3 twin, 7 double; 5 with bathroom/WC, 5 with shower/WC; all with TV, room service, hair-dryer, direct-dial telephone, radio   ✓ Dining-room, bar, 2 lounges, drying-room, garden   ⅙ No wheelchair access   ● No children under 7; dogs in bedrooms only, by arrangement; no smoking   ▭ Delta, MasterCard, Visa   £ Twin/double £56 to £76; deposit required. Set D £20. Special breaks available

---

Swinside Lodge

Grange Road, Newlands, Keswick CA12 5UE
TEL: (01768) 772948 (AND FAX)

Superior country guesthouse, offering splendid food, attentive service and classy décor, in one of the prettiest parts of the Lake District.

If you take the Portinscale road from Keswick, you skirt the western shores of Derwentwater towards the leafy Newlands Valley. It's an exceptionally beautiful area, and here, in an isolated setting below Cat Bells on the Grange road, stands this cream-painted, Victorian house. Though the exterior is unshowy, a step or two inside the door reveals that Graham Taylor's small-scale hotel reaches unusually high standards of décor and furnishings. Inspect the bedrooms, and you'll be even more convinced; stay for dinner, and it's a clear winner – one of the best of its type in the northern Lakes. There are many cheaper places in which to stay, up the road in Keswick, but none offer the style and quality of this place. The three lounges offer soothing, tasteful spaces for reading, relaxing and considering (or digesting) the dinner menu – not that it needs much considering, being a choiceless, but infinitely recommendable, feast, served punctually at 7.30pm in an equally elegant dining-room. Special dietary requirements should be notified in advance. As there's no licence, guests are encouraged to bring their own wine (no corkage charge), though complimentary sherry is served. The bedrooms are quite lavishly comfortable, with beautiful bed linen and many extras (though there are no bedside telephones); they are serviced during dinner-time.

◑ Closed Dec & Jan ⧉ From Keswick, take A66 towards Cockermouth and turn left at Portinscale; follow road towards Grange for 2 miles; ignore signs to Swinside and Newlands Valley. Private car park 🛏 2 twin, 5 double; all with bathroom/WC; all with TV, hair-dryer, radio ⌅ Dining-room, 3 lounges, drying-room, garden ⟁ No wheelchair access ◓ No children under 10; no dogs; no smoking ▭ None accepted £ Single occupancy of twin/double £72 to £85, twin/double £128 to £160. Set D £25 to £28. Special breaks available

---

KETTLEWELL North Yorkshire   map 8

Langcliffe Country House

Kettlewell, Skipton BD23 5RJ
TEL: (01756) 760243

A homely guesthouse with great views down Wharfedale.

This solid stone house is in a great spot, enjoying wonderful views down the broad expanse of the dale from the front, and overlooking the village beck at the rear. Richard and Jane Elliott's guesthouse sits on a quiet back lane in the Dales village of Kettlewell, far enough from the centre to enjoy perfect tranquillity, yet a short stroll from the pubs, in case you should fancy a break from the easy-going sociability in the house. The Elliotts prefer guests to dine together in the evening, to foster a convivial atmosphere; guests congregate in the sitting-room to choose from the options on a blackboard before dining at 7pm. The day's menu might offer oak-smoked trout salad, Dales lamb with rosemary from the garden and fresh mint sauce, then crème brûlée with fresh strawberries and mangoes; Richard and Jane used to run a pub, so the food is well executed – one guest, however, felt that dinner was rushed and was disappointed that no after-dinner drinks were offered. The house is always pleasantly decked out with plenty of fresh flowers and has seen a lot of redecoration during the last year, spruced up with new furniture, tables and lamps. Rooms 2 and 3 have the best views of the valley, though one couple found Room 3 rather cramped. More reports, please.

◑ Open all year ⧉ Kettlewell is on B6160, 6 miles north of Grassington; take road opposite Kings Head pub marked 'Access only'; hotel is 300 yards down on right. Private car park 🛏 3 twin, 3 double; family room available; most with bathroom/WC, some with shower/WC; all with TV, room service, direct-dial telephone; hair-dryer available ⌅ Restaurant, sitting-room, conservatory, garden; functions (max 12 people residential/non-residential; early suppers for children; outdoor play area ⟁ Wheelchair access to hotel (ramp) and restaurant, 1 ground-floor bedroom specially equipped for disabled people ◓ No children under 6 at dinner; dogs in bedrooms only, by arrangement; no smoking ▭ MasterCard, Visa £ Single occupancy of twin/double £56, twin/double £92, family room (rates on application); rates incl dinner; deposit required. Special breaks available

Mill House Hotel

Kingham, Chipping Norton OX7 6UH
TEL: (01608) 658188   FAX: (01608) 658492

Converted mill, with good views across the Cotswolds.

This really is rural, peaceful England at its most pastoral and pretty: the jumble of yellow-stone buildings which make up the Mill House Hotel sit in seven acres of beautifully kept grounds, with willows hanging over the millstream, a welcoming arbour and horses in fields. The millstream has been diverted so that it no longer flows under the house, but the floors in the public rooms remain completely drunken, full of dips and bumps, as if the mill workings, long since buried underneath, are struggling to re-emerge. In the flagstoned and characterful reception area are pictures of the mill in its working heyday, as well as a fascinating accounts book dating back to the early 1900s. The bar is in what was the grinding-room, so you can see cogs on the central pillar and old bread ovens in the wall next to the huge fireplace, which roars cosily in winter. Both the bar and the lounge are spacious and restful, filled with traditional, high-backed easy chairs, as well as a good assortment of books and games, whereas the restaurant has a more plush feel to it, with its pink tablecloths and curtained room dividers. The straightforward menu has hefty supplements on quite a few dishes, but if you want to avoid them you could still try such dishes as smoked-haddock salad served with a mustard dressing, followed by roast loin of pork with a cider and wine sauce.

The bedrooms are simply and sprucely done out with big beds, muted tones and good, reproduction furniture; a gradual refurbishment programme is upgrading the bathrooms. Choose one of the mid-priced rooms to be sure of a good view – it's worth the extra cost. One dissatisfied guest, who complained about his room – 'thick and visible dust' and water coming in at the window – and poor service, found the management's attitude unsympathetic. More reports, please.

◑ Open all year   ⊿ South of Kingham village, just off B4450 between Chipping Norton and Stow-on-the-Wold. Private car park   ⤙ 6 twin, 7 twin/double, 8 double, 1 four-poster, 1 family room; some in annexe; all with bathroom/WC; all with satellite TV, room service, hair-dryer, direct-dial telephone   ⌀ Restaurant, bar, lounge, drying-room, garden; functions (max 85 people incl up to 47 residential), conferences; fishing, golf; early suppers for children; cots, high chairs, toys, playroom, babysitting, outdoor play area   ⅋ Wheelchair access to hotel and restaurant, WC (M, F), 6 ground-floor bedrooms   ⊖ No dogs in public rooms; no smoking in restaurant ▭ Amex, Delta, Diners, MasterCard, Switch, Visa   £ Single occupancy of twin/double £65 to £75, twin/double £100 to £120, four-poster £100, family room £115 to £135; deposit required. Bar/bistro L £2.50 to £10; set L £14, D £23; alc L £20, D £30. Special breaks available

---

If you have access to the Internet, you can find The Which? Hotel Guide *online at the Which? Online web site (www.which.net).*

Fallowfields

Farringdon Road, Southmoor, Kingston Bagpuize OX13 5BH
TEL: (01865) 820416   FAX: (01865) 821275
EMAIL: stay@fallowfields.com

Smart, welcoming accommodation in a refined country house.

As soon as you arrive at Fallowfields, you know you're coming into someone's home. This is not an impersonal, leave-you-alone type of country house: Anthony and Peta Lloyd (and family) live here too. During an inspection meal we could hear the family having theirs outside on the patio under huge green parasols, and, between servings at breakfast, Anthony nipped out to drive his daughter to school. The seventeenth-century and Victorian Gothic house is filled with endearing family clutter: photographs, and a monster collection of elephants in all manner of shapes and sizes that Anthony has collected from around the world. Nevertheless, the atmosphere is peaceful and refined, and the hotel has proved such a success that a huge extension has been built – perfectly in keeping – of yellow stone, with arched mullioned windows. Here five new bedrooms and a conservatory will look out over the heated outdoor pool and the ten acres of organic land which the Lloyds use to grow most of the vegetables they serve at dinner. On the menu might be a delicious Fallowfields home-grown lovage soup, made to a traditional recipe and with garlic croutons, followed by medallions of pork baked in Fallowfields sloe gin with oregano, finished with a little cream. After-dinner coffee is served in the smart, yet distinctly homely sitting-room, which is filled with comfortable round sofas lining the dusky red walls. The bedrooms are a real treat, with lacy sheets, lots of antique furniture and whirlpool baths. 'As charming and delightful as ever,' reports one visitor. 'So comfortable and welcoming.'

◑ Open all year; restaurant closed Sun eve   ⬈ Turn off A420 south-west of Oxford at roundabout signposted to Kingston Bagpuize; turn right at mini-roundabout; turn left at last street lamp in Southmoor; turn left into drive. Private car park   ⬐ 2 twin, 6 double, 2 four-poster; family rooms available; all with bathroom/WC; all with satellite TV, room service, hair-dryer, direct-dial telephone, some with trouser press
⊘ 2 restaurants, bar, 2 sitting-rooms, garden; functions (max 100 people incl up to 20 residential), conferences; heated outdoor swimming-pool, tennis, croquet   ♿ No wheelchair access   ⊖ No children under 10; no dogs in public rooms; smoking in public rooms only, if other guests consent   ⊟ Amex, Delta, MasterCard, Switch
£ Single occupancy of twin/double £85, twin/double £105, four-poster £125, family room £130; deposit required. Alc D £26.50

'My colleague and I both found this woman quite incredible. She finished every whispered sentence with the word "sir" and reminded us of the characters from the sketch in the Fast Show *of the men's outfitters with the phrase, "Suit you, sir".'*
On a hotel in Northamptonshire

KINTBURY **Berkshire** map 2

Dundas Arms

53 Station Road, Kintbury, Hungerford RG17 9UT
TEL: (01488) 658263   FAX: (01488) 658568

Characterful inn turned restaurant-with-rooms, with not one water feature but two.

Suckers for traditional British waterways are likely to find this traditional inn irresistible. The whitewashed hostelry stands beside the confluence of a river and a canal, with the sluggish Kennet and Avon immobile beside the front door and the skittish Kennet slooshing eastward to the rear, right beside the picture windows and patios of the five bedrooms. The fixtures and fittings are certainly well beyond the first flush of youth, and fashion may not look kindly on the fitted wardrobes or the avocado-coloured bathroom suites, but the sheets are crisp, everything works, hot water emerges close to boiling point, and there is room enough for sitting, sleeping and stretching. Besides, the main attraction is David Dalzell-Piper's dinners. A strong local contingent favours the bar for sampling the menu, choosing from a dozen or so options from the chalked-up boards. Our inspector was impressed with a pungently cheesy crab au gratin, followed by a tasty venison casserole, but eschewed the bar's blue plates, varnished pennies and prolific stencilling for the more auditorily subdued surroundings of the cocktail room – a quirky combination of Swedish furnishings, pottery ducks and amusing culinary collages of chefs at work. A third option would have been the more traditional, narrow bistro-style dining-room. There may be no lounge to repair to, post repast, but, weather permitting, the canalside benches or riverside patios ought to outdo any yearning for chesterfields and curtains.

◑ Closed Chr to New Year; restaurant closed Sun & Mon eves   ⊠ As you drive into Kintbury off A4, hotel is first building on left after canal. Private car park   ⤆ 2 twin, 3 double; all with bathroom/WC; all with TV, direct-dial telephone   ⌗ Dining-room, cocktail room, bar   ⅙ No wheelchair access   ⬤ No children under 5; no dogs   ▭ Amex, Delta, MasterCard, Switch, Visa   £ Single occupancy of twin/double £60, twin/double £70; deposit required. Bar/bistro L, D £7 to £12; alc D £25

KNUTSFORD **Cheshire** map 8

Belle Epoque

60 King Street, Knutsford WA16 6DT
TEL: (01565) 633060   FAX: (01565) 634150

Fun, French brasserie with simple rooms, some in need of a face-lift.

Built in 1907 and originally known as the King's Coffee House, the Belle Epoque, with its gracious art-nouveau façade, is an impressive feature on Knutsford's high street. The brasserie has a flamboyant French character, with its Venetian-glass mosaic floor, deep jade-green walls and lavish indigo and emerald drapes. Flowers in oversized glass-fluted vases balance on crisp white tablecloths, while at the far end of the restaurant the grand bay window is an explosion of greenery. The walls are decorated with a collection of menus from famous restaurants worldwide. Mixed reports have reached us this year, both on food and accommodation. 'Probably the best fish and proper chips in the land', applauds one reader, while another described the food as having 'an air of being microwaved'. The bedrooms suffer in comparison with the theatrical atmosphere of the brasserie. Room 2, which provoked strong complaints from one reader, is (the owners admit) the worst: pokey and in dire need of a face-lift, with a basin in the room and pinched *en suite* toilet. Rooms 6 and 7 are more characterful, with spacious bathrooms, but still rough around the edges – flaky wooden window frames, for example. Nevertheless, one regular visitor of 14 years commends the cuisine, restaurant, rooms and general ambience as 'something special'. More reports, please.

○ Closed Sun & bank hols; restaurant closed Sun eve ▨ 2 miles from Junction 19 of M6, in centre of Knutsford. On-street parking (free); public car park nearby (25p per day) ⊨ 2 twin, 4 double; all with bathroom/WC; all with TV, room service, direct-dial telephone ⊘ Restaurant, bar; conferences (max 80 people incl up to 6 residential), functions; early suppers for children ⅓ No wheelchair access ● No children under 10; no dogs ⌷ Amex, Delta, Diners, MasterCard, Switch, Visa £ Single occupancy of twin/double £45, twin/double £55. Cooked B £5; set L £5.50; alc L, D £15.50

Longview Hotel

51 & 55 Manchester Road, Knutsford WA16 0LX
TEL: (01565) 632119   FAX: (01565) 652402
EMAIL: longview_hotel@compuserve.com

Friendly, family-run hotel with cheerful rooms, famed for Martin Bell's 'bunker'.

Situated on the busy Manchester Road, the Longview Hotel is made up of two terraced Victorian houses with well-tended gardens, separated by a dancing school. Inside, the reception area is cosy and welcoming, with its attractive period fireplace, but the real highlight is the cavernous bar. 'Bell's Bunker' was the base for Martin Bell's anti-sleaze 1997 Election campaign that resulted in his victory over Neil Hamilton – photos of the eponymous journalist-politician decorate the walls alongside a collection of old *Punch* prints. The ornate restaurant retains a Victorian feel, evoked by the floral wallpaper, rich curtains and chandelier. From the formal menu you could select dishes like grilled green-lipped mussels with a cream sauce of marjoram, bacon and orange, and swordfish steak served with chilli oil and Thai fish sauce. The bedrooms are comfortably furnished with a fine attention to detail that includes hot-water bottles, laundry bags and clothes brushes. Room 7 is fun, with its reproduction Louis XIV bed and Victorian lamps, while Room 8 has a half-tester bed. Service, overseen by Pauline and Steven West, is friendly and welcoming.

○ Closed 24 Dec to 4/5 Jan; restaurant closed Sun eve ▨ Leave M6 at Junction 19; take A556 towards Chester/Northwich as far as traffic lights; turn left to Knutsford; at roundabout, turn left. Longview is 200 yards along on right. Private car park ⊨ 6 single, 3 twin, 14 double; some in annexe; family rooms available; all with bathroom/WC; all with TV, room service, hair-dryer, trouser press, direct-dial telephone ⊘ Restaurant, bar, drying-room; leisure facilities nearby (free for guests); early suppers for children ⅓ No wheelchair access ● No dogs in public rooms;

dogs in bedrooms (£5 per night) ⊟ Amex, Delta, MasterCard, Visa £ Single £41 to
£63, single occupancy of twin/double £52 to £75, twin/double £62 to £88, family room
£78 to £93; deposit required. Bar/bistro D £6; alc D £18.50. Special breaks available

---

LACOCK Wiltshire
map 2

At the Sign of the Angel

6 Church Street, Lacock, Chippenham SN15 2LB
TEL: (01249) 730230   FAX: (01249) 730527

---

*Historic inn, with lots of character, in village preserved by the
National Trust.*

This lovely village, with its rows of half-timbered and stone cottages and
adjoining abbey, has been owned by the National Trust since 1944. Leased to the
Levis family a few years later, At the Sign of the Angel has been run by the family
ever since. Easily mistaken for the village pub, the three interlinking
dining-rooms on the ground floor have polished tiled floors, large stone
fireplaces, beams and solid wooden furnishings; the menu is traditionally
English, the atmosphere cosy. Upstairs, crooked-floored corridors lead to the
lounge, with its dark-oak panelling – somewhere to retire to for a quiet drink.
Most of the bedroooms are up here, too; some have small doorways and very low
beams, while all have dark-wood furniture in period style and neat, modern
bathrooms. Several of the rooms are in an annexe at the end of the pretty garden;
with almost as much character as those in the house, they also have more
headroom for those who are not vertically challenged.

◑ Closed Chr ⤬ In Lacock village, 3 miles south of Chippenham. Private car park
⌂ 2 twin, 6 double, 2 four-poster; some in annexe; all with bathroom/WC; all with TV,
hair-dryer, direct-dial telephone ⊘ 3 dining-rooms, lounge, garden; functions (max 45
people incl up to 20 residential); high chairs ⌖ Wheelchair access to hotel and 1
dining-room, WC (unisex), 1 ground-floor bedroom ⬤ No dogs in public rooms
⊟ Amex, Delta, MasterCard, Switch, Visa £ Single occupancy of twin/double £65 to
£75, twin/double £95 to £105, four-poster £105 to £125; deposit required. Alc L £17.50,
D £22.50. Special breaks available

LANDEWEDNACK Cornwall
map 1

Landewednack House NEW ENTRY

Church Cove, The Lizard, Helston TR12 7PQ
TEL: (01326) 290909   FAX: (01326) 290192

---

*Top-notch, very good-value Wolsey Lodge, with immaculate
accommodation in England's most southerly rectory.*

Landewednack House was built in 1683 as a rectory, and continued its religious
career right up until the 'eighties, when it retired and became a most fetching
country-house hotel. It was Georgianised in the 1730s, and an extra wing was
built by a Victorian rector to accommodate his expanding family. Peter and
Marion Stanley have furnished it throughout with elegant antiques and

sophisticated accessories, perfectly complementing the fine, cantilevered staircase, Georgian archways and stone flags. In the style of true Wolsey Lodges, guests dine *en famille*, around a single table. Marion's menus are mouthwatering, and include such starters as crab with ginger and cream and fingers of toast, followed by fillet of roast smoked salmon on a bed of leeks with sweet potato, calabrese and ginger, and finished off with home-made gooseberry ice-cream and Cornish cheeses. She also provides extra treats at breakfast with such delicacies as prunes stewed in red wine with cinnamon, home-made yoghurt or fresh melon.

The three bedrooms are particularly praiseworthy, with no luxury overlooked, and the sumptuous bathrooms have power showers. The Yellow Room has a huge, high, canopied bed and a view over the outdoor pool to the sea and headland beyond; the Red Room has a splendid four-poster and plenty of shiny antiques; while the Chinese Room has stencilled walls and silk drapes. Guests also have the use of a jacuzzi.

◑ Closed Chr ⤴ From Helston, take A3083 south; just before Lizard, turn left to Church Cove; house is ¾ mile further, on left, behind blue gates. Private car park ⌂ 1 twin, 1 double, 1 four-poster; double with bathroom/WC, 2 with shower/WC; all with TV, hair-dryer, direct-dial telephone ✇ 2 dining-rooms, lounge, drying-room, garden; heated outdoor swimming-pool, boules, croquet ♿ No wheelchair access ● No children under 16; no dogs; no.smoking ▭ MasterCard, Visa £ Twin/double £76 to £84, four-poster £80; deposit required. Set D £23

Langar Hall

Langar, Nottingham NG13 9HG
TEL: (01949) 860559   FAX: (01949) 861045
EMAIL: langarhall-hotel@ndirect.co.uk

Charming country house, reflecting the owner's tastes, with attractive, comfortable rooms.

In the gentle, quintessentially English countryside of the Vale of Belvoir stands Imogen Skirving's wonderfully idiosyncratic country hotel. The atmosphere is that of a private house – albeit one stuffed to the gables with rugs, curios, chandeliers, paintings and prints, an eclectic collection that greatly adds to the individual charm of every room. The grandest of these is the main restaurant, with its statues and Corinthian columns, which provides a suitably classic setting for food that is both simple and tasty: lettuce and sorrel soup to start with, perhaps, followed by chargrilled fillet of lamb with rosemary and garlic, and then a firmly traditional treacle tart and custard. Breakfasts (and dinners, on quieter nights) are taken in the smaller, more intimate dining-room, which has Indian-cotton drapes and pointed Gothic windows. One correspondent felt that the room was out of step with the style of the house, but praised the food and the 'friendly and helpful staff'. The bedrooms are all different, from the panelled Barristers to Edwards, an elegant four-poster, and Bohemia, once the art studio of Imogen's husband.

◑ Open all year 🅩 Behind church in Langar. Private car park 🛏 1 single, 2 twin, 5 double, 1 four-poster, 1 suite; some in annexe; family rooms available; all with bathroom/WC; all with TV, room service, hair-dryer, direct-dial telephone, some with trouser press ✅ Restaurant, 2 dining-rooms, lounge, drying-room, study, garden; functions (max 18 people incl up to 12 residential), conferences; civil wedding licence; fishing, croquet; early suppers for children; cots, high chairs, toys, babysitting, baby-listening ♿ Wheelchair access to hotel (ramp) and restaurant, 1 ground-floor bedroom ◗ Dogs by arrangement (£10 per night); smoking in one public room only ▭ Amex, Diners, MasterCard, Visa £ Single £65, single occupancy of twin/double £75 to £95, twin/double £100, four-poster £150, family room £120, suite £175; deposit required. Set L £12.50 to £15, D £15 to £20; alc D £25. Special breaks available

---

LANGHO Lancashire   map 8

Northcote Manor

Northcote Road, Langho, Blackburn BB6 8BE
TEL: (01254) 240555   FAX: (01254) 246568

A smart hotel, offering a great dining experience and delightfully furnished rooms.

On approach, the setting – on a major roundabout – is positively uninspiring, although the meadowed grounds do buffer the hotel somewhat from its immediate surroundings. The red-brick Victorian house does, however, offer a pleasant surprise upon entering it, for the interior is very much in keeping with that of a country manor; a grand, wooden staircase, smart, leather-padded bar and generous bay windows create a refined atmosphere. The ambience is on the formal side – well-dressed guests sip aperitifs and chat in subdued voices in front of an open fire while waiting to dine. And dining is very much part of the hotel's experience. Talented chef Nigel Haworth creates such dishes as local quail, fricassee of New Forest mushrooms, chive and garlic dumplings and, for the really indulgent, steamed Scottish lobster with basil, in an orange and champagne sauce; for dessert, apple-crumble soufflé, Lancashire-cheese ice-cream and apple compote – yes, all on the one plate! The bedrooms are well presented and, though individually styled, they are all of a consistently high standard, with smart *en suite* bathroooms. Finally, accompanying the good food, sophisticated company and stylish rooms is good service, which was praised by guests when our inspector visited.

◑ Closed 25 Dec & 1 Jan 🅩 Leave M6 at Junction 31 and take A59 Clitheroe road for 9½ miles; hotel is on left just before roundabout at Langho. Private car park 🛏 5 twin, 8 double, 1 four-poster suite; family rooms available; all with bathroom/WC; all with TV, room service, hair-dryer, trouser press, direct-dial telephone ✅ Restaurant, bar, 2 lounges, conservatory, garden; conferences (max 100 people incl up to 14 residential), functions; civil wedding licence; early suppers for children; cots, high chairs, baby-listening ♿ Wheelchair access to hotel (2 steps) and restaurant, 4 ground-floor bedrooms, 1 room specially equipped for disabled people ◗ No dogs; no smoking in restaurant ▭ Amex, Delta, Diners, MasterCard, Switch, Visa £ Single occupancy of twin/double £90, twin/double £110, family room £120, four-poster suite £130; deposit required. Set L £16, D £37; alc L £25, D £40. Special breaks available

LANGLEY MARSH Somerset

map 2

Langley House

Langley Marsh, Wiveliscombe, Taunton TA4 2UF
TEL: (01984) 623318   FAX: (01984) 624573

Stylish décor, good food and splendid gardens at a delightfully understated country house, carefully run by attentive hosts.

The golden grasshopper proves a distinctive insignia for Anne Wilson's interesting country house near Wiveliscombe, in the folds of the Brendon Hills; Anne and her husband Peter found the strange icon while clearing an outhouse, and decided to adopt it as the symbol of their enterprise. In fact, it's a memento of Martin's Bank, whose founder once lived here. The pristine, cream-rendered house largely masks its sixteenth-century origins, which become obvious the second you enter the atmospherically panelled hallway. Elsewhere, the house is Georgian, and it's this country-house style which sets the tone throughout the public rooms. Bold, coral walls set off the Japanese prints and wall-mounted plates in the striking drawing-room. A second sitting-room (also used for private dining) is a cheerful yellow, with lemon-and-blue gingham chairs and sofas, as befits a one-time morning room. Pretty, stencilled peach walls feature in the smart restaurant overlooking the lovely gardens. The set, four-course dinner menu, with choices only at dessert, shows judicious balance and fine execution: a typical meal might include a fanned dessert pear, marinated in walnut oil with a herb savoury, followed by roasted cod with a pine-nut crust, lemon pearl barley and a butter sauce, and then pan-fried mignons of Somerset lamb with roasted shallots and an onion and cassis purée. You could round that off with a terrine of dark and white chocolate with an almond and hazelnut meringue. The bedrooms are modishly decorated in a tasteful, country-house style.

● Open all year   ⊅ From Taunton, take B3227 to Wiveliscombe; turn right (signposted Langley Marsh); hotel is ½ mile on right. Private car park   ⬏ 1 single, 2 twin, 3 double, 1 four-poster, 1 family room; all with bathroom/WC; all with TV, room service, hair-dryer, direct-dial telephone; no tea/coffee-making facilities in rooms   ⊘ Restaurant, bar, 2 drawing-rooms, drying-room, conservatory, garden; croquet; early suppers for children; cots, high chairs, toys, babysitting, baby-listening, outdoor play area   ⑤ No wheelchair access   ● No children under 7 in restaurant eves; no dogs in public rooms; no smoking in restaurant and some bedrooms   ▭ Amex, MasterCard, Visa   £ Single £78 to £83, single occupancy of twin/double £78 to £83, twin/double £105 to £113, four-poster £118 to £128, family room £143 to £158; deposit required. Set D £26.50/£31.50. Special breaks available

---

LASTINGHAM North Yorkshire

map 9

Lastingham Grange

Lastingham, York YO62 6TH
TEL: (01751) 417345   FAX: (01751) 417358

Exemplary service in a traditional country house in the North York Moors National Park.

Lastingham is a delightfully sleepy village that sees little traffic, and the handsome creeper-clad hotel that lies on its outskirts is a reassuring bastion of tradition, but without a hint of the starchiness that can come with it. Originally a seventeenth-century farmhouse, Lastingham Grange became a country-house hotel in the 'twenties, and has been owned by the Wood family since the Second World War. The eminently restful atmosphere encourages you to switch off in an armchair in the bright and spacious redecorated lounge, while your needs are served with discreet correctness by the solicitous staff or Mr Wood himself: 'nothing is too much trouble', and 'whims are indulged as a matter of course', according to one satisfied guest. The evening meals won't scare the horses, sticking as they do to such classic fare as home-made soups and roasts. Likewise, the chintzy bedrooms – some of which have also received a visit from the decorators – steer clear of the vagaries of fashion, preferring to follow the path of comfort. Morning coffee, afternoon tea (with cakes and scones) and newspapers are included in the pricey rates.

◖ Closed Dec to Feb　🗷 2 miles east of Kirkbymoorside on A170; turn left (north) through Appleton-le-Moors to Lastingham. Private car park　↳ 2 single, 7 twin, 3 double; family rooms available; all with bathroom/WC; all with TV, room service, hair-dryer, trouser press, direct-dial telephone, radio　⊘ Dining-room, lounge, drying-room, garden; early suppers for children; cots, high chairs, toys, baby-listening, outdoor play area　ᒼ No wheelchair access　◗ No dogs in public rooms; no smoking in dining-room　⊏ None accepted　£ Single £76 to £79, single occupancy of twin/double £76 to £79, twin/double/family room £143 to £149. Set L £16.50/£20, D £30. Special breaks available

---

LAVENHAM Suffolk　　　　　　　　　　　　　　　　　map 6

The Angel

Market Place, Lavenham, Sudbury CO10 9QZ
TEL: (01787) 247388　FAX: (01787) 248344
EMAIL: angellav@aol.com

A village pub with tasty and good-value food and a welcoming atmosphere.

A stay at the Angel will enable you to enjoy some of the loveliest views of this outstanding Suffolk village. Slap bang on the wide Market Place, its cream-washed walls face the remarkable half-timbered Guildhall just opposite. Unlike most buildings in Lavenham, this pub has fairly straight walls, but that shouldn't deceive you about its age. Inside you'll find exposed medieval beams and, upstairs in the hall-like lounge, an ornate plasterwork ceiling several centuries old. The focus is, of course, the pub, which is very much a meeting place for locals both young and old, with village notices posted up around the bar. You can eat in the bar or in the more formal restaurant, which is on the other side but not cut off from the convivial pub atmosphere. Once again visitors have praised the cooking for its excellence and good value. Our inspector had deliciously fresh asparagus with a butter and herb sauce, followed by one of the Angel's old favourites, steak and ale pie and then a tasty raspberry crème brûlée. One reporter said about the service: 'Each member of staff was intent on giving every guest the best possible time.' We thought that some of the bedrooms were looking rather tired; however, one reader recommended Room 7 as cosy and well-equipped.

◗ Closed 25 & 26 Dec ↗ In Lavenham's Market Place. Private car park; on-street parking (free) ⇌ 1 twin, 6 double, 1 family room; most with shower/WC exc 3 double with bathroom/WC; all with TV, room service, hair-dryer, direct-dial telephone ⌖ Restaurant, bar, lounge, drying-room, garden; tennis courts nearby (free for guests); early suppers for children; cots, high chairs, toys, baby-listening ♿ Wheelchair access to hotel (ramp)and restaurant, 1 ground-floor bedroom ⊖ No children in restaurant after 9pm; dogs in bar only and bedrooms by arrangement, smoking in bar and bedrooms only ▭ Amex, Delta, MasterCard, Switch, Visa £ Single occupancy of twin/double £40 to £50, twin/double £65 to £75, family room £75 to £85; deposit required. Bar/bistro L, D £10; alc L £15, D £16. Special breaks available

---

Great House

Market Place, Lavenham, Sudbury CO10 9QZ
TEL: (01787) 247431   FAX: (01787) 248007
EMAIL: greathouse@surflink.co.uk

A stylish French restaurant-with-rooms that has had an excellent programme of redecoration this year.

Situated on the street corner opposite the Angel Hotel, this restaurant-with-rooms is a building in considerable contrast to its neighbour. With its fine porticoed entrance and serried line of Georgian sash windows, it certainly lives up to its name. The interior, however, offers a few surprises: the French owners, Martine and Régis Crépy, have employed many French staff, and there is a modern, sophisticated feel to the furnishings. To your left on entering is a cocktail bar lined with turquoise wood panel units and clustered with armchairs set among low lights. The restaurant to the right has been completely redesigned, and now has much lighter colours – pale red and magnolia – and a smart stripped-pine floor. In summer, guests can also use the secluded walled garden, reached via a secret pathway. A set three-course evening meal might begin with marinated grilled chicken drumstick and sauté chicken livers, followed by baked tuna and potato fish-cake on fried aubergines with a red-pepper coulis, and perhaps finally a choice from a mountain of French cheeses. Unfortunately, the weekends are always hectic, and this led one guest to complain to us that they felt rushed during their meal and were finished in less than an hour. The bedrooms, many with ancient exposed beams, have been upgraded this year with new carpets and bold colour schemes. The bathrooms now look particularly sumptuous, with marble sink tops and some nice design touches.

◗ Closed 3 weeks in Jan; restaurant closed Sun & Mon eves if no bookings ↗ In Lavenham's Market Place. On-street parking (free); public car park nearby (free) ⇌ 1 twin, 3 double, 1 four-poster; family rooms available; all with bathroom/WC exc four-poster with shower/WC; all with TV, room service, hair-dryer, direct-dial telephone ⌖ Restaurant, bar, lounge, garden; functions (max 80 people incl up to 10 residential), conferences; leisure facilities nearby (free for guests); early suppers for children; cots, high chairs, toys, baby-listening, outdoor play area ♿ No wheelchair access ◔ No children in restaurant after 9pm; no dogs in public rooms; no smoking in restaurant ☐ Amex, Delta, MasterCard, Switch, Visa £ Single occupancy of twin/double £55 to £65, twin/double £70 to £82, four-poster £82 to £102, family room £70 to £102 plus £15 to £20 per child over 2; deposit required. Bar/bistro L £3.50 to £12; set L £10 to £13, D £18; alc Sun L £18, D £27.50. Special breaks available

The Swan

High Street, Lavenham, Sudbury CO10 9QA
TEL: (01787) 247477   FAX: (01787) 248286

A chain hotel that has made the most of this unique and large collection of medieval buildings.

Lavenham is one of East Anglia's most notable, historic villages, and the medieval, half-timbered buildings of the Swan are some of the finest examples that you will find here. The hotel is actually made up of a collection of several houses, including the village's wool hall; not surprisingly, it is full of odd-shaped rooms, low ceilings and creaky corridors, which give it a cosy and warm feel, despite alterations made in the need to suit modern tastes. There's an open-plan design to the public areas, with plenty of secluded corners with tartan armchairs where you can sit and have tea, disturbed only by the sound of ticking clocks. If you fancy something stronger, there's also an authentic bar, with a stone-tiled floor, leather sofas around the walls and mementoes left by US servicemen who were stationed nearby during the Second World War. Surprisingly, the Swan also has some decent garden space, including a lawn exclusively for the use of residents. You can dine in some splendour in the hall-like restaurant, which has lots of natural light supplemented by some large, ironwork chandeliers. Some of the bedrooms retain the historic character, but others can be rather dark (not helped by the beige and green colour schemes); the newly refurbished rooms, however, have nice, tiled bathrooms.

◑ Open all year ⊿ In centre of Lavenham. Private car park ⇤ 7 single, 13 twin, 21 double, 3 four-poster, 2 suites; all with bathroom/WC; all with TV, room service, hair-dryer, trouser press, direct-dial telephone; mini-bar on request ✓ Restaurant, 2 bars, 5 lounges, garden; functions (max 50 people residential/non-residential), conferences; civil wedding licence; early suppers for children; cots, high chairs, babysitting, baby-listening ⅋ No wheelchair access ◔ No smoking in some bedrooms ☐ Amex, Delta, Diners, MasterCard, Switch, Visa £ Single £75, single occupancy of twin/double £85 to £95, twin/double £120, four-poster £140, suite £145; deposit required. Continental B £8, cooked B £10; bar/bistro L £3.50 to £13; set L £10/£13, D £25; alc D £37.50. Special breaks available

---

LEAMINGTON SPA Warwickshire   map 5

The Lansdowne   𝓛

87 Clarendon Street, Leamington Spa CV32 4PF
TEL: (01926) 450505   FAX: (01926) 421313

Town-centre hotel with a hint of French charm.

In the centre of Leamington the monkey-puzzle tree and bold green walls of the Lansdowne are easily spotted – the latter in need of sprucing up, something owners Gillian and David Allen promise is in hand. Inside, the bold colours continue in the public areas, with greens and reds dominating. The bar is a cosy nook lit by spotlights; the marble mantelpiece is laden with dozens of red wines – this is a very convivial house. Stylish touches appear in the dining-room too, with handwritten menus that change daily: maybe home-made mushroom and burgundy pâté to start, followed by a baked fillet of sea bream and then a selection of desserts and coffee in the bar with home-made shortbread biscuits. The atmosphere is relaxing and reflects the Allens' love of things French.

Bedrooms lack the striking elegance of downstairs, with stripped pine furniture and the occasional noisy bathroom extractor fan. Thoughtful touches are there, however: each has a little basket of goodies, including plasters, sewing kit and – should the conviviality flow too freely – some paracetamol.

◑ Open all year; restaurant closed Sun eve (except residents)　🚹 In town centre, at junction of Warwick Street and Clarendon Street. Private car park　🛏 5 single, 3 twin, 5 double, 1 family room; most with shower/WC, others with bathroom/WC; all with TV, hair-dryer, direct-dial telephone, clock radio　✥ Dining-room, bar, lounge, garden; early suppers for children　🖮 Wheelchair access to hotel (1 step) and restaurant, 2 ground-floor rooms　● No children under 5; no dogs; no smoking in dining-room
🗀 Delta, MasterCard, Switch, Visa　£ Single £50, single occupancy of twin/double £55, twin/double £64, family room £74 (one child only); deposit required. Set D £16/£19; alc D £23. Special breaks available

---

York House

9 York Road, Leamington Spa CV31 3PR
TEL: (01926) 424671　FAX: (01926) 832272

Pleasant, good-value small hotel, with a family atmosphere.

Sue and Robert Davis's three-storey, red-brick Victorian house is well placed in Leamington Spa – close to the Pump Room Gardens and a few minutes' walk from the high-street shops. Externally, it's a handsome house, with clematis scaling the walls and hanging baskets; inside, it's an attractive mix of period furniture, rich colours and family photographs that create a pleasant, homely atmosphere. The bedrooms represent good value, particularly if you stay in a room with a shared bathroom. Most have modern pine furniture and a bright, chintzy style, and the twin and family rooms are quite spacious. Sue's cooking is of the straightforward family-food variety: lasagne, gammon steaks, or lighter snacks, such as omelettes. Afterwards, coffee can be taken in the lounge, with its chaise longue and tasselled curtains.

◑ Closed Chr & New Year; dining-room closed Sun eve　🚹 From main parade, turn into Dormer Place, left into Dale Street, then left into York Road. Private car park
🛏 2 single, 4 twin, 2 double; family rooms available; 4 with shower/WC; all with TV, room service, hair-dryer, direct-dial telephone, some with mini-bar, trouser press
✥ Dining-room, lounge; early suppers for children; cots, high chairs, babysitting
🖮 No wheelchair access　● Dogs in 1 bedroom only; no smoking in dining-room and

some bedrooms ⬜ Diners, MasterCard, Visa £ Single £22 to £27, single occupancy of twin/double £30 to £40, twin/double £40 to £55, family room £60; deposit required. Light L £6.50; set D £13; alc D £14.50. Special breaks available

---

LEEDS West Yorkshire

map 9

42 The Calls

42 The Calls, Leeds LS2 7EW
TEL: 0113-244 0099   FAX: 0113-234 4100
EMAIL: hotel@42thecalls.co.uk

Jonathan Wix's modern, designer, waterfront hotel still leads the way in Leeds.

Not satisfied with the many plaudits that he regularly receives for his stunning, ultra-smart conversion of three riverside corn and flour mills in a once seedy, run-down area of Leeds just south of the city centre, Jonathan Wix's refurbishment and upgrading programme at '42' continues apace. The public areas now have air-conditioning, the linen is more opulent and the new bathrobes are so luxuriously weighty that Mr Wix hopes that they will be too big to fit into guests' luggage! With one eye fixed firmly on the business community, the bedrooms at 42 The Calls offer an uncommonly high level of facilities – CD and cassette players, speakers in the bathrooms, phones everywhere and an ingenious hatch for delivering room-service meals, including the expansive breakfast choices (although you should think twice before missing out on starting the day in the gorgeous, arty breakfast room). Facilities aside, the buildings' original, Victorian features, such as wooden joists, cast-iron pillars and even the odd hoist (once used for hauling grain up from quayside) protruding from the ceiling, have been slickly blended with cream-painted, brick walls and bold, modernist colour schemes. As long as noise from the Tetley brewery doesn't concern you, ask for one of the rooms with a river view. Although separately owned, two smart restaurants – Pool Court at 42 and Brasserie Forty Four – cohabit with the hotel and share its reputation for service, style and quality; both allow you to charge the tab to your hotel account. One reader voiced a couple of reservations about the service and price, but concluded, 'I would always recommend it to others.'

◑ Closed Chr; restaurants closed Sun eve ⬀ In centre of Leeds, opposite Tetley Brewery Wharf on river. Private car park (free Mon to Thur; £4.95 per day Fri to Sun); on-street parking (metered) ⇥ 7 single, 9 twin, 14 twin/double, 8 double, 3 suites; family rooms available; all with bathroom/WC; all with satellite TV, room service, hair-dryer, mini-bar, trouser press, direct-dial telephone, radio, CD player ✷ 2 restaurants (separately owned), breakfast room, bar, lounge; functions (max 55 people incl up to 41 residential), conferences; fishing; early suppers for children, served in bedroom; cots, high chairs, toys, babysitting, baby-listening ♿ Wheelchair access to hotel and Pool Court restaurant, WC (unisex), no wheelchair access to breakfast room, lift to bedrooms, 1 room specially equipped for disabled people ● Dogs by arrangement only; smoking in six bedrooms only ⬜ Amex, Delta, Diners, MasterCard, Switch, Visa £ Single £65 to £95, single occupancy of twin/double £65 to £120, twin/double £65 to £145, family room (room rate + £5 per child), suite £130 to £220; deposit required. Continental B £9, cooked B £12; bistro L £9 to £12, D £20; alc L, D £29.50. Special breaks available

Haley's

Shire Oak Road, Headingley, Leeds LS6 2DE
TEL: 0113-278 4446   FAX: 0113-275 3342
WEB SITE: www.virgin.com/hotels/haley's-hotel&restaurant.htm

Victorian villa in a smart and affluent suburb of Leeds, catering for business and conference clientele, as well as leisure travellers.

Headingley needs no introduction for cricket-lovers, but to those not familiar with the environs of Leeds this leafy and surprisingly lively suburb has the feel of a well-to-do Victorian village. Haley's sits in a leafy lane near the university – unmissable among its more sedate neighbours thanks to an incongruous concoction of red-slate turrets atop a mock-Tudor layer grafted on to a yellow-stone base. The interior is more stylistically coherent, and its up-market, restrained décor features handsome fireplaces, plush drapes and the quietly luxurious tones of toffee and cream. The lounge is not, however, the sort of place in which you would switch off with a good book: the groups of upright chairs around tables create a setting more conducive to business meetings, and the impression that Haley's is geared to a conference clientele during the week is reflected in the room rates that plunge at weekends. The bedrooms are divided between the main house and the Bedford House annexe next door, a recently converted, Victorian, Grade II-listed stone house. All share an air of understated Edwardian opulence, with antiques, rich fabrics and the sort of top-notch bathroom fittings and facilities that are *de rigueur* for business travellers. Jon Vennell's modern English cuisine also gets a thumbs-up, with starters like a warm scallop mousse, then maybe sesame-roasted cod, and a rum-and-raisin crème caramel for pudding.

◑ Closed 26 to 30 Dec; restaurant closed Sun eve (exc residents)   ⊅ Just off A660 in Headingley, between Yorkshire and Midland banks. Private car park   ⊨ 9 single, 4 twin, 16 double; family rooms and suites available; some in annexe; all with bathroom/WC; all with TV, room service, hair-dryer, trouser press, direct-dial telephone, iron   ⊘ Restaurant, bar, lounge, library; conferences (max 25 people residential/non-residential), functions; civil wedding licence; early suppers for children; cots, high chairs, baby-listening   ♿ No wheelchair access   ● No dogs; smoking in bar and some bedrooms only   ⊟ Amex, Delta, Diners, MasterCard, Switch, Visa   £ Single £105 to £110, single occupancy of twin/double £112 to £130, twin/double £120 to £140, family room £150, suite £185 to £225; deposit required. Set Sun L £15.50; alc D £26. Special breaks available

Prices are what you can expect to pay in 1999, except where specified to the contrary. Many hoteliers tell us that these prices can be regarded only as approximations.

LEINTWARDINE **Herefordshire** map 5

Upper Buckton Farm

Leintwardine, Craven Arms SY7 0JU
TEL: (01547) 540634

Superior guesthouse accommodation on a Marches farm.

'Whatever you consider your highest rating, the Lloyds deserve it,' reckons an American family. More plaudits stack up for the smartest guesthouse/B&B we recommend in the area. Though the Georgian house sits alongside a rough-and-ready farmyard, it looks out over a pretty garden and the farm's meadowland around the River Teme, and has an air of understated elegance inside. It is, however, Yvonne Lloyd's cooking, served at individual, polished tables, that receives the most fulsome praise from readers: 'most imaginative, and able to fulfil our odd dietary requirements'; 'not a single item of food that was not excellent'. A sample dinner might be melon and Parma ham, roast beef (from their own livestock) and Yorkshire pudding, and sticky toffee pudding followed by cheeses. Yvonne's husband Hayden serves sherry beforehand in the cosy sitting-room (there is no longer any need to bring your own wine as they have a table licence), and afterwards you can retire with coffee in front of the fire, or, if it's fine, under the verandah overlooking the lawn. The bedrooms benefit from fine rural views and some antique pieces; only one is fully *en suite*, but the others have their own bathroom.

◑ Open all year ⬛ Take A4113 from Ludlow towards Knighton; at Walford crossroads turn right for Buckton; Upper Buckton is second farm on left. Private car park ⬛ 2 twin/double, 1 double; twin/doubles with bathroom/WC (not *en suite*), double with shower/WC; all with hair-dryer ✧ Dining-room, lounge, garden; fishing, croquet; early suppers for children; cot ⬛ No wheelchair access ⬤ Children by arrangement; no dogs or smoking ⬛ None accepted £ Twin/double £60; deposit required. Set D £18

LEWDOWN **Devon** map 1

Lewtrenchard Manor

Lewdown, Okehampton EX20 4PN
TEL: (01566) 783256   FAX: (01566) 783332

A most fetching country house, with an extravagant, yet unostentatious, feel about it.

From the outside, this fabulous old manor house has more of the look of a French château than a seventeenth-century Englishman's castle, but the date is carved in English stone above the front door – 1620. The house has obviously been well loved during its long history, not least by the Reverend Sabine Baring Gould, who wrote 'Onward Christian Soldiers' here. Outside, a long avenue of beech trees marks just the beginning of the walk around the grounds, which will take you past the lake with the waterfall, the field with the horses, and will bring you back to the herb garden and the more formal sunken gardens in front of the house. Inside, all is dark panelled and creaky, with fascinating, fresco-like paintings of alchemical human attributes in the breakfast room, stained glass in the dining-room, and plenty of over-the-top, highly polished, antique furniture. Ornate stucco graces the ceilings, and former ladies of the house stare down in beatific fashion from the 40-plus oils around the walls. The place is vast, and you may get lost... but the bedrooms are reassuring in scale and comfortable, done out with equally heavy furniture (Melton has the four-poster which apparently belonged to the wife of Charles I) and muted colours. The menu is no less extravagant, with such adventurous dishes as shredded chicken confit with wuntun crisps, Asian greens and wasabi dressing, followed by chump of South Devon lamb with black-olive blini, roasted-fennel tortellini and basil gravy – though one reporter found the portions 'very tiny' and the desserts disappointing, and also questioned the practice of serving the previous night's speciality breads (tomato and olive oil, curry, etc.) toasted for marmalade the following morning.

○ Open all year ⊿ Take old A30 to Lewdown, then take road signposted Lewtrenchard. Private car park ⊫ 4 twin, 2 double, 2 four-poster, 1 suite; all with bathroom/WC; all with TV, room service, hair-dryer, direct-dial telephone; no tea/coffee-making facilities in rooms ⊘ Dining-room, breakfast room, bar, 2 lounges, garden; functions (max 50 people incl up to 18 residential), conferences; civil wedding licence; fishing, clay-pigeon shooting; early suppers for children ⓺ No wheelchair access ● Children under 8 by arrangement; dogs in bedrooms only, by arrangement; no smoking in dining-rooms ⊟ Amex, Diners, MasterCard, Switch, Visa £ Single occupancy of twin/double £80 to £95, twin/double/four-poster £145, suite £150; deposit required. Set L £20, D £30. Special breaks available

---

LEWES East Sussex   map 3

Millers

134 High Street, Lewes BN7 1XS
TEL: (01273) 475631   FAX: (01273) 486226
EMAIL: millers134@aol.com

A one-off B&B, full of treasures, run with a fine eye for detail.

Essentially a family home, Millers has just two guest bedrooms that owners Teré and Tony Tammar let out for B&B. It is a picturesque sixteenth-century timber-framed house in Lewes's conservation area, refronted in brick during Georgian times. The name derives from the nineteenth-century millers who sold their flour from the front parlour; this parlour has also been used as a barber's shop and tobacconist, and is now the guests' breakfast room and lounge, with a flagstoned floor, armchairs, huge fireplace and beamed ceiling. Hearty breakfasts, including yoghurt and summer-fruit compotes, are served at a large pine table. Evening meals are not provided, but there's a wealth of restaurants nearby to choose from. Both bedrooms contain four-posters. The Rose Room has Victorian furniture – including the mahogany bed – with prints on the walls and a simple, whitewashed *en suite* bathroom. The Studio has a vaulted ceiling and a small shower-room in what was possibly once a priest-hole. Millers is a child-free environment: the bedrooms are not suitable for extra beds, and the profusion of precious knick-knacks would prove too tempting for small fingers to resist.

◑ Closed 4 & 5 Nov, 20 Dec to 4 Jan ⤢ In central Lewes, just up St Anne's Hill from Shelleys Hotel. On-street parking (free) ⛨ 2 four-poster; 1 with bathroom/WC, 1 with shower/WC; both with TV, hair-dryer ✓ Breakfast room/lounge, drying-room, garden ♿ No wheelchair access ⊖ No children; no dogs; no smoking ▭ None accepted £ Four-poster £50

Shelleys Hotel

137 High Street, Lewes BN7 1XS
TEL: (01273) 472 361   FAX: (01273) 483152

Self-indulgence reigns supreme at this chic hotel, previously owned by the Shelley family.

After battling up the bustling High Street, with its milling crowds and busy shops, it comes as a welcome relief to enter the cool confines of this elegant, pale yellow building. Previous incarnations have included periods as an inn called the Vine and as an officers' military hospital, but since the late 1970s the hotel has been part of the Thistle Group, which has stylishly refurbished the interior. Don't leave the comfort of the sofas in the lounge without asking to see behind one of the locked doors: on the back is an intriguing bit of family history – all the heights of generations of the Hodgkin family (owners 1800–1875) as they were growing up. Each bedroom from the smallest (Room 11, a cute single with wood panelling and leaded windows) to the biggest (Room 1, a palace with a wide sweep of windows overlooking the garden) has been decorated with panache, with every little creature comfort catered for. Tea-lovers will revel in the outstanding selection in the rooms. Some of the bathrooms can be rather overwhelming in their expanses of patterned marble, especially if you're feeling a bit the worse for wear after the night before! You can enjoy a light lunch – maybe a chargrilled Mediterranean vegetable sandwich – in the clubby bar, or adjourn to the restaurant for something more filling, like red-mullet terrine followed by baked pork fillet en croûte with caramelised apples.

◑ Open all year ⤢ In centre of Lewes. Private car park ⛨ 1 single, 8 twin, 8 double, 1 four-poster, 1 suite; all with bathroom/WC; all with satellite TV, room service, hair-dryer, trouser press, direct-dial telephone ✓ Restaurant, bar, lounge, garden; functions (max 120 people incl up to 37 residential), conferences; early suppers for children; cots, high chairs, babysitting, baby-listening ♿ No wheelchair access ⊖ No dogs in public rooms; no smoking in some bedrooms ▭ Amex, Delta, Diners, MasterCard, Switch, Visa £ Single £115, single occupancy of twin/double £131, twin/double £149, four-poster £220, suite £204 (prices valid till Jan 1999); deposit required. Continental B £10, cooked B £12.50; bar/bistro L £8; set L £14.50/£17.50, D £26; alc L £25, D £32. Special breaks available

If you make a booking using a credit card and find after cancelling that the full amount has been charged to your card, raise the matter with your credit card company. It will ask the hotelier to confirm whether the room was re-let, and to justify the charge made.

LIFTON **Devon**   map 1

Arundell Arms

Lifton PL16 0AA
TEL: (01566) 784666   FAX: (01566) 784494

*Comfortable hotel, which takes full advantage of its proximity to the
Tamar and serves up good food besides.*

Fishing is a serious business at the Arundell Arms: the Tamar River and its four
tributaries which flow nearby are well stocked with salmon, and in season many
of the hotel's guests are anglers. All this outdoor life means that appetites are
hearty, so sustenance of both the solid and liquid varieties flows freely. The bar
menu offers simple ploughman's lunches, as well as more substantial fare like
mignon of beef fillet, while the grand dining-room has a classic Anglo-French-
with-a-twist menu: you could start with a salad of grilled sweet peppers with
Parmesan shavings, pickled anchovies and rocket leaves, followed by poached
fillet of chicken with a tarragon tartlet and a hot vinaigrette of baby vegetables.
After dinner, guests can help themselves to the decanter of port in the
comfortable lounge, which is restfully done out with flagstoned floors, oriental
rugs, a blazing fire on chilly evenings and plenty of books and magazines.
Fortunately, the fluvial focus of the hotel does not extend to hundreds of stuffed
fish in the public rooms – instead the character of the old coaching-inn is left to
speak for itself, and fascinating it is, too: the tackle shop in the garden was
originally an octagonal cock-fighting pit, the conference room and games room
were once a school, and the dining-room served as the village assembly room.
The bedrooms are done out in co-ordinating fabrics, with an antique or two for
good measure, and have spruce, modern bathrooms.

◑ Closed Chr ⊡ Just off A30 in Lifton. Private car park ⊨ 8 single, 11 twin, 9
double; some in annexe; all with bathroom/WC exc 5 singles with shower/WC; all with
TV, room service, hair-dryer, direct-dial telephone ⊘ 1 dining-room, 2 bars, lounge,
drying-room, conference room, games room, garden; functions (max 100 people incl up
to 40 residential), conferences; fishing; early suppers for children; cots, high chairs
⅙ No wheelchair access ● Children discouraged from dining-room eves; no dogs in
dining-room, dogs £3.50 per night in bedrooms; no smoking in dining-room
⊟ Amex, Diners, MasterCard, Switch, Visa ⊡ Single £68, single occupancy of
twin/double £83, twin/double £108, annexe room £39 to £78; deposit required.
Bar/bistro L, D £3.50 to £20; set L £15/£18, D £27.50; alc L £27.50, D £34.50. Special
breaks available

LINCOLN **Lincolnshire**   map 9

D'Isney Place

Eastgate, Lincoln LN2 4AA
TEL: (01522) 538881   FAX: (01522) 511321

Large, up-market B&B, within strolling distance of the cathedral.

This smart Georgian house with Victorian additions stands close to the
magnificent cathedral – near enough for the cathedral-close wall (built in 1285)

to form the back wall of the hotel's spacious garden. This is a particularly pleasant spot from which to admire the spires, but if poor weather drives you indoors there are no public rooms – not necessarily a drawback if you are out all day and eat out in the evening. Breakfasts are served in the rooms, which are generally comfortable and attractive but vary in size and views. The best of them have whirlpool baths and antique furniture, but the smaller, cheaper rooms have showers and no views. The bedrooms' style fits well with the period of the house, and there are useful extras like fresh milk on the tea tray and bathrobes. Room 38, with its mahogany half-tester and leather armchairs, is the pick of them.

○ Open all year   ☒ On Eastgate, 100 yards from cathedral. Private car park
🛏 1 single, 3 twin, 12 double, 1 four-poster; some in annexe; suites and family rooms available; most with bathroom/WC, some with shower/WC; all with TV, direct-dial telephone, some with hair-dryer, trouser press   ⍋ Garden; cots, high chairs
♿ Wheelchair access to hotel (ramp), 9 ground-floor bedrooms   ● Smoking in some bedrooms only   ▭ Amex, Delta, Diners, MasterCard, Switch, Visa   £ Single £48, single occupancy of twin/double £58, twin/double £72 (in annexe £104), four-poster £92, family room £82, suite £144 (1998 prices); deposit required. Special breaks available

---

LITTLEBURY GREEN Essex

map 6

Elmdon Lee

Littlebury Green, Saffron Walden CB11 4XB
TEL: (01763) 838237 (AND FAX)

Wistaria-clad, Georgian farmhouse with large bedrooms, in genteel surroundings.

There is some wonderful, rolling countryside in this part of north Essex, and this eighteenth-century farmhouse enjoys some great views of it. If you fancy a walk, you might not even need to leave the family estate, as Diana Duke's son, Robert, farms some 900 acres around here. The house has a comfortable, well-lived-in feel, and has a nice, airy lounge with tempting armchairs and family photos dotted around. The dining-room is enormous, and is probably more suitable for a banquet than a quiet evening meal, with guests eating communally. On the day we visited, Mrs Duke was preparing a meal for her guests of tomato and basil mousse with avocado, and then baked gammon with a raisin sauce, followed by lemon tart and strawberries. As with many Wolsey Lodges, it is best to let her know in advance if you will be dining in. Of the four bedrooms, two can be described as enormous, but even the other two are hardly small. Only one has an *en suite* bathroom, but the others have private bathrooms close by. The bedrooms' decoration is slightly old-fashioned, but everything about them is tidy and comfortable.

Don't forget that other hotels worth considering are listed in our Round-ups near the back of the Guide.

◑ Closed Chr ⚡ On outskirts of Littlebury Green, between B1383 and B1039 west of Saffron Walden. Private car park ⬆ 1 single, 2 twin, 1 double; all with bathroom/WC (not all *en suite*); all with TV, hair-dryer ⚶ Dining-room, lounge, TV room, garden ♿ No wheelchair access ● No children; no dogs ⬜ Diners, MasterCard, Visa £ Single £33, single occupancy of twin/double £33, twin/double £60; deposit required. Set D £18.50

LITTLE PETHERICK Cornwall   map 1

Molesworth Manor

Little Petherick, Padstow, Wadebridge PL27 7QT
TEL: (01841) 540292

Exceptionally friendly welcome in a fabulous seventeenth-century country house.

You have to drive slowly through the village of Little Petherick, as the road dips through verdant hedges, humps over bridges and forges up steep hills. It feels very much like England in days gone by, as if you were arriving in a horse-drawn carriage. You then sweep up the crunchy drive to this country house, and are greeted in truly agreeable style by owners Peter Pearce and Heather Clarke. You can keep pretending to be a lord or lady of the manor by looking in the passageway for all the (now disconnected) bells to the bedrooms – his lordship, her ladyship, the cook and the butler could all ring for attention. Now the whole of the ground floor is given over to five interconnecting public rooms for guests to use as they choose. No meals are served (except children's suppers) but Peter will open a bottle of Chablis for you (apparently what starts off as a crab picnic, brought back from Padstow, often becomes a bit of a party), or you can while away many a happy hour in the plush red drawing-room. The breakfast room has 21 boxes of cereal, and the morning room is lined with books for guests to read. The bedrooms are all different: some have thick walls, small windows and are high in the eaves (the Cook's Room is pretty in pink); others are more formal and dignified, with big brass beds and antique furniture. There's even a converted chapel, complete with bell and weathercock.

◑ Closed Nov to 1 Jan ⚡ On A389 from Wadebridge to Padstow; pass through St Issey into Little Petherick; hotel is 300 yards beyond humpback bridge, on right. Private car park ⬆ 1 single, 1 twin, 8 double, 1 family room; all with bathroom/WC exc 2 with shower/WC; no tea/coffee-making facilities in rooms ⚶ Dining-room, drawing room, breakfast room, TV/morning room, music room/library, drying-room, conservatory, garden; early suppers for children on request; high chair ♿ No wheelchair access ● No dogs; no smoking ⬜ None accepted £ Single £21, single occupancy of twin/double £21 to £40, twin/double £33 to £60, family room £61

Some hotels may offer facilities that we haven't space to list, such as a safe, modems, video recorders etc. Ask when booking if this is important to you.

LITTLE SINGLETON Lancashire map 8

Mains Hall

Mains Lane, Little Singleton, Poulton-le-Fylde FY6 7LE
TEL: (01253) 885130   FAX: (01253) 894132
EMAIL: mains.hall@blackpool.net
WEB SITE: www.blackpool.net/mains_hall/index.htm

---

*Attractive, small country-house hotel, built by sixteenth-century
monks as a resting place for travellers.*

Approached via a long private drive, Mains Hall seems an obvious choice for a
secluded hideaway, a view that must have been shared by the Prince Regent
(later to become King George IV) as he wooed and secretly married the owner,
Maria Fitzherbert, here. Weddings are still big business at Mains Hall, with most
receptions being held in the self-contained conservatory Garden Room, while
the main rooms of the hotel are in the dazzlingly white sixteenth-century house
with a neat, well-tended garden stretching out in front. The most striking room
inside has to be the lounge hall, with elaborately carved wooden panelling
dating from 1536. Of the two dining-rooms, the smaller one has the edge in
intimacy over the more formal and elegant one next door, if romance is on your
mind; both offer the same menu for example, avocado and blue cheese pithiviers
or pork Stroganov followed by a chocolate and pear crème brûlée. The cosy bar is
the most relaxed public area and has the feel of a smart pub lounge.

The 11 bedrooms vary greatly in size and décor; Room 2 (the bridal suite) is
sunny, bright and dominated by the large four-poster bed, although its *en-suite*
shower-room is rather small. Room 1, by contrast, has a much smarter bathroom
and another impressive bed. Some rooms (such as Room 3) are more modern but
still comfortable.

◖ Open all year ⊡ From Junction 3 on M55, follow signs to Fleetwood (A585) for 5
miles (ignore signs to Singleton); hotel is ½ mile past second set of traffic lights, on right.
Private car park ⊨ 3 twin, 3 double, 1 four-poster, 3 family rooms, 1 suite; some in
annexe; all with shower/WC exc 1 twin; all with TV, room service, hair-dryer, trouser
press, direct-dial telephone ⊘ 2 dining-rooms, lounge hall, conservatory, bar,
drying-room, library, garden; functions (max 200 people incl up to 17 residential),
conferences; civil wedding licence; early suppers for children; cots, high chairs
ঌ Wheelchair access to hotel (ramp) and restaurant, 2 ground-floor bedrooms
◕ None ▭ Amex, Diners, MasterCard, Visa £ Single occupancy of twin/double
£40 to £55, twin/double £50 to £100, four-poster £100, family room £70 + £10 per child,
suite £90 + £10 per child; deposit required. Set Sun L £10; alc D £20.50

LITTLESTONE-ON-SEA Kent map 3

Romney Bay House

Coast Road, Littlestone-on-Sea, New Romney TN28 8QY
TEL: (01797) 364747   FAX: (01797) 367156

---

*Successful and welcoming house, in which both bedrooms and food
are of a very high standard.*

Jennifer and Helmut Görlich have expanded their wonderful seaside house by adding a new wing containing four bedrooms (bringing the total to 11). All the bedrooms are different. Room 8 has an *'Out of Africa'* theme, and its cane furniture, cream décor, mosquito netting and sea views give it a calm, colonial feel; its tiled bathroom has a shower cabinet and free-standing bath. Sea views and *en suite* bathrooms also come with Rooms 9 (a double with oak furniture and cream walls) and 10 (a twin, whose colour scheme of blue, white and touches of yellow gives it a Provençale atmosphere). Room 11 has a striking *bateau lit* and views of the golf course. The Görlichs have also rearranged the dining-room, splitting it up to create a small sitting area and a separate overspill into the conservatory. Cane furniture and blinds blend with a finely checked aquamarine tablecloth topped by crisp white covers in the evening. Jennifer is the cook, and by her own admission finds she is getting 'overpopular'. A typical dinner might comprise lobster tails with pasta, followed by fillet of beef with wild-mushroom sauce, and then fresh strawberries in tuile baskets. Her breakfasts are lavish: full cooked or continental, with cheese, cold meat, fruit and croissants.

◑ Closed Chr　▣ From New Romney, head for Littlestone; at sea, turn left and follow signs for hotel. Private car park　🛏 1 single, 2 twin, 6 double, 2 four-poster; 6 with bathroom/WC, 5 with shower/WC; all with TV, room service, hair-dryer　⦸ Dining-room/conservatory, bar, 2 lounges, library, garden; functions (max 80 people incl up to 21 residential), conferences; fishing, golf, tennis, croquet　&. No wheelchair access　● No children under 14; no dogs; no smoking in some public rooms or bedrooms　▭ Delta, Diners, MasterCard, Switch, Visa　[£] Single £45, single occupancy of twin/double from £50, twin/double £70 to £110, four-poster £105; deposit required. Light L £6.50 to £10.50; set D £28. Special breaks available

---

LITTLE STRETTON Shropshire map 7

Mynd House Hotel

Little Stretton, Church Stretton SY6 6RB
TEL: (01694) 722212　FAX: (01694) 724180

Modest small hotel, offering interesting food and a vast selection of wines.

Little Stretton isn't the prettiest Shropshire village (though it does boast a thatched church), and this red-brick, Edwardian house, above a fairly main road and modern housing, isn't the best placed of the county's hotels. Most rooms do, however, enjoy pleasant views across the valley, and the owners, Robert and Janet Hill, are keen to promote the surrounding area, providing details, for example, of specially devised walks, and offering breaks themed on nearby attractions. Shropshire produce and recipes feature strongly in Janet's dinners, served in a small dining-room decked out with lacy cloths – perhaps mushroom soup made with local sheep's milk, or apple pie laced with local cider brandy. Rob looks after the front of house and all things potable, including a fascinating selection of wines that runs to 200 half-bottles, with daily and weekly choices. Skip the cheapest bedrooms in the modern extension, and ask for maybe Ashbracken, with its interesting, nineteenth-century bed made for a Paris exhibition, or Hazler, a suite with a four-poster bed, conservatory sitting area and spa bath. If you're feeling sociable, you could retire to a snug sitting-room, warmed by a wood-burning stove, or the bar.

◖ Closed Jan and 2 weeks in summer   ⬕ Turn off A49 at sign for Little Stretton, 1¼ miles south of Church Stretton; hotel is in main street of village. Private car park ⬛ 2 twin, 2 double, 1 four-poster mini-suite, 1 suite; all with bathroom/WC; all with TV, room service, hair-dryer, direct-dial telephone   ⬗ dining-room, bar, 2 sitting-rooms, garden; conferences (max 15 people incl up to 6 residential); cots, high chairs, toys, baby-listening   ♿ No wheelchair access   ● No dogs in public rooms, charge for dogs in bedrooms; smoking in bar only   ⬓ Amex, Delta, MasterCard, Switch, Visa   ⬓ Single occupancy of twin/double £45 to £60, twin/double £65 to £80, suite £90 to £115; deposit required. Bar/bistro L £8; set D £28. Special breaks available

---

LITTLE WALSINGHAM Norfolk   map 6

Old Bakehouse

33 High Street, Little Walsingham, Norwich NR22 6BZ
TEL: (01328) 820454 (AND FAX)
EMAIL: chrispadley@compuserve.com

Behind this Georgian façade is a popular restaurant, friendly hosts and some comfortable rooms.

The famed shrine of Our Lady of Walsingham makes this no ordinary village, and the Old Bakehouse, just yards away in the high street, is no ordinary restaurant-with-rooms. Come holy days and holidays, the village is packed with pilgrims and sightseers, whom Helen and Chris Padley have been welcoming to their establishment with good humour and sumptuous food for some years now. The hall-like restaurant dominates, and seats considerably more people than there are hotel guests. Chris's straightforward cooking features such starters as mushrooms and bacon in a brandy and cream sauce, followed by breast of chicken stuffed with mango and served with a mild, creamy curry and almond sauce, and then Alaskan meringue cream. They have also instituted a cheaper Thursday special, after being inundated with visitors last winter following a similar, bargain offer. Breakfast is taken in the former oven room, which dates back to 1550, and a curious, stone staircase leads you downstairs to the snug, corn-cellar bar. 'We work on the assumption that guests will enjoy the same things as we do when we go on holiday,' says Helen, and she explains that that means a relaxed atmosphere and easy-going hosts. The three bedrooms are simply and freshly decorated with country quilts and pine furniture, and new carpets have been laid this year.

◖ Closed 2 to 3 weeks Jan & Feb, 1 week June, 1 week Nov; restaurant closed Mon eve   ⬕ In centre of Little Walsingham on B1105, 5 miles north of Fakenham. On-street parking (free eves); public car park nearby   ⬛ 1 twin, 2 double; 1 double with bathroom/WC, 2 with shower/WC; all with TV, hair-dryer   ⬗ Restaurant, breakfast room, bar/lounge; functions (max 40 people incl up to 6 residential); early suppers for children; high chair   ♿ No wheelchair access   ● Children discouraged from restaurant; dogs in bedrooms only, by arrangement; no smoking in restaurant, discouraged in bedrooms   ⬓ Delta, MasterCard, Switch, Visa   ⬓ Single occupancy of twin/double £28, twin/double £45; deposit required. Set Sun L, D £13.50; alc D £25

Monaughty Poeth

Llanfair Waterdine, Knighton LD7 1TT
TEL: (01547) 528348

Simple, but outstandingly hospitable, B&B on a working farm on the Welsh borders.

Wales is 100 yards from the front door of this red-brick Victorian farmhouse, and its picturesque, sheep-dotted uplands and valley floor straddle both countries. Staying here is a deeply rural experience: expect mud and corrugated out-buildings – maybe a sheepdog will be the first to greet you – and talk of how many lambs were born the previous night. Jocelyn Williams has perfected the art of being a B&B landlady, inviting new arrivals in for a cuppa with her farmer husband in their sitting-room, and phoning around local pubs to see which is open that evening for a meal. Formerly a local schoolteacher – copies of a children's book that she has written are for sale in the hall – she now serves a mammoth full English breakfast in one of the neat and welcoming front rooms. The other operates as a comfy guests' sitting-room, with farming pictures on the walls and a TV (there being none in the bedrooms). There are just two pretty, carefully maintained bedrooms. Our inspector stayed in the double at the rear of the house, which has a handsome brass bed but a mattress that has seen better days. This room has its own loo and basin, and is next door to the communal bathroom. The other is a larger twin with better views but no *en suite* facilities.

◖ Closed Dec & Jan   ⊅ Coming from Knighton along B4355, turn right opposite Knucklas village; farm is 500 yards along this road just beyond bridge. Private car park   ⊷ 1 double, 1 twin/double; family room available; 1 with WC   ⊘ Sitting-room, breakfast room, garden; fishing   ⅙ No wheelchair access   ● No children under 7   ▭ None accepted   £ Single occupancy of twin/double £23, twin/double £38, family room £48

The Angel   **NEW ENTRY**

Bicester Road, Long Crendon, Thame, Aylesbury HP18 9EE
TEL: (01844) 208268   FAX: (01844) 202497

Up-and-coming restaurant-with-rooms, specialising in fish dishes, with three stylish bedrooms.

Chalked above the bar at the Angel are the day's fish dishes, specialities of the house. The fish comes fresh from Billingsgate every day, so the 20-odd choices are constantly changing – when we inspected, on offer were crispy fried trout on a bed of roast vegetables with a chilli-butter sauce, or pan-fried fillet of monkfish served on wilted spinach with a tomato and basil cream. There are also plenty of meaty and vegetarian dishes on the regular menu, some with an oriental or Mediterranean twist. You can make your decision while sitting in one of the lovely old chesterfields set around the wood-burner in the light, stylish bar, with its stripped-wooden floor and pale beams, or in the restaurant proper, which has several sections. There's a conservatory for ultra-civilised, relaxed dining in rattan chairs amid fresh flowers, or the Old Kitchen for a more intimate meal. The whole place has been designed to make the best of the original features of the 400-year-old building; clever use of colour and light has created a low-key yet sophisticated little place. Breakfast is taken in the Small Dining-Room, all wood and flagstones, with a few of the 150 wines on offer on display, and a section of plaster removed from the wall to reveal the original laths and mud. There are only three guest bedrooms, two of which look out over the pretty garden to the rear of the house; they are spruce and bright, with lots of antiques, wonky walls, co-ordinating colours and good-quality bathrooms.

○ Open all year; restaurant closed Sun eve ⬈ On B4011 Thame to Bicester/Banbury road. Private car park ⬐ 3 double; family room available; 2 with bathroom/WC, 1 with shower/WC; all with TV, room service, hair-dryer, direct-dial telephone ⬥ Restaurant, bar/lounge, conservatory; functions (max 65 people incl up to 6 residential), conferences; early suppers for children; cots, high chairs ⬦ No wheelchair access ● No dogs; no smoking in bedrooms ⬜ Delta, MasterCard, Switch, Visa £ Single occupancy of twin/double £55, twin/double/family room £65; deposit required. Cooked B £5; bar/bistro L £3.50 to £10; alc L £17.50, D £22.50

LONGHORSLEY Northumberland

map 10

Linden Hall

Longhorsley, Morpeth NE65 8XF
TEL: (01670) 516611 FAX: (01670) 788544

Formal large-scale country hotel with golf course and health spa.

Linden Hall has passed through many hands – including a spell as a hospital in the Great War – since John Dobson, the great architect of Georgian Newcastle, designed it for local bigwig Charles William Bigge. Quite clearly, a man whose position and social milieu took in the worlds of banking, politics, literature, philosophy and science needed a house that was up to the job of impressing people, and in this respect Linden Hall is no disappointment. From the moment you pass through the Tuscan-inspired portico into the grandiose public areas, you can't dispute the masculine authority of the moulded ceilings, period fireplaces and heavily swagged curtains – a correct setting for the formal style of service the hotel favours. The current owners aim its appeal squarely at a modern clientele that is also out to impress – namely, corporate conferences, wedding receptions and private functions. Favouring the up-market traditional country-house idiom, it performs with aplomb, offering a golf course and health spa as well as the lavish Dobson restaurant (where men are expected to don jacket and tie). The bedrooms are plush and have lots of facilities and extras – as one expects at these prices. Weekend breaks and packages aimed at golfers offer keener prices.

○ Open all year ⬈ On A697, 1 mile north of Longhorsley. Private car park ⬐ 2 single, 15 twin, 25 double, 5 four-poster, 3 suites; family rooms available all with bathroom/WC exc 1 double with shower/WC; all with TV, room service, hair-dryer, trouser press, direct-dial telephone ⬥ 2 restaurants, 2 bars, lounge, library, 2 conservatories, games room, garden; functions (max 200 people incl up to 98 residential), conferences; civil wedding licence; golf, gym, sauna, solarium, indoor heated swimming-pool, tennis, putting green, snooker, pitch & putt, clay-pigeon shooting, croquet; leisure facilities nearby (free to guests); early suppers for children; cots, high chair, babysitting, baby-listening   ♿ Wheelchair access to hotel (ramp) and restaurant, 16 ground-floor bedrooms, 1 specially equipped for disabled people ● Dogs in two bedrooms only; no smoking in public rooms; smoking in bedrooms if requested on booking   ▭ Amex, Delta, Diners, MasterCard, Switch, Visa   £ Single £98, twin/double £125, four-poster £185, family room (rates on application), suite £195; deposit required. Set L £17, D £26.50. Special breaks available

---

LONG MELFORD Suffolk   map 6

Black Lion/Countrymen Restaurant

The Green, Long Melford, Sudbury CO10 9DN
TEL: (01787) 312356   FAX: (01787) 374557

A traditional-looking seventeenth-century inn, in a great location, with a style all of its own.

It might not be noticeable at first, but this is a house full of small collections of objects. The first clue is the hat-stand in the entrance hall, with a different type of hat on every peg; further inside, you are confronted by a cabinet of ornaments containing such things as teddy bears and other furry animals. It's the craze for quirky collecting that adds a lot of charm to the surroundings. Janet and Stephen Errington have given over a lot of space to the celebration of food in their bistro and formal restaurant. The bistro is in an attractive corner room, with windows looking out to the green and across at Melford Hall; one wall is covered with prints and posters about wine, while some carved wooden jazzmen do their thing over on the other side. Through a doorway is the informal bar, with amusing sporting prints and a row of toby jugs. The restaurant looks less inviting in comparison, as it is tucked away at the back of the house. Meanwhile, not an inch of space appears untouched in the lounge, with plates and yet more plates on the walls. The bedrooms are all very attractive, with plenty of antique furnishings and beds, and no shortage of space in most.

◑ Closed Jan; restaurant & bistro closed Sun & Mon eves   ⊿ On village green, 2 miles north of Sudbury on A134. On-street parking (free)   ⊨ 2 twin, 3 double, 2 four-poster, 1 family room, 1 suite; all with bathroom/WC; all with TV, hair-dryer, direct-dial telephone   ⊘ Restaurant, bistro, bar, lounge, garden; functions (max 9 people residential), conferences; early suppers for children; cots, high chairs, toys, baby-listening   ♿ No wheelchair access   ● No dogs in public rooms; no smoking in some public rooms   ▭ Amex, Delta, MasterCard, Switch, Visa   £ Single occupancy of twin/double £50 to £60, twin/double £70 to £80, four-poster £80, family room £90, suite £105; deposit required. Bar/bistro L, D £10; set D £21; alc L £16.50, D £21. Special breaks available

---

If you have a small appetite, or just aren't feeling hungry, check if you can be given a reduction if you don't want the full menu. At some hotels you could easily end up paying £30 for one course and a coffee.

New House Farm

Lorton, Cockermouth CA13 9UU
TEL: (01900) 85404 (AND FAX)

*High-quality farmhouse accommodation in picturesque location
with excellent cooking and a seasonal tea-shop business.*

A classic whitewashed farmhouse and substantial outbuildings dating from the
seventeenth century offer Hazel Hatch plenty of scope for her thriving guest-
house-cum-tea-shop. The house is instantly welcoming in bright country styles,
and the structure and original features are exposed in stripped pine, stone
fireplaces, flagged floors and dark beams. You can see the effort involved in
renovation from the 'progress report' photos on the walls. There are two small
sitting-rooms downstairs, both cosy in warm, sunny colours and furnished with
antiques. Dried hops and vases of fresh flowers deck the rooms, plus rugs,
polished stones, interesting pictures and copper ornaments – just enough to
make the house seem personal and lived in without being irrelevantly cluttered.
There are just three bedrooms, each named after the view it surveys and
decorated with the same panache as the rest of the house. Mouthwatering
five-course dinners incorporate local produce, and, as if that weren't enough,
Hazel opens a day-time café/tea-shop in the harness-decked stone cowshed (The
Barn) during the summer. Fifteen acres of fields, ponds and woods surround the
farm, which guests are welcome to explore.

○ Open all year ⚡ On B5289 between Lorton and Loweswater, 6 miles south of
Cockermouth. Private car park 🛏 2 twin/double, 1 double; 1 in annexe; all with
bathroom/WC exc double with shower/WC; all with hair-dryer ⌁ Dining-room, 2
sitting-rooms, drying-room, garden ⚬ No wheelchair access ⬤ No children under
10; no dogs in public rooms; no smoking ▭ None accepted £ Single occupancy of
twin/double £35 to £45, twin/double £65 to £70; deposit required. Set D £20

Winder Hall NEW ENTRY

Low Lorton, Cockermouth CA13 9UP
TEL: (01900) 85107

*Tastefully renovated, historic manor house, with many intact period
features and a quiet, riverside setting.*

Parts of this Grade II-listed building date back a very long time, though most of
the interior is late-nineteenth-century in style. Mary and Derek Denman are
rapidly upgrading their recently established B&B business here, and it is now a
place of considerable style. The six guest rooms overlook serene views of the
Lorton Vale and the River Cocker, which burbles past the house. Original
features, such as stone mullions, leaded lights and oak panelling, create talking
points, and there are several imposing fireplaces. The master bedroom (did
Charles II sleep here?) has a Tudor-looking, oak four-poster. Maps and walking
guides drum up your enthusiasm for exploring some of the lovely countryside of
the northern and western Lake District, which is less crowded and tourist-

trampled than that of the eastern Lakes. The Denmans are planning to offer further facilities, including dinners and a second four-poster room, in 1999; in the meantime, you can get a decent meal at the Wheatsheaf Inn, close by in the village. Breakfasts at Winder Hall, however, are no mean affairs, with smoked fish, hams, cheeses and home-made preserves on the menu. Packed lunches and hot drinks are available on request.

◖ Closed Chr & Jan ⚡ From Keswick, take A66 west to Braithwaite, then B5292 Whinlatter Pass to Lorton; at T-junction, turn left to Low Lorton. Private car park ⌂ 1 twin, 3 double, 1 four-poster; family rooms available; some with bathroom/WC, some with shower/WC; all with TV, hair-dryer, clock radio ⚗ Dining-room, lounge, garden ♿ No wheelchair access ● No children under 8; no children under 12 in dining-room eves; no dogs; no smoking ▭ Delta, MasterCard, Switch, Visa ⚞£⚟ Single occupancy of twin/double £35, twin/double £60, four-poster £70, family room £75; deposit required. Set D £16. Special breaks available

---

LOWER BEEDING West Sussex   map 3

South Lodge

Brighton Road, Lower Beeding, Horsham RH13 6PS
TEL: (01403) 891711   FAX: (01403) 891766
EMAIL: inquiries@southlodgehotel.dial.iql.co.uk
WEB SITE: www.southlodgehotel.co.uk

Grand Victorian house, with friendly staff and lovely grounds.

On a fine spring day, you will see the grounds at their best – 93 acres filled with rhododendrons by the first owner, Frederick Duncane Godman, a noted explorer and botanist. He had this grand pile built as a family house, and the heavy Victorian style inside is today nicely offset by the friendly and helpful staff. The public areas are grand and wood-panelled, with massive display cases and plenty of comfortable seating. The Camellia Restaurant is named after a 100-year-old camellia growing on an old Tudor wall that was incorporated into the 'new' building. Guests can try the signature menu – five courses, perhaps featuring carpaccio of beef with rocket salad, confit of duck with vanilla and cherries, and a raspberry and lemon-curd roulade topped with raspberry sorbet – as well as an expensive à la carte menu. The bedrooms are grand and of a good size, perhaps featuring chandeliers, oil paintings and heavy old furniture that matches the house. There are some nice touches, like a tin of home-baked biscuits by the bed and a cuddly cat to put outside if you don't want to be disturbed. The bathrooms tend towards the luxurious, with large white towels and bathrobes, and glass decanters of smellies. Some bathrooms have wonderfully aggressive showers and rain bars to give you a total pounding.

◖ Open all year ⚡ On A281 at Lower Beeding, just south of Horsham. Private car park ⌂ 1 single, 14 twin/double, 20 double, 2 four-poster, 3 suites, 1 four-poster suite; all with bathroom/WC; all with TV, room service, hair-dryer, direct-dial telephone; no tea/coffee-making facilities in rooms ⚗ Restaurant, bar, lounge, games room, garden; functions (max 80 people incl up to 77 residential), conferences; civil wedding licence; tennis, putting green, snooker, clay-pigeon shooting, boules, croquet; early suppers for children; cots, high chairs, toys, babysitting, baby-listening

 ♿ Wheelchair access to hotel (ramp) and restaurant, WC (unisex), 9 ground-floor bedrooms, 1 room specially equipped for disabled people ◑ No children under 9 in restaurant eves; no dogs; no smoking in restaurant 📳 Amex, Delta, Diners, MasterCard, Switch, Visa £ Single £140, twin/double £165 to £205, suite £285 to £315; deposit required. Continental B £10.50, cooked B £13; set L £18.50, D £37; alc D £50 to £65. Special breaks available

---

LOWER SLAUGHTER Gloucestershire   map 5

Lower Slaughter Manor

Lower Slaughter, Cheltenham GL54 2HP
TEL: (01451) 820456   FAX: (01451) 822150
EMAIL: lowsmanor@aol.com

A fairly formal ambience pervades this extremely plush country-house hotel.

Slaughter means 'muddy place' in Anglo-Saxon – an entirely inappropriate description, both of the heavenly, though heavily visited, little village, and of this seventeenth-century listed manor. Under the same ownership as Buckland Manor in Buckland (see entry), it is shielded from day-trippers picnicking in deck chairs beside the village stream by soaring trees and a lawn mowed in picturesque stripes, and it overlooks a seductive, walled back garden, too. The smartly attired staff – many of whom are French – fuss over guests in the refined, elegant and carefully designed rooms, the most memorable being the two dining-rooms, on account of their ornate plaster ceilings. The bedrooms justify their high price tags by their size (the coach-house rooms are especially capacious), swanky bathrooms and copious 'extras' (sherry, fruit, biscuits, towelling robes, etc.). The manor has built a high reputation for its cuisine, but the chef has changed in the last year. However, the format – namely a very pricey table d'hôte dinner menu – has remained the same, as has the culinary ambition evident in such dishes as breast of duck with braised figs in a passion-fruit *jus*.

◑ Open all year 🗺 Situated off A429 towards 'The Slaughters'; hotel is on right of lane approaching village centre. Private car park 🛏 10 double, 2 four-poster, 3 suites; some in annexe; all with bathroom/WC; all with TV, room service, hair-dryer, trouser press, direct-dial telephone; no tea/coffee-making facilities in rooms ⚙ 2 dining-rooms, 3 lounges, library, garden; conferences (max 40 people incl up to 15 residential); heated indoor swimming-pool, tennis; leisure facilities nearby (free for guests) ♿ No wheelchair access ◑ No children under 12; no dogs 📳 Amex, Delta, Diners, MasterCard, Switch, Visa £ Single occupancy of double £135 to £300, double £150 to £215, four-poster £300, suite £300 to £350; deposit required. Set L £25, D £45; alc L £20, D £55. Special breaks available

---

It is always worth enquiring about the availability of special breaks or weekend prices. The prices we quote are the standard rates for one night – most hotels offer reduced rates for longer stays.

Ivy House Farm

Ivy Lane, Oulton Broad, Lowestoft NR33 8HY
TEL: (01502) 501353   FAX: (01502) 501539

A smart farm conversion on the Broads, which is now established as a restaurant-with-rooms.

While the Norfolk Broads might get a trifle busy during the summer, one can see what the owners Caroline Sterry and Paul Coe mean when they describe their farm as 'a hidden oasis'. Once you are on the property there are 40 acres of marshland and meadows, dotted with ponds, where their flock of rare-breed sheep graze amid a genuine air of tranquillity. For the past couple of years, since they expanded their operation, the Crooked Barn restaurant has been the focus of attention. As the name suggests, this is a cavernous building with exposed timbers that makes a pleasant place to dine and look out through large windows to a pebble and water garden in the courtyard. The cooking is described as 'new world', and the menu descriptions go into exhaustive detail. For instance, you could start with king scallops marinated in garlic and herbs flash-fried with home-made spaghetti Nero surrounded with fresh parsley and garlic pesto, followed by rare fillet of Scottish beef served on a crostini topped with roasted ratatouille and a red-pepper sauce. Guests staying the night can relax in a bright, modern-looking conservatory with cane chairs and sofas and a blue-and-white stone-tiled floor. There are bedrooms in the original farmhouse or in the newer Court Yard conversion. The choice here is between the polished, brighter look of the latter and the comfortable familiarity of the former.

◑ Open all year   ⬛ From A146 (Norwich to Lowestoft road), turn into Ivy Lane (beside Esso petrol station) and drive over small railway bridge. Private car park ⬛ 3 twin, 8 double, 1 family room; some in annexe; all with bathroom/WC exc 2 with shower/WC; all with TV, room service, hair-dryer, direct-dial telephone, some with trouser press ⬥ Restaurant, 2 lounges (bar service), conservatory, garden; functions (max 70 people incl up to to 24 residential), conferences; early suppers for children, by arrangement; cots, high chairs ⬥ Wheelchair access to hotel and restaurant, WC (unisex), 11 ground-floor bedrooms, 2 specially equipped for disabled people ⬤ No smoking in bedrooms ⬜ Amex, Delta, Diners, MasterCard, Switch, Visa £ Single occupancy of twin/double £65, twin/double £89, family room £94; deposit required. Bistro L £8.50; set L £18, D £20; alc D £30. Special breaks available

Loxley Farm

Loxley, Warwick CV35 9JN
TEL: (01789) 840265 (AND FAX)

Friendly B&B in a converted barn less than four miles from Stratford.

In a pretty village, Loxley Farm stands out as prettier than all the rest: a fourteenth-century cruck cottage, bedroom windows snuggled in the thatch, and an old-fashioned country garden all around. When our inspector arrived, Mrs Horton was cooking a pie on the range, and the delicious smell had brought the cat to the door. Breakfast is the only chance to step inside and absorb something of the wonderful atmosphere in the main house, with its oriental rugs on stone-flag floors and low, crooked beams. The guest rooms are actually a few yards up the garden in the 'shieling', a converted seventeenth-century thatched barn. These are less characterful than the cottage but very pleasant: the Garden suite has a fine little conservatory extension overlooking the cottage and garden, while the Hayloft suite has a small kitchen and sitting-room. Both are neatly decorated with white walls and exposed timbers – flowers from the garden giving a homely touch. The bathrooms have a corner bath and shower.

◑ Closed Chr & New Year ⇗ Turn off A422 at sign for Loxley; go through village and turn left at bottom of hill; Loxley Farm is third on right. Private car park ⇌ 2 suites, both in annexe; both with bathroom/WC; both with TV, hair-dryer ✓ Garden; croquet, lawn badminton, clock golf; cot ⅚ No wheelchair access ▭ None accepted ⓔ Suite £60; deposit required

---

LYDFORD Devon

map 1

Castle Inn

Lydford, Okehampton EX20 4BH
TEL: (01822) 820242   FAX: (01822) 820454
EMAIL: castle1lyd@aol.com

Wecoming pink hostelry in charming Devon village.

The Castle Inn is one of those village pubs you can rely on to provide good food, a warm welcome and a comfortable bed. Set in the pretty village of Lydford, which itself nestles in the soft Devon countryside, the Castle is painted an inviting pale pink, and has a useful garden for sunny days, and plenty of interesting-looking paths setting off through the fields behind. Inside, the cosy olde-worlde style is set off by heavy furniture, a snug with two huge old settles, open fires, and some idiosyncratic touches – a crazy mirror in the entrance, and a plaque saying 'Fred called time in 1991' on the bar. You can eat in the beamed and chintzy dining-room, or in the bar, where our inspector pronounced her leek, red-pepper and almond tart 'not bad at all'. An extension has recently been completed, housing a cosy new (but antique-filled) lounge area and new bedrooms, all of which are very smartly done out in bold colours, with good bathrooms.

◑ Open all year ⇗ Next to Lydford castle and opposite public car park. Private car park ⇌ 1 single, 4 double, 1 four-poster, 2 family rooms, 1 suite; most with bathroom/WC, 3 with shower/WC; all with TV, room service, direct-dial telephone; some with hair-dryer ✓ Dining-room, bar, lounge, drying-room, garden; functions (max 250 people incl up to 17 residential), conferences; early suppers for children; cots, high chairs ⅚ Wheelchair access to hotel and restaurant, WC (M, F), 1 ground-floor bedroom ● Dogs in some bedrooms only; no smoking in some public rooms and some bedrooms ▭ Amex, Delta, Diners, MasterCard, Switch, Visa ⓔ Single £35, single occupancy of double £42 to £63, double £62 to £85, four-poster £68, family room £82 to £91, suite £85; deposit required. Bar/bistro L, D £6.50; set L, D £16; alc L, D £23. Special breaks available

---

LYME REGIS Dorset　　　　　　　　　　　　　　　　　　　　　map 2

Hotel Alexandra

Pound Street, Lyme Regis DT7 3HZ
TEL: (01297) 442010　FAX: (01297) 443229

Mixed reports on the food at this comfortingly traditional resort hotel.

Lazy lunch-timers or takers of afternoon tea on the great sward of lawn that slopes towards the cliffs at Lyme Regis's Hotel Alexandra may feel that they've wandered into the pages of a Mary Wesley novel. Dapper gents in blazers and panama hats pour tea for their elegantly coiffed spouses, while parents in sunglasses, with sweaters draped across their shoulders, smile indulgently at their offspring, who wheel and dive down the banks, arms outstretched and making aeroplane noises. The generations snuggle easily into the Hotel Alexandra, like feet into a comfy pair of old slippers.

The hotel starts with certain natural advantages: the position – up the hill from the town – and its large garden overlooking Lyme Bay could hardly be bettered. There's even some off-street parking, though you may be glad to take up the offer of the experienced staff to shoehorn your car into the limited available car-park space. The building, parts of which date back to 1735, has enough traditional character to set it apart from most seaside hotels. The public rooms are liberally peppered with interesting artifacts, from the photos of old Lyme that line the bar to the model sailing ships and display cases of ceramics and old bottles that you'll find in the sitting-room and reception area. The flat-roofed conservatory, popular for lunches and children's teas, is rather better to look out from than to gaze upon, but the dining-room, pretty in pastel Regency stripes, is an elegant affair. The subject of food sharply divides our correspondents, with one reporter opining that dinners were 'very poor (far too many things on offer)'; others will brook no criticism, leaping to the kitchen's defence and asserting that 'dinner, especially, is something to look forward to'. What's beyond doubt is that there's a very traditional air to the menu, with such offerings as cream of mushroom soup with sherry, and beef Wellington with a Madeira glaze, setting the tone.

The bedrooms in the main house, attractively furnished and decorated in surprisingly bold modern colours, are more inviting than the less characterful rooms in the extension. Guests generally pronounced themselves well satisfied, though one lamented 'a bathroom reminiscent of the 1940s'. Most, however, concurred with the view of one correspondent, who concluded: 'The standard and the warm welcome remain constant and that today is something to be treasured.'

◐ Closed Jan　◪ Head up main street of town (Broad Street) away from the sea; take left fork (by cinema) into Pound Street. Private car park　⌐┛ 2 single, 6 twin, 19 double; some in annexe; family rooms available; all with bathroom/WC exc 1 single with shower/WC; all with TV, room service, hair-dryer, direct-dial telephone　⊘ Dining-room, bar, sitting-room, conservatory, garden; functions (max 80 people incl up to 52 residential); early suppers for children; cots, high chairs, baby-listening &. No wheelchair access ● No young children in dining-room eves; dogs in bedrooms only, by arrangement (£3 per night); no smoking in dining-room and some bedrooms ☐ Amex, Diners, MasterCard, Switch, Visa £ Single £40 to £50, single occupancy of twin/double £60 to £70, twin/double £90 to £110, family room £110 to £125; deposit required. Bar/bistro L, D £5; set L £12.50, D £22.50. Special breaks available

---

LYMINGTON Hampshire

map 2

Gordleton Mill

Silver Street, Hordle, Lymington SO41 6DJ
TEL: (01590) 682219 FAX: (01590) 683073

An idyllic slice of Provence in the heart of Hampshire.

Seen from the road, the creeper-covered seventeenth-century façade of Gordleton Mill looks attractive enough, but this is one of those rare places where the approach from the back is even better. After parking in the generous-sized car park, you walk over a little bridge, past ducks dabbling in a stream jumping with fish and fringed with reeds and rhododendrons, to the terrace of the restaurant. On a sunny Sunday, it was hard to imagine a more idyllic spot for an inspection lunch. The arrival of Stephen Smith to replace Toby Hill has not dimmed the Provençale influences – indeed, a starter of chilled tomato consommé with broad beans and basil was the essence of southern France in a spoonful. Slices of perfectly cooked sea bream, interleaved with paper-thin layers of deep-fried aubergine and slivers of sweet tomato surrounded by gazpacho sauce, was sensational summer eating. The puddings were less deft, but the service (mostly French) was young, charming and relaxed. One correspondent, however, had a 'singularly tasteless meal'. In the evening, or in less clement weather, the restaurant itself maintains the southern feel with its tiled floor, white-painted beams, and a rustic fireplace displaying bottled fruit. Smokers have their own, light-panelled lounge, which has cheery wallpaper, and several of the nine bedrooms allow smoking. A non-smoking guest who complained that their room smelt of stale tobacco smoke had the bill halved and the bed linen completely changed while they were at dinner, which solved the problem. In general, the bedrooms have received the same attention to detail and quality of furnishings as the rest of the hotel, and a half-bottle of champagne is included in the room rate. Avon Water, with a small balcony overlooking the millstream, is the favourite with guests.

◑ Closed 1 to 17 Nov; restaurant closed Sun & Mon eves ⚡ Approaching Lymington from the north on A337, pass under railway bridge, go straight across at mini-roundabout and take first turning on right into Sway Road, which becomes Silver Street; hotel is 1½ miles on right. Private car park ⊨ 4 twin/double, 3 double, 2 suites; all with bathroom/WC; all with TV, hair-dryer, direct-dial telephone ⌘ Restaurant, bar, 2 lounges, garden; functions (max 45 people incl up to 12 residential); fishing &. No wheelchair access ● No children under 7; no dogs in public rooms; smoking in

1 lounge and some bedrooms only ⬜ Amex, Delta, Diners, MasterCard, Switch, Visa £ Single occupancy of twin/double £97, twin/double £137, suite £219; deposit required. Set L £16.50 to £20; alc D £35. Special breaks available

Stanwell House

13–15 High Street, Lymington SO41 9AA
TEL: (01590) 677123   FAX: (01590) 677756

Georgian hotel undergoing splendidly modernist revamp, though occasionally style wins out over service.

First impressions are important, and, as soon as you pass beyond the hotel's Georgian frontage on Lymington's busy High Street, you know that this is somewhere different. Modern metalwork stair rails and mirror frames, strong, jewel-like colour schemes of deep gold, imperial purple and fuchsia pink, plus velvet cushions and drapes aplenty, provide visual sustenance for seekers of style and comfort alike. The main seating area is the flagstoned conservatory, decorated in a restful combination of cane furniture, squashy banquettes and pot-plants, with a pretty garden tucked away beyond it. The atmospheric restaurant, which has dark, unvarnished floorboards, is divided by drapes of slubbed silk in orange and pink; there's also a less formal bistro/bar, where more colourful walls form a backdrop to an eclectic mix of wooden Georgian tables, purple stools and a metal-topped bar. Our inspector was disappointed, then, to be shown to a small double room with faded pink-sprigged wallpaper, whose bland contract furniture looked a little worse for wear. If it's a four-poster voluptuously swathed in red velvet that you fancy, be sure to specify a refurbished room when you book. The young Anglo-French service was charming, but rather hit and miss: a request to the reception for a hair-dryer, which should have been in the room, elicited a promise to bring one up, but it never appeared, while at breakfast our eggs Benedict took an age to arrive (and were hard and lukewarm when they did so). Dinner, too, lacked consistency of standards: the home-cured gravad lax had little flavour; the calf's liver was nicely cooked but under-seasoned; while the chargrilled chicken appeared without skin or any other evidence of char, let alone grill, though its accompanying savoury bread-and-butter pudding with tapénade was splendid.

◑ Open all year　🅿 In centre of Lymington. On-street parking (free)　🛏 2 single, 8 twin, 13 double, 3 four-poster, 2 suites; most with bathroom/WC, some with shower/WC; all with TV, room service, hair-dryer, trouser press, direct-dial telephone, some with mini-bar　🍴 2 restaurants, bar, conservatory/lounge, garden; functions (max 80 people incl up to 54 residential), conferences; civil wedding licence; sailing; early suppers for children; cots, high chairs, baby-sitting, baby-listening　⅙ No wheelchair access　◖ No smoking in 1 restaurant and some bedrooms ⬜ Amex, Delta, Diners, MasterCard, Switch, Visa £ Single £50, single occupancy of twin/double £75, twin/double £95, four-poster £110, suite £130; deposit required. Bar/bistro L, D £4.50; set L £5, D £20; alc L, D £25. Special breaks available

See page 6 for a brief explanation of how to use the Guide.

Parkhill Hotel

Beaulieu Road, Lyndhurst SO43 7FZ
TEL: (01703) 282944   FAX: (01703) 283268

Unstuffy, homely country-house hotel with a fruity past and a rosy future.

The New Forest is more renowned for its heathland and gorse bushes than its pineapples, but, believe it or not, these spiny fruit used to grow here at Parkhill. How successfully is a different matter, but their presence remains: look out for the stone fruit on top of the gables and outside the front door. Even the key rings are brass pineapples. Apart from being the home of the man who introduced *Ananas comosus* to England, Parkhill has had other past lives as a hunting lodge and a boys' school. Since becoming a hotel, it has had its fair share of illustrious guests, including General Eisenhower, T S Eliot and the Duke of Clarence. Present-day guests can enjoy the sweeping views from their comfy sofa beside the lounge's log fire, or while enjoying an appetising meal in the conservatory extension to the restaurant. Stilton, cream cheese and port parfait wrapped in spinach might be followed by a seafood medley on a fricassee of baby vegetables and rounded off with tarte Tatin. One disappointed reader didn't appreciate the pricey menu and the 'sporadic' service he encountered (put down to a wedding reception going on during his stay). On the accommodation front, the best or 'feature' rooms have great views and more space, particularly the double-aspect Room 1. Across the drive is a dinky mini-suite in the converted stable block, perfect for added privacy.

◗ Open all year 🔁 From Lyndhurst take B3056 to Beaulieu; Parkhill is about 1 mile further on, on right. Private car park 🛏 5 twin, 9 double, 2 four-poster, 3 suites; some in annexe; all with bathroom/WC; all with TV, room service, hair-dryer, trouser press, direct-dial telephone, some with fridge ⌀ 1 restaurant, conservatory, bar, lounge, library, garden; functions (max 120 people incl up to 40 residential), conferences; civil wedding licence; fishing, heated outdoor swimming-pool, putting green, clay-pigeon shooting, croquet; early suppers for children; cots, high chairs, babysitting, baby-listening ♿ No wheelchair access ● No dogs in public rooms and some bedrooms; no smoking in some public rooms or some bedrooms
▭ Amex, Delta, Diners, MasterCard, Switch, Visa £ Single occupancy of twin/double £99 to £115, twin/double £110 to £126, four-poster £124 to £136, suite £140 to £156 (prices valid till Jan 1999); deposit required. Bar/bistro L £5; set L £16, D £27; alc L £17, D £35. Special breaks available

---

Fenwicks   NEW ENTRY

Lower Goatacre, Lyneham, Calne SN11 9HY
TEL: (01249) 760645 (AND FAX)

Spruce guesthouse run with great attention to detail by energetic, jolly owners.

Running a busy guesthouse wouldn't be most people's idea of downshifting, but Margaret Fenwick and her husband decided to do just that after Fen's early retirement. Their large, secluded, fairly modern, almost ranch-like house stands in a wonderful garden, complete with tinkling fountain and attractive terrace that fans out into extensive meadowland where junior guests can happily run wild. The guests' sitting-cum-dining area is a bright, airy space with soothing pastel décor enlivened by fascinating prints of costumes from a 1919 Bolshoi production. These and a Chinese screen, plus a host of personal knick-knacks, add interest to a room where the large dining table is the central focus. The couple also let non-dining guests have the run of their personal sitting-room while dining residents are eating in the lounge. Dinner might be wild-mushroom soup, followed by chicken stuffed with mango and banana and wrapped in smoked bacon, followed by sticky toffee pudding and cheese. Guests are also welcome to browse along the well-stocked bookshelves of a small study. The bedrooms are neat and shiny as a new pin, cheerfully decorated, and feature pine or reproduction furniture, plus cosseting extras such as fresh flowers and fruit, electric blankets in winter, and a choice of hard or soft pillows.

◑ Open all year ⊿ From Lyneham take A3102 towards Calne; after 1 mile turn left at bus shelter down Goatacre Lane; bear right at Harts Close and fork right at bottom of hill. Private car park ⤷ 1 single, 1 twin, 1 double; family rooms available; double with bathroom/WC, 2 with shower/WC; all with TV, room service, hair-dryer, direct-dial telephone ⌽ Dining-room/lounge, bar, drying-room, garden ᨠ No wheelchair access ● No children under 9; no dogs; no smoking ▭ Amex ⌸ Single £28, single occupancy of twin/double £35, twin/double £45, family room £52; deposit required. Set D £13.50 (by arrangement)

LYNMOUTH Devon   map 1

Rising Sun Hotel

Harbourside, Lynmouth EX35 6EQ
TEL: (01598) 753223   FAX: (01598) 753480
EMAIL: risingsunlynmouth@easynet.co.uk
WEB SITE: www.castlelink.co.uk/gratton/rsun.htm

Picture-postcard inn, bang on the harbour, with some newly refurbished designer bedrooms and a confident restaurant.

The Rising Sun is the kind of place to which people want to retire, so perfect is its position on the harbourside of Lynmouth, with views of the inspiring Exmoor coastline, and so cute is its thatched roof and terraced garden. Benches surrounded with flowers outside the low-beamed public bar provide the ultimate viewing spot for all that happens in the harbour, and the pub is usually crowded with locals, as well as visitors. The inn is, in fact, four fishing cottages tumbling down a little path; one is thatched, the rest tiled, but all of them were, apparently, used for smuggling. Up the path is the annexe, housing more bedrooms, and at the top is the irresistible (but expensive) Shelley's Cottage, where the romantic poet honeymooned with his 16-year-old bride, Harriet. You too can sleep in the four-poster here, under the thatched roof, with roses twining around the door. Back in the main part of the inn is the cosy, panelled restaurant, where a small but imaginative menu offers such dishes as pan-fried scallops on a bed of spinach and salad leaves drizzled with lobster oil, followed by roasted cannon of lamb coated with sesame seeds, with bubble and squeak and a carrot and thyme *jus*. The peaceful guests' lounge has a little viewing verandah, so you don't have to wrestle with the hordes in high season. If Shelley's Cottage is beyond you, stay in the recently refurbished rooms in the main house – they may be small, but they are extremely plush; those in the annexe seem drab by comparison.

◖ Open all year ⊠ Next to harbour in Lynmouth. On-street parking (restricted in summer); public car park nearby (£2 per day) ⊨ 2 single, 5 double, 8 four-poster, 1 suite; some in annexe; some with bathroom/WC, some with shower/WC; all with TV, room service, direct-dial telephone, some with hair-dryer ⌀ Restaurant, bar, lounge, drying-room, garden; fishing; leisure facilities nearby (reduced rates for guests) ♿ No wheelchair access ● No children under 7 exc by arrangement; dogs in bar only; no smoking in bedrooms ▭ Amex, Delta, Diners, MasterCard, Switch, Visa £ Single £55, single occupancy of double £70, double £99, four-poster £120, suite £140; deposit required. Bar/bistro L £8; set L £16.50, D £27.50; alc L, D £33. Special breaks available

---

LYNTON Devon   map 1

Highcliffe House

Sinai Hill, Lynton EX35 6AR
TEL: (01598) 752235 (AND FAX)

High-class high Victoriana set high on a hill overlooking the Bristol Channel.

Highcliffe House was built in the 1870s, billed a 'gentleman's summer residence', and owner John Bishop continues the theme, making the most of his expertise as an antique-dealer in classic Victoriana. Crossing the threshold is like stepping back in time to the days of heavy colours and curtains, warming-pans and crystal chandeliers. This is a house filled to the brim with period furniture, bric-a-brac, candelabra and collections of crystal and plates. Dark floral wallpaper contrasts strongly with a red carpet, and the windows have heavy drapes, pelmets *and* ruched curtains. In the lounge the lovely window seat is decorated with plush cushions and lace, and on a clear day you can see Wales across the Bristol Channel far below. John has 'a passion for clocks', so there are plenty in evidence, ticking away merrily in their discordant rhythms. According to the brochure, the 'cuisine embodies the best of Victorian values', but the menu is not remotely strait-laced and includes treats such as marinated herring fillets with a warm potato and dill salad in a crème fraîche dressing, followed by gallette of Barbary duck breast on a bed of braised lentils in a juniperberry *jus*. The bedrooms are the *pièce de résistance*, flamboyantly furnished with huge antique beds and rich colours. All have sea views, and lots of those satisfying little extras, such as complimentary sherry and bottles of spring water.

◑ Closed Dec & Jan; restaurant closed Sun eve   ⓩ Take A39 westwards through Lynmouth; at top of hill fork right; turn left at public car park; go up Sinai Hill; hotel is on left. Private car park   ⬅ 1 twin, 4 double, 1 four-poster; all with bathroom/WC; all with TV, room service, hair-dryer   ⊘ Dining-room, 2 lounges, conservatory, garden; � No wheelchair access   ⊖ No children; no dogs; no smoking   ▭ Amex, Delta, MasterCard, Switch, Visa   £ Single occupancy of twin/double £53, twin/double/four-poster £84; deposit required. Set D £25

Valley House

Lynbridge Road, Lynton EX35 6BD
TEL: (01598) 752285

Endearingly old-fashioned Victorian home on steep hill, run by hospitable hosts.

Lynton is in the part of north Devon known as the little Switzerland of England, famous for its steep valleys, hairpin bends and temperate climate. Inspired by the location, the builders of Valley House (ingenious Victorian folk) decided to follow the style of colonial Himalayan hill stations. As a result, the corridors and landings in the house are at the back, giving every room a superb view down the wooded hill – from some you can see down the cleft of the valley to the sea. The garden, too, is worthy of a more mountainous region, tumbling as it does down the steep valley-side, with shrubs and trees clinging on for dear life. Inside, Russell and Joan Herbert's house is not remotely fancy or flamboyant, just plain traditional (some might say old-fashioned), with the character of the house in evidence everywhere, from the beautiful doors to the original wooden windows. Plants, twists of dried flowers and family knick-knacks add homely touches to the small bar, and squashy velour sofas provide comfortable places to relax in the lounge. There are plenty of books and games, as well as a piano, for indoor entertainment. Menus, too, follow a conventional mode, but Russell and Joan will discuss preferences with guests beforehand – a typical meal might be avocado with smoked salmon and prawns, followed by fillet of beef en croûte, finishing off with a gin and tonic sorbet. The bedrooms are done out in calm beiges, creams and pinks; some of the *en suite* shower-rooms are rather cramped. The best have large balconies to take full advantage of the house's position.

◑ Closed Nov to Jan   ⓩ On B3234 Lynmouth to Barnstaple road, at top of Lynton Hill. Private car park   ⬅ 1 twin, 5 double; family rooms available; all with shower/WC exc 2 doubles with bathroom/WC; all with TV; hair-dryer on request   ⊘ Dining-room, bar, lounge, conservatory, garden   ⓕigure No wheelchair access   ⊖ No children under 12; no smoking; small dogs only, by prior arrangement   ▭ Amex, Delta, MasterCard, Switch, Visa   £ Single occupancy of twin/double £22 to £26, twin/double £44 to £52, family room £55 to £65; deposit required. Alc D £16. Special breaks available

---

Prices are what you can expect to pay in 1999, except where specified to the contrary. Many hoteliers tell us that these prices can be regarded only as approximations.

MALMESBURY Wiltshire map 2

Old Bell

Abbey Row, Malmesbury SN16 0AG
TEL: (01666) 822344   FAX: (01666) 825145

*Bags of character and an enlightened attitude to children at a lovely
thirteenth-century inn.*

The honey-stoned, creeper-clad building that now houses the Old Bell was
originally built as a guesthouse for the Abbey. Almost 800 years later, it finds
itself still dispensing hospitality, this time most notably to children and their
world-weary parents, who come to enjoy the liberal and sympathetic regime.
The child-friendly policy is the brainchild of co-owner Nigel Chapman, the
éminence grise behind Woolley Grange in Bradford-on-Avon (see entry) and
Moonfleet Manor in Weymouth (see Round-up section). In addition to the usual
family-hotel accoutrements of baby-listening and junior meal sittings, this
manifests itself in the lively, toy-laden playroom, where parents can entrust
their offspring to the care of trained nannies. Parents thus have the chance to
explore the fine, and distinctly grown-up, public rooms, including the smart bar
and a brace of comfortable lounges. The main restaurant runs the depth of the
hotel and affects a certain Edwardian grandeur with its sparkling chandeliers,
carved, high-backed chairs and tied-back blue drapes. The food has been
imaginative and well judged but a new chef was promoted in the summer –
reports on the meals welcome. Decent furniture and Victorian-style bathroom
fittings are the norm in the bedrooms in the main house; the distinguished Abbot
Colerne room teams these with a stand-alone cast-iron bath and a view of the
Abbey green. A Japanese theme prevails in the bedrooms in the extension of
converted outbuildings.

◑ Open all year ⤢ From M4 Junction 17 follow A429 for 5 miles to Malmesbury; at
main roundabout follow town-centre signs until facing market cross; turn left and Old
Bell is next to Abbey. Private car park ⟵ 3 single, 3 twin, 13 double, 1 four-poster, 8
family rooms, 3 suites; some in annexe; most with bathroom/WC, 3 with shower/WC; all
with TV, room service, hair-dryer, direct-dial telephone ⊘ 2 restaurants, bar, 2
lounges, playroom, garden; functions (max 80 people incl up to 52 residential),
conferences; civil wedding licence; early suppers for children; cots, high chairs, toys,
playroom, babysitting, baby-listening, outdoor play area ⅙ No wheelchair access
● No dogs or smoking in restaurant ▭ Amex, Delta, Diners, MasterCard, Switch,
Visa £ Single/single occupancy of twin/double £75, twin/double from £90,
four-poster £145, family room from £125, suite £170; deposit required. Bar/bistro L, D
£15; set L £15, D £20/£26. Special breaks available

---

*The Which? Hotel Guide is one of many titles published by Which?
Books. If you would like a full list, write to Which? Books, Castlemead,
Gascoyne Way, Hertford X, SG14 1LH, or access our web site at
www.which.net/.*

Newstead Grange

No under 10s

Norton, Malton YO17 9PJ
TEL: (01653) 692502   FAX: (01653) 696951

Elegant Georgian country house, with lovely antiques, attractive gardens and welcoming owners.

Pat and Paul Williams' lovely house has so few hotel trappings that it's not obvious to find, having only a modest name plaque to announce that you're at Newstead Grange. Their classy family home is packed with lovely antique furniture and such period features as handsome marble and pine fireplaces and window shutters. Pat used to be an art teacher, so many of the watercolours on the walls are her own work. Guests are encouraged to get to know one another in order to foster an atmosphere of country-house cordiality, and two grand lounges kitted out with oriental rugs on their wooden floors, a grand piano and Edwardian furniture provide impressively convivial surroundings. Nor are the bedrooms lacking in style or finery: each has its own charm – swagged curtains, antique furniture in oak, pine and mahogany from France and Belgium, and Royal Doulton china in which to make your tea. Pickering – one of the best rooms – has a Victorian mahogany half-tester bed and, together with Wertheimer, a double aspect over the two-and-a-half acres of garden, with its mature copper beeches and chestnuts and flower-strewn lawn. Fresh, organic produce from the fruit trees and vegetable garden is used with enthusiasm in Pat's daily set dinners that feature such dishes as courgette and bacon frittata, haddock julienne and lemon and almond soufflé.

◗ Closed early Nov to mid-Feb   🚗 On B1248, 2 miles south-east of Malton. Follow Beverley signs out of Malton. Newstead Grange is on left, ½ mile beyond last houses, at junction with Settrington road. Private car park   🛏 4 twin, 4 double; 5 with bathroom/WC, 3 with shower/WC; all with TV, hair-dryer   ⊘ Dining-room, 2 lounges, garden   ⅙ No wheelchair access   ● No children under 10; no dogs; no smoking   ☐ MasterCard, Visa   £ Single occupancy of twin/double £40 to £45, twin/double £65 to £79; deposit required. Set D £17. (Prices valid till Jan 1999.) Special breaks available

The Cottage in the Wood

Holywell Road, Malvern Wells, Malvern WR14 4LG
TEL: (01684) 575859   FAX: (01684) 560662

Family-run, country-house eyrie, on the wooded slopes of the Malvern Hills.

The name is misleading: the complex that commands a bird's-eye view over the Vale of Evesham turns out to be a substantial country-house hotel. Most of the action takes place in the Georgian dower house, specifically in the cosy bar – which offers an amazing selection of spirits – and the traditionally elegant sitting-room and restaurant, whose floor-to-ceiling windows allow you to lap up the views. The creative, largely English cuisine (for example, venison might be prepared in a chocolate sauce) has received praise. The bedrooms are spread between the main house and two annexes: the beamed Beech Cottage and the Coach House. They vary enormously (as is reflected in the tariff), from the spacious to the rather cramped, and from the swish and antique-furnished to the small, modern pine creations in the Coach House, where most have a balcony or terrace in compensation. Each, however, comes with such endearing touches as home-made biscuits and binoculars for those with a view. This is a family enterprise through and through: John and Sue Pattin are hands-on owners, their daughter Maria is the manager and son Dominic the chef. The Pattins pride themselves on their service. Complaints and suggestions made on room questionnaires, from increasing fruit-salad portions to improving bedroom lighting, are scrupulously analysed.

◗ Open all year ⤢ 3 miles south of Great Malvern off A449; turning is signposted, opposite garage. Private car park ⤶ 4 twin, 13 double, 3 four-poster; some in annexe; all with bathroom/WC; all with TV, limited room service, hair-dryer, direct-dial telephone, video, some with trouser press ⍟ Restaurant, bar, sitting-room, garden; conferences (max 14 people residential/non-residential); leisure facilities nearby (free for guests); early suppers for children; cots, high chairs, baby-listening ♿ No wheelchair access ● Dogs in some bedrooms only, by arrangement; no smoking in restaurant ▭ Amex, Delta, MasterCard, Switch, Visa £ Single occupancy of twin/double £70 to £80, twin/double £90 to £145, four-poster £120 to £145; deposit required. Set L £11 to £16; alc L, D £28. Special breaks available

---

MANCHESTER Greater Manchester   map 8

Crowne Plaza Midland

Peter Street, Manchester M60 2DS
TEL: 0161-236 3333   FAX: 0161-932 4100
WEB SITE: www.crowneplaza.com

Smart business hotel with leisure facilities in the heart of Manchester.

The Crowne Plaza Midland (formerly Holiday Inn Crowne Plaza) is very much a business hotel but with a hint of old-world elegance, particularly in its exterior – an imposing red-brick Edwardian façade. Inside, the elegance is continued in marble corridors dating back to 1903 and the airy reception area with its glass atrium. The Terrace Lounge provides a smart comfortable area to meet and chat over coffee; alternatively, drinks can be had from the Octagon Court Bar. Of the hotel's restaurants, the main Trafford Room sticks largely to buffets and a carvery. Gourmets, however, will be interested to hear of other developments in the past year. The lemon-yellow brasserie is now a branch of Nico Central, headed by Clive Fretwell, who used to be head chef of the Manoir aux Quat' Saisons. Here you can opt for two or three courses, along the lines of sushi with pickled vegetables, asparagus risotto, braised lamb shank with coconut sauce and Chinese greens, or tomato and mozzarella tart with pesto. As we went to press we heard that Paul Reed, from the Chester Grosvener Hotel, was to take over in the French restaurant. The bedrooms stick to the corporate style and are cheerful, spacious and comfortable – every bed in the hotel is a double (seven doubles, called 'syndicate rooms', have a bed that folds into the wall, so that meetings can be held). Three floors are set aside for smokers. With its extensive conference and banqueting facilities, the hotel is very much geared to corporate guests, but good packages attract a growing leisure clientele.

◐ Open all year ⚡ In city centre, just north of Oxford Road and adjacent to G-Mex Centre. Public car park nearby (£5 per 24 hours for guests) 🛏 227 double (incl 7 syndicate rooms), 62 two doubles, 7 junior suites, 7 full suites; all with bathroom/WC; all with satellite TV, 24-hour room service, air-conditioning, hair-dryer, mini-bar, direct-dial telephone, in-house movies, trouser press, ironing facilities ✦ 3 restaurants, 2 bars, lounge; functions (max 500 people residential/non-residential), conferences; civil wedding licence; gym, sauna, solarium, heated indoor swimming-pool; cots, high chairs ♿ Wheelchair access to hotel and restaurant (ramps), WC (unisex), no ground-floor bedrooms, but lift, 1 room specially equipped for disabled people ● None ⊟ Amex, Delta, Diners, MasterCard, Switch, Visa £ Double/two doubles £160 to £200, junior suite £225, full suite £450; deposit required. Cooked B £13.50; (Trafford) set L £15, D £19; alc D (French restaurant) £40. Special breaks available

Etrop Grange

Thorley Lane, Manchester Airport, M90 4EG
TEL: 0161-499 0500   FAX: 0161-499 0790

No danger of missing your flight if you stay at this attractive hotel close to the airport.

Etrop Grange appears to be in something of a time warp. Within a baggage trolley's trundle of this attractive Georgian villa are the modern, box-shaped buildings of Manchester airport – yet from inside the hotel you would be hard-pressed to notice it. Strangely enough, even the noise of the airport doesn't seem to permeate the calm of the surroundings. Regular visitors to Etrop will notice some startling changes this year, with a new 24-bedroom extension now added. Indeed there have been improvements to all the bedrooms, although there are still some which are a little short of space. The public rooms are particularly comfortable, and an effort has been made to keep to period styling as much as possible. One also notices a definite attempt to keep things relaxed and informal, despite the presence of so many business guests. We found the food disappointing on inspection, with our expectations perhaps raised a little too much by the menu descriptions.

◐ Open all year ⚡ Leave M56 at Junction 5, follow signs for Terminal 2 and take first left at roundabout; turn immediately left, and hotel is 400 yards further on. Private car park 🛏 2 single, 4 twin, 49 double, 7 four-poster, 2 suites; all with bathroom/WC; all with TV, room service, hair-dryer, trouser press, direct-dial telephone ✦ Restaurant, bar, 2 lounges, library, conservatory, garden; functions (max 150 people incl up to 126 residential), conferences; leisure facilities nearby (reduced rates for guests); early suppers for children; cots, high chairs, babysitting ♿ Wheelchair access to hotel (ramp) and restaurant (1 step), 7 ground-floor rooms ● None ⊟ Amex, Delta, Diners, MasterCard, Switch, Visa £ Single £115, single occupancy of twin/double £115, twin/double £135, four-poster £150, suite £160; deposit required. Continental B £7.50, cooked B £10.50; bar/bistro L, D £6; set L £12.50, D £27.50; alc L £16.50, D £27.50. Special breaks available

Malmaison | NEW ENTRY |

Piccadilly, Manchester M1 3AQ
TEL: 0161-278 1000   FAX: 0161-278 1002

Sexy, stylish hotel in the heart of Manchester with great weekend rates.

From the outside there doesn't seem much to get excited about – a harsh fusion of Stalinesque grey and an angular red-brick building (once an old cotton-mill warehouse) opposite Piccadilly station. Manchester's bustle is left outside as you enter a cool, modernist interior with black-and-white checked floor and black asymmetrical furnishings evocative of the Empire *bateau lit* style. Guests descend into a dark, seductive bar oozing jazz, with crimson-and-black velvet sofas. The chic art-nouveau French Brasserie evokes an atmosphere of Belle Epoque, with its fine wrought-iron filigree work, coffee-brown walls and crisp white table-tops. The atmosphere is classy and stylish, from the mood-creating pin-point lighting to the omnipresent jazz sounds. For intimate gatherings the Salon Privé provides the perfect setting and features a fabulous wine display on the wall. The Malmaison group takes pride in its name, and it seems nothing escapes the Malmaison branding, including the signatured bottles of wine and mini-bar munchies. The bedrooms maintain the style: simplistic Mondrian colour schemes dominate – striped black-and-white bed covers set against sombre grey, striped walls, interrupted by red chairs and outsized lamps. The attention to detail is captivating: rooms have their own CD players, in-house movies, bespoke toiletries (Arran Aromatics) and corks which say *'notre vin'* on the outside and *'votre vin'* on the inside! If all this doesn't sufficiently tempt, amuse or tantalise, there's still the 'gymtonic' – a new kind of health, fitness and life-style club complete with hi-tech gym, beauty and treatment rooms, not to mention the peppermint 'sanarium'!

◖ Open all year   ▨ Near Piccadilly railway station. On-street parking (metered); public car park nearby (£10 per day)   ⟻ 15 twin, 89 double, 8 suites; all with bathroom/WC; all with satellite TV, room service, hair-dryer, mini-bar, trouser press, direct-dial telephone, CD-player, in-house movies   ✇ Brasserie, bar, lounge; conferences (max 50 people residential/non-residential); gym, sauna, solarium, health and beauty rooms; leisure facilities nearby (free for guests); early suppers for children, in brasserie from 6pm or served in bedroom; cots, high chairs   㐧 Wheelchair access to hotel and restaurant, WC (unisex), lift to bedrooms, 5 rooms specially equipped for disabled guests   ● No dogs; no smoking in some bedrooms   ▭ Amex, Delta, Diners, MasterCard, Switch, Visa   £ Single occupancy of twin/double £99, twin/double £99, suite £165; deposit required. Continental B £8.50, cooked B £10.50; bar L £5; alc L £15, D £20. Special breaks available

Victoria & Albert Hotel

Water Street, Manchester M3 4JQ
TEL: 0161-832 1188   FAX: 0161-834 2484

Characterful warehouse conversion, offering Carlton-themed rooms and efficient service.

The Victoria & Albert Hotel is an attractive, red-brick former warehouse, situated on the River Irwell, across from where 'Coronation Street' is filmed. In 1992, following the successful opening of the Granada film studios, the Victorian & Albert warehouse (originally built in 1844) was converted into a hotel. The warehouse structure contributes to a stylish interior – the reception area is spacious, and the red brick and exposed beams create a warm atmosphere. Watson's Bar, on the lower ground floor overlooking the river, provides residents with a cosy lounge area for chatting, or an informal meeting place for business guests; in one of the corners, a large TV provides added entertainment. A pine terrace area, that follows the periphery of the bar, is a pleasant spot for afternoon tea, as it overlooks the river. The bedrooms are fun, individually themed around such Granada productions as 'Sergeant Pepper', with the warehouse décor – bare brick and arched windows – adding to their style. The hotel staff are on the ball and offer high standards of service, including valet car-parking and the loading and unloading of luggage on and off shiny brass trolleys by bellboys. Changes to come later this year include new leisure facilities, a pool and extra rooms.

◑ Open all year; 1 restaurant closed Sun eve ⤢ In city centre, beside River Irwell and Granada Studios. Private car park ⤔ 23 twin, 125 double, 8 suites; all with bathroom/WC; all with TV, room service, hair-dryer, mini-bar, trouser press, direct-dial telephone, ironing facilities, video ✧ 2 restaurants, bar, lounge, conservatory, garden; functions (max 400 people incl up to 312 residential), conferences; sauna, solarium; leisure facilities nearby (free for guests); early suppers for children; cots, high chairs ⅊ Wheelchair access to hotel and restaurants, WC (unisex), lift to bedrooms, 2 rooms specially equipped for disabled people ● No dogs; no smoking in some bedrooms ▭ Amex, Delta, Diners, MasterCard, Switch, Visa £ Single occupancy of twin/double £90 to £149, twin/double £99 to £185, suite £250 to £450 (prices valid till Oct 1998); deposit required. Continental B £10 (free at weekends), cooked B £13.50; bar/bistro L £10, D £20; alc D from £35. Special breaks available

---

MARKINGTON North Yorkshire   map 9

Hob Green

Markington, Harrogate HG3 3PJ
TEL: (01423) 770031   FAX: (01423) 771589

Traditional country-house hotel with friendly service in 800 acres of peaceful countryside.

In a fast-moving world where fashions come and go overnight, Hob Green provides a reassuring haven for those wanting to lead life at a slower pace. The austere aspect of the eighteenth-century house is soon forgotten amid its restful surroundings, buffered by hundreds of acres of gentle countryside from the outside world. Starting from the hearty welcome in the woodsmoke-perfumed reception lounge, it is quickly apparent that, although old-school in character, this is not a starchy sort of hotel. Fresh flowers brighten up a lived-in, slightly dated décor where attractive inlaid antique furniture, squidgy sofas and the odd grandfather clock set the tone; the elegant drawing-room and conservatory-style sun room revel in views over broad lawns. The bedrooms can't compete with the public rooms for restrained style, but are pleasant enough, each with an individual décor that ranges from homely and cottagey to modern and bright. Room 10 has a lovely double aspect over the Victorian kitchen garden whose produce goes into the hearty old favourites with a modern twist on the menu. Duck terrine with Cumberland sauce might pave the way for a traditional roast or lamb's liver with caramelised onions.

◑ Open all year ⬕ From Harrogate, take A61 towards Ripon; at Ripley, join B6165 to Pateley Bridge; after 1 mile turn right signposted Fountains Abbey; after 2 miles turn right at Drovers Inn; Hob Green is 1 mile further. Private car park ⬕⟶ 3 single, 5 twin, 2 double, 1 four-poster, 1 suite; all with bathroom/WC; all with TV, room service, hair-dryer, mini-bar, direct-dial telephone; trouser press on request ⬗ Restaurant, drawing-room, conservatory, garden; conferences (max 12 people residential/non-residential); croquet; early suppers for children; cots, high chairs ⬕ No wheelchair access ⬤ No dogs in public rooms ⬚ Amex, Delta, Diners, MasterCard, Switch, Visa £ Single £80, single occupancy of twin/double £85, twin/double £90 to £99, four-poster £105, suite £115; deposit required. Bar/bistro L £5; set L £12.50; alc D £21.50. Special breaks available

---

MARTINHOE Devon   map 1

Old Rectory

Martinhoe, Parracombe, Barnstaple EX31 4QT
TEL: (01598) 763368   FAX: (01598) 763567

Peaceful, friendly old house on rural hilltop near the sea.

The Old Rectory has new owners, but the transition seems to have been flawless. Geoff Wilson and Jane and Dennis Bennett have continued right where John and Suzanne Bradbury left off, providing comfortable accommodation and good food in a very welcoming, calm environment. One satisfied guest who visited recently told us that 'nothing was too much trouble for the new proprietors (in fact on one occasion they even washed and dried our extremely muddy walking gear)', and they also liked the complimentary tea or coffee made throughout the day on request, in addition to tea-making facilities in the room.

Set on a stretch of the most fetching coastline, the large, cream-painted, late Georgian house nestles in a tiny hamlet. A small stream burbles through the garden, which is sprinkled with inviting-looking places to sit and soak up the peace. Inside, the muted décor and small, well-kept public rooms continue the meditative theme; one lounge is done out in pinks, peaches and pale greens with comfy armchairs, and there's a useful little library on the landing. In the conservatory a flamboyant vine makes you feel more outdoors than in. If you time it right you can feast on sweet black grapes at harvest time, otherwise you will have to make do with a five-course dinner taken in the hushed dining-room under the grandfather clock, with a pretty posy of flowers on each plate. On the menu might be a grapefruit and kiwi cocktail, followed by tomato and sweetcorn soup, and then pork and prunes with redcurrant sauce. The bedrooms are spacious and pastel-coloured, with lace curtains and big beds, but the bathrooms are a tad old-fashioned and could perhaps do with some shower attachments, rather than the ubiquitous plastic jug.

◑ Closed Nov to Easter ◪ Off A39, between Parracombe and Lynton, signposted Woody Bay and Martinhoe. Private car park 🛏 3 twin, 4 double, 1 suite; most with bathroom/WC, some with shower/WC; all with TV, room service, hair-dryer ✓ Dining-room, 2 lounges, library, conservatory, vinery, garden ♿ Wheelchair access to hotel (2 steps) and restaurant, 2 ground-floor bedrooms, 1 partially equipped for disabled people ⊖ No children under 14; no dogs; no smoking ▭ None accepted £ Single occupancy of twin/double £69, twin/double £130, suite £140 (rates incl dinner); deposit required. Special breaks available

MARYPORT Cumbria map 10

The Retreat

£

Birkby, Maryport CA15 6RG
TEL: (01900) 814056

Distinctive Victorian house in a little-known part of Cumbria, a good base for exploring the coast and north-western Lakes.

Set back behind Birkby village green, just north of Maryport, the Retreat offers only distant glimpses of the waves a mile away. Its Victorian owner, Captain Joseph Cuthbertson, may have seen enough of them after a seafaring life. Certainly it seems a peaceful place now, though the lively and welcoming Geisslers make it anything but moribund. Rudi's origins may be guessed from a sharp look at the white-painted façade, where a small panel is picked out with the colours of Germany's flag. The interior of the house is full of interest, with monumental doors, imposing mahogany furniture and unusual plasterwork in the bar/lounge. The pictures are worth investigating too, particularly the 'fashion through the ages' watercolours in the restaurant, painted by Alison's aunt. Rudi is the resident chef, preparing hearty quantities of straightforward fare like duckling with orange sauce or poached salmon in white wine. When the Geisslers first moved here in 1976 they ran the Retreat as a restaurant; accommodation was added only six years ago. Surprisingly in such a substantial house, there are just three bedrooms, all spacious and handsomely furnished, with their own shower-rooms. Rear rooms overlook the walled gardens, a mosaic of lawns and flowerbeds.

◑ Closed Chr ◪ About 2 miles north of Maryport, just off A596, in hamlet of Birkby. Private car park 🛏 1 twin, 2 double; all with shower/WC; all with TV, room service, hair-dryer ✓ Restaurant, bar, lounge, garden ♿ No wheelchair access ⊖ No dogs; no smoking in restaurant ▭ Delta, MasterCard, Visa £ Single occupancy of twin/double £34 to £39, twin/double £47 to £52. Set D £18. Special breaks available

Where we know an establishment accepts credit cards, we list them. There may be a surcharge if you pay by credit card. It is always best to check when booking whether the card you want to use is acceptable.

MATLOCK BATH **Derbyshire** map 5

Hodgkinson's

150 South Parade, Matlock Bath, Matlock DE4 3NR
TEL: (01629) 582170   FAX: (01629) 584891

Flamboyant Victoriana and stylish bedrooms in this comfortable, town-centre hotel.

Near the chip shops and cheap thrills of the amusement arcades, Malcolm Archer's and Nigel Shelley's tall, plain Georgian house stands rather austerely aloof. Not that the glum exterior bears any relation to its contents, which is a splendid selection of the kitsch and the curious: a pineapple-shaped lamp on the bar, pith helmets, gold-painted tables and sepia portraits in the lounge and small restaurant. If the décor suggests a love of the colourful and richly ornamented, the cooking unashamedly follows suit: chicken might be served with brandy, cider and tarragon, lamb with honey and lavender (if there is a complaint, it is that the food can be over-complicated), and, as for puddings, they are worthy of the name. Service is formal but never staid. The bedrooms continue Nigel's inspired interior designs, with antique pieces of furniture adding to the pleasure. All have showers only and, apart from Room 2, look out on to the main road, which can be busy.

◗ Open all year; restaurant closed Sun eve   ⤢ In centre of Matlock Bath, on A6. Private car park   ⤶ 1 single, 6 double; all with shower/WC; all with TV, direct-dial telephone   ✅ Restaurant, bar, 2 lounges, drying-room, garden; conferences (max 12 people incl up to 7 residential)   ♿ No wheelchair access   ⊖ No dogs in public rooms   ⊟ Amex, Delta, Diners, MasterCard, Switch, Visa   £ Single £35, single occupancy of double £50 to £60, double £60 to £90; deposit required. Set D £19.50 to £24.50. Special breaks available

MAWNAN SMITH **Cornwall** map 1

Budock Vean

Helford River, Mawnan Smith, Falmouth TR11 5LG
TEL: (01326) 250288   FAX: (01326) 250892

Huge, well-loved golfing establishment, recently refurbished – public rooms are much brighter, but bedrooms still lack character.

It's all change at Budock Vean. Gone are the stags' heads (well, most of them), the tapestries and stone cladding, and in come parquet floors, smart, creamy walls and designer furniture. Visitors have constantly praised the 200-year-old rambling hotel's 'beautiful grounds' and 'superb setting by the Helford River', as well as the 'friendly, helpful and efficient staff' – we'll see what they make of the major internal face-lift. When we inspected, the reception and lounges had been completed, done out in sophisticated russets and yellows, with Persian rugs on wooden floors and furniture fit for the millennium. The huge, formal dining-room (jacket and tie will still be required) is due for a similar overhaul, so say goodbye to the fake beams and welcome to recessed lighting and a light, airy atmosphere. The menu remains reassuringly classical, however, full of straightforward English dishes with a smattering of the more adventurous, such as confit of duck with home-made piccalilli, followed by roast sirloin of beef with a crisp Yorkshire pudding and gravy. Less formal dining is offered in the green, spruce Country Club restaurant. The bedrooms remain as they were – spacious, straightforward and rather batchelorish, with dull but spotless bathrooms. A health spa has been added to the already extensive facilities, the pool continues to have 'the warmest water we have ever encountered in a hotel pool', and the golf course, bar and shop are still the major attractions.

◑ Open all year ⤢ Travelling south, fork right at Red Lion in Mawnan Smith; hotel is on left. Private car park ⤇ 9 single, 22 twin, 20 double, 1 four-poster, 3 suites; all with bathroom/WC; all with TV, room service, hair-dryer, direct-dial telephone ⟡ Dining-room, restaurant, 2 bars, 4 lounges, TV room, conservatory, games room, garden; functions (max 30 people residential/non-residential), conferences; civil wedding licence; golf, heated indoor swimming-pool, tennis, putting green, snooker, croquest, driving nets, health spa, billiard room; early suppers for children; cots, high chairs, babysitting ♿ No wheelchair access ● Children by arrangement, no children under 8 in restaurants eves; no dogs in public rooms; no smoking in some public rooms ▭ Delta, Diners, MasterCard, Switch, Visa £ Single £69 to £89, single occupancy of twin/double £103 to £133, twin/double/four-poster £138 to £178, suite £168 to £208 (rates incl dinner); deposit required. Bar/bistro L £3 to £7; set Sun L £10. (Prices valid until end 1998.) Special breaks available

---

Carwinion

❁ ℒ

Mawnan Smith, Falmouth TR11 5JA
TEL: (01326) 250258   FAX: (01326) 250903

Friendly, slightly eccentric welcome, a wild, unmanicured garden and countrified bedrooms in this home-from-home.

'The house is comfortable in the slightly faded manner of any home accompanied by many generations of the same family: portraits, objects d'art [sic] and collections of oddities are all there to be enjoyed' – so says Carwinion's brochure, and we cannot sum it up any better. The wording sums up the attitude of Anthony Rogers and his wife Jane, who run the B&B side of things, as well as managing to stop the gardens taking over the house – surprisingly there is little foliage inside, with only some restrained succulents in the hallway by the grandfather clock. Anthony's grandfather founded the fabulous gardens, which are visited by devotees in summer (or do they come only to sample the cream teas on the terrace?); a secret garden is being hidden this year, and a Japanese garden is under way. You'll find lots of ponds, walkways and streams, woodland areas full of ferns and a wild-flower meadow, as well as the famous bamboos, on your walk down to the coastal path. Camellias bloom in January, and wild flowers, primroses and bluebells run riot. Inside, the bedrooms are very large and comfortably furnished in spruce country style. An evening meal is available on request and consists of 'what's local and what's fresh': perhaps prawns and mango, or a crab salad. Herbs, and occasionally fruit, come from the garden.

◑ Open all year ⤢ In Mawnan Smith, turn left at Red Lion pub; Carwinian is 500 yards up hill, on right. Private car park ⬥ 2 twin, 1 double; all with bathroom/WC; all with TV, hair-dryer ⟡ Dining-room, TV room, drying-room, library, garden; functions (max 100 people incl up to 6 residential), conferences; early suppers for children; high chair ♿ No wheelchair access ● No dogs or smoking in bedrooms ▭ None accepted £ Single occupancy of twin/double £33, twin/double £57; deposit required. Set D £18. Special breaks available

---

Meudon Hotel

Mawnan Smith, Falmouth TR11 5HT
TEL: (01326) 250541   FAX: (01326) 250543
EMAIL: info@meudon.co.uk
WEB SITE: www.meudon.co.uk

Surprising architectural combinations and a gorgeous garden at this endearingly family-run hotel.

Mark Pilgrim is, in his own words, 'faced with a perennial problem – the 'sixties' conversion'. Where lesser men may have given up and knocked the whole lot down, he is resolute in his decision, however, to solve this riddle with an 'imaginative approach'. And perhaps he is right to resort to disguise (creepers) rather than the bulldozer, for the rather 'Crossroads'-style appendages to the wonderful, Victorian, main building do have a charm all of their own; indeed, the whole place fairly beguiles the visitor. It's been in the family for over 30 years; Grandad lives here, as does Mark's family, and there's incredible loyalty among the staff (Gabriel, the head waiter, has been here for 30 years, the chef for 14). There's no need to move on, it seems, when you can hang out at Meudon Hotel with the Pilgrims and the famous, first-generation, antipodean ferns in the vast, subtropical garden. The combination of styles continues inside, both in the public rooms and the bedrooms (these are mostly in the sixties parts). Delicate antiques jockey for position with old-fashioned, high-backed chairs and the rather garish carpets are happily overwhelmed by fresh flowers and foliage from the garden – indeed, in the restaurant it's difficult to tell whether you are inside or outside. A typical dinner menu might include salmon and avocado pear drizzled in a blue-cheese and chive dressing, followed by a choice of soups, and then roast leg of West Country lamb garnished with a minted carrot tartlet. Mark produces a newsletter that features recipes, along with news of renovations and disguises. One disgruntled reader was unhappy that the 'sheets were changed only once during the week we stayed' and that the specials on the menu carried a surcharge, and we have to agree that at these prices this does irritate.

◑ Closed Jan & Feb ⤢ Leave A39 at Hillhead roundabout and follow signs to Maenporth (ignore signs to Mawnan Smith). Hotel is ½ mile past Maenporth beach, on left. Private car park ⬥ 23 twin/double, 2 'executive' double, 1 four-poster, 1 family room, 2 suites; all with bathroom/WC; all with TV, room service, hair-dryer, trouser press, direct-dial telephone ⟡ Restaurant, bar, 3 lounges, drying-room, games room, garden; functions (max 100 people incl up to 60 residential), conferences; snooker; fishing nearby; golf nearby (free for guests); early suppers for children; cots, high chairs, babysitting, baby-listening, outdoor play area ♿ Wheelchair access to hotel (ramp) and restaurant, 14 ground-floor bedrooms, 2 rooms specially equipped for disabled people ● Dogs in bedrooms only (£6 per day) ▭ Amex, Delta, Diners, MasterCard,

348

Switch, Visa ꜰ£꜖ Single occupancy of twin/double £80, twin/double £140, executive double/four-poster/family room £170, suite £200; deposit required. Bar/bistro L £5 to £10; set Sun L £15, D £25. Special breaks available

---

MAXSTOKE Warwickshire map 5

Old Rectory

Church Lane, Maxstoke B46 2QW
TEL: (01675) 462248   FAX: (01675) 481615

Easy-going peace and quiet just a few minutes from the motorway and NEC.

The first thing you spot on approaching the Old Rectory are the towering, ivy-clad ruins of the Augustinian priory in whose grounds the Victorian rectory was built. Chris and Judy Page run their family home with an informal and relaxed atmosphere. A sign hanging in the hall reads 'Reward. Husband and dog missing' – and it is certainly very tempting to wander off into the expansive garden, past the old carp pond and fruit trees to the woods, or to take a turn in the rowing boat. There are only two bedrooms, both of which are spacious and furnished with some attractive, old pieces. As you might expect in a family home, there is the odd surprise – like the globe in the bathroom, or the children's toys scattered at the bottom of the stairs. Breakfasts are served in the dining-room at separate tables, most visitors heading off to nearby Coleshill for dinner. Also within easy striking distance is the NEC.

◑ Closed Chr ⊿ Leave M42 at Junction 6; follow A45 south for 2 miles; turn left by Little Chef restaurant and continue for 3 miles to a T-junction; turn left and entrance is at bottom of hill on bend through gateway to left. Private car park ⤙ 1 twin, 1 double; family room available twin with bathroom/WC, double with shower/WC; both with TV, hair-dryer ✧ Dining-room, lounge, garden; outdoor play area ⅃ No wheelchair access ● No dogs or smoking ▭ None accepted ꜰ£꜖ Single occupancy of twin/double £34, twin/double £50, family room £68; deposit required

---

MELDRETH Cambridgeshire map 6

Chiswick House

Meldreth, Royston SG8 6LZ
TEL: (01763) 260242

Quiet village location for this rustic, half-timbered farmhouse B&B with a good choice of rooms.

You will find obvious traces of both Tudor and Jacobean architecture in this house, but it must date from before 1318, when there's evidence that a lady lived here. It's exactly 100 years since the Elbourn family connection with the house began, and John and Bernice Elbourn have been living here for 20 years now. Their knowledge and appreciation of the history of their surroundings also means that there has been much care and thought put into both the restoration work and making their guests' stay comfortable. While old features abound, there is also a modest conservatory, added by the couple, where breakfast is served in fine weather. The bedrooms are split between the main farmhouse and the converted stable block – the latter are more suitable for children. Those in the farmhouse are smaller and darker, but more characterful, while the others have high ceilings, pine furniture and floral fabrics.

◑ Closed Chr ⤢ In Meldreth village, 1 mile west of A10, 8 miles south of Cambridge. Private car park ⤶ 2 twin, 4 double; some in annexe; 1 twin with bathroom/WC, 5 with shower/WC; all with hair-dryer, some with TV ✓ Dining-room, lounge, conservatory, garden; cots, high chairs, baby-listening ♿ No wheelchair access ● No dogs in public rooms; no smoking ▭ None accepted £ Single occupancy of twin/double £35, twin/double £42; deposit required

---

MELKSHAM Wiltshire
map 2

Sandridge Park

Melksham SN12 7QU
TEL: (01225) 706897   FAX: (01225) 702838

Fine country house set amid handsome grounds and gardens.

As wartime billets go, General Eisenhower probably found his temporary occupation of the fine Bath-sandstone mansion of Sandridge Park an experience to remember. The understated entrance on the main Calne to Melksham road gives little hint of the splendours awaiting those who follow the long, winding, private road that leads to Andrew and Annette Hoogeweegen's imposing house, which stands amid 30 acres of park and woodland. The tone is set immediately in the lofty, sky-blue reception hall, on which a baby grand piano and fine marble fireplace bestow a definite sense of occasion. Despite the grand proportions of the public areas, Annette has, by judicious positioning of family photographs, china and glassware, retained the welcoming feel of a family home. Impeccably tasteful decoration and fine garden views make the classically elegant drawing-room a spot where you'll wish to linger. The boldly blood-red dining-room provides an interesting gallery for a collection of contemporary art, and a worthy venue for Annette's dinner-party-style food: perhaps fresh garden asparagus with melted butter, followed by paupiettes of halibut with braised fennel and a lemon sauce accompanied by home-grown vegetables, and finally a raspberry crème brûlée. The spacious bedrooms are delightfully furnished and decorated in a restful country-house style, using lots of pastels and florals.

◑ Closed Chr ⤢ From Melksham, take A3102 towards Calne; hotel is 2 miles along on left. Private car park ⤶ 1 twin, 3 double; all with bathroom/WC; all with TV, some with trouser press; hair-dryer available ✓ Dining-room, drawing-room, TV room, drying room, garden ♿ No wheelchair access ● No children under 16; no dogs; no smoking in bedrooms ▭ MasterCard, Visa £ Single occupancy of twin/double £40, twin/double £80; deposit required. Set D £20

Please let us know if an establishment has changed hands.

Shurnhold House

Shurnhold, Melksham SN12 8DG
TEL: (01225) 790555   FAX: (01225) 793147

Lovely gardens add to the attraction of a Jacobean manor, carefully run by a friendly hostess.

The seventeenth-century occupants of Sue Tanir's Shurnhold House wouldn't have had to contend with the traffic on the A365, which represents the wistaria-clad manor's only real drawback. The ever-resourceful Sue has accepted the challenge presented by the proximity of the road, and a high hedge both screens and muffles the impact of the traffic, leaving guests free to admire the beautiful formal garden and terrace at the front of the house. Once indoors, guests are confronted by a riot of beams, flagstones and inglenooks, amply testifying to the house's age. There's an autumnal feel to the sitting-room, an elegant and tasteful affair, scattered with antiques. High-backed chairs, silver candlesticks and an interesting variety of prints, watercolours and wall-hangings add texture to the dining-room, where breakfast is served. The bedrooms, two of which have four-posters, are more cottagey than the public rooms, often featuring pine furniture and floral soft furnishings. 'We could not have asked for more pleasant discreet service... Highly recommended', concluded one correspondent, who also singled out the comfortable rooms, attractive gardens and 'excellent' breakfast for special praise.

◐ Open all year ⊿ Set back off main A365 road to Bath, 1 mile from Melksham. Private car park ⤓ 1 twin, 3 double, 2 four-poster, 1 suite; family rooms available; all with bathroom/WC; all with satellite TV, room service, hair-dryer, direct-dial telephone, some with trouser press ⊘ Dining-room, bar, 2 sitting-rooms, garden; croquet; baby-listening ♿ No wheelchair access ● Dogs in bedrooms only, by arrangement; smoking in bar and 1 sitting-room only ▭ Amex, MasterCard, Visa £ Single occupancy of twin/double £48 to £50, twin/double £68 to £78, four-poster £78, family room/suite £88 to £98; deposit required. Continental B £3.50, cooked B £5.50

Toxique

187 Woodrow Road, Melksham SN12 7AY
TEL: (01225) 702129   FAX: (01225) 742773

Rambling farmhouse with rooms that are as stylish as the well-regarded food.

Woodrow Road, a suburban street heading out of Melksham and into open countryside, is an unlikely setting for an innovative restaurant-with-rooms. On the face of things this low-slung, honey-stoned farmhouse is an unexceptional sort of place, whose climbing roses and partial cloak of creeper create expectations of hearty food and rustic charm. Be prepared to have your preconceptions well and truly upset: owners Helen Bartlett and Peter Jewkes have taken this quasi-rural shell and have imported startling interior-design layouts that wouldn't look out of place in a catalogue of cutting-edge metropolitan chic. Things kick off with a bang in both the midnight-blue reception area and the lounge, with its pine-cone cornicing and a decadently rich colour scheme of blue, purple and gold. The beamed Mediterranean Room is dominated by a large landscape mural. It's a stylish setting for such dishes as salad of scallops, chicory, fennel and orange, followed by breast of Trelough duck with figs, dauphinois potatoes and spiced red cabbage, and then a lemon mascarpone mousse with glazed kumquats. The individually styled bedrooms are memorable and distinctive, from the Zen-like, floaty simplicity of the Oriental Suite, to the louche splendour of the Rococo Suite, the pristine, stiff-upper-lip restraint of the Colonial Suite, and the startling exoticism of the Moroccan Suite.

◐ Open all year (occasional closures); restaurant closed Sun to Tue eves 🔁 Take Calne Road at Melksham centre mini-roundabout; turn left into Forest Road and Toxique is on left. Private car park 🛏 5 suites; all with bathroom/WC; all with room service, hair-dryer, some with TV ✅ 2 restaurants, bar, lounge, garden; functions (max 40 people incl up to 10 residential); early suppers for children; cot, high chairs ♿ No wheelchair access ⬤ No dogs; no smoking in public rooms ▭ Amex, Delta, MasterCard, Switch, Visa £ Single occupancy of suite £95, suite £160 (rates incl dinner); deposit required. Set L £18.50 to £22

MELLOR Lancashire

map 8

Millstone Hotel `NEW ENTRY`

Church Lane, Mellor, Blackburn BB2 7JR
TEL: (01254) 813333   FAX: (01254) 812628
EMAIL: millstone@shireinns.co.uk
WEB SITE: www.openworld.co.uk/shireinns

The cosy atmosphere of a traditional pub with the conveniences of a modern hotel.

Don't be misled by the uneventful beige stone façade of the Millstone, with its front car park right on Church Lane. Inside, the atmosphere is warm and inviting. The Millstone was formerly a farmhouse; today, the focus is the spacious wood-panelled Millers Bar, with an open fire and relaxed, jovial pub atmosphere. It's a popular spot with locals for sampling pints of award-winning Thwaites ale. Parts of the public areas, like corridors and skirting boards, were on the worn side when we inspected, but refurbishment was planned for July 1998. The main restaurant offers a more formal environment: a smart open fireplace, spot-lit paintings and quietly ticking grandfather clock create a more subdued setting for dinner guests. The 24 rooms are comfortable and of a high standard; even the smallest have decent-sized *en suite* bathrooms. The six annexe rooms in the courtyard, most recently decorated, show keen attention to detail – crisp white bathrobes, Bronnley soaps and heated towel-rails; writing bureaux in the rooms reveal the Millstone's popularity with corporate guests.

◐ Open all year 🔁 Leave M6 at Junction 31, following signs to Clitheroe; 3 miles along A59 turn right at roundabout just after British Aerospace, following signs for Mellor. Private car park 🛏 3 twin, 2 twin/double, 16 double, 3 suites; some in annexe; all with bathroom/WC; all with TV, room service, hair-dryer, trouser press, direct-dial telephone ✅ Restaurant, bar, lounge, private dining-room; functions (max 80 people incl up to 50 residential), conferences; leisure facilities nearby (free for guests); early suppers for children; babysitting, baby-listening ♿ Wheelchair access

(1 step) to hotel and restaurant, 8 ground-floor bedrooms, 1 specially equipped for disabled people ● No dogs in public rooms; no smoking in restaurant and some bedrooms ⊟ Amex, Delta, Diners, MasterCard, Switch, Visa £ Single occupancy of twin/double £52 to £89, twin/double £72 to £94, suite £94 to £104. Bar/bistro L £6, D £17; set D £21; alc L £13.50, D £25. Special breaks available

---

MERE Wiltshire   map 2

Chetcombe House

Chetcombe Road, Mere, Warminster BA12 6AZ
TEL: (01747) 860219   FAX: (01747) 860111

Welcoming hosts at a friendly, unpretentious hotel, well placed for exploring a host of first-class sights.

Colin and Sue Ross's late-'thirties detached house seems a fairly unremarkable sort of place; however, readers, and our inspectors, have down the years been unanimous in praising the couple's warmth and commitment to their guests, which have helped to raise their unassuming enterprise way above the run of the mill. Although the A303 Exeter road streams past the front, double glazing and an acre of garden help to muffle its effect and, as compensation, there are views over Blackmore Vale from the rear-facing rooms. First-time visitors to the area can 'cram' on its delights in a lounge made cosy by a wood-burning stove, where Sue and Colin have assembled an impressive range of local information. The Rosses are both enthusiastic and knowledgeable about the area. Sue is a keen exponent of locally sourced produce, embellished where possible by herbs from the kitchen garden, so guests might enjoy such traditional English fare as artichoke soup, followed by braised pork chops with mushrooms, and then baked apple royal and cheese. The bedrooms are light, airy and agreeably furnished in a brisk, modern style with lots of pine and rattan.

◑ Open all year ⊿ Just off A303, before reaching Mere (from the east). Private car park ⊨ 1 single, 1 twin, 2 double, 1 family room; 2 with bathroom/WC, 3 with shower/WC; all with TV, direct-dial telephone; hair-dryer on request ⊘ Dining-room, bar, lounge, garden; functions (max 25 people incl up to 10 residential); early suppers for children; cots, high chairs, toys, baby-listening ⅙ No wheelchair access ● No dogs in public rooms; no smoking ⊟ Amex, MasterCard, Visa £ Single £31, single occupancy of twin/double £35, twin/double £53, family room £69; deposit required. Set D £15 to £16.50. Special breaks available

---

MERIDEN West Midlands   map 5

Forest of Arden

Maxstoke Lane, Meriden, Coventry CV7 7HR
TEL: (01676) 522335   FAX: (01676) 523711/523885
WEB SITE: www.marriott.com

Good leisure facilities mark out this large golfing hotel.

Architectural purists would have kittens if they were to see the grand columns in the atrium and reception lounge of this modern, leisure-oriented hotel: the carpet appears to be neatly tucked under them and they have a hollow, plywood ring when rapped. But then why linger (long enough to notice the Muzak and ciggie machines) when there is a decent-sized swimming-pool, as well as two 18-hole golf courses and a dozen other ways to keep in shape? This is a place that goes in for active body-pampering: on weekend mornings the hotel bustles with people heading for breakfast after a swim or a round of golf. The restaurant is a large, open-plan area which extends into a pleasant cocktail bar with a log fire and cosy corners – there is also a café-bar which serves snacks and light meals. The bedrooms are well equipped and comfortable, featuring the smart, mock-Georgian décor beloved of hotel designers. In-house movies and useful extras like an iron and ironing board complete a very smooth package.

◑ Open all year ▣ Leave M42 at Junction 6 and take A45 to Coventry; go straight on at Stonebridge flyover; after ¾ mile turn left into Shepherds Lane and continue for 1½ miles to hotel. Private car park ↜ 74 twin, 140 double, 1 suite; all with bathroom/WC; all with TV, room service, hair-dryer, mini-bar, trouser press, direct-dial telephone ✵ 2 restaurants, 5 bars, lounge, games room; functions (max 400 people residential/non residential), conferences; fishing, golf, gym, sauna, solarium, heated indoor swimming-pool, tennis, putting green, croquet; leisure facilities nearby (free for guests); early suppers for children; cots, high chairs, baby-listening ♿ Wheelchair access to hotel and restaurant, WC (M, F), 66 ground-floor bedrooms, 5 specially equipped for disabled people ● Dogs by arrangement; no smoking in 1 restaurant and some bedrooms ▭ Amex, Delta, Diners, MasterCard, Switch, Visa £ Single occupancy of twin/double £71 to £139, twin/double £78 to £139, suite £200 to £278; deposit required. Continental B £9.50, cooked B £11.50; bar L, D £10; set L £16.50; alc D £22.50. Special breaks available

---

MIDDLE CHINNOCK Somerset   map 2

Chinnock House

Middle Chinnock, Crewkerne TA18 7PN
TEL: (01935) 881229 (AND FAX)

Distinguished, tastefully furnished house, thoughtfully run by careful hosts.

The *Venus de Milo* is perfectly formed but incomplete; the same cannot be said of Guy and Charmian Smith's delightful Georgian home, despite the presence of a full-size replica of the said fair lady in the hallway. Everywhere you look in this seemly, detached house you will find items to surprise, delight or intrigue, whether in the restful sitting-room, the dignified dining-room, which is lined with framed maps, or the bright, airy conservatory. This is just the place in which to brush up on your gardening techniques by browsing through some of the many horticultural tomes that you'll find dotted around the house, inspirations to the Smiths as they cultivate their extensive and attractive gardens, where a swimming-pool provides a welcome, if surprising, facility. The dinner menus are designed to reflect guests' preferences, and will often involve garden produce in such dishes as roasted red peppers with garlic and tomatoes, followed by salmon on a bed of leeks and ginger, and then strawberries and cream. The bedrooms are traditionally and handsomely furnished in an agreeably understated way.

◑ Open all year 🚲 Next door to rectory, opposite church in Middle Chinnock. Private car park 🛏 2 twin, 1 double; all with bathroom/WC; tea/coffee-making facilities, hair-dryer, trouser press available ✓ Dining-room, sitting-room, conservatory, garden; heated outdoor swimming-pool; cots, babysitting &. No wheelchair access ● No dogs; no smoking ▭ None accepted £ Single occupancy of twin/double £35, twin/double £55; deposit required. Set D £22

MIDDLEHAM North Yorkshire   map 8

Castle Keep   **NEW ENTRY**

Castle Hill, Middleham, Leyburn DL8 4QR
TEL: (01969) 623665
EMAIL: castle.keep@argonet.co.uk

Two cosy rooms above a restaurant-cum-tea-shop with a lively young proprietor.

Joanne Long seems to have as much energy as one of the famous Middleham racehorses that pass by on their way to the Gallops, as her tea-shop and restaurant is busy from breakfast until dinner. Set back from the road by a cobbled terrace with wrought-iron tables and chairs, the 300-year-old Castle Keep is an unassuming little building, painted white and hung with pretty window boxes that disguise the ancient stones, recycled by seventeenth-century builders from the looming, atmospheric ruins of the medieval castle. The interior design is all Joanne's own work; tiny narrow stairways and low ceilings make for a predictably cottagey interior, but light, sponge-finished walls and stencils add a modern zest. You can take your pick of two delightfully cosy rooms: a Victorian-style double, with a brass bed, cast-iron fireplace and seats in the window for spotting future Derby-winners; or a characterful twin, with half-tester beds, where the low oak beams above mean that you would be well advised not to jump up with a start in the night. The intimate tea-room serves equally well as a breakfast room, and is a romantic setting for candlelit evening meals that might feature Whitby crab pâté, or wild-boar and pheasant pie. Joanne's culinary special subject is puddings, so leave room for maybe hot and sticky brandy pudding, or cinnamon torte with a red-berry coulis.

◑ Open all year 🚲 Turn off market square by Black Swan pub. Castle Keep is 50 yards up on left. Off-street parking (free) 🛏 1 twin, 1 double; twin with bathroom/WC, double with shower/WC; both with TV, hair-dryer ✓ Breakfast room, lounge; early suppers for children &. No wheelchair access ● No smoking in bedrooms ▭ Delta, MasterCard, Visa £ Single occupancy of twin/double £33 to £35, twin/double £46 to £50. Light L £5 to £10, set D £13.50. Special breaks available

---

'At breakfast we asked, "Do you have any jam instead of marmalade?" "No", came the reply. "We make our own jam – this year it's marmalade." I think it was my wife's guffaw of incredulity which extracted a dish of damson jam from the owner's private store.'
On a hotel in Northamptonshire

Greystones

Market Place, Middleham, Leyburn DL8 4NR
TEL: (01969) 622016
WEB SITE: www.yorkshirenet.co.uk/accgde/greystones

A neat and homely guesthouse with a solicitous landlady who is an accomplished cook.

There is something reassuring about hosts like Frances and Keith Greenwood, who know that when you arrive at a hotel there are few pleasures more welcome and relaxing than tucking into coffee and superb home-made scones, jam and shortbread by a log fire. The lounge where afternoon tea is served is the heart of the family home, where you can read or watch TV. But who wants to stay in when the grandstand view of the comings and goings in Middleham's bustling market square beckons you to have a look around? Its four pubs, serving some of Yorkshire's finest ales, like Black Sheep and Theakston's, and a couple of tea-shops act as magnets for visitors and locals alike – or you could stroll up to the moor above the town to track down the seat from which Turner is said to have painted. Many of Frances's guests are regulars at the dinner table, who know that they are on to a good thing with her professional and impeccably presented home cooking. You might start with Wensleydale cheese tart, then a roast leg of lamb followed by lemon tart with ginger ice-cream – everything is home-made, from the delicious sauces to the oatmeal biscuits that accompany superb local cheeses. Bedrooms are trim, with pretty décor, resident knitted dolls or teddies and nice touches like home-made biscuits and a choice of herbal or fruity teas; those at the front of the house have excellent views through the market square to the dales beyond.

◑ Closed Dec & Jan (not New Year) 🔁 In centre of Middleham. On-street parking (free) 🛏 1 twin, 2 double, 1 family room; all with shower/WC exc 1 double with bathroom/WC; all with hair-dryer ⊘ Dining-room, lounge, drying-room; early suppers for children; cots ♿ No wheelchair access ⬤ No children under 5; no dogs or smoking ☐ None accepted £ Single occupancy of twin/double £35, twin/double £55 to £60, family room £70 to £75; deposit required. Set D £16. Special breaks available

---

Millers House

Market Place, Middleham, Leyburn DL8 4NR
TEL: (01969) 622630   FAX: (01969) 623570
EMAIL: hotel@millershouse.demon.co.uk
WEB SITE: www.millershousehotel.demon.co.uk

An elegant, small hotel with charming owners and classy bedrooms.

This good-looking Georgian house is set back a little way from Middleham's market square, so light sleepers can snooze happily through the daily crack-of-dawn equine parade. Owners Judith and Crossley Sunderland take a welcoming, hands-on approach to running their intimate and quietly stylish hotel – an ideal venue for themed weekends based around wine-tasting and horse-racing. Ornate period mouldings set off the smart bar and dining-room, where black-and-white photos continue the racing theme, and a pleasant conservatory expands the dining space with views into the peaceful walled garden. The Sunderlands' love of wine makes for an interesting list to accompany the likes of crab cakes with herb butter, then roast monkfish in Parma ham with ratatouille. But it is in the bedrooms that the hotel's character comes alive with a flourish. Wensleydale, a romantic four-poster room with beautifully painted plaster friezes, is not for the shy – a huge free-standing claw-foot bath is left unenclosed as a main feature of the room. Those on the top floor have extra character from sloping roofs with exposed beams – Wharfedale, with a rich blue colour scheme, hand-painted furniture and a view clear to the ruins of Middleham Castle, is the best of these.

◗ Closed Jan ↗ Set back off market square in Middleham. Private car park ⊫ 1 single, 3 twin, 2 double, 1 four-poster; all with bathroom/WC exc 1 single; all with TV, room service, hair-dryer, direct-dial telephone ⊘ Restaurant, bar, drying-room, conservatory, garden; functions (max 20 people incl up to 13 residential), conferences ⅋ No wheelchair access ● No children under 10; no dogs; smoking in lounge only ▭ Delta, MasterCard, Switch, Visa £ Single £38, single occupancy of twin/double (rates on application), twin/double £76, four-poster £91; deposit required. Set D £20.50. Special breaks available

---

Waterford House

Kirkgate, Middleham, Leyburn DL8 4PG
TEL: (01969) 622090   FAX: (01969) 624020

Intimate restaurant with rooms full of antiques and charm, on Middleham's village square.

Everyl and Brian Madell's home is a shrine to good food and wine, as well as being brimful of Victorian, Regency and Georgian antiques. The heart of the house lies in the small-scale restaurant, where prints, paintings and sundry *objets d'art* hem in the diners, creating a memorably intimate setting for one of Everyl's dinners. Her culinary repertoire sticks to tried-and-tested principles, kicking off with perhaps a chicken and duck liver terrine with cranberry sauce, followed by a fish or game dish of the day or the odd excursion into experimental mode that produces dishes like sole and banana with cream sauce. Pudding may come in the form of chocolate torte with coffee-bean sauce or Yorkshire curd tart. One couple pronounced the breakfasts and New Year's Eve dinner 'excellent', but felt undue pressure to eat in the hotel every evening of their five-night stay. Oenophiles' ears may prick up when they realise that the wine list extends to around a thousand bins, with many gems at a sensible mark-up and a more than ample choice of house wines available by the generously-sized glassful. Creaky, sloping floors and gnarled beams figure prominently in the romantic bedrooms, and the provision of treats is incredible – fresh fruit, chocolates, real milk, filter coffee and a whole bottle of sherry, Crabtree & Evelyn smellies... the list goes on. Most rooms overlook the cobbled square at the front of the house, so you may not need the radio alarm in the morning – not due to traffic noise, which is negligible, but because of the gentle clatter of thoroughbred hooves on their way to an early morning work-out.

○ Open all year ▣ In centre of Middleham, just off market square at top of hill on road to Leyburn. Private car park ▭→ 1 double, 2 four-poster, 2 family rooms; all with bathroom/WC exc 2 four-poster with shower/WC; all with TV, room service, hair-dryer, direct-dial telephone, clock radio ⊘ Restaurant, 2 lounges, drying-room, garden; functions (max 25 people incl up to 12 residential), conferences; civil wedding licence; early suppers for children; cot, high chairs, toys, playroom, babysitting, baby-listening, outdoor play area ⅖ No wheelchair access ● No dogs in public rooms; smoking in 1 lounge only ▭ Delta, MasterCard, Switch, Visa £ Single occupancy of twin/double £50 to £60, twin/double £70 to £80, four-poster £85 to £90, family room £90 to £105. Set L £18.50, D £20.50; alc L £23.50, D £25. Special breaks available

---

MIDHURST West Sussex   map 3

Angel Hotel

North Street, Midhurst GU29 9QA
TEL: (01730) 812421   FAX: (01730) 815928

Storming food and good service in a stylishly chic coaching-inn.

Plum in the middle of Midhurst's busy main street, the Angel has long played a prominent part in this little market town's history, and not just as a watering-hole for locals and visitors alike – until the late 1800s the smart conference room on the first floor was the local court-house. These days the only decisions being made are those of the diners below, who pack the Brasserie and more formal Cowdray Room. The former is a homely mix of beams and lemon yellows, and serves a wide-ranging menu – maybe aubergine and red- pepper terrine followed by lamb hotpot with mashed potato. Across the corridor in the Cowdray Room the atmosphere is a bit less relaxed, but the food is just as tempting, though the prices are higher for dishes like smoked trout and oyster-mushroom salad or pan-fried loin of veal with polenta. The building's late Georgian façade hides a Tudor interior, so the bedrooms at the front have more beams and uneven walls than you'd expect, particularly Room 1, which contains a four-poster. Towards the back of the hotel, the rooms are much newer but furnished in the same tasteful style, with rich colours and plush fabrics. Some, such as Rooms 21 and 22, have the added bonus of views of the ruins of Cowdray Castle; standard doubles, like Room 16, can be a bit cramped.

○ Open all year ▣ In centre of Midhurst on A272; easily identifiable by Union Jack on façade. Private car park ▭→ 4 single, 12 twin, 12 double, 2 four-poster, 2 suites; some in annexe; family rooms available all with bathroom/WC exc 2 single with shower/WC; all with TV, room service, hair-dryer, direct-dial telephone, no tea/coffee-making facilities in rooms ⊘ 2 restaurants, bar, lounge, garden; conferences (max 28 people residential/non-residential), functions; civil wedding licence; early suppers for children; cots, high chairs, baby-listening ⅖ Wheelchair access to hotel (ramp) and restaurants, 1 ground-floor bedroom specially equipped for disabled people ● No smoking in public rooms and some bedrooms ▭ Amex, Delta, Diners, MasterCard, Switch, Visa £ Single from £95, single occupancy of twin/double £95 to £130, twin/double from £105, four-poster from £185, family room from £169, suite from £185; deposit required. Set L £16.50, D £22; alc L £30, D £35. Special breaks available

Spread Eagle

South Street, Midhurst GU29 9NH
TEL: (01730) 816911   FAX: (01730) 815668
EMAIL: i.fleming@virgin.net

Ancient, rambling inn, with an abundance of beams and character.

The twentieth century has finally arrived at the Spread Eagle ('The Spread' to friends and locals alike) with the opening of the spanking new health club. Now you can sweat away the day's cares in the gym or sauna, or take a dip in the alarmingly dark pool – all this cheek-by-jowl with an honourably ancient inn, which has been tending to travellers' needs since 1430. To ease the step back in time, a bright, airy conservatory, with padded wicker chairs and pot-plants, has been created to connect the club with the rest of the hotel. From here on, dumbbells and jacuzzis are replaced by heavy beams and log fires, most prominently in the restaurant. Amid the stiff, white napery and sparkling crystal, you could enjoy a wild-guinea-fowl terrine, seared tuna loin on an endive salad, and then warm pancake tagliatelle with lemon-curd ice-cream – a delicate dessert that is much more appetising than it sounds! Hanging over diners' heads all the while is a plethora of Christmas puddings, each one personalised, wrapped and gently improving all year; yuletide guests get an extra pudding, which dangles decoratively until the next Noël, when it's taken down and devoured. Up a creaking stair or two, the bedrooms vary as much in size and style as they do in price. The luxurious feature rooms, such as the White Room, with its four-poster bed and open brick fireplace, are top dollar. The less extravagant standard rooms are more simply furnished, but still offer a comfortable and pleasant night's rest.

◑ Open all year ⤢ In Midhurst, off A272. Private car park ⬛ 26 twin, 4 double, 8 four-poster, 2 suites; some in annexe; all with bathroom/WC; all with TV, room service, hair-dryer, direct-dial telephone ✅ Restaurant, bar, 2 lounges, conservatory, garden; functions (max 95 people incl up to 80 residential), conferences; civil wedding licence; gym, sauna, solarium, steam room, heated indoor swimming-pool, health and beauty treatment rooms; leisure facilities nearby (reduced rates for guests); early suppers for children; cots, high chairs, babysitting, baby-listening ♿ No wheelchair access
● No smoking in restaurant and some bedrooms; dogs £5 per night ▭ Amex, Diners, MasterCard, Switch, Visa £ Single occupancy of twin/double £85 to £130, twin/double £128 to £156, four-poster/suite £188 to £198; deposit required. Set Sun L £16.50, D £29.50. Special breaks available

---

MILBORNE PORT Dorset   map 2

Old Vicarage   ❘NEW ENTRY❘

Sherborne Road, Milborne Port, Sherborne DT9 5AT
TEL: (01963) 251117   FAX: (01963) 251515

Delightful accommodation at a grand Victorian vicarage – a new venture for a pair of acclaimed ex-London restaurateurs.

The Dorset countryside may seem a very different proposition from London's western fringes, but it's here that Jörgen Kunath and Anthony Ma have come to establish their new enterprise. The large Victorian vicarage of honey-coloured stone is an imposing pile, complete with escutcheoned portico. The interior is just as flamboyant, with high-ceilinged rooms and a bold and cheerful sense of colour setting off a collection of interesting antiques and family heirlooms; oriental prints and plates and a Vietnamese cabinet add interest to a well-proportioned sitting-room. 'A place with a very remarkable interior – almost a museum housing a highly individual collection of beautiful things', wrote one satisfied guest, who was also struck by food 'presenting an interesting mix of East and West'. In a striking dining-room, where guests can dine on Friday and Saturday nights (and on the Sunday of bank holiday weekends), sand-coloured walls, bamboo chairs and a bas relief draw the eye. Dinner might offer a mediterranean fish soup, followed by breast of duck with plums in a spicy port-wine sauce, baked pear and ginger treacle pudding with toffee sauce, and local cheeses. The three bedrooms in the main house are individually designed – the Chinese room, with its spectacular half-tester, standing out. The smaller coach-house annexe rooms are attractively decorated with florals, and furnished with an agreeable mix of old and new items. They're cheaper – though less characterful – than those in the house.

❶ Closed Jan; restaurant closed Sun to Thur eve ☑ 2 miles east of Sherborne, off A30 at western end of Milborne Port. Private car park ⬅ 1 single, 2 twin, 3 double, 1 family room; some in annexe; all with bathroom/WC; all with TV, hair-dryer, direct-dial telephone ✅ Dining-room, lounge, drying-room, library, garden; functions (max 80 people incl up to 13 residential), conferences; croquet; early suppers for children ♿ No wheelchair access ● No children under 5; dogs in annexe bedrooms only; smoking in lounge only ▭ Amex, Delta, MasterCard, Switch, Visa £ Single £25 to £28, single occupancy of twin/double £32 to £55, twin/double £50 to £90, family room £95 to £100; deposit required. Set D £19 to £24. Special breaks available

---

MILDENHALL Suffolk   map 6

Riverside Hotel

Mill Street, Mildenhall, Bury St Edmunds IP28 7DP
TEL: (01638) 717274   FAX: (01638) 715997

Pleasing interiors and attractive bar and restaurant at this business-style Georgian-mansion hotel.

Just past the parish church, on the edge of Mildenhall, you will find this fine, upstanding Georgian house that dates back to 1720. It was built on the banks of the River Lark by a mill owner who could stand at its windows and look across at his lofty mill opposite. Nowadays it is owned by two sisters, Carolyn Child and Alison Lardner, and their respective husbands, John and Keith, and usually one, or both, is involved in the day-to-day running of the hotel. The main strengths of the Riverside Hotel are the features and attractive furnishings of the public rooms, which give it an extremely warm and relaxed feel. There's a clubby bar lined with bookshelves, with a large brass chandelier overhead and low lighting that is easy on the eye. It leads through french windows to a patio and a pleasant lawn stretching down to the river. The Terrace Restaurant is in an extension to the house, and has large picture windows along one side, giving it a conservatory effect. A meal might start with tiger prawns wrapped in filo pastry with a spicy tomato salsa, followed by a quartet of lamb cutlets with colcannon and a dark onion sauce. Upstairs, there is a mixture of rooms, some with newer fittings than others, some with small windows that don't let in a lot of light, but generally well furnished. There are also three cottage rooms overlooking the car park.

○ Open all year ⤢ Take A1101 to Mildenhall; at mini-roundabout turn left; hotel is last building on left as you leave town. Private car park � 3 single, 5 twin, 8 double, 1 four-poster, 4 family rooms; some in annexe; most with bathroom/WC, some with shower/WC; all with TV, room service, hair-dryer, trouser press, direct-dial telephone, radio ⏚ Restaurant, 2 bars, lounge, drying-room, garden; functions (max 100 people incl up to 35 residential), conferences; fishing; early suppers for children; cots, high chairs, baby-listening ⅙ No wheelchair access ● No dogs in restaurant; no smoking in some public rooms ▭ Amex, Delta, Diners, MasterCard, Switch, Visa £ Single £55, single occupancy of twin/double £63, twin/double £84, four-poster £94, family room £84; deposit required. Bar/bistro L, D £6; set L, D £17.50; alc L, D £23. Special breaks available

---

MINCHINHAMPTON Gloucestershire   map 2

Hunters Lodge

Dr Brown's Road, Minchinhampton, Stroud GL6 9BT
TEL: (01453) 883588   FAX: (01453) 731449

Homely yet comfortable B&B, in an Arts and Crafts Movement house.

Situated just outside the small hilltop town of Minchinhampton, Hunters Lodge lies on the edge of the grassy Minchinhampton Common (owned by the National Trust), which, as well as a golf course, contains well-preserved Iron Age earthworks. With its leaded windows, latch front door and weatherbeaten slate roof, to the untrained eye the house looks like a classic ancient Cotswold dwelling, but it turns out to have been built in 1925. Margaret and Peter Helm are extremely friendly and helpful hosts (as a qualified county tour guide, Peter is a mine of information on the area). Guests are encouraged to make full use of a lounge stocked with books, sightseeing literature and local restaurant menus, as well as the large garden and its terrace. The well-received, hearty breakfasts are taken communally around an antique refectory table alongside a fine old dresser. The three large bedrooms are more modestly furnished. Only one is *en suite* (a double with a small shower-room), but the other two have their own bathroom (with a bath), and dressing gowns are provided for the trip down the corridor.

○ Closed Chr ⤢ Turn off A419 at Brimscombe, signposted to Minchinhampton and Burleigh. Follow this road to open common at top of hill; turn left at T-junction and take second right into Dr Brown's Road. Private car park � 1 twin, 2 double; 1 double with bathroom/WC; all with TV, hair-dryer ⏚ Breakfast room, lounge, conservatory, garden ⅙ No wheelchair access ● No children under 10; no dogs; no smoking ▭ None accepted £ Single occupancy of twin/double £30, twin/double £40 to £46; deposit required

MINEHEAD **Somerset**   map 1

Periton Park Hotel

Middlecombe, Minehead TA24 8SN
TEL: (01643) 706885 (AND FAX)

Attractive grounds and a courteous welcome at a country-house hotel a stone's throw from the seaside.

If the word 'Minehead' immediately conjures up images of 'Hi-de-hi' and holiday camps, then Periton Park could be the mantra with which to exorcise the demons. This rather splendid, mid-Victorian house, set amidst considerable grounds high above the A39, exudes restrained good taste, from its pristine façade to the Minton tiles that lead from the porch into the hallway and then into comfortable but dignified public rooms. White archways add depth and interest to the Suffolk-pink drawing-room, where guests gather before dinner to peruse the menu, or relax on chesterfields or comfy armchairs with coffee and a liqueur afterwards. Dinner, served in the bright, half-panelled former billiard room, offers a reasonable choice of inviting country-house fare. The well-equipped bedrooms are spacious and pleasantly, if unremarkably, decorated in a modish country-house style, teaming bold florals with a mix of interesting old and newer furniture. On our inspection visit the hosts were unfailingly attentive without being obtrusive, carrying bags and offering good advice on local sights and attractions.

◑ Closed Jan ⊡ On south side of A39 Minehead to Porlock road. Private car park
⊨ 4 twin, 4 double; all with bathroom/WC exc 2 doubles with shower/WC; all with TV, room service, hair-dryer, direct-dial telephone ⊘ Restaurant, drawing-room, drying-room, garden; functions (max 150 people incl up to 16 residential), conferences; leisure facilities nearby (reduced rates for guests); early suppers for children
& Wheelchair access to hotel (2 steps) and restaurant, 1 ground-floor bedroom specially equipped for disabled people ● No children under 12; dogs in some bedrooms only, by arrangement; smoking in drawing-room and some bedrooms only
▭ Amex, Delta, MasterCard, Switch, Visa £ Single occupancy of twin/double £52 to £58, twin/double £84 to £96 (1998 prices); deposit required. Set D £22.50. Special breaks available

---

MOLLINGTON **Cheshire**   map 7

Crabwall Manor

Parkgate Road, Mollington, Chester CH1 6NE
TEL: (01244) 851666   FAX: (01244) 851400
EMAIL: sales@crabwall.com
WEB SITE: www.crabwall.com

Plush, stylish rooms in a country-house hotel popular with business people.

A short drive from Chester and close to the motorway network, Crabwall Manor is still surprisingly quiet, surrounded largely by fields. The central part of the building is Grade II-listed, built of red-brick and looking like a mini-castle with turrets and crenellated walls, while much newer and more modern-looking extensions radiate out from it. Inside, however, the joins between old and new are seamless – so, although the sense of history is slightly lost, the interior is undeniably plush and luxuriously decorated. A comfortable lounge, dominated by a huge inglenook fireplace, is flanked on one side by a large snooker room decorated in very masculine colours and several conference rooms. The bar, made up of two rooms and boasting good views, leads through to the formal conservatory-style restaurant, where a tempting menu includes options such as medallions of beef with roast shallots, garlic and red-wine sauce or poached quail breast on a potato pancake with a sherry *jus*.

The bedrooms are as comfortable and well equipped as you would expect of a hotel of this standard. Some rooms, such as the luxurious William suite, go beyond expectations, with a lounge area and open fire housed in one of the turrets. Prices are high, and service is professional if a litle impersonal; under the dress code 'guests wearing denim jeans will not be permitted in public areas after 7pm'.

○ Open all year ⚡ Leave M56 (western end), turn left at roundabout on to A5117 (signposted Queensferry and North Wales); at roundabout turn left on to A540; hotel is 2 miles along on right. Private car park 🅿️ 42 twin/double, 6 suites (incl 1 four-poster suite); family rooms available; all with bathroom/WC; all with TV, room service, hair-dryer, trouser press, direct-dial telephone, no tea/coffee-making facilities in rooms ✓ Restaurant, 2 bars, 2 lounges, conservatory, snooker room, conference rooms, garden; conferences (max 100 people incl up to 48 residential), functions; civil wedding licence; snooker, clay-pigeon shooting, croquet; leisure facilities nearby due to open Dec 1998 (free for guests); early suppers for children; cots, high chairs, babysitting ♿ Wheelchair access to hotel and restaurant (ramp), WC (unisex), 20 ground-floor bedrooms, 1 specially equipped for disabled people ● No dogs; no smoking in bedrooms; smoking in bar area only ▭ Amex, Delta, Diners, MasterCard, Switch, Visa £ Single occupancy of twin/double £110, twin/double £150, four-poster/suite £175, family room £150 + £20 per child, babies free (1998 prices); deposit required. Continental B £7, cooked B £10; alc L, D £30. Special breaks available

---

MONKTON COMBE Bath & N.E. Somerset map 2

Monkshill

Shaft Road, Monkton Combe, Bath BA2 7HL
TEL: (01225) 833028 (AND FAX)

Large, lavishly furnished Edwardian house, with spectacular views.

With one-and-a-half acres of neat, terraced gardens dotted with low stone walls and fruit trees, and with views that plunge down to the Avon Valley, Michael and Catherine Westlake's splendid, creeper-clad B&B occupies the crest of the hill above the village, providing spectacular vistas, especially from the front-facing twin room. Family mementoes share top billing with antiques and collectables in this rather grand and cultured home, so you'll find photographs of the Westlake daughters (as well as paintings by one of them) brightening and humanising the elegant, airy sitting-room, and a treasured Miss England sash among the profusion of fresh flowers in the breakfast room. The bedrooms are tastefully and lavishly furnished and feature vibrant colours and classy fabrics.

➊ Closed Chr ⤢ Take B3062 south from Bath; at top of hill turn left into North Road, then right into Shaft Road. Private car park ⇥ 1 twin, 2 double; 1 double with bathroom/WC, twin with shower/WC; all with TV, hair-dryer ✦ Dining-room, sitting-room, conservatory, garden; croquet; cots, high chairs, toys, babysitting ♿ No wheelchair access ✿ No dogs in public rooms; no smoking ▭ MasterCard, Visa £ Single occupancy of twin/double £45 to £60, twin/double £60 to £75; deposit required

---

MONTACUTE Somerset   map 2

Milk House

The Borough, Montacute TA15 6XB
TEL: (01935) 823823

Civilised accommodation at a homely restaurant-with-rooms in a delightful Somerset village.

Lee Dufton's delightful, mullioned, creeper-draped house on the corner of the main square of the picture-postcard village of Montacute has an intriguing history: it's the fifteenth-century successor of an earlier building that supplied milk to a nearby Cluniac priory, so the tradition of catering on this site goes back almost a thousand years. Make your way beyond the glowing golden ashlar frontage of the house, and Lee and her husband Bill may lead you through the rambling house to a sunny terrace and delightfully large, walled garden, where comestibles for the kitchen, including herbs, fruit and vegetables, are lovingly tended. The interior reflects the diverse interests of Lee, a larger-than-life character and something of a raconteur. She originally came to this country from South Africa as a young actress, and later became an art teacher, so you'll find various of her works among the souvenirs of a lifetime's travel in a sitting-room that would be homely but for the huge inglenook that reinforces the house's vintage. Another inglenook provides the focal point in a small, but well-stocked, library. Wall-hangings and antique tables add character to the restaurant, where Lee might serve creamed-walnut soup, followed by fillet of wild salmon with sorrel sauce, and then French toffee'd apple tart. The bedrooms are furnished and decorated in contrasting styles. One suggests a light, Japanese influence, while another is darker and more mysterious.

➊ Closed mid-Oct to mid-Apr; restaurant closed Sun, Mon, Tue eves ⤢ In village square, opposite entrance to Montacute House. On-street parking (free) ⇥ 1 twin, 2 double; all with bathroom/WC; all with hair-dryer ✦ Restaurant, sitting-room, library, garden; functions (max 30 people incl up to 6 residential) ♿ No wheelchair access ✿ No dogs; no smoking ▭ None accepted £ Single occupancy of twin/double £30 to £40, twin/double £48 to £58; deposit required. Cooked B £5; set D £22.50; alc D £25.50. Special breaks available

---

The Guide *office can quickly spot when a hotelier is encouraging customers to write a letter recommending inclusion. Such reports do not further a hotel's cause.*

Wigham

Morchard Bishop, Crediton EX17 6RJ
TEL: (01363) 877350   FAX: (01363) 877350

Wonderful thatched longhouse serving home-produced food and offering good accommodation.

Wigham is a farm tucked away on the far side of a valley, approached through fields filled with all manner of interesting varieties of animal, past an outdoor pool. The fairy-tale Devon longhouse is all thatched roofs and bulging walls, tiny doors, porches and windows, and chunky sculpted furniture. The dining table, window ledges, chairs and bedside tables are beautifully hewn from single pieces of elm and yew – really Hobbit-like. Tapestries adorn the walls, sheepskin rugs are scattered around the flagged floors, beams loom low and huge oak settles are in place by the fire. This is not your average hideaway – the Chilcotts are serious country-dwellers, and the reading matter on the coffee table is *Thatching Today* and magazines on organic farming; you can buy wool and local watercolours. The bedrooms are excellent, again with the superb sculpted furniture, done out in up-market country rustic style. There are even video recorders in the bedrooms – you can choose from a selection of films in the snooker room. The Chilcotts use home-reared meat and organic vegetable in their evening meals. There's no choice of starter or main course, but likes and dislikes are discussed when you book, so give plenty of notice. Typical dishes might include fishballs with coriander sauce, grilled lamb steaks or stir-fried beef with ginger and garlic.

◑ Open all year   ▣ ¾ mile north-west of Morchard Bishop, in the direction of Chulmleigh. Private car park   ⊨⇥ 4 double, 1 four-poster; family rooms available; all with bathroom/WC; all with TV, room service, hair-dryer, direct-dial telephone, video   ⊘ Dining-room, bar, 2 sitting-rooms, snooker room, garden; functions (max 14 people); heated outdoor swimming-pool; early suppers for children, by arrangement   ♿ No wheelchair access   ● No children under 8; no dogs; no smoking   ▢ Switch, Visa   £ Single occupancy of double £105, double £138 to £140, four-poster £158, family room £138 + £35 for 1 child/£50 for 2 children (rates incl dinner); deposit required. Special breaks available

Morston Hall

Morston, Holt NR25 7AA
TEL: (01263) 741041   FAX: (01263) 740419
EMAIL: reception@morstonhall.demon.co.uk
WEB SITE: www.morstonhall.demon.co.uk

A large brick farmhouse close to the Norfolk coast, with a simple, elegant feel and a well-known restaurant.

Situated just off the coastal road, Morston Hall is a plain flint-and-brick style Victorian farmhouse surrounded by a lovely, well-kept garden. In spring, a wistaria graces the walls, adding a softening effect to the severe stonework, while guests can sit outside at wooden tables and look across at the big skies and flat, but never dull, countryside that stretches away southwards. The proprietors, Galton and Tracy Blackiston, are a young couple who, together with Justin Fraser, have created a comfortable, but informal, country home, with the restaurant as its centrepiece. A recent redecoration has given it a striking look, with strong colours to the fore. This leads through to a stylish conservatory, with blue cane furniture and a stripped floor, that looks out to a pretty ornamental pool. Guests stay on a dinner, bed and breakfast basis, and dinner is served at 8pm on the dot. A typical four-course, no-choice menu might start with a warm apple boudin on sauté wild mushrooms with a whole-grain mustard sauce, followed by steamed halibut on a confit of fennel with a tomato-butter sauce, then roast best end of lamb with a rich niçoise *jus* and, finally, chilled caramel cream with crème anglaise and a sugar cage. While some bedrooms, such as the Sandringham and Beeston, are enormous, one reader on a repeat visit found their room on the small size: 'only one of us could move round it at any one time (the other lying on the bed to get out of the way!)'.

◗ Closed 1 Jan to Feb   ▨ On A149, 2 miles west of Blakeney. Private car park
▙—┙ 1 twin, 5 double; all with bathroom/WC; all with TV, room service, hair-dryer, direct-dial telephone   ⊘ Restaurant, 2 lounges, drying-room, conservatory, garden; functions (max 40 people incl up to 12 residential), conferences; early suppers for children; cots, high chairs, toys, babysitting, baby-listening   ♿ No wheelchair access   ● No dogs in public rooms; no smoking in restaurant   ⊟ Amex, Delta, Diners, MasterCard, Switch, Visa   £ Twin/double £160 to £180 (rates incl dinner); deposit required. Set L £18. Special breaks available

---

MOULSFORD Oxfordshire map 2

Beetle & Wedge

Ferry Lane, Moulsford, Wallingford OX10 9JF
TEL: (01491) 651381   FAX: (01491) 651376

Popular, distinctive hotel, with two restaurants, fronting the river in Toad and Ratty territory.

'Why Beetle & Wedge?', we hear you asking. Well, you'll have to ask your hostess, Kate Smith, to explain this fascinating (but rather complicated) historical anecdote as she shows you the photos of the gabled, handsome hotel way back then, which take up a considerable amount of wall space in the graceful sitting-room. The place exudes stories – Jerome K Jerome wrote *Three Men in a Boat* here, and Kenneth Grahame, of *The Wind in the Willows* fame, lived just upriver. The riverside location is still suitably inspiring, with cow-filled fields stretching out beyond the water and the odd craft passing lazily by. If boaters feel so inclined, they can moor at the Boat House – Kate's rustic, flagged and wooden alternative eatery, which is full of characterful beams and good charcoal smells – and sample such dishes as half-a-dozen rock oysters, or game pie with braised fennel and mashed potatoes. In summer, the Beetle & Wedge really comes into its own: you can eat on the patio by the Boat House or on the lawn in the Watergarden, or you can enjoy your drink down at the end of the jetty. More formal dining takes place in the restaurant in the main house, where the other half of the team, Richard Smith, serves up classic dishes with exciting twists, such as a pheasant and foie-gras salad with wild mushrooms and a truffle sauce, or Dover sole with a lobster and vegetable casserole and Chardonnay sauce. The bedrooms are fittingly extravagant, with huge, canopied beds and plenty of interesting antiques. Most are in the main house, some in the cottage – choose one with a river view and pay extra.

◖ Closed 25 Dec; 1 restaurant closed Sun & Mon eves ⃞ In Moulsford, turn towards river via Ferry Lane. Private car park ⟞ 6 double, 1 four-poster, 1 family room, 2 suites; some in annexe; all with bathroom/WC; all with TV, limited room service, hair-dryer, direct-dial telephone ⬦ 2 restaurants, bar, conservatory, sitting-room, garden; functions (max 20 people residential/non-residential), conferences; early suppers for children; cots, high chairs, toys, babysitting, baby-listening ⅙ Wheelchair access to hotel and restaurant, WC (unisex), 2 ground-floor bedrooms ◖ No dogs in public rooms and some bedrooms; no smoking in restaurants or bedrooms; ⃞ Amex, Delta, Diners, MasterCard, Switch, Visa ⃞ Single occupancy of double £90 to £110, double £135, four-poster/family room/suite £150; deposit required. Bar/bistro L, D £25; set L £27.50, D £35; alc L, D £27.50. Special breaks available

---

MULLION Cornwall   map 1

Polurrian Hotel

Mullion, Helston TR12 7EN
TEL: (01326) 240421   FAX: (01326) 240083

Grand, solid, old-style hotel in tremendous spot, geared towards families.

There's a tradition of staff v. families in cricket and rounders games and a crèche with a full-time nanny on call in summer – such is this hotel's enthusiasm for its younger guests. Indeed, when we inspected, tables for the under-10s were being set in the Marconi Lounge, and Bernard, the faithful retainer, was gearing up to entertain. Bernard thought about retirement a while ago, but stayed on by public demand. Families come back year after year to this wild retreat by the sea, and there's plenty for them to do: a well-equipped leisure centre offers swimming, squash, weights and massage; there's a secret beach reached by a steep cliff path; while the outdoor pool provides endless fun. The house itself is a remote, stately Edwardian building. Inside, the décor, in muted pastels, creates a peaceful atmosphere. The accent is on the views rather than the colour scheme, although fresh flowers, daily weather charts and meteorological predictions are pleasing additions. Both restaurants have spectacular, carved high-backed chairs and, of course, the view – in high summer the sun sets as late as 10pm. The menu offers a choice of three dishes at each course; a salad of crab with prawns could be followed by sauté collops of pork with Puy lentils, rounded off with a blackcurrant and apple pie served with a vanilla anglaise sauce. The simply furnished bedrooms, which are done out in pastels, are spacious and calming.

◑ Open all year ⤢ Mullion is signposted from A3083 at Penhale, between Helston and the Lizard. Private car park ⤙ 1 single, 8 twin, 10 double, 4 four-poster, 12 family rooms, 4 suites; all with bathroom/WC; all with TV, room service, hair-dryer, direct-dial telephone, some with trouser press ⌀ 2 restaurants, bar, 2 lounges, TV room, drying-room, 2 games rooms, garden; functions (max 100 people incl up to 78 residential), conferences; gym, sauna, solarium, heated indoor and outdoor swimming-pools, putting green, tennis, squash, snooker, croquet; early suppers for children; cots, high chairs, toys, playrooms, babysitting, baby-listening, outdoor play area ♿ Wheelchair access to hotel and restaurants, 8 ground-floor bedrooms ⊜ No dogs in public rooms (£6 per night in bedrooms); no smoking in some public rooms ▭ Amex, Delta, Diners, MasterCard, Switch, Visa £ Single £76, single occupancy of twin/double £96, twin/double/four-poster/family room £90 to £180, suite £210 (rates incl dinner); deposit required. Bar/bistro L £5. Special breaks available

---

MUNGRISDALE Cumbria   map 10

The Mill

Mungrisdale, Penrith CA11 0XR
TEL: (017687) 79659   FAX: (017687) 79155

A fine location in the northern fells for this small, cottagey hotel.

A simple, whitewashed former miller's house dating from 1651, the Mill stands by a trout stream amid pretty gardens. It makes a pleasant touring base for a less well-known area of the Lakes, around the John Peel country of Caldbeck. An unobtrusive house of few architectural pretensions in typical Cumbrian style, it retains some period character and even has a footnote in Lakeland history: Wordsworth and Coleridge slept here in 1801. (The similar-looking Mill Inn next door, which also has rooms, must baffle some visitors – so do not confuse the two.) The main lounge has chintzy furniture and an open fireplace where drinks are served and dinner menus perused, and a couple of smaller seating areas are available. The narrow, oblong proportions give it a 'waiting-room' look, though owners Richard and Eleanor Quinlan have done their best, with books, magazines and pictures, to give guests the opportunity to avoid staring at each other. The dining-room is similarly simple, with plain wooden furnishings and outsized, precarious-looking candles made by bolting unused stubs together. Richard Quinlan stays mostly front of house, while Eleanor cooks. Dinner (included in the room rates) is a well-prepared set menu with vegetarian options and several choices at the pudding stage. The bedrooms are simple and unremarkable.

◑ Closed Nov to Feb ⤢ Hotel is 2 miles north of A66, signposted midway between Penrith and Keswick. Private car park ⤙ 4 twin, 5 double; 6 with bathroom/WC, 1 with shower/WC; all with TV, room service, hair-dryer ⌀ Dining-room, 2 lounges, drying-room, conservatory, garden; fishing; early suppers for children; cots, high chairs ♿ No wheelchair access ⊜ No dogs in public rooms; no smoking in dining-room ▭ None accepted £ Single occupancy of twin/double £56 to £66, twin/double £86 to £101 (rates incl dinner); deposit required. Special breaks available

---

Prices are quoted per room *rather than* per person.

Hotels
of the Year

Here is our pick of hotels for this edition. They are not necessarily the most sumptuous or the most expensive in the book – in some cases, far from it – but we felt they deserved special mention this year, not just in their particular category, but for all-round excellence.

Standard bearers

Glorious grounds

Places to be seen

Seaside stunners

Business bases

Superior B&Bs

Farmhouse specials

Restaurants with rooms

Notable new entries

Idyllic inns

Island hideaways

Something different

Personal touches

Summer Lodge

Standard bearers

The Goring
London (page 42)

Gravetye Manor
East Grinstead
(page 220)

The Ley
Innerleithen
(page 579)

**One Devonshire
Gardens**
Glasgow (page 575)

Summer Lodge
Evershot (page 230)

The Goring

Glorious grounds

Gliffaes Country House
Crickhowell (page 632)

Linthwaite House
Bowness-on-
Windermere (page 125)

Places to be seen

The Hempel London
(page 46)

The Howard
Edinburgh (page 569)

St Tudno Hotel

Seaside stunners

Hotel Riviera
Sidmouth (page 448)

Royal Hotel
Ventnor (page 496)

St Tudno Hotel
Llandudno (page 644)

Royal
Hotel

Business bases

42 The Calls
Leeds (page 312)

The Copthorne
Newcastle (page 373)

The Halkin
London (page 44)

Turnberry Hotel
Turnberry (page 616)

Superior B&Bs

Bales Mead
West Porlock (page 513)

Forge Cottage
Chilgrove (page 175)

Haydon House
Bath (page 94)

Tor Down House
Belstone (page 101)

Farmhouse specials

Fishers Farm
Shefford Woodlands
(page 441)

Manor Farm
Botallack (page 118)

Rowanfield
Ambleside (page 74)

Upper Buckton Farm
Leintwardine
(page 314)

Rowanfield

Restaurants with rooms

Altnaharrie Inn
Ullapool (page 617)

The Cross
Kingussie (page 590)

Great House
Lavenham (page 309)

Mulberry House
Torquay (page 480)

Seafood Restaurant
Padstow (page 393)

Great House

Notable new entries

Hotel du Vin & Bistro
Tunbridge Wells (page 486)

Kennel Holt
Cranbrook (page 197)

Idyllic inns

The Crown
Portpatrick
(page 602)

Inn on the Green
Cookham Dean
(page 191)

Nobody Inn
Doddiscombsleigh
(page 211)

Peacock Inn
Redmile
(page 407)

Rose and Crown
Romaldkirk
(page 412)

Rose and Crown

Isle of Eriska

Island hideaways

Glenmachrie
Port Ellen (page 601)

Isle of Eriska
Eriska (page 572)

Something different

Huntsham Court
Huntsham (page 287)

West Usk Lighthouse
St Brides Wentlooge
(page 663)

**Whitstable Oyster
Fishery Co**
Whitstable (page 517)

West Usk Lighthouse

Personal touches

Little Orchard House
Rye (page 419)

Trebrea Lodge
Tintagel (page 480)

Trebrea
Lodge

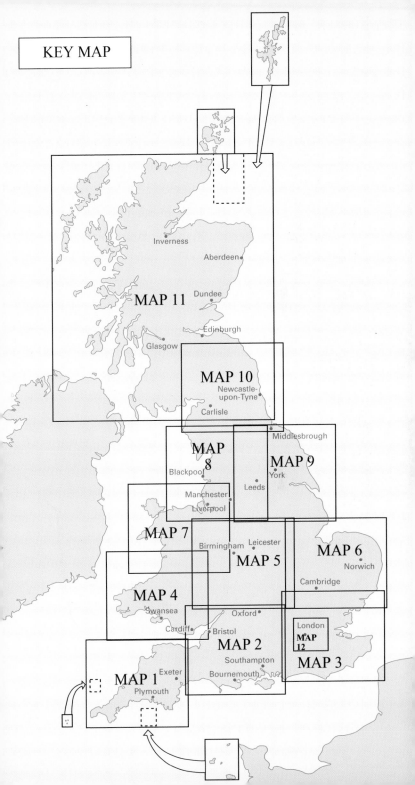

KEY MAP

MAP 11

Inverness
Aberdeen
Dundee
Edinburgh
Glasgow

MAP 10
Newcastle-upon-Tyne
Carlisle
Middlesbrough

MAP 8
Blackpool
Manchester
Liverpool

MAP 9
York
Leeds

MAP 7
Birmingham
Leicester

MAP 5

MAP 6
Norwich
Cambridge

MAP 4
Swansea
Cardiff
Bristol
Oxford

MAP 2

London
MAP 12

MAP 3
Southampton
Bournemouth

MAP 1
Exeter
Plymouth

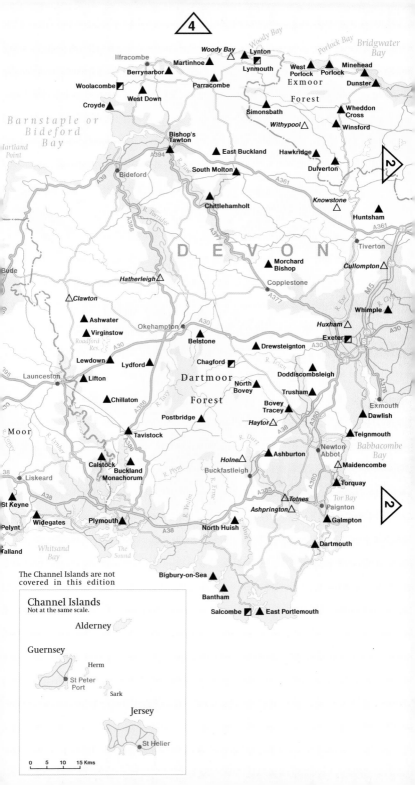

Ilfracombe

Woody Bay

Lynton
Lynmouth

Martinhoe

Berrynarbor

Porlock Bay

Bridgwater Bay

West Porlock
Porlock
Minehead
Dunster

Exmoor

Woolacombe

Parracombe

West Down

Forest

Croyde

Simonsbath

Wheddon Cross
Winsford

Barnstaple or Bideford Bay

Withypool

Hartland Point

Bishop's Tawton

East Buckland

Hawkridge

Bideford

A394

R. Taw

South Molton

A361

Dulverton

A39

R. Torridge

Chittlehamholt

Knowstone

Huntsham

D E V O N

A377

Tiverton

Morchard Bishop

A386

Hatherleigh

Copplestone

Cullompton

R. Exe

M5

Whimple

R. Culm

Clawton

Bude

Ashwater

Virginstow

Okehampton

A30

Belstone

Huxham

Exeter

A30

A35

Roadford Res.

Lewdown

A30

Lydford

Chagford

Dartmoor

Drewsteignton

A386

Launceston

Lifton

Chillaton

Forest

North Bovey

R. Teign

Doddiscombsleigh

Trusham

Exmouth

R. Tavy

Postbridge

Bovey Tracey

Haytor

Dawlish

Teignmouth

Tavistock

R. Dart

Newton Abbot

Babbacombe Bay

M o o r

Holne

Ashburton

Maidencombe

Liskeard

Calstock

Buckland Monachorum

R. Plym

Buckfastleigh

A385

A380

Torquay

St Keyne

Totnes

Tor Bay

Paignton

Pelynt

Widegates

R. Lynher

Plymouth

A38

Ashprington

Galmpton

Talland

North Huish

R. Avon

R. Erme

Dartmouth

Whitsand Bay

The Sound

Bigbury-on-Sea

The Channel Islands are not covered in this edition

Bantham

Salcombe
East Portlemouth

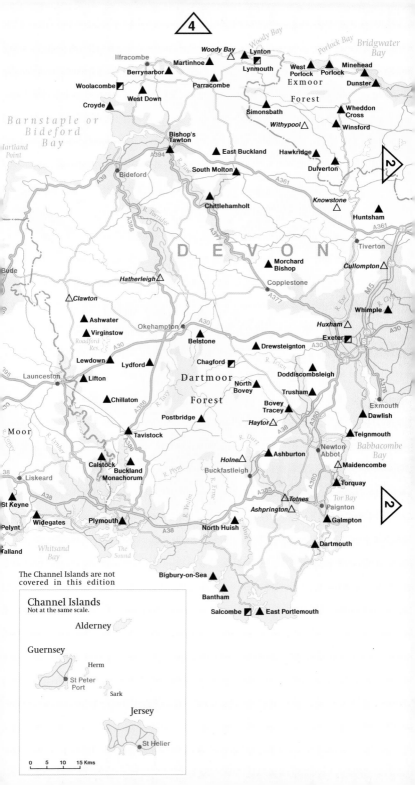

Channel Islands
Not at the same scale.

Alderney

Guernsey

Herm

St Peter Port

Sark

Jersey

St Helier

0   5   10   15 Kms

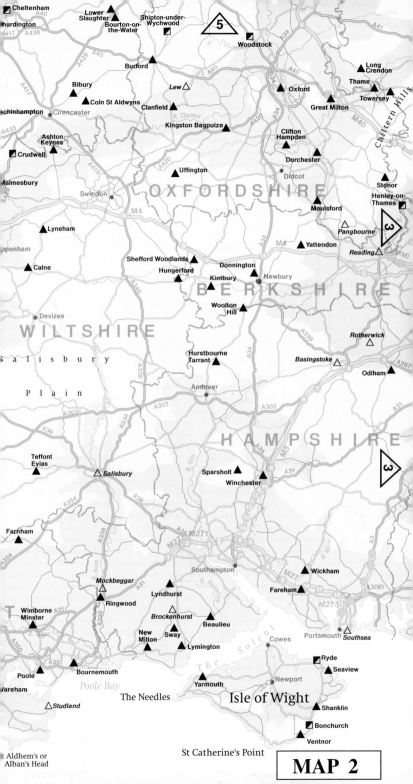

Cheltenham
hurdington
A40
A436
A417
A429 A40
Lower Slaughter
Bourton-on-the-Water
Shipton-under-Wychwood
5
Woodstock
A34
A40
A41
Long Crendon
Thame
Towersey
Chiltern Hills
M40
Burford
Bibury
Coln St Aldwyns
Clanfield
R. Thames
Kingston Bagpuize
Lew
Oxford
Great Milton
A420
Cirencester
achinhampton
A433
Ashton Keynes
Crudwell
OXFORDSHIRE
Clifton Hampden
Dorchester
A417
A419
Malmesbury
Swindon
M4
Uffington
Didcot
Stonor
Henley-on-Thames
A420
Moulsford
Lyneham
Pangbourne
3
A34
M4
Yattendon
Reading
Calne
Shefford Woodlands
Hungerford
Donnington
Kintbury
Newbury
BERKSHIRE
openham
A346
Devizes
WILTSHIRE
Woolton Hill
A339
Rotherwick
alisbury
Plain
A338
Hurstbourne Tarrant
A34
Basingstoke
A287
Odiham
Andover
A303
A303
A31
A36
HAMPSHIRE
M3
3
Teffont Evias
A354
Salisbury
Sparsholt
Winchester
A34
A31
A36
A338
R. Test
A3
Farnham
A354
A36 M271
M27
A3(M)
Southampton
R. Beaulieu
Wickham
Mockbeggar
Lyndhurst
Fareham
M27
M275
Wimborne Minster
Ringwood
Brockenhurst
Beaulieu
Cowes
Portsmouth
Southsea
A31
R. Stour
New Milton
Sway
Lymington
The Solent
Ryde
Seaview
A35
A350
Poole
Bournemouth
Yarmouth
Newport
Wareham
Poole Bay
The Needles
Isle of Wight
Shanklin
Studland
Bonchurch
Ventnor
St Catherine's Point
t Aldhem's or Alban's Head

MAP 2

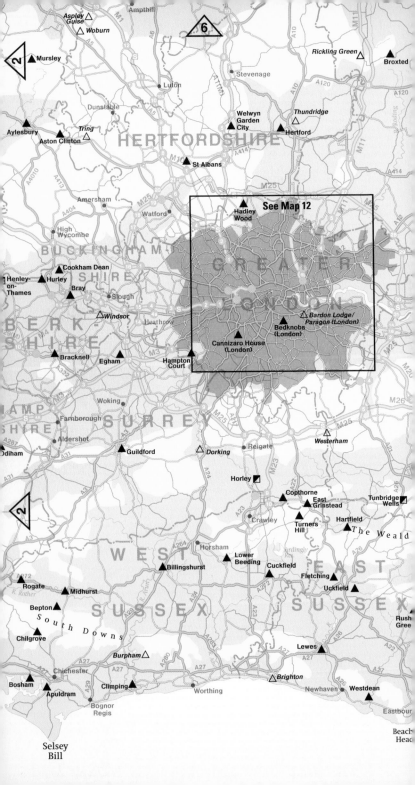

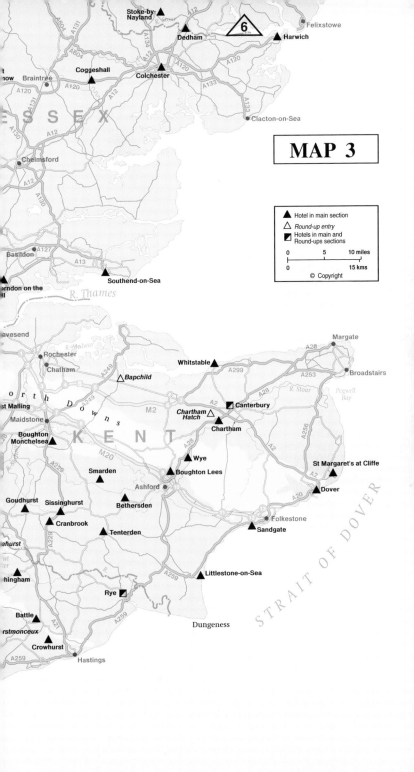

MAP 3

▲ Hotel in main section
△ Round-up entry
◩ Hotels in main and Round-ups sections

0   5   10 miles
0   15 kms
© Copyright

MAP 4

▲ Hotel in main section
△ *Round-up entry*
◣ Hotels in main and
   Round-ups sections

0	5	10 miles
0		15 kms
© Copyright

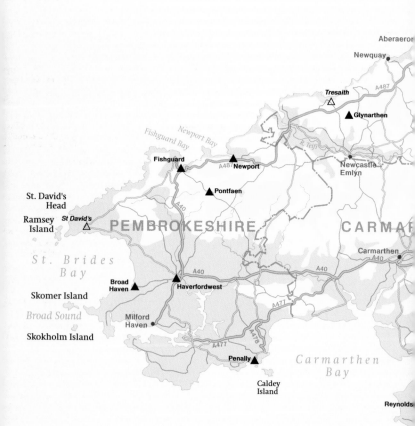

CARDIGAN

BAY

Aberaeron
Newquay

Tresaith
△
▲ Glynarthen

Fishguard Bay *Newport Bay*

Fishguard ▲ ▲ Newport

Newcastle
Emlyn

▲ Pontfaen

St. David's
Head
Ramsey   *St David's*
Island   △   PEMBROKESHIRE   CARMAR

Carmarthen

St. Brides
Bay

Skomer Island

Broad Sound

Skokholm Island

Broad
Haven ▲   ▲ Haverfordwest

Milford
Haven •

Carmarthen
Bay

Penally ▲

Caldey
Island

Reynolds

BRISTOL

MAP 5

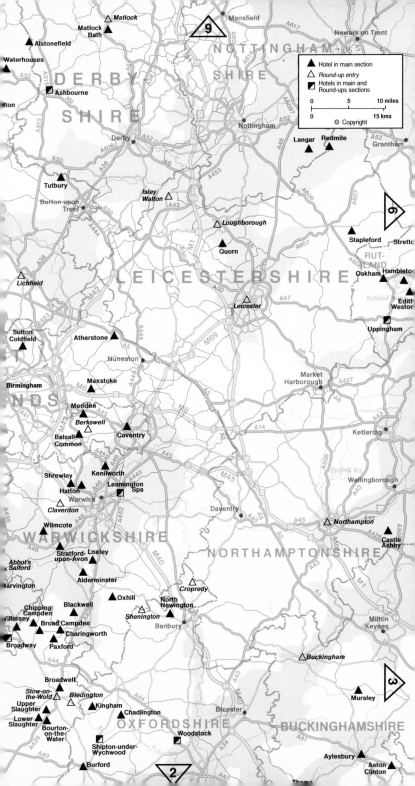

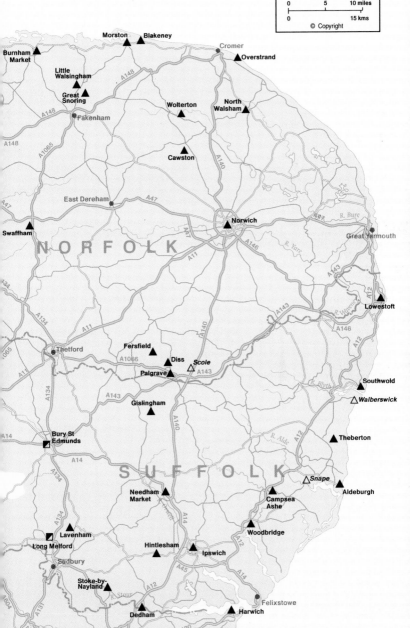

MAP 6

- ▲ Hotel in main section
- △ Round-up entry
- ◪ Hotels in main and Round-ups sections

0 — 5 — 10 miles
0 — 15 kms
© Copyright

NORTH SEA

NORFOLK

SUFFOLK

Burnham Market
Morston
Blakeney
Cromer
Overstrand
Little Walsingham
Great Snoring
A148
Fakenham
Wolterton
North Walsham
A140
Cawston
East Dereham
A47
Norwich
R. Bure
Swaffham
R. Yare
Great Yarmouth
A11
A146
A143
Lowestoft
Thetford
Fersfield
A1066
Diss
Scole
Palgrave
A143
Southwold
R. Blyth
Walberswick
Gislingham
A140
Theberton
R. Alde
Bury St Edmunds
A14
Snape
Needham Market
Campsea Ashe
Aldeburgh
Lavenham
Long Melford
Hintlesham
Woodbridge
Ipswich
Sudbury
A45
A12
R. Stour
Stoke-by-Nayland
Felixstowe
Dedham
Harwich
Coggeshall
Colchester
A120
Braintree

9

3

MAP 7

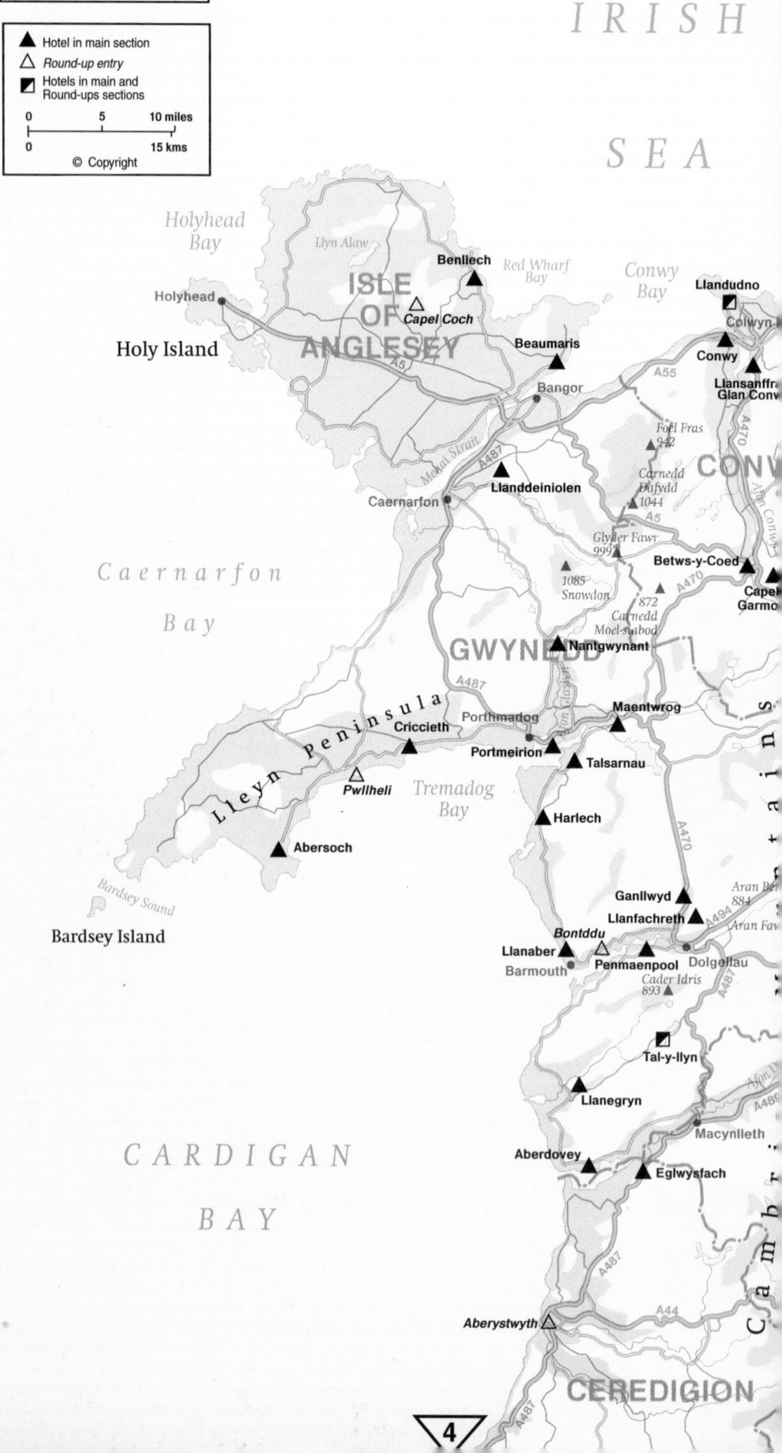

Hotel in main section ▲
Round-up entry △
Hotels in main and ▰
Round-ups sections

0 — 5 — 10 miles
0 — 15 kms
© Copyright

IRISH

SEA

Holyhead Bay

Llyn Alaw

Holyhead

Holy Island

ISLE OF ANGLESEY

Benllech ▲
Capel Coch △

Red Wharf Bay

Beaumaris ▲

Bangor

Conwy Bay

Llandudno ▰
Colwyn

Conwy ▲
Llansanffr
Glan Conw ▲

A55

Foel Fras 942

CON

Caernarfon

Caernarfon Bay

Llanddeiniolen ▲

Carnedd Dafydd 1044

Glyder Fawr 999

Betws-y-Coed ▲
Capel Garmo ▲

1085 Snowdon

872 Carnedd Moel-siabod

GWYNEDD

Nantgwynant ▲

A487

Porthmadog

Maentwrog ▲

Lleyn Peninsula

Criccieth ▲
Portmeirion ▲
Talsarnau ▲

Pwllheli △

Tremadog Bay

Harlech ▲

Abersoch ▲

Bardsey Sound

Bardsey Island

Ganllwyd ▲
Aran Be 884
Llanfachreth ▲

Bontddu △

Llanaber ▲
Barmouth

Penmaenpool ▲
Dolgellau

Cader Idris 893

Tal-y-llyn ▰

Llanegryn ▲

Macynlleth

CARDIGAN

Aberdovey ▲
Eglwysfach ▲

BAY

Aberystwyth △

CEREDIGION

4

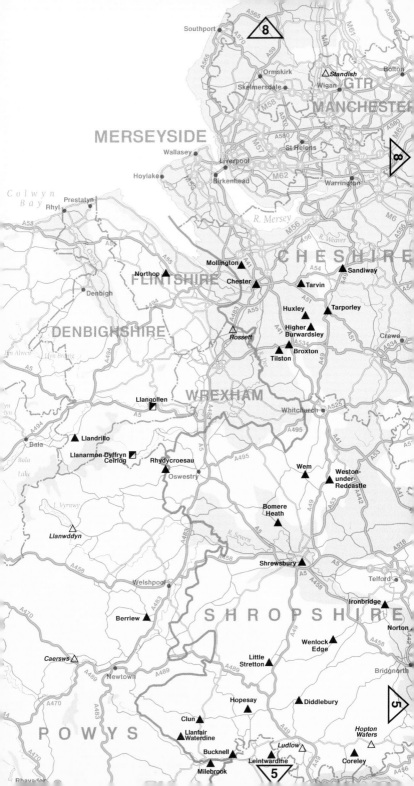

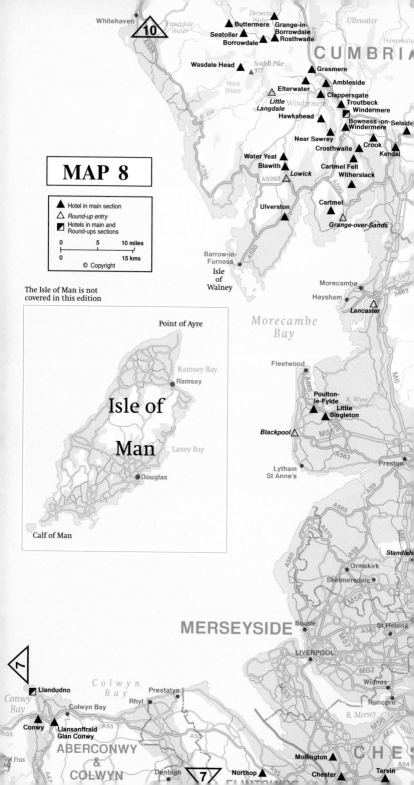

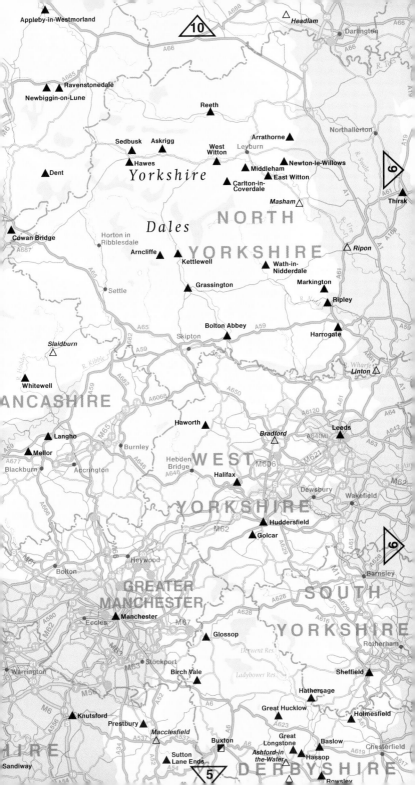

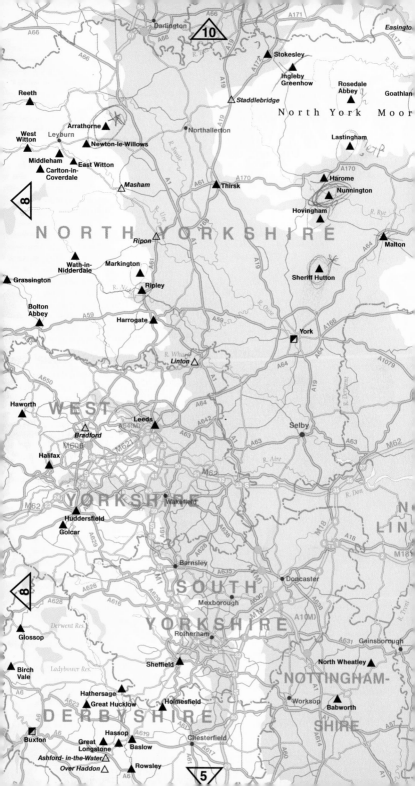

▲ Hotel in main section
△ Round-up entry
◪ Hotels in main and Round-ups sections

0   5   10 miles
0   15 kms
© Copyright

Whitby
Dunsley

A171

A170

▲ Scarborough

A64

▲ Filey

A165

Flamborough
▲
Flamborough Head

● Bridlington

Bridlington Bay

Yorkshire Wolds

A166

A165

A163

EAST RIDING
OF YORKSHIRE

A1079

A1035

A165

△
Walkington

KINGSTON
UPON HULL

● Kingston
upon Hull

A63

R. Humber

▲ Winteringham
● Barton-upon-Humber

A15

A160

RTH
:LNSHIRE

● Scunthorpe

A18

M180

A159

A15

A46

A173

N.E.
LINCOLNSHIRE

● Grimsby

Spurn Head

A18

A16

A631

A1103

A46

▲
Swinhope

A15

The Wolds

● Louth

East Barkwith ▲

A158

A158

A16

A57

▲ Lincoln

LINCOLNSHIRE

A158B

A158

● Skegness

△6△

uothquan

'into '07

Peebles

A72 Walkerburn

Galashiels

Innerleithen

Kelso

Culter Fell 755

Melrose   St Boswells

B O R D E R S

St Mary's Loch

Hart Fell 808

Jedburgh

Hawick

T h e   C h e v i

Moffat

Caldcleugh 608

Queensberry 697

Kielder Water

D U M F R I E S   &
G A L L O W A Y

R. Esk

Daer Res.

R. Nith

Dumfries

R. Eden

Brampton

Carlisle

Alston

Maryport

Ireby

Cross Fell 893

Bassenthwaite
Lake

Bassenthwaite

Cow Green Res.

Cockermouth

Skiddaw 931

Mungrisdale

Penrith

Workington

Bassenthwaite Lake

Brougham

Lorton

Applethwaite

A66

Watermillock

Braithwaite

Derwent Water

Keswick

Threlkeld

Ullswater

Ullswater

Whitehaven

Ennerdale Water

Krummock Water

Grange-in-Borrowdale

Haweswater

Appleby-in-Westmorland

Buttermere

Rosthwaite

C U M B R I A

Seatoller   Borrowdale

Wasdale
Head

Grasmere

Wast Water

Ravenstonedale

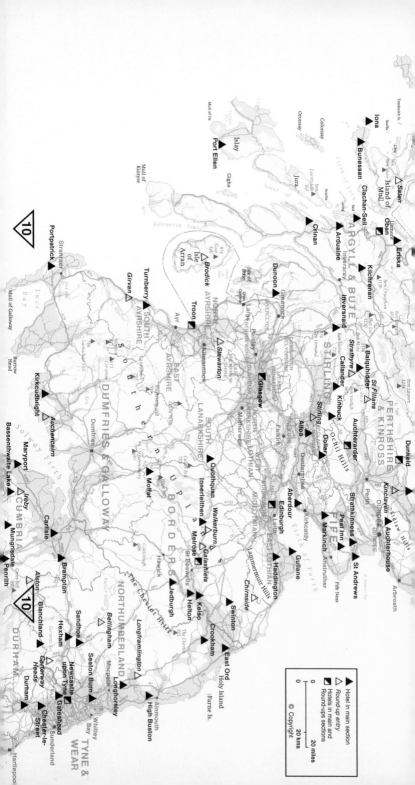

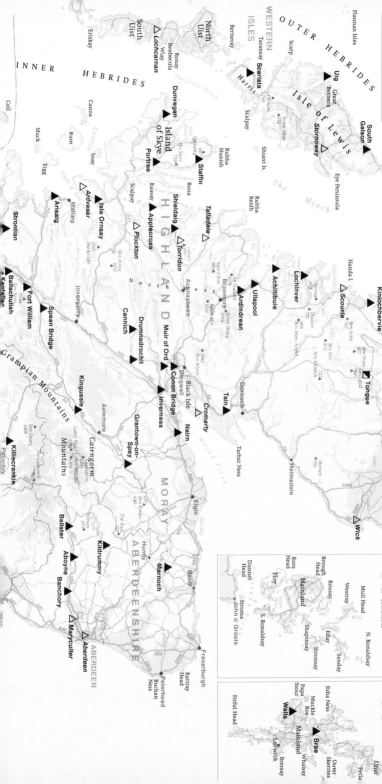

MAP 11

INNER HEBRIDES

OUTER HEBRIDES

WESTERN ISLES

Flannan Isles

North Uist
Benbecula
Ronay
Wiay
South Uist
Eriskay
△ Lochcarnan

Taransay
Scarp
Berneray
Scalpay
Harris
△ Scarista
Shiant Is.

Isle of Lewis
Great Bernera
▲ Uig
Butt of Lewis
Eye Peninsula
△ Stornoway
▲ South Galson

Coll
Canna
Rum
Muck
Eigg
Soay

Dunvegan
Island of Skye
▲ Portree
△ Staffin
Raasay
Rona
Rubha Hunish

△ Ardvasar
Isle Ornsay
▲ Strontian
▲ Arisaig
Mallaig
△ Applecross
△ Plockton
△ Shieldaig
△ Torridon
△ Talladale
Rubha Reidh

HIGHLAND

Ballachulish
Kentallen
Fort William
Spean Bridge
Invergarry
Cannich
Drumnadrochit
Muir of Ord
Achnasheen

Killiecrankie
Pitlochry

Kingussie
Aviemore
Cairngorm Mountains
Grantown-on-Spey

Grampian Mountains

Ballater
Aboyne
Banchory
△ Maryculter
Aberdeen

ABERDEENSHIRE

Kildrummy
▲ Marnoch
Huntly
Banff
Elgin

MORAY

Nairn
▲ Inverness
Conon Bridge
Black Isle
Dingwall
△ Cromarty
Tain
Dornoch

Helmsdale

△ Ullapool
Ardindrean
▲ Lochinver
▲ Achiltibuie
Baosbheinn

▲ Kinlochbervie
△ Scourie
Handa I.
Cape Wrath

▪ Tongue
△ Thurso
Wick
Dunnet Head
Duncansby Head
Stroma

Fraserburgh
Peterhead
Buchan Ness
Rattray Head

Mull Head
Westray
N. Ronaldsay
Rousay
Sanday
Eday
Mainland
Stronsay
Shapinsay
Hoy
S. Ronaldsay
John o' Groats
Brough Head

Esha Ness
Muckle Roe
Papa Stour
▲ Walls
Mainland
△ Brae
Lerwick
Bressay
Whalsay
Outer Skerries
Fetlar
Unst
Fitful Head

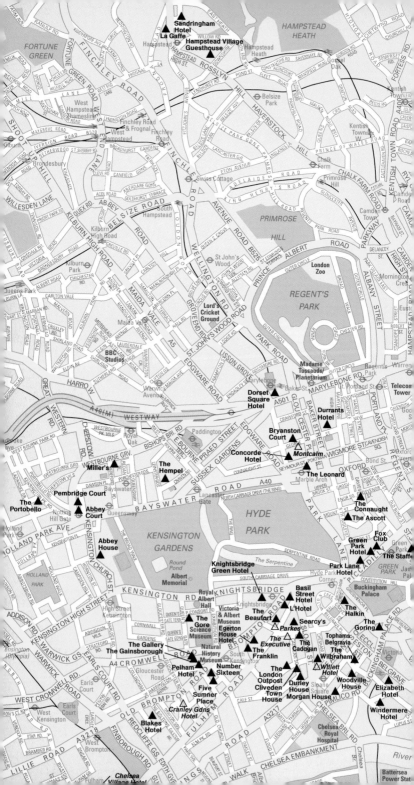

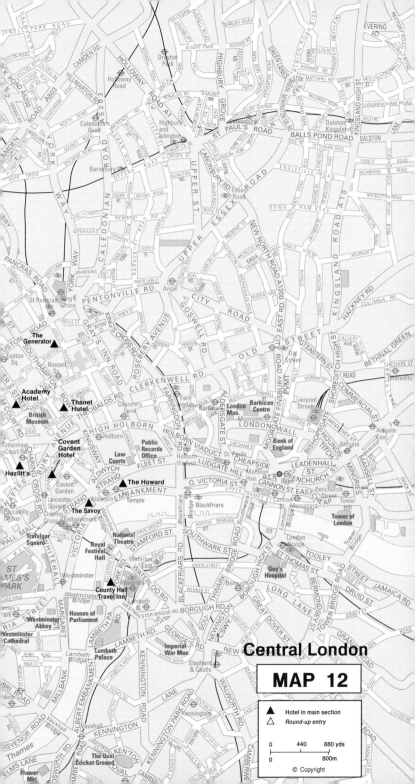

Central London

MAP 12

▲ Hotel in main section
△ Round-up entry

0	440	880 yds
0	800m	

© Copyright

The tales they tell

We were given one small tablet of soap for the two of us for the two nights and we eked it out on the second night. The tissue container was almost empty and when used up was not replaced. A breakfast tray with food on, left in the corridor by another resident in the morning, was still there that evening when we went to bed. Next morning, although the tray had been removed, lumps of croissant were scattered all over the corridor.
On a hotel in Wales

The main evening's entertainment was overhearing the proprietors take a young waiter to task for asking permission to go home, having completed his three hours. This request triggered a lengthy lecture as to their expectations of their staff and how this young man should aspire to exude confidence and a professional style when carrying a spoon and fork so that he could engage in conversation with dining guests. This dressing down took place in the main dining-room next to the sitting-room where we were having our coffee, so we could hear every word.
On a hotel in the West Country

I turned up to inspect a hotel but the receptionist refused to let me through the front door, saying that I failed the "smell test". Trying not to sound offended, I said that I realised I had been on the road for a week, but that I had had a bath that morning. "Oh, that's not the problem," said the receptionist. "The problem is you're wearing deodorant." It turned out that the proprietor was allergic to all "artificial" scents, including perfume, polish – in fact, anything that had scent added. Needless to say, I felt I could not recommend the hotel.
Inspector's report

MURSLEY **Buckinghamshire** map 5

Richmond Lodge

Mursley, Milton Keynes MK17 0LE
TEL: (01296) 720275

Rural B&B with welcoming hosts and handsome surroundings.

A stay at this tall Edwardian country villa is likely to feel like a family occasion, with Christine and Peter Abbey much involved with their guests'comings and goings. Breakfast is taken beside the blue Aga and pine dresser in the family kitchen, with the opportunity to peruse the extensive supply of local tourist information; an evening meal, if requested, is served in the dignified dining-room, around an old oak table, or relocated to the patio, weather permitting. Christine's former life as a hotel manager has obvious organisational benefits, and it is fun anticipating the influence of Peter's part-time shepherding duties when it comes to stirring visitors from their post-prandial reveries. The three bedrooms are identified by their co-ordinated colour schemes, with Green overlooking the front paddock, Yellow enjoying the best views over the surrounding downs (and the now formidable cedar, planted by Percy Thrower) and Blue, tight for space but pleasantly light. Yellow and Blue share a bathroom. Those of a sporting bent can opt for tennis on the Lodge's grass court, or a more sedate game of croquet out on the lawn. Given the isolated feel of the Lodge, it's a surprisingly short walk along the lane into Mursley, a quiet village with a collection of attractive thatched cottages.

◖ Closed Chr & New Year ⤓ Off B4032 east of Mursley village; hotel is signposted. Private car park ⇖ 2 twin, 1 double; 1 twin with bathroom/WC; all with TV, room service, some with hair-dryer; tennis, croquet ⊘ Dining-room, lounge, garden; early suppers for children ♿ No wheelchair access ⬤ No children under 6; no dogs; no smoking ⬚ None accepted £ Single occupancy of twin/double £26 to £30, twin/double £45 to £48; deposit required. Set D £12.50 (by arrangement)

NEAR SAWREY **Cumbria** map 8

Buckle Yeat

Near Sawrey, Hawkshead LA22 0LF
TEL: (015394) 36538   FAX: (015394) 36446

Charming, tea-shop B&B, in the heart of Beatrix Potter land.

It's impossible to visit either of the Sawrey villages without becoming acutely aware of the Beatrix Potter industry. You can't avoid it at Buckle Yeat either, as this pretty, whitewashed cottage is immortalised in *The Tale of Tom Kitten*. Furry-animal phobics need not be alarmed, however: Buckle Yeat's brand of charm is gratifyingly untwee. Its spacious, well-furnished lounge incorporates good, solid, antique pieces and restful, green wing armchairs and sofas; plain walls offset exposed ceiling timbers and a cheerful log fire. The breakfast room in the converted outbuildings next door functions as a popular tea-shop during the daytime, offering scones and home-made cakes to hungry hordes at simple, well-spaced pine tables, amid a restrained sprinkling of rustic artifacts of bygone times. A few tables stand outside, by the small gardens, for fair-weather diners. Upstairs, a half-dozen or so cottagey bedrooms ring the changes with sprigged wallpapers and curtains and neat, practical furniture. The beds have good-quality mattresses, the landings and stairways glow and the bathrooms gleam with attention. To supplement the cream teas, step next door for good pub food at the Tower Bank Arms.

◑ Open all year ⚡ In centre of Near Sawrey. Private car park 🛏 1 single, 2 twin, 4 double; family rooms available; 3 with bathroom/WC, 3 with shower/WC; all with TV, hair-dryer ✥ Lounge, breakfast room, garden; cots, high chairs ♿ No wheelchair access ● No dogs in public rooms; no smoking in bedrooms ▭ Amex, Delta, MasterCard, Switch, Visa £ Single £25, single occupancy of twin/double £35, twin/double £50, family room £55; deposit required

---

Ees Wyke

Near Sawrey, Ambleside LA22 0JZ
TEL: (015394) 36393

Conspicuously hospitable small country hotel in idyllic spot. Good dinners are an optional extra.

It's clear from the start that this is a house of some standing. A large Georgian building overlooking Esthwaite Water, Ees Wyke was once the holiday home of Beatrix Potter. It was here that she discovered her attachment to Near Sawrey, and subsequently made her home at Hill Top. The Potter industry now brings many pilgrims to the village, but at Ees Wyke you can, if you like, avoid any references to Squirrel Nutkin or Peter Rabbit, and simply revel in magnificent views, super food and tranquillity. Margaret and John Williams are lively, welcoming folk, and Ees Wyke's popularity owes as much to their personalities as to its intrinsic assets. The light, peachy dining-room is the centre of attention in the evenings – a splendid corner position with double-aspect windows takes full advantage of the views. Inventive five-course menus offer plenty of choice, such as duck with a blackcurrant sauce or scampi and scallops in a vermouth sauce. The older parts of the house are furnished in a mix of smart contemporary and solid antique pieces enlivened by upbeat colour schemes. Bedrooms vary in style and outlook: Blue is stylish and tasteful with wonderful views, Lilac has rather more routine furnishings, but all are comfortable and well kept. The top-floor rooms have sloping ceilings and exposed rafters.

◑ Closed Jan to Feb ⚡ At edge of village on road to Hawkshead. Private car park 🛏 3 twin, 5 double; most with shower/WC; all with TV, hair-dryer ✥ Dining-room, 2 lounges, drying-room, garden; functions (max 20 people incl up to 16 residential); fishing ♿ No wheelchair access ● No children under 10; no dogs or smoking in public rooms ▭ Amex £ Single occupancy of twin/double £46, twin/double £92. Set D £12 (residents), £22 (non-residents). Special breaks available

---

Hotels in our Round-ups towards the end of the Guide *are additional hotels that may be worth a visit. Reports on these are welcome.*

Sawrey House

Near Sawrey, Ambleside LA22 0LF
TEL: (015394) 36387   FAX: (015394) 36010
EMAIL: sawreyhous@aol.com

A handsome, Victorian property, with views of Esthwaite Water.

Near Sawrey, as all Beatrix Potter fans know, is something of a tourist honey-pot, so it's reassuring that you can find such complete peace and seclusion so close to the village centre. The location of Sawrey House is exceptional: surrounded by three acres of beautifully kept gardens; some favoured, west-facing rooms enjoy mouthwatering vistas of one of Cumbria's most picturesque lakes. Stone terraces guide the eye gently down to velvety lawns, with mature trees and rhodo-dendrons beyond; you may glimpse a deer munching some of this appetising vegetation from time to time, though these creatures are not encouraged. The welcoming Whitesides look completely at home here, though it's a fairly recent venture for them (in previous ages, the house variously served as a vicarage, a recuperation home for shell-shocked soldiers and a walkers' hotel). The spacious bedrooms have been done up in considerable style, with matching fabrics and excellent bathrooms. Plenty of light and restful public space is offered by a smartly furnished lounge, a cosy bar and a more recent restaurant extension equipped with a slightly incongruous, self-playing piano. Half-board terms are not obligatory, but most residents are more than happy to sample the wholesome dinners.

◑ Closed mid-Nov to 24 Dec and 3 to 31 Jan   ⊿ Situated on B5285 from Hawkshead. Private car park   🅿 1 single, 6 twin, 4 double; some in annexe; family room available; some with bathroom/WC, most with shower/WC; all with TV, some with hair-dryer ✅ Restaurant, bar, lounge, drying-room, garden; functions (max 35 people incl up to 21 residential), conferences; croquet; early suppers for children; cots, high chairs, toys, baby-listening   ♿ No wheelchair access   ◆ No children in restaurant eves; dogs in bedrooms only, by arrangement (£3 per night); smoking in bar only   🗀 Delta, MasterCard, Visa   £ Single £35 to £42, single occupancy of twin/double £40 to £60, twin/double £80 to £84, family room £90 to £94; deposit required. Set D £15 (residents), £19.50 (non-residents). Special breaks available

---

NEEDHAM MARKET Suffolk   map 6

Pipps Ford

Needham Market, Suffolk, Ipswich IP6 8LJ
TEL: (01449) 760208   FAX: (01449) 760561

A large, ancient farmhouse with plenty of home comforts, as well as home cooking using garden produce.

This sixteenth-century half-timbered farmhouse is actually within an Area of Outstanding Natural Beauty on the River Gipping. The only thing that slightly spoils this rural idyll is the proximity of the A14, but guests have not reported any problems about noise to us. Owner Raewyn Hackett-Jones is a dab hand in her country kitchen, where she bakes bread and cures ham; there are also home-produced eggs, preserves and honey, while the vegetables and herbs are organically home-grown. A typical meal might start with parsnip, apple and fresh-ginger soup, then loin of pork with mustard seeds, coriander, and a wine and cream sauce, and finally a hot treacle sponge pudding with custard. Meals can be taken in the elegant conservatory, which teems with semi-tropical plants during the summer; guests sit around a single long table, on bamboo chairs, looking out on to the large, well-tended gardens. The bedrooms are divided between the main house and four more modern-looking rooms in the Stables cottage. Each bed has a patchwork quilt, and there are plenty of antiques in evidence, as well as bright and fresh fabric colours. In winter, you'll find a log fire burning in the inglenook fireplace, and all the other ingredients of an old English farmhouse – exposed beams, low ceilings and a cosy, timeless feel.

◑ Closed Chr & New Year; dining-room closed Sun eve ⤢ Follow private road off roundabout where A140 joins A14. Private car park ⤙ 3 twin, 3 double, 1 four-poster; some in annexe; all with bathroom/WC; all with hair-dryer ⟡ Dining-room, conservatory, 2 lounges, TV room, garden; functions (max 40 people incl up to 14 residential), conferences; fishing, tennis; early suppers for children ⟁ Wheelchair access to hotel (ramp) and dining-room, 4 ground-floor bedrooms partially equipped for disabled people ● No children under 5; no dogs; no smoking in bedrooms ▭ None accepted £ Single occupancy of twin/double £43, twin/double £45 to £70, four-poster £70; deposit required. Set D £18. Special breaks available

---

NEWBIGGIN-ON-LUNE Cumbria

map 8

Low Lane House NEW ENTRY

Newbiggin-on-Lune, Kirkby Stephen CA17 4NB
TEL: (015396) 23269

Wonderful value and warm hospitality in a house of great character between the Lakes and Dales.

No prizes for guessing the age of this Westmorland farmhouse: the date 1684 is obligingly inscribed on its exterior. Few houses that have been so comfortably modernised retain so much of their past. Besides the beams, fireplaces and panelling that you might expect in a house of this period, a keen eye will spot dozens of fascinating details. Delicately double-arched windows with deep sills indicate the thickness of the original walls, and a built-in bureau of dark oak with intricate drawers survives in the dining-room (a classic rent or spice cupboard typical of older Cumbrian farmhouses). If you're interested, ask Mrs Paxman to show you the original bread oven near the stairs, or the curious Aesop's fables-themed Victorian tiles in a cloakroom. Even without such unusual features, however, Low Lane House would be a lovely place in which to stay. Set on a quiet offshoot of the A685 Kirkby Stephen road, the house commands views of an enticing swathe of open countryside and Pennine foothills. The whole house is beautifully kept and very welcoming, with just three simply furnished, but charming, bedrooms, all with attractive outlooks and thoughtful extras like radios and electric blankets. None has its own bathroom facilities, but sharing such a pretty bathroom is no hardship for these reasonable rates. Dinners (pre-booked) are even better value, featuring local produce from the garden and well-chosen wines. Janet and Graham Paxman will happily share their knowledge of the local area with visitors. Chickens, pigeons and other animals live here, too.

◑ Closed 31 Oct to 1 Mar ⤢ From M6 Junction 38, take A685 for 7 miles towards Scotch Corner; turn left to Kelleth and hotel is third on left. Private car park ⤷ 1 single, 1 twin, 1 double; all with hair-dryer ⊘ Dining-room, lounge, drying-room, garden ⌕ No wheelchair access ◕ No children under 8; no dogs; no smoking ⊟ None accepted £ Single £18, single occupancy of twin/double £18, twin/double £36. Set D £12 (by arrangement)

NEWCASTLE UPON TYNE Tyne & Wear   map 10

The Copthorne

The Close, Quayside, Newcastle upon Tyne NE1 3RT
TEL: 0191-222 0333   FAX: 0191-230 1111

A lively, business-oriented hotel in the centre of Newcastle with extensive views along the River Tyne.

The Copthorne certainly boasts Newcastle's prime city-centre location, smack on the waterside with three of the famous bridges in sight, and shopaholics are well catered for by the nearby shopping centres – so be prepared to pay heftily for the privilege.The River Tyne is the natural focus for the whole complex. In its centrepiece, the marble-floored atrium lobby, a lounge area offers leather seats looking out on the waterborne activity, and whether you opt to eat à la carte in the swanky Le Rivage restaurant or more casually in Harry's bar and restaurant, with a fishy themed carpet and modern art hung around the walls, the river is inescapable. Harry's menu runs the whole gamut of international dishes, from boeuf bourguignon or lamb tahini with couscous to the exoticism of Geordie stottie cakes. If pangs of conscience bite after a bout of gastronomic over-indulgence, a smart health club with yet more river views could help restore a feeling of equilibrium. Needless to say, all the bedrooms look over the river; colour schemes are bright and cheerful and, for those on a generous executive expense account, 'Connoisseur' rooms come with extra facilities, bigger beds and french windows opening on to a balcony – there's also a separate, more luxurious lounge, where a self-service breakfast awaits in the morning.

◑ Open all year; restaurant closed Sun eve ⤢ From intersection of A69 and A1, take A695 for City centre; follow signs for Quayside (B1600); hotel is on right, just short of High Level Bridge. Private car park ⤷ 24 twin, 122 double, 10 suites; family rooms available; all with bathroom/WC; all with satellite TV, room service, hair-dryer, mini-bar, trouser press, direct-dial telephone, modem point ⊘ 2 restaurants, bar, lounge; conferences (max 220 people incl up to 156 residential), functions; gym, sauna, solarium, heated indoor swimming-pool; cots, high chairs, babysitting ⌕ Wheelchair access to hotel and restaurant, WC (unisex), lift to bedrooms, 1 room specially equipped for disabled people ◕ No smoking on one bedroom floor; no dogs in public rooms ⊟ Amex, Delta, Diners, MasterCard, Switch, Visa £ Single occupancy of twin/double £135, twin/double/family room £160, suite £195 to £270; deposit required. Continental or cooked B £12; bar/bistro L £8, D £12; set L, D £11; alc L £13, D £15. Special breaks available

Malmaison NEW ENTRY

104 Quayside, Newcastle upon Tyne NE1 3DX
TEL: 0191-245 5000   FAX: 0191-245 4545

Glitzy new warehouse conversion on Newcastle's recently gentrified waterfront.

The southernwards march of the Malmaison chain continues apace: having zigzagged across from Edinburgh to Glasgow, the brand set up shop on the banks of the Tyne at the end of 1997. After transforming a redundant seamen's mission and a nineteenth-century neo-Grecian church, the chain's scouts alighted on a former Co-operative Wholesale Society warehouse to be their representative in the north-east. The exuberant wrought-ironwork on the façade trumpets the hotel's arrival, and on entering guests descend from street level to a deliciously decadent reception area, from which curling art-deco stairs (which seem to have been borrowed from a great Tyne-built liner) lead up to a mezzanine-level bar/brasserie. Here, the subdued lighting and plush, retro-styled décor – all marbled panels, etched glass, purple-velvet chairs and lacquered boxes – exude a slightly risqué sophistication. Curving etched-glass panels divide the striped spoon-backed chairs and banquettes in a smart restaurant lined with French jazz-age posters. The attentive staff, in long, emblazoned aprons, serve brasserie classics like red-onion and feta tart, perhaps followed by a fish-cake with buttered spinach, beurre blanc and frites, and finally a chocolate mousse with caramelised bananas.

The lift which whisks you up to the bedrooms ticks off the floors in a throaty French accent, garnering a grin that breaks into a broad smile as you enter a vast, individually designed boudoir, boldly decorated with lavish soft furnishings and classy fabrics. Unsightly, but useful, business-traveller accoutrements, including an iron with board and trouser press, are carefully tucked away out of sight. The bathrooms, with bespoke toiletries and bags of space, mirror the style and space of the rest of the hotel. The value for money is astonishing.

◗ Open all year. Private car park   ⊠ In Newcastle, travelling north-east on A186, turn right past law courts into Sandgate; turn right into the Swirle and right again into Quayside   ⟼ 10 twin, 88 double, 18 suites; family rooms available; all with bathroom/WC; all with TV, room service, hair-dryer, mini-bar, trouser press, direct-dial telephone, ironing facilities   ✅ Restaurant, bar/brasserie, 2 lounges; conferences (max 60 people residential/non-residential); gym, sauna, solarium; cots, high chairs, babysitting   ♿ Wheelchair access to hotel and restaurant, WC (unisex), lift to bedrooms, 5 rooms specially equipped for disabled people   ● No dogs; no smoking in some bedrooms   ▭ Amex, Delta, Diners, MasterCard, Switch, Visa   £ Single occupancy of twin/double £95, twin/double/family room £95, suite £145 to £165; deposit required. Continental B £8.50, cooked B £10.50; set L £10/£12, D £25; alc L, D £25. Special breaks available

---

'After we arrived a chap arrived plus spaniel which was immediately released and promptly killed one of the family's prize chickens. Even that episode didn't upset the welcome they gave.'
On a hotel in the West Country

map 2

Chewton Glen

Christchurch Road, New Milton BH25 6QS
TEL: (01425) 275341   FAX: (01425) 272310
EMAIL: reservations@chewtonglen.com
WEB SITE: www.chewtonglen.com

*Unsurpassed extravagance, limitless possibilities for self-indulgence,
and stratospheric prices.*

Lavish luxury. That's the only way to describe Chewton Glen, where the real
world is just something you catch a glimpse of on the satellite TV which nestles
in one corner of your near-palatial room. A bewildering array of bedrooms, at a
jaw-dropping range of prices, is on offer, but rest assured that whichever you
stay in, it will be furnished with immaculate taste in harmonious colours and
sumptuous fabrics. The top-of-the-range suites could easily be mistaken for
plush apartments in Mayfair. Every room has a name and number, the former
coming from the titles, characters and ships found in the books of Captain
Marryat, a resident in the 1840s. If you tire of savouring your room, there are
plenty of opportunities for relaxation, from unwinding in one of the spacious,
sunny lounges, surrounded by fresh flower displays, to being pampered in the
state-of-the-art health club, or even strolling in the extensive grounds. The
conservatory, a symphony in white, is a fresh, summery alternative to the
grandiose main restaurant, but in either location you could revel in such dishes
as ravioli of pigeon with a fricassee of wild mushrooms, braised pork cheeks and
lobster, and, if you've room, roasted seasonal fruits flambé with home-made
ice-cream.

◑ Open all year   ⊿ From A35, turn towards Walkford and Highcliffe; take second left
turning after Walkford into Chewton Farm Road; hotel is on right. Private car park
🛏 20 twin/double, 34 suites; some in annexe; all with bathroom/WC; all with satellite
TV, room service, hair-dryer, direct-dial telephone, some with mini-bar; no tea/
coffee-making facilities in rooms   ⊘ 3 restaurants, bar, 3 lounges, conservatory,
garden; functions (max 120 people incl up to 108 residential), conferences; civil
wedding licence; golf, gym, sauna, heated indoor and outdoor swimming-pools, tennis,
croquet; early suppers for children   ♿ Wheelchair access to hotel and restaurant, WC
(unisex), 11 ground-floor bedrooms   ⦁ No children under 7; no dogs; no smoking in
restaurants and 1 lounge   ▭ Amex, Delta, Diners, MasterCard, Switch, Visa
£ Twin/double from £220, suite from £430; deposit required. Continental B £9, cooked
B £16.50; light L from £8, set L £13.50/£18.50, set Sun L £27.50, D £48. Special breaks
available

---

*'The food has been described as "universally splendid": presumably in
Mr Spock's universe, not mine. Game terrine came warm and soggy on
the edges and still frozen in the middle where the microwave had failed to
penetrate.'*
On a hotel in Dumfries & Galloway

Trenance Lodge   NEW ENTRY

83 Trenance Road, Newquay TR7 2HW
TEL: (01637) 876702   FAX: (01637) 878772

Homely accommodation and ambitious cooking in this edge-of-town lodge.

In brash, unsophisticated Newquay, it's good to find a place serving up excellent food in a relatively quiet location. Trenance Lodge is situated over the hill from the front, with its loud bars and surf shacks, tucked away in a rather suburban part of the town. Jennie Bromell and Mac Mackenzie run a spruce, homely establishment catering for 'foodies', as they like to term their customers. The emphasis is on unusual dishes – not only is Jennie 'a real stickler for fresh fish', but you'll also encounter warm kangaroo salad, Caribbean bananas, or chargrilled ostrich among the starters, and for a main course you could sample fillets of megrim sole in a tempura batter with a chilli dipping sauce. While the culinary offerings are ambitious, the accommodation is distinctly straightforward, with more than a touch of Dralon in an interior that's inoffensive and traditional. However, the pastel-coloured public rooms, the pub-style bar and the simple, floral bedrooms are comfortable and spacious. Outside, a pretty garden and a patio terrace with wrought-iron furniture look out over the back of Newquay and the fields beyond.

---

❶ Open all year   ⊿ From Bodmin, take A392 to Newquay; go across roundabout at Quintrell Downs; turn right past King's Head pub and carry on for 1 mile to second miniroundabout; hotel is directly opposite. Private car park   ⮡ 1 twin, 4 double; all with bathroom/WC exc 2 doubles with shower/WC; all with TV, room service, hair-dryer, some with trouser press   ⍟ Restaurant, bar, lounge, garden; functions (max 50 people incl up to 10 residential), conferences; heated outdoor swimming-pool   ⅙ No wheelchair access   ⬤ No children under 10; no dogs; smoking in some public rooms only   ▭ MasterCard, Visa   £ Single occupancy of twin/double £30 to £38, twin/double £50 to £60; deposit required. Bar/bistro L £8, D £12; set L £10, D £16; alc L £12, D £20. Special breaks available

---

Trevelgue Hotel   NEW ENTRY

Watergate Road, Porth, Newquay TR7 3LX
TEL: (01637) 872864   FAX: (01637) 876365
EMAIL: trevelguehotel@btinternet.com

A children's paradise, but plenty for grown-ups too.

From the front, Trevelgue Hotel is just another faceless monstrosity, with hundreds of blank windows signalling anonymity. But drive your car round to the car park and watch the fun begin. First there's the mini adventure playground and the ships to play on, and then there's the ivy and creepers painted all over the back of the building. And that's just the outside. Hold your breath for the extremely well-executed 'fun' interior, which starts with an ethnic approach (all tapestries and carved ornamental birds), and then leads on to a pure celebration of children's imaginations, all done out in funky pastels. In the children's restaurant little doors on the walls open up to reveal cartoon characters; there's a crèche filled with the brightest toys imaginable, an indoor pool, children's clubs for all ages, and a room filled with computer games, table tennis and table football for older kids. The place is huge – it feels more like the kind of hotel you'd find in Spain than nestling on the Cornish coast.

Adults' needs are attended to in equally ambitious style. The bar is chic in blue with stained-glass effects, and the lounge is bright and relaxed with yellow walls and comfy round-backed chairs. Free squash, tennis, volleyball, aerobics (the list is endless) means everyone is kept happy. The restaurant has proper waiter service – no buffets (thank goodness) – with dishes such as grilled goats' cheese on a bed of balsamic-dressed beetroot and seasonal leaves, followed by braised leg of lamb in Beaujolais with roasted root vegetables. The bedrooms are all family-sized, with children getting the pool-side view in the best ones. Up to two children come free, and children's discounts are available all year. So bring the kids, book well ahead and enjoy.

◑ Closed Chr and 3 Jan to 12 Feb ↗ Leave Newquay on coastal road B3276 towards Padstow; go through Porth; hotel is at top of hill on right. Private car park ⊷ 2 single, 2 twin, 70 suites; family rooms available; all with bathroom/WC; all with TV, hair-dryer, direct-dial telephone ⊘ 2 restaurants, bar, 2 lounges, TV room, drying-room, games room, garden; functions (max 280 people residential/non-residential), conferences; civil wedding licence; fishing, golf, gym, sauna, solarium, heated indoor and outdoor swimming-pools, tennis, squash, volleyball, putting green, pitch & putt, croquet; early suppers for children (free teas for under-7s); cots, high chairs, toys, playrooms, babysitting, baby-listening, outdoor play area, 4 children's clubs ♿ Wheelchair access (ramps) to hotel and restaurant, 10 ground-floor bedrooms, 1 specially equipped for disabled people ⬤ No children under 7 in 1 restaurant eves; no dogs; smoking in 1 public room only ▭ MasterCard, Switch, Visa £ Single £33 to £55, single occupancy of twin £33 to £55, twin £66 to £110, family room/suite £66 to £138 (rates incl dinner for adults and children over 7, free tea for under-7s); deposit required. Bar/bistro L £6; set D £12.50 (non-residents)

Whipsiderry Hotel NEW ENTRY

Trevelgue Road, Porth, Newquay TR7 3LY
TEL: 01637 874777 (AND FAX)
EMAIL: whipsiderry@cornwall.net
WEB SITE: www.cornwall.net/whipsiderry/

Wholesome family hotel just outside Newquay, with a confident restaurant and extremely friendly hosts.

The brash, buzzy vibe of Newquay does not appeal to everyone, so this hotel, just along the coast in the more civilised neighbouring hamlet of Porth, may be a good option. Ann and Dick Drackford have been running this unpretentious, friendly hotel for 26 years, and some guests are now so familiar with the place that they waltz into the kitchen and cook their own starters! Humans are not the only creatures to make themselves at home here – a family of badgers (complete with babies) regularly comes for a snack on the front lawn. There's nothing remotely flashy about the hotel – instead it offers a great welcome and good home comforts. The Green Lounge, not surprisingly, is furnished with lots of green squashy sofas, and looks out over the verandah towards the big headland of Newquay, while the old-fashioned bar is bright and airy. The Drackfords pride themselves on their cooking, and have gone for a more formal feel in the peachy dining-room, with fresh flowers and plants arranged among the tables. The six-course dinner menu is written in French with English translations, so expect authentic Gallic cuisine – a salmon and peach terrine in a pastry case might be followed by French onion soup, and then a savoury seafood crêpe served with a white-wine sauce. The bedrooms are smallish and spruce, with functional, rather than stylish, bathrooms, and are decked out with reproduction or new pine furniture.

◑ Closed Jan to Mar, Nov to Dec (open Chr) ⤢ Leave Newquay on coastal road B3276 towards Padstow; after ½ mile turn left at Trevelgue Road. Private car park ⇖ 2 single, 2 twin, 11 double, 7 family rooms; some with bathroom/WC, most with shower/WC; all with TV, hair-dryer ⍋ Dining-room, bar, 2 lounges, TV room, drying-room, games room, garden; functions (max 100 people incl up to 50 residential), conferences; sauna, heated outdoor swimming-pool; early suppers for children; cots, high chairs, toys, baby-listening, outdoor play area ⅋ No wheelchair access ● None ▭ Amex, MasterCard, Switch, Visa £ Single £23 to £34, single occupancy of twin/double £29 to £39, twin/double £45 to £66, family room £57 to £83; deposit required. Bar/bistro L £4; set D £15; alc D £28. Special breaks available

---

NEWTON-LE-WILLOWS North Yorkshire   map 8

The Hall   `NEW ENTRY`

Newton-le-Willows, Bedale DL8 1SW
TEL: (01677) 450210   FAX: (01677) 450014

Tranquil, Georgian, country house, whose décor with a difference and accommodating owner have earned many compliments from readers.

Screened from the tiny Bedale village of Newton-le-Willows by walls, mature copper beeches and an imposing, wrought-iron portal, the Hall puts on the sober face of a Georgian country house for the outside world. Once you're inside this wonderful hideaway, however, a different picture unfolds amid a riot of idiosyncratic opulence where you certainly don't need to stand on ceremony. Owner Oriella Featherstone – 'a fabulous hostess' – 'runs the establishment very professionally but with a markedly personal touch... she makes a point of anticipating every need'. She has blended *objets*, like the 200-year-old, carved-wooden pillars from India, with tapestries, French and Italian antiques and heavy, tied-back drapes, to create an air of agreeably eccentric clutter. The drawing-room – which is full of character as a result of such details as a fancy gilt mirror and lamps made from Italian altar candlesticks – is a sumptuous spot in which to unwind or listen to music; french windows open into an acre of lovely gardens. Oriella likes her guests to feel at home, so there's tea, coffee and home-made fruitcake in the kitchen, while an honesty bar is always open. Evening meals, arranged in advance, can be quite an occasion in the dining-room, where guests sit around a huge banqueting table set with wax-laden candlesticks. The bedrooms are of a good size, and each has a distinct character: Apollo, for example, is romantic and flowery, with a bathroom big enough to run around in; while Aphrodite has its own dressing-room-cum-bathroom and a splendid garden view. 'Definitely recommend the main suite with 7-foot bed!' enthused yet another fan.

◑ Open all year   ⃞ Leave A1 at Leeming Bar and turn off A684 to Bedale; turn right at main street; ½ mile out of Bedale, turn left to Newton-le-Willows; turn right at T-junction, left at Wheatsheaf pub, then immediate right through the Hall's gates. Private car park
⮑ 1 twin, 1 double, 1 suite; all with bathroom/WC exc double with shower/WC; all with TV, hair-dryer   ⃝ Dining-room, bar, drawing-room, TV room, drying-room, garden   ♿ No wheelchair access   ⊖ No children under 13; dogs in tack room only
⃞ None accepted   £ Single occupancy of twin/double £40, twin/double £80, suite £90; deposit required. Set D £25 (by arrangement)

NORTH BOVEY Devon

map 1

Blackaller Hotel

North Bovey, Moretonhampstead, Newton Abbot TQ13 8QY
TEL: (01647) 440322 (AND FAX)
WEB SITE: www.intellect-net.com.west/country/hotel/devon/blackaller.htm

Well-loved hotel in deepest, darkest Devon, run with much care and attention to detail.

Letters of praise for this hotel have rolled in this year – Hazel Phillips and Peter Hunt are definitely producing a winning formula at Blackaller. One reader found it 'an oasis of peace and quiet'; Peter calls it a desert island, and you do feel cut off from the normally hurried pace of life here. The seventeenth-century woollen mill has a 'delightful, large riverside lawn, with deckchairs – a pleasure to come home to after a day's strenuous pursuits' (note the use of the word 'home'). Another reader 'enjoyed the friendly atmosphere combined with the quietly professional management by Peter, and the outstanding food cooked by Hazel'. The food features highly in our readers' commendations – 'high standards with a consistency of quality', and 'quite superb, with fresh organic produce and home-produced eggs and honey' – and positive reports have come, too, from vegetarians. Dinner is taken in the rustic, spruce restaurant on proper pine tables; the five-course menu might feature little spicy avocado crumbles with a cherry-tomato and basil dressing, followed by leek and potato soup, and then baked chicken breast with a mushroom and spinach stuffing, wrapped in bacon. The décor throughout the hotel is of the fresh, country-living style, with lots of pine and stripped floors, although the sitting-room is more traditional. Look out for Peter's spinning wheel and sitar. The bedrooms are of a good size, with huge, inviting-looking beds, and the bathrooms are most fetching, although one (otherwise satisfied) reader found the absence of a shower a 'major drawback'.

◑ Closed Jan & Feb; restaurant closed Mon eve   ⃞ Take A382 to Moretonhampstead, then follow signs to North Bovey; hotel is at edge of village. Private car park   ⮑ 1 single, 4 twin/double; all with bathroom/WC; all with TV, room service, hair-dryer, some with trouser press   ⃝ Restaurant, bar, sitting-room, drying-room, library, garden; functions (max 20 people incl up to 9 residential), conferences; fishing, croquet; leisure facilities nearby (reduced rates for guests); early suppers for children, by arrangement; high chairs, babysitting, baby-listening   ♿ No wheelchair access ⬤ No children under 12; no dogs in public rooms; no smoking in bedrooms 🗀 None accepted   £ Single £30 to £31, single occupancy of twin/double £40 to £45, twin/double £72; deposit required. Set D £22. Special breaks available

---

NORTH HUISH Devon   map 1

Brookdale House

North Huish, South Brent TQ10 9NR
TEL: (01548) 821661   FAX: (01548) 821606

Dignified, spacious country house with interesting features, set in a secluded valley.

Brookdale House is a sprawling old Victorian rectory, complete with mullioned windows, a pond and a waterfall at the bottom of the garden. Peace reigns supreme here in the midst of rolling, wooded farmland. The house is welcoming and informal; the dusky pink carpet throughout seems somehow comforting, and the plethora of squashy sofas in the lounge positively demand to be lazed upon; open fires burn all year round. Gill Mikkelsen is a most congenial hostess. Ask her to tell you the story of the outrageously extravagant cornice in the dining-room – it took two winters (and several hundred tipples) for a previous owner to paint the fruit and flowers in gorgeous pastels. Don't get a crick in your neck, though, because the menu ('English with a French slant') deserves perusal: you might try a grilled goats' cheese and aubergine tian with sweet and sour cherry tomatoes, followed by fillet of venison with a glazed pear and red-wine sauce. Bedrooms are spacious, calm and attractively done out in country style, sprinkled with antiques here and there. The bathrooms have fun dressing-room lights around all the basins.

◑ Open all year   ⤢ From A38, take South Brent exit; follow Avonwick signs; turn right at Avon Inn, then next left; continue to top of hill and turn right; hotel is on right at bottom of valley. Private car park ⇤ 8 double; some in annexe; all with bathroom/WC; all with TV, room service, hair-dryer, trouser press, direct-dial telephone   ✧ 2 dining-rooms, lounge, garden; functions (max 50 people incl up to 16 residential), conferences; civil wedding licence; leisure facilities nearby (reduced rates for guests)   ♿ No wheelchair access   ⬤ No children under 12 (exc Sunday L); dogs in annexe rooms only   🗀 Amex, Delta, MasterCard, Switch, Visa £ Single £65, single occupancy of double £65, double £100; deposit required. Set Sun L £12; alc L £12.50, D £17. Special breaks available

---

NORTH NEWINGTON Oxfordshire   map 5

La Madonette

North Newington Road, Banbury OX15 6AA
TEL: (01295) 730212   FAX: (01295) 730363

Bonhomie and home comforts guaranteed at this appealing old mill house.

The spring floods of 1998 may have washed away the stone bridge, but fortunately the rising water stopped short of Patti Ritter's mill cottages – a clutch of slate roofs amid a copse of tall willows and poplars. The main mill house is three storeys of lichen- and wistaria-coated stone, and cows startle guests by seeming to wander past the upstairs windows (there is a grassy hillock beside the house). An appropriately homely style of white woodchip, flowery counterpanes and baskets of dried flowers give a suitably cottagey feel to all the bedrooms. The brass four-poster in Room 2 comes draped in fine broderie anglaise, Room 5 has a lacy coronet over the bed, and the last vestiges of formica elsewhere are being replaced with a mixture of new and antique pine. Patti dissolved into tears of laughter when asked how she would describe the colour of the giant corner bath in Room 3 – we settled on 'mid-brown'. More rooms, with upstairs bedrooms and downstairs pine kitchenettes, may be available in the self-catering Banbury-brick cottages beside the millstream. Breakfast is taken in a small dining-room beneath a timbered ceiling, while the reception doubles as a guest lounge, with easy chairs facing a pine dresser well stocked with wine and spirits.

○ Open all year ⊿ From Banbury Cross take B4035 for approx 2½ miles, then turn right for North Newington (last turning before Broughton village). Guesthouse is ¼ mile, on right. Private car park ⊨ 1 twin, 1 double, 1 four-poster, 2 family rooms; 2 with bathroom/WC, 3 with shower/WC; all with TV, room service, hair-dryer, direct-dial telephone ⊘ Dining-room, bar, lounge, TV room, garden; conferences (max 24 people incl up to 5 residential); heated outdoor swimming-pool; cots, high chairs, babysitting, baby-listening ⅙ No wheelchair access ● No dogs; smoking discouraged ▭ Delta, Diners, MasterCard, Switch, Visa £ Single occupancy of twin/double £39, twin/double £48 to £55, four-poster £75, family room £68; deposit required. Set D £13 (by arrangement). Special breaks available

---

NORTH WALSHAM Norfolk   map 6

Beechwood Hotel ⟨NEW ENTRY⟩

Cromer Road, North Walsham NR28 0HD
TEL: (01692) 403231 FAX: (01692) 407284

A large Georgian house within the town that has been brought up to a high standard by its enthusiastic owners.

There was no shortage of visitors ready to sing the praises of this hotel and its warm and effusive owners. 'Before you leave you're already thinking about booking your next visit,' one guest told us. Others spoke of the friendly and genuine welcome. Don Birch and Lindsay Spalding are keen to make their guests feel at ease, and it's noticeable that the staff have a good working relationship with each other. The creeper-clad house had been the home of local doctors since it was built in 1800, and retains many touches of bygone days in the attractive, tiled entrance hall. The public rooms are small and intimate, and guests tend to linger – especially in the lounge – after their meal. There's also a long, lawned garden with many quiet areas, including a secluded fountain. Agatha Christie was a regular guest at the house in the 'thirties, and the standards of the bedrooms today would no doubt impress even her: fireplaces have been restored, there are antique beds, and the original lighting is also in place, while the bathrooms are pristine, with marble fittings. Room 7 is a lovely room, with a brass bedstead and stand-alone bath.

○ Open all year ⤢ Leave Norwich on B1150. On entering North Walsham, turn left at first set of traffic lights and right at the next; hotel is 150 yards on left. Private car park ⊨ 2 twin, 6 double, 1 four-poster; 6 with bathroom/WC, 3 with shower/WC; all with TV, room service, direct-dial telephone, some with hair-dryer, trouser press ⊘ Restaurant, bar, lounge, garden; early suppers for children ♿ No wheelchair access ● No children under 10; no smoking in bedrooms; dogs £5 per night ▭ Delta, MasterCard, Switch, Visa £ Single occupancy of twin/double £44, twin/double £64, four-poster £74; deposit required. Set L £9, D £21. Special breaks available

---

NORTH WHEATLEY Nottinghamshire   map 9

The Old Plough

Top Street, North Wheatley, Retford DN22 9DB
TEL: (01427) 880916

Friendly and unstuffy B&B with up-market rooms.

This fine-looking, whitewashed house, once a Victorian pub, is now the family home of the Pasleys – Pauline being the creative force behind the kitchen and the restrained, tasteful décor. The three bedrooms are spacious and beautifully kept, and feature fine, old furniture, Victorian fireplaces and lots of little knick-knacks dotted about – Matrushka dolls, rubber ducks and seashells in the very large and well-equipped bathroom of the twin-bedded Room 5. The best double room is Room 4, with its fine four-poster and view over the village to the fields – slippers and bathrobes are provided, as the bathroom is across the hall. Downstairs, there is an elegant dining-room with a single breakfast table – dinners *en famille* are not the feature that they once were, but suppers can be provided by prior arrangement. Eggs come from the free-range hens roaming around the garden, and there are home-made preserves and bread, too. In the evenings, the chintzy drawing-room is a pleasant place in which to sit and chat to other guests.

○ Open all year ⤢ On A620 between Retford and Gainsborough, 200 yards from Wheatley Church. Private car park ⊨ 1 twin, 1 double, 1 four-poster; all with bathroom/WC (not all *en suite*); all with TV, hair-dryer ⊘ Dining-room, drawing-room, drying-room, garden; functions (max 20 people incl up to 6 residential), conferences ♿ No wheelchair access ● No children under 16; no dogs; no smoking ▭ None accepted £ Single occupancy of twin/double £30, twin/double/four-poster £60

Denotes somewhere you can rely on a good meal – either the hotel features in the 1999 edition of our sister publication, The Good Food Guide, *or our inspectors thought the cooking impressive, whether particularly competent home cooking or more lavish cuisine.*

NORTON Shropshire

map 5

Hundred House

Bridgnorth Road, Norton, Shifnal TF11 9EE
TEL: (01952) 730353   FAX: (01952) 730355
EMAIL: hphundredhouse@compuserve.com

Bustling, immensely likeable Georgian inn furnished with joie de vivre.

The Phillips family have got just about everything right here, applying a creative and light touch throughout. The interconnecting bar, brasserie and restaurant areas marry old features, such as an antique kitchen range, quarry tiles and beams, with art-nouveau stained glass, seating covered in multicoloured leather patches, and dried herbs, flowers and hops that hang in abundance. Punters come from afar for the eclectic and imaginative English and continental food – from a cassoulet of wild boar, pork and duck confit, to a Greek salad with home-made focaccia bread, and a salmon, cider and mussel soup. You're encouraged to garnish your food with a batch of herbs set out on each table, and these come from the inn's own garden, which turns out to be a significant attraction in its own right, not only for the multitude of labelled herbs but also for its fine floral displays. The herb theme persists in the names of the (very feminine) bedrooms; romantics should pay extra for a superior such as Fennel & Dill, which comes with a swing and an old brass bed. The hotel's only obvious drawback is its position, hard up against a busy A-road, though road-facing bedrooms are double-glazed.

◑ Open all year; restaurant closed Chr night   🔁 Midway between Telford and Bridgnorth on A442. Private car park   🛏 1 single, 3 twin, 6 double; family rooms available; all with shower/WC; all with TV, room service, hair-dryer, direct-dial telephone   ⊘ Restaurant, brasserie, bar, garden; functions (max 30 people incl up to 19 residential), conferences; early suppers for children; cots, high chairs, baby-listening   ♿ No wheelchair access   ● Dogs in bedrooms only, by arrangement   ▭ Amex, Delta, MasterCard, Switch, Visa   £ Single £69, single occupancy of twin/double £79, twin/double £85 to £109, family room £109; deposit required. Brasserie L, D £12; alc L, D £20 to £25. Special breaks available

NORWICH Norfolk

map 6

By Appointment

25–29 St George's Street, Norwich NR3 1AB
TEL: (01603) 630730 (AND FAX)

A fifteenth-century house turned into a clubby Victorian-style boudoir by its extravagant hosts.

Tim Brown and Robert Culyer describe the bedrooms in this Aladdin's cave of a house as 'something special', and that's probably an understatement. After a precipitous climb up into the eaves of this rabbit warren of a building in a quiet street near the centre of Norwich, you come upon a riot of Edwardian and Victorian theatrical flamboyance in the bedrooms: a monogrammed dressing-table set, vases of ostrich feathers, a teddy bear on a chair and over-the-top bathrooms. Downstairs there are six tiny dining-rooms painted in rich greens, reds, blues and yellows, with swagged drapes. The menus are written up on blackboards, and there are flower arrangements all around. Tim does the cooking, and the food is as exuberant as the rest of the surroundings, with dishes such as apricot- and pistachio-stuffed loin of lamb with a sauce of tomatoes, honey, garlic, rosemary and thyme, or breast of pheasant on a bed of caramelised apples with a calvados sauce. The guests' drawing-room doubles as an antiques shop, and all the pieces you see are for sale.

◑ Closed 25 & 26 Dec; restaurant closed Sun & Mon eves ◢ On junction of St George's Street and Colegate. Private car park ↤ 1 single, 1 twin, 2 double; all with bathroom/WC (2 not *en suite*); all with TV, hair-dryer, trouser press, direct-dial telephone ✧ 6 dining-rooms, drawing-room; functions (max 60 people incl up to 7 residential), conferences ৬ No wheelchair access ● No children under 8; no dogs; smoking in drawing-room only ⊟ Delta, MasterCard, Switch, Visa ⬚ Single £65, single occupancy of twin/double £65, twin/double £85. Alc D £26

Catton Old Hall

Lodge Lane, Catton, Norwich NR6 7HG
TEL: (01603) 419379   FAX: (01603) 400339
EMAIL: catton.old.hall@netcom.co.uk

Fine, seventeenth-century family home, with stylish bedrooms and a friendly welcome.

Roger and Anthea Cawdron originally bought this fine, Jacobean house – now surrounded by the suburbs of Norwich – in 1989, and since then they have done an impressive job of renovating it. It's full of exposed beams, mullioned windows and, notably, there is an impressive inglenook hearth in the smartly designed lounge. There are plenty of antiques and original features to keep guests intrigued during their stay, and a tasteful use of fabrics and colours is much in evidence. The bedrooms are named after people who have lived in the house itself or have associations with Catton, including Anna Sewell of *Black Beauty* fame. This bedroom is probably the nicest, and has a dramatically sloping ceiling up into the eaves and a big, plush bathroom. John Norman is said to be haunted and, if you are lucky, the ghost might come and sit on the end of the bed. Fresh milk is available in a fridge outside the rooms for ease of tea-making. It is advisable to book ahead for the set dinner, which Anthea cooks herself. Many of her dishes are based on tips and advice from her son, who is a chef, and guests might start with a cream of Stilton and cider soup, and then enjoy fillet of Scottish salmon poached in a Chardonnay and tarragon sauce, followed by rum-flamed bananas.

◑ Open all year; dining-room closed Sun eve ◢ 2½ miles north-east of Norwich; Lodge Lane is just off Spixworth Road. Private car park ↤ 2 twin/double, 4 double, 1 four-poster; all with bathroom/WC exc 1 twin/double with shower/WC; all with TV, room service, hair-dryer, trouser press, some with direct-dial telephone ✧ Dining-room, lounge, drying-room, garden ৬ No wheelchair access ● No children under 15; no dogs; no smoking in some bedrooms ▭ Amex, Delta, Diners, MasterCard, Switch, Visa £ Single occupancy of twin/double from £48, twin/double £66 to £85, four-poster £90; deposit required. Set D £21. Special breaks available

---

NUNNINGTON North Yorkshire   map 9

Ryedale Country Lodge

Station Road, Nunnington, York YO6 5XB
TEL: (01439) 748246   FAX: (01439) 748346

A village railway station turned into a peaceful small hotel with a make-over from new owners.

A long narrow patch of lawn, now a playground for a colony of rabbits, is the only evidence that Ryedale Lodge started life as a Victorian country railway station. The location is so peaceful, a mile or so from Nunnington village, that one wonders who on earth might have once got on or off a train here, although for modern car-borne travellers York, the North Yorkshire Moors and the coastal towns of Scarborough and Whitby are just a short drive away. Peter and Gerd Handley took over the hotel in 1997; they have totally refurbished the public rooms and are making their way through the bedrooms. The lounge now luxuriates in lovely sumptuous fabrics and is packed with attention-grabbing interior-design features – such as large stone statues – set against a dramatic red colour scheme. Alternatively, guests can switch off in a conservatory-style lounge with a décor of bentwood furniture and oriental rugs on a tiled floor, which looks through huge sliding doors on to a sleepy vista of rolling fields. Upstairs, old formica-style furniture in the bedrooms has been replaced, and bathrooms are being upgraded with the addition of showers; the pick of the bunch are the Blue Room, which has the best views (even from the loo!), and the Peach Room with its lovely antiques and tapestries. The restaurant, too, has had a makeover; giving it an intimate and stylish feel. Here you could try monkfish and chive tart, continuing with venison casserole and then chocolate bread-and-butter pudding.

◑ Closed 2 weeks in Jan ⌨ Between Helmsley and Malton; 1 mile west of Nunnington village. Private car park ⌔ 2 twin, 5 double; family rooms available; all with bathroom/WC; all with TV, room service, hair-dryer, direct-dial telephone ⌘ Restaurant, lounge, drying-room, conservatory, garden; fishing, pitch & putt, croquet; leisure facilities nearby (free for guests) ᕮ Wheelchair access to hotel and restaurant, WC (M, F), 1 ground-floor bedroom ● No dogs ▭ Delta, MasterCard, Switch, Visa £ Single occupancy of twin/double £40, twin/double £70, family room £80; deposit required. Bar L £7; alc D £22

The text of the entries is based on inspections carried out anonymously, backed up by unsolicited reports sent in by readers. The factual details under the text are from questionnaires the Guide *sends to all hotels that feature in the book.*

OAKAMOOR Staffordshire

map 5

Bank House

Farley Lane, Oakamoor, Stoke-on-Trent ST10 3BD
TEL: (01538) 702810 (AND FAX)
EMAIL: john.orme@dial.pipex.com

*Friendly country home with good gardens, convenient for Alton
Towers and the Peak District.*

Tucked away in a lane close to Alton Towers, Muriel and John Egerton-Orme's
red-brick house is something of a discovery. For a start, the large two-storey
house looks old but is new (it has been rebuilt with old bricks, giving the
Egerton-Ormes a chance to introduce underfloor heating and big picture
windows); then there is Muriel's warm and welcoming personality, which gives
the house a sociable atmosphere. A pleasant sitting-room has a log fire for chilly
evenings, and an elegant dining-room is the setting for breakfasts and dinners.
The well-priced four-course meals follow a set, no-choice, menu: perhaps cream
of asparagus soup to start, followed by poached salmon with hollandaise sauce,
then a cheeseboard (including local varieties like Dovedale and Buxton Blue),
and finally a selection of sweets, such as Bakewell tart or raspberries and cream.
Bedrooms are comfortably furnished, some looking out on the garden, which
John and Muriel have been steadily landscaping.

○ Closed Chr week ☑ Follow signs for Alton Towers via Alton village, passing theme
park main entrance (on right); after road turns sharply left, continue 400 yards, then take
left turn down narrow lane; Oakamoor is second house on left. Private car park
🛏 2 twin, 1 four-poster; family rooms available; all with bathroom/WC; all with TV,
room service, hair-dryer, trouser press, direct-dial telephone ✅ Dining-room,
sitting-room, drying-room, library, conservatory, garden; early suppers for children; cot,
high chair ♿ No wheelchair access ● Smoking in sitting-room only, if other guests
consent ▭ MasterCard, Visa £ Single occupancy of twin £41 to £51, twin £74,
four-poster £66; deposit required. Set D £21. Special breaks available

---

OAKHAM Rutland

map 5

Barnsdale Lodge

The Avenue, Rutland Water North Shore, Oakham LE15 8AH
TEL: (01572) 724678 FAX: (01572) 724961

Much-extended farmhouse, with a good range of restaurants.

That Barnsdale Lodge is a success is reflected in the extensions and improvements that were going on when our inspector called: more bedrooms along
one side to complete the courtyard and children's garden games out on the lawn.
The original farmhouse is still there, of course, with its stone floors and big
beams, but modern signs in the hotel-chain style clash with the feeble stab at an
Edwardian atmosphere, which is at its most successful in the restaurant. This is
the best room: clubby and intimate, with dark, rich colours and Vanity Fair
prints. The Buttery bar, further along the building, offers less formal dining at
similar prices: anything from a ploughman's to home-made pork, Stilton and

leek sausages. The bedrooms are spacious and well equipped; thick stone walls help give them a cosy feel and keep out any noise from the various weddings and conferences. Room 9, with its four-poster and old roof beams, is particularly attractive.

◖ Open all year ⊡ On A606, 2 miles east of Oakham. Private car park ⟜ 8 single, 9 twin, 17 double, 3 four-poster, 2 family rooms, 6 suites; some in annexe; all with bathroom/WC exc 4 singles with shower/WC; all with TV, room service, hair-dryer, trouser press, direct-dial telephone, ironing facilities ⟡ 4 restaurants, 2 bars, lounge, conservatory, function room, garden; functions (max 220 people incl up to 84 residential), conferences; civil wedding licence; pitch & putt; early suppers for children; cots, high chairs, babysitting, baby-listening, outdoor play area ⟐ Wheelchair access to hotel and restaurants, WC (unisex), 15 ground-floor bedrooms, 2 rooms specially equipped for disabled people ⬤ No smoking in some bedrooms; no dogs in restaurants; £10 per dog per stay ⊟ Amex, Delta, Diners, MasterCard, Switch, Visa £⠿ Single £60, single occupancy of twin/double £60, twin/double £80, four-poster/suite £100, family room £95; deposit required. Bar/bistro L, D £10 to £15; set Sun L £18; alc L, D £25. Special breaks available

---

Lord Nelson's House

Market Place, Oakham LE5 6DT
TEL: (01572) 723199 (AND FAX)
EMAIL: lordnelson@rutland.on-line.co.uk
WEB SITE: www.rutland-on-line.co.uk

A charming and homely town-centre B&B with friendly hosts.

In between giving poetry readings and writing a Yorkshire-dialect version of Shakespeare, as well as autobiography, Malcolm Darby also manages to run this delightful small hotel with his wife Sylvia. Located in the centre of Oakham with views of the ancient butter cross and water pump, the building is a coaching-inn that dates back to the fifteenth century. The Darbys are still making discoveries as they undertake renovations and alterations, the latest being an Elizabethan inglenook fireplace and oven in the cosy breakfast room. Like all the rooms in the house, this contains a striking and eclectic mix of curios, knick-knacks, posters and plates. Next to it is a smart sitting-room; both rooms are neatly tricked out with ribbons and flounces – the bold colour schemes help to steer things clear of fussiness. Upstairs, all the bedrooms are different, with Nelson and Lady Emma having the edge: the first for its masculine, clubby good looks rather than the small bathroom, the latter for its four-poster and feminine charm. Sylvia does light suppers on request: home-made soup, perhaps, followed by smoked fillet of trout and home-made tarts.

◖ Open all year ⊡ In centre of Oakham. Private car park ⟜ 2 twin, 1 double, 1 four-poster; all with bathroom/WC; all with TV, room service, hair-dryer, direct-dial telephone, clock radio ⟡ Breakfast room, bar, sitting-room, drying-room, garden; functions (max 30 people incl up to 8 residential), conferences; early suppers for children; cots, high chairs, babysitting, baby-listening ⟐ No wheelchair access ⬤ Dogs by arrangement; no smoking ⊟ MasterCard, Switch, Visa £⠿ Single occupancy of twin/double £55, twin/double £65, four-poster £75; deposit required. Light supper (residents only) £5 to £10

ODIHAM Hampshire map 2

George Hotel

100 High Street, Odiham, Hook, Basingstoke RG29 1LP
TEL: (01256) 702081 FAX: (01256) 704213

Heaps of history and lashings of seafood in a bustling market town.

A portrait of a rather youthful George III swings in the wind outside, beneath the flag of St George, but this characterful inn goes back much further than the eighteenth century. Back in 1540, when Englande was merrie and Henry VIII was notching up wives four and five, a certain 42-year-old building was granted its first licence. Since then, the George Hotel has been part of more history than you could shake a stick at, acting as the area's assizes court until 1882, giving birth to the Royal Veterinary College, and serving as an Inland Revenue office in the nineteenth century. Much of the past is on view in the old courtroom, now the restaurant, which has flagstones which are said to have come from Bradford Cathedral and a resplendent fireplace. Anyone partial to a spot of seafood will be well fed here, perhaps feasting on a trio of smoked fish, followed by fillet of sea bass on cucumber noodles with saffron cream; non-fish dishes are also available. The food side of the George Hotel has recently expanded to take in an old shop, Next Door, which is now a pleasant café/bistro serving all-day breakfasts, sandwiches, pasta cream teas and bistro suppers. Up above, there are also new bedrooms, which, though a tad less atmospheric than the beam-laden rooms in the old inn, are thoughtfully furnished and comfortable, as are the rooms in the old coach-house and outhouse at the back. Of the olde-worlde rooms, Room 1 is just that, complete with Elizabethan wall murals.

○ Open all year; restaurant closed Sat L and Sun eve ◪ In centre of Odiham village. Private car park ⬅ 7 single, 2 twin, 15 double, 2 four-poster; some in annexe; family rooms available; all with bathroom/WC exc 1 single with shower/WC; all with TV, room service, hair-dryer, direct-dial telephone, some with mini-bar; trouser press available ⬦ Restaurant, café/bistro, bar, lounge, garden; functions (max 12 people residential/non-residential), conferences; cots, high chairs ⬥ No wheelchair access ● No dogs in public rooms; no smoking in some bedrooms ▭ Amex, Delta, Diners, MasterCard, Switch, Visa £ Single £50 to £70, single occupancy of twin/double £50 to £70, twin/double £70 to £80, four-poster £95, family room £85 to £95; deposit required. Bar/bistro L, D £5 to £10; set L £14.50, D £12; alc L, D £27.50. Special breaks available

OLDBURY West Midlands map 5

Jonathan's

16 Wolverhampton Road, Oldbury B68 0LH
TEL: 0121-429 3757 FAX: 0121-434 3107
EMAIL: bookings@jonathans.co.uk
WEB SITE: www.jonathans.co.uk

Unexpected Victorian delight in dour surroundings close to M5.

Nobody could accuse Jonathan's of doing things by halves: a love of Victoriana is stamped on every room of this distinctive hotel and restaurant. Once inside, you are enveloped in the Victorian passion for ornamentation and decoration: no wallpaper is left unpatterned and no picture frame ungilded. For some this might be overpowering, but for most it is simply fun, and the effect of cosiness and intimacy is popular with business people for small conferences and meetings. The panelled dining-room continues the period theme in the menu, if not the cooking: 'first removes' might include steamed mussels or chicken-liver and mushroom pâté, 'middle removes' a raspberry or blackcurrant water ice, then 'main removes' steak, kidney and smoked oyster pudding, or a pot-roast knuckle of lamb. Puddings stick to tradition, with dishes like spotted dick, Bakewell tart and trifle. The bedrooms are solidly furnished and full of surprises – like a piano, or twin baths, or a billiard table – but hidden behind all the books and china are also the usual modern comforts.

○ Open all year; restaurant closed Sun eve　↗ At junction of A456 and A4123. Private car park (guarded, £2.50 for duration of stay)　⊨ 8 single, 2 twin, 21 double, 2 four-poster, 11 suites; family rooms available; all with bathroom/WC; all with TV, room service, hair-dryer, direct-dial telephone, ironing facilities　⌀ 2 restaurants, 4 bars, 2 lounges, library, conservatory; functions (max 100 people incl up to 88 residential), conferences; leisure facilities nearby (free for guests); early suppers for children; high chairs, babysitting　と No wheelchair access　● No dogs in public rooms　▭ Amex, Delta, Diners, MasterCard, Switch, Visa　£ Single £75, single occupancy of twin/double £85, twin/double £85, four-poster/family room/suite £125; deposit required. Bar/bistro L, D £6; set L, D £28.50; alc L, D £30. Special breaks available

Sea Marge　NEW ENTRY

16 High Street, Overstrand, Cromer NR27 0AB
TEL: (01263) 579579　FAX: (01263) 579524

A splendid Edwardian holiday mansion, recently turned into a comfortable hotel, with lawns stretching down to the sea.

After an eventful history that included a sad period of dereliction, the Sea Marge has come under the wing of Mark and Liz Mackenzie, who were new to the hotel trade but who, in two years, have revived some of the building's former glory and put some heart into the hotel. One reader recommended it to us whole-heartedly after a stay over Christmas: 'We felt like house guests not hotel guests, it was just a feeling of total comfort.' The mock-Tudor house was built in 1909 by the banker Sir Edward Speyer, when the north Norfolk coast was at its most fashionable. Much of the original wood panelling still remains, as well as some of the European art treasures that were shipped over by the owner during the house's construction. The lofty bar has a sixteenth-century marble fireplace and a minstrels' gallery with medieval woodcarvings; from here, there are views across the sweeping lawns to the bracing coastline, and guests congregate here and on the long patio terrace in summer. The Mackenzies have added wood panelling to the restaurant and installed bright new bathrooms, some with corner or free-standing baths. The bedrooms are of a good size, with plump beds, and some have original, hand-painted Delft tiles in their fireplaces.

○ Open all year ⟋ From Cromer, take B1159 to Overstrand; turn left on to High Street by village sign; pass pub on left; hotel is set back off road on left. Private car park ⤙ 1 single, 4 twin, 11 double, 2 four-poster; family room available; most with bathroom/WC, 2 twins with shower/WC; all with TV, room service, hair-dryer, direct-dial telephone ⊘ Restaurant, bar, 2 lounges, garden; functions (max 60 people incl up to 34 residential), conferences; croquet; leisure facilities nearby (reduced rates for guests); cots, high chairs ⅄ No wheelchair access ● No smoking in restaurant or bedrooms; dogs in 1 lounge and some bedrooms only (£4.50 per night) ▭ Delta, MasterCard, Switch, Visa £ Single £36, single occupancy of twin/double £46 to £56, twin/double £72 to £78, four-poster £92, family room (room rate + £15 per child); deposit required. Bar/bistro L, D £7; set L, D £17; alc L, D £17.50. Special breaks available

---

OXFORD Oxfordshire   map 2

Cotswold House

363 Banbury Road, Oxford OX2 7PL
TEL: (01865) 310558 (AND FAX)

Good-value B&B, well positioned for exploring the city and the local sights.

As its name suggests, Anne and Jim O'Kane's attractive modern house is a recreation of the regional style, with diamond-shaped leaded lights and dark-wood frames set into the orderly local stone. Though it's situated firmly in suburbia, its half-timbering, its wheel-backed chairs and Anne's eye for pretty floral patterns recreate the style of a country cottage. All six bedrooms are in pristine condition – with small, but sparkling, shower-rooms – and show their hosts' thoughtful appreciation of guests' needs with little extras like mini-fridges, magazines and talcum powder.

Jim is much in demand after breakfast, delivering tried-and-trusted advice on local attractions, guided walks and driving routes, and he strongly recommends leaving the car on the forecourt if you are heading for the city centre – an efficient bus service passing the front door runs frequently, covering the two miles into town. Those repairing to the immaculate sitting-room might meet Harry, the attention-loving, dark-grey tortoiseshell cat, and shouldn't fail to notice the original manuscript page from Morse author Colin Dexter's *A Walk in the Woods*, in which Jim features, greeting visitors and consulting the booking register.

○ Closed Chr ⟋ Turn off A40 ring-road, following A4165 towards city centre; house is ¼ mile along, on right. Private car park ⤙ 2 single, 2 twin, 2 double; family room available; all with shower/WC; all with TV, hair-dryer, fridge ⊘ Sitting-room ⅄ No wheelchair access ● No children under 5; no dogs; no smoking ▭ None accepted £ Single £41, single occupancy of twin/double £55 to £59, twin/double £60 to £62, family room (room rate + £10 to £15 per child); deposit required

---

Don't forget that other hotels worth considering are listed in our Round-ups near the back of the Guide.

Old Parsonage

1 Banbury Road, Oxford OX2 6NN
TEL: (01865) 310210   FAX: (01865) 311262
EMAIL: oldparsonage@dial.pipex.com

Highly individual experience right in the city centre.

The Old Parsonage ploughs an individual and distinctive furrow. Behind the centuries-old casing of mellow stone and mullions, a suave and stylish operation is afoot: a glossy lobby broadens into a fashionably distressed cocktail bar, then turns up steps to a crowded dining area thick with mahogany tables, an eclectic selection of prints and photos and a brace of stuffed Thames bream. A universally youthful staff in soft, cotton polo shirts glide about: 'faultless, cheerful and efficient throughout', according to one satisfied guest, who would return again 'without a moment's hesitation'. If anything, the hotel is a victim of its own success, for it is hugely popular with socialising Oxonians as well as residents. Such acclaim creates a lively atmosphere, but it can cause frustration for residents waiting for a free table – not just for dinner, but for breakfast especially. The latter is a treat, with refreshingly tart juice, home-made preserves and quality sausages; our inspector's evening meal was spoilt, though, by a briny teriyaki sauce accompanying the duck breasts and a cremated chocolate tart. The bedrooms can be rather compact, but come well equipped and dressed in quality checks, chintz and much marble. Those on the north side overlook the rear of an unprepossessing college; otherwise the church and accompanying greenery provide an admirable view for a city-centre establishment.

◑ Closed 25, 26 Dec   ⤢ Two minutes from centre of Oxford, at north end of St Giles, at fork. Private car park   ⤶ 1 single, 6 twin, 19 double, 4 suites; family rooms available; all with bathroom/WC; all with satellite TV, room service, hair-dryer, mini-bar, direct-dial telephone, some with trouser press; no tea/coffee-making facilities in rooms   ⌦ Restaurant, bar, lounge, terrace, roof terrace, garden; punting; babysitting, baby-listening   ♿ No wheelchair access   ⊖ No dogs   ▭ Amex, Diners, MasterCard, Switch, Visa   £ Single £95, single occupancy of twin/double £125, twin/double £150 to £175, family room/suite £205; deposit required. Alc L £25, D £28

The Randolph

Beaumont Street, Oxford OX1 2LN
TEL: (01865) 247481   FAX: (01865) 791678

An Oxford tradition undergoing a major face-lift.

Major changes were afoot behind the Gothic arches of Oxford's landmark lodgings when our inspector called last spring. It would be sacrilegious to tamper with the ribbed vaulting, nutty oak panelling and splendid, square, cantilevered staircase in the entrance hall, but a brasserie was being planned to replace the sober residents' lounge, the vaults were to be converted into cafés and assorted amusements, and Marco Pierre White had designs on the crusty dining-room. An army of designers has already completed work on the bedrooms – most recently on the fourth floor, where the former staff quarters now provide acres of space in the half-tester suites, and ample room in the superior doubles. The standard doubles on the lower floors are considerably more confining, though the high quality of the fixtures and fittings, and the tastefully muted colour schemes, are consistent across the board. Whatever emerges from the upheaval, the Randolph is likely to remain the place for afternoon tea and scones. Feedback on the fallout from all the changes would, however, be most welcome.

◑ Open all year ⚁ In centre of Oxford, opposite Ashmolean Museum. Private car park (£12 per day) ⬛➛ 32 single, 16 twin, 61 double, 1 four-poster, 9 suites; family rooms available; all with bathroom/WC; all with satellite TV, room service, hair-dryer, trouser press, direct-dial telephone, some with mini-bar ⊘ Dining-room, bar; functions (max 200 people incl up to 100 residential), conferences; early suppers for children; cots, high chairs, babysitting, baby-listening ⚕ Wheelchair access to hotel (ramp) and dining-room, lift to bedrooms ⬤ No dogs in dining-room; no smoking in some bedrooms ▭ Amex, Delta, Diners, MasterCard, Switch, Visa £ Single £125 to £135, single occupancy of twin/double £155 to £165, twin/double/family room £155 to £165, four-poster £185 to £195, suite £225 to £235; deposit required. Continental B £10.50, cooked B £13.50; alc L £20, D £28. Special breaks available

---

OXHILL Warwickshire
map 5

Nolands Farm

Oxhill, Warwick CV35 0RJ
TEL: (01926) 640309   FAX: (01926) 641662
EMAIL: nolandsfm@compuserve.com
WEB SITE: www.stratford-upon-avon.co.uk/nolandsfm.htm

Peace and privacy at a farmhouse B&B right in the centre of England.

As you stand on the porch next to the log pile, listening to nothing but the wind, the lambs and the pheasants, Sue and Robin Hutsby's farm feels utterly lost in deep countryside. It's a conveniently accessible remoteness, however, with Stratford and the M40 just ten miles in either direction. The farm provides plenty of distractions for visitors: walks, animals to look at, milk for the breakfast table. 'It was the homely atmosphere I enjoyed,' wrote one correspondent. 'Breakfast was served with a smile.' The bedrooms are outside the main house, in a pleasant stable conversion. All are spacious, with simple but comfortable furnishings and lots of exposed beams. In the evenings there are armchairs in the rooms if you don't fancy socialising in the dining-room or small bar. Dinners are served by arrangement – straightforward traditional cooking, maybe featuring home-made soups and a roast. Breakfast brings home-made sausages with the home-produced milk.

◑ Closed Dec to 15 Jan; dining-room closed Sun & Mon eves ⚁ 8 miles east of Stratford, just off A422 Stratford to Banbury road; farm is signposted from A422 1 mile east of Pillerton Priors. Private car park ⬛➛ 1 single, 1 twin, 3 double, 2 four-poster, 1 family room; all in annexe; all with shower/WC exc four-posters with bathroom/WC; all with TV, clock radio, some with hair-dryer ⊘ Dining-room, bar, lounge, drying-room, conservatory, garden; functions (max 30 people incl up to 15 residential), conferences; fishing, clay-pigeon shooting; bicycles for hire ⚕ No wheelchair access ⬤ No children under 7; no dogs; no smoking in some public rooms and some bedrooms

MasterCard, Visa £ Single £25 to £30, single occupancy of twin/double £25 to £35, twin/double £36 to £40, four-poster £40 to £46, family room £55; deposit required. Set D £17. Special breaks available

---

PADSTOW Cornwall map 1

Seafood Restaurant, St Petroc's Hotel, Middle Street Café

Riverside, Padstow PL28 8BY
TEL: (01841) 532700   FAX: (01841) 532942

Choose from luxury above the famous Seafood Restaurant, mid-range at St Petroc's, and budget at the newly opened rooms above the Middle Street Café, in Rick Stein's ever-expanding empire.

Rick Stein's rule in Padstow may be expanding – the newly opened rooms above the Middle Street Café are a welcome budget addition to his empire – but the whole domain remains pleasingly low-key and relaxed. It's very much a family affair, with Jill Stein's dad playing the piano in the Seafood Restaurant on Tuesdays and Fridays, and Rick still doing most of the cooking. Of all the options, the Seafood Restaurant is the most formal, both in terms of the bedrooms above and the restaurant below, but even this is unstuffy and approachable. The menu offers such selections as fish and shellfish soup with rouille and Parmesan, followed by fillet of haddock with beurre rouge and gnocchi, which come simply served in the white-walled, parquet-floored restaurant. You pour your own wine and the service is efficient and incredibly friendly, but such is the demand for a table here that you may find yourself having to eat at 9.30pm at the second sitting.

At St Petroc's in New Street, the bedrooms are less flash, but comfortable, well equipped and kitted out with good, old furniture. The bar and restaurant area are as trendily stylish as the astonishingly reasonably priced, bistro-style food.

The three rooms over the (very good-value) Middle Street Café are small but perfectly formed, featuring over-long drapes at the windows and top-class fabrics. Parking is tricky, however, and you may end up leaving your car down in the car park by the Seafood Restaurant and walking the short distance up the hill. There's also the Stein delicatessen for snacks, if you've any room.

◖ Closed 20 to 27 Dec & 31 Dec   ⟲ Seafood Restaurant is on quayside in Padstow; St Petroc's Hotel is just above Strand; Middle Street Café: go to Seafood Restaurant for key and directions. Private car park   ⮢ 1 single, 3 twin, 24 double, 3 family rooms; most with bathroom/WC, some with shower/WC; all with TV, hair-dryer, direct-dial telephone, some with mini-bar, room service   ⊘ 3 restaurants, 2 bars, lounge, library, conservatory, garden; (no public rooms at Middle Street Café); early suppers for children, by arrangement; cots, high chairs, babysitting   ⅃ No wheelchair access
● No children under 6 in restaurants eves; no smoking in some public rooms
▤ Delta, MasterCard, Switch, Visa   £ Seafood & St Petroc's: single £29 to £35, single occupancy of twin/double £68 to £83, twin/double £90 to £110, family room £106 to £126; Middle Street Café: single occupancy of double £41 to £56; double £55 to

£75, family room (room rate + £16 for over-6s, children under 6 free). Deposit required. (1998 prices) Bar/bistro L, D £20; set L £28, D £34; alc L £40, D £50 (prices valid till spring 1999)

PAINSWICK Gloucestershire   map 2

Cardynham House NEW ENTRY

The Cross, Painswick, Stroud GL6 6XX
TEL: (01452) 814006   FAX: (01452) 812321

An unforgettable B&B in a wonderful fifteenth-century house above a tea-shop; simply amazing value.

For accommodation of this quality and character, you'd pay at least double in a hotel. Every bedroom in the Grade II-listed Cardynham House, which stands next to a pub in the centre of this silvery old wool town, is a stunner. Five of the six have four-poster beds, the other a half-tester. Each boasts the richest of fabrics, the boldest of colour schemes and the most arresting of antiques, and is strongly themed. For example, Old Tuscany has Latin inscriptions on its walls, Palm Springs focuses on a white-draped water bed, and The Highlands is decked out in tartan. Only Medieval Garden has a bath, but the rest have compact shower-rooms with quality modern fittings. Several rooms are ideal for families, as they have an extra bed, or – in the case of Dovecot, a massive, multi-beamed room up under the eaves – an extra two beds. Its name comes from the fact that the Californian artist-owner Carol Keyes keeps doves, which can sometimes make uninvited appearances in the room. Breakfast is served amid the stone walls and hanging baskets of the March Hare, a tea-shop that transforms into a Thai restaurant in the evenings. The phenomenal breakfast choice runs to omelettes, bubble and squeak, cinnamon toast, porridge and American pancakes or a waffle with maple syrup.

◑ Closed Chr; restaurant closed Sun, Mon & Tue eves   ▨ 3 miles north of Stroud on A46; take first right past church into Victoria Street; at end turn left; entrance to house is round left of March Hare. On-street parking (free)   ⤶ 1 double, 5 four-poster; family rooms available; 1 with bathroom/WC, 5 with shower/WC; all with TV, room service, hair-dryer, direct-dial telephone   ⊘ Lounge, conservatory, garden   ⅙ No wheelchair access   ● No dogs   ⊡ None accepted   £ Double/four-poster £65, family room £83; deposit required. Set D £18

PALGRAVE Suffolk   map 6

Malt House

Denmark Hill, Palgrave, Nr Diss IP22 1AE
TEL: (01379) 642107   FAX: (01379) 640315
EMAIL: malthouse@mainline.co.uk

Distinctive B&B with approachable, chatty hosts and a fascinating collection of oriental antiques.

From the outside this seventeenth-century house in pale stone, sitting discreetly behind a hedge at the end of an attractive village, gives no clue to the treasures within. Marj and Phil Morgan spent over 20 years in Hong Kong, and their home is a testament to those days and to their own good taste. Sitting rather incongruously in this quintessentially English home are fine Persian carpets, Japanese wood-block prints and an extraordinarily fine embroidered picture of an old Chinese man. The Morgans are only too happy to show you their collection and to talk about their days in the Far East. The couple have decided to stick to bed and breakfast, and dinners are no longer served, but they are happy to drive you down to one of the many eateries in the area. Other changes include some dramatic work to the walled garden. There's a new pond, complete with a pergola and statues of ducks, tortoise and teddy bear. The three bedrooms are all equally attractive, with an emphasis on bright colours.

◗ Closed 15 Dec to 5 Jan ⬛ 1 mile west of Diss on A143 Bury St Edmunds to Norwich road; house is on village green behind church. Private car park ⬛ 1 twin, 2 double; all with bathroom/WC exc 1 double with shower/WC; all with TV, 1 with trouser press; hair-dryer available ⬥ Dining-room, lounge, drying-room, garden; early suppers for children; cots, high chairs, baby-listening, outdoor play area ⬥ No wheelchair access ◗ No children under 2; no dogs or guide dogs; no smoking ⬛ Delta, Diners, MasterCard, Switch, Visa £ Single occupancy of twin/double £30 to £35, twin/double £60; deposit required

---

PARRACOMBE Devon   map 1

Heddon's Gate Hotel

Heddon's Mouth, Parracombe, Barnstaple EX31 4PZ
TEL: (01598) 763313   FAX: (01598) 763363
EMAIL: info@hgate.co.uk

Splendidly old-fashioned lodge, in fabulous, remote Exmoor location.

Amid the tumultuous landscape of Exmoor, with its lost valleys, steep hills and hairpin bends, the hotel is approached along a long, long drive, with the woods and dells on all sides just crying out to be explored. Proprietors Heather and Bob Deville do a roaring trade in packed lunches for their guests' midday nourishment on the moor. You can expect a warm welcome in the evening, too, in this extremely traditional establishment, where the only concessions to modernity are in the kitchen and the office – and there's also a new recycling centre, of which Bob is very proud. Darkly patterned floral wallpaper, heavy, swagged curtains with tasselled pelmets, dark-green chesterfield sofas, tapestries on the walls and stags' antlers above the roaring fire create an old-fashioned, lived-in atmosphere. The public rooms are a good size, and there's a useful little library; everywhere large picture windows make the best of the views. The five-course dinners are served on lacy tablecloths; you might try curried-banana soup, followed by escalopes of smoked salmon served with a Chardonnay and chive sauce, then roast tenderloin of pork stuffed with prunes and wrapped in streaky bacon. The capacious bedrooms are notionally themed – the Chinese Room features some oriental pictures and furniture, while Grandmother's Room has a splendid, embossed bathroom suite, and Servants' Quarters is endowed with a separate sitting area.

◑ Closed Nov to Easter   ⁊ From A39, 4 miles west of Lynton, take road signposted Martinhoe and Woody Bay. Take next left; carry straight on at next crossroads and down steep hill; hotel drive is on right. Private car park   ⚏ 1 single, 4 twin, 4 double, 2 four-poster, 3 suites; some in annexe; all with bathroom/WC exc 1 four-poster with shower/WC; all with TV, room service, hair-dryer, direct-dial telephone   ⊘ Dining-room, bar, 2 lounges, library, games room, garden   ⅙ Wheelchair access to hotel (1 step) and dining-room, WC (M, F), 3 ground-floor bedrooms   ● Children must be old enough to dine at 8pm; no dogs or smoking in dining-room   ⊟ Amex, MasterCard, Switch, Visa   £ Single £57 to £67, twin/double £107 to £133, four-poster £113 to £133, suite £118 to £151 (rates incl dinner). Special breaks available

---

PAXFORD Gloucestershire   map 5

Churchill Arms   NEW ENTRY

Paxford, Chipping Campden GL55 6XH
TEL: (01386) 594000   FAX: (01386) 594005

Outstanding food and fetching bedrooms in a laid-back, small-scale Cotswolds pub.

The setting is pure Cotswolds: across the lane from this mellow-stone old inn, a tiny church pokes into a sheep-dotted field and a Hovis sign hangs from a building. The pub itself – with its requisite beams and inglenook fireplace, mix of flagged, tiled and carpeted flooring, hotchpotch of round-back and bentwood chairs and tatty armchairs, and mishmash of tables – looks unsmart. But this turns out to be the venue for some of the best pub grub in Gloucestershire. On most nights, everyone from American tourists to London media types battles for a table – there are no reservations, even for residents. The short menu is nonchalantly scrawled on blackboards by the bar, where everyone must order. Our inspector recently chose a fluffy crab and spring-onion tart, followed by pan-fried calf's liver in a sensational mushroom and chorizo sauce with a bowl of olive-oil mash; a prune and Armagnac tart or a passion-fruit mousse and ice-cream loomed next, but he couldn't last the distance. Most punters choose from the small, but well-chosen, wine selection rather than knock back pints. The service is speedy and smiley – indeed, the whole pub is imbued with an atmosphere of professionalism yet also jollity. The bedrooms are extremely good looking, with antiques, chic soft furnishings and designer tea things (proper coffee and fresh milk are provided), plus smart new bathrooms with deep baths. Rooms 3 and 4 are of a good size, but Rooms 1 and 2 are indisputably small.

◑ Open all year   ⁊ On B4479, in centre of village. On-street parking (free)
⚏ 4 double; all with bathroom/WC; all with TV, hair-dryer, direct-dial telephone
⊘ Bar, garden   ⅙ No wheelchair access   ● No dogs; no smoking in bedrooms
⊟ Delta, MasterCard, Switch, Visa   £ Single occupancy of double £40, double £60. Bar L, D £5 to £18

See page 6 for a brief explanation of how to use the Guide.

| PELYNT **Cornwall** | map 1 |

Jubilee Inn

Pelynt, Looe PL13 2JZ
TEL: (01503) 220312   FAX: (01503) 220920

Well-meaning hostelry, more eating-house than drinking-house, with patriotic innuendo and cosy bedrooms.

Patriotism is a big theme in this pleasing pub, but the feeling is one of tongue-in-cheek humour rather than national pride, with Victoria looking distinctly unamused on many of the walls, and Our Liz gazing down only slightly more benevolently. They cast their regal stares around this cosy hostelry, which boasts plenty of idiosyncracies as well as a big menu and welcoming bedrooms. When the local church invited the Bishop of Truro to bless the new local beer, Trelawney's Pride, all the worshippers came for a tipple here at the pub; and if you look at the watercolours on the fabulous, airy, glass-encased wood-and-stone staircase, you'll see artists' impressions from 1953 on how to revamp the place. Elsewhere, tradition reigns supreme, from the drunken-looking exterior to the wooden settles around the beamed bar and the flags in the courtyard. The 'Bill of Fare', however, is far more cosmopolitan, with dishes ranging from local scallops with crispy bacon to chicken tikka masala; and the Jubilee mixed grill, with sauce diable ('not for the faint-hearted'), sounds a challenge. The cosy bedrooms come complete with wonky ceilings and chunky, carved antiques.

◗ Open all year   ⤢ In Pelynt village, 4 miles north of Looe. Private car park ⬛ 6 double, 1 four-poster, 2 family rooms; all with bathroom/WC exc 1 double with shower/WC; all with TV, room service, hair-dryer, direct-dial telephone   ✓ Restaurant, 3 bars, lounge, games room, garden; functions (max 150 people incl up to 20 residential); early suppers for children; cots, high chairs, toys, playroom, babysitting, baby-listening, outdoor play area   ♿ No wheelchair access   ● None   ▭ MasterCard, Switch, Visa   £ Single £36, single occupancy of double £36, double £59, four-poster £65, family room £74; deposit required. Bar/bistro L, D £5 to £16. Special breaks available

| PENRITH **Cumbria** | map 10 |

North Lakes Hotel

Ullswater Road, Penrith CA11 8QT
TEL: (01768) 868111   FAX: (01768) 868291
EMAIL: nlakes@shireinns.co.uk
WEB SITE: www.openworld.co.uk/shireinns

Unusually designed business hotel, conveniently situated on the M6.

Little about the location or the exterior of this modern chain hotel has much initial appeal: it stands on a dull plot of flattish, Eden Valley land surveying the M6 motorway roundabout at Junction 40. As you concentrate on finding the correct slip-road exit, a glimpse of its low-rise, functional architecture may seem even less enticing. Inside, however, the hotel is unexpectedly pleasing. The open-plan reception areas look rather like the inside of a giant Alpine chalet or hunting-lodge, with exposed stonework and cheerfully blazing fireplaces. In the airy, skylit roof spaces high overhead, huge rafters, which once graced Preston's railway station, can be seen; massive pots and baskets of dried flowers add a natural look. Comfortable, well-designed seating and eating areas extend from the entrance foyer, each with its own decorative theme. There's a smart, contemporary restaurant down a few steps, a snug bar with another open fireplace, and a bright, self-service cafeteria offering a splendid range of interesting snacks and sandwiches on speciality breads. Close by, the hotel's other main draw is visible – its leisure centre, which includes a large swimming-pool with whirlpool. The bedrooms (in two price grades) are predictably similar, with inoffensive, co-ordinated, contract décor and practical, modern fittings. Efficient glazing keeps out all but a faint hum of traffic noise.

◑ Open all year ⓩ Leave M6 at Junction 40; hotel is located just off the roundabout, first right, off Ullswater Road. Private car park ⇒ 40 twin, 11 double, 2 four-poster, 2 four-poster suites, 20 family rooms, 9 suites; all with bathroom/WC; all with TV, room service, hair-dryer, trouser press, direct-dial telephone ⊘ Restaurant, cafeteria, 5 bars, lounge, games room, garden; functions (max 250 people incl up to 188 residential), conferences; civil wedding licence; gym, sauna, solarium, heated indoor swimming-pool, squash; early suppers for children; cots, high chairs, playroom in leisure centre ⅙ Wheelchair access to hotel and restaurant (ramp), WC (M, F), 22 ground-floor bedrooms, 2 rooms specially equipped for disabled people ● No dogs in public rooms; no smoking in restaurant and some bedrooms ☐ Amex, Delta, Diners, MasterCard, Switch, Visa Ⓔ Single occupancy of twin/double £102, twin/double £125, four-poster/suite £152, family room £140. Bar/bistro L £5.50; set L £11 to £15, D £19.50; alc L, D £24. Special breaks available

---

PENZANCE Cornwall	map 1

Abbey Hotel

Abbey Street, Penzance TR18 4AR
TEL: (01736) 366906   FAX: (01736) 351163

Gracious hosts and relaxed sophistication in private-house atmosphere.

There's something incredibly balanced about the Abbey Hotel: the grandeur is palpable, yet it sits at the top of the slipway, overlooking docks and derricks. When we inspected, the Duke of York was about to arrive, yet the focus was on more mundane matters – the bath in Room 3 had overflowed, and hostess Jean Shrimpton (yes, *the* Jean Shrimpton, a.k.a. Mrs Cox) was rushing about in an anorak, just about to go out and buy flowers to add to those already filling every room. This 200-year-old granite house feels expensive yet lived in, is sophisticated without being swanky, and is not too proud to show a few scuffs here and there and what's more, gets away with it. The drawing-room, which looks out to a lovely walled garden, with tumbling honeysuckle and hydrangea, is distempered in a warm pink, lined with books, and filled with squashy sofas and fascinating knick-knacks that Jean and her husband have picked up on their travels, including Buddha figurines, a bronze peacock fireguard and a Pollock's toy theatre. A big, open fireplace and heavy round tables dominate the small dining-room, where dinner is an intimate event; you might try carrot and cardamom soup, followed by salmon and quenelles of hake with a stock cream sauce. A huge Rajasthani map of the cosmos hangs above the landing, and the bedrooms come in all shapes and sizes, from the grand and spacious to the more cosy. All are flamboyantly decorated in bold colours, with lace and antiques.

◑ Closed Chr ⚡ On entering Penzance, take seafront road; after 300 yards, just before bridge, turn right; after 10 yards, turn left and drive up slipway; hotel is at top. Private car park ⤇ 2 single, 1 twin, 2 double, 1 family room, 1 suite; one in annexe; 4 with bathroom/WC, 3 with shower/WC; all with TV, room service, hair-dryer ⌗ Dining-room, drawing-room, garden; croquet; early suppers for children; cots, babysitting ⅋ No wheelchair access ⬤ No children under 7; no dogs in public rooms ▭ Amex, Delta, MasterCard, Visa £ Single £70 to £75, single occupancy of twin/double £90 to £140, twin/double £90 to £140, family room £120 to £140, suite £140 to £200; deposit required. Set D £24.50. Special breaks available

PLYMOUTH Devon   map 1

Athenaeum Lodge

4 Athenaeum Street, The Hoe, Plymouth PL1 2RQ
TEL: (01752) 665005 (AND FAX)

Classic, simple B&B, handy for town centre and seafront.

This is the kind of unpretentious establishment that succeeds totally at what it sets out to do: provide cheap, clean accommodation in a useful location. Margaret and Tony Rowe have provided home comforts for regulars for years now, and they remember when guests want kippers (if you're new you have to order them in advance). The small terraced house has small, spick-and-span bedrooms – all simple and good value – and now all but the top-floor rooms have tiny *en suite* shower-rooms. The top-floor rooms share a pretty, pine-panelled shower-room. Breakfast is taken on wooden tables decorated with fresh flowers, under a picture of a crazy restaurant by Beryl Cook (the artist herself used to live next door). No evening meal is served, but there are plenty of eateries within walking distance.

◑ Closed 24 Dec to 2 Jan ⚡ From A38 follow city-centre signs, then take road signposted The Hoe, Barbican and seafront; after ¾ mile, turn left at Walrus pub; lodge is at top of road, on right. Private car park; on-street parking (£2 per day, free Sun) ⤇ 1 single, 2 twin, 4 double, 3 family rooms; 6 with shower/WC; all with satellite TV, hair-dryer ⌗ Dining-room ⅋ No wheelchair access ⬤ No children under 5; no dogs; no smoking ▭ Delta, MasterCard, Visa £ Single £17 to £18, single occupancy of twin/double £24 to £32, twin/double £30 to £38, family room £40 to £48; deposit required

The text of entries is based on unsolicited reports sent in by readers and backed up by inspections. The factual details are from questionnaires the Guide *sends to all hotels that feature in the book.*

POOLE **Dorset**   map 2

Mansion House

Thames Street, Poole BH15 1JN
TEL: (01202) 685666   FAX: (01202) 665709

Expansion plans afoot at a dashing eighteenth-century house close to Poole's bustling Quay.

A colonnaded portico adds an exuberant touch to the rather sombre façade of this partly creeper-clad, red-brick Georgian town house. It gives a little clue to the elegance encountered inside, where a graceful, pillar-flanked staircase ascends to a landing where an assemblage of portraits, antiques and a gilt-framed mirror create a stunning focal point. Something of the style is echoed in the pretty blue-and-white residents' lounge, though many of those entering the building will be members of the hotel's dining club, who make their way straight to the large, modern, part-panelled bar/restaurant, where clever lighting helps add to the sense of space. The menu, which features a good range of fish dishes, might offer seared fresh tuna loin with spicy lentils and wasabi vinaigrette, breast of duck with raspberries and a green-peppercorn sauce, followed by British and Irish cheeses with walnut bread. Alternatively, guests might choose from the fare offered on the blackboard in the beamed, rather pubby, JJ's Bistro, described by one dining-club member, who was disappointed to be told that the restaurant was full, as 'downmarket'. The bedrooms adopt a fresh, country-house look, with lots of florals, tied-back drapes and a pleasant mix of reproduction and good, old furniture. Four bedrooms are being added in an adjacent extension.

◑ Open all year; main restaurant closed Sun eve & Sat L; bistro closed Sun L
⏏ Approaching Poole from Southampton on A31, follow signs for Channel ferry; at lifting bridge turn left on to Poole Quay; take first road on left (Thames Street); hotel is opposite church. Private car park ⏏ 9 single, 8 twin, 11 double; family rooms available; all with bathroom/WC; all with TV, room service, hair-dryer, trouser press, direct-dial telephone; no tea/coffee-making facilities in rooms ⊘ Restaurant, bistro, 2 bars, lounge; functions (max 30 people incl up to 28 residential), conferences; civil wedding licence; early suppers for children; cots, high chairs, babysitting, baby-listening ⅄ No wheelchair access ⊖ No children under 5 in main restaurant eves; no dogs ⊟ Amex, Delta, Diners, MasterCard, Switch, Visa £ Single £60 to £85, single occupancy of twin/double £70 to £90, twin/double/family room £95 to £125; deposit required. Bar/bistro L £9.50, D £14; set L £14.50, D £26.50. Special breaks available

---

PORLOCK **Somerset**   map 1

Oaks Hotel

Porlock, Minehead TA24 8ES
TEL: (01643) 862265 (AND FAX)

Relaxing seaside hotel, run with an eye for traditional values.

'Quite the friendliest hotel, the friendliest proprietors, and the friendliest guests

I have ever encountered,' wrote one correspondent of her stay at Tim and Anne Riley's traditional hotel, set just above the pretty seaside town of Porlock. Guests continue to be impressed by the care and courtesy shown by the couple, from the moment the car draws up (when Tim appears, to help with the bags), to the offer of a welcoming pot of tea and the arrival of sherry (and an ever-replenished fruit bowl) in the bedrooms. Japanese wall-mounted plates add interest to a comfortable lounge (which overlooks the town's roofscape), and seaside prints breathe an air of jollity into the small bar. Floral drapes frame the picture windows in the bright dining-room, where guests might enjoy a duck and mushroom salad with orange sauce, followed by sauté fillet of monkfish with lime and ginger, then an Exmoor venison and mushroom pie, and finally banana and stem-ginger ice-cream. The bedrooms are attractively furnished in a mixture of antique, reproduction and more modern items, and are decorated in a classy country-house style.

◑ Closed Nov to mid-Mar ⤢ On A39, west of Minehead; hotel is on left as you enter village. Private car park ⌸ 3 twin, 6 double; all with bathroom/WC; all with TV, limited room service, hair-dryer, direct-dial telephone ⌀ Dining-room, bar, 2 lounges, garden ⅃ No wheelchair access ● No children under 8; no dogs in public rooms; smoking in 1 lounge only ⊟ Delta, MasterCard, Switch, Visa ⌹ Single occupancy of twin/double £53, twin/double £85. Set D £26. Special breaks available

---

PORTSCATHO Cornwall
map 1

Roseland House

Rosevine, Portscatho, Truro TR2 5EW
TEL: (01872) 580644   FAX: (01872) 580801

Windswept location, fine views and cosy atmosphere at this very off-the-beaten-track hotel.

Such is the feeling this hotel inspires of being in a protected outpost, safe and warm from the prevailing winds, that it's rather fun to fantasise about the chilly life of a smuggler – while sitting with a drink in your hand, in one of the most squashy and inviting sofas in the residents' lounge, listening only to the ticking of the grandfather clock, or among the abundant plants and fresh flower arrangements in the conservatory dining-room. And nary a draught will bother you. If, on the other hand, the weather is conducive, you could stroll down the sleek lawns to the wooded path descending to the private beach, and act it out for real... Then, having built up an appetite, you could try the six-course dinner – asparagus soup, salad niçoise, roast loin of pork served with calvados apple sauce and a herb stuffing, chocolate mousse, cheeses and coffee. When we inspected, the hotel was filled with the welcoming smells of fresh flowers and baking bread. One satisfied guest praised details like the freshly ground coffee and cafetière in the bedrooms, as well as the 'superb' food and 'slick and friendly' service. Upstairs, all but one of the bedrooms has a sea view, and they are pleasingly, simply done out in pale colours and pine furniture (they were due for refurbishment in 1998). Bathrooms are spacious and fresh.

◗ Closed Chr & New Year; occasionally Jan   ⬚ Hotel is signposted 2 miles south of Ruan High Lanes, off A3078. Private car park ⬚⤏ 5 twin, 3 double, 1 four-poster, 1 suite; family rooms available; 8 with bathroom/WC, 2 with shower/WC; all with TV, room service, hair-dryer, direct-dial telephone   ⬚ Dining-room, bar, 2 lounges, conservatory, garden, private beach; functions (max 150 people incl up to 20 residential); fishing, swimming from private beach; early suppers for children; cots, high chairs, baby-listening   ⬚ No wheelchair access   ● No dogs; no smoking ⬚ Amex, MasterCard, Switch, Visa   £ Single occupancy of twin/double £55 to £85, twin/double/four-poster £84 to £130, family room (children under 10: room rate + 25%) (rates incl dinner); deposit required. Bar/bistro L £5; alc Sun L £13.50. Special breaks available

---

POSTBRIDGE Devon   map 1

Lydgate House

Postbridge, Yelverton PL20 6TJ
TEL: (01822) 880209   FAX: (01822) 880202

Excellent value for money at this homely yet smart hotel bang in the middle of Dartmoor.

Just inside the door of this hotel is another door, gaily muralled and proudly labelled Boot Room. This sums up the feel of the place – pretty and homely, yet sensible and practical. Judging by the surrounding countryside (the East Dart River running through the garden, and wilderness in all directions), this room gets filled with walking gear rather often. Everywhere you look an enticing path leads off across Dartmoor. And the hotel is a happy, peaceful place to restore oneself from all that outdoor activity, with welcoming squashy sofas and a big wood-burner in the sitting-room, and plenty of books, games and CDs should the weather prove inclement. Breakfast and supper are taken in the conservatory at the back of the house; with flowers both inside and out, the room feels really verdant. In summer there's a danger of invasion by cream-tea-seekers, so it's best to be out exploring at this time. The menu caters well for veggies and non-veggies alike. Bedrooms are straightforwardly done out in fresh country style, with the odd piece of prettily painted furniture among the pine. The single room deserves a mention for its wonderful mural of damsels pouring water into your bath.

◗ Closed 4 Jan to 28 Feb   ⬚ Off B3212 in Postbridge; turn between humpback bridge and East Dart pub. Private car park ⬚⤏ 1 single, 6 double, 1 family room; most with bathroom/WC, 3 double with shower/WC; all with TV, hair-dryer   ⬚ Dining-room/conservatory, bar, sitting-room, drying-room, garden; functions (max 16 people residential/non-residential); fishing; early suppers for children; cots, high chairs   ⬚ No wheelchair access   ● Dogs in sitting-room if other guests consent; smoking discouraged   ⬚ Delta, MasterCard, Switch, Visa   £ Single £32, single occupancy of twin/double £40, twin/double £57, family room £90; deposit required. Set D £16.50. Special breaks available

---

Report forms are at the back of the Guide; *write a letter or email us if you prefer. Our email address is: "guide.reports@which.net".*

River House

Skippool Creek, Thornton-le-Fylde, Thornton Cleveleys FY5 5LF
TEL: (01253) 883497   FAX: (01253) 892083

Stunning location, comfortably worn accommodation, good food and wonderfully quirky hosts.

If you are one of those people who likes to check into a hotel and then retire to the comfort of your room to lounge about and watch TV, River House will not be for you. The bedrooms are not conducive to lounging – though comfortable enough, they are undeniably a little worn and shabby in places. Despite this, you're likely to be hooked after just one visit. For a start, it's hard to imagine a more evocative setting, at the end of a bumpy track and overlooking Skippool Creek. At low tide the ranks of yachts and boats sit on scrubby grass tethered to crooked wooden jetties, but at high tide they bob about on water that comes right across the road – a front bedroom will afford you fantastic views. Downstairs the delightfully cosy bar, with its roaring log fire and settle benches, is at its best at dusk, with candles flickering on the tables. Solo guests won't be on their own for long, as the owners, Bill and Linda Scott, are happy to while away the evening chatting to you; Bill has a bottomless well of anecdotes to share. He's slowly carving out a career as a TV chef, and the food served in the large dining-room is excellent. Try the salmon mikado, a lovely concoction of salmon fillets in a sake and teriyaki sauce (although, like most dishes, it's not cheap; main courses cost £16 to £20).

◗ Open all year; restaurant closed Sun eve   ⬛ From Poulton-le-Fylde, take A585 for Fleetwood; follow road through 3 sets of traffic lights; at roundabout take third exit, towards Little Thornton; immediately on right is Wyre Road leading to Skippool Creek; house is at end of road on left. Private car park   ⬛ 3 twin, 1 double; all with bathroom/WC; all with TV, room service, hair-dryer, trouser press, direct-dial telephone   ⬳ Dining-room, bar, lounge, conservatory, garden; functions (max 100 people incl up to 8 residential), conferences; early suppers for children; cot   ⬛ No wheelchair access   ⬤ No children in dining-room after 7pm; no dogs in public rooms   ⬛ Delta, MasterCard, Switch, Visa   ⬛ Single occupancy of twin/double £65, twin/double £80. Set L, D £25; alc L, D £32. Special breaks available

White House Manor

Prestbury, Macclesfield SK10 4HP
TEL: (01625) 829376   FAX: (01625) 828627

Highly original, themed rooms in charming hotel, with its restaurant five minutes' walk into picturesque village.

The façade may be that of a simple, unassuming, red-brick country house, but the cars in the car park (Jags, MR2s) are more revealing of what to expect inside. The atmosphere is warm and welcoming, and guests help themselves to drinks from the honesty bar in the conservatory. The bedrooms – impeccably executed and imaginatively themed – are the focal point. Trafalgar exudes history and masculinity; an abundance of rich, burgundy drapes and gold braid sets the decadent tone of this single room. A more feminine atmosphere is to be found in Earl Grey, a twin bursting with sunflower yellow and Wedgwood blue, with dressers laden with bone china. The White House Manor doesn't have a dining area for guests (breakfast is served in bedrooms or the conservatory), but its restaurant – only a five-minute walk into the picturesque village of Prestbury – offers an à la carte or a set menu. Dishes include a terrine of smoked salmon, champagne and crème fraîche on a cucumber cappuccino, followed by char-grilled Cornish sea bass with niçoise vegetables and an anchovy dressing. As we went to press, Judith and Ryland Wakeham were nearing completion of two new *en suite* bedrooms, an enlarged reception and an additional residents' lounge.

◗ Closed 25 Dec; restaurant closed Sun eve ⚡ 2 miles north of Macclesfield on A538. Private car park ⛳ 3 single, 1 twin, 5 double, 2 four-poster; some with bathroom/WC, most with shower/WC; all with TV, room service, hair-dryer, mini-bar, trouser press, direct-dial telephone ✓ Restaurant (off-site), bar, 2 lounges, drying-room, conservatory, garden; functions (max 40 people incl up to 19 residential), conferences; early suppers for children; cots, high chairs, toys, babysitting, baby-listening 🚫 No wheelchair access ⬤ No dogs; no smoking in bedrooms ▭ Amex, Delta, Diners, MasterCard, Switch, Visa £ Single £40 to £70, single occupancy of twin/double £70 to £85, twin/double £70 to £100, four-poster £110 to £120; deposit required. Continental B £5.50, cooked B £9; light L £7; set L £15, D £18; alc L, D £25. Special breaks available

---

QUORN Leicestershire   map 5

Quorn Country Hotel

66 Leicester Road, Quorn, Loughborough LE12 8BB
TEL: (01509) 415050   FAX: (01509) 415557

Smart, efficiently run hotel, mainly catering for business people.

At bright Sunday lunch-times, Quorn comes alive with day-trippers who have headed out of Leicester and Loughborough to the country – the town is indelibly associated with the idea of 'country' through its hunting history, even if the truth is that creeping development has taken away much of the character of the place. Quorn Country Hotel reflects that change: during the midweek it is a business-oriented hotel, while at weekends it serves Sunday lunches and caters for up-market wedding parties (grooms occasionally drop in by helicopter). Dining takes place either in the Orangery or the cosy Shires Restaurant, the latter divided into four small sections, with button-back seats in alcoves and an intimate atmosphere. Duck is the speciality of the house – they use a double-roasting technique and serve it with either plum or orange sauce – but you will find fish, ostrich, guinea-fowl and hare, too. For less formal meals, there are bar snacks, and drinks can be served in the gardens by the River Soar. The bedrooms reflect the tastes of midweek customers: they are smart and reasonably spacious, are all well equipped with satellite television and mini-bars and have full 24-hour room service. Those not on expense accounts should ask about the good-value weekend breaks.

◑ Open all year; 1 restaurant closed Mon eve, only snacks Sat L ⚡ In village of Quorn, signposted from A6 just south of Loughborough. Private car park ⌗ 8 twin, 8 double, 1 four-poster, 1 suite; family rooms available; all with bathroom/WC; all with satellite TV, 24-hour room service, hair-dryer, mini-bar, trouser press, direct-dial telephone ✧ 2 restaurants, bar, lounge, drying-room, conservatory, garden; functions (max 120 people incl up to 16 residential), conferences; civil wedding licence; fishing; leisure facilities nearby (reduced rates for guests); early suppers for children; cots, high chairs, baby-listening ⅙ Wheelchair access to hotel (ramp) and restaurants, 9 ground-floor bedrooms, 1 room specially equipped for disabled people ● No dogs in public rooms; no smoking in some bedrooms ⊟ Amex, Diners, MasterCard, Switch, Visa £ Single occupancy of twin/double £93, twin/double £104, four-poster/suite £125, family room £135; deposit required. Continental B £5, cooked B £9; bar/bistro L £12.50, D £18; set L, D £20; alc L, D £30. Special breaks available

---

RAVENSTONEDALE Cumbria   map 8

Black Swan

Ravenstonedale, Kirkby Stephen CA17 4NG
TEL: (015396) 23204   FAX: (015396) 23604

Well-kept village hostelry in the Eden Valley.

Handily placed for exploring an interesting and relatively little-known stretch of country between the Lakes and the Dales, the Black Swan has an established and confident air. It dates back to the turn of the century and looks solidly prosperous, with tall gables of Lakeland stone. It's in the middle of a pretty village, but it feels quiet, and has access to a private stretch of the Eden and a lake stocked with brown trout. The interior is reassuringly traditional in the style of many good inns, but has its own distinctive character too. The cosy bars downstairs are where most visitors congregate, taking advantage of blazing log fires and comfy, unsurprising seating, though there's plenty of interest on the walls if you take a good look, from local prints and photos to modern works. There's a separate, but rather less inviting, residents' lounge upstairs. More successful is the dining-room, a light and dignified space handsomely furnished with Chippendale-style chairs and silver-domed tureens. The food matches the surroundings and includes local game and fish and regional cheeses. The agreeably decorated bedrooms all differ but meet good standards, with a strong emphasis on comfort and character; most have their own bathrooms. The former police station next door (The Nick) is now converted into self-catering units.

◑ Open all year ⚡ Leave M6 at Junction 38 and take A685 for Brough; turn off at sign for Ravenstonedale. Private car park ⌗ 6 twin, 4 twin/double, 10 double; family rooms available; most with bath/WC, some with shower/WC; all with TV, hair-dryer, direct-dial telephone ✧ Restaurant, 2 bars, lounge, TV room, garden; functions (max 120 people incl up to 40 residential), conferences (max 12 people); fishing, tennis; early suppers for children; cots, high chairs ⅙ Wheelchair access to hotel and restaurant, WC (M, F), 3 ground-floor bedrooms, 1 specially equipped for disabled people ● Dogs in back bar only ⊟ Amex, Delta, Diners, MasterCard, Switch, Visa £ Single occupancy of twin/double £45, twin/double £70 to £86. Bar L, D £4 to £8; set L £10, D £23; alc L, D £13 to £20. Special breaks available

Tarn House Farm   NEW ENTRY

Ravenstonedale, Kirkby Stephen CA17 4LJ
TEL: (015396) 23646

Superior and welcoming farmhouse B&B on the fringes of the Pennines.

You can work up a fair speed along the bouncy A683 fell road between Sedbergh and Kirkby Stephen. This substantial farmhouse is almost concealed behind protective walls below the road and if you pass it, you've missed a treat, for among the myriad farmhouse B&Bs in Cumbria this is definitely one for the album. It's a down-to-earth working farm, with gumboots by the door and dogs in the yard. Michael and Sally Metcalfe-Gibson raise sheep and keep dairy cattle, though Michael is not a lifelong farmer. Sally welcomes a handful of paying guests (rarely more than four at a time), and offers good home-cooked dinners by prior arrangement (bring your own wine). It's no humdrum property: the crest on the stone entrance dates it to 1664 and it was the first slate-roofed farm built in the area – a house of some distinction. There's a sense of history in its fascinating period features, plus lots of good-quality, solid country furniture and photos, pictures and artifacts of family interest. Guests may use a handsome sitting-room, with a big stone inglenook fireplace. The dining-room next door (a former dairy or pantry) has kept its magnificent, original stone shelving. There are just a trio of rooms to let, light and quietly decorated in simple country style.

◑ Closed Chr   ⊅ On A683, 4 miles south-west of Kirkby Stephen (farm is on left). Private car park   ⤙ 1 single, 1 twin, 1 double; family room available; all with room service   ⊘ Dining-room, sitting-room, drying-room, garden; fishing; early suppers for children; cots, high chairs, toys, babysitting, outdoor play area   ⅅ No wheelchair access   ⬤ No dogs; no smoking   ⊟ None accepted   £ Single £18, twin/double £35, family room £40. Set L £6, D £12 (by arrangement). Special breaks available

---

REDMILE Leicestershire   map 5

Peacock Farm

Redmile, Nottingham NG13 0GQ
TEL: (01949) 842475   FAX: (01949) 843127

Rural B&B with restaurant and family-oriented atmosphere.

The Need family started doing B&B from their eighteenth-century farmhouse 24 years ago, the business passing to Nicky Need a few years back. It's an unpretentious, family-oriented style well suited to the rambling collection of stables and outbuildings where you can play snooker, drink in the small bar or even stable your horse for the night. The Feathers Restaurant (now with new chef Paul Reisenbüchler) is rustic in décor, and menus are chalked up on the blackboard: plenty of game and fresh fish is the order of the day, plus snacky items like tapas and soups. In the main farmhouse bedrooms are given a fresh cottagey look; all have showers, and those in the coach-house annexe have wood panels and plenty of potted plants (if you are with the family, these are the rooms to choose for children). Some rooms have views across to Belvoir Castle, seat of the Duke of Rutland, whose coat of arms features the peacock that gives the farm its name.

○ Open all year ⊿ ½ mile north-west of village. Private car park ⬏ 1 twin, 1 double, 7 family rooms; some in annexe; all with shower/WC; all with TV, hair-dryer ⊘ Restaurant, bar, lounge, TV room, drying-room, games room, garden; functions (max 40 people incl up to 24 residential), conferences; children's unheated outdoor swimming-pool, croquet; early suppers for children; cots, high chairs, toys, playroom, babysitting, baby-listening, outdoor play area ♿ Wheelchair access to hotel (ramp) and restaurant (1 step), 5 ground-floor bedrooms ○ Dogs in 1 bedroom only; smoking in bar only ⊟ Amex, Delta, Diners, MasterCard, Switch, Visa £ Single occupancy of twin/double £35, twin/double £49, family room £49 + £10 for 1 child, £18 for 2 children, £24 for 3 children; deposit required. Bar/bistro L £7.50; set L, D £14.50; alc L, D £18.50. Special breaks available

Peacock Inn

Main Street, Redmile, Nottingham NG13 0GA
TEL: (01949) 842554   FAX: (01949) 843746

Stylish restaurant, good traditional bar and luxurious bedrooms at this country inn near Belvoir Castle.

The Peacock Inn has been a popular dining-out spot for locals for some years now, and demand for tables in the à la carte restaurant can be high at weekends – so book ahead; it is certainly worth the extra planning – the Garden Room is a smart, bright space with quarry-tiled floor, cane furniture and carefully faded colours – the whole has a *fin de siècle* café atmosphere. The cooking leans towards France in its influences, with the occasional added exotic touch: Thai spiced mussels as a starter, for example, followed by seared fillet of turbot on saffron noodles tossed with baby lobster tail, asparagus and white wine. Our inspection meal was beautifully cooked and served, finishing with a mascarpone cheese mousse topped with seasonal berries. Meals can be taken in the bar too: a busy watering-hole made up of small interlinking rooms. The bedrooms are spacious and carefully furnished with antique pieces; bathrooms are stylish and well equipped, with strong showers. Beds are turned down for guests, and a nightcap left on the bedside table; there is no tea tray, but room service will bring that essential early-morning cuppa. Breakfasts in the Garden Room are very good, although it would be nice to have fresh orange juice rather than bottled.

○ Open all year ⊿ In village, next to church. Private car park ⬏ 8 double, 1 family suite; all with bathroom/WC; all with TV, room service, hair-dryer, trouser press, direct-dial telephone; dry-cleaning/laundry service available; no tea/coffee-making facilities in rooms ⊘ 2 restaurants, bar, lounge, drying-room, garden; functions (max 160 people incl up to 16 residential), conferences; early suppers for children; high chair, mother-and-baby room ♿ No wheelchair access ○ No dogs; no smoking in bedrooms ⊟ Delta, MasterCard, Switch, Visa £ Single occupancy of double £75, double £90, family suite £130; deposit required. Bar/bistro L, D £8; alc L, D £22.50. Special breaks available

Arkleside Hotel

Reeth, Richmond DL11 6SG
TEL: (01748) 884200 (AND FAX)
EMAIL: arkleside.hotel@dial.pipex.com

Relaxed and friendly hotel, with modest rooms and lovely views, in a Dales village.

Dorothy Kendall and Richard Beal exchanged busy careers in the NHS and BT for a less stressful existence in the bucolic idyll of Swaledale, but the experience of many years spent caring for people is, happily, a hard habit to break, so the hotel is run with friendly warmth and a solicitous approach. The evening starts in the stone-walled bar, where guests can relax over a pint of draught Theakston's and soak up the views from the patio and garden along Swaledale to Fremlington Edge. Dorothy's dinners are wholesome affairs, with a few choices at each course; special gourmet weekends give guests a chance to sample and discuss fine wines. Heaps of leaflets and books on the area show the owners' love of the Dales, which they share with walkers and painters on special guided breaks. There's not much scope for cat-swinging in the bedrooms, but a gradual redecoration programme over the last few years has resulted in a homely style, with lacy drapes and patchwork quilts; all rooms have showers except the slightly gloomy cottage suite, which has the only *en suite* bath. Sloping ceilings give Rooms 2, 3 and 4 more character to add to their splendid views of the valley.

◗ Closed 1 Jan to 10 Feb   ⬙ From Richmond, follow signs to Reeth; turn right by war memorial; hotel is 100 yards beyond post office. Private car park   ⬗ 2 twin, 4 double, 2 twin/double, 1 suite; suite in annexe; all with shower/WC exc cottage suite with bathroom/WC; all with TV, room service, hair-dryer   ⬥ Restaurant, bar, lounge, drying-room, garden; functions (max 24 people incl up to 18 residential), conferences   ⬤ No wheelchair access   ⬤ No children under 10; dogs in bar and bedrooms only, smoking in bar only   ▭ MasterCard, Visa   £ Single occupancy of twin/double £31 to £41, twin/double £62, suite £62 to £75; deposit required. Set D £18. Special breaks available

---

Burgoyne Hotel

On the Green, Reeth, Richmond DL11 6SN
TEL: (01748) 884292 (AND FAX)

Fine views of Swaledale in a tranquil Dales village hotel.

Occupying Reeth's prime spot at the head of the pretty village green, the Burgoyne Hotel looks sternly above its handsome, three-storeyed neighbours hemming the green to the dramatic beauty of Swaledale – seven of the eight rooms bask in this view, so make sure to bag one. Peter Carwardine and Derek Hickson have presided over the Burgoyne for nearly a decade now, their mission being to provide their customers with caring, individual service and a peaceful ambience. A well-kept front garden employs a hedge to buffer guests from the seasonal tourist invasion. Inside, plush lounges with open fires and an elegant

formal dining-room decorated in a restful deep green continue the feeling of
well-being. Orthodox English country-house cooking is Peter's forte, backed up
by Derek's nose for good wines; the four-course menu might start with
home-made fish-cakes with a prawn and tomato coulis, then a hearty
rump-steak and mushroom pie, rounded off with the simplicity of a fresh-fruit
salad or local Dales cheeses. Neat, relaxing décor and plenty of home comforts
coupled with cushioned window seats (in the rooms that come with a view)
make for enticing bedrooms – a ground-floor twin opens straight on to the
garden – and in the few that have bathrooms across the corridor, bathrobes and
slippers are thoughtfully provided.

◑ Closed 2 Jan to 13 Feb ☑ Hotel overlooks the green in Reeth. Private car park
🛏 3 twin, 4 double, 1 four-poster; all with bathroom/WC exc 1 with shower/WC; all
with TV, room service, hair-dryer, trouser press, direct-dial telephone ✓ Dining-room,
2 lounges, drying-room, garden; functions (max 50 people incl up to 16 residential);
early suppers for children; cots, high chairs, baby-listening ♿ Wheelchair access to
hotel (5 steps, assistance) and dining-room, 1 ground-floor bedroom specially
equipped for disabled people ● No children in dining-room eves; dogs in lounges
and bedrooms only (not unattended in bedrooms; £4 per night); smoking in 1 lounge
only ▭ MasterCard, Visa £ Single occupancy of twin/double £60 to £70,
twin/double £70 to £135, four-poster £135; deposit required. Set D £23. (Prices valid till
Mar 1999.) Special breaks available

RHYDYCROESAU Shropshire   map 7

Pen-y-Dyffryn

Rhydycroesau, Oswestry SY10 7JD
TEL: (01691) 653700 (AND FAX)

---

*Snug little country-house hotel in a fine position, with striving and
attentive hosts and good food.*

This sturdy, early Victorian rectory sits in splendid isolation on the side of a
valley in wild and hilly country close to the Welsh border. Audrey and Miles
Hunter try to help guests make the most of the surroundings, providing folders
of walks, packed lunches and details of the local birdlife. For those who want to
stay indoors, they have created a restful and civilised atmosphere in, for
example, the bar/lounge, with its crackling fire, Windsor chairs and fetching soft
furnishings, and a further sitting-room which is heavier on Victoriana. Candlelit
dinners, served to a backdrop of operatic music, have improved since the
Hunters took on a new chef in 1997. A reader judged them 'absolutely delicious';
this was largely borne out by an inspection meal whose highlight was tender
slivers of pan-fried pigeon breast arranged on a black pudding. The next thing
that needs an upgrade is the crockery. Miles ensures the evenings flow smoothly,
taking orders and dispensing drinks and unobtrusive chat. Many of the tasteful
and carefully conceived bedrooms enjoy fine valley views, including the
Rector's Room in the main house and two smart new coach-house rooms, which
also benefit from a private terrace. A small quibble: towels are rather on the mean
side.

◑ Closed Jan **⊿** From Oswestry town centre follow signs for Llansilin (B4580); hotel is 3 miles west of Oswestry, on left. Private car park **⤶** 1 single, 4 twin, 3 double, 1 four-poster, 1 family room; 2 in annexe; all with bathroom/WC exc 2 with shower/WC; all with TV, room service, hair-dryer, trouser press **⊘** Restaurant, bar/lounge, garden; functions (max 70 people incl up to 20 residential), conferences; fishing; leisure facilities nearby (reduced rates for guests); early suppers for children; cots, high chairs, baby-listening **⅋** Wheelchair access to hotel (2 steps) and restaurant, 1 ground-floor bedroom **⊜** No dogs in public rooms after 6.30pm; no smoking in some public rooms **⊟** Amex, Delta, MasterCard, Switch, Visa **£** Single £50 to £53, single occupancy of twin/double £50 to £53, twin/double £67 to £74, four-poster £80 to £90, family room £85 to £92; deposit required. Set D £18.50 (1998 price). Special breaks available

---

RINGWOOD Hampshire   map 2

Moortown Lodge

244 Christchurch Road, Ringwood BH24 3AS
TEL: (01425) 471404   FAX: (01425) 476052

A good base for exploring the New Forest, with competent home cooking.

Owner and chef Jilly Burrows-Jones runs this welcoming roadside hotel with her husband, Bob. She doesn't consciously set out to provide a French cuisine, but guests often comment that the food she serves makes them feel as if they are in France. True, the couple are committed Francophiles – witness the recently refurbished lounge, which has French pictures, maps and wine memorabilia scattered around the place, alongside family photos and signed photographs of personalities with whom Jilly worked when she was at the BBC. The restaurant, which is next on the list for a face-lift, seats a maximum of 24 and, although open to non-residents, is usually filled with overnight guests. Jilly tries to use local produce, and a typical menu might consist of freshly made soup, followed by chicken breast with wild forest mushrooms or lamb with blackcurrants. She varies the menu daily. Bedrooms are named after herbs and have flowery wallpapers and co-ordinated curtains and bed-coverings.

◑ Closed 24 Dec to mid-Jan **⊿** 1½ miles south of town centre, on B3347. Private car park; on-street parking (free) **⤶** 1 single, 2 twin, 2 double, 1 four-poster, family rooms available; 2 with bathroom/WC, 3 with shower/WC; all with TV, room service, direct-dial telephone; hair-dryer available **⊘** Restaurant, bar, lounge; functions (max 50 people incl up to 11 residential); leisure facilities nearby (reduced rates for guests); early suppers for children; cots, high chairs **⅋** No wheelchair access **⊜** No dogs; no smoking in restaurant and some bedrooms **⊟** Amex, MasterCard, Visa **£** Single £30 to £32, single occupancy of twin/double £38 to £45, twin/double £50 to £70, four-poster £60 to £80, family room £60 to £80; deposit required. Set D £18. Special breaks available

---

We mention those hotels that don't accept dogs; guide dogs, however, are almost always an exception. Telephone ahead to make sure.

Boar's Head

Ripley, Harrogate HG3 3AY
TEL: (01423) 771888   FAX: (01423) 771509
EMAIL: boarshead@ripleycastle.co.uk
WEB SITE: www.ripleycastle.co.uk/boarsheadhotel/

*An up-market country-inn hotel in the village on the historic Ripley
Castle estate.*

Sir William Ingilby belonged to the dictatorial old school of 'Lords of the
Manor', and he disapproved of locals on the estate deserting a pew in the church
for one in Ripley's three flourishing coaching-inns and banned Sunday
drinking. The landlords left in protest, leaving the village dry until 1990, when
the former Star Inn re-opened in style as the Boar's Head. Antiques and ancestral
oils on loan from Ripley Castle are a suitable accompaniment to a quietly elegant
décor in two comfy lounges where huge, fresh floral sculptures scent the air. The
smart burgundy-and-blue restaurant offers an intimate and romantic setting
with sumptuous drapes and arched windows, while a bar/bistro displays a more
casual style than the rest of the hotel. Both serve up creative modern food
(although cheap it is not) by well-reputed chef Steven Chesnutt; red mullet and
scallops with tomato and basil might lead you on to pork with aubergine purée
and sage linguini, with a pear and pecan tart to finish. The bedrooms, all smart
and stylish, are split between the main house, the courtyard and the Birchwood
annexe – it's worth paying extra for the elegance and opulence of the superior
rooms in the main house, such as Cathedral, which has an arched ceiling and
hand-painted celestial friezes of angels and trumpets.

◐ Open all year ▣ 3 miles north of Harrogate on A61. Private car park; on-street
parking (free) ⊨ 21 twin/double, 4 double, 1 family room; some in annexe; all with
bathroom/WC; all with satellite TV, room service, hair-dryer, mini-bar, trouser press,
direct-dial telephone ✓ Restaurant, bar, 2 lounges, garden; functions (max 250
people incl up to 50 residential), conferences; civil wedding licence; fishing, tennis,
clay-pigeon shooting, croquet; early suppers for children; cots, high chairs, babysitting,
baby-listening, outdoor play area   ⅙ Wheelchair access to hotel and restaurant, WC
(unisex), 4 ground-floor bedrooms, 1 specially equipped for disabled people
◑ No children under 14 in restaurant eves ⊟ Amex, Diners, MasterCard, Switch,
Visa £ Single occupancy of twin/double £90, twin/double £105 to £125, family room
£125 to £145; deposit required. Bar/bistro L £12, D £18; set L £18, D £30; alc L £22, D
£35. Special breaks available

Mizzards Farm

Rogate, Petersfield GU31 5HS
TEL: (01730) 821656   FAX: (01730) 821655

*Up-market B&B in a sixteenth-century farmhouse with a
wonderfully tranquil setting.*

With beautiful, landscaped gardens running down to the river Rother and surrounded by rolling hills of green fields, it comes as no surprise to learn that you're in the middle of a designated Area of Outstanding Natural Beauty, although that description can certainly not be applied to the track that you must drive down to get here: it's a bumpy, rutted, overgrown number, so take care! If your bones need a rest after all that shaking, the huge drawing-room is the perfect place for you, with its calm, pastel décor, huge brick fireplace, comfy sofas and garden views. Or you could head straight up the wooden staircase to the conservatory on the first floor, and relax in wicker chairs surrounded by pot-plants. The two smaller bedrooms are done out in smart blues and whites, but it is the master bedroom that grabs the attention. Reminders of its glittering past are obvious in the columned, octagonal canopy over the bed, the electric curtains and the gloriously kitsch mirror lights in the voluminous bathroom; imagine how it used to be before Harriet and Julian Francis toned it down – at least the mock-animal-fur wall-coverings have gone! Breakfast – 'one of the best I've had anywhere', reported one reader, although her husband found the tiny corner basin in the bathroom too small to enable him to shave – is taken in the flagstoned, galleried entrance hall.

◑ Closed Chr ⛶ Travel south from crossroads in Rogate; cross bridge and take first road on right. Private car park ⇱ 1 twin, 1 double, 1 four-poster; all with bathroom/WC; all with TV, hair-dryer ⊘ Drawing-room, drying-room, conservatory, garden; heated outdoor swimming-pool ⅙ No wheelchair access ● No children under 8; no dogs; no smoking ▭ None accepted £ Single occupancy of twin/double £34 to £40, twin/double £56, four-poster £62; deposit required

---

ROMALDKIRK Co Durham   map 10

Rose and Crown

Romaldkirk, Barnard Castle DL12 9EB
TEL: (01833) 650213   FAX: (01833) 650828
EMAIL: hotel@rose-and-crown.co.uk
WEB SITE: www.rose-and-crown.co.uk

An eighteenth-century coaching-inn, with excellent food and pleasant rooms, in an archetypal English village.

The wonderful thing about Teesdale is its remoteness; on the breezy roof of England, the Rose and Crown in Romaldkirk lies close to some of the country's last remaining true wilderness. Once inside Christopher and Alison Davy's classic, village-green inn it quickly becomes apparent this is not a simple pub. True, the cosy bar has a log fire in a stone hearth, gleaming copper and brasses and a snoozing cat in the prime, fireside seat – but how many pubs adorn their tables with fresh flowers? What draws many guests to this lonely spot is the promise of Christopher's superb modern cuisine – which readers have praised – prepared from the region's best and freshest produce. Simple, oak-panelled elegance sets the tone in the restaurant, seen at its best in candlelight. Our inspector enjoyed an excellent four-course menu, including fresh mussels with cream and Cotherstone cheese, then chargrilled, corn-fed chicken with watercress noodles, and finally a decadent dessert of walnut and syrup tart with calvados ice-cream. The Davys have brought in a new interior designer to make yet further improvements to the characterful bedrooms. Grumbles about the plumbing in the stable annexe have been laid to rest with a new boiler; their new colour schemes, rich fabrics and luxury bathrooms now make these some of the best rooms in the hotel. Those in the main house feature antique and pine furniture and a stylish décor; they are also gradually getting a makeover, with upgraded bathrooms. One disadvantage of staying in old inns is the noise from creaky floors above, which one reader found disturbing.

◑ Closed 25, 26 & 31 Dec ⤢ 6 miles north-west of Barnard Castle on B6277. Private car park ⤵ 5 twin, 4 double, 1 family room, 2 suites; some in annexe; most with bathroom/WC, some with shower/WC; all with TV, room service, hair-dryer, direct-dial telephone, some with trouser press ⌘ Restaurant, bar, lounge, drying-room; functions (max 30 people incl up to 12 residential); civil wedding licence; early suppers for children; cots, high chairs, toys, baby-listening ⅙ Wheelchair access to hotel and restaurant, 5 ground-floor bedrooms ● No children under 6 in restaurant eves; no dogs in public rooms; no smoking in restaurant ▭ MasterCard, Switch, Visa ⓔ Single occupancy of twin/double £60, twin/double £82, family room £94, suite £90; deposit required. Set L £13, D £24. Special breaks available

---

White Horse Farm Hotel

Rosedale Abbey, Pickering YO18 8SE
TEL: (01751) 417239   FAX: (01751) 417781

An unpretentious pub at the heart of the North York Moors with characterful carved wood from a West Riding church in the restaurant.

According to the estate agent's dictum, White House Farm boasts the three indispensable elements that a property should have: location, location, location. The pub sits in splendid isolation, perched above the somnolent village of Rosedale Abbey, the sort of spot where walkers take a break from yomping across the moors in order to sink a pint or two. Massive tree-trunk pillars, bare stone walls and the biggest set of buffalo horns you have ever seen set the tone in the bar – fight for one of the choice window seats to sample the heart-warming, hand-pulled ales from Theakston's and Black Sheep. From this vantage point, you are rewarded with simply awe-inspiring views across a tree-crossed green patchwork, topped with a bleak crown of open moor. New owners Stuart and Sarah Adamson are omnipresent and go out of their way to ensure that a lively and convivial atmosphere reigns. If you're in need of more than just liquid sustenance, a Barnsley chop in the bar might just hit the spot, or you could try something more ambitious in the Misericord Restaurant, which is quirkily fitted out with oak panels, pews, pillars and stained glass salvaged from a church. The primary reason to stop here is of course for the splendid setting and pub ambience, rather than for the rooms – adequate, but nothing to get excited about; ask for one facing that superb view.

◑ Open all year ⊿ Leave Pickering on A170 towards Thirsk; turn right after 2 to 3 miles on to Rosedale road. Private car park ⨼ 3 twin, 11 double, 1 family room; some with bathroom/WC, most with shower/WC; all with TV, room service, hair-dryer, direct-dial telephone ⊘ Restaurant, bar, lounge, drying-room, garden; functions (max 60 people incl up to 32 residential), conferences; early suppers for children; cots, high chairs, baby-listening ⅃ No wheelchair access ● No dogs; no smoking in restaurant ⊡ Amex, Delta, Diners, MasterCard, Switch, Visa £ Single occupancy of twin/double £43 to £48, twin/double £66 to £75, family room £71 to £80; deposit required. Bar L £6, D £10; set Sun L £9; set D £16 to £19. Special breaks available

---

ROSS-ON-WYE Herefordshire
map 5

Upper Pengethley Farm

Ross-on-Wye HR9 6LL
TEL: (01989) 730687 (AND FAX)

Unassuming charm and low prices make this friendly farmhouse B&B exceptional.

You need to keep your eyes peeled for the unobtrusive sign marked 'Farmhouse B&B' off the busy A49. A rough track leads to this mellow-brick eighteenth-century house, peacefully set among fields and gardens. It's emphatically a family home, where Sue and Julian Partridge's children are being raised alongside the sheep and other stock on this busy working farm. But if guests stay, they are made extremely welcome, offered a pot of tea with fresh milk on arrival, provided with masses of hot water and drying space for wet clothes and, in the mornings, a jolly good breakfast in a room near the family kitchen, one wall entirely filled by a huge china-decked pine dresser. The pretty, cosy bedrooms are interestingly decorated (Sue Partridge has an eye for colours and fabrics) and furnished in warm, cottagey styles. A small upper sitting-room for guests offers a place to read or watch TV. Evening meals are not available but there are several excellent country pubs within easy driving distance, and plenty of choices in nearby Ross.

◑ Closed Oct to March ⊿ Just off A49, 4 miles from Ross-on-Wye, next to the Pengethley Manor Hotel and Pengethley Nurseries. Private car park ⨼ 1 twin, 1 double; all with bathroom/WC; all with TV, hair-dryer ⊘ Dining-room; cots, high chairs, baby-listening ⅃ No wheelchair access ● No smoking; no dogs in public rooms ⊡ None accepted £ Single occupancy of twin/double £25, twin/double £40; deposit required

---

ROSTHWAITE Cumbria
map 10

Hazel Bank

Rosthwaite, Borrowdale, Keswick CA12 5XB
TEL: (017687) 77248   FAX: (017687) 77373

Well-loved, traditional guesthouse, in one of Cumbria's most beautiful locations.

Borrowdale is a prime site in the Lake District, and Hazel Bank has been offering a well-tried formula here for the best part of two decades, so it has a considerable following of eager devotees. Small wonder, then, that this large, Victorian house was solidly booked for an entire off-season week of dreadful weather forecasts, when other hoteliers were lamenting the slow start to the season. Gwen and John Nuttall know what their guests like, and if some might find the décor a trifle dated and on the florid side, there's no questioning the high standards of housekeeping, or the warmth of the hospitality. Throughout, Hazel Bank exudes a personal and contented feel. There's plenty of comfortable space for guests to sit in and the house is in a marvellously peaceful location, in well-kept grounds with woodland behind. The bedrooms (all named after local fells) are spacious; some sport coronet drapes and there is one four-poster. Dinners are an important part of the scene; John cooks, and the highly traditional, local fare receives rave reviews. An honour bar is available in a small room to one side of the hall. Outside, velvety lawns and mature trees sweep down towards a humpback bridge near the roadside.

◑ Closed Nov to Mar ◪ From Keswick, follow B5289 signposted Borrowdale; just before Rosthwaite village, turn left, crossing river over humpback bridge. Private car park 🛏 1 single, 3 twin, 1 double, 1 four-poster; all with bathroom/WC; all with TV, hair-dryer ✓ Dining-room, lounge, drying-room, garden ♿ No wheelchair access ⊖ No children under 11; no dogs in public rooms; no smoking ▭ Delta, Diners, MasterCard, Switch, Visa £ Single £48, twin/double/four-poster £95 (rates incl dinner); deposit required

ROWSLEY Derbyshire map 9

Peacock Hotel

Rowsley, Matlock DE4 2EB
TEL: (01629) 733518 FAX: (01629) 732671
WEB SITE: www.jarvis.co.uk

Up-market inn with thoughtful hosts and well-equipped bedrooms.

This handsome stone-built house in the centre of Rowsley was once dower house to the Dukes of Rutland but has been a hotel since 1820, accumulating an impressive roll of famous visitors: Longfellow and Emperor Maximilian of Mexico among them. The attraction, then as now, is that of an up-market inn with trout fishing – rod-racks still feature in the reception, and the hotel has 12 rods on the Derbyshire Wye and two on the Derwent. In the older part of the house, at the front, is a chintzy lounge leading on to a cosy bar with hand-pulled beer and exposed stone walls. The three dining-rooms run down one side of the house and open out through french windows on to the pretty gardens. Original chairs and tables by 'Mouseman' Thompson of Kilburn set the atmosphere of sturdy elegance, and are no worse for being a little time-worn. The table d'hôte and à la carte menus can be mixed and matched as desired, giving a wide choice: smoked trout mousse to start, perhaps, followed by roast rack of lamb and then an orange-blossom crème brûlée. The bedrooms are characterful but by no means old-fashioned, with video/TV and a complimentary blank cassette (should dinner coincide with your favourite programme). Other extras include perfume, brandy and even a pre-threaded sewing kit. With their floral covers, leaded lights and antique furniture (in all but two), these are very pleasant rooms.

◑ Open all year 🅿 On A6 in Rowsley, 5 miles north of Matlock. Private car park
🛏 2 single, 4 twin, 8 double, 2 four-poster; family rooms available; most with bathroom/WC, some with shower/WC; all with TV, video, room service, hair-dryer, trouser press, direct-dial telephone ✅ Restaurant, bar, lounge, drying-room, garden; functions (max 24 people residential/non-residential), conferences; fishing; early suppers for children ♿ No wheelchair access ● No children under 4 in restaurant eves; no dogs in public rooms; no smoking in restaurant ▭ Amex, Delta, Diners, MasterCard, Switch, Visa £ Single £70, single occupancy of twin/double £80 to £95, twin/double £85 to £105, four-poster £110; family room (children sharing with parents free); deposit required. Continental B £7, cooked B £9.50; bar/bistro L £8; set L £14, D £22.50; alc L £20, D £28. Special breaks available

---

RUAN HIGH LANES Cornwall map 1

Hundred House Hotel

Ruan High Lanes, Truro TR2 5JR
TEL: (01872) 501336 FAX: (01872) 501151

Calm and peaceful family-run hotel on a main (but not busy) road.

Yes, the roadside location is a disadvantage, but there are lawned gardens to the side and rear, and once you're inside you hardly notice the road. The interior has a feeling of calm and spaciousness, which starts as soon as you enter the beautiful hallway, boldly done out in dark, floral wallpaper, with an old woven rug over parquet flooring. The lounge is countrified and more sophisticated, filled with squashy sofas, china ornaments and a big fireplace (with a fire lit on chilly days). The bar is homely and welcoming and shows evidence of green fingers in the small fruiting mandarin tree and abundant pot-plants. Foliage is everywhere in the conservatory, too, which is furnished nicely with Lloyd Loom chairs, but has an unfortunate view of the car park. In the dining-room, whose tables are well positioned for conversation, the five-course dinner menu offers traditional dishes with inventive twists: melon with raspberry sauce might be followed by roast loin of lamb stuffed with apricots and served with a tarragon cream sauce, finishing with a plum and soured-cream flan. Home-made fudge accompanies coffee. When we inspected, Kitty and Mike Eccles were also rustling up several cream teas for unexpected guests. The bedrooms are named after local coves, and are either peachy and cosy, like St Anthony, or cool and pretty, like Gerrans.

◑ Closed end Oct 🅿 Take A3078 to St Mawes; hotel is 4 miles beyond Tregony on right, just before Ruan High Lanes. Private car park 🛏 2 single, 4 twin, 4 double; 6 with bathroom/WC, 4 with shower/WC; all with TV, hair-dryer, direct-dial telephone
✅ Dining-room, bar, lounge, library, conservatory, garden; croquet ♿ No wheelchair access ● No children under 8; no dogs in public rooms; no smoking in some public rooms ▭ Amex, Switch, Visa £ Single £39 to £42, single occupancy of twin/double £59 to £63, twin/double £78 to £84; deposit required. Set D £24. Special breaks available

Stone House

Rushlake Green, Heathfield TN21 9QJ
TEL: (01435) 830553   FAX: (01435) 830726

Fantastic food, lovely hosts and glorious grounds at this Tudor/ Georgian manor house.

From the sleepy village green, you can't miss the imposing stone walls of this 1,000-acre estate, which has been the Dunn family home since 1495. Progressing through the gates and along the sweeping drive, you face a house which looks remarkably like the setting for a Jane Austen novel – the Georgian façade gives it grandeur, there is an ornamental lake where our lovestruck heroine could steal a kiss and beautiful gardens for strolling arm-in-arm. The interior is equally elegant, with a choice of public rooms – the graceful drawing-room with log fires, fine furniture and a liberal smattering of family photos, or the library, with reading material in plenty and a piano. Wood features big time in the dining-room: panelled walls, antique dressers, window seats and beautiful tables provide a perfect setting for a delicious dinner of courgette soup, escalopes of pork with a port and prune sauce, and then treacle tart with lemon. At the top of the grand staircase, decorated in a swathe of peach, are the two best rooms, both with four-posters, huge bathrooms and exquisite furnishings. Further back, both in time and in the house, bedrooms in the Tudor wing are slightly smaller, but the beams and sloping floors compensate for the comparative lack of space.

◑ Closed 24 Dec to 1 Jan   From Heathfield take B2096 towards Battle; take fourth right to Rushlake Green; in village, with green on right, turn left and continue to crossroads; entrance is on left. Private car park   1 single, 3 twin/double, 2 four-poster, 1 suite; all with bathroom/WC; all with TV, room service, hair-dryer, direct-dial telephone, some with trouser press   ✅ Dining-room, drawing-room, library, games room, garden; functions (max 14 people residential/non-residential), conferences; fishing, snooker, clay-pigeon shooting, croquet, archery ♿ No wheelchair access ● No children under 9; no dogs in public rooms None accepted   Single £55 to £75, twin/double £105 to £123, four-poster £145 to £180, suite £145 to £180. Set D £25. Special breaks available

Biskra Beach Hotel   **NEW ENTRY**

17 St Thomas Street, Ryde PO33 2DL
TEL: (01983) 567913   FAX: (01983) 616976

Peaceful beach-front hotel in the centre of Ryde, with tasteful décor and a feeling of simple luxury.

A refurbishment in early 1998 has completely transformed the Biskra Beach Hotel, sweeping away the flock wallpaper and gaudily patterned carpets in favour of the harmonious tones of pale lemon and mossy green. Situated on a quiet road, away from the shops and bustle of the traditional seaside town of

Ryde, the hotel backs on to an expanse of sandy beach. The ground-floor bar and dining-room are spacious and light, and offer a wide selection of food and wines. You can wander past the collection of well-spaced, chunky pine tables on to the terrace and, from there, directly on to the beach. An alternative restaurant, the Cellar Bar, is in the basement. To wake up to the sound of the sea, opt for Room 3 or 4, both of which have large balconies facing the sands. All the bedrooms are fresh and peaceful, with rustic pine furniture and inviting, crisp white bed linen. Barbara Newman, the director, is friendly and unassuming, and justifiably proud of the considerable alterations.

◑ Closed 23 to 26 Dec ⌷ Hotel is short walk from Ryde pier. Private car park; public car park nearby (£1.80 per day) ⌷➔ 3 twin/double, 6 double; family rooms available; 5 with bathroom/WC, 4 with shower/WC; all with TV, room service, hair-dryer, mini-bar, direct-dial telephone ⌀ 2 restaurants/bars, lounge, drying-room, study, garden; functions (max 50 people incl up to 15 residential), conferences; civil wedding licence; leisure facilities nearby (reduced rates for guests); early suppers for children; babysitting, baby-listening ⓰ No wheelchair access ● No dogs ⌷ Amex, Delta, MasterCard, Switch, Visa £ Single occupancy of twin/double £35 to £48, twin/double £48; family room £68; deposit required. Bar/bistro L, D £10; alc L, D £20. (Prices valid till Sept 1998)

RYE **East Sussex**   map 3

Jeake's House

Mermaid Street, Rye TN31 7ET
TEL: (01797) 222828 FAX: (01797) 222623
EMAIL: jeakeshouse@btinternet.com
WEB SITE: www.s-h-systems.co.uk/hotels/jeakes.html

An excellent B&B in the heart of historic Rye, one of England's quaintest towns.

Landladies don't come much nicer than Jenny Hadfield, who's around for a little light banter in the evening or a cheery smile over breakfast. She obviously takes great pride in her house. Peer through the creepers which climb all over the front of the house, and you'll see a plaque recording not only the time and date when the foundation stone was laid (noon, 13 June 1689), but also the position of the heavenly bodies at that moment. Built as a wool storehouse, in later life it became a Quaker meeting-house and then a Baptist chapel, a past seen most easily in the high-ceilinged breakfast room. In fact, it's rather Tardis-like in appearance: compact from the outside, but rambling and labyrinthine inside. A Victorian style pervades the bedrooms, where stripes or bold florals feature in the décor. Aiken is a firm favourite, thanks to its four-poster and lovely views. A couple of rooms share a bathroom, which, in the case of the single (Room 7), entails a dash along the gallery of the breakfast room. Breakfast is accompanied by classical music and, more than likely, the attentions of one of the Siamese cats. Vegetarians are well catered for.

○ Open all year ⊡ Centrally located in old Rye. Private car park (£2.50 per day) 🛏 1 single, 1 twin, 6 double, 1 four-poster, 2 family rooms, 1 suite; most with bathroom/WC, 2 with shower/WC; all with TV, limited room service, hair-dryer, direct-dial telephone, radio ⊘ Breakfast room, bar, 2 lounges; leisure facilities nearby (reduced rates for guests); baby-listening ♿ No wheelchair access ● No dogs in public rooms; no smoking in breakfast room ▭ MasterCard, Visa £ Single £26, single occupancy of twin/double £36 to £59, twin/double £49 to £65, four-poster £65, family room £86, suite £89; deposit required. Special breaks available

Little Orchard House

West Street, Rye TN31 7ES
TEL: (01797) 223831 (AND FAX)

Inviting, yet informally elegant, B&B run by a well-travelled, welcoming owner.

There are few towns more picturesque than Rye and few B&Bs more delightful than this one. When the steep streets are crammed with tourists teetering precariously along on the cobbles, Sara Brinkhurst offers an oasis of homeliness where you can relax and unwind in peace. After an informal welcome in the charmingly rustic kitchen, you're free to lounge about in the cosy sitting-room, surrounded by dried flowers and cats of all shapes, sizes and colours. Only two of them, the Russian blues called Golly and Tatty, will respond to your attention: the others are all crafted from wood or china. More animals – teddy bears, this time – are on hand upstairs in each of the three bedrooms, the most elegant of which is Lloyd George, so named because the former prime minister is reputed to have stayed here. The pale-yellow panelling is the original Georgian décor, and the fireplace is carved from local Sussex marble. Both of the other rooms have four-poster beds, though the Garden Room's is far more impressive, fashioned as it is from a storm-felled oak tree. Breakfasts are taken at the long, scrubbed table in the kitchen, looking out into the walled garden with its flowering cherry tree.

○ Open all year ⊡ West Street is off the High Street in Rye. Private car park (£2.50 per day); on-street parking (free) 🛏 1 twin, 2 four-poster; all with bathroom/WC exc 1 four-poster with shower/WC; all with TV, hair-dryer, clock radio; some with fridge ⊘ Breakfast room, sitting-room, library, garden ♿ No wheelchair access ● No children under 12; no dogs; no smoking in 2 bedrooms ▭ Delta, MasterCard, Visa £ Single occupancy of twin £45 to £65, twin/four-poster £64 to £84; deposit required

Old Vicarage

66 Church Square, Rye TN31 7HF
TEL: (01797) 222119   FAX: (01797) 227466

Peaceful B&B in town centre with cheerful hosts and good breakfasts.

Breakfasts are taken very seriously at this lovely, marshmallow-pink B&B and are the responsibility of Julia Masters, who runs the place with her husband,

Paul. Home-made bread and yoghurt have now been added to a mouthwatering menu that includes the local butcher's prize-winning sausages, Romney Marsh mushrooms, free-range eggs and freshly baked scones (accompanying marmalade and jams also home-made, it goes without saying). The Old Vicarage, pink roses around its door, lies in an elegant church square in the centre of Rye, with good views of surrounding medieval houses and cobbled streets. Its Georgian façade belies the building's true age – it is around 400 years old (and was last used as a vicarage in 1896). All five bedrooms come with *en suite* shower- or bathroom and a hospitality tray which now includes fudge. The atmosphere in the rooms is decidedly rustic: you are likely to find whitewashed or Laura Ashley décor, pine furniture and wood beams. The attic room is particularly attractive. There is a cosy lounge, equipped with local guidebooks, where Paul dispenses evening sherry.

◑ Closed Chr　🔃 Enter old town by Landgate Arch to High Street; take third left into West Street; hotel is by St Mary's Church. Private car park (£2.50 per day)　🛏 1 double, 2 four-poster, 1 family room, 1 suite; all with shower/WC exc family room with bathroom/WC; all with TV, hair-dryer, trouser press　⚱ Dining-room, lounge, TV room, garden　♿ No wheelchair access　⬤ No children under 8; no dogs; smoking in lounge only　🚭 None accepted　💷 Single occupancy of double £45 to £55, double £50 to £59, four-poster £51 to £60, family room £65 to £75, suite £59 to £60; deposit required. Special breaks available

---

ST ALBANS Hertfordshire　　　　map 3

Sopwell House

Cottonmill Lane, Sopwell, St Albans AL1 2HQ
TEL: (01727) 864477　FAX: (01727) 844741

An efficient country-house hotel with extensive facilities and a broad appeal.

This business-oriented hotel and country club is a thriving enterprise that simply keeps on growing: the original creamy-beige Georgian house, set among thickets of rhododendrons and mature trees, has already been supplemented with various bedroom extensions and conservatories, and further expansion was under way as we went to press. Among the facilities on offer are the Magnolia Restaurant (so called for the magnificent trees that emerge among the white-damask-covered tables and disappear through the glass roof) and a 'twenties-period brasserie that adjoins a magnificent art-deco pool spanned by a black iron footbridge. Elsewhere, you'll find an informal terrace lounge, a dark, snoozy bar and a rich-pink traditional lounge with green-leather buttonbacks. Football fans will be hypnotised by the 'Hall of Fame' corridor and its framed signed shirts from FA-Cup winners and a host of international stars. The bedroom corridors are a warren, but, once installed, you can expect plenty of space, all the requisite features, and frills provided either by coronet beds or four-posters, swagged curtains and baby ferns or palms. The extensive spa and gym facilities are justly popular, as are weekend weddings, and don't be surprised should you bump into the stars of Arsenal's double-winning team: the club regularly uses the hotel as a training base. We have received another complaint this year about service and poor food – more reports, please.

◑ Open all year; Magnolia restaurant closed Sun eve ⊠ Turn off M25 at Junction 21A and follow signs to St Albans; join A414; turn left and follow signs for Sopwell. Private car park ⤶ 12 single, 20 twin, 30 double, 22 four-poster, 6 family rooms, 2 suites; some in annexe; all with bathroom/WC; all with TV, room service, hair-dryer, trouser press, direct-dial telephone, some with mini-bar ⊘ 2 restaurants, 2 bars, 2 lounges, conservatory, games room, garden; functions (max 230 people incl up to 60 residential), conferences; civil wedding licence; gym, sauna, solarium, heated indoor swimming-pool, croquet; early suppers for children; cots, high chairs ⅊ Wheelchair access to hotel (ramp) and restaurant, lift to bedrooms ● None ▭ Amex, Delta, Diners, MasterCard, Switch, Visa £ Single £73 to £110, single occupancy of twin/double £76 to £120, twin/double £100 to £136, four-poster £110 to £145, family room (room rate + £10 per child), suite £165; deposit required. Continental B £9, cooked B £11; bar/bistro L, D £13; set L £17, D £23.50; alc L £30, D £40. Special breaks available

---

ST BLAZEY Cornwall   map 1

Nanscawen House

Prideaux Road, St Blazey, Par PL24 2SR
TEL: (01726) 814488 (AND FAX)
EMAIL: keithmartin@compuserve.com
WEB SITE: www.ourworld.compuserve.com/homepages/keithmartin

Traditional on the outside, surprising on the inside, this rural retreat is a real delight.

From the outside, everything about this japonica- and wistaria-clad, double-fronted house seems quintessentially English, down to the wild flowers and rabbits in the gardens. If you look around closely, however, you'll find clues to the 'different' nature of the establishment – there's a heated outdoor pool and a whirlpool spa hidden away (so you can, if you feel inclined, watch the stars while drinking your digestif and soaking in the tub). This voguish approach to the hotel business continues inside: downstairs, the open-plan rooms are simply gigantic, with beautiful parquet floors, a help-yourself honesty bar, and an array of tropical plants. Breakfast – usually taken in the conservatory – is freshly squeezed orange juice, croissants and smoked salmon. There are only three bedrooms, but Rashleigh is as big as a ballroom (the bed looks tiny) and has a spectacular bathroom, done out in 'cancan' pink and complete with bows and flounces. Treffry and Prideaux are more conventionally sized, but are just as flamboyantly decorated in feminine style. Evening meals are not served, but Keith Martin can recommend local eateries.

◑ Closed 25, 26 Dec ⊠ From A390 heading towards St Austell, turn right in St Blazey directly after railway crossing; hotel is 1 mile on right. Private car park ⤶ 1 twin, 1 double, 1 four-poster; all with bathroom/WC; all with TV, hair-dryer, direct-dial telephone ⊘ Drawing-room, conservatory/breakfast room, garden; outdoor heated swimming-pool, whirlpool spa ⅊ No wheelchair access ● No children under 12; no dogs; no smoking ▭ MasterCard, Visa £ Twin/double/four-poster £74; deposit required. Special breaks available

ST BRIAVELS Gloucestershire

map 2

Cinderhill House [NEW ENTRY]

St Briavels, Lydney GL15 6RH
TEL: (01594) 530393   FAX: (01594) 530098

Industriously run guesthouse with a long and interesting history and superb views.

Cinderhill House sits on a hillside on the edge of the village of St Briavels, basking in panoramic views over the thickly wooded Wye Valley and yards from an English Heritage twelfth-century castle. The beamy, flagstoned former farmhouse is extremely old itself. Owner Gillie Peacock has unearthed evidence that it was once a bloomery, or ironworks, that produced arrowheads and quarrels used at Agincourt. Gillie's hospitality is highly praised, and her food – she is a trained cook – has been described in glowing terms. Dinners (served in a refined, antique-furnished dining-room and offering choices except at the main course) feature home-made soups and ice-creams, and farmhouse cheeses – likes and dislikes are discussed beforehand. Breakfasts are equally appetising, with locally smoked bacon and maybe even salmon fishcakes, and afternoon tea and high tea for children are also available. Bedrooms in the main house have much character but simple washing facilities (a tub bath or shower). For more space and privacy, ask about the three smartly furnished cottages created out of the nearby outbuildings, two of which have four-poster beds. They are let on a B&B basis when not booked to self-caterers, and include accommodation designed for less mobile visitors.

◑ Closed 10 Jan to 6 Feb   ⬕ From B4228 turn off into village; at castle take Cinderhill (steep road); house is on right after 100 yards. Private car park   ⬅ 1 twin, 1 twin/double, 1 double, 1 four-poster, 1 family room, some in annexe; 3 with bathroom/WC, 1 with shower/WC; all with hair-dryer, some with TV   ⊘ Dining-room, lounge, drying-room, games room, garden; table tennis, darts; early suppers for children; cots, high chairs   ⅙ No wheelchair access to house and restaurant, 1 ground-floor bedroom partially equipped for disabled people in annexe cottage (meals can be served in cottage)   ● Children discouraged in dining-room eves; no dogs; smoking in lounge only   ⬒ None accepted   £ Single occupancy of twin/double £45, twin/double £60 to £64, four-poster/family room £74; deposit required. Set D £15 to £21

ST HILARY Cornwall

map 1

Ennys

Trewhella Lane, St Hilary, Penzance TR20 9BZ
TEL: (01736) 740262   FAX: (01736) 740055
EMAIL: ennys@zetnet.co.uk

Wonderful, isolated farmhouse retreat with sophisticated welcome and lots of attention to detail.

This is the kind of place you dream about for a holiday in Cornwall – a farmhouse at the end of a very long lane, a mile from any road, with an old, wild garden full of hidden corners, a yard full of animals, good company and breakfasts, and scrumptious bedrooms. Indeed the name 'Ennys' means oasis or island in old Cornish. Gill Charlton (who came here on holiday many times, dreamt a bit and then decided to buy the place) has taken over the helm from Sue White, but is still keen to emphasise that 'it's not a hotel, it's a farmhouse'. She's not planning on changing much about Ennys 'because it works so perfectly as it is' except – and this is not a small exception – there will be no more evening meals. Instead, a Cornish cream tea is included in the price of the room. Gill points out that there are plenty of good eateries within striking distance, so with any luck guests will still climb the stairs to the spruce, countrified bedrooms with happy hearts. Breakfast will not disappoint, however, with home-made bread, free-range eggs and porridge providing energy for swimming in the outdoor pool, or simply going for a walk accompanied by the exceedingly friendly cat.

◑ Closed 20 Nov to 15 Feb (open Chr & New Year)   ⊿ 2 miles east of Marazion on B3280; just before Relubbus, turn left into Trewhella Lane. Private car park   ⟻ 1 twin, 2 four-poster, 2 suites; some in annexe; family rooms available; all with bathroom/WC exc four-posters with shower/WC; all with TV, hair-dryer   ✥ Dining-room, lounge, garden; heated outdoor swimming-pool, tennis; high chairs, baby-listening   ♿ No wheelchair access   ● No children under 2; no dogs; no smoking in bedrooms   ▭ Delta, MasterCard, Visa   £ Single occupancy of twin £40, twin £60, four-poster £63 to £70, family room £85, suite £70; deposit required

---

ST KEYNE Cornwall   map 1

Old Rectory

St Keyne, Liskeard PL14 4RL
TEL: (01579) 342617   FAX: (01579) 342293

Old-fashioned, genteel country-house hotel in idyllic rural spot.

It's as if the rector left this typically Cornish country house yesterday, despite the fact that proprietors Pat and John Minifie are most definitely not locals – they come from the south-east. They've kept the secluded, rural feel very well, and there are sycamores, oaks and maples in the garden. From the gates, you can tramp off across the surrounding fields, preferably arriving back in time for supper – taken in the best room in the house, which features cheerful, yellow walls, white cloths and crystal glasses. A vegetarian inspection meal consisted of deep-fried Camembert with Cumberland sauce, while meatier options might be roast poussin stuffed with lemon balm and garlic, or sirloin steak topped with pesto and black olives, served with provençal vegetables in puff pastry. Petits fours and coffee are taken in the family-style drawing-room, which is furnished with a smattering of antiques and some old-fashioned sofas. John Minifie is a most affable host, and will suggest various expeditions and walks in the area. The bedrooms are floral and pretty, although the bathroom in a four-poster room is a little old-fashioned, with a noisy extractor fan.

◑ Closed Chr & New Year; restaurant closed Sun eve   ⊿ On B3254, 3 miles south of Liskeard. Private car park   ⟻ 1 single, 2 twin, 3 double, 2 four-poster; family rooms available 4 with bathroom/WC, 3 with shower/WC; all with TV   ✥ Restaurant, bar, drawing-room, drying-room, garden; functions (max 25 people incl up to 15 residential);

early suppers for children; cots, high chairs, babysitting   ♿ Wheelchair access to hotel and restaurant, WC (unisex), 1 ground-floor bedroom specially equipped for disabled people   ⊜ No smoking in bedrooms; dogs £2 per night   ▭ MasterCard, Visa   £ Single £30 to £40, single occupancy of twin/double £40 to £45, twin/double £52 to £58, four-poster £60 to £70, family room £70; deposit required. Set L £13.50, D £19.50. Special breaks available

Well House

St Keyne, Liskeard PL14 4RN
TEL: (01579) 342001   FAX: (01579) 343891

Extremely smart and composed small country-house hotel, sumptuously done out and carefully run.

The cosmopolitan nature of this hotel comes as a surprise, hidden away as it is in deepest, rural Cornwall, but host Nick Wainford will soon make you feel at home – and if he can't, then the tribe of wagging-tailed King Charles spaniels certainly will. They'll lead you around the dignified Victorian house (built at the turn of the century by a tea planter), down the stepped, well-formed gardens, past the swimming-pool and ponds, over the bridges across the stream, round past the tennis court and back to the front door, which is covered in creepers so dense that you have to look twice to find it. Inside, the house is spacious. Nick's partner, Ione Nurdin, has created an ultra-civilised, airy environment, using plush, yet unobtrusive, fabrics and stylish pastel colours. The morning sun streams into the sitting-room, while the dining-room has yellow walls, upholstered designer chairs, pink tablecloths, fresh flowers and fabulous views. The menu may include goats'-cheese ravioli, followed by breasts of pigeon with a wild-mushroom sauce, with a selection of West Country cheeses and a passion-fruit soufflé to finish. Nick is an expert on claret, so you can expect an interesting wine list. The bedrooms are sumptuous in a traditional kind of way, while the two terrace rooms go for ethnic glamour.

◑ Open all year   ⊿ Pass through St Keyne, past church and take road to St Keyne Well; hotel is ½ mile from church. Private car park   ⊫ 3 twin, 5 double, 1 family room; all with bathroom/WC; all with TV, room service, hair-dryer, trouser press, direct-dial telephone; no tea/coffee-making facilities in rooms   ⊘ Dining-room, bar, sitting-room, garden; functions (max 150 people incl up to 19 residential), conferences; heated outdoor swimming-pool, tennis; early suppers for children; cots, baby-listening   ♿ No wheelchair access   ⊜ No children under 8 in dining-room eves   ▭ Amex, Delta, Diners, MasterCard, Switch, Visa   £ Single occupancy of twin/double £70 to £95, twin/double £100 to £160, family room £160 to £180; deposit required. Set L, D £22/£27/£30.50. Special breaks available

---

'We were woken at 1 a.m. on the first night by a telephone call from a guest who had lost his way. Apparently reception was somehow mixed up with our line. We were told an engineer was coming the following week, but no apology was forthcoming, and we had similar calls on two successive nights.'
On a hotel in East Sussex

ST MARGARET'S AT CLIFFE Kent map 3

Wallett's Court

Westcliffe, St Margaret's At Cliffe, Dover CT15 6EW
TEL: (01304) 852424   FAX: (01304) 853430
EMAIL: wallettscourt@compuserve.com
WEB SITE: www.wallettscourt.com/

Lovingly renovated historic house, with classy cuisine, a short hop from the ferries at Dover.

A sign beside the front door proclaims this to be a 'historic building of Kent', which is not a vain boast as it was recorded in the Domesday book and has associations with Eleanor of Castile and William Pitt, among others. This must have been hard for members of the Oakley family to believe when they first saw Wallett's Court in 1975, when it was empty, almost derelict and overgrown. 'Anyone buying it would have to be mad,' Chris Oakley is quoted as saying, but 20-odd years later it has been tenderly transformed into a fine hotel, all the while keeping its historic feel. This is most prominent in the restaurant, where the brick fireplace, tapestried chairs and beamed ceiling create a wonderful ambience in which to enjoy a superb meal. Chris conjures up a culinary extravaganza using primarily local ingredients – for example, Canterbury river-bed watercress soup and then roasted Romney Marsh lamb with a mélange of woodland mushrooms, all served with home-baked organic bread. The characterful, comfortable bedrooms in the main house come complete with uneven, creaking floors, whereas those in the converted farm buildings are more modern in appearance, but just as well furnished. As we went to press, the old barn was being converted into a health spa with four more bedrooms attached, one with its own access to the pool.

◑ Closed 24 to 28 Dec   ⊠ From M20 or A2 take A258 Dover to Deal road, and first right turning for Westcliffe; hotel is 1 mile further on, on right. Private car park
⊨ 1 single, 2 twin, 1 twin/double, 10 double, 2 four-poster, 1 suite; some in annexe; family rooms available; all with bathroom/WC; all with TV, room service, hair-dryer, direct-dial telephone   ⌀ Restaurant, bar, 2 lounges, TV room, drying-room, conservatory, garden; functions (max 30 people incl up to 16 residential), conferences; gym, sauna, solarium, steam room, heated indoor swimming-pool, tennis, putting green, pitch & putt, croquet; early suppers for children; cots, high chairs, babysitting, baby-listening, outdoor play area   ⴲ No wheelchair access   ● No children in restaurant after 8pm; no dogs; no smoking in restaurant, discouraged in bedrooms
▭ Amex, Delta, Diners, MasterCard, Switch, Visa   £ Single £40, single occupancy of twin/double £60 to £105, twin/double £75 to £90, four-poster £90, family room £85, suite £120; deposit required. Bar/bistro L £7.50; set D £23.50; alc D £30. Special breaks available

---

Prices are what you can expect to pay in 1999, except where specified to the contrary. Many hoteliers tell us that these prices can be regarded only as approximations.

St Martin's

Lower Town, St Martin's TR25 0QW
TEL: (01720) 422092   FAX: (01720) 422298

A haven of excellence, with superb hospitality, in the only hotel on the island.

Every year we receive positive reports on this well-loved hotel, not least about how nice it is to be greeted by the manager, Keith Bradford, on your arrival at the quayside. People come back year after year (one reader calls it her 'all-time favourite') to sample the good food and high standards of accommodation and housekeeping. 'The staff were as friendly and helpful as ever', and 'nothing is too much trouble' are oft-quoted commendations – even visiting dogs are given individual towels and menus. The hotel is built as a cluster of cottages by the side of a sandy beach; most guests spend their days having 'exciting adventures' on the water, and you can watch the sun set from the cheerful blue-and-yellow restaurant. The menu remains as indulgent and fish-oriented as ever, with such starters as cobbler of halibut with thyme, smoked artichoke and mushroom ravioli, followed by lamb and venison noisettes with foie-gras escalope, lamb and rosemary *jus*. The bedrooms tend to the luxurious, and are decked out in bright florals with modern furnishings.

◐ Closed Nov to Feb   ⤴ Flights from Southampton, Bristol, Exeter, Plymouth, Newquay or Land's End; helicopter and then boat from Penzance. There are no cars on the Isles of Scilly   ⟼ 15 twin/double, 1 double, 2 four-poster, 10 family rooms, 2 suites; all with bathroom/WC; all with TV, room service, hair-dryer, direct-dial telephone; no tea/coffee-making facilities in rooms   ⊘ Restaurant, bar, lounge, TV room, games room, garden; functions (max 60 people residential); civil wedding licence; fishing, heated indoor swimming-pool; early suppers for children; cots, high chairs, babysitting, baby-listening   ⅙ No wheelchair access   ● No children under 12 in restaurant eves; no dogs in public rooms and some bedrooms   ▭ Amex, Delta, Diners, MasterCard, Switch, Visa   £ Single occupancy of twin/double from £95, twin/double from £190, four-poster £200 to £270, family room £240 to £310, suite £280 to £350 (rates incl dinner); deposit required. Light L £10. Special breaks available

Atlantic Hotel

St Mary's TR21 0PL
TEL: (01720) 422417   FAX: (01720) 423009
EMAIL: atlantichotel@btinternet.com

Rambling old inn in prime position on the harbour, with a restaurant that juts out over the water.

The Atlantic Hotel is perfectly positioned to cater for people arriving and leaving the island, but it serves as very much more than just a stopping-off place. You need to book in advance for tables in the restaurant, as well as for rooms with views, as the place is deservedly popular with locals – it's even harder to make sure of a window seat. Despite its popularity, the place is extremely friendly and relaxed, and caters well for guests of all ages, with children being especially welcomed by manager Luke Paulger. The four-course menu tends heavily towards the fishy, as might be expected – you could try smoked salmon and tuna salad Marie Rose, followed by cream of oak-smoked chicken soup, and then fresh Scillonian-caught haddock with prawn Bercy sauce. The bedrooms and public rooms are done out cheerfully in florals, but most people gravitate towards the busy bar, with its views and buzzing atmosphere. It's worth paying the extra for a bedroom with a sea view.

◑ Closed Nov to Feb ⤢ Take helicopter, boat or plane from Penzance. There are no cars on the Isles of Scilly ⬌ 1 single, 8 twin, 12 double, 1 four-poster, 2 family rooms; all with bathroom/WC exc 1 double with shower/WC; all with TV, hair-dryer, direct-dial telephone ⊘ Restaurant, bar, lounge; functions (max 60 people incl up to 48 residential), conferences; early suppers for children; cots, high chairs ⅗ No wheelchair access ● Dogs £8 per night ▭ MasterCard, Switch, Visa £ Single £67 to £76, single occupancy of twin/double £100 to £110, twin/double £134 to £152, four-poster £150 to £164, family room £159 to £177; deposit required. Set D £21.50. Special breaks available

---

ST MAWES Cornwall map 1

Idle Rocks Hotel

Harbourside, 1 Tredenham Road, St Mawes, Truro TR2 5AN
TEL: (01326) 270771   FAX: (01326) 270062

Comfortable hotel, with good service, in great seaside location.

A collection of black-and-white photographs in the corridor shows the Idle Rocks Hotel in its previous incarnations: it was one of the first houses built in the village, right by the harbour (the original slipway is still visible outside); then it became a bakery. It is still very much a focal point of the village: position yourself on the terrace at the front, and you are practically in the sea, overlooking the harbour, yet you can view the rest of the village spreading itself around the coast. If the weather is inclement, the inside of the hotel is consolingly decorated in determinedly warm tones – plush fabrics in red and purple dominate the public rooms – and there are literally dozens of places to sit to take in the panorama. A picture of a sailing race in the harbour takes up the whole of one wall in the restaurant, so you get a real nautical feel even when the curtains are drawn. The menu offers plenty of local seafood, but there's no shortage of meaty choices either: a crisp filo tulip of marinated cucumber and chicken-liver pâté served on a sweet-mustard sauce might be followed by escalopes of pork layered with sun-dried tomatoes and wafers of Parmesan cheese with a red-wine sauce. The bedrooms are each decorated with a picture of the bird that they are named after, as well as fresh flowers. Those in the house are luxurious; try to get the sea views. Those in the attractive annexe (across the road and up a slight incline) are more spacious and equally well furnished.

◑ Open all year ⚹ By harbour in St Mawes. Private car park (£4 per day); public car park nearby (free) ⬑ 3 single, 4 twin, 11 double, 4 four-poster, 2 family rooms; some in annexe; most with bathroom/WC, some with shower/WC; all with TV, room service, hair-dryer, direct-dial telephone ⚹ Restaurant, bar, 2 lounges; functions (max 60 people incl up to 12 residential), conferences; civil wedding licence; leisure facilities nearby (reduced rates for guests); early suppers for children; cots, high chairs, babysitting, baby-listening ⚹ No wheelchair access ⚫ No smoking in restaurant and 1 lounge ▭ Amex, Delta, MasterCard, Switch, Visa £ Single £44 to £67, single occupancy of twin/double £66 to £101, twin/double £94 to £134, four-poster £102 to £154, family room £108 to £134; deposit required. Bar/bistro L £6; set D £24; alc D £26. Special breaks available

Rising Sun

The Square, St Mawes, Truro TR2 5DJ
TEL: (01326) 270233   FAX: (01326) 270198

Stylish refurbishment and cosmopolitan atmosphere in very friendly seaside hotel.

It is a great surprise and even greater pleasure to walk through the doorway of this hotel. From the outside the white, 1930s building, with its pale blue doors and window surrounds and its unpretentious plastic tables and chairs outside on the patio, appears rather uninspiring – yet the interior is welcoming and confident. A recent refurbishment in modern country style radiates with the brightness of a new pin: flagged floors, huge chunky sofas, rattan furniture, stripped-pine fixtures, colourwashed walls, tartan banquette seats, Indian coffee tables – the list goes on. In the restaurant (part of which is in a bright conservatory) the menu veers back towards the traditional; you might try a prawn and crab platter, followed by pork medallions served on a walnut croûton with a blueberry and red-wine sauce. Upstairs, the bedrooms are coolly assured. Fabrics and furniture have been chosen with luxury in mind: sophisticated brass beds, gorgeous bathrooms, more squashy sofas. The attention to detail even incorporates a copy of the *Radio Times* in each room.

◑ Open all year ⚹ In St Mawes. Private car park ⬑ 2 single, 2 twin, 5 double; family rooms available; some with bathroom/WC, some with shower/WC; all with TV, room service, hair-dryer, trouser press, direct-dial telephone ⚹ Restaurant, 2 bars, lounge, drying-room, conservatory, patio; early suppers for children; high chairs ⚹ No wheelchair access ⚫ None ▭ Delta, MasterCard, Switch, Visa £ Single £30 to £45, single occupancy of twin/double £70, twin/double £90, family room £90 + £10 per child under 13, £15 per child 13 and over; deposit required. Bar/bistro L, D £5; set D £19.50

'When I rang the bell at one hotel the owner left some bacon under the grill to come and answer the door, and it caught fire. I rushed into the kitchen with him to battle with the flames, helped to put it out and resumed the inspection.'
Inspector's report

Soar Mill Cove Hotel

Soar Mill Cove, Salcombe TQ7 3DS
TEL: (01548) 561566   FAX: (01548) 561223

Luxurious retreat in splendid coastal spot, run with great enthusiasm.

It's a surprise when you first see the Makepeace family's hotel: after such a long drive along tiny roads down to a picture-perfect bay, you happen upon what looks like a lost motel. But don't be disillusioned – it was meant to be that way: the stone, slate and glass one-storey building blends into the valley floor, and is almost invisible on this dramatic stretch of National Trust coastline. Anyway, the interior and surroundings more than make up for the hotel's uninspiring exterior. There's an 'Enid Blyton-type cove', complete with rock pools and a warm bathing pool (naturally formed by a sand bar), and 3½ miles of civilisation-free walks in each direction. The hotel is now run by the larger-than-life Keith Makepeace and his sister Caroline. Keith is justifiably proud of his highly professional kitchen, which uses mainly organic ingredients (many of which come from the kitchen garden) and produces home-made jams and marmalades. Dinner, taken in the mulberry-coloured, formal restaurant, is a flamboyant affair: a haddock taster may be followed by consommé of lobster and saffron, and then roast saddle of venison with a garlic brioche crust, olive mash and roasted peppers. The plush décor of the public rooms continues through into the bedroooms, all of which have huge beds, doors to little patios, and fresh milk.

◑ Closed mid-Nov to Chr, 2 Jan to mid-Feb   ☑ From A381, turn right at Marlborough and follow signs towards sea and hotel. Private car park   ⬐ 6 twin, 7 double, 1 four-poster, 4 family rooms, 3 suites; all with bathroom/WC; all with TV, room service, hair-dryer, trouser press, direct-dial telephone   ✓ Restaurant, bar, lounge, drying-room, games room, garden; fishing, heated indoor and outdoor swimming-pools, tennis, putting green; early suppers for children; cots, high chairs, toys, playroom, baby-listening, outdoor play area   ♿ Wheelchair access to hotel and restaurant, 21 ground-floor bedrooms   ● Dogs in bedrooms only, by arrangement, smoking in bar only   ▭ MasterCard, Switch, Visa   £ Single occupancy of twin/double £100 to £155, twin/double £140 to £225, four-poster £165 to £250, family room £175 to £281, suite £210 to £340; deposit required. Set D £35; alc L £21, D £35. Special breaks available

[handwritten] Aug 2001   £667 pp/wk. B+B+D   ch<5 £25%   cl>5 £33%

South Sands   **NEW ENTRY**

South Sands, Salcombe TQ8 8LL
TEL: (01548) 843741   FAX: (01548) 842112

Straightforward, child-friendly hotel, right on very safe beach.

South Sands is the sister hotel of Tides Reach (see entry), but has a very different feel to it: children under eight aren't allowed at Tides Reach, whereas here they are positively welcomed, and the accommodation is geared towards having youngsters around. It's comfortable, but without frills and ornaments because 'parents can't be on pins as to Don't touch this, don't touch that'. This doesn't mean that there's no character, however: the terrace bar (which opens directly on to the beach) has a distinctly nautical theme and feels like a ship's deck – there's a highly polished floor, ships' wheels, lobster pots and a frieze depicting maps of the world. Kids have their meals here at the chunky pine tables. Grown-ups dine in the pretty yellow restaurant, from a menu that might offer pan-fried fillet of mackerel with strips of vegetables and prawns, or braised shoulder of lamb filled with mushrooms and thyme; supplements are charged for such dishes as local scallops or grilled duck breast. The bar-cum-lounge is done out very traditionally, with solid chesterfields, and there's a separate playroom and a large indoor pool decorated with a pretty mural by local artist Pam Merlin. The bedrooms are fresh and functional; some (such as Room 4) have great views across the bay.

○ Closed Nov to Mar ⊅ Follow A381 from A38 to Salcombe, then follow signs to South Sands. Private car park ⫣ 2 single, 9 twin, 10 double, 9 family suites; all with bathroom/WC; all with TV, room service, hair-dryer, direct-dial telephone, radio ⌁ Restaurant, 2 bars, lounge, drying-room; steam room, heated indoor swimming-pool; leisure facilities nearby (reduced rates for guests); early suppers for children; cots, high chairs, toys, playroom, baby-listening ⅋ No wheelchair access ● No children under 7 in restaurant eves; no dogs in public rooms ☐ Amex, Delta, MasterCard, Switch, Visa £ Single £47 to £88, single occupancy of twin/double £47 to £88, twin/double £94 to £166, family suite £118 to £233 (prices valid till Mar 1999); deposit required. Bar/bistro L £9.50, D £15; set D £21.50; alc D £28.50. Special breaks available

Tides Reach

South Sands, Salcombe TQ8 8LJ
TEL: (01548) 843466   FAX: (01548) 843954

Excellent service and plenty of pampering at this friendly hotel.

If this hotel were a dog, it would be the kind of small one that thinks it's as big as a Great Dane. The Tides Reach aims to offer its guests the facilities and standards of a big hotel, while maintaining an extremely friendly atmosphere. It is certainly a comfortable place, with pretty public rooms, gardens with subtropical trees and an ornamental lake – complete with fountain and fish – and the beach just across the road. The staff are very helpful, and there seem to be plenty of them, while the (astonishingly tropical) swimming-pool and leisure complex is a real bonus. The colourful restaurant has large picture windows, which allow you to take in the views while dining from a menu with plenty of fish choices.The bedrooms are well decorated and spacious, though an ill-fitting shower curtain led to a flooded bathroom during our inspection stay. The best of them have a balcony that looks over the cove – it's worth paying extra if you enjoy lazing round the hotel during the day.

○ Closed Dec & Jan ⊅ Follow A381 to Salcombe; turn right in Salcombe at seafront and follow signs to South Sands. Private car park ⫣ 17 twin, 18 double, 3 family suites; all with bathroom/WC; all with TV, room service, hair-dryer, direct-dial telephone ⌁ Restaurant, 2 bars, 3 lounges, drying-room, games room, garden; gym, sauna, solarium, heated indoor swimming-pool, squash, snooker; leisure facilities nearby (free for guests)   ↿ No wheelchair access ● No children under 8; no dogs in public rooms; no smoking in some public rooms and some bedrooms ☐ Amex, Delta, Diners, MasterCard, Switch, Visa ℒ Single occupancy of twin/double £75 to £94, twin/double £136 to £188, family room/suite £220 to £284 (rates incl dinner); deposit required. Bar/bistro L £5. Special breaks available

---

SANDGATE Kent   map 3

Sandgate Hotel   **NEW ENTRY**

Wellington Terrace, The Esplanade, Sandgate, Folkestone CT20 3DY
TEL: (01303) 220444   FAX: (01303) 220496

Wonderful food and bags of French charm at this English seaside hotel.

Overlooking the main coastal road and shingle beach, the Sandgate Hotel faces France, both literally and metaphorically. Zara Gicqueau is from Sandgate, but her husband Samuel comes from the Loire, and the influence of his homeland pervades the whole hotel, from the paintings of Loire vineyards in the restaurant to the welcome lack of pretentiousness in the décor and the solicitous attitude of the young, largely French staff. Such a combination clearly appeals to local tastes: on a wet, blustery spring evening the lounge and restaurant were full of birthday celebrants, dining with gusto on Samuel's well-judged, perfectly balanced menus. Foie gras with Sauternes jelly, monkfish with asparagus and spring onions, duckling breast with honey glaze and sesame seeds all made an appearance on the *prix fixe* menu, while, from an à la carte where fish dishes outnumbered meat courses, scallops with thin slices of black truffle on potato purée was an outstanding success. And therein lies the rub: with 15 rooms and only seven or eight tables in the restaurant, residents are not guaranteed dinner reservations – and that, early ferries apart, would be the main reason for staying over. The bedrooms are perfectly comfortable, if on the small side, and have well-planned bathrooms; those at the front have attractive sea views, though they may also have traffic noise to contend with. Breakfast croissants and *pain au chocolat* are baked every day – you're asked to order the evening before, so that they don't run out. For traditionalists there's also the full English fry-up in addition to freshly squeezed juice and cereals.

◕ Closed mid-Jan to mid-Feb & first week Oct; restaurant closed Sun & Mon eve
■ On A259, main coastal road opposite the sea. Coming from Hythe, hotel is on left before main village where antique shops line both sides of road. Private car park
🛌 2 single, 2 twin, 11 double; all with bathroom/WC exc 2 single with shower/WC; all with TV, room service, direct-dial telephone ✓ Restaurant, bar, lounge, terrace; cot, high chair, baby-listening ↿ No wheelchair access ● No dogs; no smoking in restaurant ☐ Amex, Delta, Diners, MasterCard, Switch, Visa ℒ Single £42, single occupancy of twin/double £49 to £67, twin/double £54 to £72; deposit required. Set L, D £20.50 (weekdays), £29.50 (weekends); alc L, D £37.50

The **Guide** *is totally independent, accepts no free hospitality, and survives on the number of copies sold each year.*

SANDHOE Northumberland
map 10

The Courtyard

Mount Pleasant, Sandhoe, Corbridge NE46 4LX
TEL: (01434) 606850   (AND FAX)

A farmhouse converted into a stylish B&B above the Tyne Valley.

The magnificent views over the Tyne Valley alone make it worth tracking down the Courtyard, lost among narrow lanes high on a hillside above Corbridge in Hadrian's Wall country. Owner Bill Weightman's building skills have fused perfectly with his wife Margaret's long track record as a landlady to create a luxurious B&B from little more than derelict farm buildings. Yet this is no pocket-sized cottagey affair; the dining-room and sitting-room are designed on a sprawling, ranch-like scale, full of solid antiques, gilt mirrors, stone fireplaces and a red wood-burning stove. With flagstone floors underfoot and exposed roof beams above, it all looks original, but the beams, doors and much of the final structure were imported from other buildings. The edges are softened with rich damask and velvety fabrics, fresh lilies, dried-flower arrangements and tribes of teddies, creating a luxurious, if slightly fussy, interior. The three bedrooms are certainly a cut above the average B&B, too, fitted out with classy fabrics, and including a canopied bed and a four-poster. The bathrooms bear Margaret's personal stamp too, with her own hand-painted tiles made in a kiln in the house.

◑ Open all year   ⤢ From Corbridge go north up A68; very soon take road on left signposted Sandhoe; go across crossroads, then turn right at T-junction. The Courtyard is 100 yards along on left. Private car park   🛏 1 twin, 1 double, 1 four-poster; all with bathroom/WC, exc twin with shower/WC; all with TV, room service, hair-dryer
⚘ Dining-room, sitting-room, conservatory, garden   ὦ No wheelchair access
● No children under 14; no dogs; no smoking   ☐ None accepted   £ Single occupancy of twin/double £50 to £55, twin/double £55 to £65, four-poster £75

SANDIWAY Cheshire
map 7

Nunsmere Hall

Tarporley Road, Sandiway, Northwich CW8 2ES
TEL: (01606) 889100   FAX: (01606) 889055
EMAIL: nunsmere@aol.com
WEB SITE: www.prideofbritainhotels.com

A sophisticated turn-of-the-century manor, with impeccable rooms, in sumptuous grounds.

Nunsmere Hall is as sophisticated as its aristocratic name and history suggest: it was the former home of Sir Aubrey Brocklebank, one of the designers of the *Queen Mary*, the great transatlantic liner. A smart, seemingly never-ending, gravel driveway leads up to the gracious and solid red-brick manor house, which is surrounded by manicured lawns, picturesque gardens and a 60-acre lake. All is equally elegant inside, especially the guests' lounge, with its elegant, moulded ceiling, chunky sofas and tasteful rugs, and the Crystal Restaurant, with its wood panelling and smart furnishings. The imaginative dishes on the dinner menu might include caramelised sea scallops with a cassoulet of split peas and Alsace bacon, and breast of Barbary duck on sugared figs with braised leg meat and a foie-gras soufflé. The desserts are positively dangerous: chilled white-chocolate and lime tart with milk-chocolate quenelles, for example, or, for the suicidal, the caramel trio: sugar-frosted vanilla rice with hot caramel soufflé and iced praline. You can give your stomach a rest in the Captain's Bar, a cheerful, pine-panelled bar area, with a solid stone fireplace, that overlooks the terrace and rose garden. The comfort and indulgence continues in the bedrooms, with attention to detail evident in dried flowers and Chinese door stops.

◑ Open all year ⏣ Off A49, 4 miles south-west of Northwich. Private car park ⤶ 10 twin, 20 double, 1 four-poster, 5 suites; family rooms available; all with bathroom/WC; all with TV, 24-hour room service, hair-dryer, trouser press, direct-dial telephone ✅ Restaurant, bar, lounge, library, games room, garden; functions (max 150 people incl up to 72 residential), conferences; civil wedding licence; putting green, snooker, croquet; archery by arrangement; early suppers for children; cots, babysitting, baby-listening ♿ Wheelchair access to hotel (3 steps) and restaurant, WC (unisex), 2 ground-floor bedrooms ● No children under 12; no dogs ☐ Amex, Delta, Diners, MasterCard, Switch, Visa £ Single occupancy of twin/double £90 to £130, twin/double £140 to £175, four-poster £225 to £325, family room £190 to £200, suite £250 to £325; deposit required. Continental B £8.50, cooked B £13.50 (cooked B incl in room rate Fri to Sun); bar/bistro L £6.50; set L £17.50/£20; alc D £35

SANDRINGHAM **Norfolk**   map 6

Park House

Sandringham, King's Lynn PE35 6EH
TEL: (01485) 543000   FAX: (01485) 540663

Relax in the countryside at this hotel designed exclusively for people with disabilities and their carers for a one- or two-week stay.

You won't get a better chance of rubbing shoulders with royalty than at Park House: it is actually set within the beautiful Sandringham estate and is only a matter of yards from the Queen's own front door. It also happens to be the birthplace of the late Diana, Princess of Wales, and so attracts one or two onlookers at its railings. However, once inside this rather dour example of a Victorian country pile, hardly anything remains of the house's former royal connections. Its broad proportions are ideally suited for wheelchair use, and the emphasis in each of the public rooms is always on space and manoeuvrability. While the choice of browns and beiges for the decoration can be a little uninspiring, there are some particularly attractive areas, such as the hall-like conservatory, which has a games room to one side, and the dining-room, with its panoramic picture windows that look across the cricket pitch. The enticing menus might include cheese and chive roulade, followed by salmon and prawn vol-au-vent, and then banoffi tart. If guests need any care assistance during their stay, there is a daily charge. The bedrooms are of a good size, if plainly decorated (only one is without a view), and the bathrooms are as one would expect: bright and well equipped.

◑ Open all year ▣ Turn right (east) off A149, 3 miles north of Knight's Hill roundabout, and follow hotel signs. Private car park ⟻ 8 single, 8 twin; plus 1 single, 2 twin in annexe flat (non-disabled guests); main house: singles with shower/WC, twins with bathroom/WC; annexe flat: 1 bathroom/WC; all with TV, room service, direct-dial telephone; hair-dryer on request ✅ Dining-room, bar, lounge, TV room, library, conservatory, games room, garden; functions (max 100 people incl up to 34 residential), conferences; heated outdoor swimming-pool, jacuzzi, snooker, croquet; early suppers for children; cots, high chairs ♿ Wheelchair access to hotel and dining-room, WC (unisex), 16 rooms specially equipped for disabled people, 7 ground-floor bedrooms, lift ⬤ No dogs; smoking in conservatory only ☐ MasterCard, Visa £ Single £44 to £86, twin £70 to £154; deposit required. Set L £7.50, D £14.50. (Prices valid till Jan 1999.)

SCARBOROUGH North Yorkshire map 9

Interludes

No under 16s ℒℒ

32 Princess Street, Scarborough YO11 1QR
TEL: (01723) 360513   FAX: (01723) 368597
EMAIL: interludes@mcmail.com
WEB SITE: www.interludes.mcmail.com

A small hotel in the old town area of Scarborough, with a strong thespian theme.

Cobbled streets rise steeply from the working fishing harbour into Scarborough's charming old town conservation area, where Interludes forms part of a row of simple Georgian houses. Set back from a quiet street, the south-facing terrace is a real sun-trap, and inside Ian Grundy and Bob Harris greet their guests with an equally sunny reception – their performance wins rave reviews, with guests lauding the 'friendly, welcoming atmosphere' and 'brilliant hospitality'. The theatrical flavour of the hotel is immediately apparent: framed theatre posters, photos and memorabilia set against a bold backdrop of blues and creams and vivid modern patterns. Ian and Bob's packaged breaks to Scarborough's Stephen Joseph theatre have a strong following, and guests can discuss the current theatrical offerings over dinner around two shining mahogany tables, or while relaxing on the lounge's twin chesterfields. Four of the five bedrooms, named after famous theatres, have sea views – for the pick of these, the top floors are worth the climb. Antiques and four-poster or canopied beds are the stars of the show in a cosy, slightly fussy décor – Wyndham has a brass bed with a lacy canopy, and on a clear day you can see 15 miles across South Bay, all the way to the lighthouse on Flamborough Head.

◑ Closed 2 weeks late autumn & early spring ▣ Follow tourist signs to harbour; take small road up hill between Newcastle Packet pub and Princess café; Princess Street is second turning on left. On-street parking (free); public car park nearby (£3 per day) ⟻ 2 twin, 1 double, 2 four-poster; 1 twin with bathroom/WC, most with shower/WC; all with TV, hair-dryer, clock radio, some with trouser press ✅ Dining-room/bar, lounge, sun patio ♿ No wheelchair access ⬤ No children under 16; no dogs; smoking in lounge only ☐ MasterCard, Visa £ Single occupancy of twin/double £28 to £30, twin/double £46 to £54, four-poster £54; deposit required. Set D £12.50. Special breaks available

Seatoller House

Seatoller, Borrowdale, Keswick CA12 5XN
TEL: (017687) 77218 (AND FAX)

House-party atmosphere and hearty dinners in deepest Borrowdale.

New managers have arrived at this much-loved Cumbrian establishment, but regulars will be relieved to hear that its well-tried formula is unchanged. Seatoller is a one-off. Can these simple lodgings really engender such a convivial brand of hospitality? If its faithful *habitués* have any say, the answer's a resounding yes. This modest, low-slung seventeenth-century house stands by a sharp bend in the village centre, just before the Borrowdale road begins its ascent to the Honister Pass. Inside, the beams, carved oak furniture and open fires give a friendly air to the twin sitting-rooms, while the communal dining-room is even plainer, with polished slate flags and wooden tables. Bedrooms, named after British mammals (Hedgehog, Badger, and so on), date from a bygone era of rustic charm: all rush-seat chairs and sprigged wallpapers and with separate bathrooms of varnished pine and cork tiles. The boot room, where you can dry out wet clothes (a much-needed facility in England's wettest valley), or the tea bar (help yourself to complimentary drinks and home-made cake after long walks) may start a few conversations going. These swell to an amiable crescendo during choiceless but inventive set dinners and gel to firm camaraderie over drinks by the fire. On Tuesdays Seatoller House serves no dinners, so track down Ann Pepper (its previous manager) in the Yew Tree Restaurant next door.

○ Closed Dec to Feb; restaurant closed Tue eve   ◪ 8 miles south of Keswick on B5289. Private car park   ⤲ 3 twin, 3 double, 3 family rooms; one in annexe; all with bathroom/WC (not all *en suite*); no tea/coffee-making facilities in rooms   ✅ Dining-room, sitting-room, drying-room, library, tea room, boot room, garden; early suppers for children   ⅙ No wheelchair access   ● No children under 5; no dogs in public rooms; smoking in library only   ▭ None accepted   £ Single occupancy of twin/double £30, twin/double £57, family room £69; deposit required. Set D £10; packed lunches available

Horton Grange

Seaton Burn, Newcastle upon Tyne NE13 6BU
TEL: (01661) 860686   FAX: (01661) 860308
EMAIL: andrew@horton-grange.co.uk
WEB SITE: www.horton-grange.co.uk

Relaxing country hotel on the edge of Newcastle, with superb food in a stylish restaurant.

If Newcastle's inner-city sprawl holds no attraction for you, Seaton Grange is an oasis of calm and understated elegance on the outskirts of the city, just a short way off the A1. The countryside hereabouts is rather bleak and featureless, and the Georgian villa's stones are blackened by atmospheric pollution, but as soon as you walk on to the dark-oak floor and soft rugs in the woodsmoke-perfumed reception, a softly comforting aura descends. Plump, green-damask sofas, antiques and deliciously scented fresh lilies set a suitably soft-focus scene for the Pre-Raphaelite prints that hang in the refined lounge. This mood of gentle relaxation continues in the appealing bedrooms: high ceilings with plaster cornices give a sense of space, and chunky antiques, coupled with brass fittings and thick towels and robes in the bathrooms, add to the feel-good factor. The bedrooms in the Peach House annexe are smaller and aimed more at single business travellers. The stylish new restaurant opened in summer 1997 and is a treat – huge paper lanterns and light ash furniture create a Scandinavia-meets-Japan setting in which to tackle one of chef Steven Martin's esteemed four-course dinners. The number of choices at each course is generous; crab with cucumber and dill salad and lime mayonnaise might be a first choice, followed by sea bass on spiced couscous, then rich orange tart with chocolate sauce and honeycomb ice-cream.

◑ Closed Chr and New Year; restaurant closed Sun eve　⤢ From A1 take A19 exit; at roundabout take first exit; after 1 mile turn left (signposted Ponteland and airport); hotel is 2 miles on right. Private car park　⤆ 4 single, 5 double; some in annexe; all with shower/WC; all with TV, room service, hair-dryer, direct-dial telephone; no tea/coffee-making facilities in rooms　⚥ Restaurant, bar, lounge, garden; functions (max 45 people incl up to 14 residential); civil wedding licence; fishing　♿ Wheelchair access to hotel (3 steps) and restaurant (1 step), WC (unisex), 4 ground-floor bedrooms　◒ No dogs; no smoking in bedrooms or restaurant　▭ Amex, Delta, MasterCard, Switch, Visa　£ Single £59, single occupancy of double £74, double £90. Set D £34

Seaview Hotel

High Street, Seaview PO34 5EX
TEL: (01983) 612711　FAX: (01983) 613729

Well-run hotel in tiny, seaside town, with good food, great service and stylish rooms.

Even on a rainy Friday lunch-time out of season, the Seaview Hotel was a bustling hive of activity, with everyone working smoothly, efficiently and, best of all, cheerfully. On our inspection visit, staff were attending to lunch-time diners, local drinkers and the organisers of an auction, as well as hotel guests. It is this constant hard work and enthusiasm, together with Nicky and Nick Hayward's attention to detail and anticipation of needs, which ensure that the hotel's gleaming reputation is unlikely to become tarnished. As one reader summed up: 'A real treat! All the charms of an old seaside hotel, with every modern convenience.' You could spend your entire stay reading the framed accolades that line the corridor but your time would be better spent enjoying the hospitality and comfort for which the hotel is renowned. Lunch is served in the front bar, with views down to the pebbly beach, and in the locals' bar – a snug, wood-panelled nook, crammed with nautical artifacts. In the evening, diners can choose between two stylish restaurants, one of which is no-smoking – whether you are fresh off your boat or dressed to the nines, you'll fit in. Main courses might consist of roasted salmon fillet with spinach mash and mustard sauce, or knuckle of lamb cooked with shredded beetroot, port and potatoes.

Away from the activity of the public rooms, guests can take in the sea views from the residents' lounge, playing cards or board games, or taking afternoon tea. The bedrooms are elegantly decorated with bright colours and bold, patterned fabrics. Extras include a sewing kit, full-sized bottles of shampoo, a local map and a selection of books in each room. The hotel is family-friendly, with a three-bedroom, self-contained apartment and a children's menu, but is far from being overrun with infants. The secret of the Seaview Hotel is that it caters, thoughtfully and seemingly effortlessly, for all its guests.

◑ Closed Chr; restaurant closed Sun eve exc bank hol weekends ⏏ Take B3330 from Ryde and follow signs to Seaview; hotel is on High Street. Private car park 🛏 2 single, 1 twin, 8 twin/double, 2 double, 2 suites; family rooms available; most with bathroom/WC, 2 with shower/WC; all with TV, room service, hair-dryer, direct-dial telephone ✇ 2 restaurants, 2 bars, lounge, drying-room, conservatory; functions (max 50 people incl up to 30 residential), conferences; early suppers for children; cots, high chairs, babysitting, baby-listening ♿ No wheelchair access ● Children under 5 discouraged from restaurants (after 7.30pm); no dogs in restaurants; no smoking in 1 restaurant and some bedrooms ▭ Amex, Delta, Diners, MasterCard, Switch, Visa ⓔ Single £55, single occupancy of twin/double £60 to £85, twin/double £85 to £110, family room (twin/double rate + £10.50 per child), suite £110 to £170; deposit required. Bar/bistro L £14; set Sun L £14; alc L, D £19.50. Special breaks available

---

SEAVINGTON ST MARY Somerset   map 2

The Pheasant

Water Street, Seavington St Mary, Ilminster TA19 0QH
TEL: (01460) 240502   FAX: (01460) 242388

Agreeable accommodation in a converted seventeenth-century farmhouse, with friendly service from an energetic young couple.

On first impression, the Pheasant looks every inch the English country pub: all thatched roof, creeper cladding and honey-coloured stone. In fact, this restaurant-with-rooms has never been a pub, having started life as a farmhouse in around 1610. Pub-like qualities abound, however, not least in the heavily beamed bar, with its green-leather chairs, log-burning fire and inglenook bedecked with pheasant-decorated plates. Ceiling and vertical beams, leaded windows, exposed stone walls and a pastel colour scheme give a cosy feel to the two-sectioned restaurant, where guests might enjoy a warm salad of chicken livers, followed by pan-seared Quantock duck breast with a peach and blueberry sauce, and then a pudding. The two bedrooms in the main house, Dunster and Winsham, retain their original beams, and have more character than those in the converted stable across the courtyard. All the bedrooms, as well as the two suites in the converted dairyman's cottage, feature cheerful colour schemes and lavish, co-ordinating fabrics. The young owners (and recent first-time parents), Mark and Tania Harris, are striving to import little personal touches to make the smart rooms genuinely special.

◐ Open all year; restaurant closed Sun eve　⊅ From South Petherton roundabout on A303, follow signs to Ilminster local services; turn left by Volunteer Inn; the Pheasant is 300 yards further on, on right. Private car park　⊨ 3 twin, 2 double, 1 four-poster, 2 suites; some in annexe; family rooms available; all with bathroom/WC; all with TV, room service, hair-dryer, trouser press, direct-dial telephone, some with mini-bar
⊘ Restaurant, bar, lounge, garden; functions (max 64 people incl up to 16 residential), conferences; early suppers for children; cots, high chairs, babysitting　& No wheelchair access　● No dogs in public rooms (£7.50 per night in bedrooms); smoking in bar and bedrooms only　▭ Amex, Delta, MasterCard, Switch, Visa
£ Single occupancy of twin/double £70, twin/double/four-poster £90, family room £110, suite £120; deposit required. Alc L £16, D £24. Special breaks available

---

SEDBUSK North Yorkshire　　　　　　　　　　　　map 8

Stone House

Sedbusk, Hawes DL8 3PT
TEL: (01969) 667571　FAX: (01969) 667720
EMAIL: daleshotel@aol.com

An Edwardian country hotel with wonderful views over
Wensleydale and a lively young manager.

Chris Taplin is the keen and energetic new hand at the helm of Stone House – his parents retired recently after many years running the family hotel. In spite of the dark and sober feel of the house – oak panelling, green leather sofas, a log fire in the stone hearth of the lounge, a snooker table in the library – this is a relaxed and approachable country hotel that doesn't want to rest on its laurels. A continuing programme of sensitive extensions and redecoration has added extra bedrooms and more space to the restaurant to avoid overcrowding, while a tastefully converted gazebo, now panelled in oak, provides more area for relaxing. The Taplin penchant for collecting – thimbles, Dinky cars, teapots among other items – remains undimmed. The bedrooms are all pleasantly fitted out with simple décor, and some have distinct plus points: the ground-floor conservatory rooms come with a little conservatory-lounge opening into the garden and a mix of bentwood and pine furniture – Room 9 has the prime corner spot with uninterrupted views over Wensleydale. Rooms 18 and 19 in the coach house have equally desirable views, while Room 1, a grand four-poster room, has a bed made by grandfather Taplin.

◐ Closed Jan　⊅ From Hawes take road signposted Muker for ½ mile; turn right towards Askrigg; hotel is 500 yards on left. Private car park　⊨ 1 single, 8 twin, 10 double, 3 four-poster; some in annexe; family rooms available; most with bathroom/WC, some with shower/WC; all with TV, hair-dryer, direct-dial telephone
⊘ Dining-room, bar, lounge, drying-room, library, conservatory, games room, garden; functions (max 50 people incl up to 43 residential), conferences; tennis, croquet, snooker; early suppers for children; cots, high chairs, baby-listening　& Wheelchair access to hotel (ramp) and restaurant, 6 ground-floor bedrooms　● No smoking in some public rooms and bedrooms　▭ Delta, MasterCard, Switch, Visa　£ Single £34, single occupancy of twin/double £39 to £44, twin/double £57 to £67, four-poster £80, family room £92; deposit required. Set D £17.50. Special breaks available

SELSIDE Cumbria map 8

Low Jock Scar [NEW ENTRY]

Selside, Kendal LA8 9LE
TEL: (01539) 823259 (AND FAX)

*An idyllic streamside setting and lovely gardens enhance this
friendly country guesthouse handily situated between Lakes and
Dales.*

A brief drive through light woodland, past walls of mossy stones, transports
visitors from the fast through-traffic on the A6 to a much more peaceful world.
Here, in an acre of beautifully kept and sheltered grounds beside a babbling
brook, stands an isolated stone-built house, successfully combining traditional
Cumbrian-style architecture with modern comfort. Alison and Philip Midwin-
ter have made the interior of this pleasant family home as appealing and
welcoming as its surroundings. A spacious, well-furnished lounge full of books
and maps offers plenty of scope for relaxing and planning walks and local drives.
The dining-room is in a conservatory extension, simply arranged with wooden
tables; Austrian blinds frame inviting views of the rear gardens amid a
burgeoning display of house plants and a collection of old-fashioned soda
siphons. The cuisine is straightforward, satisfying home cooking – you may need
a walk after the five-course dinner so as to make room for a classic Cumbrian
breakfast. Picnic lunches are available on request. Five good-sized bedrooms,
attractively but unfussily decorated in pine, feature floral duvets and plain walls.

◖ Closed 1 Nov to 15 March ⬀ 5 miles north of Kendal on A6 (1 mile past Plough
Inn), turn down lane on left. Private car park ⬅ 1 twin, 4 double; one in annexe; 2
with bathroom/WC, 1 with shower/WC; ⬥ Dining-room/conservatory, lounge,
garden ⬥ No wheelchair access ◖ Children/dogs by arrangement; no smoking
⬜ None accepted £ Single single occupancy of twin/double £31 to £36, twin/double
£45 to £55; deposit required. Set D £16; packed lunches available

---

SHANKLIN Isle of Wight map 2

Foxhills [NEW ENTRY]

30 Victoria Avenue, Shanklin PO37 6LS
TEL: (01983) 862329 FAX: (01983) 866666

*Relaxed hosts offer walking breaks and home-cooked food at this
Victorian house on the outskirts of Shanklin.*

It is well worth the walk away from Shanklin's centre to find Foxhills, an
elegant, sandy-coloured Victorian house on a tree-lined road. Smoking and pets
are not allowed, and special arrangements have to be made for children, but the
rules stop there, and the emphasis is on unwinding. Stuart Granshaw and
Michael Waller, the pleasant owners, run courses on Relaxation for Living in the
hotel out of season. Walking breaks are also available, led by Stuart, who devises
the walks to take in coastal scenery and the more gentle chalk downlands.
Michael's speciality is cooking, and he has created an imaginative selection of

dishes for the restaurant that recently opened to the public. Since taking over in 1997 the new owners have refurbished imaginatively with a modern touch. Walls colourwashed in bold pink greet you in the hall and this is typical of the fresh, colourful décor throughout. Room 6, decorated in pink with dark-wood furniture, is the largest of the bedrooms, with huge bay windows looking over the road. The sedate lounge and dining-room give on to lawns at the side of the house – a pleasant place to sit, although overlooked slightly by the road.

○ Closed Jan ⤢ From centre of Shanklin take A3020 towards Newport; Foxhills is less than ½ mile along on left. Private car park ⤶ 2 single, 2 twin, 3 double, 1 four-poster; 4 with bathroom/WC, 2 with shower/WC, 1 with WC only; all with TV, direct-dial telephone, hair-dryer; mini-bar available ✓ Dining-room, lounge, drying-room, garden; functions (max 40 people incl up to 14 residential), conferences; whirlpool spa, aromatherapy treatment room; leisure facilities nearby (reduced rates for guests); early suppers for children ⅙ No wheelchair access ● Children by arrangement; no dogs; no smoking ▭ Delta, MasterCard, Switch, Visa £ Single £25, single occupancy of twin/double £35, twin/double £50, four-poster £60; deposit required. Light L £4.50; set L £9.50, D £15. Special breaks available

---

SHEFFIELD South Yorkshire   map 9

Whitley Hall

Elliott Lane, Grenoside, Sheffield S35 8NR
TEL: 0114-245 4444   FAX: 0114-245 5414

An Elizabethan country-house hotel with lovely gardens, popular with Sheffield's business-conference and wedding clientele.

As you wind down a leafy lane through gentle hills toward Whitley Hall, the unlovely environs of Sheffield evaporate, and you could almost believe yourself enfolded in the depths of the countryside. Honey-coloured stone, gables wrapped in creepers, and 30 acres of grounds where peacocks roam and ducks glide on an ornamental lake announce a country mansion in the classic mould – although the house has seen a lot of tinkering since 1584, when the ancient builder carved his message for posterity (that 'William Parker made this worke') into a headstone near the kitchen. The hotel's style is friendly and relaxed, though it's business guests who predominate during the week. The bedrooms vary from a functional, light, modern décor adequate for weekday business stays, all the way to the honeymooners' extravaganza in the Peacock room, with its mullioned windows, high ceiling and suitably baronial four-poster. Five-course dinners are a snip at under £20 per person and offer modern English choices such as sauté chicken livers with garlic crostini, and chicken with sun-dried tomatoes in tarragon and paprika cream.

○ Closed bank hols ⤢ Off A61 Sheffield to Barnsley road at Grenoside. Private car park ⤶ 2 single, 7 twin, 7 double, 1 four-poster, 1 family room; suite available; all with bathroom/WC exc 1 single with shower/WC; all with TV, room service, trouser press, direct-dial telephone, some with hair-dryer ✓ Restaurant, bar, lounge, garden; functions (max 120 people incl up to 34 residential), conferences; civil wedding licence; putting green, clay-pigeon shooting, croquet; early suppers for children; cots, high chairs, baby-listening ⅙ No wheelchair access ● No dogs in public rooms; no smoking in restaurant ☐ Amex, Delta, Diners, MasterCard, Switch, Visa £ Single £65, single occupancy of twin/double £65, twin/double £85, four-poster £99, family room £95, suite £175; deposit required. Set L, D £9.50/£12/£20; alc L £14, D £21. Special breaks available

---

SHEFFORD WOODLANDS Berkshire map 2

Fishers Farm

Ermin Street, Shefford Woodlands,
Hungerford RG17 7AB
TEL: (01488) 648466   FAX: (01488) 648706

Smashing secluded working farm and welcoming family home.

The driveway should have a 'Beware of the rabbits' sign, for the emboldened bunnies scamper freely among the rolling acres of productive pasture. Mary Wilson for one, though, might be relieved to see fewer of the lovable pests, as they play havoc with the landscaped shrubbery in front of her splendid red-brick farmhouse. This is truly a place to escape from the urban jungle, though it is located only an unlikely mile or two from the M4 motorway. Mary, with her husband Henry, provides a welcoming family-home atmosphere in which to unwind. An open fire awaits in the beamed sitting-room, while a wood-burning stove warms the dining-room on cooler days. The bright Spanish tiles above the fireplace draw numerous admiring comments. The three bedrooms are appealingly cottagey, with beamed ceilings, cream walls and pine furniture. A 10-metre heated indoor pool is available for those wishing to work off hearty farmhouse breakfasts, while the farm's own lamb or local trout might feature in one of Mary's evening meals (provided by arrangement). Zelda, the beautiful smoky grey Weimaraner, is a hit with children – not least because she rightly associates them with extra walkies and play.

◑ Open all year ⚡ Leave M4 at Junction 14 and take A338 towards Wantage; after 1 mile turn left on B4000; pass Pheasant Inn on right; Fishers Farm is first drive on right. Private car park ⬅ 2 twin, 1 double; family rooms available; most with bathroom/WC; tea/coffee-making facilities, hair-dryer, direct-dial telephone available on request ✧ Dining-room, sitting-room, garden; heated indoor swimming-pool, croquet; early suppers for children, by arrangement ⚗ No wheelchair access ● No dogs; smoking in sitting-room only ☐ None accepted £ Single occupancy of twin/double £35, twin/double £50, family room £60; deposit required. Set D £18. Special breaks available

---

SHEPTON MALLET Somerset map 2

Bowlish House

Wells Road, Shepton Mallet BA4 5JD
TEL: (01749) 342022 (AND FAX)

Warm welcome at a comfortable Georgian restaurant-with-rooms.

'It was a dull day when we arrived for our three-night stay, but once inside our spirits lifted, and we were made most welcome by Bob Morley, who turned out to be an excellent host.' So began one letter describing a successful stay at Bob and Linda's large Georgian house in the sleepy market town of Shepton Mallet. Stained glass, wood panels and arched pilasters in the reception hallway immediately set a gracious tone, which is echoed in the comfortable lounge, where the combination of oil paintings, a marble fireplace, a chessboard and a selection of magazines creates an instantly relaxing feel. More art features in the small, panelled bar. Linda's food is appropriate fare for the elegant dining-room, where architectural prints, Italianate pictures and a large gilt-framed mirror conjure up images of an ordered, less frenetic time. Dinner, described by one correspondent as 'excellent', might offer toasted Somerset goats' cheese on a roasted red-pepper croustade with salad leaves, followed by fillet of brill with a warm fresh tomato and coriander salsa, and an Italian dark chocolate and almond torte with chocolate sauce and mascarpone. Polished furniture complements the bright colours in part-panelled bedrooms, furnished in a quiet, low-key way.

◑ Closed 1 week in autumn, 1 week in spring ⊿ ¼ mile from centre of Shepton Mallet on A371 Wells road. Private car park ⏢ 1 twin, 2 double; family rooms available; all with bathroom/WC; all with TV ⊗ Dining-room, bar, lounge, conservatory, garden; functions (max 35 people incl up to 6 residential), conferences; early suppers for children, by arrangement; cot ᵶ No wheelchair access ⬤ No dogs in public rooms ⬜ Amex, MasterCard, Visa £ Single £48, single occupancy of twin/double £48, twin/double £58, family room (£58 + £10 per child); deposit required. Cooked B £3.50; set L (first Sun of month) £14.50, D £22.50

Charlton House

Charlton Road, Shepton Mallet BA4 4PR
TEL: (01749) 342008   FAX: (01749) 346362
EMAIL: reservations-charltonhouse@btinternet.com

Beautiful country-house hotel with plenty to admire.

This fine Georgian house has been turned into a hotel that could be used as a decorating guide. The opulence is in the yards of fabrics used and in the detail, rather than in a forbiddingly perfect atmosphere. The individual pieces of heavy, old wooden furniture look as if they've seen a bit of life, and the lounge is filled with stylish yet comfortable groupings of settees and easy chairs. At night the candles are lit, and the rich, warm colours of the restaurant provide a fine romantic setting. The hotel is a popular venue for weddings, when it will be closed to those not attending the event. The staff are young and friendly. On inspection the food was a bit of a disappointment. From the set dinner menu, the duck breast with fig Tatin and port sauce was wonderfully sticky, but the pear with bitter-chocolate sauce lacked the required bitterness about it, and 'cheese with date-and-walnut bread' was served with biscuits until our inspector objected, when one slice of bread was produced. Helpings throughout were rather mean. Bedrooms are as interesting as you might expect. We liked Room 3, done out in blue-and-white reversed fabric and with a wonderfully airy bathroom.

❍ Open all year 🅿 On A361, 1 mile from Shepton Mallet. Private car park
🛏 1 single, 4 twin, 7 double, 2 four-poster, 3 suites; some in annexe; most with
bathroom/WC, 2 with shower/WC; all with satellite TV, room service, hair-dryer,
direct-dial telephone ✅ Restaurant, lounge, conservatory, garden; functions (max 80
people incl up to 36 residential), conferences; civil wedding licence; fishing, sauna,
solarium, heated indoor swimming-pool, tennis, croquet; early suppers for children;
cots, high chairs, toys, babysitting 🚫 No wheelchair access ● Dogs in 1 bedroom
only; no smoking in restaurant 🗀 Amex, Delta, Diners, MasterCard, Switch, Visa
£ Single £85, single occupancy of twin/double £95, twin/double £125, four-poster
£210, suite £210 to £285, family room (room rate + £15 cot, £25 bed); deposit required.
Cooked B £5; set L £12.50, D £27.50; alc L £17.50, D £36.50. Special breaks available

---

SHERIFF HUTTON North Yorkshire map 9

Rangers House

Sheriff Hutton Park, Sheriff Hutton, York YO6 6RH
TEL: (01347) 878397 (AND FAX)

Easy informality in an idiosyncratic country house on the peaceful
estate of a Jacobean stately home.

The coat of arms of James I, evidence of a long pedigree of royal connections,
adorns the entrance of this seventeenth-century house, built originally from the
stones of Richard III's castle as a brewhouse and stable for the royal hunting
lodge. In spite of its grand history, owners Sid and Dorianne Butler manage to
inject a healthy dose of fun and irreverence into their fascinating home. The main
hall makes a grand impression with its gallery and mahogany panelling, but
what draws the eye is the multitude of off-beat and arcane objects that make you
want to point and ask what everything is – the Italian antique crib full of teddies,
a huge drum, a fancy inlaid piano and an agreeable clutter of everyday bits and
bobs that immediately put you at ease. The conservatory is the alternative
sitting-room, perfect for children (or children at heart, of whatever age) to escape
into an eclectic and rather wacky disorder, including kites on the roof and jungly
prints. In one of the bedrooms an unusual fireplace-cum-oven is left from the
days when the house's ground floor served as stabling, and grooms lived
upstairs. The rooms are generally small and cottagey, but full of character – even
if you have one that's not *en suite*, the bathrooms are just a few feet away. Guests
can discuss dinner in advance – all produce is fresh and local, and is likely to
feature pheasant, venison or fish according to season.

❍ Open all year 🅿 At southern end of Sheriff Hutton, on a private road leading to
Sheriff Hutton Park. Private car park 🛏 1 single, 1 twin, 3 double, 1 family room; 1
double with bathroom/WC, 1 single with shower/WC, 1 double with WC only; all with
hair-dryer ✅ Dining-room, 2 lounges, conservatory, garden; functions (max 120
people incl up to 12 residential); early suppers for children; cot, babysitting, baby-
listening, games & garden games 🚫 No wheelchair access ● No dogs
🗀 None accepted £ Single £34, single occupancy of twin/double £45, twin/double
£64 to £68, family room £78; deposit required. Set D £24. Special breaks available

---

Prices are quoted per room *rather than* per person.

ENGLAND

Daneswood House

Cuck Hill, Shipham, Winscombe BS25 1RD
TEL: (01934) 843145   FAX: (01934) 843824
EMAIL: daneswoodhousehotel@compuserve.com

Turn-of-the-century homeopathic retreat, reincarnated as a comfortable country-house hotel.

The private, helter-skelter-like path ascending from the Cheddar road leads new arrivals to Daneswood House – and to fine views of the Mendips. Built as part of the Edwardian craze for spas and hydrotherapy, this large, pebble-dashed house, with its striking box bay windows, has sprouted an extension or two down the years as it metamorphosed into a country-house hotel, now run by long-time owners David and Elise Hodges. There's a nostalgic feel in the air from the second you go in through the conservatory entrance to encounter rattan chairs and an old His Master's Voice gramophone, and there's a similarly timeless feel in the spacious lounge-cum-bar, where you'll find enough books and games to while away a rainy afternoon. In the past year, the frieze in one of the two spacious dining-rooms has been restored to its original polychromatic splendour. Here you might dine on baked goats' cheese and onion Tatin, followed by roast fillet of sea bass with saffron noodles on a coconut and coriander beurre blanc, and finally a raspberry brûlée tartlet. There's a second, light conservatory, which is often used for serving breakfast. The bedrooms are generally spacious, with those in the main house showing considerable attention to detail. The rooms in the extension, such as the ground-floor Room 10, although on the face of it less characterful, redeem themselves with such innovations as a galleried bedroom or spa bath.

◐ Open all year   ⬚ South of Bristol; 1½ miles off A38 towards Cheddar. Private car park   ⬚ 2 twin, 6 double, 1 four-poster, 3 suites; family rooms available; all with bathroom/WC exc 2 doubles with shower/WC; all with TV, room service, hair-dryer, trouser press, direct-dial telephone   ⬚ Restaurant, lounge/bar, 2 conservatories, garden; functions (max 70 people incl up to 24 residential), conferences; early suppers for children; cots, high chairs, baby-listening   ⬚ No wheelchair access   ⬚ Dogs in bedrooms only, by arrangement   ⬚ Amex, Delta, Diners, MasterCard, Switch, Visa   £ Single occupancy of twin/double £65 to £75, twin/double £80 to £90, four-poster £100, suite £125, family room (room rate + £10 per child); deposit required. Set L £13; alc L, D £28. Special breaks available

Innsacre Farmhouse

Shipton Lane, Shipton Gorge, Bridport DT6 4LJ
TEL: (01308) 456137 (AND FAX)

A dash of French rustic style at a comfortable seventeenth-century farmhouse deep in a Dorset gorge.

From the outside, this low-slung, honey-stone house, cradled by surrounding hills, might appear to be just one more farmhouse B&B. Closer acquaintance, however, soon reveals that Jayne and Sydney Davies's home puts an unusual spin on the genre, importing a style and colours more usually associated with rustic France than with deepest Dorset. The heart of the place is a darkly mysterious sitting-room/bar/dining area with a heavily-beamed ceiling, chunky stone walls, a huge settle and a massive rough-stone inglenook. Modern artworks and fine ceramics add a sophisticated touch. Breakfast and supper (except on summer Saturdays) are served here at hearty tables, paired by ladder-back chairs. Jayne's good-value evening fare might involve roast yellow-pepper and carrot soup with olive-and-tomato bread, followed by slow-roasted duck with roast apple, and cinnamon-poached pears with butterscotch sauce. Beams, art-deco and antique or basket-weave items are appropriate for the spacious bedrooms decked out in sumptuously rich, deep colours.

◗ Closed Chr & New Year; dining-room closed Sat eve Easter to end-Sept
⤢ From Dorchester turn off A35 after 13 miles, taking second turning signposted Shipton Gorge (ignore first signpost). Innsacre is first entrance on left down this road. Private car park ⤣ 1 twin, 3 double; all with bathroom/WC; all with TV; hair-dryer available ⊘ Dining-room/bar/sitting-room, garden ♿ No wheelchair access ⬗ No children under 9; no smoking in bedrooms; dogs £5 per visit ▭ Delta, MasterCard, Switch, Visa £ Single occupancy of twin/double £45 to £58, twin/double £58 to £65 (1998 prices); children sharing with parents half price; deposit required. Tray supper £10.50; set D £14.50. Special breaks available

---

SHIPTON-UNDER-WYCHWOOD Oxfordshire   map 2

Lamb Inn

Upper High Street, Shipton-under-Wychwood, Chipping Norton OX7 6DQ
TEL: (01993) 830465   FAX: (01993) 832025

Atmospheric hostelry in picture-postcard village, with stylish bedrooms.

Shipton is the kind of village you find in novels – yellow-stone houses with leaded windows nestling contentedly behind walled gardens under shaggy trees – and the Lamb Inn is suitably full of character, living up to the sign outside advertising 'Erstwhile accommodation'. Originally three small cottages, it became a pub and a butcher's shop several centuries ago, and since then has been knocked through to create a wonderfully rickety, cosy old inn. Stripped floors, shiny antique tables and spruce old settles are the order of the day here. Daily newspapers hang on racks in the bar, where a fire blazes away on chilly days; the fire also warms the small, red lounge, with its big armchairs and bookcase of reading matter. From here a double staircase takes you up to the characterful bedrooms, which are named after local villages – Bruern has a chunky, funky four-poster and sloping ceilings. The Lamb offers several choices for eating. In the bar there's a buffet every lunch-time, or, in the evening, you can try dishes like smoked trout mousse, followed by Cotswold pie. For more formal dining, the rustic, beamed restaurant has an imaginative, extensive menu offering delicacies such as scallops with Pernod and bacon, followed by roast lamb steak with potato-and-rocket mash and a redcurrant *jus*.

◑ Open all year; restaurant closed Sun & Mon eves   ⊉ Just off A361 at edge of village, 4 miles north of Burford. Private car park   ⊫┓ 1 twin, 2 double, 2 four-poster; all with bathroom/WC; all with TV, hair-dryer, direct-dial telephone   ⊘ Restaurant, bar, lounge, garden; functions (max 30 people incl up to 10 residential), conferences; high chairs   ⅙ No wheelchair access   ● None   ⊟ Amex, Delta, MasterCard, Switch, Visa   £ Single occupancy of twin/double £65, twin/double £75, four-poster £95; deposit required. Bar/bistro L £9, D £10; alc Sun L £17, D £20. Special breaks available

---

SHREWLEY Warwickshire   map 5

Shrewley House

Hockley Road, Shrewley, Warwick CV35 7AT
TEL: (01926) 842549   FAX: (01926) 842216

Up-market B&B, with spacious, elegant rooms and friendly, considerate hosts.

Liz Green has been changing the rooms around in her smart country home since last year, bringing a new bedroom, Rose, into action, as well as a new breakfast room. The latter looks out across the lawn and farmland, and has a grey marble fireplace and elegant, homely willow-pattern crockery; next door is a small, chintzy sitting-room. There are no evening meals served here, but Liz can do tray suppers if necessary. The two best bedrooms differ quite markedly in feel: Joanne's is bright and airy, with a pine four-poster bed, sprigged wallpaper and a large bathroom; Rose is more Victorian in atmosphere, and has an elegant four-poster in dark, polished wood, opulent wallpaper and period furniture. The south-facing aspect of these two just gives them the edge over Samantha's and Robert's. All have fresh fruit, flowers, TV, plenty of books and lots of other useful little extras. Dotted around the house are Green family pictures, which add to the homely atmosphere.

◑ Open all year   ⊉ On B4439, 3 miles north-west of Warwick. Private car park   ⊫┓ 2 double, 2 four-poster, 1 family room; one in annexe; all with bathroom/WC; all with TV, room service, hair-dryer, direct-dial telephone; trouser press available   ⊘ Dining-room, sitting-room, drying-room, garden; leisure facilities nearby (reduced rates for guests); cots, high chairs, toys, babysitting, baby-listening, outdoor play area   ⅙ No wheelchair access   ● No smoking   ⊟ Diners, MasterCard, Visa   £ Single occupancy of double £38, double £55, four-poster £60, family room £64; deposit required

---

Albright Hussey

Ellesmere Road, Shrewsbury SY4 3AF
TEL: (01939) 290571   FAX: (01939) 291143

A venerable old manor that has been much extended into a thriving, mid-sized hotel.

Surrounded by open farmland a couple of miles north of Shrewsbury, the hotel is a faintly bizarre agglomeration of buildings – a skew-whiff, black-and-white timbered cottage wedged between a very old red-brick and stone extension and a very new brick addition. Albright Hussey's history is fascinating: records date it back to the Domesday Book and show that it was used during the Civil War as a garrison for Charles I's troops. Thanks to the engaging Florentine owner, Franco Subbiani, visitors can now be put up in considerably more comfort. He has recently expanded the enterprise greatly, adding nine new bedrooms that are relieved of ordinariness by antique beds, and function rooms that are intelligently separated from the main goings-on of the hotel. It's still more enjoyable to stay in the old buildings, however, and to embark on Matterhorn-like climbs across the sloping floors. If you want to splash out, ask for one of the three big 'suites' located here, such as Hussey, which has a four-poster bed and a canopied spa bath. Downstairs, the bar and lounge, with their thickly patterned carpets and unrelaxing chairs, are uninspiring. However, the restaurant's two dining-rooms, where French and British cuisine is served, are atmospherically panelled and beamed, despite their kitsch Royalist portraits and armour.

● Open all year   ⌷ On A528, 2½ miles north of Shrewsbury. Private car park ⌷ 4 twin, 5 double, 4 four-poster, 1 suite; family rooms available; all with bathroom/WC; all with TV, room service, hair-dryer, trouser press, direct-dial telephone   ⌷ Restaurant, 2 bars, lounge, function rooms, drying-room, garden; functions (max 220 people incl up to 30 residential), conferences; civil wedding licence; croquet; early suppers for children; cots, high chairs, babysitting, baby-listening, outdoor play area   ⌷ Wheelchair access to hotel and restaurant, WC (unisex), 2 ground-floor bedrooms, 1 room specially equipped for disabled people   ● Dogs in bedrooms only, by arrangement (£10 per night)   ⌷ Amex, Delta, Diners, MasterCard, Switch, Visa   £· Single occupancy of twin/double £73 to £85, twin/double £95, four-poster/suite £135, family room £165; deposit required. Bar/bistro L £7.50; set L £12.50, D £20; alc L, D £26. Special breaks available

The Greenway

Shurdington, Cheltenham GL51 5UG
TEL: (01242) 862352   FAX: (01242) 862780

One of the best Cotswolds country-house hotels: a wonderful setting, first-rate modern cuisine and high levels of comfort.

Though the creeper-clad Elizabethan manor is only a short distance from the outskirts of Cheltenham, it stands in seven acres of glorious gardens and looks out on to the hills of the Cotswolds. This is a confident enterprise, run on a tight rein by the much-in-evidence owner David White. The captivating, traditional public rooms offer a feast of venerable features, such as panelling and flagstoned floors, complemented by choice antiques and quality soft furnishings. One of the loveliest spots is the conservatory half of the restaurant, which opens on to an alluring terrace set round a lily pond, where lunch and pre-dinner drinks are served in fine weather. There is nothing traditional about Peter Fairclough's much-applauded, fancy cuisine, however: a lobster salad with pickled courgettes, and honey ice-cream with a deep-fried banana ravioli, appeared on a spring à la carte. Save room for breakfast: its mouthwatering menu offers every conceivable early-morning dish. High standards are equally apparent in the bedrooms, most of which feature king-sized beds. A coach-house allocation is no hardship, since the bedrooms here are particularly spacious, and incorporate original beams and exposed bricks.

◗ Open all year ⊿ Coming from Cheltenham on A46, in Shurdington on left. Private car park ⌁ 2 single, 16 twin, 1 suite; some in annexe; all with bathroom/WC; all with satellite TV, room service, hair-dryer, direct-dial telephone; no tea/coffee-making facilities in rooms ⊘ Restaurant, bar, 2 lounges, drying-room, garden; functions (max 64 people incl up to 36 residential), conferences; civil wedding licence; croquet ♿ Wheelchair access to hotel (ramp) and restaurant, WC (F), 4 ground-floor bedrooms, 1 room specially equipped for disabled people ● No children under 7; no dogs; no smoking in restaurant and some bedrooms ▭ Amex, Delta, Diners, MasterCard, Switch, Visa £ Single £90, twin £140 to £195, suite £225; deposit required. Set L £10, D £32; alc L £19.50, D £32. Special breaks available

---

Hotel Riviera

The Esplanade, Sidmouth EX10 8AY
TEL: (01395) 515201   FAX: (01395) 577775
EMAIL: enquiries@hotelriviera.co.uk
WEB SITE: www.hotelriviera.co.uk

The quintessential English seafront hotel, immaculately run by the Wharton family.

There are pictures dotted around the Hotel Riviera of Sidmouth in 1870, when the water apparently lapped at the hotel's doorstep, and houses along the front were difficult to sell. Not any more – the sea is kept at bay by the promenade, and the Riviera occupies a prime position. The Wharton family has been running this smart, Georgian establishment for the past 20 years, but standards have not slipped, judging by the orderly interior. The dining-room is pretty in pink, with swagged curtains and formal place-settings; the seven-course dinner menu might include terrine of asparagus and wild mushrooms, consommé celestine, and steamed fillet of salmon and scallops with a champagne sauce and celeriac mousse. Pianist John Gooch entertains guests in the plush bar, and the lounge is filled with Queen Anne sofas. One satisfied reader told us she 'thoroughly enjoyed her stay'; 'the staff were very professional, pleasant and helpful', though she would have been glad to have had 'a little conversation here and there – it would have helped me relax more in the formal atmosphere of the dining-room'. The bedrooms are graded according to their sea view; there are plenty of good singles, and all rooms are done out in strawberries-and-cream or peaches-and-cream colour combinations.

◐ Open all year ⊉ At centre of Esplanade. Private lock-up garage (£3.25 per night); on-street parking (free) ⊨ 7 single, 12 twin, 6 double, 2 suites; all with bathroom/WC; all with TV, room service, hair-dryer, trouser press, direct-dial telephone, radio, video ⊘ Dining-room, 2 bars, lounge, drying-room, conservatory, garden; functions (max 85 people incl up to 47 residential), conferences; leisure facilities nearby (some reduced rates for guests); early suppers for children; cots, high chairs, babysitting, baby-listening ⅄ Wheelchair access to hotel (ramp) and dining-room, lift to bedrooms, 2 rooms specially equipped for disabled people ● Dogs in bedrooms only, by arrangement (£6 per day) ▭ Amex, Delta, Diners, MasterCard, Visa £ Single £70 to £80, single occupancy of twin/double (rates on application), twin/double £120 to £140, suite £170 to £190; deposit required. Set L £15, D £25; alc L, D £20. Special breaks available

---

SIMONSBATH Somerset   map 1

Simonsbath House

Simonsbath, Minehead TA24 7SH
TEL: (01643) 831259   FAX: (01643) 831557

Unassuming country hotel in the heart of Exmoor, with charming public rooms and woodland setting.

Three hundred years ago the Warden of the Forest of Exmoor decided to build a house at the spot where all the forest tracks appeared to meet; Simonsbath House was the result. Over the years the white-harled, partly creeper-clad house has sprouted a variety of extensions, becoming something of an architectural jumble with a tower-like structure as its central focus. The hotel's history is immediately apparent on entering the panelled sitting-room, where heraldic devices flourish above a fireplace that exudes the scent of woodsmoke; it's an atmospheric place to relax on the comfy sofas in autumnal shades. The cosy library/bar provides an alternative retreat. Moody landscapes by Ken Hildrew fit snugly into the panels of an attractive mint-green dining-room where guests can dine on hearty fare such as leek and potato soup, venison steak braised in a red-wine sauce, traditional bread-and-butter pudding, and cheese. Three of the bedrooms boast four-posters, but others are more homely, though comfortable, with emulsioned anaglypta walls and reproduction furniture cheered up by bright, co-ordinated soft furnishings.

◐ Closed Dec & Jan ⊉ On B3223, in village. Private car park ⊨ 3 twin, 1 double, 3 four-poster; all with bathroom/WC; all with TV, room service, hair-dryer, direct-dial telephone, some with tea/coffee-making facilities ⊘ Dining-room, bar/library, sitting-room, drying-room, garden ⅄ No wheelchair access ● No children under 10; no dogs ▭ Amex, Delta, Diners, MasterCard, Switch, Visa £ Single occupancy of twin/double £56 to £66, twin/double £96, four-poster £96; deposit required. Bar/bistro L £7.50; set D £20. Special breaks available

Sissinghurst Castle Farm

Sissinghurst, Cranbrook TN17 2AB
TEL: (01580) 712885   FAX: (01580) 712601

Peaceful, friendly B&B on the doorstep of Sissinghurst Gardens.

With its deep-red brick, castellated gables, creeper-clad walls and heavy chimneys, this looks more like the backdrop for a Victorian romantic novel than a working farmhouse. Built in 1855, it was bought, along with its more famous neighbour, by Vita Sackville-West and Harold Nicolson in 1930, which precipitated the Stearns family's involvement: James Stearns' grandparents became the farm's tenants, and it was passed down to him. He was born here, and a fair proportion of his family still lives on the estate, now owned by the National Trust. It's very much a family affair, very much a family home. Informal hospitality abounds, from the bright, summery sitting-room, to the smart dining-room, where guests eat breakfast *en famille*. Even Fly, the dog, helps the mood by lounging in front of the TV – cartoons and music shows are his favourites. Up the fairly grand staircase and past the stag's head, all the bedrooms are spacious and prettily decorated. Not all have *en suite* bathrooms but, for those that don't, the shared bathroom is commodious, and has its own sofa (in case that long, hot bath leaves you gasping) and lovely views.

○ Closed Chr   ☑ 1 mile out of Sissinghurst towards Biddenden; turn left down lane marked Sissinghurst Castle Gardens; hotel is on right. Private car park   ⌁ 1 single, 2 twin, 3 double; family rooms available; 1 double with bathroom/WC; all with TV, hair-dryer   ✅ Dining-room, sitting-room, garden; conferences (max 30 people incl up to 6 residential); croquet   ♿ No wheelchair access   ● No children under 5; no dogs; no smoking   ▭ None accepted   ⌂ Single £23 to £26, single occupancy of twin/double £50, twin/double £52 to £56, family room (room rate + £5 for 5-yr-old, £6 for 6-yr- old, etc.); deposit required. Special breaks available

Bell Inn

Bell Lane, Smarden, Ashford TN27 8PW
TEL: (01233) 770283   FAX: (01233) 820042

No-frills pub accommodation in a lovely country setting.

Near the attractive village of Smarden, this is first and foremost a pub, with a clutch of four rooms. It was built as a farmhouse in 1536 and an early document describes a blacksmith's forge on the site – a role it fulfilled until 1907. It became a registered ale house in 1630, becoming known as the Bell over 100 years later. So carefully have records been kept that Craig and Jackie Smith can produce a full list of publicans – from one Josias Quy in Charles I's reign to themselves in the present day. The Smiths have carefully preserved the ancient character of the place (brick floors, beams, large inglenook fireplaces and lumpy plaster walls) and enhanced it with furniture made from old barrels and with riding tack on the walls. Residents have a separate entrance, and bedrooms are comfortable, decorated in pink and green colour schemes. Curtains and upholstery are carefully co-ordinated, and there are good views over orchards and fields. None of the rooms is *en suite*: two shared shower-rooms on the landing serve all four bedrooms. A fridge on the landing is stocked with milk, yoghurt and juices and you are expected to help yourself to cereals and make toast with a toaster provided. There is no breakfast room – tables and chairs are provided in the rooms.

◑ Open all year   🔲 In village of Smarden off B2077 between Charing and Biddenden. Private car park   🛏 3 twin, 1 double; all with TV   ✣ 2 restaurants, 3 bars, games room, garden; functions (max 200 people incl up to 8 residential); early suppers for children   ⅃ No wheelchair access   ◒ No dogs in bedrooms; no smoking in 1 bar ▭ Amex, Delta, MasterCard, Switch, Visa   £ Single occupancy of twin/double £30, twin/double £37 to £42; deposit required. Bar L, D £2.50 to £8

SOMERTON Somerset   map 2

The Lynch

4 Behind Berry, Somerton TA11 7PD
TEL: (01458) 272316   FAX: (01458) 272590

Friendly B&B in a tastefully furnished Georgian house with its own lake.

The market town of Somerton was the ancient capital of Wessex, but it's to the Georgian period we owe Roy Copeland's country house on the shores of its own lake, where black swans glide serenely. To make the most of the splendid setting, guests ascend to the glass canopy that seems to have alighted on the roof, like a miniature greenhouse, to enjoy the view over lovely copses, Victorian fruit trees and a quaint topiary chess set. Breakfast is taken in a bright, elegant room extending into the former butler's pantry, where Roy has set aside a sitting area in which guests can consult guidebooks and tourist information to help plan their itineraries. The first-floor bedrooms, including the four-poster Goldington, adopt a classic, period look with graceful furniture and sumptuous soft furnishings. Second-floor rooms are less grand, the combination of stencilled beams and quilted bedspreads evoking a cheerful, cottagey style.

◑ Closed Chr & New Year   🔲 On northern edge of Somerton. Private car park 🛏 1 twin, 2 double, 1 four-poster, 1 family room; all with bathroom/WC; all with TV, hair-dryer, direct-dial telephone   ✣ Dining-room, lounge, garden; functions (max 175 people in marquee, incl up to 11 residential)   ⅃ No wheelchair access   ◒ No dogs; no smoking   ▭ Amex, MasterCard, Visa   £ Single occupancy of twin/double £45 to £53, twin/double £49 to £75, four-poster £65 to £75, family room £69; deposit required.

It is always worth enquiring about the availability of special breaks or weekend prices. The prices we quote are the standard rates for one night – most hotels offer reduced rates for longer stays.

SOUTHEND-ON-SEA Essex   map 3

Pebbles

190 Eastern Esplanade, Thorpe Bay, Southend-on-Sea SS1 3AA
TEL: (01702) 582329 (AND FAX)
WEB SITE: www.yell.co.uk/sites/pebbles-guest-house

An Edwardian terraced guesthouse with all the best qualities of a traditional seaside establishment.

The first thing you will notice about Pebbles is the impressive display of flowers at the front: pots, hanging baskets, tubs and containers with a profusion of colour sprouting forth. It's a show that should win some prizes, and it's no surprise that the owner, Edna Christian, has carried off awards in several competitions. She puts it down to the seafront location, which gets plenty of fresh air and light. The high standards of her garden are reflected indoors as well, where the simply furnished interior is brightened up with more pot-plants. There's also a rooftop garden, complete with pergola, which makes up for the fact that there's no guests' lounge. The bedrooms are modern with good pine furniture, matching duvets and satisfyingly bright and tidy shower-rooms – some have a sea view, although these might get some noise from the road outside. Pebbles is principally a B&B, but evening meals can be served on request.

◑ Open all year   ⤢ On seafront; 1 mile east of pier. On-street parking (free)
↳ 1 single, 1 twin, 3 double; all with shower/WC; all with TV, limited room service; hair-dryer available   ✅ Dining-room, roof terrace; early suppers for children; cots, high chairs   ♿ No wheelchair access   ⬤ No dogs; no smoking in public rooms
▭ MasterCard, Visa   £ Single £26, single occupancy of twin/double £26, twin/double £42; deposit required. Light L £2; set D £12.50 (by arrangement)

SOUTH MOLTON Devon   map 1

Marsh Hall

South Molton EX36 3HQ
TEL: (01769) 572666   FAX: (01769) 574230

Spacious, Victorian house, run by most welcoming folk.

Judy and Tony Griffiths came to Marsh Hall from London some six years ago, but their enthusiasm for, and evident love of, their classic, red-brick Victorian home remains undiminished. Guests are welcomed by name, like long-lost friends, and are immediately shown around the huge, booming house. The Griffiths are not the types to stuff the rooms full of antiques, preferring instead to let the character of the place speak for itself, as it does loud and clear, from the daring, tiled floor in the hallway, to the stained-glass window on the landing. As a result, there's a really spacious feel to the house; the galleried landing is itself as big as a volleyball court. The décor throughout is on the old-fashioned side – the lounge is done out in creams and pale greens, with plenty of floral sofas to lounge on around the fire, while a patterned carpet may dazzle you in the bar. Judy discusses the menu with you on arrival; expect good home cooking rather than anything too flamboyant. At our inspection meal in April, most of the vegetables were fresh from the garden. The bedrooms, too, could be described as old-fashioned, but they are large, spruce and homely, with fine bathrooms. The view across the soft Devon hills is marred by the A361, but the road is far enough away for the house to merit our 'peaceful' symbol, so don't be put off.

◑ Open all year   ⊿ Turn off A361 at sign for North Molton; after ¼ mile turn right and right again. Private car park   ⊏—⊤ 1 single, 2 twin, 3 double, 1 four-poster; 5 with bathroom/WC, 2 with shower/WC; all with TV, room service, hair-dryer, direct-dial telephone   ⊘ Dining-room, bar, lounge, conservatory, garden; functions (max 20 people incl up to 13 residential), conferences   ⅙ No wheelchair access   ● No children under 12; no dogs   ▭ MasterCard, Switch, Visa   £ Single £47, single occupancy of twin/double £52, twin/double £75, four-poster £95; deposit required. Bar/bistro L £10; set D £20. Special breaks available

---

Whitechapel Manor

South Molton EX36 3EG
TEL: (01769) 573377   FAX: (01769) 573797

Fabulously quirky, Elizabethan country house, with lots of character, big bedrooms and good food.

This is a house that can tell a story or two: a gentle lady ghost (who leaves a peaceful atmosphere behind) has been seen in the bedroom named after a Mr De Basset, pretender to the English throne, who built the house in 1575. A wonky, wooden Jacobean screen separates the entrance from the Great Hall – watch your head on the low, skew-whiff doorway – and in the last century another of the owners had a secret door built into the cupboard between Rooms 2 and 3 so that his maidservant could visit him at night. The low-slung, brown-stone house has two impressive, gabled wings flanking the central section, and a formal garden with ponds and walled areas. Inside, William-and-Mary stucco plasterwork (painstakingly restored) and overmantels do nothing to disguise the drunken nature of the floors and ceilings, while graceful, period antiques add elegance to the country character of the rooms. You'll find open fires everywhere for most of the year, and you can choose between the peaceful Oak Room, which is lined with fabulous, heavy panelling, or the more masculine bar, with its blue leather sofas. The dinner menu is sophisticated and correspondingly expensive, featuring such mouthwatering dishes as spiced monkfish with couscous and crème fraîche, followed by roast saddle of venison with truffled celeriac, braised lentils and thyme. There's also a fine selection of West Country cheeses. Proprietor Charles Brown believes in providing his guests with that 'extra spot of luxury', so in the bedrooms, along with the antiques and huge beds, you'll find big, fluffy bath towels, complimentary mineral water and plenty of fruit. The best rooms are south-facing, with a view over the garden to the front of the house.

◑ Open all year   ⊿ Leave M5 at Junction 27 and follow signs to Barnstaple; at second roundabout, turn right; hotel is a further 1 mile down an unmarked track. Private car park   ⊏—⊤ 2 single, 4 twin, 3 double, 2 suites; all with bathroom/WC; all with TV, room service, hair-dryer, direct-dial telephone; no tea/coffee-making facilities in rooms   ⊘ Dining-room, bar, 2 lounges, drying-room, garden; functions (max 50 people incl up to 16 residential), conferences; civil wedding licence; croquet; leisure facilities nearby

(reduced rates for guests); early suppers for children; cots, high chairs, baby-listening
  ♿ No wheelchair access ● No dogs ▭ Delta, Diners, MasterCard, Switch, Visa
£ Single £70, single occupancy of twin/double £95, twin/double £110 to £150, suite
£170; deposit required. Set L £20, D £34. Special breaks available

---

SOUTHWOLD Suffolk   map 6

The Crown

90 High Street, Southwold IP18 6DP
TEL: (01502) 722275   FAX: (01502) 727263

Relaxed inn with good food and decent bedrooms.

Owned by Adnams, this old posting-inn was rebuilt in about 1750 and renamed
the New Swan – as a direct rival to the Old Swan in the market place (see next
entry). Nowadays it provides a relaxed and informal bolt-hole, with a friendly
young staff under new manager Anna Bostedt, formerly of the Groucho Club in
London. Inside, the feel is light and modern, with yellow walls and stripped
floors. There are old wooden tables and settles in the front bar, which operates as
a neighbourhood brasserie, serving pots of coffee and an interesting bar menu:
grilled skate wing, perhaps, followed by hot bread-and-butter pudding. The
restaurant is a sort of side room off the front bar (book a table when you book
your room, if you want to eat here) and serves a three-course menu, with a good
choice of fish dishes – perhaps seared sea bass and red fish fillets with baby
spinach and yellow oyster mushrooms, and proper puddings, such as apple-
and-lime baked sponge pudding. Upstairs are bedrooms disarmingly described
in the brochure as 'small... decent, simple'. They are plain and simple, but nicely
so, with interestingly shaped ceilings. New bathrooms have been put in this
year, although not all rooms are *en suite*, and you may have to walk a few steps
down the corridor.

◑ Closed 1 week at beginning of Jan ↗ In centre of Southwold. Private car park
⤺ 2 single, 4 twin, 5 double, 1 family room; 8 with bathroom/WC, 1 with shower/WC;
all with TV, hair-dryer, direct-dial telephone; no tea/coffee-making facilities in rooms
⊘ Restaurant, brasserie, 2 bars, lounge; functions (max 30 people incl up to 22
residential), conferences; early suppers for children, by arrangement; cots, high chairs
 ♿ No wheelchair access ● Dogs in 1 bar only; smoking in bedrooms and bars only
▭ Amex, Delta, Diners, MasterCard, Switch, Visa £ Single £54, single occupancy of
twin/double £54, twin/double £68, family room £94. Cooked B £4; bar/bistro L, D £8.50;
set L £14/£17, D £19/£23

The Swan

Market Place, Southwold IP18 6EG
TEL: (01502) 722186   FAX: (01502) 724800

A traditional base right at the heart of this sedate resort.

This lovely old coaching-inn occupies pride of place, right on the market place of
this sleepy seaside resort. Inside, the lounge is the place to relax, for summer
cream teas or Sunday morning coffee with the papers; its large bay windows

make it a fine vantage point for surveying the town's life. The lounge bar at the back is rather more modern in tone, with black leather settles, burnt orange walls and a real fire. While children are officially tolerated, there are lots of warning notices about their behaviour, which, in the way of such notices, come over as unfriendly and unwelcoming to families. The restaurant is justly popular and, a rather nice idea, has three fixed-price menus with choices on each – and you can swap between them. One is sort of traditional English (baked wing of skate followed by roast lamb), one rather more adventurous (potted North Sea prawns in a light oyster-and-anchovy butter with pumpernickel, followed by breast of duck carved on to a butter-bean broth with bacon), and one is a Frenchified gourmet menu. Service on a busy Saturday was bustlingly efficient, after rather a long wait when first called to the table. The bedrooms vary widely – and divide our readers. Many, especially dog-owners, like the modern garden rooms out the back by the Adnams Brewery; others prefer the more traditional-style rooms in the main house.

○ Open all year　🅿 In Southwold's market square. Private car park　🛏 5 single, 19 twin, 19 double, 1 four-poster, 1 suite; some in annexe; all with bathroom/WC exc 2 double with shower/WC; all with TV, room service, hair-dryer, direct-dial telephone; trouser press available; no tea/coffee-making facilities in rooms　✅ Restaurant, bar, lounge, study, garden; conferences (max 88 people incl up to 45 residential), functions; croquet; early suppers for children; cots, high chairs, babysitting, baby-listening　♿ Wheelchair access to hotel and restaurant, WC (unisex), 18 ground-floor bedrooms, 1 specially equipped for disabled people　● No children under 5 in restaurant after 7pm; dogs in some bedrooms only; no smoking in restaurant　🗀 Amex, Delta, Diners, MasterCard, Switch, Visa　£ Single £51, single occupancy of twin/double £79, twin/double £97 to £125, four-poster £160, suite £150; deposit required. Bar/bistro L £8; set L £13.50/£15.50, D £22/£28.50/£34. Special breaks available

---

SPARSHOLT Hampshire　　　　　　　　　　　　　　　　　　　map 2

Lainston House

Sparsholt, Winchester SO21 2LT
TEL: (01962) 863588　FAX: (01962) 776672
EMAIL: enquiries@lainstonhouse.com
WEB SITE: www.hants.gov.uk/tourist/hotels/lainstonhouse

Splendid vistas and good service – with a lofty price-tag attached.

The long, winding drive from the road up to this William-and-Mary house inevitably raises expectations, but it's not until you stand on the terrace at the back of the hotel that you appreciate its wonderful view over a circular dew pond and an avenue of limes stretching away into the distance. The 63 acres of parkland surrounding Lainston House provide plenty of scope for exploration, from the ruined twelfth-century chapel and pets' graveyard to the octagonal columbarium and slightly ragged topiary garden. Like the garden, the interior makes the most of the basic structure and materials without unnecessary embellishment. With its splendid curved, panelled bar fashioned from a cedar tree felled in 1930, the Cedar Room requires little in the way of frills (copies of *Reader's Digest* condensed classics sitting rather incongruously beside bound volumes of *Punch* from the early part of the century). The panelled dining-rooms and long, thin drawing-room share its view over the limes at the back of the house, and are unostentatious in style, with plenty of fresh flowers and the occasional oil painting or piece of Chinese porcelain. The set candlelit dinner menu (seven courses including sorbet, consommé and coffee and petits fours) looks incredible value compared with the à la carte, and on inspection proved to be the better executed – sea bass from the carte was overcooked and dry. One reader also felt that the food was expensive. Service is young and friendly. The bedrooms, divided between the main house and the stable block, mix antiques with good-quality reproductions and modern pine. At these prices, though, you expect perfection, and our inspector was troubled by various niggles, such as the hot tap of one of the basins not working, poor lighting on the dressing-table – and being woken at 2am by a radiator sounding like a pneumatic drill.

◑ Open all year ⤢ 2½ miles from centre of Winchester, just off B3049 to Stockbridge. Private car park ⬔ 6 single, 8 twin, 18 double, 2 four-poster, 1 family room, 3 suites; some in annexe; all with bathroom/WC exc 1 single with shower/WC; all with TV, room service, hair-dryer, direct-dial telephone, some with trouser press; no tea/coffee-making facilities in rooms ⬙ 2 dining-rooms, bar, lounge, library, 4 meeting-rooms, garden; functions (max 200 people in marquee, incl up to 68 residential), conferences; civil wedding licence; fishing, tennis, putting green, clay-pigeon shooting, croquet, archery, bowls; early suppers for children; cots, high chairs, babysitting, baby-listening ♿ Wheelchair access to hotel and restaurant (ramps), 16 ground-floor bedrooms, 2 specially equipped for disabled people ⬤ None ▭ Amex, Delta, Diners, MasterCard, Switch, Visa £ Single £95, single occupancy of twin/double £140, twin/double £140, four-poster £260, family room £260 to £275, suite £275; deposit required. Continental B £10, cooked B £12; set L £15.50/£18.50, D (Fri, Sat) £35.50; alc D £45. Special breaks available

---

STAMFORD Lincolnshire   map 6

George of Stamford

71 St Martins, Stamford PE9 2LB
TEL: (01780) 750700   FAX: (01780) 750701
EMAIL: georgehotelofstamford@btinternet.com
WEB SITE: www.georgehotelofstamford.com/georgehotelofstamford

Smartly decorated and historic inn, right in the heart of Stamford.

This fine old coaching-inn is easily spotted on what was once the Great North Road through the centre of Stamford: an eighteenth-century gallows sign proclaims the name right across the road. Hopefully those old coach travellers, swinging in through what is now the main restaurant, would still recognise the place, with its log fires, cosy bars and blackened beams. Modern travellers are received with an offer of help with luggage and a polite suggestion that a jacket and tie might be needed for dinner in the restaurant. Don't imagine that this is simply a pub – it is more a well-heeled hotel, with a public bar and a history. The bedrooms are cosy and thoughtfully equipped, though there is no tea tray – tea is delivered to the room free of charge in the morning on request. Also free of charge is the long walk that comes with rooms at the rear of the hotel – ask for a front room near the stairs if that is a problem. For breakfasts and less formal dining, there is the Garden Lounge, which is attractively decked out with potted plants. The food served on our inspection was good; helpings, however, were either miserly or mammoth, and the noise of the kitchen extractor fans was irritating. More atmospheric is the candlelit and panelled main restaurant, of which Mr Pickwick would have certainly approved.

◑ Open all year 🔁 From A1, take roundabout signposted B1081 to Stamford; hotel is on left, at first set of traffic lights. Private car park 🛏 10 single, 9 twin, 24 double, 3 four-poster, 1 suite; most with bathroom/WC, some with shower/WC; all with satellite TV, room service, hair-dryer, trouser press, direct-dial telephone; no tea/coffee-making facilities in rooms ✅ 2 restaurants, 2 bars, 2 lounges, garden; conferences (max 55 people incl up to 47 residential), functions; civil wedding licence; croquet; early suppers for children; cots, high chairs, babysitting, baby-listening ৬ No wheelchair access ◗ No dogs in restaurants ⊟ Amex, Delta, Diners, MasterCard, Switch, Visa £ Single £78 to £98, single occupancy of twin/double £88 to £98, twin/double £100 to £155, four-poster £145 to £175, suite £135 to £145; deposit required. Bar L £5; set L £13.50/£16.50; alc L, D £35. Special breaks available

---

STANTON WICK Bath & N.E. Somerset   map 2

Carpenters Arms

Stanton Wick, Pensford, Bristol BS39 4BX
TEL: (01761) 490202   FAX: (01761) 490763
EMAIL: carpenters@dial.pipex.com

Agreeably rustic bedrooms in a popular country inn on the edge of the Mendips.

The terrace of stone-fronted, creeper-smothered former miners' cottages that make up the Carpenters Arms is very much the focal point of the tiny village of Stanton Wick. This means that you may find the locals lingering on the beer terrace that runs across the front of the building, or nursing their pints in the traditionally pubby interior, with its beamed ceiling, horse brasses and open fire. Exposed, chunky-stone walls reiterate the rustic feel in a small but comfortable lounge. Hearty bar meals (along the lines of chicken chasseur and chilli con carne) are served in Cooper's Parlour, a more casual alternative to the three interlinked rooms that make up the restaurant. Offerings here include fish bisque, followed by peppered lamb fillet with a mint and caper sauce, and then various home-made puddings. The well-appointed bedrooms are decorated in a neat, nicely co-ordinated cottagey style, with lots of cheerful pine.

◑ Open all year 🔁 Near junction of A37 and A368. Private car park 🛏 3 twin, 9 double; all with bathroom/WC; all with TV, room service, hair-dryer, trouser press, direct-dial telephone ✅ 2 restaurants, bar, lounge, garden; functions (max 50 people incl up to 24 residential), conferences; early suppers for children; cot, high chairs, baby-listening ৬ No wheelchair access ◗ Dogs in bar only; no smoking in bedrooms ⊟ Amex, Delta, Diners, MasterCard, Switch, Visa £ Single occupancy of twin/double £53, twin/double £70; deposit required. Bar/bistro L, D £12; set Sun L £13; alc L, D £19. Special breaks available

---

Reports are welcome on any hotel, whether or not it is in the Guide.

Stapleford Park

Stapleford, Melton Mowbray LE14 2EF
TEL: (01572) 787522   FAX: (01572) 787651
EMAIL: reservations@stapleford.telme.com
WEB SITE: www.stapleford.co.uk

Sumptuous transatlantic-style country house, with top-notch leisure facilities.

Stapleford Park was old enough to have been renovated and restored in 1633, although much of it is either Victorian or recent additions (all done without a note of disharmony, it should be said). Since passing to entrepreneur Peter de Savary, the house has become a country club and hotel that does nothing by halves. Offering falconry, golf, riding, clay-pigeon shooting and archery, there is also a 22-metre-long swimming-pool and a futuristic gymnasium. If your habits are more Churchillian, then the library has a vast humidor whose cigars – worth £300 – will waft you back to 1878 (the year they were rolled). This is really an English country house that is rooted somewhere in the mid-Atlantic. Genteel visitors from the past might pale at the thought of bedrooms being named after the businesses that designed them; they would require smelling salts in the Pirelli single (think calendars), but then Crabtree & Evelyn would surely revive them. There is something for all tastes – assuming that all pockets are deep enough. Downstairs, the rooms are equally faultlessly stylish and opulent, particularly the main dining-room, with its Grinling Gibbons woodcarving. The food is in the country-house style, with plenty of salmon and venison plus an 'adult nursery dish' – perhaps a chicken and mushroom casserole with buttered greens and mash. Service is unstuffy and friendly, but gentlemen do require jackets.

◐ Open all year ◪ In Stapleford, approx 5 miles east of Melton Mowbray. Private car park ⇨ 1 single, 35 twin, 11 double, 2 four-poster, 2 suites; some in annexe; family rooms available; all with bathroom/WC; all with TV, room service, hair-dryer, trouser press, direct-dial telephone, CD player; no tea/coffee-making facilities in rooms ⌁ 4 restaurants, bar, 3 lounges, library, conservatory, games room, garden; functions (max 200 people incl up to 101 residential), conferences; civil wedding licence; fishing, golf, gym, sauna, solarium, heated indoor swimming-pool, tennis, clay-pigeon shooting, croquet, riding, shooting, archery, falconry, cycling; early suppers for children; cots, high chairs, babysitting, baby-listening, outdoor play area ⑤ No wheelchair access ● No children under 10 in restaurants eves; no smoking in bedrooms; dogs £5 per night ▭ Amex, Diners, MasterCard, Visa ⟦£⟧ Single/twin/double from £194, single occupancy of twin/double from £194, four-poster from £329, family room from £271, suite from £441; deposit required. Bar/bistro L £12, D 17.50; set D £39.50; alc L £18.50 (prices valid till Nov 1998)

The text of entries is based on unsolicited reports sent in by readers and backed up by inspections. The factual details are from questionnaires the Guide *sends to all hotels that feature in the book.*

Angel Inn

Stoke-by-Nayland, Colchester CO6 4SA
TEL: (01206) 263245   FAX: (01206) 263373

*A superior pub-and-restaurant operation that delivers good service
and even better food.*

Stoke-by-Nayland is a rather strange-shaped village, as its houses face outwards
around the exterior of a huge green. At one of these 'corners' is the rather plain,
square brick frontage of the Angel Inn, which looks like a row of houses rather
than an inn. It's quite close to the roadside, which means that passers-by can
gaze through the windows into the long bar room and across at the tempting
menu chalked up on the blackboards that cover a whole wall. You can eat either
here, or more formally in the dramatically different Well Room, with its high,
raftered ceiling of exposed beams and its minstrels' gallery. The food is of an
extremely high standard; our inspector had a fabulously fresh bream, baked
with a sweetly spicy Thai chilli-and-tomato glaze, which was followed by a
tangy and feather-light mixed-fruit steamed pudding with vanilla sauce. The
staff at the Angel Inn are extremely friendly and helpful, and will offer you fresh
milk to accompany the tea- and coffee-making facilities in the bedrooms. The
rooms are bright, with a good eye for colour schemes shown in the decoration.

◑ Closed 25 & 26 Dec   ⊡ In centre of village at junction of B1087 and B1068. Private
car park   ⚐ 1 twin, 5 double; one in annexe; all with bathroom/WC; all with TV, room
service, hair-dryer, direct-dial telephone   ✅ Restaurant, 2 bars, lounge; early suppers
for children   ⟁ Wheelchair access to hotel (1 step) and restaurant, WC (M, F), 1
ground-floor bedroom   ● No children under 8; no dogs   ▭ Amex, Delta, Diners,
MasterCard, Switch, Visa   ⌧ Single occupancy of twin/double £46, twin/double £62;
deposit required. Bar/bistro L £6.50, D £10; alc L £13, D £17

Chapters

27 High Street, Stokesley, Middlesbrough TS9 5AD
TEL: (01642) 711888   FAX: (01642) 713387

*A lively bistro-with-rooms, in a Georgian coach-house with one-off
interior décor.*

This large and vivacious bistro comes as a pleasant surprise in a handsome, but
off-the-beaten tourist-track, spot like Stokesley – and in order to fix their
enterprise firmly in your memory, Catherine and Alan Thompson have
employed some pretty off-the-wall ideas in the domains of interior design and
cuisine alike. Most striking are the murals, born of an act of faith when the
owners struck a deal with some Newcastle art students, who unleashed their
creative talents on the walls in exchange for a few days' bed and board. Suitably
arresting designs thus adorn the bistro, along with food-oriented representations of fish and cafetières, in an ambience of cheerful chic spiked with jazz.

Upbeat, modern food that takes its cue from an eclectic bag of influences is the keynote: you could start with Indonesian-style fish-cakes with a curried Malibu sauce, followed by sea bass with ratatouille and wild-mushroom mash – the puddings are rather more orthodox, but no less tempting. At the back, a conservatory-style restaurant plays second fiddle to the front-facing bistro, offering a more peaceful alternative venue. Upstairs, dragons and snakes coil along the bedroom corridors around the bright and immaculate rooms (less exuberantly decorated than the rest of the premises). Some are a bit on the tight side, so go for one of the generously sized ones that overlook Stokesley's market-place at the front.

◑ Closed Chr & 1 Jan   🔼 In centre of Stokesley. Public car park nearby   🛏️ 2 single, 2 twin, 9 double; most with bathroom/WC, 3 with shower/WC; all with TV, room service, direct-dial telephone, some with hair-dryer   ⊘ 2 restaurants, 2 bars, lounge, garden; functions (max 150 people incl up to 25 residential), conferences; early suppers for children; cots, high chairs, baby-listening   ♿ No wheelchair access   ● No dogs in public rooms   ▭ Amex, Delta, Diners, MasterCard, Switch, Visa   £ Single £40 to £52, single occupancy of twin/double £40 to £55, twin/double £55 to £65. Bar/bistro L £6 to £10, D £12 to £15; alc L £20, D £30. Special breaks available

---

STON EASTON **Somerset**   map 2

Ston Easton Park

Ston Easton, Bath BA3 4DF
TEL: (01761) 241631   FAX: (01761) 241377
EMAIL: stoneaston@cityscape.co.uk

Sumptuous country house; grand, but not haughty.

Ston Easton Park's pedigree is impressive. Take a large Palladian mansion, add grounds originally landscaped by Humphry Repton and an interior replete with tinkling chandeliers, exuberant plasterwork and a panoply of pilasters, and you may feel that you've wandered on to a film set. No bogus backdrop, this, however – rather the real McCoy: a magnificent country home run with style and élan, without a hint of simpering sycophancy. It's just the place for splurging a bit on a special occasion. The entrance lounge is a gorgeous affair, flaunting a feast of eye-catching flourishes, from faux Corinthian pillars to soaring pediments and *trompe l'oeil* panels, and a host of carefully positioned, gracious chairs and sofas. The library, itself a fine room, is less outré and a more relaxing spot to which to retire for an after-dinner drink. Guests are required to dress for dinner, which is taken in one of the elegant twin restaurants. It's capital food at capital prices; a typical meal might include an appetiser, followed by grilled Loch Fyne oysters with a Sauternes sabayon, then baked sea bass on a bed of roast peppers with thyme, and finally a bitter-chocolate and walnut cheese torte. The bedrooms are lavishly furnished and decorated in an appositely grand country-house style.

◑ Open all year   🔼 Off A37, 11 miles south of Bristol and Bath. Private car park   🛏️ 14 double, 6 four-poster; suites available; all with bathroom/WC; all with TV, room service, hair-dryer, direct-dial telephone, some with mini-bar, trouser press; no tea/coffee-making facilities in rooms   ⊘ 2 restaurants, 2 lounges, library, games room, garden; functions (max 50 people incl up to 40 residential), conferences; tennis, snooker, croquet; early suppers for children; cots, high chairs, toys, babysitting, baby-listening   ♿ No wheelchair access   ⬭ No children under 7 exc babes in arms; no dogs   ▢ Amex, Delta, Diners, MasterCard, Switch, Visa   £ Single occupancy of double/four-poster £140 to £320, double £185 to £300, four-poster £315 to £360, suite £405; deposit required. Continental B £8.50, cooked B £12.50; bar/bistro L £5 to £18; set L £11/£16, D £39.50; alc L £30, D £60

STONOR Oxfordshire   map 2

Stonor Arms

Stonor, Henley-on-Thames RG9 6HE
TEL: (01491) 638866   FAX: (01491) 638863

Confident country hotel and restaurant in the depths of rural Oxfordshire.

The hugely characterful village of Stonor is strung out along the road, giving hotel arrivals a full view of the chocolate-box-type cottages and farmyards (complete with doe-eyed cows) which nestle under the ridge behind. Rare red kites circle languidly above (courtesy of the local landed gentry which has reintroduced them) and deer come to visit from Stonor Park. In this idyllic pastoral setting sits the eighteenth-century Stonor Arms, looking innocuous enough from the outside but bristling with confidence inside. The rustic bar area is done out in stylish bohemian colours, and is crammed with endearingly moth-eaten, comfortable antique sofas, a piano and plenty of rowing para-phernalia (we are, after all, within spitting distance of Henley), while the lounge is more refined, with ornate mirrors and co-ordinating colours. Lunches are served in a bright and airy conservatory, whose windows, heavily hung with dried hops, look out on to the pretty gardens. The modern European dinner menu is ambitious, featuring such dishes as confit of chicken and rabbit with French beans and a mustard dressing, followed by roast monkfish with a crab beignet on tomato risotto, asparagus and butter sauce – but one couple, otherwise happy with their room and the service, found the food 'pretentious but unappetising'. The bedrooms are indeed satisfying, making the best use of the converted barn in which they are housed; they are understated and muted but huge, with luxurious bathrooms and plenty of antique furniture.

◑ Open all year   ▣ In centre of Stonor village, 4 miles from Henley-on-Thames. Private car park   ⌁ 6 twin, 4 double; all with bathroom/WC; all with TV, room service, hair-dryer, direct-dial telephone   ⌂ Restaurant, bar, lounge, 2 conservatories, garden; functions (max 20 people residential/non-residential), conferences; civil wedding licence; early suppers for children; cots, high chairs, baby-listening   ♿ Wheelchair access to hotel (ramp) and restaurant, WC (unisex), 6 ground-floor bedrooms, 1 room specially equipped for disabled people   ⬭ No children under 12 in restaurant after 7pm; no smoking in restaurant   ▢ Amex, Delta, MasterCard, Switch, Visa £ Single occupancy of twin/double £80 to £90, twin/double £95 to £105; deposit required. Bar/bistro L, D £8; alc L, D £30. Special breaks available

---

Please let us know if an establishment has changed hands.

Caterham House

58/59 Rother Street, Stratford-upon-Avon CV37 6LT
TEL: (01789) 267309   FAX: (01789) 414836

A chic town-house hotel with stylish bedrooms.

Proximity to the Royal Shakespeare Theatre is a big attraction for guests at
Dominique and Olive Maury's Georgian town house – both members of the
audience and the cast can be at performances on time. But this beautifully
decorated house has a lot more going for it than just geography. There is the
stylish bar and lounge, with its classical *trompe l'oeil* and white leather sofas, and
then there is the light, airy breakfast room for freshly baked croissants in the
morning – the French influence is there, but it is never too strong to rule out
kippers or full English breakfasts. Bedrooms are carefully decorated with an
elegant mix of old and new furniture. Room 12 is particularly spacious and has
an attractive patchwork bedspread and brass bedstead; Room 4 is an interesting
shape with terracotta colours, Austrian blinds and a neat shower-room. All are
delicately understated in blues and lemon yellows. In the evenings, there are
many restaurants within easy walking distance.

◑ Closed 25 Dec   ⊡ In centre of Stratford, opposite police station. Private car park
⊫ 5 twin, 8 double, 1 family room; some in annexe; all with shower/WC exc 1 double
with bathroom/WC; all with TV, limited room service, hair-dryer; tea/coffee-making
facilities available   ⊘ Breakfast room, bar, lounge, drying-room; conferences (max 25
people incl up to 14 residential); high chairs, babysitting   ⅃ No wheelchair access
● No dogs in public rooms   ▭ MasterCard, Visa   £ Single occupancy of
twin/double £65, twin/double £68 to £72, family room £78; deposit required

---

Victoria Spa Lodge

Bishopton Lane, Stratford-upon-Avon CV37 9QY
TEL: (01789) 267985   FAX: (01789) 204728
EMAIL: ptozer@victoriaspalodge.demon.co.uk
WEB SITE: www.scoot.co.uk/victoria_spa

Friendly atmosphere and spacious rooms at this good-value B&B.

Paul and D'reen Tozer's handsome Victorian hotel stands beside the Stratford
canal: a very useful position, as the tow-path provides a pleasant walk either to
Mary Arden's cottage or to the theatre and Stratford town centre. The hotel
welcomed the then Princess Victoria as its inaugural guest (she slept in Room 5,
not that the Tozers make any great fuss about that). The Lodge is a straightforward small hotel, rather prettily decorated. The large breakfast room has lacy
tablecloths and a collection of Wedgwood dotted about, with twin fireplaces and
some period prints as historical reminders. Simply furnished bedrooms are
spotlessly clean and spacious, with fresh flowers adding colour. For families or
groups the best option is taking both Rooms 6 and 7 in the attic, where the huge
old beams and thick floors give extra privacy. Otherwise Room 1 is pleasant,
with its smart blue-and-white-striped décor, Victorian fireplace, and

shower-room. At breakfast Paul cooks while D'reen serves, and between them they create a friendly and relaxed atmosphere.

◑ Open all year ⚡ 1½ miles north of Stratford, take first left at roundabout where A3400 and A46 intersect; Lodge is on right. Private car park ⟼ 1 twin, 3 double, 3 family rooms; all with shower/WC; all with TV, hair-dryer ⌗ Breakfast room, lounge, garden; cots, high chairs ♿ No wheelchair access ⬤ No dogs; no smoking ▭ MasterCard, Visa £ Single occupancy of twin/double £40 to £50, twin/double £50 to £60, family room £70 to £85; deposit required

---

STRETTON Rutland   map 6

Ram Jam Inn

Great North Road, Stretton, Oakham LE15 7QX
TEL: (01780) 410776   FAX: (01780) 410361

Time-saving stopover on the A1 with a hint of sophistication.

Travellers have been pulling off the Great North Road for a night's rest at the Ram Jam for at least 200 years – and for centuries before that when the inn had other names. The two-storey, creeper-clad building is quite attractive and, though only yards from the speeding traffic, is surprisingly peaceful once you are ensconced in the rear bar or restaurant. The latter is smartly decorated with plaid curtains and polished oak floor. A well-balanced menu offers a good selection of dishes: Stilton and garlic mushrooms to start, perhaps, followed by pork normande. On our inspection Mike Littlemore and Margaret Cox had been owners for just a few days – but, as Mike has been the manager for the past seven years, no alterations to the friendly and unobtrusive atmosphere are expected. The bedrooms are unfussy and smart with striped papers and pine furniture. Room 6 is particularly well positioned, overlooking an extensive orchard at the rear of the house, and the A1 and its traffic are easily forgotten.

◑ Open all year ⚡ On west side of A1, about 9 miles north of Stamford. Private car park ⟼ 5 twin, 1 double, 1 family room; all with bathroom/WC; all with TV, direct-dial telephone; hair-dryer available ⌗ Restaurant, bar, lounge, garden; functions (max 120 people incl up to 14 residential), conferences; leisure facilities nearby (reduced rates for guests); early suppers for children; cots, high chairs ♿ No wheelchair access ⬤ No dogs; no smoking in some public rooms ▭ Amex, Delta, MasterCard, Switch, Visa £ Single occupancy of twin/double £45, twin/double £55, family room £70; deposit required. Cooked B £5.50; bar/bistro L, D £6; alc L, D £17

STURMINSTER NEWTON Dorset   map 2

Plumber Manor

Sturminster Newton DT10 2AF
TEL: (01258) 472507   FAX: (01258) 473370
EMAIL: plumbermanor@btinternet.com

Good food at a refreshingly unstuffy and easy-going restaurant-with-rooms.

It's hard not to be won over by a host who enquires whether your pre-dinner gin and tonic is to be 'an orphan or a family measure', as Richard Prideaux-Brune does when dispensing good cheer from behind the bar of his family's ancestral home, now a wonderfully unpretentious restaurant-with-rooms. The Jacobean house, with its mullioned and leaded windows, stands in substantial grounds, but it's a comfortable, well-worn sort of place, and the family (which has been around for 300 years) doesn't affect any airs, simply inviting guests to relax and eat, drink and sleep well. Archie and Bertie, a pair of delightful black Labradors, mooch around the bright, comfortable, lemon-walled sitting-room, waiting for guests to tickle their tummies. The room also houses the bar, above which a long-barrelled musket hangs, reminding guests of the manor's field-sports associations. There are three dining areas – one in peach and one in blue, both sedate and elegant, and one pretty, stencilled, barrel-vaulted section (sometimes given over to private parties). Our inspector enjoyed a meal of gravad lax and smoked trout, followed by loin of pork with apricot, not to mention the lemon and ginger torte and chocolate gâteau from the sweet trolley (cruelly, you're encouraged to choose more than one). One correspondent described the food as 'excellent' and breakfast as 'splendid'. The bedrooms in the main house are plainly furnished with a mix of old and newer items, and have a daintily countrified décor. The only drawback of Room 1 was the small, rather narrow, bathroom. Those in the barn conversion are larger, with bright and modern soft furnishings. One guest felt slightly nonplussed by the 'idiosyncratic house-keeping', though all appeared well on our inspection visit.

◗ Closed Feb ⊡ 2 miles south-west of Sturminster Newton on road to Hazelbury Bryan. Private car park ⌸ 14 twin, 2 double; some in annexe; all with bathroom/WC; all with TV, room service, hair-dryer, trouser press, direct-dial telephone ⊘ Restaurant, bar, sitting-room, garden; conferences (max 80 people incl up to 16 residential); tennis; early suppers for children; cots, high chairs ⟨ Wheelchair access to hotel and restaurant, WC (unisex), 10 ground-floor bedrooms, 2 rooms specially equipped for disabled people ◗ No dogs in public rooms and some bedrooms ▭ Amex, Diners, MasterCard, Switch, Visa £ Single occupancy of twin/double £75 to £90, twin/double £115 to £140. Set Sun L £17.50, D £17.50 to £29. Special breaks available

---

SUTTON COLDFIELD West Midlands

map 5

New Hall

Walmley Road, Sutton Coldfield B76 1QX
TEL: 0121-378 2442   FAX: 0121-378 4637

Top-notch country house with excellent grounds and friendly staff.

New Hall may look the grand country house, complete with tower, moat and dinner-time dress code, but any expectation of pomposity is rapidly dispelled: 'Beware,' reads the sign in the drive, 'slow-moving hedgehogs.' Then there's the signed photo of Cher – in the Gents – and the topiary that mimics the crenellations. There is a sense of humour and fun here that communicates itself to staff and guests, creating a warm, friendly atmosphere. Seen from the gravel drive, the house's history reveals itself from left to right: first twelfth-century undressed grey stone, then warmer sixteenth-century red stone, followed by neatly cut Victorian masonry and finally twentieth-century brick. Inside, things are not so clear: the drawing-room, with its stone-mullioned and leaded windows, looks every inch part of the Victorian country house – except that it was built in 1990. The restaurant has bare stone walls, stained glass and the grandeur born of centuries – this time quite legitimately, as it is the oldest part of the building. Dinner menus are a good mix of traditional and modern: maybe a haddock and whisky soup for starters, then rack of lamb with a chicken mousse wrapped in Parma ham on couscous, and, to finish, a hot ginger and syrup sponge with honey ice-cream. The bedrooms are all tastefully furnished and well equipped: the choice is to stay in the older part or to look at it. If you choose the former, then the Albatross suite has it all: four-poster bed, good bathroom and period furniture.

◑ Open all year ⓩ Leave M42 at Junction 9, taking A4097; at B4148 turn right; follow road for 1 mile, keeping left at fork; New Hall is on left. Private car park ⌷➔ 4 single, 16 twin, 32 double, 2 four-poster, 6 suites; all with bathroom/WC; all with satellite TV, room service, hair-dryer, trouser press, direct-dial telephone, some with mini-bar
⚓ Restaurant, bar, 2 lounges, drawing-room, garden; functions (max 50 people residential/non-residential), conferences; golf, tennis, putting green, croquet; early suppers for children; cots, high chairs, babysitting, baby-listening ♿ Wheelchair access to hotel only, 24 ground-floor bedrooms, 1 specially equipped for disabled people ◓ No children under 8; no dogs; no smoking in some public rooms and some bedrooms ▭ Amex, Delta, Diners, MasterCard, Switch, Visa £ Single and single occupancy of twin/double £135 to £160, twin/double £160 to £185, four-poster £205, suite £215; deposit required. Continental B £11, cooked B £13.50; set L £26.50 to £29.50, D £34.50 to £48.50; alc L £20.50, D £35.50. (Prices valid till Jan 1999.) Special breaks available

---

SUTTON LANE ENDS Cheshire   map 8

Sutton Hall

Bullocks Lane, Sutton Lane Ends, Macclesfield SK11 0HE
TEL: (01260) 253211   FAX: (01260) 252538

An atmospheric pub oozing history, with adequate rooms and straightforward food.

Set amid stunning grounds at the end of a long, sweeping drive, the black-and-white Tudor façade of Sutton Hall immediately draws you into the past. Inside, an abundance of sixteenth-century oak and open log fires generates a warm and welcoming atmosphere; the collection of guns and the suit of armour are totally at home in this setting. The bar is convivial, with business guests socialising and conversing in a lively manner. The restaurant provides a calmer setting, and the dishes on the menu stick to traditional offerings: medallions of pork, grilled steak and pan-fried salmon, for example. Another quiet spot is the library – the big stone hearth above the fireplace showing the Sutton family's coat of arms granted by the queen in 1580 is not to be missed. After the characterful pub, the bedrooms are comfortable, if not overly exciting; some are wood-panelled. The single, which is let only as a last resort, is particularly bland, missing out on the four-poster beds provided in the other rooms; bathrooms are dated.

◗ Open all year ⊿ Off A523 in village of Sutton Lane Ends. Private car park
🛏 1 single, 8 four-poster, 1 four-poster suite; all with bathroom/WC; all with TV, room
service, hair-dryer, trouser press, direct-dial telephone ⊘ Restaurant, bar, library,
garden; functions (max 150 people incl up to 19 residential), conferences; civil wedding
licence; croquet; leisure facilities nearby (free for guests); early suppers for children;
cots, high chairs, baby-listening, outdoor play area ⅙ No wheelchair access
● No dogs in public rooms (£5 per night in bedrooms) ▭ Amex, Delta, Diners,
MasterCard, Switch, Visa £ Single (rate on application), single occupancy of
four-poster £75, four-poster £90, four-poster suite (rate on application); deposit
required. Bar/bistro L, D £5.50 to £14; set L £13; alc D £24

SWAFFHAM Norfolk map 6

Strattons

4 Ash Close, Swaffham PE37 7NH
TEL: (01760) 723845   FAX: (01760) 720458

---

*Fabulously original designs in the bedrooms and good food in this
cheerfully run hotel.*

This unusual Queen Anne villa is just off the market place in Swaffham, at the
end of a fine circular gravel drive. Behind the intriguing façade, Les and Vanessa
Scott have pretty much succeeded in recreating some of the sumptuous
easy-living character of the villa's past. The public rooms are heaped with
antiques and Victorian bits and pieces; sofas and armchairs are festooned with
cushions, and walls are covered with paintings and sketches. Les is described by
guests as 'an engaging and pleasant host', while Vanessa, who rather unfairly
describes herself as 'general dogsbody', has won heaps of praise for her
'wonderful' cooking. A meal might start with spinach roulade served with
gravad lax and tomato and basil dressing, followed by scallop pudding with
saffron seafood custard, and finally rhubarb and ginger burnt cream. The
striking dining-room, with its bright mural of typical Norfolk countryside, has a
rustic feel with exposed red brick and a pine dresser. The former library has been
converted into a bedroom – walls a deep shade of red with a dark purple border
and matching curtains, a red chesterfield by the fireplace and an enormous heavy
wooden four-poster. The Scotts have also restored the attic bedroom, making it
larger and introducing Japanese décor. One guest felt the informality went too
far: 'Should guests be faced with jokey handwritten notes about how to use the
toilet, how not to use the broken sash window?'

◗ Closed Chr and 2 weeks in summer ⊿ At north end of market-place, behind shop
fronts. Private car park 🛏 1 twin, 5 double, 1 family room, 1 four-poster suite; all
with bathroom/WC; all with TV, room service, hair-dryer, direct-dial telephone, radio,
some with mini-bar ⊘ Dining-room, lounge, drying-room, garden; early suppers for
children; cots, high chairs, toys, baby-listening ⅙ No wheelchair access
● No smoking ▭ MasterCard, Switch, Visa £ Single occupancy of twin/double
£65 to £95, twin/double £95, family room £145, four-poster suite £140; deposit
required. Set D £25

See page 6 for a brief explanation of how to use the Guide.

Nurse's Cottage   NEW ENTRY

Station Road, Sway, Lymington SO41 6BA
TEL: (01590) 683402 (AND FAX)
EMAIL: nurses.cottage@lineone.net

Lovely little cottage guesthouse, run with energetic enthusiasm, in the heart of the New Forest.

This is a place where a bit of tender loving care is part of the very fabric of the building: dating from the turn of the century, it was home for over 50 years to the village's district nurses, and their memory lives on – each room is named after one. These days, the emphasis is on R&R, and the food is certainly light years away from anything served up by medical establishments. Owner/proprietor/ chef/chief-bottle-washer Tony Barnfield is on hand to cater to his guests' needs. Leaving behind a radio career, which included interviewing Mrs Thatcher and playing 'toptastic' tunes on Radio 1, he transformed this simple, white-painted cottage into an inviting, friendly, licensed guesthouse. He delights in creating meals from local ingredients, all eaten in the smart blue-and-white Garden Room; a typical menu might include an avocado, orange and prawn salad, then New Forest venison and red-wine casserole, and finally banana flambé. Over 70 wines are available, with one produced in Sway's own vineyard among the French, Australian, Chilean and even Chinese offerings. Of the three bedrooms, Southerden is a twin in cheery yellow colours, while Lipscombe is small but perfectly formed. The *en suite* bathrooms have recently been upgraded, so that, while they're still on the bijou side, they are bright and fresh.

❶ Closed 9 Nov to 16 Dec, 17 to 21 Jan, 21 Feb to 11 Mar   ⏏ In centre of Sway village, next to post office. Private car park   ⤶ 1 single, 1 twin, 1 double; all with bathroom/WC; all with TV, room service, hair-dryer, mini-bar, trouser press, direct-dial telephone   ✅ Dining-room/ lounge, garden; conferences (max 15 people incl up to 3 residential); early suppers for children   ♿ No wheelchair access   ● No children under 10; no smoking   ▭ Amex, Delta, MasterCard, Switch, Visa   £ Single £50, single occupancy of twin/double £60, twin/double £85; deposit required. Set D £20; alc L £15. Special breaks available

---

Hoe Hill

Swinhope, Binbrook, Market Rasen LN8 6HX
TEL: (01472) 398206

Quiet, charming house with friendly sociable hostess.

Rosemary and Marjory are getting on a bit now but still like to meet guests out on the lawn: 'Like two old girls on the prom,' says Erica Curd of her Jacob sheep. It's all part of the friendly atmosphere that pervades this well-kept eighteenth-century house on a quiet road north of Binbrook. A former nurse, Erica is now a chef of some reputation, giving demonstrations in her immaculate country kitchen and providing evening meals by arrangement – fresh fish from nearby

Grimsby is one popular choice; another would be rack of venison followed by baked pears in cassis or a lemon posset. Appropriately, the dining-room is particularly welcoming, with a log fire burning on a chilly evening and jars of home-made marmalades piled up on the window ledges. The sitting-room, though comfortable, lacks the same sparkle, but its real feature is the garden beyond the french windows – a swathe of lawn and trees with those two friendly old ladies pottering about. Bedrooms are spacious and nicely decorated with a mix of old and new furniture: the Garden Room is particularly pleasant for its view, and the *en suite* bathroom with corner bath and separate shower.

◑ Closed Jan & owners' holiday 🖅 On B1203, 1 mile north of Binbrook. Private car park 🛏 1 twin/double, 2 double; twin/double with bathroom/WC; all with hair-dryer; TV, trouser press available ⌁ Dining-room, sitting-room, drying-room, garden; croquet; early suppers for children, by arrangement; toys, books, outdoor play area ♿ No wheelchair access ● No children under 5; no dogs; smoking in sitting-room only ⊟ None accepted £ Single occupancy of twin/double £20 to £30, twin/double £36 to £50; deposit required. Light supper £5; set D £14. Special breaks available

---

TALLAND Cornwall
map 1

Talland Bay

Talland, Looe PL13 2JB
TEL: (01503) 272667   FAX: (01503) 272940

Impeccable small hotel on the coastal path, good for walking.

When we inspected, tea and cakes were being served in the lounge; this treat is included in the room rates, so residents flock back to the hotel feeling ravenous. ('It's all this walking,' said one tanned and hungry guest as he walked through the door.) If you go down the stepped terraces of the (almost sub-tropical) garden, past the pool and the palm trees, you have to stop – if you walked any further you would wade right into the surf, so close is this hotel to the sea. Whichever way you turn, you will be able to walk for miles along some of the most beautiful coastal paths in England. The sound of the sea permeates every room, from the spectacularly oak-panelled restaurant to the pretty-in-peach lounge, creating a feeling of extreme peace and tranquillity. The bedrooms are particularly fetching, with fresh flowers on the antique furniture and fluffy towels in the rather glamorous bathrooms. Dinner is a banquet-like affair: you might start with a filo pastry basket of creamy scrambled egg with Parma ham laid on a fresh tomato sauce, and follow it with noisettes of Cornish lamb with puy lentils and rice and a fresh mint sauce. Vegetarians are well catered for, too.

◑ Closed Jan 🖅 In Looe, take Polperro road for 2 miles to sign for hotel at crossroads; turn left down hill; hotel is on left. Private car park 🛏 3 single, 8 twin, 3 double, 2 four-poster, 2 family rooms, 1 suite; some in annexe; all with bathroom/WC; all with TV, room service, hair-dryer, trouser press, direct-dial telephone ⌁ Restaurant, bar, lounge, library, games room, garden; functions (max 50 people incl up to 40 residential), conferences; sauna, heated outdoor swimming-pool, putting green, croquet; early suppers for children; cots, high chairs, baby-listening ♿ No wheelchair access ● No children under 5 in restaurant eves; no dogs in public rooms, £4 per night in bedrooms, by arrangement ⊟ Amex, Diners, MasterCard, Switch,

---

Visa £ Single £44 to £79, twin/double £98 to £118, four-poster £128 to £158, family room £123 to £173, suite £108 to £138; deposit required. Bar L £8.50; set D £21; alc D £36. Special breaks available

---

TARPORLEY Cheshire map 7

The Swan

50 High Street, Tarporley CW6 0AG
TEL: (01829) 733838 FAX: (01829) 732932
EMAIL: c.sharp@virgin.net

Charming and relaxed coaching-inn located in an equally charming village.

Tarporley is so pretty that it has the feel of a film set about it – one long street edged by smart Georgian cottages and terraced houses, with a sign outside the church proclaiming the accolade of Best Kept Village (achieved several times now). In the middle of this bustling high street is the Swan, which manages to be three things at once – up-market pub, attractive restaurant and welcoming hotel. The red-brick Georgian façade was added in 1789, and the three-storey building, with its two bay windows, dominates the street. Through the front door you're straight into the comfy lounge area, stuffed with the kind of sofas which are just begging for you to collapse into with your newspaper and a pint. Tucked into one of the bays is the tiny wooden-floored bar, while the other houses the restaurant, whose wooden floorboards and slightly scuffed paintwork give it a lived-in and welcoming feel. There is also an alternative bar and eating area with flagstoned floors, wooden settle benches and horse brasses adorning the beams. Our inspector enjoyed a main course of pork medallions with apple and cider, but felt that the starter, warm seafood salad, wasn't up to the same standard. Bedrooms are divided between the main building and a converted coach-house; although all are comfortable, they are not quite as appealing as the public rooms. The staff, however, are welcoming and friendly, contributing to a wonderfully relaxed atmosphere.

◑ Open all year; restaurant closed Sun eve ⤧ On Tarporley High Street. Private car park ⇥ 3 single, 10 twin, 5 double, 1 four-poster; some in annexe; family rooms available; all with bathroom/WC; all with TV, trouser press, direct-dial telephone, some with hair-dryer ⌀ Restaurant, 2 bars, lounge; functions (max 100 people incl up to 35 residential), conferences; early suppers for children; cots, high chairs ♿ Wheelchair access to hotel and restaurant, WC (unisex), 3 ground-floor bedrooms ● No dogs in public rooms, dogs in some bedrooms only ▭ Amex, Delta, MasterCard, Switch, Visa £ Single £55, single occupancy of twin/double (rate on application), twin/double £73, four-poster £85, family room £83; deposit required. Bar/bistro L £6, D £12

Willington Hall

Willington, Tarporley CW6 0NB
TEL: (01829) 752321 FAX: (01829) 752596

Personally run country-house hotel in lovely, rural surroundings.

Sitting at the end of its very long drive and surrounded by fields, Willington Hall looks like an ancestral family seat – which is close to the truth, for, although run as a country-house hotel, it is still co-owned by Richard Tomkinson, whose great-grandfather built it in 1829. Family portraits adorn the walls, and there's a definite lived-in homely atmosphere, yet the faded grandeur can still impress. The study bar, with its high ceiling and comfy window seats, boasts magnificent views of the rolling Welsh hills, and you can opt for a good-value bar meal here, such as salmon crumble pie or spinach pancake with cheese sauce. The breakfast room also has great views and leads into a second dining-room, which is small, cosy and rather formal (as is the adjacent Pink Room, a private dining-room but used on busy Saturday evenings for the restaurant overspill). The restaurant menu relies largely on traditional English fare, such as smoked trout with horseradish sauce followed by rack of lamb. The bedrooms vary in size, but all are furnished with a mix of solid old furniture and antiques and are comfortable. The large Room 1 has the best views, while Room 2, a good-sized twin, is sunny and fresh, with flowers stencilled on the walls behind the beds. Rooms 8 and 9 are decent-sized singles, their high ceilings giving an extra sense of airiness.

◑ Closed 25 Dec; restaurant closed Sun eve   ⊿ Travelling north-west on A51 to Chester, turn right at Bull's Head in Clotton; hotel is 1½ miles further, on left. Private car park   ⊫ 2 single, 5 twin, 3 double; family rooms available; all with bathroom/WC; all with TV, room service, direct-dial telephone, some with hair-dryer   ⊘ 3 dining-rooms, 2 bars, lounge, drying-room, garden; functions (max 75 people incl up to 20 residential), conferences; civil wedding licence; tennis; early suppers for children; cots, high chairs, babysitting, baby-listening   ⅃ No wheelchair access   ● No dogs in public rooms   ▭ Amex, Delta, Diners, MasterCard, Switch, Visa   £ Single £45, single occupancy of twin/double £55, twin/double £75, family room £80. Continental B £4, cooked B £6; bar L, D £8; alc L, D £17.50

TARVIN Cheshire

map 7

Grove House   NEW ENTRY

Holme Street, Tarvin, Chester CH3 8EQ
TEL: (01829) 740893   FAX: (01829) 741769

Charming family home with fabulous rooms and warm hospitable atmosphere.

Although Grove House sits just off the busy road junction of the A51 and A54, the pretty one-acre garden, with its attractive cedar and monkey-puzzle, manages effectively to eradicate sounds of traffic. Behind the smart red-brick Victorian façade is an elegant, immaculate house that nevertheless retains an air of relaxing warmth. Throughout the interior various artifacts hint at the Spiegelberg family's passion for travel, for example their foreign doll collection and fabulous Javanese shadow puppets. They also have a keen interest in music – on the landing is a cluster of musical instruments, including a didgeridoo, drums and a piano, and the youngest son shows great talent as a percussionist in the National Children's Orchestra. The three bedrooms are charming; the king-sized double and the twin both have *en suite* bathrooms, while the smaller double has a private bathroom on the landing. Downstairs, double doors open from the lounge on to the garden. In the dining-room, smart china adds a touch of formality to breakfast. Helen doesn't offer dinner but is full of suggestions for restaurants just a couple of miles away.

◐ Closed Chr & New Year ⤢ From A51 east of Chester, turn on to A54 at roundabout; go up slight hill; house is at top on left, just before turning on right into village. Private car park ⤶ 1 single, 1 twin, 1 double; 1 with bathroom/WC, 1 with shower/WC; all with TV, hair-dryer, 1 with trouser press ⊘ Dining-room, lounge, drying-room, garden; croquet ♿ No wheelchair access ● No children under 12; no dogs; smoking in lounge only ▭ None accepted £ Single £23, single occupancy of twin/double £28 to £35, twin/double £40 to £56; deposit required

---

TAVISTOCK Devon

map 1

Horn of Plenty

Gulworthy, Tavistock PL19 8JD
TEL: (01822) 832528 (AND FAX)

Consistently good restaurant-with-rooms in elegant Victorian house.

This attractive, double-fronted Victorian house is reassuring in its rooted Englishness, covered as it is with creepers and surrounded by rhododendrons, camellias and azaleas. Inside, the welcome and décor are equally sure; elegantly proportioned rooms are set off by stripped floors and sophisticated floral walls, while confident staff make you feel at home. The restaurant is the focal point of the house, but the bar and drawing-room are just as comfortable, with big squashy sofas and rugs on the floor; in the bar two old teddies look very much at home in a high chair – as well they might, for the fireplace (which opens to the dining-room as well) is certainly one to relax in front of. One exuberant diner told us the food was 'to die for'; on the menu you might find celeriac ravioli filled with rabbit confit ragoût with a grain mustard sauce, followed by baked monkfish wrapped in prosciutto with ratatouille and a white-wine sauce. The bedrooms are outside, in a converted barn, where they overlook a pretty walled garden. Each has its own balcony or patio, and is excellently done out in fresh pine. Some have attractive pitched ceilings, and all have good-quality bath- or shower-rooms.

◐ Closed 25 & 26 Dec ⤢ 3 miles west of Tavistock on A390, turn right at Gulworthy Cross and follow signs to hotel. Private car park ⤶ 6 twin/double; all in annexe; all with bathroom/WC exc 2 with shower/WC; all with TV, room service, hair-dryer, mini-bar, direct-dial telephone ⊘ Restaurant, bar, lounge, garden; functions (max 50 people incl up to 12 residential), conferences; civil wedding licence; golf club nearby (reduced rates for guests) ♿ Wheelchair access (ramps) to hotel and restaurant, WC (M, F), 4 ground-floor bedrooms ● No children under 13; no dogs in public rooms; no smoking in restaurant and bedrooms ▭ Amex, Delta, MasterCard, Switch, Visa £ Single occupancy of twin/double £70 to £85, twin/double £95 to £110; deposit required. Cooked B £7.50; set L £10.50 to £18.50; alc D £32.50. Special breaks available

---

This denotes that the hotel is in an exceptionally peaceful situation where you can be assured of a restful stay.

TEFFONT EVIAS Wiltshire   map 2

Howard's House

Teffont Evias, Salisbury SP3 5RJ
TEL: (01722) 716392   FAX: (01722) 716820

Swiss-style country mansion in a picture-postcard English village.

The village of thatched cottages in the depths of rural Wiltshire is England at its chocolate-box best, which makes the neo-Alpine appearance of Howard's House all the more surprising. The house was originally built in 1623, and is now run by a direct descendant of one Christopher Mayne, who bought it in 1632. Today's continental appearance is a legacy of the grand tour taken by a family member at the beginning of the Victorian era, which inspired the building of an extension and alterations to the roof line. The interior owes its fresh, contemporary feel to a radical refurbishment a decade ago. Only the stone fireplace and exposed beams hint at the house's vintage, in a lounge notable for its cool green and yellow décor and its outlook over an ornamental pond and patio. A double aspect makes the plant-filled restaurant bright, yet intimate. It's a classy setting for Paul Firmin's accomplished food; perhaps a chicken and goats' cheese timbale with black olives and a basil and beetroot ravioli, followed by rock salmon with a shrimp bisque and a saffron risotto, and finally a passion-fruit crème caramel with vanilla syrup and tropical fruits. Boldly bright or modishly pastel colours add to the appeal of the well-appointed and attractively furnished bedrooms.

◑ Closed 25 to 27 Dec   ⬕ On B3089, 9½ miles west of Salisbury; in Teffont Magna follow signs to hotel. Private car park   ⬳ 1 twin, 6 double, 1 four-poster, 1 family room; all with bathroom/WC; all with TV, room service, hair-dryer, direct-dial telephone; no tea/coffee-making facilities in rooms   ⬥ Restaurant, lounge, garden; functions (max 70 people incl up to 18 residential), conferences; croquet; early suppers for children; cots, high chairs, baby-listening   ♿ No wheelchair access   ● Smoking in lounge only   ☐ Amex, Delta, Diners, MasterCard, Switch, Visa   £ Single occupancy of twin/double £75, twin/double £95 to £115, four-poster £135, family room £140; deposit required. Set L £18.50, D £25. Special breaks available

---

TEIGNMOUTH Devon   map 1

Thomas Luny House

Teign Street, Teignmouth TQ14 8EG
TEL: (01626) 772976

Imposing house built in 1800 in quay area of town, providing high-class accommodation.

Thomas Luny made his fortune painting moody nautical scenes and ships of war on tossing seas – a far cry from the house he built in the docklands of Teignmouth, which virtually emanates symmetry and repose. The double-fronted house, approached through rather a grand archway, has satisfying proportions and a crunchy gravel courtyard. John and Alison Allan run a refined and elegant operation here, despite the location; the walls around the house keep away any hint of the surrounding factories and loading yards. The lounge runs the full depth of the house, so is very light, and the fire is lit on chilly days. Breakfast is taken communally around an antique table under an old grandfather clock, and there's a small south-facing back garden. The bedrooms have different themes: Chinese has an oriental flavour, whereas Luny tends to the nautical. All are exceedingly well done out, with fascinating chests instead of the usual luggage racks, and spotless bathrooms.

◑ Closed Jan 🔁 In Teignmouth, follow signs to quay; after turning off inner relief road, take first left into Teign Street. Private car park 🛏 2 twin, 1 double, 1 four-poster; all with bathroom/WC; all with TV, hair-dryer, direct-dial telephone, radio; no tea/coffee-making facilities in rooms ✓ Breakfast room, lounge, garden ♿ No wheelchair access ● No children under 12; no dogs; no smoking in public rooms 🛏 None accepted £ Single occupancy of twin/double £35, twin/double/ four-poster £70. Special breaks available

---

TENTERDEN Kent   map 3

Brattle House

Watermill Bridges, Tenterden TN30 6UL
TEL: (01580) 763565

Top-notch B&B – with dinner if you want – run by an amiable, jolly couple.

Once you've met Mo and Alan Rawlinson, you'll understand why so many of the guests come back year on year. They are such a friendly couple, welcoming you into their home so that you feel like a long-lost relative just arrived from Australia. Taller guests, if they're not familiar with the house, might feel less at home – some of the beams are so low that anyone over six foot has to stand between them. Expect a few bumped foreheads, especially in the sitting-room. Much better just to sit down and admire the tranquil view across the lovely garden to the valley beyond. Breakfast is taken in the adjoining hexagonal conservatory, and so is dinner if the weather is good enough. Otherwise dinner is eaten in the more formal dining-room, and the Rawlinsons join their guests around the table. Mo rustles up a mean feast, often using her mother's well-thumbed 1930s recipe book for inspiration – maybe watercress and salmon mousse, duck with kumquats and then marmalade bread-and-butter pudding. Both Mo and Alan are vegetarian, so they're happy to cater for like-minded souls if you let them know. The two spacious bedrooms at the front have brick fireplaces and padded seats in the bay windows, while the double at the back enjoys wonderful views. All three are stylish, both in décor and furnishings.

◑ Closed Chr & New Year 🔁 From Tenterden head for Hastings on A28; go downhill past signpost for Cranbrook and widening of A28; turn right into Cranbrook Road (country lane); house is ¼ mile on left. Private car park 🛏 1 twin, 2 double; all with shower/WC; all with hair-dryer ✓ Dining-room, sitting-room, conservatory, garden ♿ No wheelchair access ● No children under 14; no dogs; no smoking 🛏 None accepted £ Single occupancy of twin/double £40 to £45, twin/double £60 to £70; deposit required. Set D £20. Special breaks available

Calcot Manor

Tetbury GL8 8YJ
TEL: (01666) 890391   FAX: (01666) 890394

Large, bustling country-house hotel, which excels in its welcome to families.

Though it backs on to open fields several miles outside Tetbury, this sizeable complex is no peaceful hideaway: focused around a lovely old manor, it extends into a pub and a bewildering array of outbuildings that have been converted into bedroom annexes. The family accommodation, in a block next to the outdoor pool, is outstanding. The smart, spacious rooms and suites here have a bunk and/or sofa or armchair beds, along with a video, access to a library of tapes, mini-fridges and a listening system connected to reception. A qualified nanny supervises a well-stocked playroom for at least four hours a day. If you're not staying *en famille*, ask for a room in the main house. Eating at Calcot Manor is something of a treat, whether in the Conservatory Restaurant, which adopts a chic, contemporary style, or less formally in the extremely popular Gumstool Inn, a tasteful modern extension to the manor. The breakfasts are well regarded, and the restaurant and pub serve eclectic, international brasserie-style fare. High tea is available for children.

◑ Open all year   ⬕ 3 miles west of Tetbury on A4135, just before intersection with A46. Private car park   ⌘ 15 twin, 2 double, 1 four-poster, 5 family rooms, 4 suites; some in annexe; all with bathroom/WC; all with TV, room service, hair-dryer, trouser press, direct-dial telephone, some with video, fridge; tea/coffee-making facilities available   ⊘ 2 restaurants, 2 bars, lounge, conservatory, garden; functions (max 150 people incl up to 50 residential), conferences; civil wedding licence; heated outdoor swimming-pool, tennis, croquet; leisure facilities nearby (reduced rates for guests); early suppers for children; cots, high chairs, toys, playrooms, babysitting, baby-listening, outdoor play area   ♿ Wheelchair access to hotel (ramp) and restaurants, WC (unisex), 15 ground-floor bedrooms   ◔ No children in main restaurant eves; no dogs   ▭ Amex, Delta, Diners, MasterCard, Switch, Visa   £ Single occupancy of twin/double £95, twin/double £110 to £155, four-poster £155, family room £155 to £160, suite £160; deposit required. Bar/bistro L, D £16; set L £12.50; alc L, D £25. Special breaks available

Tavern House

Willesley, Tetbury GL8 8QU
TEL: (01666) 880444   FAX: (01666) 880254

High-quality B&B in a former staging-inn on the edge of a hamlet in the Cotswold countryside; traffic noise may be a problem.

Tim and Janet Tremellen's seventeenth-century house has a lot going for it. It's a classic, rambling, mellow-stone Cotswold building that backs on to an inviting walled garden as meticulously maintained as the rest of the enterprise. The Tremellens provide first-rate hospitality, in the form of a friendly welcome, detailed advice on where to eat locally, and fresh milk on tea trays. It's a pleasant enough surprise when sophisticated hotels turn down beds in the evening and give you exactly what you want at breakfast, pleasanter still in a small B&B like this. Breakfasts themselves, served in a small dining-room where hunting scenes on table-mats and walls complement a pair of stuffed pheasants, are beautifully presented, and offer any variation on the traditional English theme. The spruce bedrooms come with pink and matching floral schemes, roomy bathrooms and the odd beam. However, the noise of traffic whizzing right past the house on the A433 intrudes through the leaded windows; if it's not warm, the double glazing can reduce the disturbance.

◑ Open all year　▣ On A433, 4 miles south-west of Tetbury. Private car park; on-street parking (free)　🛏 1 twin, 3 double; all with bathroom/WC; all with TV, hair-dryer, trouser press, direct-dial telephone　✅ Dining-room, lounge, garden　♿ No wheelchair access　⊖ No children under 10; no dogs; smoking in lounge only　💳 MasterCard, Visa　💷 Single occupancy of twin/double £45 to £55, twin/double £59 to £63; deposit required. Special breaks available

---

THAME Oxfordshire　　　　　　　　　　　map 2

Old Trout　NEW ENTRY

29–30 Lower High Street, Thame OX9 2AA
TEL: (01844) 212146　FAX: (01844) 212614

Exciting restaurant-with-rooms, with new owners and the smallest bedroom door in hotel history.

When Mark and Ruth Jones took over the Old Trout (formerly Thatchers) last year, they went the whole hog and gutted the place, right back to the flagstoned floors and the drunken doorways, so that it matched the fabulously bulging, thatched exterior. A sign outside dates it to 1550 – but were people really this short back then? The old kitchen houses part of the restaurant, and the waiting staff have to stoop, but nothing beats the diminutive door to Room 1, which opens between wildly bent original beams and can't be more than three feet high. The rest of the place is tall enough though, and oozing with character. A piano by the front door has wonderfully smelly cheeses on top, specials of the day are chalked on the blackboard above the huge fireplace, rustic wooden tables fill the different rooms, there are nooks and crannies with more tables, and chunky antique furniture and black-and-white prints in heavy frames decorate the restaurant in higgledy-piggledy fashion. Leading through to the garden is a new, airy conservatory, done out in coir matting and red walls, where you can dine in a less intensely ancient environment. Fish features strongly on the modern, unpretentious menu; or you could try roasted and chargrilled vegetables with pesto and Parmesan, followed by calf's liver with celeriac purée, thyme and port sauce. If you can, stay in the bedrooms in the main house (avoiding Room 1 if you have a bad back), which are simply done out with more coir flooring, muted tones and minimal furniture, so you get the full effect of the misshapen walls and ceilings. The bedrooms in the modern annexe are unfortunately box-like, crammed with a heavy four-poster bed and not much else, but adequate for replete diners.

◗ Closed Chr & 2 weeks in Aug; 1 restaurant closed Sun eve ⤧ On main High Street in Thame. Private car park ⤶ 1 single, 2 double, 4 four-poster; some in annexe; 4 with bathroom/WC, 3 with shower/WC; all with TV, room service, trouser press, direct-dial telephone, some with hair-dryer ⟐ 2 restaurants, bar, conservatory, garden; functions (max 60 people incl up to 13 residential) ⟐ No wheelchair access ⊖ No dogs ▭ Delta, MasterCard, Switch, Visa ⓔ Single £55, double/four-poster £75; deposit required. Bar/bistro L £4 to £6, D £8 to £10; alc L £25, D £27.50. Special breaks available

---

THEBERTON Suffolk   map 6

Theberton Grange

Theberton, Leiston IP16 4RR
TEL: (01728) 830625 (AND FAX)
EMAIL: stay@thebertongrange.co.uk
WEB SITE: www.thebertongrange.co.uk

A fine Victorian house in the depths of the countryside, with good cooking and attentive hosts.

In the hallway of Theberton Grange are two framed photographs of children with the title 'Your hosts' underneath. It's a nice little touch that sets the tone for the friendly and welcoming home of Paul and Dawn Rosher. Their large, pale-red-brick Victorian farmhouse with steep-pitched roofs is deep in a remote bit of countryside and within easy reach of the coast. Paul is a dapper and very affable host, and before dinner he chats to guests about their day and discusses the menu before dashing off to prepare the food himself. Meanwhile you can relax in the lovely, light, spacious lounge and help yourself to a drink from the honesty bar. Dotted around is military memorabilia which gives a clue to Paul's former career in the army. At 7.30pm you are called into the tidy dining-room, with tables in regimental lines, classical music drifting across the room from the CD player and views through the windows to the lawns and a small sunken garden. A typical meal might include a fluffy broccoli and cheese tartlet, followed by a generous portion of poached salmon with noisette potatoes, cauliflower cheese and french beans and finally a chocolate roulade with raspberry sauce. Upstairs the bedrooms are comfortable without being showy; some are quite large, and they all have good plump beds and smart bathrooms.

◗ Closed Chr; dining-room closed Sun eve ⤧ Go through Theberton on B1122 from Yoxford; on leaving village turn immediately right at small crossroads, then first left. Private car park ⤶ 1 twin, 5 double; most with bathroom/WC, 1 with shower/WC; all with TV, clock radio ⟐ Dining-room, lounge, terrace, garden ⟐ No wheelchair access ⊖ No children under 9; no dogs; smoking in lounge only ▭ Visa ⓔ Single occupancy of twin/double £50, twin/double £75 to £80; deposit required. Set D £19.50. Special breaks available

---

Where we know an establishment accepts credit cards, we list them. There may be a surcharge if you pay by credit card. It is always best to check when booking whether the card you want to use is acceptable.

Sheppard's

Front Street, Sowerby, Thirsk YO7 1JF
TEL: (01845) 523655   FAX: (01845) 524720

Small-scale restaurant and bistro complex with rustic rooms on the edge of Thirsk.

Sheppard's was originally a cluster of farm buildings around a cobbled courtyard opposite the local church. As the popularity of the family's enterprise grew, the old stables and granaries were gradually colonised, changing a simple farmhouse B&B into the busy restaurant complex it is today. The rustic Mediterranean-style bistro is the heart and soul of the set-up, lit by a plant-festooned atrium and kitted out with the exposed brick walls, polished flagstones and chunky furniture that set the tone in most of the public areas. The menu dips into the modern global basket of ingredients to offer starters like goats' cheese and mango in filo and main courses such as guinea-fowl with basil and tomato *jus* or pork with black-pudding mash. Alternatively, the restaurant has more ambitious concoctions to tempt you into a plush and more formal setting on a mezzanine level with exposed beams above. The former hayloft above the bistro and restaurant houses the bedrooms, which are pretty in a cottagey style that revolves around bright fabrics, pine furniture and modern prints.

◑ Closed first week Jan 🔃 Take Sowerby road from Castle Gate, Thirsk; ½ mile from Thirsk market-place. Private car park 🛏 2 twin, 5 double, 1 four-poster; all with bathroom/WC; all with TV, hair-dryer, direct-dial telephone ✅ 2 restaurants, bar, lounge; functions (max 100 people incl up to 16 residential), conferences ♿ No wheelchair access ● No dogs; no smoking in some bedrooms ▭ Delta, MasterCard, Switch, Visa £ Single occupancy of twin/double £62, twin/double £85, four-poster £88; deposit required. Bar/bistro L £9, D £15; alc L £18, D £25.50

Thornbury Castle

Castle Street, Thornbury, Bristol BS35 1HH
TEL: (01454) 281182   FAX: (01454) 416188
EMAIL: thornburycastle@compuserve.com
WEB SITE: www.bestloved.com

A luxury hotel that is as historic a place in which to stay as anywhere in England.

When its builder, the Duke of Buckingham, was beheaded for treason in 1521, Thornbury Castle passed into royal hands; if you stay here, you'll be following in the footsteps of Henry VIII, Anne Boleyn and Mary Tudor. With its host of crenellations, arrow slits and oriel windows (some of which were reckoned so fine that they were copied in Windsor Castle), the first sight of this complex, which comprises a turreted main building, various wings and towering walls surrounding extensive gardens, is simply awesome. The interior delivers the expected baronial grandeur in spades – most notably in the lofty ceilings and in the tapestries and Tudor portraits hanging from the walls. There is the odd kitschy element: for example, a suit of armour in the reception, and Muzak, described as 'terrible' by one reader, who was also underwhelmed by the service. Generally, however, this is a sophisticated enterprise. The bedrooms (called bedchambers) are typically massive and atmospheric, particularly the several top-of-the-range four-poster rooms, but as much attention is generally placed on comfort as on antiquity – though one visitor had to sleep in her dressing-gown as there was no spare blanket in her room. The highly regarded dinners (jacket and tie required for men) offer elaborately presented, but none too overwrought, dishes. To wash them down, you could choose a palatable, fruity white wine produced by the castle's own vineyard.

---

① Closed 4 days in Jan ⤴ In Thornbury, turn into Castle Street at bottom of hill; hotel entrance is to left of church. Private car park ⇝ 2 single, 4 twin, 3 double, 9 four-poster, 1 family room, 1 suite; all with bathroom/WC; all with TV, room service, hair-dryer, trouser press, direct-dial telephone; tea/coffee-making facilities available ✥ 3 restaurants, lounge, library, garden; functions (max 30 people residential/non-residential), conferences; civil wedding licence; croquet, archery ♿ No wheelchair access ● No children under 12; no dogs; no smoking in restaurants ▭ Amex, Delta, Diners, MasterCard, Switch, Visa £ Single £85 to £105, single occupancy of twin/double £105 to £120, twin/double £120 to £135, four-poster £170 to £235, family room £295 to £335, suite £195 to £335; deposit required. Cooked B £9; set L £18.50, D £34.50

THRELKELD **Cumbria**   map 10

Blease Farm   NEW ENTRY

Blease Road, Threlkeld, Keswick CA12 4SF
TEL: (017687) 79087 (AND FAX)

Rooms with a view in a super farmhouse at the foot of Blencathra.

High above the A66 and the roadside village of Threlkeld stands this eighteenth-century stone farmhouse. The amazing views all around (when weather permits) are admirably freeze-framed by the house's multiple windows. Immediately behind, majestic Blencathra soars to over 2,800 feet (or 868 metres, as all modern maps less impressively declare). Mountains are an important part of John Knowles's life. He's climbed many of the most awesome Himalayan peaks, and the house is full of mountaineering books, maps and photos. He and Ruth moved to Blease Farm about five years ago, and since then have spent their formidable combined energy on doing it up. It now provides some of the most attractive farmhouse accommodation anywhere in the Lakes. It's no longer a working farm, though 40 acres of grazing land are still attached to the house, on which sheep, horses and chickens roam. Ruth's forte is the garden, steeply landscaped and with a trout pond fed by a beck which ingeniously supplies power for the house.

Inside, the house is stylish and immaculately kept; it's also relaxing and personal. Guests may make use of a well-furnished sitting-room stacked with books, videos and a baby grand piano. Beyond is a sun lounge embellished with serious walking maps (which guests may borrow), and a chess set. Ruth cooks traditional Lakeland breakfasts, and dinners several nights a week (by arrangement, as are packed lunches). The bedrooms are named after mountains – mind that steep incline on the floor of K2. They're all different, but equally appealing, with many well-considered features (hooks on doors, good bedside lights, decent power showers, adequate storage space). John and Ruth have made a point of sleeping in all the rooms themselves to discover any shortcomings. It's hard to think of any.

◑ Open all year ⤤ From A66 east of Keswick turn north into Threlkeld, then north again into Blease Road for less than ½ mile. Private car park ⬛ 1 twin, 2 double; all with bathroom/WC exc twin with shower/WC; all with TV, hair-dryer, clock radio ⦵ Dining-room, 2 lounges, TV room (satellite), drying-room, library, conservatory, garden; fishing ⸝ No wheelchair access ◔ No children under 12; no dogs; no smoking ⬚ None accepted ⑂ Single occupancy of twin/double £34, twin/double £58, family room £80. Set D £18

Tilston Lodge

Tilston, Malpas SY14 7DR
TEL: (01829) 250223 (AND FAX)

Immaculate and tranquil B&B with superb bedrooms and thoughtful hosts.

It is impossible to find fault with Tilston Lodge and the excellent way Kathie Ritchie runs this up-market B&B. Set in 16 acres of garden and pasture (for the rare breeds of sheep that the Ritchies rear), it started life as a gentleman's hunting lodge back in Victorian times. The views from many of the windows remain little changed – even the road that runs in front of the house is an old Roman Road. The rooms downstairs are all immaculate, with a smart, tiled hallway opening out into a comfortable and stylish sitting-room (complete with piano) and bay-windowed dining-room with its carved wooden fireplace. The real draw, however, is the three bedrooms. The Rose Room has a four-poster bed, antique furniture and a lovely view, as does the recently redecorated twin room. Saving the best till last, the light and airy Pine Room is luxuriously large, with a four-poster (pine) bed, stencilled cream walls, and a couple of comfy armchairs from which to admire the view from the four windows. The large *en suite* bathroom is big enough for a tub and stand-alone shower. All the bedrooms have lots of thoughtful little extra touches, like nail-polish remover and decanters of sherry.

◑ Open all year ⤤ In Tilston village, turn left at T-junction (signposted Malpas); lodge is 200 yards on right. Private car park ⬛ 1 twin, 2 four-poster; all with bathroom/WC; all with TV, hair-dryer, some with trouser press ⦵ Dining-room, sitting-room, drying-room, garden ⸝ No wheelchair access ◔ No dogs; no smoking ⬚ None accepted ⑂ Single occupancy of twin/double £40 to £45, twin/double £60, four-poster £68. Special breaks available

TINTAGEL **Cornwall** map 1

Trebrea Lodge

Trenale, Tintagel PL34 0HR
TEL: (01840) 770410   FAX: (01840) 770092

Wonderfully dignified retreat, with uninterrupted views and a handful of mysteries.

Overlooking the church, cliffs and sea, this grey-stone Cornish manor house has a few secrets – the curious arrow-shaped pond in the drive, the smugglers' hidey-hole leading to a concealed room (discovered 40 years ago), and the Napoleonic ghost spotted in the quarry will get you thinking. The original house dates back to 1315, and though it received a Regency face-lift and two new wings in 1790, it was not extended backwards – as a result, it remains one room deep, so all the bedrooms have views westwards towards the sea (and sunset), and eastwards over the beautifully unkempt stepped grounds behind the house. Inside, calmness and dignity prevail, inspired by the mutedly rich colours and fabrics, polished flagstones, fully panelled walls and fresh flowers. The best room in the house is the snug – you just want to curl up on the squashy pink sofa in front of the fire, a drink from the honesty bar in hand, and read your favourite book. In the intimate dining-room, a late-summer menu may offer a warm cheese and asparagus tart, followed by a pan-fried salmon fillet with lime and ginger, and may finish with vanilla-flavoured Swiss meringues with a strawberry coulis, and finally Cornish Yarg and Stilton. Most of the bedrooms are in the main house – the one in the annexe is provided with an umbrella for rainy days (watch out for the drunken stairs). All are furnished most pleasingly with antiques and plush individual touches.

◑ Closed Jan, 1 to 13 Feb   ⬚ Leave Tintagel on Boscastle road; turn right at RC church; turn right at top of lane. Private car park   ⬚ 3 twin, 3 double, 1 four-poster; one in annexe; 4 with bathroom/WC, 3 with shower/WC; all with TV, hair-dryer, direct-dial telephone   ⬚ Dining-room, lounge, drying-room, garden   ⬚ No wheelchair access   ● No children under 12; smoking in 1 public room only; dogs £3.50 per night   ⬚ Amex, Delta, MasterCard, Switch, Visa   £ Single occupancy of twin/double £58 to £63, twin/double £70 to £90, four-poster £90; deposit required. Set D £21.50. Special breaks available

TORQUAY **Devon** map 1

Mulberry House

1 Scarborough Road, Torquay TQ2 5UJ
TEL: (01803) 213639

Gentle, graceful restaurant-with-rooms, providing good food and a real welcome.

Very rarely has our inspector felt as welcome as when she arrived one rather blustery evening at Lesley Cooper's dainty and refined establishment among the leviathan seaside hotels of Torquay. Inside, classical music, the smell of good cooking, a cup of herbal tea and a quick soak in the (huge) tub restored body and mind in time to sample some of Lesley's famous food. The restaurant is pretty in white, with lots of prints and pictures on the walls, occasional eclectic knick-knacks, lace tablecloths and chunky tableware from the local pottery. On the menu (chalked on a blackboard) might be a light tomato soup prepared with cream and chives, followed by a mushroom risotto (with arborio rice), Parmesan shavings and pine-nuts, and then the 'most sublime' chocolate and truffle torte. Care and thought have been poured into this place, from the bottles of wine on the landing for guests who are thirsty in the middle of the night to the restfully furnished bedrooms filled with antiques and books. Two extra things would make it perfect – fresh milk, and a fluffy bathrobe to wear across the landing if you're in the room without *en suite* facilities. But it's Lesley's gentle, peaceful character that sets this place apart – quiet, elegant, utterly charming.

◑ Open all year ⊿ From middle of Torquay seafront, turn up Belgrave Road; Scarborough Road is first right; house is on left at end. On-street parking (free) ⊨ 1 twin, 2 double; doubles with bathroom/WC (1 not *en suite*), twin with shower/WC; all with TV, room service, hair-dryer, mini-bar ✇ Restaurant functions (max 30 people incl up to 6 residential), conferences; early suppers for children; babysitting, baby-listening   占. No wheelchair access ● No dogs; no smoking ⊟ None accepted ⒠ Single occupancy of twin/double £35, twin/double £50; deposit required. Set L £8; alc L, D £15. Special breaks available

---

Upper Green Farm

Manor Road, Towersey, Thame OX9 3QR
TEL: (01844) 212496   FAX: (01844) 260399

Gorgeous thatched farmhouse with pond, bedrooms in converted outbuildings and the warmest welcome you could ask for.

On the night of our inspection, Marjorie Aitken dashed off to attend the birth of a grandchild, leaving husband Euan to hold the fort and scramble the free-range eggs at breakfast. Next morning all the guests were asking how things were going, and messages were relayed constantly. All this just goes to show how effortlessly you become absorbed into the family here – Euan's gregarious personality and the joy of the place combine to make you feel immediately at home. Added to this, there's the livestock: Euan will give you the low-down on the habits of geese and ducks, as you feed them breakfast, and Leo the cat patrols the beautiful lawns, the pond, complete with willows, and the spotless farmyard in a most proprietorial fashion. Most of the bedrooms are in the converted Paradise Barn and wistaria-clad milking shed on one side of the farmyard, with two in the fifteenth-century thatched farmhouse on the other side. All are faultlessly restored and filled with antiques, fascinating old pictures, lacy covers and the occasional stuffed bird. There are TV and video units in the bedrooms, with a supply of movies on the dresser in the guests' sitting-room, so if the views (clear to the Chiltern Hills) are not enough for you, you won't be bored. Breakfast is taken in the beamed and countrified barn, under old hayricks and beside a row of geraniums on the window ledge. Euan and Marjorie don't serve an evening meal but are more than willing to help you choose from plenty of good local eateries.

◑ Closed Chr to New Year   ⊡ From Thame ring-road take Towersey exit; farm is just past Towersey Manor on left. Private car park   ⟋ 1 single, 2 twin, 7 double; some in annexe; most with bathroom/WC, some with shower/WC; all with TV, hair-dryer
✧ Breakfast room, lounge, garden; pitch & putt, croquet   ⟏ Wheelchair access to hotel and breakfast room, 4 ground-floor bedrooms, 2 specially equipped for disabled people   ● No children under 13; no dogs; no smoking   ▭ None accepted
£ Single £40, single occupancy of twin/double £40 to £48, twin/double £48 to £60; deposit required.

TRESCO Isles of Scilly   map 1

Island Hotel

Tresco TR24 0PU
TEL: (01720) 422883   FAX: (01720) 423008

Continued praise for this grande dame of hotels on the beautiful island of Tresco.

'The fact that we have stayed at the Island Hotel for the past eight years and have booked to go again next year must speak for itself,' writes one satisfied regular. School holidays are a particularly busy time, with the same weeks automatically booked for you the following year. This magic is worked by a combination of excellent service ('Ivan Curtis, the manager, obviously has a knack of choosing the right staff'), high standards of housekeeping – a new innovation is to be asked if you would 'like turning down' while you are dining – comfortable accommodation and a great location. Huge picture windows make the most of the views from the sitting-room, but be prepared to stay for more than a few days if you want to qualify for prime window seats in the dining-room – a strict pecking order operates. The food is thought to be 'better than last year'; the six-course table d'hôte menus might start with chargrilled medallion of fresh swordfish with chives, capers, anchovies and fresh rosemary served with a ginger and chilli salsa, followed by woodland mushroom and fennel soup, and then braised lamb shanks with crushed new potatoes and chives served with a sweet garlic sauce. The bedrooms in the Flower wing have their own balconies and sitting areas, and four new suites have been added to the hotel's beach side, while some of the old rooms in the house have been converted into three spruce family suites.

◑ Closed Nov to Mar   ⊡ Take helicopter from Penzance to Tresco; car park at heliport; there are no cars on island   ⟋ 5 single, 41 twin/double, 2 suites; family rooms available; some in annexe; all with bathroom/WC; all with TV, room service, hair-dryer, direct-dial telephone, some with mini-bar   ✧ Restaurant, bar, lounge, drying-room, study, games room, garden; conferences (max 50 people residential), functions; heated outdoor swimming-pool, tennis; early suppers for children; cots, high chairs, toys, playroom, babysitting, baby-listening   ⟏ Wheelchair access to hotel (ramp) and restaurant, 3 ground-floor bedrooms   ● No dogs   ▭ Amex, Delta, MasterCard, Switch, Visa   £ Single £80 to £110, single occupancy of twin/double £120 to £165, twin/double £160 to £310, family room £228 to £363, suite £125 to £195; deposit required. Set D £32.50

Mortal Man

Troutbeck, Windermere LA23 1PL
TEL: (015394) 33193   FAX: (015394) 31261
EMAIL: the-mortalman@btinternet.com

*Traditional Cumbrian pub-with-rooms in picturesque location
north of Windermere.*

Among all the scenic spots of the Lake District, it would be hard to better the
countryside around Troutbeck village. The windows of the Mortal Man inn look
out on grandly rolling green hills and the bleaker moors of Kirkstone beyond.
It's sheep country; Beatrix Potter owned land here, as a highly respected
Herdwick farmer. This white-painted pub on the edge of the village has been a
local landmark since 1689, and its rather foreboding name is soon dispelled by
the comical sign. It recently passed from family to company ownership and is
now undergoing a steady overhaul. The new owners seem to be keeping its
charms intact: sealed-unit double glazing, for example, efficiently keeps out the
draughts while still transmitting the full glory of the fell views. The bars are
typically furnished with wooden settles and wheel-back chairs and feature
beams and open fires. Next door, a pleasantly furnished residents' lounge offers
more upholstered comfort – help yourself to coffee. The restaurant's mud-
coloured furnishings, though well kept, could do with a face-lift, but cheering
efforts are made with china, pictures and plants. The bedrooms, too, are a bit
short on character, but are nevertheless spacious, light, warm, quiet and well
equipped, and have the views. The staff are young, informal and friendly.

◗ Open all year   ⊠ Troutbeck is on A592, 3 miles north of Windermere. Private car
park   ⊨ 6 twin, 7 double; family rooms available; all with bathroom/WC; all with TV,
hair-dryer, trouser press, direct-dial telephone   ⊘ Restaurant, 2 bars, lounge,
drying-room, conservatory, garden; functions (max 27 people residential/non-
residential), conferences; early suppers for children; high chairs   ⅙ No wheelchair
access   ● No dogs in restaurant   ⊟ Amex, Delta, Diners, MasterCard, Switch, Visa
£ Single occupancy of twin/double £56 to £61, twin/double £112 to £122, family room
(room rate + £30 to £35 per child) (rates incl dinner); deposit required. Bar L £4. Special
breaks available

Old Manor

Trowle, Trowbridge BA14 9BL
TEL: (01225) 777393   FAX: (01225) 765443
EMAIL: queen.anne.house@dial.pipex.com
WEB SITE: www.accomodata.co.uk/060295/

*Hybrid medieval/Queen Anne house, with a series of converted
outhouses, offering good-value accommodation.*

With a pedigree that dates back to the Domesday book, Barry and Diane
Humphreys' Old Manor is a house that's entitled to feel pretty pleased with

itself. It has metamorphosed over the years, so that its medieval core has acquired a rather grand Queen Anne frontage, while more recent times have seen the once-derelict old barn and stable block converted to provide a harmonious cluster of additional accommodation. The décor in the public rooms, including the three spacious lounges, enthusiastically embraces a rustic theme, so you can expect to see lots of stripped pine, exposed stone and chintzy drapes, set off by strong, confident colours. Farmhouse chairs and dried flowers suspended from the beams set the tone in a restaurant that is dominated by a huge stone fireplace. The fairly simple menu embraces a clutch of old favourites, such as oeufs florentine, followed by fresh local trout with prawns and almonds, and then treacle pudding with custard. The bedrooms vary in style and size, with some featuring antique half-tester or four-poster beds, while the rooms upstairs in the main house have massive A-frame beams hewn from a single tree. For something a bit different, stay in one of the split-level four-poster suites in the converted barn.

◑ Closed Chr; restaurant closed Sun eve ⊿ On A363, between Bradford-on-Avon and Trowbridge. Private car park ⊨ 1 single, 1 twin, 9 double, 3 four-poster; some in annexe; family rooms and suites available; all with bathroom/WC; all with TV, room service, hair-dryer, direct-dial telephone, some with mini-bar ⊘ Restaurant, 3 lounges, library, conservatory, garden; early suppers for children; cots, high chairs, baby-listening ♿ Wheelchair access to hotel (ramp) and restaurant, 9 ground-floor bedrooms ● No dogs; smoking in 1 lounge and some bedrooms only ▭ Amex, Delta, Diners, MasterCard, Switch, Visa £ Single £49, single occupancy of twin/double £58, twin/double £55 to £70, four-poster £70 to £85, family room £65 to £80; deposit required. Alc D £18.50

TRURO Cornwall
map 1

Alverton Manor

Tregolls Road, Truro TR1 1ZQ
TEL: (01872) 276633   FAX: (01872) 222989
EMAIL: alverton@connexions.co.uk

Imposing Gothic-style pile, with ecclesiastical overtones and grand bedrooms.

This impressive 200-year-old building was a convent until 10 years ago; last Christmas, a nun who had been a resident came to visit and commented on the improvements – the sinks have been moved into the bathrooms (they had been outside the bedrooms in the corridors before), and the former mortuary (now the downstairs meeting-room) is today decidedly warmer. The ecclesiastical tone remains, however, particularly in the restaurant, where, surrounded by stone columns, you might try smoked chargrilled duck with asparagus, croûtons and bacon in an orange sauce, followed by oven-baked fillet of salmon on a bed of vegetable linguini, and, if you've room, a brandy-snap basket filled with mango mousse and summer fruits. The nuns were obviously keen horticulturists, and full-time gardeners are now needed to maintain the six acres of rare trees and shrubs. The huge chapel, which is mainly used for functions, has unfortunately been denuded of all its former character – red carpet covers the floor, and the stained-glass windows are covered with grimy drapes. Any shabbiness in the public rooms, however, is made up for in the bedrooms, which are well proportioned, have inviting beds and plush fabrics, and make clever use of the building's original features, particularly the arched, mullioned windows.

◑ Open all year ⏢ On A39 (Tregolls Road) from St Austell leading into Truro. Private car park ⇤ 6 single, 5 twin, 19 double, 4 suites; all with bathroom/WC; all with TV, room service, hair-dryer, trouser press, direct-dial telephone ⌁ Restaurant, 2 bars, lounge, drying-room, games room, garden; functions (max 220 people incl up to 62 residential); conferences; civil wedding licence; fishing, golf, snooker, clay-pigeon shooting; early suppers for children; cots, high chairs, babysitting, baby-listening ⓰ Wheelchair access to hotel (1 step) and restaurant, 3 ground-floor bedrooms, 1 room specially equipped for disabled people ◓ No smoking in restaurant; dogs £3 per night ⧠ Amex, Delta, Diners, MasterCard, Switch, Visa £ Single £67, single occupancy of twin/double £79, twin/double £99 to £114, suite £139; deposit required. Set L £14/£16.50, D £14.50; alc D £25. Special breaks available

---

TRUSHAM Devon   map 1

Cridford Inn   [NEW ENTRY]

Trusham, Newton Abbot TQ13 0NR
TEL: (01626) 853694 (AND FAX)

Attractive thatched hostelry in sleepy Devon village.

Kim and William Farrell have just taken over this old thatched pub, after returning from several years' work in Malaysia. They would have been hard-pushed to find a more established, more English place than this – it was *rebuilt* in 1081 (a chunk of the restaurant floor has been glassed over so you can see the datestone below), and there are two ghosts: a nun (the place was once a convent) and a cavalier. The public rooms are flagged and beamed; you can eat at the bar or in the more formal restaurant, which offers dishes such as home-made chicken-liver pâté, followed by French-trimmed lamb cutlets served on a rosemary-scented gravy, surrounded by a light puff pastry. Bedrooms are named after Devon rivers – Otter is a spruce yellow-and-blue room with a patchwork quilt, Teign has low beams and a very inviting bed, and Dart and Exe have good bathrooms.

◑ Closed Wed; restaurant closed Mon to Thur eve ⏢ From A38 south-west of Exeter, take B3193 and follow signs to Trusham; inn is in lower part of village. Private car park ⇤ 2 single, 2 twin, 2 double; 3 with bathroom/WC, 3 with shower/WC; all with TV ⌁ Restaurant, bar, garden; functions (max 70 people incl up to 6 residential); early suppers for children ⓰ No wheelchair access ◓ Dogs by arrangement, £3 per day ⧠ Delta, MasterCard, Switch, Visa £ Single £50, single occupancy of twin/double £60, twin/double £70; deposit required. Alc L, D £19.50

 This denotes that you can get a twin or double room for £70 or less per night inclusive of breakfast.

TUNBRIDGE WELLS Kent   map 3

Hotel du Vin & Bistro | NEW ENTRY |

Crescent Road, Tunbridge Wells TN1 2LY
TEL: (01892) 526455   FAX: (01892) 512044
EMAIL: reception@tunbridgewells.hotelduvin.co.uk

*A sequel that's as good as the original – comfortable rooms, top food
and great atmosphere.*

Following in the footsteps of a mega-successful elder sibling is never easy, but it
looks as though this younger sister will hold her own. Four years after the first
Hotel du Vin & Bistro opened in Winchester, the winning formula of 'good
quality at sensible prices' has been duplicated here, but on a bigger, bolder scale.
Messrs Basset, Chapon, Hutson and Chittick – a combination that sounds more
like a firm of lawyers than a company of hoteliers – have transformed the old
Calverley Hotel into a relaxed and discreetly elegant place in which to stay. A
Grade II-listed sandstone building dating from 1762, it has a prominent hilltop
position in the centre of town. Before dinner, you can relax in front of a log fire in
the Burgundy Bar, surrounded by excellent painted copies of famous works of
art, or play billiards in the Havana Room. The bustling bistro is a noisy place
when full, with chatter and the clink of cutlery echoing off the bare floorboards
and yellow walls. With an emphasis on modern Mediterranean cuisine, a meal
might include green-pea risotto with crab mascarpone, honey-roast confit of
duck with braised lentils, and an apple crème brûlée; vegetables are extra, and
there is a huge wine list to peruse. As in Winchester, each bedroom is sponsored
by a wine company, so corporate memorabilia feature, in a colour scheme of
cream, blue and black. Sisal carpets, fluffy bathrobes, Egyptian-cotton sheets,
CD players and fantastic showers are standard features. The only niggle in this
otherwise almost perfect establishment is having to pay extra for breakfast.

◖ Open all year   ▨ At intersection of Mount Pleasant Road and Crescent
Road/Church Road, take Crescent Road; hotel is 150 yards on right, just past Phillips
House. Private car park   ⊨ 19 twin/double, 6 double; all with bathroom/WC; all with
satellite TV, hair-dryer, mini-bar, trouser press, direct-dial telephone, radio, CD player
✅ Restaurant, bar, lounge, games room, garden; functions (max 70 people incl up to
50 residential), conferences; early suppers for children, by arrangement   ♿
Wheelchair access to hotel (1 step) and restaurant, WC (unisex), lift to bedrooms
● No dogs   ▭ Amex, Delta, Diners, MasterCard, Switch, Visa   £ Single occupancy
of twin/double £75 to £109, twin/double £75 to £109; deposit required. Continental B
£6.50, cooked B £9.50; alc L £24.50, D £27

TURNERS HILL West Sussex   map 3

Alexander House

East Street, Turners Hill, Crawley RH10 4QD
TEL: (01342) 714914   FAX: (01342) 717328

Lavish, luxurious country-house hotel, in secluded tranquillity.

If you're searching for intimate, cosy bedrooms, or subtle, unobtrusive décor, then this is definitely not the place for you. Over-the-top opulence reigns supreme at Alexander House – a fact that is instantly apparent from the moment you arrive: over the entrance door is a vast portico supported by honey-coloured stone columns of great girth, which looks unnervingly like the stage set for *Aïda*. Inside, the public rooms are lined with pale oak panelling and filled with delicate chandeliers, fine art, flamboyant furnishings and antiques. The liberal use of mirrors throughout the house magnifies the almost overwhelming effect of all this sumptuousness. As for fireplaces – well, the one in the bar is two-sided, so you can peek through the flames to the other half of the room, and the library has a cavernous, carved creation that could house a family of four. The standard bedrooms are stylish and comfortable, but pale beside the lavish suites and premium rooms – the Napoleonic four-poster in Goodwood is a scarlet-and-gold domed extravaganza, while Henley is the size of a small flat, with room after room available to roam in. If you can tear yourself away from your room, dinner offers such delights as a leek, lobster and langoustine terrine, followed by an asparagus and herb risotto with a red-pepper coulis, and then a lemon posset with a red-berry compote.

○ Open all year ⤴ Off B2110, 4 miles south of East Grinstead. Private car park ⤶ 1 single, 2 twin, 8 double, 2 four-poster, 2 suites; family rooms available; all with bathroom/WC; all with TV, room service, hair-dryer, trouser press, direct-dial telephone ✓ Restaurant, bar, lounge, TV room, library, games room, garden; functions (max 80 people incl up to 17 residential), conferences; civil wedding licence; tennis, croquet, snooker ⅄ No wheelchair access ● No children under 7; no dogs ☐ Amex, Diners, MasterCard, Switch, Visa £ Single £120, single occupancy of twin/double £120, twin/double £155, four-poster £285, family room/suite £195; deposit required. Set L £22, D £28; alc D £47. (Prices valid till Jan 1999.) Special breaks available

---

TUTBURY Staffordshire   map 5

Mill House   ℒ

Cornmill Lane, Tutbury, Burton upon Trent DE13 9HA
TEL: (01283) 813300/813634

Smart B&B in a mill house just outside Tutbury.

No large sign marks Elizabeth and James Chapman's up-market B&B, but the three-storey, red-brick Georgian mill house is unmistakable (the mill itself, now part of the Chapmans' clothes shop, is next door and still has some of its original workings). From the front of the house there are views across to Tutbury castle, a ruin since the Civil War, and the millstream flows underneath. From the window of one of the twin bedrooms, Moseley, you can watch the ducks, and even the occasional kingfisher or woodpecker, when not dipping in to one of the hundreds of books in the room. Vernon, the double room, is grander, with stylish furnishings in blue and cream, a sitting area and spacious bathroom. The breakfast room has a sturdy elegance to it too, with an inglenook fireplace, old maps on the walls and white linen. There is only one table, but those who prefer not to socialise at the start of the day need not worry – Elizabeth usually staggers breakfast times. She takes pride in serving a good breakfast: fruit followed by cereals then full English.

◑ Closed Chr & New Year   ⤵ At bottom of High Street in Tutbury village, turn into Cornmill Lane and continue ½ mile. Private car park   ⬅ 2 twin, 1 double; all with shower/WC exc 1 twin with bathroom/WC; all with TV, hair-dryer   ✅ Breakfast room, garden   ⑇ No wheelchair access   ⊖ No dogs; no smoking   ▭ None accepted   £ Single occupancy of twin/double £35 to £38, twin/double £50 to £55; deposit required.

UCKFIELD East Sussex   map 3

Hooke Hall

250 High Street, Uckfield TN22 1EN
TEL: (01825) 761578   FAX: (01825) 768025

Friendly owners and unpretentious comfort, plus Italian cooking to die for.

It's hard to believe that when Juliet and Alister Percy arrived 12 years ago this beautiful Queen Anne house was divided up into offices. Since then a lot of work and love have gone into transforming it into a gracious, comfortable hotel. The informal, personable style of the Percys is reflected in the bedrooms – not least in the naming of the first-floor rooms after famous lovers. So, if you fancy sleeping in the company of Casanova or Lillie Langtry, this is the place to come; and Madame Pompadour has room enough for a romp or two in a decadently frou-frou four-poster. Up under the eaves, via a rather steep staircase, the second-floor rooms are just numbered ('We ran out of lovers,' says Juliet); watch your head on the beams and sloping ceilings. Back down in the refined restaurant, there's a whole host of dishes not often seen this side of the Alps, from barley and lettuce soup with sauté prawns to gnocchetti in a beef ragù for starters, and pork fillet with sultanas and white wine to follow. Italian cheeses or a tempting array of desserts, such as zabaglione, make the perfect end to the meal.

◑ Closed Chr; restaurant closed Sun eve   ⤵ At northern end of High Street in centre of Uckfield. Private car park   ⬅ 1 twin, 7 double, 1 four-poster; all with bathroom/WC exc 1 twin/1 double with shower/WC; all with TV, hair-dryer, trouser press, direct-dial telephone, some with mini-bar   ✅ Restaurant, 2 lounges, garden; conferences (max 24 people incl up to 9 residential), functions; babysitting, baby-listening   ⑇ No wheelchair access   ⊖ No children under 12; no dogs; no smoking in restaurant   ▭ Amex, Delta, MasterCard, Visa   £ Single occupancy of twin/double £45 to £50, twin/double £65 to £70, four-poster £110 to £120; deposit required. Continental B £6, cooked B £8.50; set L £10/£14; alc D £25. Special breaks available

---

Horsted Place

Little Horsted, Uckfield TN22 5TS
TEL: (01825) 750581   FAX: (01825) 750459
EMAIL: hotel@horstedplace.co.uk

Stately Gothic country-house hotel with royal connections.

Lovers of fine architectural detail will enjoy this splendid example of Gothic revivalist architecture worked on by Augustus Pugin, better known for his work on the Houses of Parliament. As a private house, the home of Lord and Lady Nevill, it was visited by the Queen – and yes, you can stay in the room in which she slept (called the Windsor Suite). Now Horsted Place is operated as a relaxed country-house hotel, with relaxed staff – a good weekend bolt-hole, with its indoor pool and access to a golf course that is also part of the Horsted estate. Downstairs, the public rooms are warm and comfortable, with plenty of sofas to curl up on, fresh flowers and antiques to admire. Dinner in the Pugin Restaurant could be chosen from the long and expensive à la carte menu – cod-cake, perhaps, followed by lightly smoked local ostrich (not many people know that Sussex is known for its ostrich) on a purée of celeriac and braised shallots, pancetta and Barolo wine sauce – or from the shorter, but more reasonable, table d'hôte. There are a couple of good choices for vegetarians, too.

On the first floor are the suites, large rooms with plenty of space to relax in – though our inspector was rather put off by the pervasive smell of cigarette smoke on a winter's inspection. The double rooms in the East Wing are less lavish, but most still have room for a sitting area.

◑ Open all year   ⤵ At junction of A26 and A22, 2 miles south of Uckfield. Private car park   ⊨ 3 twin, 3 double, 14 suites; some in annexe; all with bathroom/WC; all with TV, hair-dryer, direct-dial telephone, some with room service; no tea/coffee-making facilities in rooms   ✅ Restaurant, lounge, library, garden; functions (max 150 people incl up to 40 residential), conferences; civil wedding licence; golf, heated indoor swimming-pool, tennis; early suppers for children; cots, high chairs, babysitting   ♿ No wheelchair access   ⬤ No children under 12; no dogs   ⊟ Amex, Delta, Diners, MasterCard, Switch, Visa   £ Single occupancy of twin/double £90 to £100, twin/double £90 to £100, suite £140 to £230. Cooked B £3; snack menu L, D £10; set L £18, D £30; alc L, D £33. Special breaks available

---

UFFINGTON Oxfordshire   map 2

The Craven

Fernham Road, Uffington, Faringdon SN7 7RD
TEL: (01367) 820449

Good food, a friendly welcome and immense charm at a quintessentially English cottage.

A thatched roof, roses climbing round the door, a dog wagging his tail to greet you, a white horse carved into the hillside nearby – what else could be more perfectly English? The nearby village is even delightfully sleepy. Carol Wadsworth's family has lived here for more than 20 years, though that is but a fraction of the cottage's 300-odd years of history – it started life as a hostelry, and was mentioned in *Tom Brown's Schooldays* as a 'low-lying wayside inn'. Be prepared for its higgledy-piggledy interior: beams so low you have to stoop, a stone spiral staircase, twisting corridors and stairs, and no two windows the same. Carol has furnished the place with charming antiques and decorated in bold, stylish colours. Guests can enjoy her ready conversational style as they sit around the communal table for dinner in the L-shaped kitchen – let her know in advance if you want to dine in. On the (suitably English) menu might be watercress soup, followed by pork in scrumpy cider with lots of fresh vegetables, and home-made ice-cream to round off the meal. The best of the bedrooms is the *en suite* four-poster room on the ground floor; the others share a bathroom, reached along a creaky corridor, but all are endearingly done out with lacy bedspreads and embroidered Victorian pillowslips.

◖ Open all year   ⛝ On the northern outskirts of Uffington, south-west of Oxford. Private car park   ⇥ 1 single, 1 twin, 1 double, 2 four-poster, 1 family room; one in annexe; half with shower/WC; all with room service, hair-dryer   ⊘ Breakfast room, dining-room, lounge, drying-room, garden; functions (max 14 people residential/non-residential), conferences; early suppers for children; babysitting   ♿ Wheelchair access (1 step), 2 ground-floor bedrooms, 1 specially equipped for disabled people ● No dogs or smoking   ⬚ Diners, MasterCard, Visa   £ Single £26, single occupancy of twin/double £30, twin/double £52, four-poster £60, family room £65; deposit required. Set D £15.50 to £17.50

ULLINGSWICK Herefordshire   map 5

The Steppes

Ullingswick, Hereford HR1 3JG
TEL: (01432) 820424   FAX: (01432) 820042

Both food and accommodation are hard to fault in this superbly run hotel-restaurant.

The original white-painted farmhouse dates mostly from the sixteenth century, but the antique-looking courtyard outbuildings housing the bedroom accommodation are clever reconstructions in period style by owner Henry Howland, a one-time solicitor who has discovered an impressive talent and enthusiasm for ambitious DIY. Apparently deep in rural seclusion, the Steppes is actually within easy reach of Hereford. The main house contains the public rooms, which are thoroughly personal, interesting spaces. They include a cosy cellar bar with cobbled floors and stone walls, a relaxing sitting-room with smart sofas and a stone fireplace, and the dining-room, where Tricia Howland's excellent cooking is served – book ahead for dinner, or hungry non-residents may snap up your place. The courtyard bedrooms are warm, charming, spacious and thoughtfully equipped with masses of extras, including fresh milk in the fridge for your morning tea, and helpful information packs.

◖ Closed Dec till Chr, Jan after New Year   ⛝ Just off A417 Gloucester to Leominster road. Private car park   ⇥ 2 twin, 4 double; all in annexe; all with bathroom/WC; all with TV, room service, hair-dryer, mini-bar, direct-dial telephone, radio   ⊘ Dining-room, bar, sitting-room, drying-room, garden   ♿ No wheelchair access ● No children under 12; no dogs in public rooms; smoking in sitting-room only ⬚ Amex, Delta, MasterCard, Switch, Visa   £ Single occupancy of twin/double £50, twin/double £80 to £90; deposit required. Set D £26. Special breaks available

---

Many hotels put up their tariffs in the spring. You are advised to confirm prices when you book.

Sharrow Bay

Ullswater, Penrith CA10 2LZ
TEL: (017684) 86301   FAX: (017684) 86349

A Lakeland legend, determined to keep the show going after the sad demise of its founder.

This year, the fiftieth anniversary of Sharrow Bay's inauguration as Britain's first real country-house hotel, saw Francis Coulson's death. Truly the end of an era in hotel-keeping – except that things go on much as before on the southern shores of Ullswater, just as its former owner wished. Brian Sack, Sharrow Bay's co-owner, holds the reins, with the loyal band of staff assembled over many years, plus two energetic new managers, Nigel Lawrence and Nigel Lightburn. For many devotees, Sharrow Bay is simply the best that the Lake District (or anywhere else for that matter) can offer by way of luxury accommodation. Beautifully located in 12 acres of picturesque foreshore grounds, it is furnished in a mannered, overblown decorative style which has come to be known as 'Sharrow Bay' – crystal, clocks, cherubs, candlesticks, china and chintz. As the staff admit, they couldn't change things if they wanted to – their guests simply won't let them. So Sharrow Bay lives on, continually refurbished in faithful replicas of itself. And its success is remarkable. The cooking still glows undimmed in all major food guides; the service is faultlessly attentive ('they chat everyone up,' remarked one guest); the cosseting and the location remain utterly seductive.

○ Closed Dec to late Feb   ↗ Leave M6 at Junction 40 and follow signs for Ullswater; at Pooley Bridge turn right for Howtown; follow road for 2 miles to lakeside. Private car park   ⊨ 3 single, 20 twin/double, 3 cottage suites; some in annexe; most with bathroom/WC, 1 with shower/WC; all with TV, room service, hair-dryer, trouser press, direct-dial telephone, some with mini-bar; no tea/coffee-making facilities in rooms ⊘ 2 dining-rooms, 4 lounges, drying-room, conservatory, garden; conferences (max 12 people residential)   ⅃ No wheelchair access   ● No children under 13; no dogs; no smoking in bedrooms   ▭ MasterCard, Switch, Visa   £ Single £115 to £145, single occupancy of twin/double £190, twin/double £290 to £360, suite £340 to £360 (rates incl dinner). Set L £35, D £46. Special breaks available

Bay Horse

Canal Foot, Ulverston LA12 9EL
TEL: (01229) 583972   FAX: (01229) 580502
EMAIL: reservations@bayhorse.furness.co.uk
WEB SITE: www.furness.co.uk/bayhorse

Superb location on Morecambe Bay for this sophisticated and well-managed pub.

Ulverston itself is a fine little market town, but to reach the Bay Horse you have to pass through some fairly unprepossessing outskirts, including a Glaxo-

Wellcome drug factory. At the far end of the road, however, you'll find this yellow-painted pub which virtually paddles in Morecambe Bay at high tide. A former coaching-inn for the perilous short-cut across the bay's shifting sands, the original building dates back to the 1750s and retains an old-world charm in the twin-roomed bar. Though simply furnished, it's far from run-of-the-mill, with fresh flowers, magazines to read on the wide window sills, and animal cartoons on the walls – and is extremely well kept (visit the award-winning loos). Most attention focuses on the restaurant, a glazed extension overlooking the sea; here Robert Lyons, a Tovey-trained protégé turned hotelier, works culinary wonders. The bedrooms are in a sympathetically designed modern wing to one side. Named after the wading birds that frequent the mud-flats at low tide, all but one (the cheapest) enjoy wonderful views and are contemporary and comfortable, with books, games and lots of extras. Bring your binoculars, bird-lovers – and work up an appetite.

◖ Open all year From A590 on outskirts of Ulverston, follow signs for Canal Foot. Private car park 3 twin, 4 double; all with bathroom/WC; all with TV, room service, hair-dryer, trouser press, direct-dial telephone; no tea/coffee-making facilities in rooms Restaurant, bar, conservatory; functions (max 50 people incl up to 14 residential); civil wedding licence No wheelchair access No children under 12; no dogs in public rooms MasterCard, Switch, Visa Single occupancy of twin/double £85, twin/double £160. Bar/bistro L £12.50; set L £17; alc L, D £23. Special breaks available

---

UPPER SLAUGHTER Gloucestershire   map 5

Lords of the Manor

Upper Slaughter, Bourton-on-the-Water, Cheltenham GL54 2JD
TEL: (01451) 820243   FAX: (01451) 820696

A former rectory in a dreamy spot, now an up-market, well-managed country-house hotel.

If you're considering staying here, chances are that you're also weighing up Lower Slaughter Manor (see entry) just down the road. In terms of location, there's little to choose between them; the village of Upper Slaughter is idyllic – albeit in a less picture-perfect way than Lower Slaughter – and the hotel surveys eight lovely acres of gardens and parkland, including a small lake. The honey-coloured building – seventeenth century, with extensive Victorian, and sympathetic modern, additions – is less stylised and intimate, and the atmosphere somewhat more casual, than its competitor down the road. Its sitting-room and bar are perhaps the most enjoyable rooms, both for their unaffected elegance and views of the grounds. The restaurant, split between a chic main dining-room and conservatory, is the setting for fine dinners, which are praised for their first-class ingredients and lack of over-elaboration. If you really want to push the boat out, opt for the chef's no-choice, seven-course *menu dégustation*. The swish bedrooms have a pleasingly lived-in, rather than squeakily pristine, look. The choicest, available at most price levels, lie at the front of the main house, overlooking the grounds; others are located in the converted barn and granary to the rear.

◑ Open all year 🔁 Upper Slaughter lies west of A429, between Stow-on-the-Wold and Bourton-on-the-Water. Private car park 🛏 2 single, 10 twin, 12 double, 3 four-poster; family rooms available; all with bathroom/WC; all with TV, room service, hair-dryer, direct-dial telephone; no tea/coffee-making facilities in rooms ⊘ Restaurant, bar, sitting-room, 2 libraries, garden; functions (max 60 people incl up to 50 residential), conferences; civil wedding licence; fishing; early suppers for children; cots, high chairs, babysitting, baby-listening 🦽 Wheelchair access to hotel and restaurant, 7 ground-floor bedrooms ● No dogs; no smoking in restaurant ▭ Amex, Delta, Diners, MasterCard, Switch, Visa £ Single £95, single occupancy of twin/double from £130, twin/double £130 to £195, four-poster £195 to £265, family room (room rate + £20 per child); deposit required. Bar/bistro L £10 to £12; set L £17/£20, D £32/£36.50; alc L £45, D £51. Special breaks available

---

UPPINGHAM Rutland map 5

Lake Isle

16 High Street East, Uppingham, Oakham LE15 9PZ
TEL: (01572) 822951 (AND FAX)

Stylish high-street restaurant-with-rooms noted for its comprehensive cellar.

Uppingham has one of England's prettiest high streets, and right in the middle is Claire and David Whitfield's town-house restaurant and hotel. With its swagged curtains, old pine furniture and displays of plate on dressers, the restaurant has something of a French farmhouse atmosphere – a style which continues up into the bedrooms, all named after French wine-growing regions. Décor and furnishings vary, but all are well equipped with welcome extras like home-made biscuits, sherry, fruit and iced water. There is a pleasant sitting-room – cosy with terracotta walls and Austrian blinds – as well as the bar, which has been recently extended. David's five-course table d'hôte dinners show an inventive touch: five-bean and sun-dried tomato soup, perhaps, followed by a brochette of mussels and scallops on wild rice, roast duck breast, and finally cheeses with home-made malt loaf, desserts and coffee. There should be a wine to suit most tastes from the choice of about 300 – including one of the best selections of half bottles you could hope for.

◑ Open all year 🔁 In Uppingham's High Street, reached via Reeves Yard. Private car park 🛏 1 single, 2 twin, 7 double, 2 suites; suites in annexe; family rooms available; all with bathroom/WC exc single with shower/WC; all with TV, limited room service, hair-dryer, trouser press, direct-dial telephone ⊘ Restaurant, bar, sitting-room, garden; functions (max 40 people incl up to 23 residential), conferences; early suppers for children 🦽 No wheelchair access· ● No dogs in public rooms; smoking restricted in restaurant ▭ Amex, Diners, MasterCard, Visa £ Single and single occupancy of twin/double £52, twin/double £69, four-poster £74, family room/suite £79; deposit required. Set L £10.50 to £13.50, D £22.50 to £25.50 (prices valid till Mar 1999). Special breaks available

---

Use the index at the back of the book if you know the name of a hotel but are unsure about its precise location.

Welland Court

Upton upon Severn, Worcester WR8 0ST
TEL: (01684) 594426 (AND FAX)

Posh B&B in a grand, rural home with high-quality bedrooms.

Welland Court goes one step further than the common practice among up-market B&Bs of having no sign to indicate that guests are welcome – here there is no mention of even the house's name. That Philip and Elizabeth Archer should riposte 'Is there a sign at Buckingham Palace?' perhaps gives some idea of just how imposing their Georgian-fronted house is. It stands in a supremely peaceful spot at the end of a no-through lane, surveying its 23 acres of land that includes a trout-stocked lake (free fishing on offer) and the Malvern Hills beyond. Inside, not all is what it seems. For example, the pillars in the palatial black-and-white tiled hall turn out to be *faux*-marble rather than the real thing, while beams and even exposed wattle and daub in the bedrooms reveal the house to be far older (fifteenth-century, to be exact) than its façade suggests. The bedrooms are enchantingly furnished with antiques, and come with pleasing touches such as clothes brushes, mini-decanters of whisky, and a turn-down in the evening. The sitting-room is perhaps too formal to be user-friendly, and breakfast may be more relaxed when served in the conservatory than amid the family silver in the dining-room.

◑ Closed 25 Dec 🅿 From Upton upon Severn go 3 miles west on A4104; turn left at telephone kiosk; follow signs for Welland Court. Private car park 🛏 2 twin, 1 double; all with bathroom/WC; all with TV, hair-dryer ✥ Dining-room, sitting-room, conservatory, drying-room, garden; functions (max 50 people incl up to 6 residential); fishing ⅙ No wheelchair access ⬤ No dogs ⊟ None accepted £ Single occupancy of twin/double £43, twin/double £65; deposit required. Set L £15, D £35 (by arrangement)

Curdon Mill

Vellow, Williton, Taunton TA4 4LS
TEL: (01984) 656522 FAX: (01984) 656197

Good food at a family-run former mill deep in the Somerset countryside.

This lonely spot at the foot of the Quantocks provides an agreeable setting for Richard and Daphne Criddle's converted mill house. An abundant creeper smothers the lines of the detached red-sandstone building, and this, plus a lovely front garden, a glorious terrace complete with outdoor swimming-pool, and the presence of free-ranging chickens, confirm that here's a place where you can enjoy a little of the good life. You'll be in the pink in the cosy sitting-room, where assorted candy-coloured and dusky tones are set off by floral-patterned sofas and winged armchairs, while a variety of huntin' 'n' shootin' prints, market scenes and a vision of the mill by a local artist line the walls. Things move up a gear in the relentlessly rustic restaurant, which retains the heavy metal paraphernalia of the mill's winding shaft, as well as a well-laden dresser, beams and polished wooden tables. Daphne Criddle's food features home-grown or locally sourced produce wherever possible, so the terrine of trout with herb salad that kicks off your dinner may have been tickled from the millstream. Follow it up with West Country fillet of beef with celeriac dauphinois and truffle *jus*, and finally a board of local farmhouse cheeses. The bedrooms are handsomely furnished: Walnut is notable for its fine walnut bed and suite, Candy is delicately feminine and River allows you to be lulled to sleep by the babbling brook.

◑ Open all year; restaurant closed Sun eve　▣ Take turning to Yellow off A358; hotel is 1 mile further on, on left. Private car park　🛏 3 twin, 3 double; 1 twin with bathroom/WC, 5 with shower/WC; all with TV, room service, hair-dryer　⌖ Restaurant, bar, sitting-room, garden; functions (max 65 people incl up to 12 residential), conferences; civil wedding licence; fishing, heated outdoor swimming-pool, clay-pigeon shooting　♿ No wheelchair access　● No children under 8; kennel for dogs; smoking in sitting-room only　▭ Amex, Delta, MasterCard, Switch, Visa　£ Single occupancy of twin/double £40, twin/double £60; deposit required. Bar/bistro L £5.50; set D £19.50; alc L £12.50, D £22.50

VENTNOR Isle of Wight　　　　　　　　　　　　　　　　map 2

Hillside

Mitchell Avenue, Ventnor PO38 1DR
TEL: (01983) 852271 (AND FAX)

Good-value, relaxing and friendly hotel with views over Ventnor.

Brenda Hart is as relaxed and unpretentious as this simple, thatched hotel set at the foot of overgrown hills above Ventnor. The family memorabilia on the landing, the freely roaming cats and slightly worn sofas make the hotel feel lived in and encourage you to relax. You could try out the rocking chair in the lounge, help yourself to reading matter from the stacks of magazines and crowded bookshelves, or just sit on comfy sofas in the bar. Corridors are painted sunny yellow or peach, and bedrooms are individually styled with floral fabrics and a selection of Victorian furniture. Brenda and Peter are continually making improvements; this year they have added baths and are planning to create another single room, in response to demand from guests. By November, all rooms should be *en suite*, but meanwhile, where necessary, bathrobes are provided for the short hop across the landing. In another considerate gesture, those in bedrooms without sea views are offered a window seat in the dining-room. Meals are home-cooked by Brenda and her daughter and include a good selection of vegetarian dishes. At the far end of the dining-room, the plant-filled conservatory opens on to the garden and the views over Ventnor's rooftops. The gardens extend to the back of the house, with St Boniface Downs directly behind.

❍ Open all year ⤢ Just outside Ventnor, off B3327 Newport road. Private car park
⤢ 1 single, 2 twin, 7 double, 1 family room; some with bathroom/WC, some with
shower/WC; all with TV, hair-dryer ⊘ Dining-room, bar, lounge, drying-room, library,
conservatory, garden ♿ No wheelchair access ● No children under 5; no dogs in
public rooms; smoking in bar and some bedrooms only ▭ Amex, Delta, MasterCard,
Switch, Visa £ Single £20 to £23, single occupancy of twin/double £20 to £33,
twin/double £39 to £45, family room £49 to £56; deposit required. Bar L £2.50 to £4.50;
set D £9.50

Royal Hotel   NEW ENTRY

Belgrave Road, Ventnor PO38 1JJ
TEL: (01983) 852186   FAX: (01983) 855395
EMAIL: royalhotel@zetnet.co.uk

Regal atmosphere in an imposing, pale stone building set above the town's main centre.

In Ventnor's heyday as a Victorian spa town, the Royal was used as an annexe to
Osborne House for the Queen's guests. As you look down from the hotel,
catching glimpses of the sea, the atmosphere and surroundings convince you this
must be the cream of Ventnor's accommodation. Every member of staff, from
reception to room service, seems to know the importance of good service – owner
William Bailey is the younger brother of that shining star of hospitality, Nichola
Haywood at Seaview (see entry). He has transformed the hotel since buying it
from Forte four years ago and is a visible presence, walking around the tables at
breakfast, chatting with guests to ensure they are enjoying their stay. The
spacious restaurant, with its elegant high ceilings, occupies a long stretch of the
ground floor and gives pleasant views over the well-tended front gardens. Food
is well prepared and beautifully presented – main courses might include a fillet
of sea bream with mixed seafood served with tomato and red-onion salsa, or
turkey roasted with lemon, tarragon and leeks. In better weather, guests can
enjoy drinks and snacks served on the terrace and gardens, or take a dip in the
small outdoor pool. The bedrooms are equally comfortable: well proportioned
and well equipped, with fresh modern décor.

❍ Open all year ⤢ From A3055 going west into Ventnor, follow one-way system
around town; after traffic lights turn left into Belgrave Road; hotel is on right. Private car
park ⤢ 5 single, 5 twin, 15 double, 19 twin/double, 7 family rooms, 4 suites; all with
bathroom/WC; all with TV, room service, hair-dryer, direct-dial telephone ⊘
Restaurant, bar, 2 lounges, conservatory, garden; functions (max 100 people
residential/non-residential), conferences; heated outdoor swimming-pool; early
suppers for children; cots, high chairs, babysitting, baby-listening, outdoor play area
♿ No wheelchair access ● No dogs in public rooms; dogs £30 per stay; smoking in
bar, lounge and some bedrooms only ▭ Amex, Delta, Diners, MasterCard, Switch,
Visa £ Single £50, single occupancy of twin/double £70, twin/double £90, family
room up to £115, suite £130 (1998 prices); deposit required. Bar/bistro L £11; set D £20.
Special breaks available

Reports are welcome on any hotel, whether or not it is in the Guide.

Nare Hotel

Carne Beach, Veryan, Truro TR2 5PF
TEL: (01872) 501279   FAX: (01872) 501856

Country-house elegance and excellent service in an amazing location.

The landward side of the Nare Hotel is much more attractive than the seaward side – perhaps the sea winds have given the building its battened-down quality, so that the windows need triple glazing and lack character, looking out from rough-rendered walls. This said, the Nare is a very fine hotel, providing quiet luxury to those who can afford it. The setting is spectacular: right on the cliff edge, with the headland jutting out to the east, the bay swinging round to the west, and the sea breaking on to the private beach below. Inside, the low ceilings and smart country-style furniture create an intimate, classy atmosphere, with plenty of public rooms to choose from. All look out through huge french windows to the sea. The dining-room is large and formal, with tables set close together, high-backed wooden chairs, and windows on three sides; the curtains are drawn at dinner. This is a busy and proper occasion, with gentlemen in jackets, staff in uniform, and much flourishing of wine bottles. The menus are fairly traditional, along the lines of consommé or chilled melon and beef Wellington or roast pork with apricot seasoning and apple sauce; a vegetarian option, such as deep-fried cheese beignets with a red-pepper dressing, or peppered mushrooms with vegetables, is also available. The bedrooms are fabulous, with all sorts of little extras – fresh fruit, fresh milk brought in the evening by a maid, who also turns the covers down, and candles – as well as plush, bright furnishings in a chunky country style.

◐ Closed 3 Jan to 1 Feb 🔁 1 mile south-west of Veryan, on Carne beach. Private car park 🛏 5 single, 13 twin, 11 double, 1 four-poster, 3 family rooms, 3 suites; all with bathroom/WC; all with TV, room service, hair-dryer, direct-dial telephone, some with trouser press 🍴 Dining-room, 2 bars, 4 lounges, drying-room, conservatory, games room, garden; functions (max 50 people residential/non-residential); gym, sauna, heated outdoor and indoor swimming-pools, tennis, billiards; early suppers for children; cots, high chairs, babysitting, outdoor play area ♿ Wheelchair access to hotel and dining-room, 5 ground-floor bedrooms, 3 rooms specially equipped for disabled people ● No children under 7 in dining-room eves; no dogs in public rooms; no smoking in dining-room and 1 lounge ▭ MasterCard, Switch, Visa £ Single £61 to £129, single occupancy of twin/double £107 to £200, twin/double £122 to £228, four-poster £156 to £202, family room £153 to £285, suite £218 to £476; deposit required. Bar/bistro L £12; set L £13 to £15; alc L, D £33. (Prices valid till Feb 1999.) Special breaks available

 Denotes somewhere you can rely on a good meal – either the hotel features in the 1999 edition of our sister publication, The Good Food Guide, *or our inspectors thought the cooking impressive, whether particularly competent home cooking or more lavish cuisine.*

VIRGINSTOW Devon

map 1

Percy's at Coombeshead

Virginstow, Beaworthy EX21 5EA
TEL: (01409) 211236   FAX: (01409) 211275
EMAIL: percyscoombeshead@compuserve.com

Very stylish restaurant-with-rooms, plenty of animals to play with and top-notch food.

Our anonymous inspector arrived, slightly frazzled, on a muddy evening, and Tony Bricknell-Webb provided a pair of wellies and sent her off on a tramp with the dogs, down the lane and to the ponds. If she'd got there slightly earlier she could have gone out with Tina (the other half of this husband-and-wife team) on one of the horses. Then she was introduced to the new wild boarlets and, thus restored, made ready for the evening meal. Tina and Tony already run a successful eatery in London, and out here in Devon they do what they're best at (cooking) in a place they love. The restaurant is smart and modern, with a stripped floor, light-wood furniture and candles at every table. Organic produce, most of it hand-picked from the kitchen garden, is used wherever possible, and the style is up-market modern English. Our vegetarian inspection meal consisted of avocado and hummus on a bed of salad leaves with dressing, followed by 'the most scrumptiously done vegetables' with a red-wine sauce, and topped off with bitter chocolate tart with caramelised oranges and sour cream. Bedrooms in the converted barn across the way are high-class functional, rather than decorative, but have lots of room and all the necessaries, but no telephone.

◐ Open all year   ⊿ Follow signs from Metherel Cross on A3079, from St Giles on the Heath on A388, or from A30. Private car park   ⤆ 8 twin/double; all in annexe; family rooms available; 7 with shower/WC, 1 with bathroom/WC; all with TV, hair-dryer
✧ Restaurant, bar, garden; functions (max 50 people incl up to 16 residential), conferences; early suppers for children; cots, high chairs, baby-listening, outdoor play area   ♿ Wheelchair access to hotel and restaurant (ramps), 4 ground-floor bedrooms, 1 specially equipped for disabled people   ● No children under 8 in restaurant eves; no dogs in public rooms; no smoking   ▢ Amex, Delta, MasterCard, Switch, Visa
£ Single occupancy of twin/double £50, twin/double £80, family room £92; deposit required. Set L, D £18/£22

WAREHAM Dorset

map 2

Priory Hotel

Church Green, Wareham BH20 4ND
TEL: (01929) 551666   FAX: (01929) 554519

Delightful gardens at a historic, riverside hotel; some concerns about service.

No one could quibble about the splendour of the hotel's setting, reached along a little lane, adjacent to an ancient church, bounded on three sides by high walls and on the fourth by the course of the River Frome. The building itself, part red brick, part stone, seems part of the landscape – sturdy, unadorned and tranquil. Wonderful gardens and lawns, dotted with white wrought-iron furniture, slope down to the river. The interior straddles the line between country house and inn, with the traditionally plush sofa, baby grand piano and antiques of the drawing-room evoking the former, while the bar, with its electric log fire, settle-style banquettes and white woodchip walls, is more the latter. Dinner is served beneath the ancient beams of the stone-walled Abbots Cellar, where guests might dine on baked goats' cheese wrapped in filo pastry with roasted cherry tomatoes and pesto, followed by cream of mushroom and tarragon soup, and then dressed crab salad with new potatoes. There are more exposed stone walls, not to mention antlers and a parquet floor, in the breakfast room. The service here upset one guest, who, while effusive in his praise for the 'exemplary' service at dinner, found the 'service of breakfast [and, later, afternoon tea] slow and not very efficient'. This was confirmed during our inspection, when one staff member voiced to a colleague the problems of covering the reception desk while also being responsible for making up guests' tea trays. The bedrooms in the main house are decorated with traditional flair and furnished with a mix of antique and more functional items. The courtyard rooms (at the back of the house and over the cellar restaurant) are less interesting. Best, perhaps, are the riverside rooms in the Boathouse, a converted sixteenth-century barn, complete with exposed beams, vaulted ceilings and galleried entrance halls.

◑ Open all year ◪ Leave A351 for Wareham along North Causeway and enter North Street; turn left past town hall and right into Church Street leading to green. Private car park ⇐ 3 single, 5 twin, 7 double, 2 four-poster, 2 suites; some in annexe; all with bathroom/WC exc 1 double with shower/WC; all with TV, room service, hair-dryer, trouser press, direct-dial telephone, some with mini-bar; tea/coffee-making facilities available ⊘ Restaurant, breakfast room, bar, 2 sitting-rooms, drying-room, garden; functions (max 150 people incl up to 45 residential), conferences; fishing ⅙ No wheelchair access ◓ No children under 8; no dogs; no smoking in restaurant ▭ Amex, Delta, Diners, MasterCard, Switch, Visa ⟨£⟩ Single £80, single occupancy of twin/double £85 to £120, twin/double £115 to £170, four-poster £195 to £210, suite £240; deposit required. Set L £14, D £26.50 to £31.50

Bishopstrow House

Warminster BA12 9HH
TEL: (01985) 212312   FAX: (01985) 216769
EMAIL: bishopstrow_house_hotel@msn.com

Fine, timeless Georgian house, with good food and excellent leisure facilities.

For refugees from the capital, the position could hardly be better: distant enough from the smoke, yet only 20 minutes from the M4. And there's much to enjoy: swathes of creeper sweep down the fine, Georgian façade, and there are 27 acres of grounds to explore, all set in a landscape of bucolic English charm. It's here that you'll find gents in Panamas, and Miss Joan Hunter Dunns filing down to the tennis courts. The sumptuously decorated public rooms are true to the proportions of their period, and are furnished in a plush, but comfortable, style. The Mulberry Bar, shoehorned into an area at the foot of the stairs, is too much of a thoroughfare for the most relaxing of afternoon teas, despite the calorie-laden delights on offer. Dinner is a less formal affair than the setting might suggest, and the food – perhaps terrine of goats' cheese, artichoke and pesto, followed by Wiltshire ham hock with West Country mushroom risotto and roasted red onion, and finally passion-fruit crème brûlée – is imaginative and well executed. Some may protest at the 'suggested' gratuity of 15 per cent added to the bill, however. The lavish and romantic first-floor oval bedroom is the one to go for if you're entertaining a grand passion. The courtyard rooms are just as exquisitely decorated, though the Georgian proportions may be somewhat compromised – one correspondent wrote of Room 23: 'To take a medium-sized bedroom, cut off an end to create an unusably small sitting-room and to be left with a cramped bedroom is an abuse of the word "suite".' He also voiced concern over housekeeping standards and the supplement charged for porridge at breakfast, while praising the 'very relaxing' atmosphere, as well as the leisure facilities.

◑ Open all year ◪ Approaching Warminster on B3414, after a sharp left-hand bend, turn right into hotel's drive. Private car park ⌁ 1 single, 20 twin/double, 1 four-poster, 2 family rooms, 7 suites; all with bathroom/WC; all with satellite TV, room service, hair-dryer, direct-dial telephone, some with trouser press, video, CD player; no tea/coffee-making facilities in rooms ✇ 2 restaurants, bar, lounge, library, conservatory, garden; functions (max 70 people incl up to 61 residential), conferences; civil wedding licence; fishing, gym, sauna, solarium, heated indoor and outdoor swimming-pools, tennis, clay-pigeon shooting, croquet, beauty treatment rooms; early suppers for children; cots, high chairs, babysitting, baby-listening ⅙ No wheelchair access ● No smoking in restaurants and 1 bedroom; dogs £5 per night ▭ Amex, Diners, MasterCard, Switch, Visa £ Single £90 to £95, single occupancy of twin/double from £90, twin/double £155 to £170, four-poster £190 to £210, family room £155 to £170 + £25 per child over 4, suite £255 to £295 (prices valid till Mar 1999); deposit required. Cooked B £5.50; set D £29.50. Special breaks available

---

WASDALE HEAD Cumbria   map 8

Wasdale Head Inn

Wasdale Head, Nr Gosforth, Seascale CA20 1EX
TEL: (019467) 26229   FAX: (019467) 26334
EMAIL: wasdaleheadinn@msn.com
WEB SITE: www.wasdale.com/

Rugged stone-built inn amid dramatic lake and mountain scenery, under dynamic new management.

It's a long trail to reach this place from anywhere in the Lakes. There's only one road into Wasdale, and the inn lies at the far end of it. But if location is your priority, look no further. This is a fantastic spot, approached by a three-mile drive past Wastwater, England's darkest and deepest lake. At the head of the valley the simple, white-painted inn stands dwarfed by a spectacular tri-umvirate of awesome fells: Pillar, Great Gable and Scafell Pike. The cosy walkers' pub with side access is known as Ritson's Bar, after the original landlord, a great yarn-spinner in whose memory an annual contest is held to determine the world's biggest liar. Ice axes and other climbing equipment deck the walls, mementoes of intrepid Victorian climbers who set off from Wasdale clad only in tweeds. The residential section of the inn makes some concessions to guests who don't eat mountains for breakfast, with a comfy lounge of faded upholstery, cheered up by open fires and plenty of books. Abrahams Restaurant has dark oak panelling and willow-pattern china. Bedrooms in the main building are simple and quite small, but the newly converted apartments and self-catering units in the neighbouring annexe are much more spacious and stylish, with good-quality pine furniture and smart modern fabrics. Wasdale is a signal reception blackspot, so TV and radio aren't available at the hotel, and, on a more serious note, don't rely on a mobile phone to summon help on the local mountain.

◐ Open all year ☑ Turn off A595 for Gosforth or Holmrook, then follow signs for Wasdale Head. Private car park 🛏 2 single, 2 twin, 5 double, 1 four-poster, 3 suites; suites in annexe; all with bathroom/WC exc 1 single with shower/WC; all with hair-dryer, direct-dial telephone, some with mini-bar, trouser press ✓ Restaurant, 2 bars, lounge, drying-room, garden; functions (max 80 people incl up to 30 residential), conferences; early suppers for children; baby-listening 🔥 No wheelchair access ● No children in restaurant eves; no dogs in public rooms (£3 per night in bedrooms); no smoking in some public rooms and some bedrooms ▭ Amex, Delta, MasterCard, Switch, Visa £ Single £39, single occupancy of twin/double £49, twin/double/four-poster £78; suite £78 not incl breakfast; deposit required. Bar L, D £6.50; set D £18; alc D £18. (Prices valid till Jan 1999.) Special breaks available

---

WATERHOUSES Staffordshire   map 5

Old Beams

Leek Road, Waterhouses, Stoke-on-Trent ST10 3HW
TEL: (01538) 308254   FAX: (01538) 308157

An up-market restaurant-with-rooms, renowned for its food.

It's unfortunate that such a good restaurant and such smart bedrooms should be separated by the A523 – but they are, and it's the one big drawback to Old Beams. But it is one that the eighteenth-century inn manages to transcend. The restaurant is a cosy, low-ceilinged room with a log fire in the grate and a spacious, plant-filled conservatory beyond. There is a small, pretty garden – a pleasant spot to take an aperitif before sampling the top-notch cooking of Nigel Wallis. The five-course dinner might begin with appetisers and seared scallops, then go on to a sorbet and noisette of venison with wild mushrooms and a red-wine sauce, before finishing with apricot clafoutis with amaretto ice-cream. The bedrooms, over the road, are equally cultured and beautifully finished. Wedgwood is stylish and spacious with blue-and-white décor (even the TV is white), but some traffic noise does make it through the double glazing. Royal Doulton, the four-poster room across the hall, is quieter – not even disturbed by the millstream right under the window; this room, too, is carefully planned and well equipped – right down to the Roberts radio, bathrobes and slippers.

◑ Closed 3 weeks in Jan, 1 week in Aug; restaurant closed Sun & Mon eve
⊿ On A523 between Ashbourne and Leek. Private car park ⊏⊐ 4 double, 1 four-poster; all in annexe; all with bathroom/WC; all with TV, room service, hair-dryer, direct-dial telephone, radio; tea/coffee-making facilities available ⊘ Restaurant, bar, lounge, conservatory, garden; functions (max 40 people incl up to 10 residential), conferences; early suppers for children; cots, baby-listening ⑁ Wheelchair access to hotel and restaurant, WC (F), 3 ground-floor bedrooms, 1 specially equipped for disabled people ◓ No dogs; smoking in reception only ▭ Amex, Delta, Diners, MasterCard, Switch, Visa ⌷£⌷ Single occupancy of twin/double £65, twin/double £75 to £95, four-poster £120; deposit required. Cooked B £6.50; set L £17.50 to £23, D £30 to £42

WATERMILLOCK **Cumbria** map 10

Old Church Hotel

Old Church Bay, Watermillock, Ullswater, Penrith CA11 0JN
TEL: (017684) 86204   FAX: (017684) 86368
EMAIL: info@oldchurch.co.uk

Lakeshore elegance and appetising food in a wonderfully peaceful location.

A steady stream of traffic takes advantage of the Wordsworthian views along the north shores of Ullswater, but the lawns of the Old Church Hotel, safely tucked away down a 400-yard drive from the main road, reach almost to the waterfront. This tranquil, white-painted house with pretty Gothic windows dates back to 1754. The twelfth-century church which gave it its name no longer stands, but the ancient yew trees in the grounds featured in Wordsworth's writings (his famous daffodils are just up the road at Gowbarrow, but you'll find plenty more down the driveway in spring). It's a conspicuously stylish house inside: the décor is striking, demonstrating Maureen Whitemore's keen eye for colour schemes and patterns which complement the period feel of the building. The hallway cuts a dash in shades of burgundy, with a carved-oak Victorian Gothic fireplace. There are two residents' lounges (one has a bar neatly stowed away in a corner cupboard), both boldly wallpapered and tastefully furnished; the books, maps and games suggest a restful stay if the weather is bad. The dining-room is equally memorable in smart racing green, any sombreness being dispelled by the marvellous views. The bedrooms display the handsome individuality of the rest of the house. Named after the more imperious types of bird, they feature well-co-ordinated colour schemes, quality furnishings and stylish bathrooms. Food is Kevin's department, and his menus ring the changes on straightforward, appetising local produce, with three choices at each course.

◑ Closed Dec to Feb; dining-room closed Sun eve ⊿ 2½ miles south of Pooley Bridge, on A592. Private car park ⊏⊐ 2 twin, 8 double; all with bathroom/WC; all with TV, room service, hair-dryer, direct-dial telephone ⊘ Dining-room, bar, 2 lounges, garden; fishing; early suppers for children; cots, high chairs, baby-listening ⑁ No wheelchair access ◓ No children in dining-room except by arrangement; no dogs; no smoking in dining-room ▭ Amex, MasterCard, Switch, Visa ⌷£⌷ Single occupancy of twin/double £65 to £99, twin/double £90 to £130; deposit required. Alc D £25

Rampsbeck Hotel

Watermillock, Ullswater, Penrith CA11 0LP
TEL: (017684) 86442   FAX: (017684) 86688

A fine setting on the shore of Ullswater combines with smart country-house style and recommendable food.

The Rampsbeck Hotel looks mostly Victorian in style, though its earliest parts date back to 1714. It's been a hotel since 1947, and has been vastly upgraded since its change of ownership in 1983. Now it offers a spirited challenge to any of Cumbria's luxury-bracket lakeshore hotels in terms of food, style and setting. Eighteen acres of gardens and parkland surround the rambling, white-painted house, which is reached by a drive from the main Ullswater road. The handsomely furnished public rooms occupy the ground floor, offering guests a choice of two spacious lounges (one non-smoking) overlooking the grounds and lake, besides an exceptionally grand entrance hall and a more simple bar to the rear. Last orders for dinner are taken in the lounges at 8.15pm, then guests are called individually through to the picture-windowed restaurant for a block-busting table d'hôte topped and tailed by canapés, several kinds of home-made bread and luscious chocolates. The bedrooms vary in size and style, but all are spacious and luxurious, with careful attention having been paid to lighting, storage and heating. The service is exemplary: Mrs Gibb is an exceptionally professional and charming hostess, and all the staff were praised for being friendly and attentive.

◑ Closed Jan to mid-Feb   ⤴ Leave M6 at Junction 40 and take A592 to Ullswater; turn right at T-junction at lake's edge; hotel is on left after 1½ miles. Private car park ⌁ 2 single, 3 twin, 14 double, 1 four-poster, 1 suite; family rooms available; most with bathroom/WC, 2 with shower/WC; all with TV, limited room service, hair-dryer, direct-dial telephone, some with trouser press, tea/coffee-making facilities ⌂ Restaurant, bar, 2 lounges, garden; functions (max 60 people incl up to 40 residential), conferences; early suppers for children   ♿ No wheelchair access ⬤ No children under 5 in restaurant eves; no dogs in public rooms and some bedrooms; smoking in some public rooms and some bedrooms only   ▭ Delta, MasterCard, Switch, Visa   £ Single £55, single occupancy of twin/double £75 to £125, twin/double £96 to £170, four-poster/suite £170, family room £136; deposit required. Bar/bistro L £7; set L £25, D £26/£39. Special breaks available

---

Water Yeat

Water Yeat, Ulverston LA12 8DJ
TEL: (01229) 885306 (AND FAX)

Delightful country guesthouse with splendid food and effortless charm.

Once you track down the hamlet of Water Yeat on a back road south of Coniston, you'll soon spot this cream-washed farmhouse with its ancient stone barn still intact. Jill and Pierre Labat, an affable Anglo-Gallic team, run this stylish place with relaxed savoir-faire – no mean feat with a young family to bring up (the new baby of four months took a brief, well-behaved bow in the dining-room, mid-course, to universal acclaim). News of Jill's cooking has spread, and she (in the kitchen) and Pierre (front of house) use an extra pair of hands when the dining-room is packed, and the inventive five-course dinners (with a single choice at each course) sail smoothly through the evening and represent remarkable value. You can taste some very acceptable wines here, too. Parts of the farmhouse date back to the seventeenth century, so it has stacks of character, with cosy beams and roaring fires. The dining-room is full of crafts, preserves, dried flowers and painted country furniture, while the cheerful lounge with stripped pine and poppy-pattern curtains makes a relaxing place to order dinner or have coffee afterwards. The bedrooms are simple and cottagey in light floral fabrics, with older pieces of furniture and thoughtful extras like hot-water bottles and biscuits. Three acres of woodland and garden surround the house, and rambles further afield take you into unspoilt and varied countryside.

◑ Closed mid-Dec to mid-Feb; dining-room closed Sun eve   ⤧ On A5084 midway between Coniston and Ulverston. Private car park   ⬏ 3 twin, 1 double, 1 family room; all with bathroom/WC exc 1 twin/family room with shower/WC   ⌀ Dining-room, lounge, drying-room, garden; early suppers for children   ♿ No wheelchair access ⬤ No children under 4; no dogs; no smoking in bedrooms or dining-room   ▭ None accepted   £ Single occupancy of twin/double £35 to £39, twin/double £50 to £54, family room £61 to £65; deposit required. Set D £18. Special breaks available

---

Sportsman's Arms

Wath-in-Nidderdale, Pateley Bridge, Harrogate HG3 5PP
TEL: (01423) 711306   FAX: (01423) 712524

Seventeenth-century pub, with excellent food, in a tranquil Dales village.

Wath-in-Nidderdale is the sort of village so quintessentially English that it seems to belong to another age; in fact, conservation laws that forbid such frightening technology as street lamps should help to defer the day when it joins the modern world – if ever. You cross a narrow packhorse bridge straddling the River Nidd to reach the mellow yellow-sandstone inn that exudes conviviality inside and out. Ray and Jane Carter have run the Sportsman's Arms for 20 years with a down-to-earth style and humour that perhaps finds its inspiration in the framed photo of John Cleese's alter ego above the bar. The emphasis is firmly on the dining-room, where Ray's cooking sticks to an established repertoire built on top-notch regional produce. A keenly priced prix fixe menu might offer local black pudding with an apple and cider sauce, then fresh fish from Whitby or pork with Cajun spices on couscous, and an apricot and almond tart to round it all off. In a continuing programme of refurbishment and upgrading, the bedrooms are getting the stripped-pine treatment, as well as state-of-the-art showers and classy new tiles in the bathrooms, to complement their already bright and modern décor. Six new rooms in a stone barn annexe were due to be completed by the end of summer 1998.

◖ Closed 25 Dec; dining-room closed Sun eve   ⤢ In Pateley Bridge, follow signs for Ramsgill but turn off at Wath after 2 miles. Private car park   ⤺ 3 twin, 9 double, 1 four-poster; some in annexe; family rooms available; some with bathroom/WC (not all *en suite*), some with shower/WC; all with TV, room service, some with hair-dryer, direct-dial telephone   ⊘ Dining-room, bar, 2 lounges, garden; functions (max 26 people residential/non-residential), conferences; fishing; early suppers for children   ♿ No wheelchair access   ● Dogs and smoking in some public rooms only   ▭ MasterCard, Switch, Visa   £ Single occupancy of twin/double £20 to £40, twin/double £30 to £70, four-poster £80, family room £40 to £80; deposit required. Bar L £13, D £15; set L £17.50, D £21.50; alc L £25, D £26. Special breaks available

---

WELLAND Worcestershire   map 5

Holdfast Cottage Hotel

Marlbank Road, Little Malvern, Malvern WR13 6NA
TEL: (01684) 310288   FAX: (01684) 311117

Small-scale, personally run hotel, in a picturesque seventeenth-century cottage.

Though the brown and cream building was much extended in Victorian times, Stephen and Jane Knowles's little hotel still feels quintessentially cottagey. In the hall, for example, low black beams crowd over a cast-iron kitchen range, and a tin helmet hangs at the ready for anyone who may be fearful of hitting their head. The public rooms – a snoozy sitting-room focused on an open fire, a snug Victorian-styled bar, and a pretty dining-room, laid out with old oak tables and dainty flower displays – are cute without being twee. They run across the front of the house, peeking out through windows wreathed in a magnificent, ancient wistaria to a pretty terrace and large lawned garden that runs down to the main road (traffic is just audible but doesn't impinge). Not all the bedrooms match the public areas for character; ask for one in the older part of the house, such as Tinker's, which has a sloping floor, brass bed, antiques and large, beamed bathroom. Readers have praised the Knowles's first-rate service and Jane's meals, offered on a short table d'hôte menu; the rolls are home-baked and the ice-cream is home-made. 'A high standard of food and accommodation, with friendly and efficient service', conclude regular visitors.

◖ Open all year; dining-room closed Sun eve   ⤢ On A4104, halfway between Little Malvern and Welland. Private car park   ⤺ 1 single, 2 twin, 5 double; family rooms available; all with bathroom/WC exc single with shower/WC; all with TV, room service, hair-dryer, direct-dial telephone, clock radio   ⊘ Dining-room, bar, sitting-room, conservatory, garden; functions (max 15 people residential/non-residential), conferences; early suppers for children; cots, high chairs, baby-listening   ♿ No wheelchair access   ● No children under 12 in dining-room eves; dogs in conservatory and bedrooms only; smoking in bar only   ▭ Delta, MasterCard, Switch, Visa   £ Single £44, single occupancy of twin/double £52, twin/double £85, family room £95; deposit required. Set D £20. Special breaks available

Market Place Hotel

Market Place, Wells BA5 2RW
TEL: (01749) 672616   FAX: (01749) 679670

Restaurant-with-rooms in a prime position.

Owned by the same family as the Swan (see entry) up the road, this is the younger, trendier cousin. The building, long and thin, is only two minutes' walk from the cathedral – but don't expect fine views from the windows, you're more likely to get the car park. Inside, it has been decorated in a clean and contemporary style. This is best seen in the long restaurant, which has beams and oil paintings blended into its modern styling, and a small chrome-and-glass bar area. The menu offers similarly stylish dishes, and the staff, under an efficient restaurant manager, are young and friendly. Upstairs there is a rather less successful lounge area – cold rather than cosy, and used primarily as a thoroughfare to some of the bedrooms. Some bedrooms are rather small, though carefully decorated with pastel walls and painted furniture. Newer bedrooms in the old Court House have been done in Shaker style, with dark green and blue colour schemes.

◑ Open all year   ⊠ In centre of Wells. Private car park   ⬓ 1 single, 15 twin, 13 double, 5 suites; some in annexe; all with bathroom/WC; all with TV, room service, direct-dial telephone   ⊘ Restaurant, bar, 2 lounges; functions (max 67 people residential/non-residential), conferences; early suppers for children; cots, high chairs, baby-listening   ♿ Wheelchair access to hotel and restaurant, 5 ground-floor bedrooms, 1 specially equipped for disabled people   ⊖ No smoking in restaurant; no dogs in public rooms   ▭ Amex, Delta, MasterCard, Switch, Visa   £ Single £70 to £73, single occupancy of twin/double £75 to £78, twin/double £80 to £90, suite £90 to £98. Bar/bistro L £15, D £19.50; alc D £23.50. Special breaks available

---

Swan Hotel

11 Sadler Street, Wells BA5 2RX
TEL: (01749) 678877   FAX: (01749) 677647

Traditional family-run city-centre inn.

This is one of those city-centre coaching-inns that has managed to adapt just enough to ensure its continuing popularity. Although there is a row of houses in between, the hotel is set right opposite the cathedral's magnificent West Front and has some lovely views from the best bedrooms (and the garden also provides a short-cut). Step inside the front door, with the large lounge and roaring fire on your left, and you get an immediate feel for the place; décor is dark and traditional, and is perhaps cosier in winter. In the restaurant a traditional menu (perhaps avocado with prawns, followed by roast loin of pork, then apple pie with cream) is served on fine white linen cloths in a traditional setting of wood panelling. Although singles can be box-like, the best bedrooms (such as Room 40) have the view and/or heavy old four-poster beds (Room 44).

◑ Open all year ⊅ In centre of Wells, opposite cathedral. Private car park
⊨⊣ 9 single, 10 twin, 11 double, 8 four-poster; all with bathroom/WC exc 5 single with
shower/WC; all with TV, room service, direct-dial telephone, some with hair-dryer,
trouser press ✅ Restaurant, bar, lounge, TV room, drying-room, garden; functions
(max 90 people incl up to 67 residential), conferences; early suppers for children; cots,
high chairs, babysitting, baby-listening ఉ Wheelchair access to hotel and restaurant,
WC (M, F), 2 ground-floor bedrooms, 1 specially equipped for disabled people
● No dogs in public rooms ▭ Amex, Delta, Diners, MasterCard, Switch, Visa
£ Single £73, single occupancy of twin/double £78, twin/double £90, four-poster £98;
deposit required. Set L £13.50, D £17.50 (1998 prices). Special breaks available

---

WELWYN GARDEN CITY Hertfordshire   map 3

Tewin Bury Farmhouse

Tewin, Welwyn Garden City AL6 0JB
TEL: (01438) 717793   FAX: (01438) 840440

Smoothly efficient hotel business, integrated with a working farm.

The 400 acres that belong to Tewin Bury Farm have certainly been put to good
use, producing not only cattle and crops, but also clued-up conferences and
contented guests. With the hotel's various facilities dispersed among converted
outbuildings, the effect is rather like a cross between Old MacDonald's farm and
a swanky motel. The stout Georgian farmhouse now provides various
meeting-rooms; two great barns spend the weekends being showered with
confetti; while the brick and black-weatherboarded outbuildings around the
farmyard have been transformed into very smart neo-rustic bedrooms.
Depending on the original shapes of the former sheds and byres, you'll find
sloping, timbered ceilings, mezzanine levels and private patios, as well as swish,
red-marbled bathrooms and rich fabrics in muted shades. Dining is an
appropriately countrified experience, too, among the timbers, assorted patterns
of red bricks and wheel-back chairs of the Tewin Bury Pie Restaurant – the
multi-purpose tea-room, bar and restaurant. A seasonally adjusted menu might
feature a Stilton, leek and spring-onion tartlet with apple-cider mayonnaise,
pastry-wrapped lamb fillet with raspberries and mint, or poached lemon sole
with salmon mousse.

◑ Closed 24 Dec to 2 Jan ⊅ Leave A1 at Junction 6 and take B1000 towards
Hertford; farmhouse is on left. Private car park ⊨⊣ 1 single, 3 twin, 3 four-poster, 6
family rooms; some in annexe; suites available; all with bathroom/WC exc single with
shower/WC; all with TV, video, room service, hair-dryer, trouser press, direct-dial
telephone ✅ Restaurant/bar, lounge, garden; functions (max 120 people incl up to 31
residential), conferences; civil wedding licence; fishing, clay-pigeon shooting; early
suppers for children; cots, high chairs, toys, babysitting, baby-listening, outdoor play
area ఉ Wheelchair access to hotel and restaurant, WC (unisex), 2 ground-floor
bedrooms specially equipped for disabled people ● No smoking in public rooms
▭ Amex, MasterCard, Switch, Visa £ Single £70, single occupancy of twin £80, twin
£80, four-poster/suite £95, family room £105; deposit required. Bar/bistro L £5; alc D
£17. Special breaks available

Soulton Hall

Wem, Shrewsbury SY4 5RS
TEL: (01939) 232786   FAX: (01939) 234097
EMAIL: j.a.ashton@farmline.com

*Unpretentious old manor on a working farm deep in rural
Shropshire.*

The impressive Soulton Hall is an unusual, almost square, building, predating
the Tudor red brick that covers it. Any initial sense of grandeur is soon offset,
however, not only by the nearby farm outbuildings, but also by the down-
to-earth owners, the Ashtons (whose family has lived here for over 250 years),
and by the generally pleasing but unassuming furnishings inside. The
sitting-room, despite its roaring inglenook fire, is perhaps the least appealing
room, with its set of modern sofas and armchairs. More successful are the bar,
made cosy by mullioned windows and oak beams, and dining-room, whose
antique wooden tables and carved fireplace invest it with a hint of elegance.
Dinners sound fairly ambitious, and might feature several interesting
home-made elements, such as venison sausages or ice-cream. In the four
bedrooms in the main house, squeaky floors and upright and ceiling beams more
than compensate for the woodchip walls and lurid pink bedspreads. Two further
rooms in the coach-house adopt a more co-ordinated, cottagey style. Guests are
welcome to explore the estate, which includes two miles of river and ancient oak
woodland.

◐ Open all year   ⃞ 1½ miles east of Wem on B5065. Private car park   ⃤ 2 twin, 4
double; some in annexe; family rooms and suites available; most with bathroom/WC; all
with TV, room service, hair-dryer, direct-dial telephone   ⊘ Dining-room, bar,
sitting-room, drying-room, garden; conferences (max 35 people incl up to 6 residential);
fishing, clay-pigeon shooting; early suppers for children; cots, high chairs, baby-
listening   ⅙ No wheelchair access   ● No children under 9 in dining-room eves; no
dogs in public rooms; smoking in bar only   ⃞ Diners, MasterCard, Visa   £ Single
occupancy of twin/double £35 to £42, twin/double £70, family room £98, suite £80;
deposit required. Alc D £22. Special breaks available

Wenlock Edge Inn

Hilltop, Wenlock Edge, Much Wenlock TF13 6DJ
TEL: (01746) 785678   FAX: (01746) 785285

*Outstandingly run, isolated roadside pub in prime walking
territory, offering excellent, keenly priced bar food.*

The squat stone inn on this famous wooded limestone escarpment (part of which
is owned by the National Trust) looks ordinary from the outside; the many
parked cars at weekends, however, suggest that something special happens
within. The pub side of the operation amounts to just two small, beamed bar
rooms and a dining-room, all crammed with unfancy wooden tables, chairs,

pews and window seats. Every available space is often taken (even the seating within the inglenook fireplace), thanks primarily to the first-rate food. Dishes, advertised on 'whiteboards' and honestly identified as home-made, organic, vegetarian or frozen, might include a delicious venison pie or chicken and apricot tart, and good, traditional English puddings. The pub's other big draw is the efficient and very friendly service provided by the well-established owners, the Waring family. There are just three bedrooms (a fourth has recently been turned into a peaceful guests' sitting-room). Each is pretty, cosy and furnished with pine; one, a conversion of an outside loo, is like a minuscule cottage. Guests on a recent four-night stay had nothing but praise for the Warings – 'could not do enough to make our stay enjoyable' – as well as for the food, wine and their well-thought-out bedroom.

○ Closed Chr; dining-room closed Mon eve ⊠ On B4371, 4½ miles south of Much Wenlock. Private car park ⊨ 1 twin, 2 double; one in annexe; all with shower/WC; all with TV, hair-dryer ⊘ Dining-room, bar, sitting-room ⅙ No wheelchair access ● No children under 8; dogs in bar and 1 bedroom only ⊟ Amex, Delta, MasterCard, Switch, Visa £ Single occupancy of twin/double £45 to £50, twin/double £63 to £70. Bar/bistro L, D £7; alc L, D £15. Special breaks available

---

WEOBLEY Herefordshire   map 5

Ye Olde Salutation Inn

Market Pitch, Weobley, Hereford HR4 8SJ
TEL: (01544) 318443   FAX: (01544) 318216

Civilised pub in a historic village in the Welsh Marches.

The 'Ye Olde' description is stating the obvious: the pub is one of the numerous ancient buildings in vernacular black-and-white, half-timbered style that make this village one of the county's most photogenic. Inside, there is a rough-and-ready public bar for the locals to prop up, but the focus of activity is the smarter lounge bar, with dried hops hanging over the bar, a large log fire and a panoply of upright and cross beams. At its rear lies a slightly more formal restaurant area, with linen-dressed tables. The food on the separate bar and restaurant menus – such as no-nonsense steak and stout pie and sticky toffee pudding, or more ambitious concoctions like leek tartlets topped with quail's eggs – surpasses normal pub standards. The residents' quarters upstairs – namely a roomy sitting-room with a floor like a ski-slope and four beamed, cosy bedrooms featuring antique brass half-testers and a four-poster bed – are just as characterful as the rest of the establishment. For the rooms with only *en suite* showers, there is a communal bathroom with a bath.

○ Closed 25 Dec; restaurant closed Sun & Mon eves ⊠ In village centre facing Broad Street, just off A4112. Private car park ⊨ 1 twin, 2 double, 1 four-poster; 1 double with bathroom/WC, 2 with shower/WC; all with TV, hair-dryer, trouser press ⊘ Restaurant, 2 bars, sitting-room, TV room, drying-room, conservatory; functions (max 40 people incl up to 8 residential), conferences; gym ⅙ No wheelchair access ● No children in restaurant eves; dogs only in public bar and bedrooms by

arrangement; no smoking ⬜ Amex, Delta, Diners, MasterCard, Switch, Visa
£ Single occupancy of twin/double £40, twin/double £65, four-poster £70; deposit
required. Bar/bistro L, D £13; set Sun L £10.50; alc L, D £22. Special breaks available

---

WEST BEXINGTON Dorset map 2

Manor Hotel

Beach Road, West Bexington, Dorchester DT2 9DF
TEL: (01308) 897616   FAX: (01308) 897035

A racing certainty; bags of character at a manor with roots in the
Domesday book, with a popular and busy bar.

If the history (a pedigree dating back to the eleventh century) doesn't get you,
then the situation (on a windswept bluff with sweeping views down to Chesil
Beach) will. The stark, honey-coloured walls hint at a respectable, rather than
ancient, provenance, and win barely a second thought from the drinkers who
congregate on the summer lawns. You need to venture indoors to appreciate the
full medieval flavour of the place, at its most obvious in the atmospheric entrance
hallway, where the flagstones and heavily carved panelling contrast agreeably
with the modern fabrics of the drapes and seating. It's here that you'll also find
the first clue to owners Richard and Jayne Childs's passion for horse-racing,
evident from a clutch of prints. You'll find more evidence of equestrian
enthusiasm in the sea-facing lounge, before encountering it full-frontally in the
split-level, flagstoned restaurant, where hunting and other horsey prints abound
on the white, rough-stone walls, and where brasses festoon the huge fireplace.
The menu majors on fish, as you might expect in a place so close to the sea. For
more casual diners, there are lots of hearty, but imaginative, options available in
the beamed, hop-bedecked Cellar Bar, or in the light, airy conservatory. The cosy
bedrooms are furnished in a chintzy, cottagey style.

◑ Open all year; restaurant closed 25 Dec eve ⤳ Off B3127 Bridport to Weymouth
coastal road. Private car park 🛏 1 single, 3 twin, 8 double, 1 family room; all with
bathroom/WC; all with TV, room service, hair-dryer, direct-dial telephone ✓
Restaurant, bar, 2 lounges, conservatory, garden; functions (max 110 people incl up to
26 residential), conferences; civil wedding licence; early suppers for children; cots, high
chairs, baby-listening, outdoor play area 🚫 No wheelchair access ⬤ No dogs in
bedrooms ⬜ Amex, Diners, MasterCard, Switch, Visa £ Single and single
occupancy of twin/double £52 to £54, twin/double £88 to £90, family room £90 (prices
valid till Mar 1999); deposit required. Bar/bistro L, D £7; set L £15, D £19

WESTDEAN East Sussex map 3

Old Parsonage

Westdean, Alfriston, Seaford BN25 4AL
TEL: (01323) 870432 (AND FAX)

Leave your cares behind at this outstanding, serene B&B with
superb hosts.

Yet again, we've received more letters eulogising about this 'beautiful and tranquil place'. It seems that Raymond and Angela Woodhams run a near-perfect B&B, where guests are 'totally at home and made to feel most welcome'. Reputed to be the oldest small medieval house still inhabited in Britain, it was built by monks back in 1280. The walls of rough-hewn flint are lined on the inside with symmetrical blocks of local chalk, punctuated only by the small leaded windows. Gnarled beams and original stone fireplaces provide the characterful backdrop, and the Woodhams have furnished the rooms immaculately. Two of the bedrooms, Hall and Solar, are reached by twisting stone spiral staircases, and both have tremendous, high, timbered ceilings and views over the churchyard. Hall also houses a splendid four-poster, with stained-glass windows adding splashes of colour to the monastic minimalism. Breakfasts are a legend, with fresh fruit from the garden and home-made jams as well as a hearty cooked meal. It's hard to find fault with any aspect of a stay here. As one reader wrote, 'We have to leave now and feel quite tearful, wishing this was ours and we didn't have to go away.'

◗ Closed Chr & New Year ⊠ Off A259 east of Seaford. Private car park ⊫ 2 double, 1 four-poster; 2 with bathroom/WC, 1 with shower/WC (none *en suite*); all with hair-dryer ⊘ Lounge/breakfast room, library, garden ⅋ No wheelchair access ◓ No children under 12; no dogs; no smoking ⊟ None accepted £ Single occupancy of double £38 to £45, double £55 to £65, four-poster £70

WEST DOWN Devon   map 1

Long House

The Square, West Down, Ilfracombe EX34 8NF
TEL: (01271) 863242

Tea-shop by day, guests' restaurant by night, with three good bedrooms.

West Down is a sleepy village south of the coastal road, the kind of place where local children take the goat for a walk along the road, and everyone talks to each other. Martyn and Yvonne Lavender, originally from the Midlands, fit in very well in their relatively new role as proprietors. Martyn serves cream teas, pausing to position the handle of the teapot for perfect access while discussing local news. He will point out photos taken back in 1910 of the Long House in its incarnation as the village smithy, as well as the original oak beams from 1720. Today the tea-room is spacious, simple and spruce, with plain dark tables and chairs, whitewashed walls and a plethora of mouthwatering cakes. In the evening, this room becomes the guests' restaurant, with Yvonne rustling up such old favourites as salmon and broccoli roulade, followed by sweet-and-sour pork chops, and topped off with one of those ubiquitous cakes, or perhaps a summer pudding. In the lounge, floral sofas face a big, old stone fireplace, and teddies and photos brighten up the heavy dresser. The three bedrooms are bigger than you would expect, and are done out in pretty chintzes, with fresh, pine furniture.

● Closed Nov to Feb 🚗 West Down is signposted off A361, 4 miles north of Braunton. On-street parking (free) 🛏 1 twin, 2 double; all with bathroom/WC exc 1 double with shower/WC; all with TV ⍺ Restaurant, lounge, drying-room, study, garden ⅙ No wheelchair access ● No children under 8; no dogs; no smoking ⊟ None accepted £ Single occupancy of twin/double £30, twin/double £52; deposit required. Light L £5; set L £9.50, D £14

WEST MALLING Kent　　　　　　　　　　　　　　　　　　　map 3

Scott House

37 High Street, West Malling ME19 6QH
TEL: (01732) 841380　FAX: (01732) 870025

Antique-lovers will adore this excellent B&B in the middle of a bustling Kent town.

It has been another storming year for Margaret and Ernest Smith, as the laudatory letters continue to roll in: 'truly superb', 'very charming and interesting host', 'book well in advance – it's always full' is a typical selection. One eternally grateful reader gave Ernest a gold star after an unfortunate incident with a sauce bottle over breakfast – not only did he launder the stained shirt, but he also went out and bought his guest a new one at a local shop so that he could attend an important meeting that day in pristine clothing. At street level this is an antique shop, but the whole house, itself a Grade II-listed Georgian building, is a treasure-trove of goodies – marble fireplaces, cabinets crammed with porcelain and clocks aplenty. Upstairs are three cosy bedrooms, individually furnished and decked out in pale yellow or jade green. Room 1 is the most spacious, with a canopied half-tester bed and pretty shower-room. Evening meals aren't served, but Ernest has plenty of local recommendations up his sleeve.

● Closed Chr 🚗 West Malling is on A228, 1 mile from M20 Junction 4. On-street parking (free) 🛏 1 twin, 2 double; all with shower/WC; all with TV, room service, hair-dryer, trouser press ⍺ Lounge ⅙ No wheelchair access ● No children under 10; no dogs; no smoking ⊟ Amex, Delta, Diners, MasterCard, Switch, Visa £ Single occupancy of twin/double £49, twin/double £69; deposit required

---

WESTON-UNDER-REDCASTLE Shropshire　　　　　　　　map 5

The Citadel

Weston-under-Redcastle, Shrewsbury SY4 5JY
TEL: (01630) 685204 (AND FAX)

Palatial accommodation in a turreted family home.

With its towers and crenellations, and its elevated position overlooking Hawkstone Park (part golf course, part cliffy, grotto-rich terrain that is open to the public), this early nineteenth-century dower house lives up to its name. Its owner, Sylvia Griffiths, welcomes her guests along Wolsey Lodge lines – in other words, there is nothing to indicate that this is a commercial operation either at the gate or inside, where the atmosphere is instead one of a rather grand family home. The tapestry-hung, flagstoned hall leads to the dining-room, where dinners featuring such traditional dishes as salmon en croûte and chocolate roulade are served round a single, long, polished table amid gilt-framed paintings. Though the Citadel is unlicensed (bring your own wine), guests can take a pre-prandial sherry with their hosts in the fine sitting-room, with its strapwork ceiling and baby grand piano; a draped archway leads from here to a magnificent snooker room, with a full-sized table. The three bedrooms are comfortably furnished with armchairs, a dressing-table and pleasing antiques. The most fun is the Round Room, which not only occupies one of the towers, but also has a massive bathroom with a claw-foot Victorian bath.

---

① Closed Nov to Mar; dining-room closed Sun eve ⏴ 10 miles north of Shrewsbury, turn right off A49 towards Red Castle; hotel is ¼ mile out of village. Private car park ⏴ 2 twin, 1 double; 2 with bathroom/WC, 1 with shower/WC; all with TV, room service, hair-dryer, trouser press; no tea/coffee-making facilities in rooms ⊘ Dining-room, sitting-room, conservatory, games room, garden; fishing, snooker ⓺ No wheelchair access ● No children under 10; no dogs; no smoking ⬛ None accepted ⟨£⟩ Single occupancy of twin/double £45, twin/double £70; deposit required. Set D £19.50

WEST PORLOCK Somerset

map 1

Bales Mead

West Porlock, Minehead TA24 8NX
TEL: (01643) 862565

A real treat. Sumptuous B&B accommodation in a delightful house run with flair and energy by dedicated hosts.

From the second you enter the grounds of this creamy Edwardian house, which commands an elevated position over Porlock Bay, you know that it's going to be good. Tall shrubs wave in the breeze in the small, mature, interestingly stocked and immaculately kept garden. After this, the house – something of a canvas for the talents and creative energies of owners Stephen Blue and Peter Clover – comes as no disappointment. The sitting-room, pretty and elegant in blue and white and ennobled by swag-and-tail drapes, a grand piano, plus a fine collection of paintings and art-deco ceramics, pulls off the minor miracle of being both good to look at and relaxing to sit in – unquestionably stylish, yet intimate, too. At breakfast, guests sit as couples or around one candlelit table, and are invited to feast on fresh-fruit salad, Peter's home-made pastries and freshly squeezed orange juice, as well as the traditional morning staples, in an elegant, delicately pink room equipped with silverware and Royal Doulton plates. The immaculate bedrooms are furnished with care and decorated in a delightful, delicate style that wouldn't shame a country-house hotel offering rooms at three times the price. Guests are unanimous in their paeans of praise of the hosts and their enterprise.

If you have access to the Internet, you can find The Which? Hotel Guide *online at the Which? Online web site (www.which.net/).*

● Closed Chr & New Year ⊅ Midway between Porlock village and Porlock Weir; follow signposts to West Porlock. Private car park ⊨ 3 double; 1 with bathroom/WC, 1 with shower/WC; all with TV, hair-dryer, clock radio ⊘ Dining-room, sitting-room, drying-room, garden ⅙ No wheelchair access ● No children under 14; no dogs; no smoking ⊟ None accepted £ Single occupancy of double £44 to £48, double £58; deposit required

---

WEST WITTON North Yorkshire   map 8

Wensleydale Heifer

West Witton, Wensleydale, Leyburn DL8 4LS
TEL: (01969) 622322   FAX: (01969) 624183
EMAIL: heifer@daelnet.co.uk

A classic Dales pub that focuses on its food and public areas rather than its bedrooms.

At first glance, you might think that this lovely, whitewashed Yorkshire Dales inn is a simple two-up, two-down cottage. In reality, this section is a mere front for a complex that extends a good way back from the A-road that carves through the village – far enough to have room for a front lounge and cosy, panelled snug, a lively bistro with gingham tablecloths, a bright restaurant with a rustic white-stone wall, and a back bar. The food choice is more adventurous and extensive than the average pub has to offer: rabbit alla cacciatora on tagliatelle, 'posh' bangers and mash and plenty of veggie options appear on the bar/bistro menu, while Bartles Restaurant serves the likes of chicken with crayfish and chervil mousse and roast guinea-fowl with lime and lemon marmalade. The bedrooms, shared between the main inn, Rose Cottage and the Reading Room (where you can avoid the bar noise and ask for a ground-floor room that opens on to the walled garden), are generally nothing to get excited about: the furniture is functional, but the plumbing is not always so – one reader had problems with the shower in Room 16, reiterating a previously reported complaint.

● Open all year ⊅ On A684 Leyburn to Hawes road, at west end of village. Private car park ⊨ 5 twin, 5 double, 3 four-poster, 1 family room, 1 suite; some in annexe; all with bathroom/WC exc 3 doubles with shower/WC; all with TV, room service, hair-dryer, direct-dial telephone ⊘ 2 restaurants, bar, lounge; early suppers for children; cots, high chairs, baby-listening ⅙ No wheelchair access ● None ⊟ Amex, Delta, Diners, MasterCard, Switch, Visa £ Single occupancy of twin/double £55, twin/double £76, four-poster/suite £95, family room £99; deposit required. Bar/bistro L £5, D £16; alc D £25. Special breaks available

---

WHAPLODE Lincolnshire   map 6

Guy Wells

Eastgate, Whaplode, Spalding PE12 6TZ
TEL: (01406) 422239 (AND FAX)

Friendly and peaceful B&B with interesting horticultural connections.

The old country houses of Lincolnshire stand surrounded by trees and are separated by the monotonous, flat fields. Richard and Anne Thompson's eighteenth-century farmhouse is no exception: as you pass through the trees and bushes and see the lawn, with the handsome, creeper-clad house behind, it really does feel like an oasis. The Thompsons came here in 1965 to grow hothouse flowers, something they have only recently stopped doing, leaving just the outdoor daffodil and tulip business. The listed, Queen Anne house has handsome, well-proportioned rooms, furnished in a homely style. Breakfasts (and suppers on request) are served at two tables in the beamed dining-room, which – like the sitting-room next door – has views over the lawns. Anne is the friendly and lively force behind the B&B side of things – Richard concentrates on the farm, and happily shows guests around. The bedrooms are all different, but follow the same homely pattern, two with pleasant views over the garden.

◑ Closed Chr ⚡ Turn off A151 at Whaplode, 2 miles west of Holbeach; farm is first on left down Eastgate Lane. Private car park ⬛➞ 1 twin, 1 double, 1 four-poster; 2 with shower/WC, 1 with bathroom/WC (not *en suite*); TV on request ✅ Dining-room, sitting-room, garden ⅙ No wheelchair access ● No children under 5; no dogs; no smoking ▭ None accepted £ Single occupancy of twin/double £25 to £30, twin/double/four-poster £40 to £44, deposit required. Supper £10 to £12. Special breaks available

---

WHEDDON CROSS Somerset   map 1

Raleigh Manor   NEW ENTRY

Wheddon Cross, Dunster, Minehead TA24 7BB
TEL: (01643) 841484

Fine setting and good value at an agreeably homely Exmoor country house.

Originally built as a hunting-lodge for the Boeveys of Barclay's Bank, Raleigh Manor is these days run by a newcomer to the hotel business, Dorothy Sahlool. Taking on a hotel might seem a strange way of downshifting after early retirement, but the evidence of our postbag would suggest that Dorothy and her husband, Mahmoud, are making a decent go of it, with guests speaking warmly of the welcome (with tea and home-made cakes), the service – 'just say what you need and it will be done' – and the rooms. Raleigh Manor is something of a Victorian pile, but the setting, down a long farm track and overlooking a delightful, wooded combe, wins many friends. The public rooms are furnished in a robustly traditional style, with the décor tending toward modern pastels and cheerful tones. There's a homely library, as well as a roomy lounge with a games table. Large windows make the most of the views in the dining-room, which has a pretty wallcovering in mint green and coral. Dinner might involve leek and Stilton soup, baked salmon cooked in lemon and butter, fresh-fruit salad, and finally local cheeses with oatmeal biscuits. The bedrooms are attractively decorated and furnished with solid, agreeable pine furniture. It's worth treating yourself to the premium Squire's Room for its stunning views and magnificent half-tester.

○ Closed end Nov to 1 Mar ⤢ Turn left 200 yards north of Wheddon Cross down a private road; manor is 800 yards past Watercombe Farm. Private car park 🛏→1 single, 2 twin, 4 double; all with bathroom/WC exc single with shower/WC; all with TV, hair-dryer, radio ⊘ Dining-room, lounge, library, conservatory, garden; early suppers for children 🚿 No wheelchair access ● No children under 5; no dogs; no smoking ▭ Delta, MasterCard, Visa ⟨£⟩ Single £31, single occupancy of twin/double £46, twin/double £62 to £74; deposit required. Set D £16.50. Special breaks available

---

WHIMPLE Devon   map 1

Woodhayes

Whimple, Exeter EX5 2TD
TEL: (01404) 822237   FAX: (01404) 822337

Fine food and an excellent welcome at this dignified country house.

Woodhayes is all about stylish professionalism, from tea on arrival to menu discussions before dinner; even late-arriving vegetarians are fitted in without an eyelid being batted. The meal is what it's all about: people travel from miles around to eat the (necessarily) small and scrumptious helpings that make up the six-course feast. Everyone is served at once at 8pm, and because there are no menus it feels more intimate than a restaurant, despite the formality of the setting. You might start with delicate slices of mango, melon and red grapefruit, followed by tomato and basil soup, fillet of brill, roast fillet of beef with a pepper and sour-cream sauce, and finally a strawberry sablé. The pleasing Georgian house is done out effectively in plush, peachy tones, and manages to get that special combination of elegance and unstuffiness just right. The bedrooms (which are serviced while you are at dinner) have good views over the lawns, and are furnished in classic country style with delicate antiques and high, comfortable beds. As we went to press, the house was on the market; the current owners plan to work side by side with the new owners in an unusual handover period – let's hope the standards remain high. More reports, please.

○ Closed Chr & New Year ⤢ Turn off A30 Exeter to Honiton road at sign for Whimple; hotel is just before village. Private car park 🛏→3 twin, 3 double; all with bathroom/WC; all with TV, room service, hair-dryer, direct-dial telephone, radio ⊘ Dining-room, bar, lounge, library, garden; early suppers for children 🚿 No wheelchair access ● No children under 12; no dogs; no smoking in dining-room ▭ Amex, Delta, Diners, MasterCard, Switch, Visa ⟨£⟩ Single occupancy of twin/double £65, twin/double £95. Set D £27.50. Special breaks available

---

WHITEWELL Lancashire   map 8

Inn at Whitewell

Whitewell, Forest of Bowland, Clitheroe BB7 3AT
TEL: (01200) 448222   FAX: (01200) 448298

Exquisite rooms, a relaxed atmosphere and a stunning setting.

Driving through the raw, untouched landscape of the Forest of Bowland, the Inn at Whitewell comes as a sophisticated surprise. At first, its façade, with its attractive stonework (dating back to 1836), slate roof and creeping clematis, seems more reminiscent of an Oxbridge college than an inn; the muddy wellies in the entrance, however, signal a relaxed, unpretentious atmosphere. The public rooms are traditional and unfussy – the bar has exposed beams and themed sporting prints, one dining-room has white walls and an open fire – and nothing detracts from the views across the Trough of Bowland. The food, too, eschews frills and flourishes with main dishes like loin of local lamb roasted with a herb crust. In the corridor, old riding boots, fox and stag heads and a pile of old suitcases continue the rustic theme, but it's in the bedrooms that Richard Bowman really goes to town. With the help of his daughter and wife, he has created rooms of exquisite taste and character – all feature impressive sound systems, superb beds, open peat fires, antiques and highly imaginative bathrooms. Room 7 has impressive views of the Forest of Bowland and a four-poster bed set against soft-yellow walls, not to mention a fantastic brass bathtub and an antique WC. Room 5, a bright, spacious double, has an elegant writing bureau and a delicious sunken marble bath.

◑ Open all year ⤢ Whitewell is 6 miles north-west of Clitheroe. Private car park ⤶ 1 twin, 8 double, 1 four-poster, 1 suite; family rooms available; all with bathroom/WC; all with TV, room service, direct-dial telephone, radio, CD player; tea/coffee-making facilities, hair-dryer available ✇ 3 dining-rooms, bar, lounge, drying-room, garden; functions (max 200 people incl up to 22 residential), conferences; civil wedding licence; fishing, clay-pigeon shooting; early suppers for children; cots, high chairs, babysitting, baby-listening & No wheelchair access ● None ⊟ Amex, Diners, MasterCard, Switch, Visa £ Single occupancy of twin/double £53 to £65, twin/double/four-poster £74 to £87, family room £89 to £102, suite £110; deposit required. Bar/bistro L £9, D £10; alc D £27

WHITSTABLE Kent   map 3

Whitstable Oyster Fishery Co

Royal Native Oyster Stores, Horsebridge,
Whitstable CT5 1BU
TEL: (01227) 276856   FAX: (01227) 770666

A fun and funky place to stay on the beach, but not for those wanting creature comforts.

Deep carpets, fluffy bathrobes and room service are out, stylish minimalism, beachfront location and lashings of atmosphere are in. A converted fisherman's hut is not everyone's idea of an ideal place to rest a weary head, but, as a quirky alternative to your run-of-the-mill B&B, it's hard to beat. The seven black clapboard huts are a short stroll from the parent restaurant – if you're walking back at night, the road is easier on the feet than the beach and has no groynes to blunder into in the dark. Inside, the huts are more comfortable than you might expect; it's as if Barnacle Bill went shopping at IKEA: exposed floorboards painted deep red, brightly painted walls, pine furniture, and small, smart bathrooms. Nor should one forget the sea views, and the central heating. Our only quibbles were the tiny towels and lack of soap (only shower gel instead). Huts sleeping four are on two floors, with sofa-beds downstairs. Hut 2 suffers from having a ground floor only, while Hut 1 has quite a narrow, steep stepladder at its door. Breakfast isn't included, but you'll probably still be full from a gargantuan feast in the restaurant the night before: as well as oysters, you could try chargrilled scallops with a basil dressing, sea bream roasted with garlic and rosemary, and pear and almond flan – all enjoyed in a rural New England atmosphere, with scrubbed floorboards and red-and-white checked tablecloths. Further down the seafront, a new company venture was opening as we went to press: the Hotel Continental, with 23 *en suite* twin or double rooms: reports, please.

◑ Open all year; restaurant closed Sun & Mon eve Oct to May 🔁 On seafront in Whitstable. Private car park 🛏 4 double, 3 family huts; all with shower/WC; all with TV, hair-dryer ⊘ Restaurant (off-site); early suppers for children; cots ♿ No wheelchair access ⊖ No dogs; no smoking in bedrooms ▭ Amex, Delta, Diners, MasterCard, Switch, Visa £ Double £55 to £85, family hut £90 to £100; deposit required. Special breaks available

---

WICKHAM Hampshire

map 2

Old House

The Square, Wickham, Fareham PO17 5JG
TEL: (01329) 833049   FAX: (01329) 833672

Simple, understated elegance, attentive staff and superb food in the heart of Hampshire.

This fine Georgian house is an imposing feature of Wickham's pleasant village square, standing out from the pick-and-mix of English architectural styles that surrounds it. The red-brick walls are almost obscured by creepers, and the flowerbeds along the pavement are a riot of colour. Richard and Annie Skipwith have converted the house into a hotel, decorating the bedrooms in pretty florals or plain, muted colours. Room 2 at the front still has its original fireplace, but it's Room 6 at the back which comes up trumps for character – an A-shaped room with dramatically sloping ceilings and copious beams. Even Room 10, which the Skipwiths admit is used only if they're very busy, has its ardent fans. Downstairs, the old stables have been turned into a restaurant overlooking the garden, and the 'super food' could include lamb sweetbreads with fresh mint, breast of Barbary duck with fresh pears in a red-wine sauce, rounded off with a terrine of fresh-fruit sorbets.

◑ Closed Chr, Easter, 2 weeks in Aug; restaurant closed Sun eve 🔁 3 miles north of Fareham in village square; at junction of B2177 and A32. Private car park 🛏 2 single, 3 twin, 3 double, 1 family room; all with bathroom/WC; all with TV, room service, hair-dryer, trouser press, direct-dial telephone; tea/coffee-making facilities available ⊘ Restaurant, bar, 2 lounges; functions (max 50 people incl up to 17 residential), conferences; early suppers for children; cots, high chairs, baby-listening, outdoor play area ♿ No wheelchair access ⊖ No dogs ▭ Amex, Diners, MasterCard, Visa £ Single £75, single occupancy of twin/double £80, twin/double £90, family room £95; deposit required. Continental B £6, cooked B £9; set L £11/£22/£29, D £22/£29 (1998 prices). Special breaks available

WIDEGATES **Cornwall**	map 1

Coombe Farm

Widegates, Looe PL13 1QN
TEL: (01503) 240223   FAX: (01503) 240895

Delightful farmhouse retreat with gregarious hosts and plenty to do.

This 1920s gabled farmhouse is a home away from home, with proprietors Alexander and Sally Low extending a real welcome, and dogs Sam, Sacha and Mischa always ready to show you round. The public rooms are full of photographs of the family competing on horseback (the horse in question is now in semi-retirement in the field behind the house), along with trophies, cups, pots, plants and general domestic paraphernalia. There's a love-it-or-hate-it squashy velvet sofa (covered in pink and green flowers) and an open fireplace in the sitting-room, and a huge patio window in the dining-room providing sweeping views across the grounds. Food, cooked by Sally, is hearty and home-made, along the lines of soup, roast, sponge pudding, cheese and fruit. Outside, there's plenty to see and do – an inviting outdoor pool in the middle of the sloping lawn and a beamed and countrified games room housing snooker and table-tennis tables – and doves, peacocks and rabbits abound. The bedrooms in the cottage have huge stone floors and chunky wooden furniture, while those in the house are simply done out with white walls and sprigged fabrics; some retain the tiny original fireplaces.

◑ Closed Dec, Jan, Feb   ⓩ On B253 3½ miles north-east of Looe. Private car park ⌷ 3 twin, 3 double, 4 family rooms; some in annexe; all with shower/WC; all with satellite TV, hair-dryer, direct-dial telephone   ⊘ Dining-room/bar, sitting-room, games room, garden; heated outdoor swimming-pool, snooker, table tennis   ⅙ Wheelchair access (1 step) to hotel and restaurant, 5 ground-floor bedrooms   ◓ No children under 12; no dogs in public rooms (in bedrooms by arrangement); no smoking   ▭ Amex, Delta, Diners, MasterCard, Switch, Visa   £ Single occupancy of twin/double £28 to £32, twin/double £56 to £64, family room £77 to £90; deposit required. Set D £16. Special breaks available

WILLERSEY **Gloucestershire**	map 5

Old Rectory

Church Street, Willersey, Broadway WR12 7PN
TEL: (01386) 853729   FAX: (01386) 858061
EMAIL: beauvoisin@btinternet.com

Cotswolds country-cottage chic and warm hospitality.

The plaudits keep rolling in for Liz and Chris Beauvoisin's charming retreat at the heart of this Cotswolds' village. 'It surpasses several five-star hotels to me because the owners give an extra-unique personal touch,' writes one fan. Attention to detail is excellent, from the letter of confirmation to the security light in the car park and the large bottles of Crabtree & Evelyn toiletries in the bathrooms. The pale, colour-washed walls are covered with stencils done by Liz's sister-in-law – bees are a popular motif, but look out for a frog on top of a stair post and a spider's web on the wall by Liz's office. The drawing-room doubles as the breakfast room; in the evening, you can help yourself to a sherry before sinking into one of the chairs or sofas in front of the traditional stone fireplace; in the morning, you can breakfast on fresh-fruit salad and a full cooked breakfast while gazing out on the 300-year-old mulberry tree in the sheltered walled garden. The bedrooms continue the high standards, with carefully co-ordinated chintzy soft furnishings and gleaming tiled bathrooms, some making ingenious use of the space beneath the eaves. A separate coach-house a few steps from the main house offers more spacious, self-contained options for honeymooners or families.

◑ Closed Chr　🗷 Take B4632 from Broadway for 1½ miles; Church Street is opposite duck pond; go to end of lane to hotel car park. Private car park　🛏 1 twin, 3 double, 3 four-poster, 1 family room; some in annexe; all with bathroom/WC (not all *en suite*) exc 1 four-poster with shower/WC; all with TV, hair-dryer, direct-dial telephone, clock radio, some with trouser press　✅ Drawing-room/dining-room, drying-room, garden; functions (max 20 people incl up to 17 residential), conferences　♿ Wheelchair access to hotel (ramp) and dining-room, 3 ground-floor bedrooms, 2 rooms specially equipped for disabled people　● No children under 8; no dogs; no smoking　🗖 Delta, MasterCard, Switch, Visa　£ Single occupancy of twin/double £45 to £55, twin/double £79, four-poster £85 to £95, family room £89 to £94; deposit required. Special breaks available

---

WILMCOTE Warwickshire　　　　　　　　　　　　map 5

Pear Tree Cottage

Church Road, Wilmcote, Stratford-upon-Avon CV37 9UX
TEL: (01789) 205889　FAX: (01789) 262862

Pretty B&B, with friendly owners, in a historic location.

With its views across to Mary Arden's cottage (where the Bard used to visit his grandparents), Margaret and Ted Mander's partly seventeenth-century cottage is perfectly positioned for soaking up the Shakespearean atmosphere. The house – an odd amalgamation of half-timbering, brick and blue Lias stone that spans almost four centuries – is set in a pretty cottage garden. Like the architectural style of the house, the bedrooms vary; the oldest, Caroline's, has the most character, with its brass bedstead, botanic prints and delightfully uneven, white walls. Arden is similar, but larger, and has a view of the cottage from its somewhat dated bathroom. Downstairs are two cottagey sitting-rooms and an attractive breakfast room, with elm beams and a fine collection of Staffordshire pots on the dresser. Guests often like to picnic in the beautiful garden in summer, and if you prefer more independence there is a kitchen with a microwave. The rooms in the new extension share another kitchen, which has a patio area outside.

◑ Closed 24 Dec to 1 Jan　🗷 Turn off A3400 3½ miles north-west of Stratford; turn left at village green and first left again. Private car park　🛏 2 twin, 4 double, 1 family room; all with bathroom/WC; all with TV, hair-dryer　✅ Breakfast room, sitting-room, TV room, garden　♿ No wheelchair access　● No children under 3; no dogs; no smoking　🗖 None accepted　£ Single occupancy of twin/double £30 to £32, twin/double £45 to £48, family room £55 to £60

Beechleas

17 Poole Road, Wimborne Minster BH21 1QA
TEL: (01202) 841684 FAX: (01202) 849344

Unimpeachably neat rooms in a carefully run, period house with a conservatory restaurant.

The roadside position and resolutely plain, creeper-clad façade of this red-brick Georgian house might lead you to pass it by, but there are good reasons to tarry at Josephine McQuillan's agreeable small hotel, an easy drive from the bustle of Poole or Bournemouth. The parquet flooring and gentle watercolours of the hall emphasise that this is a place of restrained good taste, a style continued in the drawing-room, where pictures line the mottled-yellow walls which graciously set off the grey carpet and pastel and apricot sofas and pelmeted drapes. A similar feel pervades the restaurant, which opens into an airy conservatory section with a flowing muslin canopy above. Pastel shades are also to the fore in the bedrooms, some of which boast beams, and all of which are decorated to good effect with carefully co-ordinated bedding and a mixture of antique, reproduction or pine furniture. Extras such as Roberts radios and mineral water complement the spotless bathrooms. Consider the courtyard or lodge rooms to escape the possibility of traffic noise.

◑ Closed 24 Dec to 11 Jan ↗ Take A31 to Wimborne Minster; at roundabout take B3073; at next roundabout take A349 towards Poole; Beechleas is on right. Private car park 🚗 1 single, 2 twin, 6 double; some in annexe; all with bathroom/WC; all with TV, room service, hair-dryer, direct-dial telephone, radio; no tea/coffee-making facilities in rooms ✅ Restaurant/conservatory, drawing-room, garden; functions (max 12 people residential/non-residential), conferences; early suppers for children; cots, baby-listening ♿ No wheelchair access ● Dogs in bedrooms only, by arrangement; smoking in drawing-room only ☐ Amex, MasterCard, Visa £ Single £69, single occupancy of twin/double £79 to £89, twin/double £89 to £99. Alc L £19, D £20. Special breaks available

---

Isbourne Manor House

Castle Street, Winchcombe, Cheltenham GL54 5JA
TEL: (01242) 602281 (AND FAX)

B&B with de luxe bedrooms in a fine old listed house.

The manor – not quite as grand as its name might suggest but still a handsome golden-stone building – is well placed. On the edge of town but a mere two-minute walk from the High Street (and highly recommended food at Wesley House, see entry), it overlooks Sudeley Castle's grounds (though not the castle itself). In the front, Georgian, half of the building, you'll find a refined guests' sitting-room with honesty bar, magazines and a fire in winter, and a rather formal dining-room, where everyone takes breakfast round a single table under the gaze of one of owner Felicity King's dour-looking Scottish ancestors. This section also contains two of the bedrooms: Sudeley, with a massive reproduction four-poster bed, which is the only room with a bath, and Langley, with a much smaller Victorian brass bed. The third room, Beesmore, lurks in the eaves of the Elizabethan wing at the rear of the house; it has its own terrace, but its shower-room is down the corridor. Nonetheless, all the rooms are fairly luxurious, not only furnished with antiques, but also full of indulgent extras.

◑ Open all year ⨀ In Winchcombe, turn into Castle Street by White Hart Hotel; hotel is at bottom of steep hill. Private car park ⨼ 1 twin, 1 double, 1 four-poster; 1 with bathroom/WC, 1 with shower/WC; all with TV, room service, hair-dryer, some with trouser press ⨷ Dining-room, sitting-room, garden ⛐ No wheelchair access ⬤ No dogs; no smoking ▭ None accepted £ Single occupancy of twin/double £40 to £50, twin/double £50 to £60, four-poster £65; deposit required. Special breaks available

---

Wesley House

High Street, Winchcombe, Cheltenham GL54 5LJ
TEL: (01242) 602366   FAX: (01242) 602405

Highly rated restaurant, with characterful bedrooms, in a former merchant's house dating from the fifteenth century.

The skew-whiff, gabled, black-and-white-timbered building, named after the Methodist preacher who may have stayed here in 1779, looks as old as it is. You enter off the busy High Street into a small bar area, where a few sofas are ranged round a log fire; a little terrace at the back of the house serves as an alternative drinks' spot in summer. In between lies the thickly beamed restaurant, its white walls and linen pleasingly unfussy, as if to ensure that nothing detracts from the main reason that you are here: namely, Jonathan Lewis's confident modern European cuisine. Ingredients and flavours come in vivid combinations: maybe grilled marinated goats' cheese with a beetroot dressing and a buttermilk pancake, or guinea-fowl with a spiced plum chutney. The fish dishes and desserts (you can taste a selection for a supplement) win rave reviews, as does the perky, unforced service. The character of the building is much in evidence in the small, beamed bedrooms, which, except for one, only have space for shower-rooms. The front-facing rooms, though double-glazed, have to endure traffic noise. A few pounds extra secures you the Terrace Bedroom at the rear; it's the biggest, and has a terrace with enjoyable views over Winchcombe's ancient rooftops.

◑ Open all year; restaurant closed Sun eve ⨀ On High Street in Winchcombe. On-street parking (free) ⨼ 1 single, 2 twin, 3 double; single with bathroom/WC, most with shower/WC; all with TV, room service, hair-dryer, direct-dial telephone ⨷ Restaurant, bar, lounge, drying-room; functions (max 55 people incl up to 11 residential); early suppers for children; cots, high chairs, babysitting, baby-listening ⛐ No wheelchair access ⬤ No children in restaurant after 8pm; no dogs; no smoking ▭ Amex, Delta, MasterCard, Switch, Visa £ Single £39, single occupancy of twin/double £48, twin/double £70 to £80; deposit required. Set L £16.50, D £28.50. Special breaks available

WINCHESTER Hampshire   map 2

Hotel du Vin & Bistro

Southgate Street, Winchester SO23 9EF
TEL: (01962) 841414   FAX: (01962) 842458
EMAIL: admin@winchester.hotelduvin.co.uk
WEB SITE: www.hotelduvin.co.uk

*Stylish, popular town-house hotel with refined rooms, excellent food
– and lots of wines.*

All is not as it seems in the cool, cream sitting-room of the Hotel du Vin. If you
look closely at the mantelpiece, you'll discover that the posh white invitation
there is actually part of the *trompe l'oeil* decoration – it celebrates the hotel's
opening night in 1994. Such attention to detail is typical of the hotel; everything
thought through and nothing left to chance. Each bedroom is sponsored by a
winery, with the stylish décor incorporating company colours and corporate
memorabilia. Courvoisier is as serene as its namesake, with a view of the sunny
garden and delicate cream-and-white colour scheme. Much more overwhelming
are the intense, bold colours of Durney Vineyards, where black, burgundy and
gold predominate; even the bathroom is ostentatious, with a free-standing bath
and double-headed power shower. Rooms at the front, such as Marqués de
Cáceres, are a bit noisier because they face the street, but this is always made
clear to potential guests. Out beside the pleasant walled garden are the newer
rooms, all as discreetly elegant as those in the main house. The informal but
efficient management style is most noticeable in the bustling bistro, as
continental in its décor and feel as in its cuisine: perhaps, parfait of foie gras with
toasted brioche, then escalope of calf's liver with shallot marmalade, and sultana
crème caramel. Book in advance, even if you're a hotel guest – one reader, who
confirmed the hotel and breakfast to be excellent, was unable to eat in the bistro
when arriving late in the evening.

◑ Open all year   ⚡ In Winchester city centre. Private car park   🛏 22 twin/double, 1
suite; some in annexe; all with bathroom/WC exc 1 twin/double with shower/WC; all
with TV, hair-dryer, mini-bar, trouser press, direct-dial telephone, CD player
⚗ Bistro, bar, lounge, garden; functions (max 48 people residential/non-residential),
conferences; baby-listening   ♿ Wheelchair access to hotel (2 steps) and bistro, 4
ground-floor bedrooms, 1 specially equipped for disabled people   ● No dogs
☐ Amex, Delta, Diners, MasterCard, Switch, Visa   💷 Single occupancy of
twin/double £79 to £115, twin/double £79 to £115, suite £165; deposit required.
Continental B £6.50, cooked B £9.50; set Sun L £21.50; alc L £27.50, D £35

Wykeham Arms

75 Kingsgate Street, Winchester SO23 9PE
TEL: (01962) 853834   FAX: (01962) 854411

*Bustling, popular inn, with great food and comfy rooms, in a
historic cathedral city.*

From the outside, this couldn't be a more archetypal town pub if it tried, and inside it's the kind of pub that gives its genre a good name, featuring log fires, snug corners and good food. Perfectly positioned in a back street near the cathedral and college, the inn has been tending to the needs of pilgrims, tourists, teachers and locals since 1755. Winchester College (after whose founder the inn is named), features prominently: old desks are used as tables in the bar, and oodles of memorabilia line the walls and shelves. The converted former watchmaker's shop at the end is a quieter area in which to dine, where you could enjoy leek, courgette and garlic soup, then roast duck breast on a spiced-fruit compote, and lastly a cappuccino mousse cake. Upstairs, the bedrooms are as cosily cluttered as the bar, with Nelson and Hamilton the cream of the crop – the latter having 100-year-old, four-foot-high beds. The bathrooms are being upgraded (not before time). Across the road at the Saint George, the newly refurbished bedrooms lack the atmosphere of those over the pub, but have much better bathrooms and lovely, restful colour schemes. The College Bakehouse suite, done out in cream and blue, is particularly pleasant.

● Closed 25 Dec; dining-room closed Sun eve 🔁 Immediately south of cathedral by Kingsgate, at junction of Canon Street and Kingsgate Road. Private car park; on-street parking (free) ⇌ 1 single, 3 twin, 8 double, 1 suite; some in annexe; all with bathroom/WC exc single with shower/WC; all with TV, room service, hair-dryer, mini-bar, direct-dial telephone; some with fax/modem points ⌀ 4 dining-rooms, 2 bars, lounge, drying-room, garden; conferences (max 12 people residential/non-residential); sauna ♿ No wheelchair access ● No children under 14; no smoking in 3 dining-rooms and some bedrooms ⬜ Amex, Delta, Diners, MasterCard, Switch, Visa £ Single £45, single occupancy of twin/double £70 to £82, twin/double £80 to £92, suite £118. Bar/bistro L £5; alc L £13, D £18

WINDERMERE Cumbria   map 8

The Archway

13 College Road, Windermere LA23 1BU
TEL: (015394) 45613
EMAIL: archway@btinternet.com

A guesthouse with real personality and wonderful cooking in the heart of Windermere.

If Windermere fills you with a dread of dreary boarding houses, think again: this civilised, upbeat guesthouse is one to remember. In a tidy Victorian terrace, it's close to the centre but feels very quiet, set as it is above street level in steep gardens. In busy holiday periods, nearby day-time parking can be scarce, so bag your place in the evening. The knocked-through lounge-cum-dining-room (partly divided by the archway) contains a pleasant mix of furnishings and interesting objects, where nothing matches but everything gels. Billowing kangaroo vines festoon the bay window where a table overlooks the gardens and town beyond, and books galore are stacked in alcoves and on surfaces (and reflect Anthony's background in art history). A fire blazes cheerfully on chilly days, and classical CDs play sotto voce by the china-stacked dresser at meal-times. There are just four bedrooms, simply equipped but individualised with Victorian or Edwardian pieces and lots of family pictures, books, prints and antique patchwork quilts. The main selling point of this place, however, is undoubtedly Aurea Greenhalgh's wonderful cooking. The two-course dinners here knock spots off countless Lakeland table d'hôte menus for their freshness and flair. There's a strong emphasis on organic produce, and the breakfast, 'catering for those not so fond of English bacon and eggs, was superb,' reported one guest of the home-made yoghurt and fruit purées, freshly squeezed fruit-juice cocktails, and Aurea's lovely bread.

❶ Open all year; dining-room closed Sun & Weds eves ⓩ From Windermere Main Street, turn by Methodist church into College Road. Private car park; on-street parking (free) ⤷ 2 twin, 2 double; all with bathroom/WC exc 1 twin with shower/WC; all with TV, hair-dryer, direct-dial telephone ⊘ Dining-room, lounge, garden; early suppers for children ♿ No wheelchair access ⬤ No children under 10; no dogs; no smoking ▭ MasterCard, Visa £ Single occupancy of twin/double £34 to £39, twin/double £45 to £52; deposit required. Set D £13.50. Special breaks available

Gilpin Lodge

Crook Road, Windermere LA23 3NE
TEL: (015394) 88818   FAX: (015394) 88058
EMAIL: hotel@gilpin-lodge.demon.co.uk
WEB SITE: www.gilpin-lodge.co.uk/

Superior country-house style, in peaceful setting east of Windermere.

Exceptionally high standards mark out this Edwardian hotel, which is going from strength to strength under its energetic, professional and warmly welcoming management. Easily found on the B-road to Crook, it stands well back from any traffic noise in 20 acres of gardens. Much of its appeal lies in its unusually large amount of beautifully furnished public space, including two drawing-rooms and three dining-rooms, which ranges into skilfully added modern extensions to the rear of the house. The main drawing-room is a gorgeous oblong room, with masses of well-spaced seating arranged in cosy groups around a fireplace. The dining-rooms in the original house are intimate but formal in Chippendale style, with crystal and silver displays and many antiques, while the Courtyard Room in a partly glazed extension has William Morris 'Lemons' wallpaper and modern ladder-back seating. With all this space in which to eat it, food is understandably a high point. The bedrooms come in several categories, all splendidly comfortable, from beautiful, but unpretentious, four-poster rooms to more modern units in the Orchard Wing, with their own private terraces and jacuzzis.

❶ Open all year ⓩ From M6 Junction 36, take A590 or A591 to roundabout north of Kendal, then B5284 for 5 miles. Private car park ⤷ 4 twin/double, 6 double, 4 four-poster; family rooms available; all with bathroom/WC; all with TV, room service, hair-dryer, mini-bar, trouser press, direct-dial telephone ⊘ 3 dining-rooms, 2 drawing-rooms, garden; functions (max 14 people residential/non-residential), conferences; leisure facilities nearby (free for guests) ♿ No wheelchair access ⬤ No children under 7; no dogs; no smoking in dining-rooms and 1 lounge ▭ Amex, Delta, Diners, MasterCard, Switch, Visa £ Single occupancy of twin/double £65 to £110, twin/double £80 to £180, four-poster £120 to £180, family room £185 to £240; deposit required. Light L £8; set Sun L £16.50, D £29.50; alc L £18. Special breaks available

Holbeck Ghyll

Holbeck Lane, Windermere LA23 1LU
TEL: (015394) 32375   FAX: (015394) 34743

Ambitious and stylish country-house hotel in magnificent setting.

Recent additions, such as the full-blown health spa and the luxury 'flexible catering' units, give an air of confident expansionism to this fine hotel. It's an imposing house of undoubted character, originally built as a nineteenth-century hunting lodge and boasts art-nouveau stained glass and some very fine furniture. Throughout, the hotel is beautifully maintained and feels very inviting. Although it's professionally staffed and business-like, it still has a family-run air, and staff are noticeably welcoming. The gracefully proportioned lounges and the oak-panelled restaurant have high-quality furnishings, antiques and lots of personal touches, set off by lovely views over the immaculate, sheltered grounds. From the terraces outside, and from many of the bedrooms, guests can enjoy the full majesty of the hotel's Lakeland setting. The food is a serious but unpretentious affair of classic English cooking with French influence. There's no point stinting yourself at Holbeck Ghyll: push the boat out for a special treat, choose a room with a view, and you'll have a splendid stay.

◑ Open all year   🔃 3 miles north of Windermere on A591; turn right on to Holbeck Lane after Brockhole Visitors' Centre; hotel is ½ mile on left. Private car park
🛏 1 single, 7 twin, 5 double, 2 four-poster, 5 suites; some in annexe; family rooms available; all with bathroom/WC; all with TV, room service, hair-dryer, trouser press, direct-dial telephone, some with mini-bar, tea/coffee-making facilities, CD player
🍽 2 restaurants, bar, 2 lounges, drying-room, garden; functions (max 65 people incl up to 40 residential), conferences; civil wedding licence; gym, sauna, tennis, putting green, health & beauty spa; early suppers for children; cots, high chairs, babysitting, baby-listening   ♿ No wheelchair access   ● No children under 8 in restaurants eves; no dogs in public rooms (£3 per night in bedrooms); no smoking in restaurants
▭ Amex, Diners, MasterCard, Switch, Visa   £ Single £79 to £95, single occupancy of twin/double £130 to £140, twin/double £160 to £190, four-poster/suite £180 to £210, family room £200 to £230 (rates incl dinner); deposit required. Bar L £5.50; set L £18, D £29.50/£34.50. Special breaks available

Miller Howe

Rayrigg Road, Windermere LA23 1EY
TEL: (015394) 42536   FAX: (015394) 45664
EMAIL: lakeview@millerhowe.com
WEB SITE: www.millerhowe.com/

Same team but different leadership in this flagship country-house hotel and restaurant.

The flamboyant food impresario John Tovey retired to warmer climes this year, and his famous temple of gastronomy overlooking Windermere has passed into other hands. It's been a carefully orchestrated takeover, and few regulars will notice many changes to the fabric of the place, or in many of its staff. The magician himself, however, is a hard act to follow, and whether his invisible influence as 'consultant' can replace his dynamic showmanship at dinner remains to be seen. The idiosyncratic décor makes an immediate impact, with button-back leather furnishings, rich colour schemes and ornate statuary. The sun lounge – cool bamboo decked with ferns and palms – revels in its lake and garden views. The bedrooms are predictably comfortable, though more restrained than the public spaces; sound systems and binoculars are supplied. The restaurant, focal point of all the fuss, is a split-level, voguish space of Italianate chairs and elegant glassware. The food, of course, deserves a separate essay, but the basic dinner concept is a choiceless *tour de force* featuring wondrous ways with vegetables. Set lunches, good value at £15, are popular with non-residents (not many people could manage both lunch and dinner). Regulars will welcome the abolition of a hefty service charge (it's now 'at your discretion'). We include this top-flight establishment on the basis of 'business more or less as usual'; our inspector felt that at this critical phase in its history, however, reception staff might try a more positive charm offensive on visitors.

◑ Closed 2 Jan to 11 Feb　⊠ On A592 between Windermere and Bowness. Private car park　⊯ 1 single, 6 twin, 5 double; all with bathroom/WC; all with TV, room service, hair-dryer, trouser press, direct-dial telephone, sound system; no tea/coffee-making facilities in rooms　⊘ Restaurant, 3 lounges, conservatory, garden; conferences (max 10 residential/non-residential)　⅋ No wheelchair access ⬤ No children under 8; no dogs in public rooms (£3 per night in bedrooms) ▭ Amex, Diners, MasterCard, Visa　£ Single and single occupancy of twin/double from £95, twin/double £140 to £250 (rates incl dinner); deposit required. Set L £15, D £32. Special breaks available

---

WINSFORD Somerset   map 1

Savery's at Karslake House　NEW ENTRY

Halse Lane, Winsford, Minehead TA24 7JE
TEL: (01643) 851242 (AND FAX)

Excellent restaurant, with homely rooms, in the heart of huntin', fishin' an' shootin' territory.

At first glance, John Savery and Pat Carpenter's enterprise has the look of a roadside country pub – whitewashed walls and a simple, cottagey exterior. In fact, the building has its origins in a fifteenth-century malthouse, which becomes more obvious as you venture inside, where heavy beams and a huge inglenook add distinction to a homely sitting-room, whose tied-back floral drapes and wall-mounted plates bestow a rustic look. The restaurant, with peachy woodchip prettified by a floral border, is distinguished by John's numerous culinary awards. The food is unfussy yet well judged: perhaps chicken-liver parfait with toasted brioche, followed by venison in port wine with polenta and crispy bacon, and finally sticky toffee pudding. The neat

527

bedrooms successfully team antiques with more prosaic furniture and clean, crisp décor. Room 7, with its four-poster, is the one to go for if you're celebrating a special occasion.

◖ Closed Feb; restaurant closed Sun eve ⎘ Turn off A396 Minehead to Tiverton road at signpost to Winsford; pass the Royal Oak pub and hotel is 50 yards on right. Private car park ⇤ 1 twin, 5 double, 1 four-poster; 4 with bathroom/WC, 3 with shower/WC; all with TV, hair-dryer ⊘ Restaurant, bar, sitting-room, drying-room, library, garden; functions (max 30 people incl up to 14 residential); fishing, clay-pigeon shooting ♿ No wheelchair access ● No children under 15; dogs £2.50 per night; smoking in bar only ▭ Delta, MasterCard, Switch, Visa £ Single occupancy of twin/double £30 to £50, twin/double £40 to £70, four-poster £80; deposit required. Set D £25

WINTERINGHAM North Lincolnshire   map 9

Winteringham Fields

Winteringham, Scunthorpe DN15 9PF
TEL: (01724) 733096   FAX: (01724) 733898
EMAIL: euroannie@aol.com

A relaxed atmosphere and plush bedrooms in one of the UK's culinary centres of excellence.

Lost in countryside south of the Humber Bridge, and way off any established tourist itinerary, you may think this is truly an odd location for a restaurant-with-rooms. But the renown of Germain and Annie Schwab's place is such that guests travel the length and breadth of the country to treat themselves to such exemplary cooking. Many – to do justice to the menu and wine list – will want to stay overnight, and will find that the bedrooms are no mere afterthought, but little capsules of luxury in which to sleep off any gastronomic exertions. The sixteenth-century house, all beams and sloping floors, has an Aladdin's-cave interior of darkly romantic Victorian opulence that allows Annie to indulge her love of rich fabrics. Shared between the main house and a courtyard annexe, they are top-class and fitted out with antiques, cosseting fabrics and luxury bathrooms; those in the main house win out, thanks to their beamed ceilings and extra character – Lord Fitzhugh is worth choosing for the bathroom alone. The restaurant remains, however, the centre of this universe; the gold silk curtains, dark panelling and deep-midnight-blue décor contrast elegantly with the starched linen and candlesticks to set the scene for Germain's culinary creativity. Although the food is guaranteed to please the eye, taste is the ultimate goal, and a typical menu might feature mille-feuille of lobster with a morel sauce and then rabbit tortellini in wild-mushroom broth; for aficionados, the cheese trolley has acquired legendary status.

◖ Closed Chr, first week Mar, first week Aug, bank hols; restaurant closed Sun & Mon eves ⎘ 4 miles west of Humber Bridge, off A1077 in centre of village. Private car park ⇤ 2 twin, 3 double, 1 four-poster, 1 suite; some in annexe; 5 with bathroom/WC, 2 with shower/WC; all with TV, room service, hair-dryer, direct-dial telephone; no tea/coffee-making facilities in rooms ⊘ Restaurant, bar, lounge, conservatory, garden ♿ Wheelchair access to hotel (1 step) and restaurant, 3 ground-floor bedrooms ● No children under 8 exc babes in arms; no dogs; no smoking in bedrooms 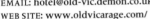 Amex, Delta, MasterCard, Switch, Visa £ Single occupancy of twin/double £85 to £120, twin/double £120, four-poster/suite £125; deposit required. Cooked B £8.50; set L £20, D £29 to £49; alc D £48

WITHERSLACK Cumbria map 8

Old Vicarage

Church Road, Witherslack, Grange-over-Sands LA11 6RS
TEL: (015395) 52381 FAX: (015395) 52373
EMAIL: hotel@old-vic.demon.co.uk
WEB SITE: www.oldvicarage.com/

Smart country-house hotel in rural seclusion, run with professional, but friendly, courtesy.

Take note of the directions before you attempt to find this hotel: it's hidden in a cat's cradle of tiny lanes. Twenty years ago, two engineering colleagues in mid-career hit on the notion of teaming up with their families for a change of life-style, and the Old Vicarage, a large grey-stone house dating from 1803 and set in five acres of mature natural gardens, orchards and woodland, took on its new role – somewhere between an up-market restaurant-with-rooms and a tranquil country-house hotel. It succeeds admirably in both departments, the Reeves and the Browns dividing the task of running the Old Vicarage between them. The food is reliably excellent and uses much local produce, including damsons and Lakeland lamb. The five-course dinners are interesting, but never over-elaborate, and it's worth saving room for both the stupendous cheeseboard and breakfast the following morning, when porridge liberally doused in whisky is served. Along with two pleasant lounges and two dining-rooms, there is a bevy of handsome bedrooms, some of which are in a well-designed modern annexe and have private patios and rather more gadgetry than those in the house, which are older and have more individual character. All are very comfortable. Special events add spice to the Old Vicarage's calendar, and there's a certain amount of small-conference trade, so you may find yourself dining with a board of directors or a carriage-load of nostalgic railway enthusiasts.

◑ Open all year ⏩ Turn off A590 into Witherslack and take first left by telephone box; hotel is ½ mile further on, on left. Private car park 🛏 4 twin, 8 double, 1 four-poster, 1 family room; some in annexe; most with bathroom/WC, 3 with shower/WC; all with TV, room service, hair-dryer, direct-dial telephone, some with mini-bar, CD player, safe ⊘ 2 dining-rooms, 2 lounges, garden; conferences (max 20 people incl up to 14 residential); tennis; leisure facilities nearby (reduced rates for guests); early suppers for children; cots, high chairs, baby-listening ♿ Wheelchair access to hotel and dining-rooms, WC (M, F), 7 ground-floor bedrooms, 1 room specially equipped for disabled people ◔ No dogs in public rooms ▭ Amex, Delta, MasterCard, Switch, Visa £ Single occupancy of twin/double from £80, twin/double from £140, four-poster £200, family room £180 (rates incl dinner); deposit required. Set L £15.50. Special breaks available

---

All entries in the Guide *are rewritten every year, not least because standards fluctuate. Don't trust an out-of-date edition.*

ENGLAND

WOLTERTON Norfolk

Saracen's Head

L

Wolterton, Erpingham, Norwich NR11 7LX
TEL: (01263) 768909

A quirky pub and restaurant in a notable building in an isolated position amid rolling countryside.

This unusual, square red-brick house with overhanging eaves was built in 1806 by Horatio Walpole as a copy of the Tuscan villas that he had encountered on his European journeys. Its idiosyncratic architectural style also suits the approach of the Saracen's Head owner and chef, Robert Dawson-Smith. Blackboards herald your arrival with slogans promising 'Heaven on Earth' and advertising the delights of the large walled garden at the back. The easy-going style is immediately apparent inside, where a battered old school map of the world adorns a wall of the parlour, which is brightened up by floral plastic tablecloths. There are other eating tables around the bar area, which serves two different rooms. You might start a meal with deep-fried Brie with apricot sauce, followed by wok-sizzled strips of sirloin with basil and tomato, and end with a dessert of old-fashioned treacle tart. The pleasant bedrooms are plain and simple; Room 1 in particular has a nice brass bed. One guest told us they had had excellent service, but their mattress was 'just about bearable'.

◑ Closed 25 Dec ⬚ 2 miles west of A140; go through Erpingham and continue straight past church, following signs for Wolterton Hall; hotel is ½ mile further on right. Private car park ⬚ 1 twin, 3 double; all with bathroom/WC; all with TV, hair-dryer ⬚ Parlour restaurant, bar, lounge, garden; functions (max 60 people incl up to 8 residential), conferences; leisure facilities nearby (reduced rates for guests); early suppers for children; high chairs ⬚ No wheelchair access ⬚ No dogs in public rooms; no smoking in bedrooms ⬚ Amex, Delta, MasterCard, Switch, Visa ⬚ Single occupancy of twin/double £35 to £40, twin/double £60; deposit required. Bar/bistro L, D £3 to £18. Special breaks available

---

WOODBRIDGE Suffolk

map 6

Seckford Hall

Woodbridge IP13 6NU
TEL: (01394) 385678 FAX: (01394) 380610
EMAIL: reception@seckford.co.uk
WEB SITE: www.seckford.co.uk/

Beautiful Elizabethan mansion, now a popular family-run business hotel.

Although the immediate surroundings, the A12 bypass at Woodbridge, are pretty mundane, this house is a splendid example of Elizabethan architecture. During the week the car park is packed with corporate BMWs, but this is no bland chain hotel; unassuming owner Michael Bunn is a very visible presence, doing much of the running round himself – and coming up with the loan of a pair of cuff links when our inspector realised he'd left his at home. Inside the

530

building are old beams, wonderful wood panelling and heavy old furniture. The large main restaurant has comfortable and well-spaced tables with tapestries around to admire. This is clearly a place where people dress up to come for an evening out, with a pricey menu. Lobster is a speciality, and there are choices for vegetarians as well as some simpler dishes such as poached salmon. Even on a buzzing Friday night our inspector was impressed with the efficiency of the service. Upstairs the bedrooms are similarly individual, some with heavy old four-posters, and the Seckford has a large balcony. The outbuildings have been converted into more bedrooms for those who prefer seclusion (or for families who need more space). And there's also a pool in the beamed barn, with an informal restaurant for feeding the children, or if you don't feel like dressing up.

◐ Closed 25 Dec   🚹 Hotel is signposted on A12 near Woodbridge. Private car park 🛏 3 single, 9 twin, 14 double, 4 four-poster, 2 suites; some in annexe; family rooms available; all with bathroom/WC; all with TV, room service, hair-dryer, trouser press, direct-dial telephone, some with mini-bar   ⊘ 2 restaurants, bar, 3 lounges, garden; conferences (max 100 people incl up to 20 residential), functions; civil wedding licence; fishing, golf, gym, solarium, heated indoor swimming-pool; early suppers for children; cots, high chairs, babysitting, baby-listening   ♿ Wheelchair access to hotel and restaurant, WC (M, F), 9 ground-floor bedrooms, 1 specially equipped for disabled people   ● Dogs £4 per night; no smoking in bedrooms   ▭ Amex, Delta, Diners, MasterCard, Switch, Visa   £ Single £79, single occupancy of twin/double £95, twin/double £110 to £120, four-poster £125, family room £125 to £150, suite £150; deposit required. Bar/bistro L, D £15; set L £13.50; alc L, D £27 (1998 prices). Special breaks available

---

WOODSTOCK Oxfordshire   map 5

Feathers Hotel

Market Street, Woodstock OX20 1SX
TEL: (01993) 812291   FAX: (01993) 813158
EMAIL: enquiries@feathers.co.uk
WEB SITE: www.feathers.co.uk/

Polished and highly characterful town-house hotel.

The Feathers has become as much a part of the fabric of Woodstock as Blenheim Palace. This seamless amalgamation of several gorgeous Georgian town houses, right in the centre of town, was preparing to expand into another neighbouring property as we visited in spring. One correspondent's recommendation – 'friendly help, excellent dining-room, nice bedroom with all the thoughtful necessities'– sums up succinctly what the hotel is about, but rather understates its sophistication. Residents with relaxation in mind have numerous options: a courtyard garden with tinkling fountain, soporific snug bar, the tartan-and-oak study (possibly too close to Johan, the whistling parrot, for quiet contemplation), or the exclusivity of the refined first-floor drawing-room. The wood-panelled and yellow-colourwashed restaurant, with its bookshelves, looks particularly fetching once the lights are dimmed. Chef Mark Treasure (poached from Michael's Nook in Grasmere) has advanced the style of rich and powerful flavours delivered with a lighter touch; duck roasted with rock salt and pepper, sea bass scented with pesto, and iced nougat parfait serve as fine examples. The bedrooms, distributed about a labyrinth of corridors, are as distinctive as the public rooms: generally comfortable, rather than generous for size, with unobtrusive decoration and gleaming bathrooms.

◗ Open all year ⤢ In centre of Woodstock, off A44. On-street parking (free); public car park nearby (free) ⤶ 7 twin/double, 10 double, 5 suites; some in annexe; family rooms available; most with bathroom/WC, 1 with shower/WC; all with TV, room service, hair-dryer, direct-dial telephone; no tea/coffee-making facilities in rooms ⊘ Restaurant, bar, drawing-room, study, garden; functions (max 60 people incl up to 44 residential), conferences; early suppers for children; cots, high chairs, babysitting, baby-listening ⟨⟩ No wheelchair access ⬤ No dogs in public rooms (£5 per night in bedrooms); no smoking in restaurant ☐ Amex, Delta, Diners, MasterCard, Switch, Visa £ Single occupancy of twin/double £88 to £156, twin/double £139 to £169, family room/suite £215 to £295; deposit required. Cooked B £8.50; bar/bistro L, D £10.50; set L £17.50/£21, D £44; alc D £37. Special breaks available

Holmwood

6 High Street, Woodstock OX20 1TF
TEL: (01993) 812266   FAX: (01993) 813233

Delightful town-centre B&B, with charming hosts.

When Christina and Roberto Gramellini headed south from York a couple of years ago, they found they couldn't entirely retire from a business in which they had made, and had royally entertained, so many friends. So they re-established their Holmwood B&B – on a slightly smaller scale – in one of the delightful eighteenth-century town houses in the centre of Woodstock. A couple visiting from Australia wrote to say that they headed straight from the airport to the new Holmwood to find 'wonderful hospitality and suites that are a true delight'. The two suites in question are a lovely pale-blue room, with a high ceiling and a bathroom so large you could set up home in it, and a light room at the top of the house with a lacy coronet bed and lots of antique pine furniture. Each has a small sitting-room supplied with magazines, mineral water and shortbread. Breakfast is taken around a long oak table: freshly squeezed juices and home-made marmalade featuring in the traditional breakfast fare.

◗ Closed Jan ⤢ On High Street in Woodstock. On-street parking (free); public car park nearby ⤶ 2 suites; both with bathroom/WC; both with TV, room service, hair-dryer; direct-dial telephone available ⊘ Dining-room, garden ⟨⟩ No wheelchair access ⬤ No children under 12; dogs in bedrooms only, by arrangement; no smoking ☐ None accepted £ Single occupancy of suite £50 to £55, suite £70 to £75; deposit required

If you make a booking using a credit card and find after cancelling that the full amount has been charged to your card, raise the matter with your credit card company. It will ask the hotelier to confirm whether the room was re-let, and to justify the charge made.

Glencot House   NEW ENTRY

Glencot Lane, Wookey Hole, Wells BA5 1BH
TEL: (01749) 677160   FAX: (01749) 670210

Splendid faux-Jacobean house, attractively situated, with easy access to Wells.

Recent investment has seen the old paper mill reinstated as one of the most child-friendly attractions at the Wookey Hole show-caves complex. In recent years Jenny Attia has also striven to restore the mock-Jacobean Glencot House, built in late Victorian times for WS Hodgkinson, the sometime owner of the mill. Hodgkinson incorporated enough period features – carved ceilings, walnut panelling and hefty beams – to produce a most convincing pastiche, while Jenny (herself exhibiting considerable magpie tendencies) has imported sufficient clocks, chandeliers, rugs and display cases of glassware to add her own stamp to a house that's brimming with character and charm, especially in the drawing-room, with its big bay window, and the panelled library, with its mullioned windows and grand piano. Somewhat surprisingly, given the laid-back, family feel of the place, explore further and you'll uncover a table-tennis room, conference facilities and even a splash-around pool and sauna. Chandeliers, a bird-of-paradise wallcovering and a beamed ceiling characterise a rather grand dining-room – though your eyes will drift inexorably towards the views of the lake and sward of lawn that leads down to the River Axe. The food is ambitious and creative: perhaps warm crab sausage with creamed leeks, followed by breast of chicken with a honey sauce, and then iced banana 'mushrooms' (meringue, with candied hazelnuts and coconut anglais). The bedrooms, a smattering of four-posters and half-testers notwithstanding, are more mundane than you might expect, if irreproachably comfortable.

◑ Closed 2 weeks after Chr   ⚡ From Wells, follow signs to Wookey Hole. On entering village, look for pink cottage on left; take sharp turn left 100 yards further on. Private car park   ⟵ 3 single, 3 twin, 2 double, 5 four-poster; family rooms available; all with bathroom/WC exc singles with shower/WC; all with TV, room service, hair-dryer, direct-dial telephone   ⊘ Dining-room, bar, drawing-room, library/TV room, drying-room, games room, garden; conferences (max 40 incl up to 13 residential); fishing, sauna, heated indoor swimming-pool, croquet; early suppers for children; cots, high chairs, baby-listening   ♿ No wheelchair access   ⬤ No children in dining-room after 7pm; dogs in 1 bedroom only, by arrangement; smoking in some public rooms only   ▭ Amex, Delta, MasterCard, Switch, Visa   £ Single and single occupancy of twin/double £58 to £62, twin/double £84 to £98, four-poster £110, family room from £96; deposit required. Set D £25.50. Special breaks available

The Guide *for the year 2000 will be published in the autumn of 1999. Reports on hotels are welcome at any time of the year, but are extremely valuable in the spring. Send them to* The Which? Hotel Guide, FREEPOST, 2 Marylebone Road, London NW1 1YN. *No stamp is needed if reports are posted in the UK. Our email address is: "guide.reports@which.co.uk".*

WOOLACOMBE Devon   map 1

Watersmeet Hotel

Mortehoe, Woolacombe EX34 7EB
TEL: (01271) 870333   FAX: (01271) 870890
EMAIL: watersmeethotel@compuserve.com
WEB SITE: www.watersmeethotel.co.uk/

Immaculate, large seaside hotel with spectacular restaurant and friendly staff.

The corniche around the golden expanse and rolling surf of Woolacombe bay is classic seaside territory, with hotels perched on the cliff, and craggy rocks tumbling down into the sea. This low, cream-painted Victorian hotel proudly occupies prime position. At the front is a tennis lawn, outdoor pool and private steps to the beach. Inside, the hotel is bright and spacious; interconnecting public rooms running the length of the building make the best of the view. Recent refurbishment has brought a designer feel – smart, blue-striped chairs contrast with the peachy walls and carpet. The hexagonal restaurant is simply splendid, with huge plants arching high above the formal, candlelit tables (be prepared to manoeuvre for a window seat); a pianist plays on Saturdays and Wednesdays. The menu is laden with ingeniously prepared classic dishes, such as crown of Lundy crab with tomato and dill salad, followed by pan-fried medallions of marinated Exmoor venison with a tawny-port sauce and mulled fruits. Bedrooms (not all had been refurbished on inspection) follow a peaches-and-cream theme, with the best, of course, having the sea views.

◗ Closed Dec & Jan   ⤢ On the seafront in Woolacombe. Private car park
🛏 10 twin, 10 double, 1 four-poster, 2 family rooms, 1 suite; all with bathroom/WC; all with TV, room service, hair-dryer, direct-dial telephone, clock radio; no tea/coffee-making facilities in rooms   ⌁ Restaurant, 2 bars, lounge, drying-room, games room, garden; conferences (max 20 people residential/non-residential), functions; indoor and outdoor swimming-pools, spa, tennis; early suppers for children; cots, high chairs   ♿ Wheelchair access to hotel (2 steps), 1 ground-floor bedroom   ● No children under 9 in restaurant eves; no dogs; no smoking in restaurant   ▭ Amex, Delta, Diners, MasterCard, Switch, Visa   £ Single occupancy of twin/double £81 to £107, twin/double £132 to £184, four-poster £166 to £218, family room £165 to £230, suite £132 to £218 (rates incl dinner); deposit required. Bar L £5. Special breaks available

---

WOOLTON HILL Hampshire   map 2

Hollington House

Woolton Hill, Newbury RG20 9XA
TEL: (01635) 255100   FAX: (01635) 255075
EMAIL: hollingtonhouse@newbury.net

An accomplished country house with a finely tuned sense of fun.

The turn-of-the-century industrial magnate who commissioned Hollington House must have had fun with the plans, for the result is an entertaining concoction of mock-Tudor, medieval and neo-Jacobean. The overall impression is one of manageable baronial splendour, with much oak panelling and many stags' heads and heavy plaster ceilings. The present owners, John and Penny Guy, have lightened the tone by distributing gems about the place from their collections of model ships, Japanese prints and seasoned luggage. The underlying levity continues in the highly individual bedrooms: Kimono follows a Japanese theme, with architectural drawings of pagodas and *trompe l'oeil* urns; Portholes, having round windows, demonstrates a maritime theme; and Upstairs Downstairs meanders along various levels beneath the rafters. Jacuzzi baths (sometimes two) are *de rigueur*, and late sleepers can signal their reluctance to be disturbed by 'putting the cat out' – a life-sized soft-toy moggie that dangles from the door knob. Dining, while not stuffy, is a more serious affair, with traditional country-house fare being given a modern treatment. On a fine evening, the balustraded terrace is the spot to start or finish with al fresco drinks while enjoying a fine, elevated view over the downs to the distant Highclere Castle.

○ Open all year ◲ From Newbury, take A343 towards Andover; follow signs to Hollington Herb Garden. Private car park ⛫ 19 double, 5 suites; some in annexe; all with bathroom/WC; all with TV, room service, hair-dryer, trouser press, direct-dial telephone; no tea/coffee-making facilities in rooms ⌀ Restaurant, lounge, study, games room, garden; functions (max 48 people incl up to 24 residential), conferences; civil wedding licence; heated indoor and outdoor swimming-pools, tennis, putting green, snooker; early suppers for children; cots, high chairs, toys, babysitting, baby-listening ⎣ No wheelchair access ● No dogs ▭ Amex, Delta, Diners, MasterCard, Switch, Visa £ Single occupancy of double from £105, double from £145, suite £275; deposit required. Cooked B £5; light L £9; set D £29.50; alc L £30, D £40.50. Special breaks available

---

Old Vicarage Hotel

Worfield, Bridgnorth WV15 5JZ
TEL: (01746) 716497   FAX: (01746) 716552
EMAIL: admin@the-old-vicarage.demon.co.uk
WEB SITE: www.oldvicarage.com

Cosseting country-house hotel in a thoroughly rural spot – a classic of its kind.

Christine and Peter Iles's up-market hotel has all the necessary features for a civilised, indulgent break. The Edwardian house stands in two acres of lawned gardens on a ridge above a sleepy village, and basks in restful views of fields stretching away into the distance. The main rooms, such as the fairly formal, parquet-floored dining-room and immediately relaxing, slate-floored conservatory sitting-room, are elegantly furnished. The individually designed bedrooms come with soothing watercolours, delicate colour schemes and sometimes antique beds, as well complimentary extras, such as sherry, fresh fruit and a newspaper. The top-of-the-range coach-house rooms cost a packet but are luxurious, with interesting distressed French furniture and whirlpool baths and, in the case of the two on the ground floor, private gardens with bench and table. After 16 years of hands-on service, the Iles are adopting more of a back-seat role, though they are still very much in evidence. They have promoted their former chef, Richard Arnold, as hotel manager, and have appointed a new head chef. The ambitious dinner menus use carefully sourced ingredients; the obscure cheeses sound fascinating.

◐ Open all year   ⤵ From Wolverhampton, take A454 towards Bridgnorth, through Hilton; take right turn to Worfield (follow brown signs); hotel is 1 mile along, at top of hill, on right. Private car park   ⟻ 3 twin, 7 double, 1 four-poster, 1 family room, 2 suites; some in annexe; most with bathroom/WC, 2 with shower/WC; all with TV, room service, hair-dryer, mini-bar, trouser press, direct-dial telephone   ✓ 3 dining-rooms, sitting-room/bar, conservatory, garden; functions (max 30 people residential/non-residential), conferences; leisure facilities nearby (reduced rates for guests); early suppers for children; cots, high chairs, babysitting, baby-listening   ♿ Wheelchair access to hotel (ramp) and dining-room, 1 ground-floor bedroom specially equipped for disabled people   ◓ No dogs in public rooms; smoking in conservatory only   ▭ Amex, Diners, MasterCard, Visa   £ Single occupancy of twin/double £70 to £100, twin/double £108 to £160, four-poster £150, family room £140, suite £160; deposit required. Set L £17.50, D £25 to £34.50. Special breaks available

---

WYE Kent   map 3

Wife of Bath

4 Upper Bridge Street, Wye, Ashford TN25 5AW
TEL: (01233) 812540   FAX: (01233) 813630

Restaurant-with-rooms run with hospitable charm and thoughtfulness.

In Chaucer's tale, the Wife of Bath is portrayed as a domineering pleasure-seeker. Nobody could accuse John Morgan or his staff of being domineering, but they certainly provide sustenance for seekers of a relaxing good time. The neat, brick-fronted restaurant façade gives way at the back to an attractive, tile-hung exterior, as well as a large garden beyond the car park, complete with fig and magnolia trees and a sunken fish pond. Inside, the stone-flagged lobby is taken up by the small bar and cushioned benches for pre-dinner drinks, while the restaurant occupies two interconnecting rooms next door. The ceilings are low ('I am 6'3" – and had a crack!' noted one visitor), but the neutral colours and well-spaced tables alleviate any feeling of being cramped. The food, drawing on eclectic influences that are seen to good effect in dishes like crab spring rolls with wasabi mayonnaise, and duck breast with a rhubarb and champagne compote, is popular with locals as well as visitors. John Morgan and his team of young staff, well trained in courteous good service, keep things bowling along. The bedrooms ('very clean, good facilities'), named after other Chaucer characters, include the Yeoman, with deep-pink walls and a four-poster, and the Friar. Out in the converted stables, the Miller and the Knight share a small kitchenette, which is stocked with milk, juice, yoghurt, cereal and bread for early departures or DIY breakfasts. Others are welcome to partake of the full-monty fry-up over in the restaurant, for an extra charge.

◑ Closed 2 weeks from 26 Dec; restaurant closed Sun & Mon eves ⤵ Leave M20 at Junction 9 and follow signs to Canterbury on A28; after 4 miles, turn right to Wye. Private car park ⤶ 2 twin, 2 double, 1 four-poster, 1 family room; some in annexe; 2 with bathroom/WC, 3 with shower/WC; all with TV, hair-dryer, direct-dial telephone, some with trouser press, fridge ⦸ Restaurant, bar, drying-room, garden; high chairs ♿ Wheelchair access to hotel and restaurant, WC (unisex), 2 ground-floor bedrooms ◓ No dogs; no smoking in some bedrooms ▭ Delta, Diners, MasterCard, Switch, Visa £ Single occupancy of twin/double £40, twin/double from £50, four-poster £80, family room £60. Cooked B £5; set L £10, D £23.50; alc L £22

YARCOMBE Devon

map 2

The Belfry

Yarcombe, Honiton EX14 9BD
TEL: (01404) 861234   FAX: (01404) 861579
WEB SITE: www.westcountry-hotels.co.uk/belfry/

Spruce, useful hotel in converted school, good for overnighting.

This old schoolhouse was constructed in 1872 from local dressed flint and Portland stone, with fine, arched windows. In 1965 it was converted into a small hotel; from the outside the only visible concessions to modernity are the dormer windows in the roof, but inside nary a trace of its previous incarnation remains – only titular references to the rooms (Upper Second, Lower Third). Tony and Jackie Rees offer simple accommodation in their spruce, bright bedrooms with built-in cupboards and dried-flower arrangements; some of them have views through the arched windows to the fields behind. Downstairs is a small lounge and a pine-panelled cottagey dining-room, with an open fire in the corner. The three-course dinners might include chicken-liver pâté, followed by apricot pork, and then home-made desserts with cream for the sweet-toothed.

◑ Open all year ⤵ On A30, 7 miles east of Honiton, in village centre. Private car park ⤶ 2 twin, 3 double, 1 family room; all with bathroom/WC exc 1 double with shower/WC; all with TV, room service, hair-dryer, mini-bar, trouser press, direct-dial telephone, clock radio ⦸ Dining-room, lounge, drying-room, garden; functions (max 40 people incl up to 13 residential); leisure facilities nearby (free for guests) ♿ Wheelchair access to hotel (1 step) and dining-room, WC (unisex), 2 ground-floor bedrooms ◓ No children under 12; no smoking in bedrooms ▭ Amex, Delta, MasterCard, Switch, Visa £ Single occupancy of twin/double £39 to £44, twin/double £59 to £68, family room £79 to £88; deposit required. Set D £15/£19; alc D £22.50. Special breaks available

---

YARMOUTH Isle of Wight

map 2

George Hotel

Quay Street, Yarmouth PO41 0PE
TEL: (01983) 760331   FAX: (01983) 760425

Elegant seventeenth-century seafront hotel, serving good food.

In the charming old fishing village of Yarmouth, the George, built on the side of the seafront castle, was transformed from local pub to elegant hotel just three years ago. The hotel was built in the seventeenth century for the Governor of the island, who lived at Carisbrooke Castle but wanted a house by the sea (and today you pay more for a room with a view). Service is formal, though with occasional glimpses of superciliousness, and perhaps lacks the personal attention of more intimate hotels. The bedrooms are stylish, varying in degrees of opulence. All have king-sized beds, some have imposing four-posters, and some display the wood-panelling that the owners have painstakingly stripped. Meals in the formal restaurant consist mostly of rich meat and fish dishes, with a good selection of puddings; a main course here might consist of galantine of rabbit with wild mushrooms and chorizo on a cardamom sauce. In the more contemporary, country-style brasserie, with its chunky pine and bright yellow walls, you can enjoy fresh, light dishes and uninterrupted views across the Solent. Through the patio doors a terrace garden leads down to the private shingly beach. When weather prevents a stroll on the beach, the wood-panelled guests' lounge, with its open fire, is an appealing after-dinner alternative.

◑ Open all year; main restaurant closed Sun & Mon eve   ⤤ In centre of Yarmouth's square. On-street parking (free)   ⬏ 1 single, 5 twin, 7 double, 1 four-poster, 2 suites; all with bathroom/WC; all with TV, room service, hair-dryer, direct-dial telephone ⚶ 2 restaurants, bar, lounge, garden; conferences (max 70 people incl up to 12 residential), functions; civil wedding licence; early suppers for children   ♿ No wheelchair access   ◓ No children under 8; dogs £7.50 per night   ☐ Amex, Delta, MasterCard, Switch, Visa   £ Single £75, single occupancy of twin/double from £90, twin/double from £130, four-poster/suite £150; deposit required. Brasserie L, D £22.50; set L £14.50/£24.50, D £37

YATTENDON Berkshire

map 2

Royal Oak

The Square, Yattendon, Thatcham RG18 0UG
TEL: (01635) 201325   FAX: (01635) 201926

Extremely stylish little hotel, with a happening brasserie as well as a fine restaurant, in an out-of-the-way village.

The Royal Oak is not the kind of place you stumble upon, unless you happen to be hopelessly lost in a tangle of lanes in Berkshire not far (although far enough) from the M4. Nevertheless, people from many miles around make the effort to get to this sleepy, rural village in order to sample the culinary delights and warm hospitality of this most cosmopolitan establishment. The outside is deceptive: the low-key old red-brick pub, lost behind swathes of wistaria and high hawthorn bushes, does not prepare you for the vivacious, chic brasserie inside – all yellow walls, flagstoned floors and wooden ceiling, with flowers everywhere. You can sample continental (but not necessarily simple) dishes in the brasserie, such as confit of duck with fennel purée and an olive sauce, or go for the three courses in the more up-market restaurant. Here you might start with a potage of oyster with clams and mussels scented with chervil and chives, followed by pan-fried Barbary-duck breast with a light ginger sauce. The bedrooms are a cut above the average, too (and priced accordingly), with well-thought-out extras – an antique vase here, plenty of cushions there, everywhere flowers. They are brightly done out in yellows and blues to match the rest of the hotel, and have spruce and shiny bathrooms.

◗ Open all year; restaurant closed Sun eve ⤢ In centre of Yattendon village. Private car park ⬆ 1 twin, 3 double, 1 suite; all with bathroom/WC; all with TV, hair-dryer, trouser press, direct-dial telephone ✧ 2 restaurants, bar, lounge, garden; functions (max 100 people incl up to 10 residential), conferences; early suppers for children; cots, high chairs ⅚ No wheelchair access ● No smoking in main restaurant, discouraged in bedrooms ▭ Amex, Delta, Diners, MasterCard, Switch, Visa £ Single occupancy of twin/double £90, twin/double £110, suite £120; deposit required. Continental B £6.50, cooked B £9.50; brasserie L 18, D £20; set L £12/£15, D £32.50; alc L £18. Special breaks available

---

The Dairy

3 Scarcroft Road, York YO2 1ND
TEL: (01904) 639367

Pretty town-house B&B with relaxed hosts and health-conscious breakfasts, situated just outside the city walls.

Let's get *The Sound of Music* puns out of the way first. This Victorian terraced house was once a town dairy operated by the Trapp family, and its present incumbent Keith Jackman plays drums, didgeridoo and harmonica in the town's music venues – put the two together and all that's missing is Julie Andrews. Inside, period detail is the order of the day, with stained-glass windows, fancy cornicing, pitch-pine doors, cast-iron fireplaces and a tiled hallway setting the scene. Simple pine furniture and flowery duvets continue the Victorian theme in the bedrooms, most of which are not *en suite*, although cassette players and a good range of extras help to compensate. Rooms that open on to the lovely, flowery courtyard are the quietest, and although this is a no-smoking house a quiet drag in the courtyard is tolerated. Two sittings are the system at breakfast, so Keith will take your order in advance when you arrive; non-meat-eaters are well catered for with vegetarian and wholefood options.

◗ Closed mid-Dec to 31 Jan ⤢ From A64 follow signs to York (west) on A1036; Scarcroft Road is on right as you approach city centre. Private car park ⬆ 1 twin, 2 double, 1 four-poster, 1 family room; 1 with bathroom/WC, 1 with shower/WC; all with TV, hair-dryer ✧ Dining-room, garden; cot, high chair, toys, secure courtyard ⅚ No wheelchair access ● No dogs in public rooms (in bedrooms by arrangement); no smoking ▭ None accepted £ Single occupancy of twin/double £28 to £38, twin/double £36 to £45, four-poster £40, family room £45 to £56

Denotes somewhere you can rely on a good meal – either the hotel features in the 1999 edition of our sister publication, The Good Food Guide, *or our inspectors thought the cooking impressive, whether particularly competent home cooking or more lavish cuisine.*

Holmwood House

114 Holgate Road, York YO2 4BB
TEL: (01904) 626183   FAX: (01904) 670899
EMAIL: holmwood.house@dial.pipex.com

Suburban B&B with keen owners and attractively furnished bedrooms.

After two years in their new enterprise Bill Pitts and Rosie Blanksby have stamped their mark on the brace of Victorian terrace houses that lie about half an hour's walk from the centre of York. The building they inherited was already well kept, but – not ones to be complacent – they have upgraded facilities and completely refurbished some rooms, which have a sprinkling of antique furniture combined with a light Laura Ashley décor and soft white duvets. Noise from the busy A-road running past the front of the building is unavoidable, despite double glazing, so if you're easily disturbed ask for a rear-facing room – which will come with the added attraction of a view over one of York's prettiest squares. Rosie and Bill go out of their way to help guests, perhaps giving lifts if taxis are unavailable, or lending you a bike; for special occasions they arrange gourmet breaks in conjunction with York's Melton's restaurant (see entry in *The Good Food Guide*) and are developing breaks for walkers. Their breakfasts will certainly set you up for the day – choose from muesli, kippers, fresh fruit, croissants or the full English job, to the accompaniment of classical music.

○ Open all year   ⤢ On A59 Harrogate road near city walls and station. Private car park   ⊨ 1 twin, 8 double, 2 four-poster; family rooms and suites available; all with bathroom/WC exc 2 with shower/WC; all with TV, room service, hair-dryer, direct-dial telephone   ⊘ Dining-room, lounge, garden; conferences (max 12 people incl up to 11 residential); baby-listening   ⅙ No wheelchair access   ● Children under 8 by arrangement only; no dogs; no smoking   ▭ Amex, Delta, MasterCard, Switch, Visa   £ Single occupancy of twin/double £40 to £65, twin/double £50 to £75, four-poster £65 to £70, family room £70 to £80, suite £115 to £135; deposit required. Special breaks available

'Breakfast on our second day was the lowest point. We were seven minutes late for breakfast. My husband had come down to forewarn of this possibility but the proprietor was unforgiving and told us twice that we were late. So when my daughter asked for orange juice she was told this was not available because it was too late, and grapefruit juice – my husband's choice – had run out so could he please settle for half a grapefruit. Our daughter was so intimidated that she resorted to eating her cereal out of a saucer rather than risking further wrath with a request for a bowl.'
On a hotel in the West Country

Middlethorpe Hall

Bishopthorpe Road, York YO23 2GB
TEL: (01904) 641241   FAX: (01904) 620176

Authentically restored stately home in huge grounds, near York racecourse.

In common with many country houses, Middlethorpe Hall fell on hard times after its heyday in the eighteenth century but has had the good fortune to come into the hands of the Historic House Hotels group, which has a fine track record, having effected the transformations of Bodysgallen Hall (Llandudno) and Hartwell House (Aylesbury) (see entries). The impressive public rooms are liberally fitted out with seventeenth- and eighteenth-century antiques and oils, chosen to be consistent with period features like the hall's marble floor, the superb carved-oak staircase and the oak panelling in one of the restaurants. The staff manage to hit the correct pitch with regard to the atmosphere, which is relaxing and devoid of any feeling of intimidation, although one visitor caught the restaurant staff on an off-day. The main house has the best bedrooms, typically with a luxurious, traditional feel created by rich fabrics, elegant antiques and fresh flowers; the Edwardian-style bathrooms (some are a bit on the cramped side) come with embossed bathrobes. The rest of the bedrooms occupy a neighbouring stable block with a modern extension, and nearby cottages have been converted into suites. Chef Andrew Wood offers two dinner menus: the gourmet version justifies its sky-high prices with the inclusion of luxury ingredients; the more down-to-earth selection could start with pan-fried John Dory with sun-dried tomatoes, move on to pork with glazed apples and a truffle sauce, and finish with a prune and Armagnac soufflé with almond custard. One reader felt that standards had dropped since his last visit.

◐ Open all year   ⏰ 1½ miles south of York, beside York racecourse. Private car park ⤢ 4 single, 9 twin, 8 double, 2 four-poster, 7 suites; some in annexe; all with bathroom/WC; all with TV, room service, hair-dryer, trouser press, direct-dial telephone, some with tea/coffee-making facilities   ⚒ 2 restaurants, drawing-room, library, garden; functions (max 50 people residential/non-residential), conferences ⟐ No wheelchair access   ◖ No children under 8; no dogs; no smoking in restaurant ▭ MasterCard, Switch, Visa   £ Single £99 to £110, single occupancy of twin/double £120, twin/double £140 to £155, four-poster £215, suite £175 to £230; deposit required. Continental B £8.50, cooked B £12.50; set L £14.50, D £28/£30; alc L £36. Special breaks available

'In respect of the current expressed concerns, it is our opinion that you are more likely to:
* win the lottery twice in succession
* be innocent and prosecuted by the CPS
* if male and over forty, to be bedded by the Spice Girls – or if female, Tom Cruise!!
than be harmed by the beef or lamb served by this establishment.'
Notice in a Cheshire hotel

Mount Royale

The Mount, York, YO24 1GU
TEL: (01904) 628856   FAX: (01904) 611171
EMAIL: reservations@mountroyale.co.uk
WEB SITE: www.mountroyale.co.uk

A welcoming hotel, run in an exemplary fashion, between York centre and the racecourse.

The main ingredient in the success of Mount Royale is the way in which Richard and Christine Oxtoby run their hotel. All guests are made to feel like the celebrities who have stayed here over the years, attracted, no doubt, by the nearness of the racecourse, as well as the medieval town centre just 15 minutes away – their photos, from Charlton Heston to Twiggy, cover the walls of the bar. As soon as you reach your room, housekeeping calls to make sure that all is well, and the enthusiastic staff put everyone at their ease during meal-times, paying particular attention to solo travellers. The cosseting interior of the two William IV terraced houses that form the hotel bulges with antiques, paintings and plants, changing to an elegant, romantic setting in the conservatory dining-room overlooking the landscaped garden; a pianist plays in the background to set the mood for the accomplished French/English cuisine, served in helpings intended to satisfy hunger, as well as to please the eye. The bedrooms are all top-notch and amply provisioned with mod cons, whether they are the standard type in the main house or the more expensive garden rooms that open through french windows on to a verandah.

◗ Open all year ⚡ On A1036 near York racecourse. Private car park 🛏 5 twin, 9 double, 3 four-poster, 6 suites; some in annexe; family rooms available; all with bathroom/WC; all with TV, room service, hair-dryer, trouser press, direct-dial telephone ⊘ Dining-room/conservatory, bar, 2 lounges, drying-room, games room, garden; conferences (max 14 people residential/non-residential); sauna, solarium; early suppers for children; cots, high chairs, baby-listening ♿ No wheelchair access
● Dogs by arrangement only; no smoking in dining-room ▭ Amex, Diners, MasterCard, Switch, Visa £ Single occupancy of twin/double from £75, twin/double/four-poster from £85, family room/suite from £130; deposit required. Alc D £28. Special breaks available

SCOTLAND

MANSFIELD HOUSE HOTEL

TAIN

Hawkcraig House

Hawkcraig Point, Aberdour, Burntisland KY3 0TZ
TEL: (01383) 860335

On the very edge of the Firth of Forth – a tucked-away guesthouse with fine views.

Aberdour is one of the historic, sunny small towns facing Edinburgh over the broad expanse of the Forth estuary. Hawkcraig House stands at the edge of the sea, just around a headland from the main beach. You would be unlikely to find it by chance, however, for it is situated at the bottom of an alarmingly steep and narrow track, with a precipitous rock face rearing up behind. There's not a great deal of space for garden or car park – though both exist – but the house itself, a white-painted, solid building, is well positioned to get the best of the sun, and guests can use the small conservatory to take full advantage of it. The views, of nearby Inchcolm island and of the distant Pentland Hills, are very fine. A downstairs lounge is warmed by a fire on chilly days, and the upstairs dining-room is the setting for Elma Barrie's home-cooked set four-course dinners (24 hours' notice required). Seafood platters are a popular option – Elma buys her seafood direct from Pittenweem up the coast – and she commends her 'Pineapple Ellis' – a recipe she got from her mother which uses fresh pineapple and whisky liqueur. The house is not licensed, so bring your own bottles. The two bedrooms are simple and straightforward, but have everything you could want.

❶ Closed Nov to late Mar   ↗ Turn off A921 in Aberdour and follow Hawkcraig road to a large car park; drive through and down a very steep access road. Private car park 🛏 1 twin, 1 double; double with bathroom/WC, twin with shower/WC; both with TV, hair-dryer; no tea/coffee-making facilities in rooms   ⊘ Dining-room, lounge, conservatory, garden   ♿ No wheelchair access   ● No children under 10; no dogs; no smoking   ▭ None accepted   £ Single occupancy of twin/double £32 to £36, twin/double £50 to £52. Set D £22 (by arrangement)

Hazlehurst Lodge

Ballater Road, Aboyne AB34 5HY
TEL: (013398) 86921   FAX: (013398) 86660

A restaurant-with-rooms which is also really an art gallery.

This is the kind of place which defies categorisation. In a small Victorian lodge, which looks from the outside as if it might be full of period fripperies, Anne Strachan has created a determinedly modern mix of gallery and restaurant. The interlinked ground-floor rooms which make up the restaurant are spotlit, the white walls and clever lighting showing off the colourful canvases, simple cherry furniture and various treasured objects. The lounge is more traditionally homely, with a stove, masses of books and comfortable sofas. The bedrooms are cool and soothing to the eye, again with white walls, as well as carefully chosen furniture and splendid showers. The same creative touch is applied to the cooking – Anne's passion; there might be crab soup, followed by rack of lamb on a confit of wild mushrooms with salad and a herby polenta. Summer pudding, stuffed with local fruit and made with cassis, would be an appropriate pudding to finish off with. Hazlehurst Lodge is not an exclusive place in the least; families are welcome and there are good facilities for children.

◑ Closed Jan ⊞ On A93 in village of Aboyne. Private car park ⤆ 3 twin/double, 2 double; some in annexe; family rooms available; all with bathroom/WC exc 1 with shower/WC; all with hair-dryer ⟡ Restaurant, 3 lounges, TV room, drying-room, library, garden; functions (max 20 people incl up to 11 residential), conferences; leisure facilities nearby (reduced rates for guests); early suppers for children; cots, high chairs, toys, playroom, babysitting, baby-listening, outdoor play area ⅚ No wheelchair access ● No dogs in public rooms; no smoking ▭ Amex, MasterCard, Visa £ Single occupancy of double £35, twin/double/family room £60 to £76; deposit required. Set D £25. Special breaks available

---

ACHILTIBUIE Highland   map 11

Summer Isles Hotel

Achiltibuie, Ullapool IV26 2YG
TEL: (01854) 622282   FAX: (01854) 622251

Long-established haven in the wilderness.

Not everyone appreciates the isolated wilderness of Wester Ross and the straggling township of Achiltibuie, which lies 15 miles from the nearest main road: one reader described the area as a 'rural agricultural slum... boasting heaps of scrap metal and rolls of fencing wire'. The lack of a TV in the bedroom and the no-choice menu offered at the hotel caused this reader problems, too. For those who are prepared to put up with such matters, however, the Summer Isles Hotel remains a much-appreciated opportunity to indulge in a few creature comforts in a part of the world where modern conveniences are not to be taken for granted. The hotel takes its name from the scattering of small islands at the mouth of Loch Broom, and it is the view of these, and of the distant mountains beyond, which draws guests to the sun lounge at sunset. The hotel is well decorated and well kept throughout, seeming much larger inside, and with far greater aspirations, than you might expect from its humble Highland-farmhouse exterior. The four-course menus are sourced from the excellent ingredients available locally; dinner is served promptly at 8pm. Aberdeen Angus beef features, as does local seafood, and the cheese is good. The bedrooms are furnished to a high standard (one does have a TV), with rocking chairs and high wooden beds (in the log-cabin annexe). Midge repellent is a necessity, as are wellies – you will need both if you intend to take advantage of the comprehensive guide to local walks which is to be found by every bed.

◑ Closed mid-Oct to Easter ⊞ 10 miles north of Ullapool on A835, turn left on to a single-track road to Achiltibuie; village is 15 miles along; hotel is 1 mile further, on left. Private car park ⤆ 4 twin, 7 double, 1 suite; some in annexe; most with bathroom/WC; all with room service, hair-dryer, direct-dial telephone, one with TV; no tea/coffee-making facilities in rooms ⟡ Dining-room, 2 bars, lounge, TV room, drying-room; functions (max 24 people residential/non-residential); fishing; early suppers for children   ⅚ No wheelchair access   ● No children under 6; no dogs in public rooms; no smoking in bedrooms   ▭ MasterCard, Switch, Visa   £ Single occupancy of twin/double £59, twin/double £88, suite £156; deposit required. Bar L £5.50, D £7.50; set D £35.50. Special breaks available

---

ALLOA Clackmannan   map 11

Gean House

Gean Park, Tullibody Road, Alloa FK10 2HS
TEL: (01259) 219275   FAX: (01259) 213827

Beautiful Lutyens-style house, sensitively run as a smart edge-of-town hotel.

Houses built for industrial magnates over the past 100 years can often be wonderful places; the money for Gean House came from the Scottish textile industry, and the Paton family used William Kerr as its architect – he was a disciple of Lutyens, as becomes obvious the moment you see the characteristic roof lines or look at the formal layout of the garden. A great deal of money has been spent on restoring the house, and on turning it into a quiet, dignified, luxurious hotel which is sensitive to its origins. Close to Edinburgh, Glasgow and Stirling, and within easy reach of good countryside, it attracts a mixture of business and leisure trade. A huge hall, complete with gallery and floor-to-ceiling bay window, leads you towards a drawing-room – carefully furnished in formal town-house style, with a rococo mirror – and to the restaurant, whose polished wood panelling reflects the gleam of the dark tables and chairs. Throughout, there are good antique carpets, *objets d'art* and plenty to admire. The bedrooms are distinctly large, carefully and coolly furnished, and contain well-chosen ornaments and paintings. The bathrooms are especially good, and one room has retained its original shower – a mammoth contraption of pipework and taps designed to spray you from all sides. Gean House has a new head chef this year, who previously worked at Inverlochy Castle – a pedigree that speaks for itself. Dinners are either three or four courses, with a choice at each stage bar the soup; venison, lamb and wild mushrooms feature, accompanied by a variety of salsas, sauces and *jus*.

◑ Open all year   ⊿ At Alloa town-hall roundabout, take third exit (B9096) to Tullibody; hotel is 1 mile further on, on left. Private car park   ⊫ 6 twin/double, 1 twin; family rooms available; all with bathroom/WC exc twin with shower/WC; all with TV, room service, hair-dryer, direct-dial telephone; no tea/coffee-making facilities in rooms   ✓ Restaurant, 2 drawing-rooms, library, garden; functions (max 50 people incl up to 14 residential), conferences; early suppers for children; high chairs, baby-listening   ⅚ No wheelchair access   ● No dogs; no smoking in restaurant   ▭ Amex, Delta, Diners, MasterCard, Switch, Visa   £ Single occupancy of twin/double £90, twin/double/family room £145 to £165; deposit required. Light L £12.50; set L £15, D £26.50/£29. Special breaks available

---

All entries, including Round-ups, are fully indexed at the back of the Guide.

Applecross Inn

Shore Street, Applecross, Strathcarron IV54 8LR
TEL: (01520) 744262   FAX: (01520) 744400

Simple, lively inn at the very end of the road.

You reach Applecross after crossing the closest thing in Britain to an Alpine pass and descending over moorland to the edge of the sea facing Skye. It is a faraway place, a monastery a long time ago, now just a few scattered houses at the end of the road. But if you end up here, the Applecross Inn makes a good place to stay overnight – or longer if the whim takes you. It is a simple pub, with a lively bar where everyone in the neighbourhood ends up sooner or later, and simple bedrooms with shared bathrooms. Room 5 at the top of the house is probably the nicest. The bar food at lunch-time is sustaining and hearty, and the meals served in the miniature dining-room in the evenings are equally good, making use of the local seafood in the shape of scallops or crustaceans. There's enough room in the residents' lounge for you not to feel cramped on a rainy day.

◐ Closed 20 Dec to 5 Jan ⊡ In Applecross village. Private car park ⤙ 1 single, 2 double, 2 family rooms; all with wash-basin ⦸ Dining-room, bar, lounge, TV room, garden; functions (max 16 people residential/non-residential); early suppers for children; cots, high chairs, toys & No wheelchair access ⊖ Smoking in bar and lounge only ⊟ MasterCard, Visa £ Single £24, single occupancy of double £33, double £48, family room £52; deposit required. Bar/bistro L, £5, D £8.50; alc D £19.50

Taigh Na Mara

The Shore, Ardindrean, Loch Broom, Garve IV23 2SE
TEL: (01854) 655282   FAX: (01854) 655292
EMAIL: tony@scotlandthegreen.co.uk
WEB SITE: www.scotlandthegreen.co.uk/taighnamara/

Lochside croft guesthouse serving gourmet vegetarian food.

An old shop by the seashore on one of Scotland's most beautiful lochs was transformed in 1989 into a 'Scottish Gourmet Vegan Farmhouse' guesthouse. According to Tony Weston and Jackie Redding, it is now 'notorious and grossly overpraised'. We would prefer 'mildly eccentric, not for everyone, but definitely different'. For a start, you get there on foot, down a steep 200-yard path from the road. Second, as Tony says, there are no chandeliers or jacuzzis, just some bikes, a dodgy dinghy and three rooms – two small ones in the crofthouse itself, and another 'honeymoon suite' in the old boathouse. The atmosphere is laid-back and friendly, the views out across the loch are terrific, and there is as much or as little to do as you want. High spot of the day will be the dinner – seaweed and coconut mousse, walnut and oyster mushroom pie, and peat bog tart – a sticky chocolate concoction. There's no licence, so you will have to lug your own bottles down from the car. Bedrooms are cosy and the kitchen range keeps the place warm, and on wet days you can thumb through Tony's book of recipes, appropriately called *Rainbows and Wellies*.

❶ Open all year ⚡ 8 miles south of Ullapool turn off A835 at sign to Letters and Loggie; hotel is 3 miles on, below Ardindrean phone box, on shore. On-street parking (free) 🛏 1 twin, 2 double; one in annexe; 1 double with bathroom/WC; all with room service, hair-dryer, some with TV ✦ Dining-room, lounge, drying-room, garden; functions (max 8 people incl up to 6 residential), conferences; early suppers for children; cots, high chairs, toys, babysitting ♿ No wheelchair access ● No children under 10 in dining-room eves; no dogs in public rooms and 2 bedrooms; no smoking in public rooms ▭ Delta, MasterCard, Switch, Visa £ Single occupancy of twin/double £42, twin/double £70 to £80 (rates incl dinner); deposit required. Alc L £8, D £15. Special breaks available

---

ARDUAINE Argyll & Bute   map 11

Loch Melfort Hotel

Arduaine, Oban PA34 4XG
TEL: (01852) 200233   FAX: (01852) 200214
EMAIL: lmhotel@aol.com

A spectacular setting for this lochside hotel south of Oban.

The Loch Melfort Hotel has a view to dream of: the sun sets right over the island-studded waters of Loch Melfort, and the mix of sea and land fades into the far distance to the south. It is entertainment enough to sit at the windows of the cocktail bar and watch the patterns of light playing over the scenery. The chief disadvantage that the Loch Melfort Hotel labours under is the presence of its bedroom extension – euphemistically known as the Cedar Wing. However much refurbishing goes on (and a lot does), nothing can really disguise the utilitarian nature of this 'chalet-style' structure. Although you will be comfortable enough there, opt for a bedroom in the main house, where the rooms have far more character, if at all possible. There have been mixed reports of the food – once the hotel's high point. These were confirmed to some extent on an early-season inspection visit, when the food was very nearly very good but was let down, for instance, by a cold salmon salad, where the fish had been allowed to cook a fraction too long and was discernibly woolly round the edges. Feedback from readers suggests that this patchiness has continued – 'fabulous seafood buffet', 'parsimonious portions'. The serving staff – brought in for the season – were amicable but inexperienced. The welcome is friendly and the facilities in the pleasant Chartroom bar, the cocktail bar, and the rewarding library are well up to scratch; the bedrooms are warm, bright and well maintained. A mistaken charge over a single-room supplement was refunded with a handsome letter of apology. And there is a general air of contentment and relaxation, which is most attractive.

---

❶ Closed Jan to mid-Feb ⚡ 20 miles south of Oban; hotel is signposted on A816. Private car park 🛏 15 twin, 11 double; family rooms available; all with bathroom/WC; all with TV, room service, hair-dryer, direct-dial telephone ✦ Restaurant, 2 bars, lounge, drying-room, library, garden; functions (max 100 people incl up to 52 residential), conferences; early suppers for children; cots, high chairs, playroom, baby-listening ♿ Wheelchair access to hotel (ramp) and restaurant, 10 ground-floor bedrooms ◐ Dogs in some bedrooms only; smoking in bar and some bedrooms only 💳 Amex, MasterCard, Switch, Visa £ Single occupancy of twin/double £65 to £82, twin/double £80 to £120; deposit required. Bar/bistro L, D £5 to £20; alc D £31.50. Special breaks available

---

ARISAIG Highland   map 11

Arisaig House

Beasdale, Arisaig PH39 4NR
TEL: (01687) 450622   FAX: (01687) 450626
EMAIL: arisaighse@aol.com

Smoothly run country house in the wilderness.

The road to the Isles is being rapidly upgraded, and reaching Arisaig House will consequently be much easier than it used to be in the days of the winding, single-track route from Fort William. This was once the big house for the Arisaig estate – several thousand acres of tumbled rock and heather – and it is a fairly formal-looking place, surrounded by the usual West Highland combination of stately conifers and a luxuriant undergrowth of rhododendrons. In fact, the old house was burnt down before the war (a common fate of remote Highland mansions before the days of electricity), and what you see today is a rebuilt version. The Smither family and Alison Wilkinson have run it as a luxurious country house in the wilderness for 16 years now, and it continues to draw praise from guests. 'A well-run hotel, friendly and the food is excellent,' writes one satisfied customer. 'When I made a mistake in ordering the wine, the opened bottle was changed at no extra cost, without hesitation.' The interior has been well thought out to combine the best aspects of the traditional shooting-lodge style of hotel with a more formal, dignified side. There is a magnificent carved staircase, and the bedrooms are big and comforting; some have their original baths.

◐ Closed Nov to Mar ⤴ On A830, 1 mile past Beasdale railway station, 3 miles east of Arisaig village. Private car park 🛏 4 twin, 3 twin/double, 5 double, 2 suites; all with bathroom/WC exc 1 double with shower/WC; all with TV, room service, hair-dryer, trouser press, direct-dial telephone; tea/coffee-making facilities available ⊘ Dining-room, bar, 3 lounges, drying-room, games room, garden; functions (max 10 people residential/non-residential), conferences ♿ No wheelchair access ◐ No children under 10; no dogs; no smoking in dining-room 💳 MasterCard, Switch, Visa £ Single occupancy of twin/double £84 to £235, twin/double £168 to £252, suite £252; deposit required. Set D £40. Special breaks available

---

Old Library Lodge

Arisaig PH39 4NH
TEL: (01687) 450651   FAX: (01687) 450219

Restaurant-with-rooms close to the silver sands of Arisaig.

With its unrivalled views of Eigg and Rum across the sea, Arisaig is part village, part crofting township, and is popular with holidaymakers for its wonderful sandy beaches. The Old Library Lodge started life as a stable, but was converted into a library in around 1810 (after Arisaig had lost much of its population during the Clearances). Now it makes a good bistro-style restaurant-with-rooms (some of which are in an annexe). Scallop-and-artichoke soup, grilled duck breast with honey-and-soy sauce, followed by raspberry-and-mascarpone mousse might be typical examples of the dishes served in the black-and-red restaurant – or on the front patio at lunch-time, if the weather permits. The bedrooms in the main house have more character, but those in the annexe have small patios overlooking the garden, and there is a comfortable residents' lounge to boot.

◑ Closed Nov to Mar   ⃕ On main road in centre of Arisaig. On-street parking (free)
⤶ 1 twin, 5 double; some in annexe; family rooms available; all with bathroom/WC exc 2 doubles with shower/WC; all with TV, hair-dryer, direct-dial telephone
⊘ Restaurant, lounge, garden; early suppers for children; cots, high chairs, baby-listening   ⅋ No wheelchair access   ⬤ No dogs; no smoking in public rooms
⌷ Amex, Delta, MasterCard, Switch, Visa   £ Single occupancy of twin/double £48, twin/double £74, family room £89; deposit required. Set D £22.50; alc L £11. Special breaks available

---

Gleneagles

Auchterarder PH3 1NF
TEL: (01764) 662231   FAX: (01764) 662134
EMAIL: ressales@guinness.com
WEB SITE: www.gleneagles.com/

Classic railway hotel turned into an all-inclusive resort complex for the well heeled.

Built in the roaring 'twenties and quickly dubbed 'the playground of the gods' (assuming the gods enjoy golf), Gleneagles at heart still looks and feels like a flagship railway hotel from the days when engine drivers were real men and gentlemen wore plus fours. Its current owners have had the good sense not to tamper with its cavernous lobby, nor its imposing staircases or its corridors, which are like an ocean liner's. Instead, they have built on the past, creating in their newly refurbished bedrooms a study in art-deco retro of subdued beiges and creams, with chunky, crafted furniture and smart bathrooms in black-and-grey mosaic, spiced up by potted palms. The older rooms are not nearly as exciting, featuring space, alabaster sinks and a mix of furniture which clings together well enough but without making you shout 'brilliant!' as you unpack the travelling trunk and hatbox. Intimacy is not what you get here – the main dining-room is best described as 'lofty and echoing' and, when full, could almost be a *palais de danse* on a busy Saturday. Instead, you get facilities – an abundance of them, from designer outlets to big-name golf courses, kiddies' clubs, dance studios, off-road driving, an equestrian school, and much more. It's an all-singing, all-dancing resort complex of the type found nowhere else between Norway and Florida, and while Gleneagles is, as it has always been, designed to appeal to our transatlantic cousins, it provides something for just about everyone, however lazy. Moreover, it's superbly run, exemplifying professionalism with a human face. There's a friendliness of service, American-style, combined with Scottish sincerity and a Jeeves-like attention to detail to make a winning combination.

◐ Open all year ⏢ On A823, just off A9, midway between Stirling and Perth. Private car park ⏢ 19 single, 58 twin, 137 double, 15 suites; family rooms available; all with bathroom/WC; all with TV, room service, hair-dryer, mini-bar, trouser press, direct-dial telephone ✧ 2 restaurants, dining-room, 3 bars, library, garden; functions (max 360 people incl up to 240 residential), conferences; facilities include: fishing, golf, gym, sauna, solarium, 2 heated indoor swimming-pools, tennis, squash, clay-pigeon shooting, off-road driving, biking, bowling, riding, falconry; early suppers for children; cots, high chairs, toys, playrooms, babysitting, outdoor play area ♿ Wheelchair access to hotel (ramp) and restaurants, WC (unisex), 14 ground-floor bedrooms, 2 specially equipped for disabled people ◐ No smoking in some public rooms and some bedrooms ⊡ Amex, Delta, Diners, MasterCard, Switch, Visa £ Single £140, single occupancy of twin/double £225 to £365, twin/double £225 to £365, family room (child up to 16 sharing with parents: room rate + £30 to £40), suite £515 to £1,250; deposit required. Bar/bistro L, D £20; set L £29, D £41; alc L £29, D £45. Special breaks available

---

AUCHTERHOUSE Angus map 11

Old Mansion House

Auchterhouse, Dundee DD3 0QN
TEL: (01382) 320366   FAX: (01382) 320400

Lovely old fortress house, with some splendid interiors.

Set in the rural hinterland of Dundee, on the edge of the Sidlaw Hills, this peaceful old stone tower house has seen a lot of history. It is typical of its time – a house that started life in the days when enemies were just as likely as friends to turn up on the doorstep, before being gradually transformed into a spacious dwelling house. What you get in places like this is a sense of history: massive walls, curious half-landings and undercrofts, some wonderful period plasterwork, but also bedrooms which have not exactly been designed for today's discerning business person. It helps if the owners care about the house, and Jannick and Maxine Bertschy are obviously making the most of theirs. The star is the Jacobean dining-room, sumptuous with its rugs and racing prints, and dominated by a magnificent moulded-plaster ceiling. Next door, a fire blazes in a small ante-room, now used as a lounge, while those who prefer thumping the ivories after dinner repair to the vaulted undercroft by the front door. Upstairs, in the library bar, dark-green walls and racks of books are the backdrop for another space for relaxation. The Bertschys are gradually refurbishing and upgrading the bedrooms, and those that are finished have been given warmth by dark, rich colours, which extend into the bathrooms. Those still to be renewed are chillier in tone, and have some fairly ancient furnishings. The dinners (three, four or five courses, according to choice, with numerous alternatives), are ambitious affairs – roast pheasant breast on a pecan rösti, or tournedos of beef on grilled polenta are typical of the mix of local ingredients and modern fashions.

◗ Open all year ⊿ 3 miles from Muirhead on B954. Private car park ⊏⊐ 2 twin, 2 double, 2 four-poster; suites and family rooms available; all with bathroom/WC; all with TV, room service, hair-dryer, direct-dial telephone ✓ 2 dining-rooms, bar, library/bar, lounge, garden; functions (max 50 people incl up to 12 residential), conferences; sauna, heated outdoor swimming-pool, tennis, clay-pigeon shooting; early suppers for children; cots, high chairs, babysitting, baby-listening ꜀ No wheelchair access ◖ No children in dining-rooms eves; dogs in bedrooms only, by arrangement; no smoking in public rooms ▭ Amex, Delta, Diners, MasterCard, Switch, Visa ₤ Single occupancy of twin/double £80, twin/double £100, four-poster £135, family room/suite £125; deposit required. Bar/bistro L £9.50, D £13; set L £18, D £28. Special breaks available

---

BALLACHULISH Highland   map 11

Ballachulish House

Ballachulish PA39 4JX
TEL: (01855) 811266   FAX: (01855) 811498

Very comfortable and friendly establishment in an ideal location.

'Ballachulish House is one of those places that it is very difficult not to be enthusiastic about,' writes one guest who found refuge in Liz Grey's beautiful, old white house last January. 'The welcome and the house was as warm inside as the weather outside was vile. . . We appreciated finding snowdrops in our bedroom. . . It is difficult to find words to express the tranquillity of the place.' Set against a backdrop of the Glencoe Mountains, and well away from the main road, Ballachulish House dates back to the eighteenth century. Inside, it is very much a family home, so much so that Liz finds some of her returning guests becoming almost proprietorial themselves. There's an elegant drawing-room and a formal dining-room, but there's also the Ceilidh Room – a mix of playroom and billiard room, with games, books, comfortable old chairs, a billiard table and a double bass. The bedrooms are some of the best features of the house. Two huge 'best rooms' at the front, stocked with fine old furniture, are the stars; there's also a lovely family suite (two bedrooms and a bathroom) up under the eaves, with sloping roofs, pine furniture and smart tartan bedspreads. In the recently opened 'new' wing, a further two bedrooms have the biggest bathrooms in the house – one of them has a neat four-poster. Liz Grey does all the cooking herself, serving up five-course dinners with a choice of main course, starter, and usually of pudding, too. Crêpes with smoked haddock, tomato-and-mint soup, fillet of venison with a port and green-peppercorn sauce, followed by chocolate Drambuie, would be a representative menu.

◗ Closed Chr & New Year ⊿ At roundabout before Ballachulish bridge, take A828 towards Oban; hotel is 200 yards further on, on left. Private car park ⊏⊐ 5 twin/double, 2 double, 1 four-poster; family rooms available; all with bathroom/WC; all with hair-dryer, direct-dial telephone ✓ Dining-room, drawing-room, games room, garden; early suppers for children ꜀ No wheelchair access ◖ No children under 3, no children under 6 in dining-room eves; dogs in bedrooms only, by arrangement; smoking in games room only ▭ Delta, MasterCard, Switch, Visa ₤ Single occupancy of twin/double £60, twin/double/four-poster £80, family room £105; deposit required. Set D £25

Balgonie Country House

Braemar Place, Ballater AB35 5NQ
TEL: (013397) 55482 (AND FAX)

Interesting house and good food on Deeside.

Built in 1898 in Arts and Crafts style, this Victorian house looks rather strange among the heather and the hills of Deeside. It was originally built by an Edinburgh lawyer for his widowed sister (no doubt he took advantage of it in the summer for holidays on Royal Deeside). Now under the ownership of John Finnie's family, it still makes a good place to stay. It's a comfortable, unpretentious house, with good-sized plain bedrooms on the first floor and rather more modern ones on the second. Equally, the bar and the lounge are well furnished in a straightforward, unflashy style, and there's croquet if the weather is fine enough to be outdoors. Four-course set dinners might include chicken-liver parfait with Cumberland sauce and a brioche, fillet of halibut in a herb crust, and a chilled minestrone of fruits with mascarpone. The cooking is delicate, and the meals served with style in the small dining-room, with its high-backed chairs.

◑ Closed 5 Jan to 10 Feb ⏺ On outskirts of Ballater, off A93 Aberdeen to Braemar road. Private car park ⏪ 3 twin, 6 double; all with bathroom/WC exc 2 double with shower/WC; all with TV, hair-dryer, direct-dial telephone, radio; tea/coffee-making facilities available ⊘ Dining-room, bar, lounge, garden; croquet; early suppers for children; cots, high chairs ♿ No wheelchair access ⬤ Discourage children in dining-room eves; no dogs in public rooms; no smoking in dining-room ▭ Amex, Delta, MasterCard, Switch, Visa £ Single occupancy of twin/double £52 to £62, twin/double £80 to £103; deposit required. Set L £17.50, D £29.50. Special breaks available

---

Darroch Learg

Braemar Road, Ballater AB35 5UX
TEL: (013397) 55443   FAX: (013397) 55252
EMAIL: darroch.learg@exodus.uk.com

Pleasing country house with good food.

Overlooking the Dee valley and Queen Victoria's favourite mountain, Lochnagar, Darroch Learg is a substantial late-Victorian house. It comes with its own mini-castle, built at the same time (they were once two separate dwellings). You can either sleep in the main house, or ask for a room in Oakhall – as the turreted, pink granite castle is called – where rooms have recently been refurbished. Fiona and Nigel Franks run Darroch Learg as a welcoming, relaxed house; families are welcome. There's plenty of space in the sitting-rooms, which have good views, and one of which is no-smoking. Bedrooms vary in size; the two rather grand four-poster rooms are decorated in light, feminine colours. Chef David Mutter serves up excellent three-course set dinners. Aberdeen Angus beef is usually on the menu – accompanied perhaps by foie gras butter, garlic cream and shallots. You might precede this with roast monkfish fillet with a saffron crab velouté, avocado salsa and crispy potatoes and follow it with a white-chocolate and pear tart with home-made rum-and-raisin ice-cream.

◗ Closed Chr & last 3 weeks Jan　⎘ On A93 at western edge of Ballater. Private car park　⊫ 1 single, 7 twin, 8 double, 2 four-poster; some in annexe; most with bathroom/WC, some with shower/WC; all with TV, room service, hair-dryer, trouser press, direct-dial telephone　✅ Restaurant, 3 sitting-rooms, conservatory, garden; functions (max 60 people incl up to 35 residential), conferences; early suppers for children; cots, high chairs, baby-listening　⅖ Wheelchair access to hotel (ramp) and restaurant, 1 ground-floor bedroom　● No dogs in public rooms; no smoking in some public rooms　⊟ Amex, Delta, Diners, MasterCard, Switch, Visa　⎣£⎦ Single £48 to £50, single occupancy of twin/double £60 to £62, twin/double £95 to £100, four-poster £115 to £140; deposit required. Light L (Mon to Sat) £12; set D £29, Sun L £17.50. Special breaks available

Stakis Craigendarroch

Braemar Road, Ballater AB35 5XA
TEL: (013397) 55858　FAX: (013397) 55447

Big, well-run resort hotel with loads of activities and facilities.

According to legend, Ballater became a resort when a local woman found a cure for her ills by bathing in a nearby peat bog. Now it's a calm, small town, largely composed of Victorian houses built by people who enjoyed the close proximity of Balmoral. Stakis Craigendarroch grafts on to the town well, providing it with a twentieth-century version of the fitness and leisure facilities that originally brought people here. The facilities are the main reason for staying, and if you have children who could get bored with deer and heather, it is ideal. There are swimming-pools, a gym, a sauna and a dry-ski slope. A crèche and children's club will take small people off your hands, perhaps taking them to the local sweet factory or on an outing further afield; there's also an adventure playground. A full fitness programme, making use of the dance studio above the gym, is now available. It's a big hotel and busy in high season, so don't expect peace and quiet or too much character. But it's a smoothly run operation, with rooms that vary from large suites with all the trimmings to humbler standard rooms. The leisure club (now with hot buffet) and the Oaks restaurant provide for those who like their food quick and simple as well as for those who want to linger over an elaborate meal.

◗ Open all year　⎘ 1½ miles west of Ballater on A93. Private car park　⊫ 13 twin, 19 double, 1 four-poster, 6 family rooms, 5 suites; all with bathroom/WC; all with satellite TV, room service, hair-dryer, trouser press, direct-dial telephone, some with mini-bar　✅ 2 restaurants, 2 bars, lounge, study, 2 games rooms, garden; functions (max 120 people residential/non-residential), conferences; gym, sauna, solarium, 2 heated indoor swimming-pools, tennis, dry-ski slope, snooker, health & beauty salon; early suppers for children; cots, high chairs, toys, playrooms, babysitting, baby-listening, outdoor play area, crèche　⅖ No wheelchair access　● No dogs; no smoking in some public rooms　⊟ Amex, Delta, Diners, MasterCard, Switch, Visa

£ Single occupancy of twin/double £134, twin/double £156, four-poster/suite £206, family room £176; deposit required. Bar/bistro L £10, D £15; set D £25; alc L £19.50, D £28.50. Special breaks available

---

BALQUHIDDER Stirling   map 11

Monachyle Mhor

Balquhidder, Lochearnhead FK19 8PQ
TEL: (01877) 384622   FAX: (01877) 384305

A jovial atmosphere and fine food in this isolated farmhouse.

It's a long way to the head of Loch Voil, down one of those single-track Highland roads that winds perilously along the loch shore through birch, oak and rowan trees. Set more or less at the end of the road, Monachyle Mhor is an old farmhouse, now painted strawberry pink, set in the ideal surroundings of rough mountainside, tranquil loch and distant blue hills. The public rooms are somewhat on the small side if the place is full, but the bedrooms, carved out of the old steading which surrounds the courtyard, are excellent, with plenty of space and character in their exposed beams, comfortable, unfussy furniture and interesting nooks and crannies to explore. The bonus – and this is what turns Monachyle Mhor into a place of outstanding merit – is the enthusiasm with which the Lewis family runs it. Much of this stems from Tom, the son in charge of the kitchen, who is passionate about his food and also about the running of the whole enterprise. You feel that if something went wrong with your stay he would take it as a personal blow. 'Relaxed competence seems to be the motto,' declares one satisfied visitor. There's a jovial feel to the place, enhanced by the real fire in the snug bar, the cosy surroundings and the aroma of good things cooking which drifts through from the kitchen. Tom's set menus have a delicious choice of puddings – his more expansive ones, with four or five choices at each stage, offer such delights as scallops with ginger stock, lamb's sweetbreads, or pan-fried entrecôte of venison.

◐ Open all year   ⤢ 10 miles north of Callander on A84; turn right at Kingshouse and continue for 6 miles; hotel is on right. Private car park   ⮠ 2 twin, 5 double, 3 suites; some in annexe; all with bathroom/WC exc 2 with shower/WC; all with TV, hair-dryer, direct-dial telephone   ⊘ 2 restaurants, bar, lounge, drying-room, conservatory, garden; functions (max 35 people residential/non-residential), conferences; fishing, clay-pigeon shooting; leisure facilities nearby (free for guests)   ⅙ Wheelchair access to hotel (ramp) and restaurant, WC (unisex), 3 ground-floor bedrooms   ● No children under 12; no dogs; smoking in bar only   ▭ MasterCard, Switch, Visa   £ Single occupancy of twin/double £48, twin/double £65, suite £84; deposit required. Bar/bistro L £15; set Sun L £17.50, D £22.50/£27.50; alc L £16

'After we arrived a chap arrived plus spaniel which was immediately released and promptly killed one of the family's prize chickens. Even that episode didn't upset the welcome they gave.'
On a hotel in the West Country

BANCHORY **Aberdeenshire** map 11

Banchory Lodge

Banchory, Aberdeen AB31 5HS
TEL: (01330) 822625   FAX: (01330) 825019

A good, traditional country hotel, in one of the nicest spots in the Dee Valley.

This is a country-house hotel which actually looks and feels like one. The famous salmon of the River Dee can be seen from the windows, leaping in the river which lies just across the lawn. Fishing rods and waders garnish the porch, and there is a general sense that life is for living outdoors, before returning to a fire and a good supper. It's a traditional place – Maggie and Dugald Jaffray like it that way, and so do their guests. You will find flowery patterns and decent, solid furniture in the bedrooms, a touch of the sporting life in the bar, and an airy residents' lounge. The gardens surrounding the house are ideal for a stroll on a fine day. The food makes nice use of local ingredients: there's salmon, of course, game, venison and Aberdeen Angus beef. It's a relaxing place, even if you don't fish, and is within easy reach of Aberdeen and the great castles and tower houses of the north-east.

◑ Open all year   ⤢ 18 miles west of Aberdeen, off A93. Private car park   ⬛⃗ 4 twin, 9 double, 2 four-poster, 7 family rooms; all with bathroom/WC exc 1 double with shower/WC; all with TV, room service, hair-dryer, direct-dial telephone   ⊘ 2 dining-rooms, bar, 2 lounges, meeting-room, drying-room, games room, garden; functions (max 110 people incl up to 50 residential), conferences; fishing; early suppers for children; cots, high chairs, toys, playroom, babysitting, baby-listening, outdoor play area   ⅙ No wheelchair access   ● No smoking in some bedrooms   ▭ Amex, Diners, MasterCard, Switch, Visa   £ Single occupancy of twin/double £82, twin/double £115, four-poster £135, family room £115 + £6 to £10 per child; deposit required. Bar/bistro L £13, D £14; set L £15.50, D £25.50; alc D £21.50. Special breaks available

---

BLAIRGOWRIE **Perthshire & Kinross** map 11

Kinloch House

Blairgowrie PH10 6SG
TEL: (01250) 884237   FAX: (01250) 884333
EMAIL: kinlochhouse@compuserve.com

A very efficient country hotel, with good facilities and a formal atmosphere.

Within easy reach of famous golf courses and salmon rivers, Kinloch House is an accomplished and smart hotel. It has grown out of a fairly plain stone house, extending first into a modern wing which tries to tone in, and then into a new leisure complex on the steep hillside behind. Highland cattle, looking newly combed, graze in front of the hotel, and creepers cover the walls. In atmosphere, David and Sarah Shentall's hotel falls somewhere between a French country château and a traditional Scottish shooting lodge. The French-style furniture, the spinet in one drawing-room and the general air of spit and polish among the personnel are reminiscent of the former. The surroundings, the field sports and the Scottish menu served in the cool, formal dining-room belong to the latter. The leisure centre is not so easily classified; it's a shoes-off, pine-panelled place of steam, scents and piped classical music. The bedrooms vary between those in the old part of the house and those in the more modern wing, and are all very generous in terms of space, with antique or reproduction furniture and bright, modern bathrooms. The vegetables come from the walled garden, which is well worth looking into on account of its striking design. The food may include loin of venison, cock-a-leekie soup and Kyle of Lochalsh prawns.

◑ Closed Chr ⤢ On A923, 3 miles west of Blairgowrie. Private car park 🛏5 single, 9 double, 5 four-poster, 2 suites; 1 single with bathroom/WC, most with shower/WC; all with TV, room service, hair-dryer, trouser press, direct-dial telephone ⌗ Dining-room, bar, 2 drawing-rooms, TV room, drying-room, conservatory, garden; conferences (max 18 people incl up to 10 residential); fishing, gym, sauna, heated indoor swimming-pool; early suppers for children; cots, high chairs, baby-listening ♿ Wheelchair access to hotel (ramp) and dining-room, 4 ground-floor bedrooms specially equipped for disabled people ● No children in dining-room eves; dogs in some bedrooms only; no smoking in dining-room ▭ Amex, Delta, Diners, MasterCard, Switch, Visa £ Single £89, single occupancy of double £140, double/four-poster £189, suite £225 (rates incl dinner); deposit required. Set L £16; alc L £14.50

BRAE Shetland   map 11

Busta House

Brae, Shetland ZE2 9QN
TEL: (01806) 522506   FAX: (01806) 522588
EMAIL: busta@mes.co.uk
WEB SITE: www.mes.co.uk/busta

A comfortable haven in the wilderness of mid-Shetland.

In the far, far north, you can tell the old houses by their trees: they are the only ones to have any, even if, as is the case with Busta House, they barely reach head height. This is one of the few places outside Lerwick worth bedding down in for an extended stay. It's an attractive, white-painted house, overlooking an inlet of the sea (a 'voe' in local dialect), and dates back to the early eighteenth century. For the most part, it now acts as a comfortable base for itinerant business people from the oil industry, and you may find yourself sharing a table with a helicopter pilot or a geologist. But many people come here for the birds, or the scenery, or just for a few days' relaxation, and the hotel caters well for them, too. In particular, it has satisfying bar food if you don't want to sit down to the more formal dinners in the restaurant, which rely heavily on the very good local seafood. There's an excellent sitting-room in the Long Room, where a peat-and-log fire smoulders on the hearth, and a smaller study/library on the first floor. The bedrooms are modern, business-style rooms, well equipped with good-quality furniture. They are not really appropriate for the resident ghost to haunt, and you are more likely to see her on the stairs or in the passages. As we went to press, Busta House was up for sale.

◑ Closed 22 Dec to 3 Jan   ⊠ From Lerwick, travel north on A970 for 27 miles; turn left at Brae to Muckle Roe; hotel is 1½ miles further on. Private car park   ⊫ 2 single, 5 twin, 8 double, 2 twin-double, 1 four-poster, 1 family room, 1 suite; most with bathroom/WC; some with shower/WC; all with TV, room service, hair-dryer, trouser press, direct-dial telephone   ⌀ Restaurant, bar, sitting-room, drying-room, library, garden; early suppers for children; cots, high chairs   ♿ No wheelchair access   ● No dogs in public rooms; no smoking in restaurant and library   ⊟ Amex, Delta, Diners, MasterCard, Switch, Visa   £ Single £70, single occupancy of twin/double £84, twin/double £91, four-poster £101, family room from £91, suite £115; deposit required. Bar/bistro L, D £9.50 to £19; set D £21/£24.50. Special breaks available

---

BUNESSAN Argyll & Bute   map 11

Ardfenaig House

Bunessan, Isle of Mull PA67 6DX
TEL: (01681) 700210 (AND FAX)

A smart, English-style country house in a remote corner of Mull.

It is easy enough to see why Jane and Malcolm Davidson abandoned their London life to buy this old shooting lodge in the westernmost corner of Mull. The position is almost perfect, with views over a tranquil sea loch, a croquet lawn running down towards the water and an atmosphere that could hardly be further from the rat race; it's also very close to the ferry terminal for Iona. Ardfenaig House is one of the smarter hotels on Mull – the décor and furnishings are of a high quality and spotless, and everything runs like clockwork. Since the Davidsons added their conservatory dining-room (with wonderful views), there are now two lounges for guests. The bedrooms are spacious, too, pervaded by a comfortable sense of peace and with some good pieces of furniture. Jane's food draws as much as possible from her garden – especially vegetables. Carrot-and-coriander soup, collops of venison pan-fried with lemon juice, and peach-and-redcurrant fool might make up the substance of one of her four-course dinners. Malcolm's launch is available for fishing trips or morning sails, and there is a rowing boat with an outboard motor for guests' use. As we went to press the hotel was on the market.

◑ Closed Nov to Mar   ⊠ Take A849 west through Bunessan; hotel is 3 miles further on, on right. Private car park   ⊫ 3 twin, 2 double; all with bathroom/WC; all with room service, hair-dryer   ⌀ Dining-room/conservatory, bar, 2 lounges, drying-room, garden; functions (max 20 people incl up to 10 residential); croquet, boating   ♿ No wheelchair access   ● No children under 12 in dining-room eves; no dogs; smoking in 1 public room only   ⊟ MasterCard, Visa   £ Single occupancy of twin/double £75 to £89, twin/double £150 to £178 (rates incl dinner). Special breaks available

Assapol House   **NEW ENTRY**

Bunessan, Isle of Mull PA67 6DW
TEL: (01681) 700258   FAX: (01681) 700445

Very friendly family establishment in good, isolated position in southern Mull.

This old white manse lies a couple of miles south of Bunessan village, on the long, bleak Ross of Mull. It is extremely well placed for the area's attractions: the Iona ferry terminal is six miles away and there are some lovely beaches within easy reach. The Robertsons – Thomas, Onny and Alex – have got the business of hotel-keeping in the wilderness down to a fine art. There's a good feel to the welcome, with just the right mix of intimacy and respect for privacy. There are two separate lounges – one chintzy and comfortable, the other more modern in style, where the books and the games are kept for those days when the drizzle descends. In fine weather, guests can sit overlooking Loch Assapol below the house, or admire Onny Robertson's rockery, which is being carefully created from a natural outcrop. The small, fairly formal dining-room is the setting for Mrs Robertson's excellent dinners – table d'hôte home cooking, with lots of fresh, local ingredients and plenty of imagination to go with them. While such items as mozzarella and fresh basil may seem no big deal in the restaurants of the south, up here they probably involve a ferry journey and a 30-mile drive, yet they appear on the table with no great fanfare, as do many other delicious things. The helpings of local cheeses are generous and the puddings are superb. The bedrooms are peaceful and comfortable, and are individually decorated in a variety of styles (the big twin Room 7, with its William Morris décor, is recommended).

◑ Closed Oct to Easter   ⇗ Take A849 towards Fionnphort; after passing Bunessan primary school, take first road on left signposted Assapol House. Private car park   ⇖ 1 single, 2 twin, 2 double; 3 with bathroom/WC, 1 with shower/WC; all with TV, hair-dryer, direct-dial telephone, radio   ✅ Dining-room, 2 lounges, garden; fishing   ♿ No wheelchair access   ● No children under 10; no dogs; smoking in 1 lounge only   ▭ MasterCard, Switch, Visa   £ Single £49, single occupancy of twin/double £86, twin/double £112 (rates incl dinner); deposit required. Special breaks available

---

CALLANDER Stirling   map 11

Arran Lodge   ℒℒ

Leny Road, Callander FK17 8AJ
TEL: (01877) 330976

High-quality stage-management in this edge-of-town guesthouse.

Like so many others, Robert Moore wanted to be an actor. He ended up doing the next best thing, perhaps: working on the stage-management side of television, and it is the skills learnt there – of positioning, presentation – even illusion, from time to time – that he brings to the running of his guesthouse. A good performance is something he delights in, and there is no doubt that his guests – the actors on his cherished sets – will feel like stars. The *pièce de résistance* of Arran Lodge is probably the bathroom that belongs to the bedroom called Lomond, a magnificent, cool room of greys and blues, with a sunken bath and a separate shower which is bigger and more powerful than an American refrigerator. The bedrooms are reminiscent of French period dramas, with frills and four-posters; those downstairs have separate little patios that open directly on to the lawns running down to the River Leny. A hidden service passage allows Robert to whip away the breakfast trays unnoticed. Upstairs, the sitting-room is bright and elegant, with good-quality modern furniture, while the big breakfast room is a study in solid, dark wood and chunky tables. Alas, evening meals are no longer on offer at Arran Lodge, but in compensation the breakfast menus have become lavish, including fish pie and other elaborate creations over and above the normal guesthouse offerings.

◑ Closed Dec to Feb ⤴ On A84, on western outskirts of Callander. Private car park ⟻ 1 double, 3 four-poster; family rooms available; 2 with bathroom/WC, 2 with shower/WC; all with TV, hair-dryer, clock radio, some with room service, trouser press ✅ Dining-room, sitting-room, drying-room, garden; fishing ⎃ No wheelchair access ◓ No children under 12; no dogs; no smoking ⬜ None accepted
£ Single occupancy of double £54 to £58, double £60 to £66, four-poster £64 to £80, family room £95 to £110; deposit required. Special breaks available

---

CANNICH Highland

map 11

Mullardoch House

Glen Cannich, Cannich, Beauly IV4 7LX
TEL: (01456) 415460 (AND FAX)

You can't get much more isolated than this converted hunting lodge.

Mullardoch House is at the end of Glen Cannich – one of three long glens which cross westward from the Cromarty Firth into the high mountains of northern Scotland. Eight miles from Cannich along single-track road, it was originally a shooting lodge, built by the Chisholms as a base for their guests to return to at the end of a long day's stalking. It has many typical features – panelling, a fine wooden staircase and a large entrance hall among them. Now Andrew Johnston is working hard to turn it into a comfortable hotel in the wilderness. It has already gone a long way towards being just that, but new carpets, better furniture, a revamped shower-room and a re-rendered exterior are helping matters along further. There is a spacious sitting-room, with a suitable selection of books and malt whiskies for wet days, a neat dining-room and a small bar (used for lunches). The bedrooms vary considerably in size, Coire Buidhe being the biggest and best, and there is a family room. All are well decorated with a mix of furniture in keeping with the shooting-lodge atmosphere. Helen Johnston used to provide all the food herself, but the business has grown to the extent that a professional chef has been recruited.

◑ Open all year ⤴ Take A831 from either Beauly or Drumnadrochit to Cannich; follow signs 8 miles up single-track road. Private car park ⟻ 2 twin, 3 double, 1 family room; all with bathroom/WC; all with TV, room service, hair-dryer ✅ Dining-room, bar, sitting-room, drying-room, garden; functions (max 35 people non-residential, 13 residential), conferences; fishing, boating, deer stalking, mountain bikes; early suppers for children; cots, high chairs, toys, baby-listening ⎃ No wheelchair access
◓ Dogs in bedrooms only, by arrangement; no smoking in dining-room or bedrooms ⬜ Amex, Delta, MasterCard, Switch, Visa £ Single occupancy of twin/double £57, twin/double £90, family room £130; deposit required. Bar L, D £5.50; set D £24

CLACHAN-SEIL Argyll & Bute map 11

Willowburn Hotel [NEW ENTRY]

Clachan-Seil, Isle of Seil, Oban PA34 4TJ
TEL: (01852) 300276   FAX: (01852) 300597
EMAIL: willowburn.hotel@virgin.net
WEB SITE: www.willowburn.co.uk/

Small, family hotel in modern building, well tucked away near Oban.

The Island of Seil is actually linked to the mainland by the so-called 'Bridge over the Atlantic'. It is a sheltered, quiet place, within easy reach of Oban and much favoured by people who enjoy boats, short walks and general tranquillity. The Willowburn Hotel, a large 'seventies house, lies halfway down the island and makes a perfect haven for a few days' relaxation. Chris Mitchell and Jan Wolfe are turning it into a comfortable and friendly base for holidaymakers. The lavish use of glass means that from the dining-room and lounge there are fine views down to the narrow Clachan Sound, with yachts, dinghies, birds, and possibly even seals, giving life to the scenery. The telescope in the lounge brings it all into focus; there is the house cat to stroke and a very useful book of local things to do and see. The dining-room, which is simply furnished and decorated, takes up most of the space on the ground floor, but there is also a bistro – actually more like a pub – for cold days, with a wood-burning stove, pine panelling and a long bar. Gradual upgrading of the bedrooms and bathrooms is under way; meanwhile, there are no obvious horrors, and everything is fresh and well kept. Chris's four-course menus offer such curiosities as Highland beef stuffed with Cheddar and served with a whisky sauce, and a seafood platter including up to 14 different kinds of fish and shellfish, as well as a vegetarian option. The wine list is excellent value.

◗ Closed Jan to mid-Mar   ⌘ Take A816 south from Oban for 7 miles; turn right at signs for Atlantic Bridge; follow signs for Easdale and Luing for 6 miles; cross over big humpback bridge and hotel is ½ mile further on, on left. Private car park   ⌘ 1 single, 3 twin, 3 double; 2 with bathroom/WC, 5 with shower/WC; all with TV, hair-dryer   ⌀ Dining-room, bistro/bar, lounge, drying-room, garden; early suppers for children; cots, high chairs   ⌖ No wheelchair access   ⬤ No dogs in public rooms; smoking in bar only   ⌷ Delta, MasterCard, Switch, Visa   £ Single £50 to £55, single occupancy of twin/double £55 to £75, twin/double £100 to £110 (rates incl dinner); deposit required. Bar/bistro L £10. Special breaks available

---

CONON BRIDGE Highland map 11

Kinkell House

Easter Kinkell, Conon Bridge, Dingwall IV7 8HY
TEL: (01349) 861270   FAX: (01349) 865902

A good combination of spacious house and friendly, guesthouse-style management.

There are many advantages to Kinkell House, one of them being the view: the low, white house stands on the edge of the hillside which slopes down to the Cromarty Firth and looks across to the mass of Ben Wyvis in the distance. Inside, this is a spacious and well-kept place, with various extensions having been grafted on to the body of a small Victorian house. Steve and Marsha Fraser run it very much as an intimate, family affair, so you have all the advantages of guesthouse-style hospitality and friendliness without the typical guesthouse constraints of lack of privacy and not many places in which to sit – there are in fact three separate sitting areas, one in a modern conservatory extension and the others in small sitting-rooms with fires, books and televisions. The bedrooms are split between the older part of the house, where they have plenty of farmhouse character, and the modern wing, where they are extremely comfortable and decked out with good-quality furniture. The dining-room is possibly the nicest room in the house, positioned to take full advantage of the view and with doors opening on to a patio for fine evenings. Marsha's food is good, honest home cooking, with a choice of four starters and four main courses, while Steve – a civil engineer in real life – does the waiting and brings the drinks as if born to it.

○ Open all year ⚡ 10 miles north of Inverness on B9169. Private car park
🛏 4 twin, 5 double; family rooms available; doubles with bathroom/WC, twins with shower/WC; all with TV, room service, hair-dryer, direct-dial telephone ⌀
Dining-room, 2 sitting-rooms, drying-room, conservatory, garden; conferences (max 30 people incl up to 9 residential); early suppers for children; cots, high chairs ♿
Wheelchair access to hotel and dining-room, WC (unisex), 1 ground-floor bedroom specially equipped for disabled people ● No dogs in public rooms; no smoking in dining-room and bedrooms ▭ MasterCard, Visa £ Single occupancy of twin/double £40 to £55, twin/double £70 to £80, family room £80 to £95; deposit required. Light L £6; alc L £12, D £21. Special breaks available

---

Crinan Hotel

Crinan, Lochgilphead PA31 8SR
TEL: (01546) 830261   FAX: (01546) 830292
EMAIL: reservations@crinanhotel.com
WEB SITE: www.connoisseurs-scotland.com/

Excellent yachtsman's hotel, serving freshly landed seafood.

The Crinan Canal meets the Atlantic in a jumble of rocky headlands and reefs. Beside the basin which lies behind the final lock stands the Crinan Hotel, a large, white building which could never be called beautiful, looming over the small cluster of cottages that is the only other sign of human habitation. It's a wonderful spot, for nothing but sea and islands lie in front of the hotel's windows, while the woods and hills, typical of this part of Argyll, shelter it from the east. The hotel's reputation is founded on its seafood restaurant, Lock 16, an enclosed, rooftop eyrie with magnificent views. The five-course menu is headed with the local shipping forecast, and the time when the prawns were landed is noted, too. Typically, there will be mussels, smoked wild salmon, jumbo prawns or clams on offer – all as fresh as you can get. There's another restaurant in the hotel (Westward), which deigns to serve meat dishes – here the food is a little cheaper, but the views are not quite as good. Not all the feedback has been positive this year: the breakfasts in particular have been disappointing, with one guest being served hard-boiled eggs and clearly burnt toast; others have complained about the free rein given to the cats in the bar, even when food is served. There's a small lounge in the reception area, and a larger, more relaxing one further into the hotel. The main bar is panelled, with barometers set into the floor. The public rooms have character and are enlivened by the magnificent murals painted by Frances Macdonald. The bedrooms barely need decoration since the views out to sea are so magnificent, but they are actually very carefully designed. Room 31, for example, in pale yellows and blues, with chunky bedside tables and wicker chairs, perfectly balances the greys, greens and blues of the world outside. Erratic water pressure led one guest to describe a shower as 'challenging'.

◑ Open all year ⚡ Follow B841 from Cairnbaan, or A82/A83 along Loch Lomond, to Crinan at north end of Crinan Canal. Private car park ⤶ 1 single, 5 twin, 15 double, 1 suite; family rooms available; most with bathroom/WC, some with shower/WC; all with TV, room service, direct-dial telephone; tea/coffee-making facilities, hair-dryer, trouser press available ⌁ 2 restaurants, 3 bars, 2 lounges, drying-room, garden; functions (max 150 people incl up to 43 residential), conferences; fishing; early suppers for children; high chairs 🦽 Wheelchair access to hotel (ramp) and restaurants, lift to bedrooms, 2 rooms specially equipped for disabled people ● No dogs or smoking in restaurant; dogs £5 per night in bedrooms ▭ Amex, Delta, MasterCard, Switch, Visa ⌷£⌷ Single £75 to £95, single occupancy of twin/double £75 to £120, twin/double £75 to £240, family room £240 + £25 per child, suite £200; deposit required. Alc D £38.50. Special breaks available

---

DERVAIG Argyll & Bute   map 11

Druimard Country House

Dervaig, Tobermory, Isle of Mull PA75 6QW
TEL: (01688) 400291   FAX: (01688) 400345
WEB SITE: www.smoothhound.co.uk/hotels/druimard.html

Very good food and friendly hosts in a pleasant Victorian house.

As country-house hotels go, Druimard is neither large nor particularly imposing, being merely a Victorian villa set on a hill just outside the hamlet of Dervaig in the north of the island. The hotel can only accommodate 14 guests, which has the advantage that it never feels institutional or anonymous, but you are likely to have to book in advance. As you might expect in a house of this period, there is a fairly formal lounge downstairs, decorated in best front-parlour style, and an attractive dining-room opposite it. A staircase leads up to the bedrooms, which vary in size but are comfortable, well equipped and, most importantly, warm. In the glass-and-wood conservatory extension which serves as a bar, Haydn Hubbard officiates, dispensing drinks and helpful advice with equal aplomb. Wendy Hubbard bubbles with enthusiasm for cooking, serving five-course set-menu dinners, topped and tailed by canapés and petits fours. If you don't like something, however, there's always an alternative on hand. The puddings are especially worth leaving room for.

○ Closed Nov to Mar   ⚡ Approached from Tobermory, hotel is on right before Dervaig. Private car park   🛏️ 2 twin, 3 double, 1 suite; some with bathroom/WC, most with shower/WC; all with TV, limited room service, hair-dryer, direct-dial telephone
✧ Dining-room, bar/conservatory, lounge, drying-room, garden; functions (max 20 people incl up to 14 residential); early suppers for children; cots, high chairs, babysitting   ♿ No wheelchair access   ● No dogs in public rooms   ⊟ Delta, MasterCard, Visa   £ Single occupancy of twin/double £70 to £72, twin/double £115 to £139, suite £124 to £156 (rates incl dinner) (prices valid till Mar 1999); deposit required. Special breaks available

---

DOLLAR Clackmannan map 11

Castle Campbell Hotel

11 Bridge Street, Dollar FK14 7DE
TEL: (01259) 742519 (AND FAX)

Excellent small town hotel, run with care and with good food.

The kilt-clad Stewart Morrison moved south a few years ago from the Royal Hotel at Cromarty, and has brought with him the formula that made that hotel such a success. In sum, this is good housekeeping, good value and good food, all presented with informality and friendliness. The Castle Campbell Hotel was originally a Georgian coaching-inn, well located in this quiet township at the foot of the Ochil Hills to serve birds of passage between Glasgow and Perth or Dundee. It is certainly a centre of local life, with people drinking pots of coffee in the deep sofas in front of the fire in the lounge, or absorbed in Alan Bristow's menus, which he describes as 'good pub food with a few extras': everything from traditional Thai dishes to 'Al's ocean pie', with seafood, sourced from Pittenweem, a speciality. You can eat either in the long, comfortable bar, or with a bit more style in the dining-room at the front of the hotel, where the tables are carefully draped with Lindsay tartan. The bedrooms are standard fare, apart from a few antique pieces to give them character, and the bathrooms are pretty small. But everything is clean, neat and in its place, and the price is right.

○ Open all year   ⚡ On main street in Dollar. Private car park   🛏️ 1 single, 7 twin/double; most with bathroom/WC exc 2 with shower/WC; all with TV, direct-dial telephone, some with hair-dryer   ✧ Dining-room, 2 bars, 2 lounges, drying-room; functions (max 80 people incl up to 12 residential), conferences; early suppers for children; high chairs, baby-listening   ♿ No wheelchair access   ● No dogs in public rooms (£5 per night in bedrooms); no smoking in bedrooms   ⊟ Amex, MasterCard, Switch, Visa   £ Single £45, twin/double £65. Bar L £7, D £8.50; alc L, D £14. Special breaks available

---

DRUMNADROCHIT Highland map 11

Polmaily House

Drumnadrochit, Inverness IV3 6XT
TEL: (01456) 450343   FAX: (01456) 450813
EMAIL: polmailyhousehotel@btinternet.com

Child-friendly country house close to Loch Ness.

Polmaily House is now into the fifth year of its incarnation as a children's paradise and frazzled-parents' haven, and the Whittington-Davises show no signs of running out of enthusiasm for the kind of life that would drive most hoteliers to distraction. What is especially remarkable is the balance that they manage to strike between the needs of adults and those of children. The conservatory, for example, doubles up as sunny café/bar and children's tea-room, and the transformation between the two is instantaneous and effective. The grown-up bedrooms are comfortable and beautifully decorated, while the restaurant and lounge would grace many a smarter hotel. Families who like to be self-contained should opt for the Garden Suites in an attractively laid-out cottage, which have a separate, three-bunk room for children and a huge king-sized bed for parents. Activities for kids – some organised, others not – range from cuddling rabbits or painting figurines to pony rides, sailing trips on Loch Ness, a lofty tree house and a perilous-looking rope swing, all surrounded by more than enough space to run riot in. There is also a covered swimming-pool and a separate playroom, with plenty of toys. Back-up services, in the shape of baby-listening, emergency supplies of nappies, and children's meals are on hand, too. The adult menu is varied and restorative, with a vegetarian option every day. Adult activities are also catered for with stalking, golf, riding and fishing in the hotel's own trout loch. There are still a few rough edges – uneven and rough slabs round the swimming-pool, for example, and some playthings which were somewhat past their sell-by date when we inspected. But the overall impression of Polmaily House is of a place that it would be difficult not to enjoy. Perhaps it would be best to be aged between seven and ten here – old enough not to fall in the trout loch, but still young enough to enjoy the rabbits.

❍ Open all year   ▨ At Drumnadrochit take A831 towards Chinook for 2 miles; hotel is on right. Private car park   ⮑ 2 single, 1 twin, 5 double, 1 four-poster, 4 family rooms, 1 suite; some in annexe; all with bathroom/WC exc singles with shower/WC; all with TV, room service, hair-dryer, direct-dial telephone   ⏺ Restaurant, bar/conservatory, lounge, library, games room, garden; functions (max 60 people incl up to 30 residential), conferences; golf, riding, fishing, heated indoor swimming-pool, tennis; early suppers for children; cots, high chairs, toys, playroom, babysitting, baby-listening, outdoor play area   ♿ Wheelchair access to hotel and restaurant, 3 ground-floor bedrooms, 1 room specially equipped for disabled people   ◖ No children under 7 in restaurant eves; no dogs in public rooms; no smoking in bedrooms   ▭ Delta, MasterCard, Switch, Visa   £ Single £42 to £61, single occupancy of twin/double £72 to £91, twin/double £84 to £122, four-poster/suite £102 to £142, family room £128 to £178; deposit required. Bar/bistro L £8; set D £25; alc D £25. Special breaks available

---

DUNKELD Perthshire & Kinross   map 11

Kinnaird

Kinnaird Estate, Dunkeld PH8 0LB
TEL: (01796) 482440   FAX: (01796) 482289

Living in the lap of luxury on Tayside.

If a party of aristocratic Edwardians were to be spirited back to Kinnaird, they might be a little shocked by the approachability and lack of obsequiousness of the staff, but they would be delighted by the comfort of the massive beds, would revel in the bathrooms and would find much that was familiar in the billiard room and the comfortable drawing-room, with its Persian rugs, tattered copy of Burke's Peerage and comforting scent of woodsmoke. 'Mr Jack [the manager] is always in the right place at the right time,' reports one admiring reader. The house owes much to the best standards of American furnishing and interior design – the result of close attention paid by the proprietor, Mrs Ward. She has left many of the original features well alone, including the unusual Italianate frescoes which enliven the formality of one of the dining-rooms, from which guests can gaze out over the valley of the River Tay to the beetle-sized cars scurrying towards Perth, a world away. Despite the air of tranquillity which pervades the place, the bedrooms, with their emperor-sized beds, are equipped with up-to-date conveniences, including a range of CDs and videos, though the terrestrial TV reception is not brilliant, so be prepared for some fuzz. Trevor Brooks's daily-changing menus look full of interest – classical in tone, but spiced up by such modern touches as polenta or Swiss chard, and old-fashioned ones, too, such as toasted rice-pudding.

◑ Closed Mon to Wed in Jan & Feb   ⬈ From Perth, take A9 until 2 miles beyond Dunkeld, then take B898 towards Dalguise; hotel is 4½ miles further on. Private car park   ⬌ 1 twin, 7 double, 1 suite; all with bathroom/WC; all with TV, video, room service, hair-dryer, direct-dial telephone, CD player, some with trouser press; no tea/coffee-making facilities in rooms   ✧ 2 dining-rooms, 2 drawing-rooms, drying-room, study, games room, garden functions (max 15 people residential/non-residential), conferences; fishing, tennis, clay-pigeon shooting, snooker   ⅙ Wheelchair access to hotel (ramp) and dining-rooms, WC (unisex), 1 ground-floor bedroom   ● No children under 12; no dogs   ▭ Amex, MasterCard, Switch, Visa   £ Single occupancy of twin/double £225 to £285, twin/double £235 to £295, suite £315; deposit required. Set L £20 to £25, D £45

DUNOON Argyll & Bute   map 11

Enmore Hotel

Marine Parade, Kirn, Dunoon PA23 8HH
TEL: (01369) 702230   FAX: (01369) 702148
EMAIL: enmorehotel@btinternet.com

Comfortable house, convenient for the ferry, with flamboyant hostess.

Angela and David Wilson are the stars of the show here, and make even first-time one-nighters feel as special as the regulars. Their white, traditional seafront villa is close enough to the ferries to make it the first stop after a flight to Glasgow (reached via a 20-minute ferry journey). Inside all is comfortable and homely, with a good-sized lounge warmed by a real fire, Morris-print furniture in clusters, and well-designed lighting that's not too bright. Angela is the hostess par excellence, making everyone feel like a house guest and dispensing drinks and bons mots while David prepares a wonderfully full-flavoured five-course dinner – perhaps creamy mushroom soup with fresh-baked bread, followed by salmon fillets in lemon and parsley sauce. Ask for cheese and you're likely to be presented with a huge slab of Tobermory to carve your own helping from. Dinner is 7.30 for 8pm for all guests – but is served at separate tables, so you're not obliged to be chummy. Upstairs, bedrooms vary in size, but are all cared for and neatly decorated in light florals. Bathrooms are light on toiletries, but do have nice large white towels.

◑ Closed Chr   ⏣ On seafront at Kirn, 1 mile north of Dunoon on A815. Private car park   🛏 2 single, 2 twin, 1 double, 3 four-poster, 2 family rooms; all with bathroom/WC exc singles with shower/WC; all with TV, room service, hair-dryer, direct-dial telephone, some with trouser press; tea/coffee-making facilities available   ⌁ Restaurant, bar, 2 lounges, study, games room, garden; functions (max 40 people incl up to 20 residential), conferences; fishing, golf, squash; early suppers for children; cots, high chairs, toys, baby-listening   ⟐ No wheelchair access   ⬤ None   ▭ Amex, Delta, MasterCard, Switch, Visa   £ Single £35, single occupancy of twin/double £59, twin/double/family room £98, four-poster £138; deposit required. Bar L £5; set D £22; alc L, D £25. Special breaks available

---

DUNVEGAN Highland   map 11

Harlosh House

Dunvegan, Isle of Skye IV55 8ZG
TEL: (01470) 521367 (AND FAX)
EMAIL: harlosh.house@virgin.net

Small hotel in the north of Skye, with good food.

Situated in a superb position, with views of the serrated ridge of the Cuillin Hills on a clear day, Peter Elford's house makes an ideal alternative to staying in or around Portree. Harlosh House is not large and you cannot expect grand bedrooms, but all are *en suite* and nicely furnished. Ask for one at the front of the house if possible, for the views. Peter is now running the whole outfit himself, but manages to cope with the housekeeping while still finding time to put together inventive, modern menus. Seared scallops with spring onions and ginger, followed by baked Dover sole in lime, lemon and coriander with a fresh herb salad, and spiced apple tart with home-made vanilla ice-cream might be the kind of meal awaiting you on your return from a hard day's walking. On bad-weather days, there's enough space and a good, homely atmosphere in the sitting-room, as well as a fire, to keep you cheerful.

◑ Closed Nov to Easter   ⏣ 3 miles south of Dunvegan on A863, follow signs for Harlosh. Private car park   🛏 4 twin, 2 double; 4 with bathroom/WC, 2 with shower/WC; all with hair-dryer   ⌁ Dining-room, sitting-room, conservatory, garden; early suppers for children; cots, high chairs, toys, baby-listening   ⟐ No wheelchair access   ⬤ No children under 7 in dining-room eves; no dogs; smoking in sitting-room only   ▭ Delta, MasterCard, Switch, Visa   £ Single occupancy of twin/double £53 to £73, twin/double £105; deposit required. Set D £27.50

'My colleague and I both found this woman quite incredible. She finished every whispered sentence with the word "sir" and reminded us of the characters from the sketch in the Fast Show *of the men's outfitters with the phrase, "Suit you, sir".'*
On a hotel in Northamptonshire

Drummond House

17 Drummond Place, Edinburgh EH3 6PL
TEL: 0131-557 9189 (AND FAX)

Very genial and comfortable B&B, with quirky bathrooms.

Drummond House is one of the better late-Georgian houses in the streets and crescents extending north of the original New Town. 'Better' means that it has flagstones and a pair of marble pillars in the entrance hall, and indulges in a sweeping oval staircase. Under the stewardship of Josephine and Alan Dougall, it makes an excellent place in which to stay, especially for those who want to escape the anonymity of larger hotels. This is a very relaxed establishment, so much so that you might be forgiven for wondering if you haven't dropped into a private home by mistake (especially as there is no sign on the door). The downstairs sitting-room, with its rugs, comfortable sofas and fig plant, has no trace of formality about it. Upstairs, the bedrooms share a common style – rugs laid over stripped floors, big Victorian dressers and chests of drawers, and large, comfortable beds (the single, too). The bathrooms in two of the rooms are large, airy places, one dignified by a shower cabinet apparently inspired by the more extravagant period of Imperial Rome. At the back of the house, the bathroom is more Ming dynasty in style, with an elaborate fabric construction decorated by Chinese vases descending over a tiny sitz bath (officially a Japanese-style deep-soak tub). Josephine and Alan make good hosts, and most facilities are on offer if you ask. One point to note: parking can be a problem if you arrive before 6pm, so ask Alan's advice when you book.

◗ Closed Chr ⃞ ¼ mile north of St Andrew Square, at east end of Great King Street. On-street parking (metered) ⌁ 1 single, 1 twin, 2 double; all with bathroom/WC exc single with shower/WC; all with hair-dryer; no tea/coffee-making facilities in rooms ⌗ Dining-room, sitting-room ⅋ No wheelchair access ● No children under 15; no dogs; no smoking ⃞ Delta, MasterCard, Visa £ Single £60 to £75, single occupancy of twin/double £85 to £105, twin/double £90 to £110; deposit required

The Howard

34 Great King Street, Edinburgh EH3 6QH
TEL: 0131-557 3500   FAX: 0131-557 6515
EMAIL: reserve@thehoward.com
WEB SITE: www.thehoward.com/

Stylish hotel in the centre of Edinburgh's New Town – determined to make an impact.

Among the late-Georgian extensions to the original New Town, Great King Street is a wide, cobbled thoroughfare, away from the noise and bustle of the town centre but well within walking distance of it (although it is a stiff climb up the hill). The Howard occupies what were once three of the grand houses on the street, and it does its utmost to live up to the tone of the area. In this, it is helped by the wealth of original features that remain, such as the curving staircases, the pillars and, in particular, the Italianate frescoes in the breakfast room, which were discovered beneath layers of wallpaper. The interior decoration of the Howard is sensitive and fairly restrained, so as not to clash with the sense of period. Only in the basement restaurant – simply called 36 – has modern minimalism taken over. This is currently one of the city's most fashionable restaurants, and even residents are strongly advised to book, in order to sample the modern cooking among the spotlights and glass panels. The bedrooms are very spacious, and are endowed with Edwardian-style baths, which one reader picked out as a particularly noteworthy plus point. Their facilities are excellent and their furnishings – including some attractive antique pieces – are in keeping with the Howard's style of subdued luxury. Overall, the standards of service are good, too, although one reader was unhappy not to have his shoes cleaned overnight.

○ Closed 24 to 28 Dec   �↗ On Great King Street, east of Dundas Street. Private car park   ⇇ 2 single, 1 twin, 10 twin/double, 2 suites; family rooms available; all with bathroom/WC; all with TV, room service, hair-dryer, trouser press, direct-dial telephone; no tea/coffee-making facilities in rooms   ⌖ Restaurant, bar, drawing-room, breakfast room; functions (max 50 people incl up to 28 residential), conferences; early suppers for children; cots, high chairs, babysitting, baby-listening   ♿ No wheelchair access   ⊖ No dogs   ▭ Amex, Delta, Diners, MasterCard, Switch, Visa   £ Single £125, single occupancy of twin/double £150, twin/double £195, suite £275; deposit required. Set L £11.50/£14; alc L £18, D £26. Special breaks available

Malmaison Edinburgh

1 Tower Place, Leith, Edinburgh EH6 7DB
TEL: 0131-468 5000   FAX: 0131-468 5002
EMAIL: edinburgh@malmaison.com
WEB SITE: www.malmaison.com

A classy and reasonably priced Docklands alternative to some of the staid and fusty city-centre hotels.

Gone are the days when Leith was grimy, industrial and decaying. Where cargo ships once docked, the new Scottish Office now stands like a modern monument to the bulldozed warehouses, while the surrounding alleyways have sprouted fountains and fashionable restaurants. Malmaison, itself something of a trendsetter, is well placed to take advantage of Leith's current trendiness. It occupies a nineteenth-century former seamen's mission – an imposing, four-square building, once with a view of ships and cranes, now overlooking large swathes of greenery, wrought-iron gates and ornamental cannons. Inside, Ken McCulloch's hotel exemplifies what has become the Malmaison style (see also under Glasgow, Manchester and Newcastle) – sophisticated, uncluttered chic, with clever lighting, high-quality fabrics and an emphasis on quiet luxury. Since last year, a further 35 rooms have been added – all with the CDs, satellite TV and food cupboards which are part of the style, and there is a fitness room in which to work off the indulgence of a stay here. Although there's now a residents' lounge, Malmaison is more attuned to the get-up-and-get-going side of life than to relaxing in peace and quiet. What one does is eat in the very attractive brasserie and see or be seen. There's a good buzz to the place; it's still very fashionable and everything works as it should.

◑ Open all year ◪ Take A900 from city centre to Leith; hotel is on waterfront. Private car park ⌂ 8 twin, 43 double, 3 four-poster, 6 suites; family rooms available; all with bathroom/WC; all with satellite TV, room service, hair-dryer, mini-bar, trouser press, direct-dial telephone, CD player ✓ Restaurant, bar, lounge; conferences (max 32 people residential/non-residential); gym; cots, high chairs, babysitting ৬ Wheelchair access to hotel and restaurant, WC (unisex), lift to bedrooms, 4 rooms specially equipped for disabled people ● Dogs in bedrooms by arrangement only ⊟ Amex, Diners, MasterCard, Switch, Visa £ Single occupancy of twin/double £95, twin/double £95, four-poster/family room £120, suite £130; deposit required. Continental B £8.50, cooked B £10.50; alc L £22, D £25. Special breaks available

---

Sibbet House   **NEW ENTRY**

26 Northumberland Street, Edinburgh EH3 6LS
TEL: 0131-556 1078   FAX: 0131-557 9445
EMAIL: sibbet.house@zetnet.co.uk
WEB SITE: www.sibbet-house.co.uk

Some slight changes of style to this well-reputed guesthouse under its new management.

This must have been quite a change for Anita and Jens Steffen, who have moved to the heart of Edinburgh from the idyllic surroundings of Kinloch Rannoch to take over from Jim and Aurore Sibbet, who pioneered the up-market city guesthouse in this part of the world. Much remains the same, and regulars will recognise the antique-packed first-floor drawing-room and the book-lined dining-room, even if everything has been freshened up by new paintwork. The place is a haven for American visitors looking for a touch of antiquity, and your fellow guests enjoying the Victorian atmosphere of the drawing-room will probably be from across the Pond. There's a lot of variation in the style of the bedrooms. Down in the basement, the Tartan Room is a smallish, pretty room, in contrast to its neighbour the Patio Room, which is a suite, complete with its own dining-room and kitchen. Upstairs, the bedrooms are lighter, benefiting from the high Georgian windows. They are big rooms, with plenty to look at, although the bathrooms are not on the same scale. In the Blue Room's bathroom, the bath seems to disappear into the wall, and large ceramic masks of sea creatures peer down at you. Anita and Jens run the place with precision, and the house seems a little more formal these days, though there are several nice touches.

◑ Open all year ◪ Fourth street north of Princes Street. Private car park ⌂ 2 twin, 1 double, 1 four-poster, 1 suite; family rooms available; all with shower/WC exc 2 with bathroom/WC; all with TV, hair-dryer, trouser press, direct-dial telephone, some with fridge ✓ Dining-room, drawing-room ৬ No wheelchair access ● No dogs; no smoking ⊟ MasterCard, Switch, Visa £ Single occupancy of twin/double £55 to £65, twin/double/four-poster £90 to £100, family room £100 to £130, suite £100 to £120; deposit required. Set D £30

ERISKA Argyll & Bute   map 11

Isle of Eriska

Eriska, Ledaig, Oban PA37 1SD
TEL: (01631) 720371   FAX: (01631) 720531
EMAIL: reserve@eriska-hotel.co.uk
WEB SITE: www.eriska-hotel.co.uk/

A genuine country-house experience in a family-run hotel.

There's a certain magic about a stay on the Isle of Eriska, first felt as the car rattles across the bridge on to the island on its approach to the house – all Scottish baronial towers and ramparts, flying the flag of St Andrew. Inside, the Buchanan-Smith family have created a wonderfully cosseting old style of comfort, with tip-top staff who make you feel like a house guest. A minimum two-night stay is required if you want to book in advance, but the experience is such that you'll have to drag yourself away. You'll need that long to wander round, admiring the tapestries and furniture (plenty of dead animals on the walls too, to offend modern sensitivities), or to stroll round the island, perhaps catching sight of the seals or petting donkeys or having a swim (no under-fives or non-swimmers). Or you can snooze by the fireside before helping yourself to tea laid out in the hall. Leave room for dinner, which is quite an affair – new chef Robert MacPherson produces a robustly flavoured menu. In keeping with the rest of the house, the bedrooms are large, comfortable and in subdued colours. Bathrooms are modern and wonderfully stocked – even a little soap powder provided for your smalls. It's also good to see a family hotel of this class welcoming *all* the family. Children will find it a civilising experience, just as much as their parents: under-10s are served a proper dinner at 6pm – with formal service, and none of this modern reliance on fish-fingers and chips. Bravo!

◐ Closed Jan   ⏌ From A85 north of Oban, turn over bridge on to A828 at Connel; continue for 4 miles to north of Benderloch; follow signs from here to Eriska. Private car park   ⊨ 1 single, 1 twin, 15 twin/double; family rooms available; all with bathroom/WC; all with TV, room service, hair-dryer, trouser press, direct-dial telephone   ⊘ Dining-room, bar, 3 lounges, library, garden; functions (max 30 people residential), conferences; golf, gym, sauna, heated indoor swimming-pool, tennis, putting green, pitch & putt, clay-pigeon shooting, croquet; early suppers for children; cots, high chairs, babysitting, baby-listening, outdoor play area   ⅙ Wheelchair access (ramps) to hotel and dining-room, 2 ground-floor bedrooms specially equipped for disabled people   ● No dogs in public rooms   ⊟ Amex, Delta, MasterCard, Switch, Visa   £ Single £115 to £160, single occupancy of twin/double £160, twin/double £195 to £230, family room (room rate + £20 per child); deposit required. Set D £37.50. Special breaks available

---

'We ordered a room service lunch of sandwiches and salad, which was almost eaten when I discovered a small slug on a lettuce leaf. Feeling quite queasy I asked for the food to be returned to the kitchen. The waiter proffered the explanation that the lettuce was "organic".'
On a hotel in East Sussex

Ashburn House   **NEW ENTRY**

4 Achintore Road, Fort William PH33 6RQ
TEL: (01397) 706000 (AND FAX)
WEB SITE: www.ark.uk.com/bb/ashburnhouse/ashburnhouse.htm

Extremely good facilities and a genuine welcome in this Highland B&B.

On the southern outskirts of Fort William a long line of guesthouses proclaims your arrival in the chief tourist base for the West Highlands. Ashburn House is one of the more substantial: a large Victorian villa with double gables front and rear, built to take full advantage of the views across Loch Linnhe to the mountains beyond. A neat garden separates it from the main road, and there is ample parking space at the back. Judging from our readers' reports, the facilities, the welcome and the value are all outstanding. At the front of the house the bedrooms are large, clad in deep blue and have king-sized beds. At the back, they are smaller but very romantic, with elaborate swags and tumbling fabrics; quieter, too, but lacking the views across the loch. Home-made shortbread and tablet are laid out for guests. Shower-rooms are mostly small, but well equipped with up-to-date furnishings. There's also a pleasing sitting-room in the modern conservatory extension, with a set of bagpipes draped over a sofa, paintings of mountains and ships, and a chess set. Breakfasts include (translated from the Gaelic) creamy porridge, and fried egg bread and fruit pudding.

◗ Closed Dec & Jan   ⊠ On A82, 500 yards south of town centre. Private car park ⇨ 3 single, 1 twin, 3 double; all with shower/WC exc 1 double with bathroom/WC; all with TV, room service, hair-dryer, clock radio   ⌀ Dining-room, sitting-room/ conservatory, drying-room, library, garden   ♿ No wheelchair access   ● No dogs; no smoking   ▭ Amex, MasterCard, Visa   £ Single £30 to £35, single occupancy of twin/double £60 to £70, twin/double £60 to £70; deposit required. Special breaks available

---

Inverlochy Castle

Torlundy, Fort William PH33 6SN
TEL: (01397) 702177   FAX: (01397) 702953
EMAIL: info@inverlochy.co.uk

Top-people's hotel, but you don't have to be a celebrity to be made to feel your comfort is all-important.

In a way, it is a pity that one of Scotland's premier hotels should be stuck in a rather uninspiring part of the Highlands. True, you can see the top of Ben Nevis if it isn't raining, but this flattish stretch of ground to the north of Fort William will never appear on a scenic calendar. Scenery apart, however, this is a hotel that deserves the buckets of praise that have been poured on it over the years, and fame has not been allowed to spoil it. A more professionally run place would be hard to imagine, but obsequiousness or trumpet-blowing are both out the question – the staff are human and open. Inverlochy Castle is a classic Scottish baronial creation, and it has been allowed to retain its atmosphere of good living without deference to modern trends. The exception, perhaps, is the bedrooms, where everything focuses on comfort and luxury, but in a careful and restrained sort of way. Elsewhere, apart from the fresco on the ceiling of the Grand Hall, there is nothing obtrusively magnificent – just furnishings and decoration of unashamedly good taste and high quality. The dinners are notable for the same virtues. Simon Hay's four-course meals use the best local produce, and are professionally cooked and presented. It's a tranquil, sumptuous experience, and you will not be bothered by celebrities going through photo shoots in the grounds, or be made to feel out of place if you just turn up for a meal.

◑ Closed 5 Jan to 12 Feb ⚡ 3 miles north of Fort William, on A82. Private car park ⊨ 1 single, 14 double, 1 four-poster, 1 suite; all with bathroom/WC; all with TV, room service, hair-dryer, trouser press, direct-dial telephone; no tea/coffee-making facilities in rooms ⊘ 3 dining-rooms, 2 lounges, drying-room, library, games room, garden; functions (max 34 people residential/non-residential), conferences; fishing, tennis, clay-pigeon shooting; early suppers for children; cots, high chairs, playroom, babysitting, baby-listening ⅃ No wheelchair access ● No children under 12 in dining-rooms eves; no dogs ▭ Delta, MasterCard, Switch, Visa ⟨£⟩ Single £180 to £215, single occupancy of double £290 to £340, double £290 to £340, four-poster/suite £390 to £440; deposit required. Set D £45 to £50; alc D £45. Special breaks available

---

GLASGOW Glasgow map 11

Malmaison Glasgow

278 West George Street, Glasgow G2 4LL
TEL: 0141-572 1000   FAX: 0141-572 1002

The original Malmaison sets the standard for cool, eclectic style in an urban setting.

You could be forgiven for being slightly thrown by the quasi-Greek-cum-Egyptian façade of this hotel in an otherwise dour Victorian part of Glasgow. That is probably a good thing, as you are unlikely to be prepared for the style of the cool yet striking reception area, which conspicuously lacks the usual sort of hotel bustle. Up the stairs you pass an extraordinary wrought-iron banister depicting Napoleon's coronation and battle scenes. The bedrooms are effortlessly stylish, with an attention to lighting effects and a reliance on bold, deep colours. A CD player and satellite television are provided for your amusement, and the chrome-and-white bathrooms have exclusive toiletries in generous bottles; it makes you feel like the house guest of some avant-garde millionaire. Owner Ken McCulloch has added a new extension which houses the Mal Café, serving mainly pizzas and pasta. The main restaurant is quite a contrast and takes you back to a traditional French style with banquettes and wooden partitioned alcoves. (See also under Edinburgh, Manchester and Newcastle.)

◑ Open all year ⚡ In city centre, just off Blythswood Square. On-street parking (free/metered); public car park nearby (£7 per day) ⊨ 10 twin, 54 double, 8 suites; family rooms available; all with bathroom/WC; all with satellite TV, room service, hair-dryer, mini-bar, trouser press, direct-dial telephone, CD player, port for laptop

⚜ 2 restaurants, 2 bars; conferences (max 16 people residential/non-residential); gym; early suppers for children; cots, high chairs, babysitting   ⎔ Wheelchair access to hotel and restaurant (lift), WC (unisex), 17 ground-floor bedrooms, 4 rooms specially equipped for disabled people   ● No dogs; smoking in some bedrooms   ▭ Amex, Diners, MasterCard, Switch, Visa   £ Single occupancy of twin/double £95, twin/double £95, family room £120, suite £165; deposit required. Continental B £8.50, cooked B £10.50; bar/bistro L £7, D £10; alc L £18, D £19. Special breaks available

---

One Devonshire Gardens

1 Devonshire Gardens, Glasgow G12 0UX
TEL: 0141-339 2001   FAX: 0141-337 1663

Still a hotel that others look up to – after many years at the top.

Glasgow is a city that breeds legends, and One Devonshire Gardens is now one of them. Bursting on to the scene at about the same time that the City of Culture was making headlines, it set new standards for the intimately luxurious small town hotel. More than a decade later it is still showing no sign of flagging, or of losing its premier position, although the competition is definitely hotting up. Among the substantial stone houses lining the Great Western Road, there is not much to distinguish it from its neighbours (in fact it spreads over three houses). Inside, however, it is as if you were entering the mansion of some great potentate of the past – perhaps Venetian, or Byzantine. There's an immediate and overwhelming sense of richness, achieved by the use of deep velvety colours, swathes of fresh flowers, fine paintings and masses of polish, and enhanced by the original features of the house – marbled columns and elaborate plasterwork. The bedrooms almost disappear among their fabrics, but there seems to be room for every desirable luxury, too. The food, eaten in the splendid, hushed dining-room, does not let the rest of the place down. This year, seared scallops and halibut with stir-fried vegetables and a Thai curry sauce has been the most popular starter. It might be followed by breast of chicken with caramelised shallots and ceps, then white-chocolate mousse with pink-grapefruit and vanilla and orange sauce. Traffic noise, despite every precaution, is one of the hotel's few problems.

◑ Open all year 🔁 In the West End of Glasgow, 2 miles from the centre, on junction of Great Western Road and Hyndland Road. On-street parking (free) ⇤ 3 twin, 12 double, 10 four-poster, 2 suites; all with bathroom/WC exc 3 double with shower/WC; all with TV, room service, hair-dryer, mini-bar, trouser press, direct-dial telephone; no tea/coffee-making facilities in rooms   ⚜ Dining-room, bar, 2 lounges, garden; conferences (max 40 people incl up to 27 residential), functions; leisure facilities nearby (reduced rates for guests); cots, high chairs, babysitting, baby-listening   ⎔ No wheelchair access   ● No dogs in public rooms; no smoking in dining-room   ▭ Amex, Diners, MasterCard, Visa   £ Single occupancy of twin/double £140, twin/double £180, four-poster £190, suite £190 to £225; deposit required. Continental B £10.50, cooked B £14.50; set L £19 to £25, D £40. Special breaks available

---

Hotels in our Round-ups towards the end of the Guide *are additional hotels that may be worth a visit. Reports on these are welcome.*

Town House

4 Hughenden Terrace, Hyndland, Glasgow G12 9XR
TEL: 0141-357 0862   FAX: 0141-339 9605
EMAIL: michael.ferguson1@virgin.net

A perfect alternative to bland business hotels – a guesthouse full of character.

Glasgow's West End is full of classy Victorian streets like Hughenden Terrace. It's a peaceful place, with a cricket club on one side and a rugby club on the other, lined with imposing Victorian houses built in the heyday of the city's mercantile prosperity. The Town House is one of them: an imposing three-storey construction of red sandstone, with large ground-floor rooms, bay windows and a flight of steps leading up to the front door. Inside, one of the chief attractions is the big living-room on the ground floor, a solid, comfortable room, without frills and fripperies but with comfortable sofas, a fire and a long bookshelf full of interesting and slightly eccentric reading matter. Bedrooms are big, lavishly equipped and have very, very comfortable beds. Some bathrooms have had to be carved out of existing rooms, but they are as well designed as space allows. Breakfasts are good, and the staff extra willing to please. There's a relaxed, understated air about the place, with a touch of humour, illustrated by the quirky selling-point chosen for the brochure: 'This Victorian Hotel... boasts amongst its many amenities the reassurance of an air-raid shelter in the garden.'

◑ Open all year   ▣ From A82, turn at sign for Hyndland into Hyndland Road; take first right, then right turning at mini-roundabout to hotel. On-street parking (free)
⇌ 3 twin, 5 double, 2 family rooms; all with shower/WC; all with TV, hair-dryer, direct-dial telephone, some with trouser press   ✅ Dining-room, living room, garden; leisure facilities nearby (reduced rates for guests); cots, high chairs   ♿ No wheelchair access   ● No dogs; smoking in living-room only   ▭ Delta, MasterCard, Switch, Visa   £ Single occupancy of twin/double £58, twin/double £68, family room £76; deposit required

---

GRANTOWN-ON-SPEY Highland   map 11

Culdearn House

Woodlands Terrace, Grantown-on-Spey PH26 3JU
TEL: (01479) 872106   FAX: (01479) 873641

Very welcoming guesthouse in the Spey Valley.

Grantown-on-Spey is downstream from the hive of outdoor activity that goes on around Aviemore, in a rather more attractive part of the Spey Valley. It's a quiet, respectable, very Victorian-looking place, and its history as a pleasant Cairngorm resort indeed goes back to the time of that queen's love affair with the Highlands. Culdearn House is a big, granite villa, well endowed with bedrooms, and with the kind of ornate drawing-room belonging to more spacious times. Here guests can relax in front of the fire, chatting to Alasdair Little – the epitome of the cheerful host – before being piped into dinner. Isobel Little's four-course set menus are much appreciated – smoked-salmon and spring-onion fish-cake, fillet of beef pan-fried with red wine and mushrooms, followed by brandy scrolls with lemon ice and raspberry coulis are typical of the dishes she serves. The bedrooms are comfortable and well decorated, usually with light colours and pale wooden furniture.

◑ Closed Nov to Feb ⟐ Enter Grantown-on-Spey on A95 from south-west and turn left at 30mph sign; hotel is opposite. Private car park ⮑ 1 single, 3 twin, 5 double; 2 with bathroom/WC, 7 with shower/WC; all with TV, hair-dryer ⊘ Dining-room, drawing-room, drying-room, garden ♿ Wheelchair access to hotel and dining-room, 1 ground-floor bedroom ● No children under 10; no dogs; no smoking in some bedrooms ▭ Amex, Delta, Diners, MasterCard, Switch, Visa £ Single and single occupancy of twin/double £60 to £65, twin/double £120 to £130 (rates incl dinner); deposit required. Special breaks available

---

GULLANE East Lothian

map 11

Greywalls

Muirfield, Gullane EH31 2EG
TEL: (01620) 842144   FAX: (01620) 842241

Smart, attractive Lutyens house, turned into a smoothly running hotel.

It may not be St Andrews, but when it comes to golf Muirfield has its adherents, and many of them, including the famous, choose to stay at Greywalls. It's only a few steps from the course, after all, and many of its rooms overlook the links. This is not primarily a golfing hotel, though, but a very beautiful country house – unmistakeably by Lutyens, with its low eaves and honey-coloured walls – and a country-house atmosphere predominates. This is especially true of the bright, scented sitting-room and the panelled library, with its open fire. The bedrooms share the atmosphere of relaxation, and are slightly feminine in tone. The rose garden was, not surprisingly, designed by Gertrude Jekyll, with a characteristic mix of formality and hidden corners, and it complements the house well. The service is correct and professional, while the food, under new head chef Simon Burns, is becoming increasingly adventurous. Carpaccio of courgettes with an aubergine mousse as a starter, followed by seared North Berwick turbot on foie gras, with mousseline of coconut to finish, are the kinds of dish on offer.

◑ Closed Nov to Mar ⟐ Off A198 in Gullane village; signposted from A1 and Edinburgh bypass. Private car park ⮑ 4 single, 17 twin, 2 double; some in annexe; all with bathroom/WC; all with TV, room service, hair-dryer, direct-dial telephone; no tea/coffee-making facilities in rooms ⊘ Dining-room, bar, 2 sitting-rooms, drying-room, library, conservatory, garden; functions (max 40 people residential/non-residential), conferences; tennis, putting green; early suppers for children; cots, high chairs, babysitting, baby-listening ♿ No wheelchair access ● No dogs in public rooms; no smoking in dining-room ▭ Amex, Diners, MasterCard, Switch, Visa £ Single £95, single occupancy of twin/double from £153; twin/double £190; deposit required. Bar L £6; set L £17.50, D £35; alc L £20. Special breaks available

---

Prices are quoted per room rather than per person.

Brown's Hotel

1 West Road, Haddington EH41 3RD
TEL: (01620) 822254 (AND FAX)

Flamboyant décor and cooking in a stylish house.

Haddington's elegant old houses combine well with the quiet county-town atmosphere. Although these days the town is largely a dormitory for workers in Edinburgh (half an hour's drive away), the big Georgian villas on the outskirts date from less frenetic times. Colin Brown and Alex McCallum have turned one of these into a small hotel of class – badly needed in an area where the 'traditional' hotel is still dominant. The classical-style mini-mansion, with its columned porch and lush garden, has been turned into a palace of rich colours and bright paintings. Mirrors, bronzes and art objects fill the sitting-room and bar, while rich fabrics clothe the rather splendid bedrooms. Many people come just for the food, which is a set four-course menu with a main-course choice (vegetarians should give advance warning). Sea bass stuffed with mousse and served in saffron sauce, wild mushroom soup, and perhaps a passion-fruit ice-cream with pink grapefruit to finish – these are the kinds of delicacy on offer, and all are cooked with love and care. If you are visiting Edinburgh, this place may well be worth the extra drive; if you are East Lothian-bound anyway, it's ideal.

○ Open all year   On main road into Haddington off A1 from Edinburgh. Private car park   1 single, 2 twin, 2 double; all with bathroom/WC exc 2 with shower/WC; all with TV, room service, hair-dryer, direct-dial telephone, some with trouser press   Dining-room, bar, sitting-room, garden; functions (max 30 people incl up to 9 residential); early suppers for children; cots   No wheelchair access   No dogs; no smoking   Amex, Diners, MasterCard, Visa   Single and single occupancy of twin/double £60 to £65, twin/double £85 to £90; deposit required. Set L £19.50, D £27.50

Sunlaws House

Heiton, Kelso TD5 8JZ
TEL: (01573) 450331   FAX: (01573) 450611
EMAIL: sunlaws.roxgc@virgin.net

Massive country house in the centre of the Scottish Borders.

With the advent of the Duke of Roxburghe's new golf course in the extensive parkland which surrounds Sunlaws House (it's still settling down, say the local enthusiasts), there's a slight danger that the hotel will change its character from smart country house to smart golfing hotel – indeed, from January it will be known as the Roxburghe Hotel & Golf Course. The emphasis on outdoor sports (there is clay-pigeon shooting and trout fishing already) now continues into the new club house, with its colourful clientele. However, Sunlaws House is still very much a traditional, rather grand, country-house hotel, with all the features you would expect – lawns, oak panelling and a Victorian conservatory full of the scent of jasmine. It's a friendly and smoothly running place, with the odd sign of wear and tear just to let you know that it's not perfect. Ranks of the duke's leather-bound books fill the library bar, and there's an elaborate, Gothic, carved fire-surround in the inner lounge. The bedrooms vary considerably in size. The Bowmont Suite is huge, with its own fireplace and old-fashioned thunderbox loo, and is correspondingly pricey. Others are not so vast, but are well equipped and furnished with a mix of modern and antique pieces. The food is served in the newly refurbished dining-room (again, not a huge space); as we went to press a new chef was settling in.

◗ Closed Chr ▢ 3 miles south-west of Kelso on A698. Private car park 🚪2 single, 7 twin, 8 double, 3 four-poster, 2 suites; some in annexe; all with bathroom/WC; all with satellite TV, 24-hour room service, hair-dryer, trouser press, direct-dial telephone ✅ Restaurant, bar/library, lounge, drying-room, conservatory, garden; functions (max 120 people incl up to 40 residential), conferences; fishing, golf, tennis, clay-pigeon shooting, health & beauty salon; early suppers for children; cots, high chairs, baby-listening ⅙ Wheelchair access to hotel (ramp) and restaurant, WC (unisex), 3 ground-floor bedrooms, 1 room specially equipped for disabled people ◗ No smoking in restaurant; dogs in bedrooms only ▭ Amex, Diners, MasterCard, Switch, Visa £ Single £105 to £110, single occupancy of twin/double £115 to £120, twin/double £140 to £145, four-poster £195 to £200, suite £245 to £250; deposit required. Bar/bistro L, D £17.50; set L £14.50, D £28.50. Special breaks available

---

INNERLEITHEN Borders   map 11

The Ley

Innerleithen EH44 6NL
TEL: (01896) 830240 (AND FAX)

One of the best guesthouses in Scotland: country location, friendly hosts, great food.

Those who know the Ley won't need reminding of its virtues. It remains as good as ever – better even, for the MacVicars have now installed power showers in all bathrooms, ranging from a glass-encased affair to a wrap-around, over-bath arrangement that looks like a cross between a Western saloon door and a device for preserving Hollywood starlets' modesty. For those who don't know the Ley, it's worth driving halfway across the Scottish Borders to find it. Hidden in woodland on the edge of wild country behind the small town of Innerleithen, it is a white, sunny house surrounded by lawns, flowers, and the sound of running water. The MacVicars run it very much as a family home, and the combination of a house that is both loved and lived in is a winning one. There's a big drawing-room with comfortable lounge-about sofas and lots of books, a dining-room that is elegant and full of gleaming silver and polished furniture, and three superb bedrooms. Each of these is named after the trees visible from the window – Copper Beech is yellow and cheerful, Douglas Fir feminine in pink and green, while Larch is almost semi-circular and blessed with light pouring in from all sides. Doreen McVicar's food draws never a harsh word; her four-course set menus titillate the palate in anticipation. Tomato-and-basil tart or curried-parsnip soup, perhaps, then breast of chicken or guinea-fowl with lime, tarragon and mustard cream, followed by rhubarb crumble or home-made ice-cream.

◑ Closed Nov to mid-Feb, April   ⤤ From Innerleithen, take B709 north; after 2 miles, turn left after golf course, and cross white bridge to hotel drive. Private car park ⤶ 2 twin, 1 double; all with bathroom/WC exc 1 twin with shower/WC; all with hair-dryer, trouser press; television available, room service (breakfast only) ⊘ Dining-room, drawing-room, TV room, drying-room, garden ♿ No wheelchair access ⊖ No children under 12; no dogs; no smoking in bedrooms or dining-room ⊟ None accepted   £ Single occupancy of twin/double £54, twin/double £88. Set D £23

INVERNESS Highland   map 11

Dunain Park

Inverness IV3 6JN
TEL: (01463) 230512   FAX: (01463) 224532
EMAIL: dunainparkhotel@btinternet.com

Interesting mix of styles and a friendly set-up make this a good base near Inverness.

At some point in the Victorian era it became fashionable to add a tower to your Scottish property. Dunain Park's owners decided to grace their Georgian building with a tower drawn from the Venetian Gothic tradition, and this now lends a curious air of exoticism to a house that is in any event a strange mix of styles, from the Georgian core to the modern extension. The interior reflects this mix. The main drawing-room is chintzy and formal, with surely more chairs and sofas than could possibly fit in. The smaller coffee lounge is less imposing, and the dining-room – a cool, elegant three-parter – is distinctly more modern. Among the bedrooms, there is a similar variation. In the old part of the house, up the stairs past one of the tallest pot-plants in the region, the bedrooms are traditional in style, decorated in quiet pinks and greens or warmer yellows and maroons. Some of the bathrooms are distinctly small: if you want to soak in a full-sized tub you would be better off in the modern extension, where the rooms, slightly more expensive, are mini-suites with much bigger bathrooms. Food, under the careful eye of Ann Nicoll, is one of the hotel's high spots. 'New influences are creeping in', she says. 'I'm aiming for lighter, more intense flavours.' Her menus feature local produce and include such good things as Shetland salmon baked in sea salt and served with a white-port, lime and ginger sauce. There's a separate steak menu – for hearty-eating American visitors, with ten variations – and all the steaks come from accredited Aberdeen Angus herds.

◑ Open all year   ⤤ 1 mile from Inverness, just off A82 towards Fort William. Private car park ⤶ 2 twin, 2 four-poster, 2 family rooms, 6 suites; some in annexe; all with bathroom/WC; all with TV, room service, hair-dryer, trouser press, direct-dial telephone; tea/coffee-making facilities available   ⊘ Dining-room, 2 drawing-rooms, drying-room, garden; sauna, heated indoor swimming-pool, badminton; early suppers for children; cots, high chairs   ♿ Wheelchair access to hotel and dining-room, 3 ground-floor bedrooms, 1 room specially equipped for disabled people   ⊖ No dogs in

public rooms; no smoking in dining-room ▭ Amex, Delta, MasterCard, Switch, Visa
£ Twin £98 to £138, four-poster £118 to £158, family room £111 to £151, suite £130 to £170; deposit required. Alc D £25. Special breaks available

Sealladh Sona

3 Whinpark, Canal Road, Muirtown, Inverness IV3 6NQ
TEL: (01463) 239209 (AND FAX)
EMAIL: cooksona@aol.com

Excellent B&B in a quiet corner of Inverness.

Sealladh Sona is the kind of B&B where overseas guests take snaps of co-proprietor Peter Cook in tartan trews standing by the ornamental thistle in the back garden, then send copies back from Australia, Hong Kong and America: in other words, a place where visitors feel they have made instant friends. The B&B is not large (just three guest rooms carved out of a couple of restored cottages on the very edge of the Caledonian Canal) but it has both comfort and character. If you are looking for a good-value stopping point in Inverness, this is it. The bedrooms are smart and warm – not big, but with everything you could want, including a compact shower-room. The two attic rooms have a good view of the canal. There's a neat residents' lounge too, with a decanter of Moniack sloe gin on the go, and stacks of useful information. Breakfasts in the sunny little dining-room are a high point; the more-than-comprehensive menu includes smoked fish, haggis, black pudding, hot fruit compote, oatcakes, crispbread and home-made marmalade, and there's even a special vegetarian cooked breakfast.

◑ Open all year ⎆ From Inverness town centre, take A862 for Beauly; turn left immediately after crossing Caledonian Canal Bridge; after lock gates, take narrow entrance to Whinpark. Private car park ⌂ 2 twin, 1 double; all with shower/WC; all with TV, hair-dryer, clock radio ✓ Dining-room, lounge, garden; cot, high chair ♿ No wheelchair access ● No dogs; no smoking ▭ Delta, MasterCard, Visa £ Single occupancy of twin/double £26 to £31, twin/double £50 to £54

INVERSNAID Stirling   map 11

Inversnaid Lodge

Inversnaid, Aberfoyle, Stirling FK8 3TU
TEL: (01877) 386254

Isolated house on Scotland's favourite loch – geared for photographers, but good for anyone.

The west bank of Loch Lomond is all traffic and tourists; the east bank is isolated and largely inaccessible by car. One of the places where a road breaks through from Loch Katrine and the Trossachs is Inversnaid. It was from here that Queen Victoria set sail on a Loch Lomond trip, and the tiny hamlet has the air of a place where nothing much has happened since. André Goulancourt is a professional photographer, and he and his partner Linda Middleton had the idea of running workshops and courses for photographers in an isolated place in beautiful surroundings. Inversnaid Lodge fitted the bill perfectly, and the old shooting lodge has now been stocked with darkrooms and the necessary equipment. However, André and Linda take in guests alongside their photographers, and although the talk around the table may occasionally verge on the technical, it is hard not to be caught up in the enthusiasm. The lodge is comfortably furnished in a homely style, and there are good views over the loch. Linda's evening meals are popular – home-made smoked mackerel pâté, braised gigot of lamb and cranberry pudding might be on offer. There's no television, and no keys to the pine-furnished bedrooms; it is very much a home from home.

◑ Closed Nov to Mar ⬕ From Aberfoyle, take B829 for 15 miles; at T-junction turn left; lodge is about 3 miles on, after church, on right. Private car park ⬔ 4 single, 4 twin, 1 double; one in annexe; all with shower/WC exc 1 twin with bathroom/WC ⬗ Dining-room, lounge, drying-room, garden ⬗ No wheelchair access ● No children under 16; no dogs; no smoking ⬕ None accepted £ Single and single occupancy of twin/double £28, twin/double £56; deposit required. Set D £15 (by arrangement)

IONA Argyll & Bute

map 11

Argyll Hotel

Isle of Iona PA76 6SJ
TEL: (01681) 700334   FAX: (01681) 700510

The place to stay while making the pilgrimage to Iona.

St Columba's isle is a beautiful place, renowned for its sense of tranquillity and spirituality. Most visitors to the island make a day-trip of it, thundering back to the Mull ferry in coaches each evening. But Iona can be at its best in the evenings, and the Argyll Hotel is a good base if you want to stay a little longer. Like everything else on Iona, it is modest and unassuming. Originally the village inn, it stands in the centre of the rows of small crofthouses down by the ferry pier. Fiona Menzies runs it in a comfortable, relaxed style in keeping with the overall atmosphere of the island. There is space enough to sit (and gaze at the views) and a pleasing dining-room, where you may dine off creamy chicken soup, beef-and-mushroom bourguignon and lemon mousse – a June example of the hotel's three-course set dinners (there is always a vegetarian option). Much of the produce comes either from the hotel's garden or from the surrounding sea, and there's even home-produced water from the hotel's spring. Don't expect much space in the bedrooms, and ask for a sea-facing one if possible. The hotel has been on the market for a couple of years, but meanwhile continues happily on its way.

◑ Closed 7 Oct to Mar ⬕ 200 yards from ferry jetty on Iona. On-street parking (free) at Fionnphort, Isle of Mull ⬔ 8 single, 4 twin, 3 double, 2 family rooms; most with bathroom/WC, 3 with shower/WC ⬗ Dining-room, 2 lounges, TV room, drying-room, conservatory, garden; functions (max 50 people incl up to 26 residential), conferences; early suppers for children; cots, high chairs, toys, baby-listening ⬗ No wheelchair access ● No smoking in some public rooms ⬕ Delta, MasterCard, Switch, Visa £ Single £33 to £45, single occupancy of twin/double £82 to £90, twin/double £82 to £90, family room £103 to £113; deposit required. Light L £9; set D £19.50. Special breaks available

ISLE ORNSAY Highland   map 11

Eilean Iarmain

Isle Ornsay, Sleat, Isle of Skye IV43 8QR
TEL: (01471) 833332   FAX: (01471) 833275

An inn of character in the south of Skye.

One of Sir Iain Noble's many and varied enterprises (which include the
controversial Skye Bridge), the Eilean Iarmain is an old nineteenth-century inn
which overlooks the tiny harbour of Isle Ornsay. The south-eastern coast of Skye
has the lushest climate and best views on the island, and this hotel is a good
place in which to take advantage of both. The atmosphere is determinedly
traditional, with an emphasis on the Gaelic side of things, and the hotel's bar is
usually full of a mix of locals and visitors. You can either eat here or in the main
restaurant, where the food is rather more ambitious; chilled ballottine of salmon,
scallops and local shellfish, oven-roasted sea bass with dill and tomato, followed
by peaches poached in Sauternes might be on offer. The bedrooms – either in the
main house or in a separate building across the drive – are attractive, although
one guest found his 'pretty basic' and reckoned that the hotel, like the bridge,
was 'leaning over the value-for-money frontier'.

◑ Open all year   ⚡ Follow A851 from Broadford, then take A852 to Isle Ornsay's
harbour. Private car park   ⚑ 4 twin, 5 double, 1 four-poster, 2 family rooms; some in
annexe; all with bathroom/WC exc 1 double with shower/WC; all with room service,
hair-dryer, direct-dial telephone, some with TV, trouser press   ⌐ Restaurant, bar,
lounge, garden; functions (max 100 people incl up to 26 residential), conferences;
fishing; early suppers for children; cots, high chairs, babysitting, baby-listening,
outdoor play area   ⅙ No wheelchair access   ● No dogs in public rooms; no
smoking in restaurant and some bedrooms   ⌐ Amex, MasterCard, Switch, Visa
£ Single occupancy of twin/double £50 to £70, twin/double £80 to £95, four-poster
£95 to £115, family room from £85; deposit required. Bar L from £5.50; set L £16.50, D
£29.50. Special breaks available

JEDBURGH Borders   map 11

Hundalee House

Jedburgh TD8 6PA
TEL: (01835) 863011 (AND FAX)
EMAIL: sheila.whittaker@btinternet.com

Sparkling B&B in a beautiful old house with lovely surroundings.

Hundalee is a fine eighteenth-century house in the middle of woods and
farmland close to Jedburgh. Sheila and Peter Whittaker have run it as a stylish
B&B for many years now, and its devotees continue to wax enthusiastic – 'bed
and breakfast should be like this', remarks one happy reader. The success of the
enterprise has as much to do with Sheila's bubbly friendliness as with the
beauty of the house, and you will feel a welcome guest. The best room is the
Georgian dining-room, illuminated by two high windows, and elegant with
green-and-white paintwork and gleaming silver. It ought to be the setting for a
formal dinner party, but the Whittakers' breakfasts are the next best thing, with

lavish amounts of good things spread out on the long, polished mahogany table. The living-room is also a gracious place, although not quite so grand. Some bedrooms have their own entrance behind the family kitchen, others are in the main part of the house. Room 4 is sweet and tiny; Room 5 is dominated by a big, red four-poster; and Room 2 is a very pretty twin in turquoise-green and rose. The standard of 'extras' would outdo many a posh hotel.

◐ Closed Nov to Mar ⚡ 1 mile south of Jedburgh, off A68. Private car park ⊫ 2 twin, 2 double, 1 four-poster; 1 with bathroom/WC, 2 with shower/WC; all with TV, hair-dryer, clock radio ✓ Dining-room, living-room, garden ⅙ No wheelchair access ● No dogs; no smoking ▭ None accepted £ Single occupancy of twin/double £20 to £35, twin/double £33 to £50, four-poster £40 to £50; deposit required

---

The Spinney

Langlee, Jedburgh TD8 6PB
TEL: (01835) 863525   FAX: (01835) 864883

The ultimate in professionally run B&Bs.

Sandra Fry's B&B has been in our guide since its inception, and shows no sign of growing stale. The original accommodation in Sandra's low, white house beside the A68 a few miles north of the English border has now been supplemented by two chalets, tucked away unobtrusively in a corner of the immaculately kept grounds. If you like your privacy, these will be a useful alternative to the main house, and they are kitted up for self-catering too. The Spinney has a large residents' lounge, somewhat formal with its high-backed chairs, rockers and stone fireplace. The main house bedrooms are simple and spacious; one has a primrose bathroom suite from the 'sixties, which Sandra reckons may suddenly become a desirable antique. Carefully stencilled putti on the walls of passage and stairway lend a curious, romantic charm to the Spinney, and the rockery garden is perfect for strolling around on a summer's evening.

◐ Closed Dec to Feb ⚡ 2 miles south of Jedburgh on A68. Private car park ⊫ 1 twin, 4 double; some in annexe; most with shower/WC; all with TV, hair-dryer ✓ Dining-room, lounge, garden ⅙ No wheelchair access ● No dogs; no smoking in bedrooms ▭ Delta, MasterCard, Visa £ Twin/double £40 to £42; deposit required

---

KELSO Borders   map 11

Ednam House

Bridge Street, Kelso TD5 7HT
TEL: (01573) 224168   FAX: (01573) 226319

Tradition and quality combine in this Borders fishing hotel.

When it comes to longevity in hotel-keeping, Ednam House, now into its seventh decade of ownership by the Brooks family, must be approaching some kind of record. In the wake of this enviable stability come certain virtues, notably a disregard of change for the sake of change, and equally a lengthy knowledge of exactly what the guest requires. The house itself is a lovely Georgian building, its front porch facing out towards Kelso's shops and monuments, its restaurant looking over a green lawn towards the rolling waters of the River Tweed. These waters are the hotel's mainstay, for many of the guests come in pursuit of salmon, and the entrance hall contains plenty of evidence of fishing activity. Two of the sitting-rooms are large, elegant, Georgian affairs, blessed with fine ceilings and comfortable, homely sofas and chairs. A passage leads to a bar, now set up for small-scale lunch-time dining, where you can sample an ostrich sandwich (becoming very popular, apparently), while stairs lead downwards to the restaurant extension. After some years during which the food was inclined to be as unchanging as the clientele, the menus have been smartened up and are a little more adventurous, while the quality has definitely improved. The five-course menus, which feature game (jugged hare, venison), salmon, Aberdeen Angus beef and such old favourites as sticky toffee pudding or apple pie, end with nice, old-fashioned savouries: devils on horseback or Scotch woodcock. The bedrooms are scattered all over the upper storeys. The best are in the oldest part of the house, under the cupola on the first-floor landing. The décor and furnishings vary considerably, as the bedrooms are upgraded gradually, year by year – some rooms have candlewick bedspreads and antique furnishings; others feature modern contract furnishing and pale pastel colours. Many overlook the river.

○ Closed Chr & New Year ☑ 100 yards from town square in Kelso. Private car park ⌂ 11 single, 21 twin/double; all with bathroom/WC; all with TV, room service, hair-dryer, trouser press, direct-dial telephone ⊘ 2 restaurants, 2 bars, 3 sitting-rooms, drying-room, garden; functions (max 200 people incl up to 20 residential), conferences; early suppers for children; cots, high chairs, baby-listening ⅙ No wheelchair access ● No dogs in restaurants; no smoking in some bedrooms ▢ MasterCard, Switch, Visa £ Single £55, twin/double £72 to £102 (1998 prices); deposit required. Bar/bistro L from £5; set L £9/£12, D £11 to £20. Special breaks available

---

KENTALLEN Highland　　　　　　　　　　　　　　　　map 11

Ardsheal House

Kentallen, Appin PA38 4BX
TEL: (01631) 740227　FAX: (01631) 740342
EMAIL: info@ardsheal.co.uk
WEB SITE: www.ardsheal.co.uk

Family house for paying guests in a superb location.

Ardsheal is one of the most historic houses on the coast between Fort William and Oban, and it certainly has the loveliest location. A one-and-a-half mile avenue winds between sea and wood, around a headland and past a series of perfect bays of golden shingle, to reach it. The original house was burnt down after the 1745 uprising, and what now stands on a little knoll above the sea is a low, rambling building in shooting-lodge style. After many years as a rather posh hotel, it has now been bought back by the family that once had to sell it to pay death duties. Neil and Philippa Sutherland take in up to 12 paying guests, running the old house very much in guesthouse style. 'We are what we are,' says Philippa; 'we are not a hotel.' One visitor reports: 'Guests will find it hard not to join in the life of the Sutherland family home during their stay.' The same writer goes on to record an environment which 'occasionally verges on the bizarre', but which has undoubted strengths. He mentions the vast log fires, the meals which were 'perhaps unexpectedly excellent' (it's all Philippa's own cooking, including the bread) and included 'proper kippers, and memorable dinners notable for the absence of potatoes during the three days of our stay.' Perhaps surprisingly for a big house, none of the rooms, apart from the billiard room, is especially large, but there is plenty of space overall: an entrance hall with two huge Gothic chairs, a small but comfortable sitting-room with grandfather clock, a big billiard room and a warm conservatory where breakfasts are served. Bedrooms vary in size, decoration and in the antiquity of the furniture, some of it inherited from the previous owners, some of it brought back from Hong Kong. There's no difference in price between the rooms, so ask if you can have one facing the loch and the mountains beyond.

◑ Open all year ◩ Off A828, 5 miles south of Ballachulish bridge. Private car park ⊨ 1 twin, 4 double, 1 four-poster; family rooms available; all with bathroom/WC exc 1 double with shower/WC; all with hair-dryer, direct-dial telephone ✓ Dining-room, bar, drying-room, library, conservatory, billiard room, garden; early suppers for children; cots, high chairs, baby-listening ᴋ No wheelchair access ● No dogs or smoking in dining-room ▭ Amex, MasterCard, Switch, Visa ⟨£⟩ Single occupancy of twin/double £39, twin/double/four-poster £78, family room £90; deposit required. Set D £24

Holly Tree

Kentallen, Appin PA38 4BY
TEL: (01631) 740292   FAX: (01631) 740345

An old railway station turned into an inn of character.

This hotel is a curious mixture of roadside pub, modern hotel and historic building. The station was built in 1903, in best art-nouveau style, and was made extra elaborate to attract Edwardian tourists; it even had its own steamer pier. Closed by Dr Beeching in 1966, the station's transformation into a hotel has been remarkably successful. The old tea-room is now the bar, and the main passage was once platform one. Various items of railway nostalgia still linger, but the overall impression in the light dining-room, with its terrific views over the loch, and in the lounge, with its central log fire, is of the famous Glasgow style, with its high-backed chairs and characteristically globular lamps. The bedrooms are all similar and remarkably large for what is effectively quite a small hotel. They are furnished with cane and wood furniture, and have neat bathrooms. The rooms upstairs have a little less space but even better views. Interior furnishings are looking a bit tired here and there. The à la carte dinners are ambitious, relying heavily on excellent seafood and local salmon. The sauces – they are keen on sauces here – range from port and redcurrant (with venison) to malt whisky, onion and cream (with poached salmon). There are vegetarian options, too. Even if you do not stay, the lunch-time food is good value.

● Closed Dec to Feb ⊿ On A828, 5 miles south of Ballachulish bridge. Private car park 🛏 5 twin, 5 double; family rooms available; all with bathroom/WC; all with TV, room service, hair-dryer, direct-dial telephone ⊘ Dining-room, bar, lounge, garden; functions (max 50 people incl up to 20 residential), conferences; fishing; leisure facilities nearby (free for guests); early suppers for children; cots, high chairs, babysitting, baby-listening ﹠ Wheelchair access to hotel and dining-room, WC (unisex), 2 ground-floor bedrooms specially equipped for disabled people ● No dogs in public rooms; no smoking in dining-room ⊟ Delta, MasterCard, Switch, Visa £ Single occupancy of twin/double £84 to £94, twin/double £97 to £117, family room £115 to £135; deposit required. Light L £5.50, D £12; alc L £12, D £26. Special breaks available

---

KILCHRENAN Argyll & Bute   map 11

Taychreggan

Kilchrenan, Taynuilt PA35 1HQ
TEL: **(01866) 833211**   FAX: **(01866) 833244**
EMAIL: taychreggan@btinternet.com

An eye for good design, a flair for food and a lovely setting for this hideaway lochside hotel.

Once a cattle-drovers' inn, now a comfortable hotel, Taychreggan's original building, with its internal courtyard, has been supplemented by a modern wing which harmonises well with the old house. The hotel is fronted by a lawn running down to the banks of Loch Awe and a day searching after the trout in the hotel's own stretch of the loch is a popular pastime. The interior of the hotel is quiet and fairly formal in tone, with the plain, rich colours of the walls and carpets given life and movement by the excellent modern paintings (Annie Paul is a collector). There's a comfortable sitting-room in crimson, with an upright piano; a bar with around 80 malt whiskies; and a formally decorated restaurant. The TV is banished to its own small room. The bedrooms in the modern wing are fairly standard, with rather small bathrooms (and baths) – bank on having a shower if you are taller than six foot. In the old house, the bedrooms have been reduced in number, creating a suite and a large bathroom out of the saved space. These rooms have a lot more character. The five-course menus draw high praise for their combination of local ingredients with flavours from further afield. A typical example would be escalopes of peppered salmon served on cuttlefish-ink risotto and complemented by a plum-tomato coulis. Venison, pheasant and smoked fish or game usually feature.

● Open all year ⊿ 1 mile east of Taynuilt (A85), turn left on to B845 and follow signs to lochside. Private car park 🛏 11 twin, 5 double, 2 four-poster, 1 suite; all with bathroom/WC; all with room service, hair-dryer, direct-dial telephone, some with trouser press, ironing facilities ⊘ Restaurant, bar, 2 sitting-rooms, TV room, 2 drying-rooms, games room, garden; functions (max 50 people incl up to 38 residential), conferences; fishing, snooker ﹠ No wheelchair access ● No children under 14; dogs in some bedrooms only, by arrangement (£2.50 per night); no smoking in some bedrooms ⊟ Amex, Delta, MasterCard, Switch, Visa £ Single occupancy of twin/double £80 to £95, twin/double £140 to £160, four-poster £210, suite £250 (rates incl dinner); deposit required. Bar L £6.50; set L £17. Special breaks available

Kildrummy Castle

Kildrummy, Alford AB33 8RA
TEL: (019755) 71288   FAX: (019755) 71345

Large Victorian country house on a historic site, with an excellent garden next door.

The real Kildrummy Castle may well have been built by Edward I to help in pacifying the Scots, and its imposing ruins lie a stone's throw from its replacement. This big, typically late-Victorian country house was built by a Colonel Ogston in the 1890s, and contains many of the features you might expect, from panelling and pediments to a magnificent carved staircase. More unusually, the Colonel commissioned a Japanese firm to create a superb garden in the 'back den' (originally the quarry from which the stone for the old castle was taken), to which hotel guests have free entry. The Colonel's house makes a good hotel, and the turn-of-the-century opulence is enhanced by a fine blend of relaxed atmosphere and professional service. Swathes of damask and huge flower arrangements grace the public rooms; bedrooms are straightforward and comfortable. In its own words, the hotel does not serve 'pretentious food' and wisely sticks with the things it knows best: game and fish and shellfish fresh from the Moray coast.

○ Closed Jan ⊅ 35 miles north-west of Aberdeen, off A97 Huntly to Dinnet road. Private car park ⌂ 1 single, 6 twin, 5 double, 2 four-poster, 2 family rooms; all with bathroom/WC exc 1 twin with shower/WC; all with TV, room service, hair-dryer, trouser press, direct-dial telephone, radio ⊘ Dining-room, bar, drawing-room, drying-room, library, games room, garden; conferences (max 20 people residential/non-residential); fishing, snooker; early suppers for children; cots, high chairs, babysitting ⅙ No wheelchair access ⊖ No dogs in public rooms; no smoking in some public rooms ▭ Amex, Delta, MasterCard, Switch, Visa ⊞ Single £75 to £80, twin/double £125 to £155, four-poster £135 to £155, family room £140 to £170. Set L £15.50, D £29; alc L, D £32. Special breaks available

Killiecrankie Hotel

Killiecrankie, Pitlochry PH16 5LG
TEL: (01796) 473220   FAX: (01796) 472451
EMAIL: killiecrankie.hotel@btinternet.com
WEB SITE: www.btinternet.com/~killiecrankie.hotel

Neat, traditional hotel, in a prime tourist area of Scotland.

The Killicrankie Hotel continues to flourish under Colin and Carole Anderson's benevolent rule. It is an old manse, bypassed by the main A9 as it winds through the pass of Killiecrankie, one of the most scenic haunts of the central Highlands. There is a nature reserve close by, as well as the fine woodlands and rocky gorges of the River Garry to explore. This is a firmly mid-range country hotel. It won't suit those who like masses of space, for the confines of the old house mean that the public rooms are a little restricted. On the other hand, the bedrooms are large and extremely well appointed. Improvements made this year include a general refurbishment of the verandah area, which serves as an extension to the homely lounge bar and now makes a very pleasing place in which to sit when it's too cold to wander around the beautiful garden. Over the past years, the hotel has gained a strong reputation for its food. Now that head chef John Ramsay has moved on and has been replaced by Mark Easton, who used to be number two in the kitchen, the food is unlikely to undergo any radical change.

◑ Closed 1 week Dec & Jan to Feb ⤢ Midway between Pitlochry and Blair Atholl on B8079. Private car park ⤙ 2 single, 1 twin, 5 double, 1 family room, 1 suite; 8 with bathroom/WC, 2 with shower/WC; all with TV, room service, hair-dryer, direct-dial telephone, radio ✅ Dining-room, bar, lounge, drying-room, garden; putting green, croquet; early suppers for children; cots, high chairs, baby-listening ♿ No wheelchair access ⊜ No children under 5 in dining-room eves; dogs in bar after 9.15pm and bedrooms only; no smoking in 1 bedroom ▭ Delta, MasterCard, Switch, Visa £ Single £63 to £84, twin/double/family room/suite £126 to £168; deposit required. Bar/bistro L £7; set D £28. Special breaks available

---

KINBUCK Stirling map 11

Cromlix House

Kinbuck, Dunblane FK15 9JT
TEL: (01786) 822125 FAX: (01786) 825450

Huge Victorian pile in rough country north of Stirling.

Cromlix House sits at the centre of a huge sporting estate and was obviously built as the centrepiece. Nothing will ever make this grey sandstone mansion into a beautiful building, but it has a certain air of imperial austerity which is not unattractive. Inside, it's a bit of a labyrinth, but some good work has been done by Ailsa Assenti in softening, even feminising, the atmosphere. The most attractive of the warm and intimate public rooms is the Red Dining Room, where a marble fireplace and heavy navy curtains offset the Moroccan-red walls. Upstairs, the library is another nice room, although it needs more books to justify its name; it can be used for dining, as can the large and elegant heated conservatory. There's also a morning room, in peppermint green. The bedrooms are spacious, tranquil and comfortable, with the past reflected in prints of romantic-style Highlanders, and, in the Upper Turret, an original bath and thunderbox. The kitchen produces ambitious dishes, including elaborate puddings. The hotel's rolling acres offer plenty of opportunities for sport, from fishing to rough shooting; but it equally makes a pleasant base from which to ramble through the woods or rough hills which surround it. The private chapel is much used for weddings but also makes a quiet and attractive place for contemplation.

◑ Closed Jan ⤢ 4 miles north of Dunblane, leave A9 and take B8033; go through Kinbuck and cross narrow bridge; hotel is 200 yards on, on left. Private car park ⤙ 3 twin/double, 3 double, 8 suites; all with bathroom/WC; all with TV, room service, hair-dryer, direct-dial telephone ✅ 3 dining-rooms, 2 lounges, library, conservatory, garden; functions (max 42 people incl up to 28 residential), conferences; fishing, tennis, croquet, clay-pigeon shooting, rough shooting; early suppers for children; cots, high chairs, babysitting, baby-listening ♿ No wheelchair access ⚫ No dogs in public rooms; no smoking in dining-rooms ▮ Amex, Delta, Diners, MasterCard, Switch, Visa £ Single occupancy of twin/double £95 to £165, twin/double £155 to £200, suite £200 to £280; deposit required. Set L £18/£25, D £38. Special breaks available

---

KINGUSSIE **Highland** map 11

The Cross

Tweed Mill Brae, Ardbroilach Road,
Kingussie PH21 1TC
TEL: (01540) 661166   FAX: (01540) 661080

Long-standing quality restaurant, now endowed with excellent rooms.

Travellers on the road between Edinburgh and Inverness have long known the Cross at Kingussie to be one of the few great eating places on the journey. Tony Hadley shifted the enterprise to a restored mill at the back of the village some five years ago and added rooms, and it's an almost faultless performance. The working floor of the old mill has been turned into an open, spacious restaurant, illuminated and heated by a fire built into a partition wall. The decoration is cool and modern – sculptures, pot-plants and white walls set off the clean formality of the tables, which are set so far apart that there is no chance of your neighbour trying to read your morning newspaper. The bedrooms in the modern extension are likewise cool and spacious. They vary in size and tone – some are clad with pine and wicker, others are more cottagey in style. On the side of the mill which overlooks the burn, the constant rush of water will lull you to sleep. Sitting space – as so often in restaurants-with-rooms – is a little restricted: just an open-plan lounge area at the head of the staircase, with white sling-back chairs, a TV and a few coffee-table books, and further seats downstairs by the reception desk. However, this is a place to eat in rather than to sit around contemplating the rain. There's a set five-course dinner menu, with a choice of main course and dessert. Ceviche of salmon, sweetcorn soup, courgette flan, breast of duck with a soy and sherry source, followed by some luscious puddings and good Scottish cheese was on the menu this spring. There's no cooked breakfast, but the superb home-made croissants are compensation enough. Tony Hadley is a good host – observant, keen to please and happy to talk – especially about his wine list, which is long and carefully balanced between the well known, the unusual, the rare and the good value; there's a fine selection of half-bottles.

◐ Closed 1 to 26 Dec & 11 Jan to 25 Feb; restaurant closed Tue eve ⛒ From traffic lights in centre of village, travel 300 yards uphill along Ardbroilach Road, then left down private drive. Private car park ↲ 2 twin, 7 double; all with bathroom/WC; all with hair-dryer, direct-dial telephone; tea/coffee-making facilities, TV available ⌽ Restaurant, lounge; functions (max 30 people incl up to 18 residential) ♿ No wheelchair access ⚫ No children under 12; no dogs; smoking in lounge only ▮ Delta, MasterCard, Switch, Visa £ Single occupancy of twin/double £95 to £115, twin/double £170 to £190 (rates incl dinner); deposit required. Special breaks available

Old School Restaurant

Inshegra, Kinlochbervie, Lairg IV27 4RH
TEL: (01971) 521383 (AND FAX)

Restaurant-with-rooms well placed to take advantage of very fresh fish.

Drive the lonely roads of north-west Sutherland late at night, and you will meet fish lorries plunging southwards from Kinlochbervie, where much of Scotland's Atlantic catch comes ashore. Rather than wait for the lorries to reach the market, you can trace them back to their source and eat the seafood almost as it comes ashore, in Tom Burt's restaurant. Far from ducking the history of his converted school, he has rather successfully melded the atmosphere of the classroom with the business of eating. The place-mats are slates, there are maps on the walls, and a tawse is hung up in memory of more disciplinarian times. Tom quotes his stuffed plaice mimosa as a great favourite, or his haddock in prawn and wine sauce. But there are also scallops, prawns and possibly turbot, and, for those who want meat, venison, steaks and grills as well. There is both a bar menu (chalked up, of course) and an à la carte version. The bedrooms are in a separate building, well furnished and smart, although – since Kinlochbervie is a utilitarian place – views are not outstanding.

◑ Closed Chr & 1 Jan　🔁 From A838 at Rhiconich take B801 to Kinlochbervie. Private car park　🛏️ 1 single, 3 twin, 1 double, 1 family room; all in annexe; 5 with shower/WC; all with TV, room service, hair-dryer, direct-dial telephone　✅ Restaurant, bar, lounge, drying-room, garden; early suppers for children; high chairs, toys　♿ No wheelchair access　⊖ No dogs or smoking in public rooms　▭ MasterCard, Switch, Visa　£ Single £29, single occupancy of twin/double £37, twin/double £48 to £58, family room £66. Bar L £3.50; alc D £13.50

Gladstone House

48 High Street, Kirkcudbright DG6 4JX
TEL: (01557) 331734 (AND FAX)

Elegant B&B in this quiet old artists' town.

South-west Scotland is blessed with several small towns that time has left in a backwater, and Kirkcudbright is one of them. Big enough to act as a hub for the surrounding country, and small enough for everyone to know everyone else, it has attractive old houses, a harbour and the remains of a castle. It has, perhaps naturally, become something of an artists' colony. Gladstone House is a large, dignified town house in the High Street (which time has also left as a quiet backwater on the edge of the town centre). This listed building is now a useful and appealing B&B, run in good style by Sue Westbrook. Rooms are spacious and bright, thanks to the large windows; the top room enjoys the best views and the most light. Breakfasts are a little special, featuring smoked salmon and scrambled eggs for those fed up with grills, and, in season, fresh fruit from local gardens. Antiques, good paintings and prints and works by local artists add to the general air of comfort and stylish antiquity.

◗ Open all year ⊋ On High Street (behind castle), 200 yards from harbour. Private car park ↵ 3 double; 2 with bathroom/WC, 1 with shower/WC; all with TV, clock radio ⊘ Dining-room, lounge, garden ♿ No wheelchair access ● No children under 12; no dogs; no smoking ▭ MasterCard, Visa £ Single occupancy of double £30 to £34, double £50 to £58; deposit required

---

LOCHINVER Highland

map 11

The Albannach

Baddidarroch, Lochinver, Lairg IV27 4LP
TEL: (01571) 844407   FAX: (01571) 844285

Good, friendly, family-run option for the far north-west.

For those who love the remote landscapes and desolation of Sutherland, Lochinver is the obvious base for a walking or touring holiday. It is a small place, dominated by the strange hump of Suilven – the closest Scotland comes to an alpine peak, and the goal of many of the hill-walkers who end up here. The Albannach is a small hotel just outside Lochinver, occupying one of those imposing-looking properties built by Victorian businessmen who amassed a fortune abroad and wanted to make a mark when they came home. Colin Craig and Lesley Crosfield run it in just the kind of style to make you welcome in the wilderness – the drying-room and conservatory are both necessities in the west coast's variable climate. Bedrooms are small, except for the stylish four-poster room and the room in what was once a byre, but they are well furnished and comfortable; in a gesture of recognition to the outside world, they now have telephones. The dining-room has been upgraded a little since last year, too, with starched white cloths and proper wine coolers. Here Lesley serves up her set five-course menus, which feature ambitious combinations of locally sourced ingredients, such as scallops and monkfish with Ayrshire ham on a bed of saffron and sea-kelp risotto with Pernod cream sauce, or a tartlet of crab with tomato and basil.

◗ Closed Jan to Feb ⊋ On entering Lochinver, turn right over old stone bridge at foot of hill, signposted Baddidarroch; after ½ mile, turn left after pottery. Private car park ↵ 2 twin, 2 double, 1 four-poster; one in annexe; all with bathroom/WC; all with hair-dryer, direct-dial telephone; TV available ⊘ Dining-room, lounge, drying-room, conservatory, garden ♿ No wheelchair access ● No children under 10; no dogs; no smoking ▭ MasterCard, Switch, Visa £ Single occupancy of twin/double £92 to £97, twin/double £124 to £134, four-poster £134 (rates incl dinner); deposit required

---

'We were woken at 1a.m. on the first night by a telephone call from a guest who had lost his way. Apparently reception was somehow mixed up with our line. We were told an engineer was coming the following week, but no apology was forthcoming, and we had similar calls on two successive nights.
On a hotel in East Sussex

Inver Lodge

Iolaire Road, Lochinver, Lairg IV27 4LU
TEL: (01571) 844496   FAX: (01571) 844395
EMAIL: inverlodge@compuserve.com

It looks like a business hotel in the wilderness, but it has many plus points.

Inver Lodge is a curious place – the product of a time when it seemed a good idea to put large, modern hotels in remote parts of Scotland, presumably in the hope that employment and business would follow in their wake. Some of them have been successful, and Inver Lodge is definitely such a one, mostly because the staff are friendly and thoughtful: here there is no sense in which you are made to feel just another itinerant destined to remain anonymous except when it comes to paying the bill. An unprepossessing, factory-like building on top of a hill outside the small town of Lochinver, the hotel is better inside than out. You immediately discover the brilliance of the views through the great picture windows – on a clear evening you can see the mountains of the Western Isles strung out on the horizon, with the sun setting behind them. The public rooms are arranged around the lobby and are smartly furnished, with the inevitable touches of Scottish 'tradition' evident here and there. The bedrooms are likewise smart and comfortable, if lacking in character. The kitchens come up with food which is very much better than you expect; seafood features strongly on the fairly plain, five-course table d'hôte menus, with several choices at the important points. Steak, salmon and venison are among the staples.

◗ Closed Nov   ⊡ In Lochinver, travel towards harbour and take first left after village hall. Private car park   ⊫ 11 twin, 9 double; all with bathroom/WC; all with TV, room service, hair-dryer, mini-bar, trouser press, direct-dial telephone   ⊘ Restaurant, bar, 2 lounges, drying-room, games room, garden; functions (max 30 people incl up to 20 residential), conferences; fishing, sauna, solarium; early suppers for children; cots, high chairs   ♿ Wheelchair access to hotel and restaurant, WC, 11 ground-floor bedrooms   ⊜ No children under 7; dogs in bedrooms only   ▭ Amex, Diners, MasterCard, Switch, Visa   £ Single occupancy of twin/double £80; twin/double £130; deposit required. Bar/bistro L £7; set D £27.50; alc D £30. Special breaks available

---

Balbirnie House

Balbirnie Park, Markinch, Glenrothes KY7 6NE
TEL: (01592) 610066   FAX: (01592) 610529
EMAIL: balbirnie@btinternet.com
WEB SITE: www.balbirnie.co.uk

Huge Georgian mansion in Silicon Glen.

This huge Georgian house, built on the back of the embryonic coal-mining industry and surrounded by stately parkland, is now a luxurious hotel, with most of its estate turned into a public park and golf course. Balbirnie House draws much of its business trade from the booming electronics industries of central Scotland – at lunch-time, the restaurant and downstairs bar/bistro are packed with executives entertaining. Unusually, for a hotel of this size, Balbirnie House remains in private hands; the Russell family guards its character jealously, and has done well in restoring Georgian dignity to a house which had once lost all its furniture and been turned into government offices. The star attraction is the long gallery downstairs – no longer hung with wonderful works of art but still with the beauty of its double-cupola ceiling intact, and retaining the bas-relief cupids dancing on the walls. It now acts as an overspill seating area for the panelled bar and the drawing-room, with its sofas and black marble fireplace. The de luxe bedrooms are large and luxurious, their quality reproduction furniture fitting well into the period style. The standard rooms are smaller, but still of a good size. The bathrooms vary a lot: as is the case with so many Georgian hotels, some have had to be carved out of existing rooms, leaving them bereft of light; others are more attractive. But all are sizeable and well fitted out. The food is sensible and straightforward, but with some interesting accompaniments to the meats, such as horseradish rösti and basil crust with the pork fillet, or spätzli, lime and honey sauce with the duck.

◖ Open all year ⤢ North of Glenrothes on A92, turn on to B9130 and follow signs to Markinch and Balbirnie Park. Private car park ⤙ 2 single, 16 twin, 9 double, 1 four-poster, 2 suites; all with bathroom/WC; all with TV, room service, hair-dryer, trouser press, direct-dial telephone ⊘ 2 restaurants, 2 bars, drawing-room, library, games room, garden; functions (max 150 people incl up to 58 residential), conferences; fishing, golf, snooker; early suppers for children, served in bedrooms; cots, high chairs, babysitting, baby-listening ⅋ Wheelchair access to hotel (ramp) and main restaurant, WC (unisex), 7 ground-floor bedrooms, 1 room specially equipped for disabled people ● No dogs in public rooms; no smoking in main restaurant ▭ Amex, Diners, MasterCard, Visa £ Single £115, single occupancy of twin/double £135, twin/double £170 to £210, four-poster £220, suite £225; deposit required. Bar/bistro L £12; set D £30.50; alc L £14, D £37. Special breaks available

---

MARNOCH Aberdeenshire map 11

Old Manse of Marnoch

Bridge of Marnoch, Huntly AB54 7RS
TEL: (01466) 780873 (AND FAX)

A friendly and smartly outfitted country house in rural Aberdeenshire.

Down by the River Deveron, in one of the quietest parts of rural Scotland, this old Georgian manse looks as tranquil as the surrounding country, although the castles and fortified houses found throughout the area show it was once a risky place to live. Nowadays these historic remains, the fishing and the distilleries of nearby Speyside are good reasons to come to this part of the world, and the Old Manse makes an excellent base. It is run by Patrick and Keren Carter as an easy-going country house full of interesting things to look at. These range from a deck plan of the *Titanic*, through an assortment of antiques to Patrick's own furniture – he is an accomplished cabinet maker, and your bedside table may be a sample of his work. The bedrooms are striking, with carved French beds, and, this year, a magnificent four-poster, bought at auction. Keren's food ranges from kedgeree, herring and fresh fruit from the garden for breakfast, to lamb noisettes in port-wine sauce, pork fillets with pear and honey and walnut tart in the evening. Plans are currently in hand to add further bedrooms and to build a new restaurant; the work is due to finish by early 1999.

◗ Closed 2 weeks Nov, Chr & New Year　☒ Just off A97 on B9117, midway between Huntly and Banff. Private car park　🖛 1 single, 2 twin, 5 double, 1 four-poster; most with bathroom/WC, 3 with shower/WC; all with TV, hair-dryer, trouser press　⌖ Restaurant, 2 lounges, drying-room, garden; fishing　♿ No wheelchair access　● No children under 12; no dogs in public rooms; smoking in 1 lounge only　▭ Delta, MasterCard, Switch, Visa　£ Single and single occupancy of twin/double £54 to £60, twin/double £85 to £94, four-poster £90 to £100; deposit required. Set D £27. Special breaks available

---

MELROSE Borders　　　　　　　　　　　　　　　　　　map 11

Dunfermline House　NEW ENTRY

Buccleuch Street, Melrose TD6 9LB
TEL: (01896) 822148 (AND FAX)

Terrific B&B in this central Borders town, characterised by friendly humour.

Some people are natural hosts, exuding an unforced friendliness and happy to share their enjoyment of life with you. It is impossible not to warm instantly to Susan and Ian Graham's welcome, and to sense that they enjoy what they do. Dunfermline House is a solid stone construction, situated virtually next door to Melrose Abbey; St Cuthbert's Way (a newish, waymarked ramble) starts nearby. None of the bedrooms is huge, but they have everything you could want in them and are fresh, bright and cheerful. There's a very small single, with a private bathroom bigger than it is; otherwise the rooms have small *en suite* shower-rooms. One bedroom contains pictures of romantic ladies gazing out at you – 'Ian's choice', says Susan. There's a small lounge ('mostly used by fishermen who bring their own bottles') and a breakfast room. Breakfasts are competent and ample, with a vegetarian choice and a healthy option. Specials are being introduced – like haggis for the overseas guests.

◗ Open all year　☒ Follow signs for Melrose Abbey; house is approx 50 yards from abbey's car park. On-street parking (free)　🖛 1 single, 2 twin, 2 double; 1 with bathroom/WC (not *en suite*), 4 with shower/WC; all with TV, hair-dryer　⌖ Lounge, drying-room　♿ No wheelchair access　● No dogs; no smoking　▭ None accepted　£ Single £24, twin/double £48; deposit required. Special breaks available

---

'We were dismayed to discover that the corporate event involved clay-pigeon shooting and target practice with a replica cannon in the grounds of the hotel. We complained as soon as the event commenced in the afternoon, pointing out that we would not have booked for that day had we known. We were told that the hotel had not itself been aware of what was to happen.'
On a hotel in West Sussex

Beechwood Country House

Harthope Place, Moffat DG10 9RS
TEL: (01683) 220210   FAX: (01683) 220889

Relaxing and friendly country-house hotel, which draws paeans of praise.

Beechwood Country House is one of Moffat's larger Victorian houses, built well up on the slope of the hill behind the town. There's a smallish garden, a good view and a sense of being more in the country than in the town. Internally, the décor is unobtrusive – not stuffed with Victoriana, or overloaded with country-house knick-knacks – and uses restful fabrics and pale colours. A grandfather clock stands by the bar, and another extraordinary clock hangs above the fire – a timepiece embedded in a ceramic plate and then surrounded by a massive wooden frame. There are two lounges – one non-smoking – and a restaurant done up in peachy hues, as well as a conservatory for the odd sunny day. The bedrooms are large and restful, with good-quality furniture, much of it in pine; bathrooms and bedrooms are well stocked with extras, including shoe-cleaning kits. The food is straightforward and very good – maybe a pheasant and chestnut terrine to start with, lemon and garlic chicken to follow, and chocolate cake to finish. Breakfast might even include chanterelle mushrooms, picked in the local beechwoods, to accompany the scrambled eggs. The house style, as our readers' letters confirm, is welcoming and outgoing. Jeff and Lynda Rogers make their guests feel instantly at home, and cater for their every need.

◖ Closed 2 Jan to 15 Feb   ⊿ At north end of Moffat; turn right at corner of St Mary's church into Harthope Place and follow signs to hotel. Private car park   ⇤ 3 twin, 3 double, 1 family room; all with bathroom/WC exc 1 double with shower/WC; all with TV, room service, hair-dryer, direct-dial telephone   ⚐ Restaurant, lounge, lounge/bar, drying-room, library, conservatory, garden; functions (max 30 people incl up to 14 residential), conferences; leisure facilities nearby (reduced rates for guests); early suppers for children; cots, high chairs, baby-listening   ⅙ No wheelchair access   ● No smoking in restaurant   ⊟ Amex, Delta, MasterCard, Visa   £ Single occupancy of twin/double £52, twin/double £74, family room £85; deposit required. Set L £14.50, D £23.50. Special breaks available

---

Well View

Ballplay Road, Moffat DG10 9JU
TEL: (01683) 220184   FAX: (01683) 220088

A place for lovers of food and wine.

Well View is fairly typical of the Victorian villas which line Moffat's quiet back streets, from the days when the town was a spa resort. Now it is mostly walkers, country-lovers and motor-borne tourists who come for a few days to this attractive part of the Borders. If you want to add serious eating and wine-drinking to these activities, Well View is the place to stay. It is a narrow, charcoal-grey three-storey house, with perhaps more of a guesthouse than a hotel feel about it. (One guest commented adversely to us about the free rein that the resident dog and cats seemed to have.) The public rooms are restrained in their décor and are not huge by any means. The bedrooms vary in size – Room 3 is particularly attractive, with a large bay window framed by hollyhock-patterned curtains. Room 6, up under the eaves, is another pleasing room, with lots of character. In the eating department, Janet and John Schuckardt really come into their own. For such a small hotel, the wine list is of a fascinating depth and complexity; it is especially strong on dessert wines, but includes worldwide representation and some fine vintages. The set, no-choice dinners run to seven courses (and that goes for vegetarians, too) for a remarkably reasonable tariff. From the tantalising menus, you might find cream of lamb's-kidney soup, roulade of pork fillet with a bacon crust and apricot and mushroom stuffing, and fillet of sea bass or vegetable cakes on a bed of baby spinach.

◑ Open all year ↗ Follow A708 out of Moffat towards Selkirk; take first left turning after fire station; hotel is 300 yards on, on right. Private car park ⇤ 2 twin, 2 double, 1 four-poster, 1 suite; 3 with bathroom/WC, 3 with shower/WC; all with TV, hair-dryer, some with trouser press ⊘ 2 dining-rooms, lounge, garden; functions (max 30 people incl up to 12 residential), conferences; early suppers for children; cots, high chairs, baby-listening ⅙ No wheelchair access ● No children under 5 in dining-rooms eves; dogs in bedrooms only, by arrangement; smoking in lounge only ▭ Amex, Delta, MasterCard, Switch, Visa £ Single occupancy of twin/double £45 to £57, twin/double £64 to £82, four-poster/suite £70 to £90; deposit required. Set L £13, D £28. Special breaks available

---

MUIR OF ORD Highland　　　　　　　　　　　　　　　　　map 11

Dower House

Highfield, Muir of Ord IV6 7XN
TEL: (01463) 870090 (AND FAX)
EMAIL: thedowerhouse@compuserve.com

An attractive home, with good food, well located in Easter Ross.

Set in the pleasant mix of woods, fields and moorland which surrounds the head of the Beauly Firth, the Dower House is not some large stone house, but actually a curious late-Victorian bungalow, built in an H shape. Its origins go back much further than the reign of Queen Victoria, but it was during the fashion for Highland holidays inspired by the queen that the house took its final shape. Today it continues as an excellent spot for a Highland holiday, notably because of the relaxed and homely way in which Robyn and Mena Aitchison run it. The earliest part of the house (with a vaulted ceiling, of all things) contains the sitting-room and dining-room. The bedrooms are at the rear of the house and are furnished in period style, with some original baths still to be found. The food is another high point. The set menus offer an assortment of good home cooking in a mixture of French and English styles, without pretentious frills. Risotto prepared with red wine and rocket, grilled monkfish with a tomato and herb sauce, and finally pear tarte Tatin would comprise a typical menu.

◖ Open all year   🗺 1 mile north of Muir of Ord on A862 Dingwall road, turn left after double-bend sign into hotel's maroon gates. Private car park   🛏 2 twin, 2 double, 1 suite; family rooms available; all with bathroom/WC exc 1 twin with shower/WC; all with TV, room service, hair-dryer, direct-dial telephone; no tea/coffee-making facilities in rooms   ✅ Dining-room, sitting-room, drying-room, garden; early suppers for children; cots, high chairs, baby-listening   ♿ Wheelchair access to hotel (1 step) and dining-room, WC (unisex), 1 ground-floor bedroom   ● No children under 6 in dining-room eves; no dogs in public rooms; no smoking in dining-room and some bedrooms   🗀 MasterCard, Visa   💷 Single occupancy of twin/double £45 to £85, twin/double/family room/suite £90 to £120; deposit required. Set L £17.50, D £25. Special breaks available

---

NAIRN Highland

map 11

Clifton House

Viewfield Street, Nairn IV12 4HW
TEL: (01667) 453119   FAX: (01667) 452836

A small hotel steeped in theatre, good cheer and good food.

If you sometimes feel that the world is too full of interchangeable and anonymous places to stay, a few nights at J Gordon Macintyre's hotel will revive your spirits. It's an extraordinary place, a theatre as well as a hotel, for it's the setting for plays (every few weeks between September and May), produced by Mrs Macintyre and acted in the round among the dining-tables. The dramatic talent has been extended into the design of all the rooms. It is not a big place, but the use of mirrors, bright colours, and swathes of fabric used to emphasise or conceal, turn it into a kind of child's hide-and-seek wonderland, where there is always something new to look at. This skill is seen at its best in Room 6 perhaps – a small single where bed and bath share the same room, but where, instead of being merely odd, the use of mirrors, partitions and curtains to create the illusion of space and separateness is magical. There's more – paintings, sculptures, photographs of past performances, even some papier-mâché geese, and flowers everywhere. It could be cluttered, but it isn't. It is comfortable in the sitting-room and distinctly stagey in the dining-room. The Macintyres are genial and friendly, and so are their staff. The food is one of the high spots of the performance. Mr Macintyre cooks twice a week, his son Charles taking over on other days. They hate drowning flavours in fancy sauces, and serve their perfect, fresh ingredients in a way designed to draw out the best. You might have poached scallops in vermouth, guinea-fowl sauté with redcurrants or turbot poached with beurre blanc, followed by proper vanilla cheesecake an inch thick.

◖ Closed mid-Dec to mid-Jan   🗺 Enter Nairn on A96, turn west at only roundabout in town, down Marine Road; hotel is ½ mile on, on left. Private car park   🛏 4 single (incl 1 four-poster), 4 twin, 2 double, 2 four-poster; all with bathroom/WC; all with room service, hair-dryer; no tea/coffee-making facilities in rooms   ✅ 2 dining-rooms, sitting-room, drawing room, TV room, drying-room, library, garden; functions (max 200 people incl up to 20 residential); early suppers for children   ♿ No wheelchair access   ● No dogs or smoking in dining-rooms   🗀 Amex, Diners, MasterCard, Visa   💷 Single £60, twin/double/four-poster £100 to £107; deposit required. Alc L £15 to £20, D £20 to £25

Manor House

Gallanach Road, Oban PA34 4LS
TEL: (01631) 562087   FAX: (01631) 563053

Smart hotel in a class of its own in this busy resort and ferry port.

The Manor House stands well away from the throng of Oban's B&Bs and guesthouses, on the edge of a headland overlooking the ferries departing for Mull and the Outer Hebrides. The only thing that might disturb the tranquillity is the lifeboat station's helicopter landing on its pad just behind the hotel – but we are assured that it is such a rare occurrence that, when it does, everyone at the bar gathers round the windows to watch. The Manor House is a smart town-house hotel in style – a little incongruous in a part of the world where most people are wearing anoraks and walking boots, but very effectively done. In fact, it's an ideal place to remind you of civilisation after a day spent ploughing through peat bogs. The lounge is a very attractive, Edwardian-style room, with a heavy gold mirror, snow scenes on the walls and a big slate fireplace. The bar is more art-deco in tone – another big room, with light panelling and fan-shaped lamps. The dining-room is different again – a formal, dark-green room, with a dark tartan carpet and big floral plates set out for dinner. The bedrooms have slightly less character, but many have lovely sea views, and they are spacious and elegant. The food is distinctly good, relying heavily on local fish and game.

○ Closed Mon & Tue Nov to end Feb   ↗ From A816, follow signs to Oban ferry terminal; hotel is 200 yards past terminal on right. Private car park   ⊨ 5 twin, 6 double; all with bathroom/WC; all with TV, room service, hair-dryer, direct-dial telephone   ⊘ Dining-room, bar, lounge, garden; functions (max 32 people incl up to 22 residential); early suppers for children   ⅙ No wheelchair access   ◕ No children under 12; no dogs in public rooms; no smoking in dining-room and bedrooms   ⊟ Amex, Delta, MasterCard, Switch, Visa   £ Single occupancy of twin/double £63 to £110, twin/double £100 to £160; deposit required. Bar/bistro L £10; set L £13, D £25; alc L, D £25. Special breaks available

Peat Inn

Peat Inn, Cupar KY15 5LH
TEL: (01334) 840206   FAX: (01334) 840530

One of Scotland's top haunts for foodies, with fine accommodation to match.

The brochure for this 'restaurant and residence' shows David Wilson, complete with chef's hat, sitting on a lamplit sofa in the middle of the road which runs through the village of Peat Inn. It is the kind of place where the night-time traffic is sparse enough to allow a camera shoot with no fear of disturbance – you need a good map to find the village, despite the fact that it is less than an hour's drive from Edinburgh or Dundee and much closer to St Andrews' famous golf courses. What causes the world to beat a path to David Wilson's door is the extraordinary quality of his cooking. The menus – the very opposite of the florid, overwritten hype found in trendier places – cannot state the quality of the food, but roasted scallops on a bed of leek and smoked bacon with a pea purée, followed, perhaps, by fillet of beef in a Madeira sauce and a little pot of chocolate, give a hint of what is on offer. Another good reason for staying here is to take full advantage of David's passion for wine – reflected in the lovingly compiled list. A third is the fact that residents get to use the best of the three dining-rooms, with its carved sideboard and windows overlooking the garden. Yet another is the quality of the split-level suites which comprise the accommodation in the separate 'residence'. King-sized beds, slippers, padded bathroom doors (perhaps so that you can sing freely inside) and plenty of space to spread yourself around in are some of their features. The residence has its own small, carefully designed sitting area, too, with striped sofas in front of a fireplace. Best of all, perhaps, David Wilson is a very nice man – without pretension, happy to see his guests enjoy themselves and his food.

◑ Closed Sun & Mon ⊅ At junction of B940 and B941, 6 miles south-west of St Andrews. Private car park ⊑→ 8 suites; all in annexe; all with bathroom/WC; all with TV, room service, hair-dryer, direct-dial telephone; no tea/coffee-making facilities in rooms ⊘ Restaurant, lounge, drying-room, garden; functions (max 20 people incl up to 16 residential); early suppers for children ₺ Wheelchair access to hotel and restaurant, WC (unisex), 1 suite specially equipped for disabled people ● No dogs or smoking in public rooms ▭ Amex, Diners, MasterCard, Switch, Visa £ Single occupancy of suite £75 to £95, suite £135; deposit required. Set L £18.50, D £28; alc D £35. Special breaks available

---

PORT APPIN Argyll & Bute   map 11

Airds Hotel

Port Appin, Appin PA38 4DF
TEL: (01631) 730236   FAX: (01631) 730535

Smart, sophisticated hotel in a lovely setting.

Betty Allen's hotel lies tucked away from the main road between Oban and Fort William in the kind of picturesque seafront village more often to be found in Cornwall than Scotland. The Airds Hotel has gained its enviable reputation through maintaining consistently high standards over the years – in service, housekeeping and, above all, in the kitchen. Even hotel inspectors are tested: Betty points out the hand-painted lamps and picture frames in one of the bedrooms: 'Only one inspector has noticed these,' she says. Put on his mettle, our inspector then discovers the full-length mirror tucked into the wardrobe, the careful choice of flower prints, from hydrangeas to primulas, and asks obscure questions about the powerful, thermostatically controlled showers in the bright, tiled bathrooms. The Airds Hotel is an old inn, and its white, simple outline conceals a good deal of the sophistication within. The conservatory hallway is a riot of flowers, and the sun-faded wicker chairs feel just right for it. The double drawing-room has that combination of a smell of woodsmoke, comfortable sofas and interesting pictures which makes you aware that the place is both lived in and cared for. The dining-room is a long, bright place, full of pictures of flowers, birds and amphibians. Here, the four-course dinners, with plenty of alternatives offered at each stage, are wafted to your table by the immaculately trained waiting staff. Lismore oysters with smoked salmon and a champagne jelly, roasted loin of lamb, and poached-pear shortcake with a caramel and lime sauce are the kinds of delicacy you can expect. You can work off any over-indulgence by taking a short walk down to the sea's edge to watch the sun setting behind the mountains of Morven.

◑ Closed 6 to 31 Jan & 20 to 27 Dec ⤳ 2½ miles off A828, midway between Ballachulish and Connel. Private car park 🛏 6 twin, 5 double, 1 suite; all with bathroom/WC; all with TV, room service, hair-dryer, direct-dial telephone; no tea/coffee-making facilities in rooms ⊘ Dining-room, 3 drawing-rooms, drying-room, conservatory, garden; early suppers for children; cots, high chairs, toys, babysitting, baby-listening ♿ No wheelchair access ● No children under 5 in dining-room eves; dogs in bedrooms only, by arrangement; smoking in 1 drawing-room only ▭ MasterCard, Switch, Visa £ Twin/double £110 to £160, suite £110 to £200; deposit required. Set D £40

PORT ELLEN Argyll & Bute   map 11

Glenmachrie [NEW ENTRY]

Port Ellen, Isle of Islay PA42 7AW
TEL: (01496) 302560 (AND FAX)

A wonderful welcome and superb food make this the most memorable guesthouse on the islands.

The flat stretch of Duich moss north of Port Ellen is not Islay's best scenery unless you are a bird-watcher, in which case it becomes full of fascination; Islay's airstrip is here, and the island's golf course. Glenmachrie farmhouse stands beside the fast main road that traverses the moor, looking rather bare and exposed. But this is the only disadvantage, for, on arrival, you are immediately swept into the warmth of Rachel Whyte's welcome. Her guesthouse is modern and neat, and her bedrooms, varying from the small to the medium-sized, are well thought out, warm and comfortable, with everything you need either in the room or readily available. Rachel and any of her family who are around are genuinely interested in their guests – even if they are there for only a night. Over pre-dinner drinks talk can range from the best place to see an otter to the complications of getting to Islay by private aircraft. It is impossible not to be infected by the genial atmosphere, even if you normally retire into a corner behind a newspaper. The food, like the welcome, shows genuine enthusiasm. On inspection, we ate nettle soup, roast pheasant and wild raspberries – the ingredients for the first and last picked by Rachel herself. It is terrific cooking, too. The breakfasts are talked about, and there is an unspoken competition to see who can work their way through the piles of dishes on offer, including fresh strawberries, compote of figs, mangoes and prunes, haggis on toast, peat-smoked haddock and home-made scones and oatcakes, in addition to the more usual offerings.

○ Open all year **⊉** On coastal side of A846, 4 miles north of Port Ellen, south of airstrip. Private car park **⊯** 3 twin, 2 double; all with shower/WC; all with TV, room service, hair-dryer, ironing facilities, radio **⌖** Dining-room, lounge, drying-room, library, garden; functions (max 20 people incl up to 10 residential), conferences; fishing; leisure facilities nearby (reduced rates for guests); early suppers for children; cots, toys, babysitting, baby-listening, outdoor play area **♿** Wheelchair access to hotel (ramp) and dining-room, WC (unisex), 1 ground-floor bedroom specially equipped for disabled people **⬤** No children in dining-room eves; no dogs in public rooms; no smoking **▭** None accepted **£** Single occupancy of twin/double £38, twin/double £56. Set D £20

PORTPATRICK Dumfries & Galloway   map 11

Crown Hotel

9 North Crescent, Portpatrick, Stranraer DG9 8SX
TEL: (01776) 810261   FAX: (01776) 810551
EMAIL: penpatrick@aol.com

A harbourfront pub with extra class.

Right on the harbour in one of south-west Scotland's most picturesque fishing villages, the Crown looks a popular smugglers' haunt: go through the self-effacing front door, and you are straight into a couple of snug bars, full of gossip and redolent with wood- and tobacco-smoke. But the bars are really just a front for a stylish, almost posh small hotel. The bistro restaurant, which takes up most of the rest of the ground floor, sets the tone, with cool tones of green, rattan furniture, wrought iron, and Glasgow style murals. Seafood, as might be expected, is the joy of the place – herring, sole, lobsters, scallops and monkfish appear on almost all the menus. The catch is local, and the cooking the work of an enthusiast. Small wonder that the restaurant seats three times as many as could ever cram into the bars. But this is not the only surprise. Mount the narrow stairs, and you find a sequence of bedrooms that have retained something of the rustic character in their panelling and small windows, but that have been beautifully refurbished with country fabrics, brass beds and striped wallpaper. Room 12 is the biggest and has a great view of the harbour, but none of the bedrooms is to be sniffed at. Nor are the bathrooms, which are mostly spacious and smart. The proprietors are not only friendly but obviously also efficient.

○ Open all year **⊉** On entering Portpatrick from A74, keep left at war memorial; continue to seafront and turn right; hotel is 100 yards on right. On-street parking (free) **⊯** 3 twin, 9 double, 1 suite; family rooms available; all with bathroom/WC; all with TV, room service, direct-dial telephone **⌖** Restaurant, 3 bars, conservatory, garden; functions (max 500 people incl up to 24 residential), conferences; early suppers for children; cots, high chairs, baby-listening **♿** No wheelchair access **⬤** No smoking in restaurant and conservatory **▭** Amex, MasterCard, Switch, Visa **£** Single occupancy of twin/double £48, twin/double/suite £72, family room £82; deposit required. Set L £7.50, D £13.50; alc L, D £30. Special breaks available

---

Many hotels put up their tariffs in the spring. You are advised to confirm prices when you book.

Knockinaam Lodge

Portpatrick, Stranraer DG9 9AD
TEL: (01776) 810471   FAX: (01776) 810435

Peace and plenty at this perfect country-house hotel – at a price.

There's something about the way in which North Americans run country hotels. Perhaps it's a slightly different and more careful eye for interior design, perhaps it is extra respect for old houses; certainly it has to do with the attention paid to the beds. Whatever the case, Pauline Ashworth and Michael Bricker, who came to Knockinaam Lodge from Toronto, have brought that extra class with them, and have turned this old shooting lodge into a wonderful hotel. From the start, it is difficult not to fall in love with the house and location. A network of country lanes leads across the neck of the Rhinns of Galloway, bringing you at length to a steep track leading down to a perfect cove shut in by headlands. Knockinaam Lodge stands on its own here, on a patch of lawn, with only the sea and cliffs for company. When you first come upon it from above, the old white house and the blue ocean seem to be from a different world, where towns and traffic play no part. Inside, everything has been done to heighten the impression of calm, and no noise, except for the ticking of clocks, disturbs the tranquillity of the house. The drawing-room and morning room lie waiting, with their comfortable country-house-style sofas and bright paintings, mostly by local artists. The bar, with its dark-green tartan chairs, is panelled and clubby, while the restaurant, a brilliant creation of strawberry and charcoal hues, is full of the reflected light of the sea glancing off the silverware. The menus, printed on glossy paper decorated with flower paintings by another local artist, understate, in their simplicity, the sheer excellence of the food. Leek and potato soup with crème fraîche and chives; steamed fillet of sea bass with saffron mashed potatoes and a rosemary beurre blanc; and chocolate-pudding soufflé with coconut ice-cream are typical dishes. The bedrooms add to the atmosphere. They are big – especially the Pond Room – and have huge beds. The Churchill Room is dignified by a vastly deep Edwardian bath, in which it is easy to imagine the great man wallowing after his secret wartime meeting with Roosevelt here.

◐ Open all year ⤧ On A75 or A77, follow signs to Portpatrick; 2 miles west of Lochans, turn left at Knockinaam sign; follow signs to hotel for 3 miles. Private car park ⤶ 1 single, 2 twin, 6 double, 1 four-poster; all with bathroom/WC exc single with shower/WC; all with satellite TV, video, room service, hair-dryer, direct-dial telephone; no tea/coffee-making facilities in rooms ⊘ Restaurant, bar, 2 drawing-rooms, drying-room, garden; functions (max 20 people residential/non-residential), conferences; leisure facilities nearby (reduced rates for guests); early suppers for children; cots, high chairs, babysitting, baby-listening, outdoor play area ♿ No wheelchair access ⬤ No children in restaurant eves; dogs in bedrooms only (£10 per night); no smoking in restaurant ▭ Amex, Diners, MasterCard, Switch, Visa ⊡ Single from £95, single occupancy of twin/double from £120, twin/double from £160, four-poster from £210 (rates incl dinner); deposit required. Bar/bistro L £7.50; set L £27. Special breaks available

---

Use the maps in the central section of the Guide *to pinpoint hotels in a particular area.*

Viewfield House

Portree, Isle of Skye IV51 9EU
TEL: (01478) 612217   FAX: (01478) 613517

An ancient family home turned into a hotel of great character.

Viewfield House has belonged to the same family of Macdonalds for close on 200 years, changing its appearance from its Georgian origins to a suitably imposing neo-Gothic Victorian mansion, complete with a tower and an entrance hall hung with trophies. Wisely, Hugh and Linda Macdonald have kept the character of the old place as unchanged as possible, one of the few concessions to modernity being the *en suite* bathrooms (although there is still an original thunderbox). You eat off Macdonald silver while admiring the portraits of slightly disapproving Macdonald ancestors gazing down on the venerable mahogany dining table. After dinner, it is through to the drawing-room – much as if you were part of an Edwardian shooting party. In style and atmosphere, Viewfield House is much closer to a home than a hotel – and this is what makes it special and not easily classified. Have no fear of the bedrooms: although some ancient Scottish houses are draughty and spartan on their upper storeys, the bedrooms here are comfortable and rather romantic, with solid Victorian furniture and plenty of space and light. Single travellers should ask for the tower room, which is absolutely tiny (and will probably need a hot-water bottle to go with it), but unique. Linda's five-course set-dinner menus might include tomato and tarragon soup, Swiss baked chicken, and chocolate and cinnamon almond cake with vanilla sauce – eaten in a setting which Dr Johnson would have appreciated.

◑ Closed mid-Oct to mid-Apr ⊿ On southern edge of Portree, just off A87; hotel driveway is opposite BP filling station. Private car park ⊨ 2 single, 5 twin, 5 double; most with bathroom/WC; all with clock radio ⊘ Dining-room, drawing-room, TV room, drying-room, garden; early suppers for children; cots, high chairs, baby-listening, outdoor play area ⅋ No wheelchair access ● No dogs in public rooms; no smoking in dining-room ▭ MasterCard, Visa £ Single £35 to £45, twin/double £70 to £90; deposit required. Set D £15. Special breaks available

---

Shieldhill

Quothquan, Biggar ML12 6NA
TEL: (01899) 220035   FAX: (01899) 221092

A very ancient fortified tower turned into a pleasant country hotel.

The fact that Shieldhill has survived the internecine strife of lowland Scottish history for 800 years says a lot for the strength with which it was built – or, perhaps, for the astuteness of the family which owned it for 750 of those years. When William Wallace trained his army close by, the tower house was already a respectable age; more was added to it in the sixteenth century. The 'New Wing' dates from 1820; Christina and Bob Lamb have recently created four new bedrooms here, adding king-sized beds, jacuzzi baths and some power showers. There are some splendid features in the old house, notably the fireplaces, panelling and high ceilings. The bedrooms are cheerfully decorated, dispelling any remaining medieval grimness from the atmosphere, and are furnished in good country-house style. The set dinner menu offers several choices at each stage; there may be wild-boar and quail's-egg salad as a starter, grilled sea bass with seafood risotto to follow, and there's always a 'chef's' grand dessert' to finish with. Wooded parkland surrounds the house, softening the stern air with which the old fortress looks out on the world.

○ Open all year ⚡ From Biggar, take B7016 towards Carnwath for 2 miles; turn left into Shieldhill Road; hotel is 1½ miles on, on left. Private car park ⚓ 1 single, 4 twin, 6 double, 3 four-poster, 2 suites; family rooms available; most with bathroom/WC, 2 with shower/WC; all with TV, room service, hair-dryer, direct-dial telephone, some with trouser press no tea/coffee-making facilities in rooms ✦ 3 dining-rooms, 2 bars, drying-room, library, games room, garden; functions (max 200 people incl up to 31 residential), conferences; snooker, clay-pigeon shooting, croquet; early suppers for children; cots, high chairs, baby-listening ♿ No wheelchair access ● No dogs in public rooms; no smoking in dining-rooms and bedrooms ☐ MasterCard, Switch, Visa £ Single £85, single occupancy of twin/double £90, twin/double £124, four-poster £136, family room £134, suite £188; deposit required. Bar/bistro L £10, D £13; set L £18.50, D £32.50. Special breaks available

---

ST ANDREWS Fife   map 11

Old Course Hotel

Old Station Road, St Andrews KY16 9SP
TEL: (01334) 474371   FAX: (01334) 477668
EMAIL: oldcoursehotel@standrews.co.uk
WEB SITE: www.standrews.co.uk/hotels/oldcours/home.htp

Everything on tap for dedicated golfers, including panoramic views of the course.

Time passes: this 'new' hotel is now almost 30 years old, but shows few signs of fading, either in its fabric or in its appeal to golfers (many from overseas), who come to play St Andrews's famous courses. It was built to be a landmark from every point of the town's golfing complex down by the West Sands, though it is not the most beautiful of buildings, with its late-'sixties roofscape. Inside, the combination of modern minimalist interior design (imported from Texas), some *trompe l'oeil work* to give the impression of stone walls where none exists, and the lavish use of wood give a feeling of smart clubbiness with overtones of antiquity. The Old Course Hotel does not yet have the patina of age and fame which you find at Turnberry or Gleneagles, but it is competing hard. A huge bowl of Madonna lilies fills the entrance lobby; rugs and polished parquet flooring mark the reception area and stone-floored passageways lead to the pro shop and conference rooms. Sensibly, given the amazing views over the Old Course, the hotel's main restaurant and panelled bar are situated on the fourth floor. Both serve good, hearty grills for exhausted golfers, seared before your eyes, combined with gentler, healthier dishes for those fresh from the extensive spa. The bar claims to be the only one with a single malt from every distillery in the country. The bedrooms are spacious and bright, with a minimalist approach to furniture and no clutter. Those facing the sea and the links carry a hefty supplement.

◑ Closed Chr ◪ As you enter St Andrews on A91, hotel is on left. Private car park 30 twin, 41 double, 37 twin/double, 17 suites; family rooms available; all with bathroom/WC; all with TV, room service, hair-dryer, mini-bar, trouser press, direct-dial telephone ✓ 2 restaurants, 2 bars, 2 lounges, library, conservatory, garden; functions (max 300 people incl up to 250 residential), conferences; golf, gym, sauna, solarium, heated indoor swimming-pool; early suppers for children; cots, high chairs, toys, babysitting ♿ Wheelchair access to hotel (ramp) and restaurant, WC (unisex), lift to bedrooms, 1 room specially equipped for disabled people ● No dogs in public rooms ▭ Amex, Diners, MasterCard, Visa £ Single occupancy of twin/double £145 to £225, twin/double £175 to £250, family room £175 to £288, suite £230 to £350; deposit required. Bar/bistro L £12.50, D £19.50; alc L £17.50, D £38.50. Special breaks available

Rufflets

Strathkinness Low Road, St Andrews KY16 9TX
TEL: (01334) 472594 FAX: (01334) 478703
EMAIL: rufflets@standrews.co.uk

Attractive country-house hotel – much used by golfers, but good for others too.

Close enough to St Andrews to be within easy reach of the courses, but far enough outside town to be genuinely in the country, Rufflets is a big, rambling house from the 'twenties, dignified by a double-gabled aspect and a formal garden of clipped yew and neat flowerbeds. Inside, the cleanliness of the place makes an immediate impression: everything sparkles. At first glance, the public rooms don't seem to have a great deal of character, but look closer and distinctly interesting touches appear. In the Garden Restaurant, for instance, the green, yellow and cherry colours actually work together very well. The drawing-room is graced by Russell Flint paintings – and it turns out that the artist was connected with the house. In the library, *trompe l'oeil* bookshelves are ranged alongside real ones beside the two steps leading down to the bar. The bedrooms come in two distinct styles. Those on the first floor are spacious, flowery and traditionally furnished. On the next floor, they are done up in rich, deep blues with modern furniture; these are apt to be smaller, but have good garden views. Food at Rufflets is distinctly good. The table d'hôte menu has several choices at each stage, and includes Brie and ham baked with oatmeal, collops of venison in sloe and rosemary *jus*, and steamed ginger pudding with butterscotch sauce.

◑ Open all year ◪ On B939 1½ miles west of St Andrews. Private car park 6 single, 7 twin, 11 double, 1 four-poster; some in annexe; family rooms available; all with bathroom/WC; all with TV, room service, hair-dryer, trouser press, direct-dial telephone ✓ Restaurant, bar, drawing-room, drying-room, library, garden; functions (max 80 people incl up to 42 residential), conferences; putting green, golf practice net; early suppers for children; cots, high chairs, baby-listening ♿ Wheelchair access to hotel (ramp) and restaurant, 3 ground-floor bedrooms, 1 specially equipped for disabled people ● No dogs; no smoking in some public rooms and some bedrooms

Amex, Delta, Diners, MasterCard, Switch, Visa £ Single £65 to £95, single occupancy of twin/double £65 to £125, twin/double/four-poster/family room £100 to £180 (+ £5 per child); deposit required. Set L £18.50, D £30

SCARISTA Western Isles   map 11

Scarista House

Scarista, Isle of Harris HS3 3HX
TEL: (01859) 550238   FAX: (01859) 550277
EMAIL: scarista@compuserve.com
WEB SITE: www.ourworld.compuserve.com/homepages/scarista

Terrific location and an ethical approach to eating in this long-standing island hotel.

The east coast of Harris is all rock, but the west coast is sand and green pasture, and Scarista House faces a wonderful sweep of clean, white beach – one of the best in the whole of the Hebrides. With the short turf of the machair as its setting, and the seabirds its closest neighbours, this really is the perfect spot for getting away from it all. For many years, under its previous owners and now under Jane and Ian Callaghan, Scarista has been a pioneer of ethical eating: no product of factory farming will appear on your plate. Something which was perhaps regarded as mildly cranky a decade ago is now coming to look increasingly like common sense; the spin-offs, of course, are the flavour and delicacy of food that comes only from the garden, the sea or carefully selected flocks and herds. Jane Callaghan places great emphasis on fish in her five-course set menus. There may be scallops baked in their shells, or lobsters (for which there is no supplement), turbot or halibut 'whenever we can get it', or there may be venison or lamb. Melon ice-cream, cold chocolate pudding, or tarts with crowdie, cream and strawberries feature among the desserts. The house has a large library (a necessity), and a peat fire warms the sitting-room. Bedrooms are individual, most being in a single-storey annexe a little way from the house. Local staff help to make the place, and, inspired by the conversation in the dining-room, some guests have even started learning Gaelic.

◖ Closed Oct to Apr   ◰ 15 miles south-west of Tarbert on A859. Private car park ⊨ 2 twin, 3 double; some in annexe; suites available; all with bathroom/WC; all with room service, hair-dryer, direct-dial telephone   ⊘ Dining-room, sitting-room, library, garden; early suppers for children; cost, high chairs   ♿ No wheelchair access ● No children over 2 and under 8; dogs and smoking in annexe rooms only ▭ MasterCard, Visa   £ Single occupancy of twin/double £70, twin/double £110, suite £125; deposit required. Light L £7.50 (residents only); set D £30

SHIELDAIG Highland   map 11

Tigh an Eilean

Shieldaig, Strathcarron IV54 8XN
TEL: (01520) 755251   FAX: (01520) 755321

Exceptional small hotel, with great food, service and sunsets.

Those who don't know this hotel, in one of the prettiest villages in the West Highlands, are always surprised by the space and style behind the unassuming frontage. From the outside it looks just like a row of terraced cottages – and, indeed, this is exactly what it once was – but inside there is space for 11 bedrooms and all the public rooms that you might want. 'Despite its size, this must be one of the great country hotels of north-west Scotland,' writes one happy guest, who goes on to mention the high standard of the rooms, the immaculate tidiness, and the quality of the sunsets. The latter, he says, turn the already memorable dinners into a spiritual experience. On the set menus you will find local ingredients – often seafood – unpretentiously cooked, but prepared with a real attention to presentation and detail. A sauté of local scallops with salsa, roast gigot of blackface lamb, and apricot mousse with a chocolate and orange sauce are typical of what is on offer. Add to all this the fact that the service is 'efficient, homely and quite unfussy', and that the packed lunches are a real pleasure, and you have a hotel well worth making a special effort to visit.

◑ Closed mid-Oct to mid-Apr　▨ In Shieldaig village, off A896. On-street parking (free)　↳ 3 single, 4 twin, 3 double, 1 family room; all with bathroom/WC exc 1 single with shower/WC; hair-dryer available　⌀ Dining-room, bar, lounge, TV room, drying-room; early suppers for children; cot, high chair　よ No wheelchair access ◒ No dogs in public rooms; no smoking in TV room and dining-room　⊟ Delta, MasterCard, Switch, Visa　£ Single £45, twin/double £100, family room from £100; deposit required. Bar L, D £5.50, set D £23.50

SOUTH GALSON Western Isles   map 11

Galson Farm Guesthouse

38 South Galson, Ness, Isle of Lewis HS2 0SH
TEL: (01851) 850492 (AND FAX)

Close to the northernmost tip of the Western Isles, a guesthouse of great friendliness.

In any season except summer the fishing and crofting townships strung out along the north-west coast of Lewis can be bleak places. But in summer, with the birdlife, the flowers and the clear light, even the utilitarian nature of the villages and the lack of trees can become charming. It is not easy to find really good places to stay this far out in the wilds, so John and Dorothy Russell's farm guesthouse is all the more welcome. Galson Farm is a substantial stone building, with fields behind running down to the Atlantic shore. Now and again the bones of Viking warriors are dug out of the sand dunes, and guests are encouraged to keep an eye open for anything unusual on their morning walks along the beach. This is a very welcoming, friendly place to stay – you can quickly become a part of the community. At the same time, it is very comfortable; the three guest rooms have been made proof against the worst weather and are warmly and cosily decorated. Dorothy's three-course dinners make use of local ingredients; seafood gratin with cockles and mussels is a favourite, as is her Snow Queen pudding (wispy sugar with meringue and lemon), or her hazelnut and peach tart. You need to say in advance that you will be eating in – and it is well worth doing so.

◑ Open all year   ⊇ From Stornoway take A857 for Port of Ness; hotel is 20 miles from Stornoway. Private car park   ⊫⊐ 2 twin, 1 double; all with shower/WC; all with room service, hair-dryer; TV available   ✅ Restaurant, 2 lounges, library/conservatory, garden; clay-pigeon shooting; early suppers for children; cots, high chairs, babysitting, baby-listening   ⅄ No wheelchair access   ● No smoking   ▭ MasterCard, Visa   £ Single occupancy of twin/double £35, twin/double £58; deposit required. Set D £16; alc D £19. Special breaks available

---

SPEAN BRIDGE Highland   map 11

Old Pines

Spean Bridge, Fort William PH34 4EG
TEL: (01397) 712324   FAX: (01397) 712433
EMAIL: goodfood.at.oldpines@lineone.net

Good food and a good family atmosphere in the Great Glen.

Old Pines is a modern chalet-style house, much bigger than it seems at first sight, as there has to be room for Bill and Sukie Barber and their eight children. Although it is not set up specifically as a hotel for families, guests with children are more than welcome, the latter generally rapidly disappearing into the huge family playroom, or into the surrounding woodlands. There are animals, bikes and toys, but there is also extensive sound-proofing – so child-free guests are unlikely to be worried by the sound of riot. (Sukie emphasises that her guests come for the food rather than the child-friendly atmosphere.) Bill, a former fish-farmer, makes the bread and smokes the fish and the duck, while Sukie, a keen adherent of the natural cooking of Scotland, produces set five-course menus. These may start with scallops, squat lobster and mussels, move on to flat mushroom soup with chicken livers, port and thyme, followed by roast cod with ratatouille and garlic mayonnaise, and finish with caramelised rhubarb flan with ginger ice-cream and orange sauce. A wood-burning stove provides the background warmth to the interconnecting restaurant and sitting-room, and everything is fresh and modern, with extensive use of pine. Bedrooms are log-cabin style, practical and comfortable.

◑ Closed 2 weeks in late Nov   ⊇ From A82, 1 mile north of Spean Bridge, take B8004 at Commando Memorial; hotel is 300 yards on right. Private car park   ⊫⊐ 1 single, 2 twin, 3 double, 2 family rooms; all with shower/WC; all with room service, hair-dryer   ✅ Restaurant, 2 lounges, TV room, drying-room, conservatory, garden; conferences (max 24 people incl up to 8 residential), functions; early suppers for children; cots, high chairs, toys, playroom, babysitting, baby-listening, outdoor play area   ⅄ Wheelchair access to hotel (ramp) and restaurant, WC (unisex), 8 ground-floor bedrooms, 5 specially equipped for disabled people   ● No dogs; no smoking   ▭ MasterCard, Switch, Visa   £ Single £55 to £60, single occupancy of twin/double £55 to £75, twin/double/family room £110 to £120 (+ from £5 per child) (rates incl dinner); deposit required. Alc L £13.50. Special breaks available

---

It is always worth enquiring about the availability of special breaks or weekend prices. The prices we quote are the standard rates for one night – most hotels offer reduced rates for longer stays.

STAFFIN Highland   map 11

Flodigarry Country House

Staffin, Portree, Isle of Skye IV51 9HZ
TEL: (01470) 552203   FAX: (01470) 552301
WEB SITE: www.milford.co.uk/go/flodigarry.html

An ideal location for exploring northern Skye, with good food and interesting history.

When it comes to letting accommodation, it helps if you have Flora Macdonald's cottage in your grounds; faxes arrive regularly from New York asking for rooms in the heroine's house, and luckily it is large enough to offer a choice of seven. The 'big hoose' itself was built by a Macdonald descendant around the turn of the century in a rather different style, for its owner favoured Moorish ideas – as you can see in the hotel's bar. The style of accommodation is somewhat different, too, for the bedrooms here are rather grand – some have king-sized four-poster beds – whereas in the cottage they are simpler, featuring rugs and brass or iron beds. Staffin has some of the oddest volcanic landscapes in Britain and you are only a short drive from the pinnacle of the Old Man of Storr or the tumbled rocks of the Quiraing. The third great advantage of the place is the food; the seafood is especially good. On the table d'hôte menu you might find baked monkfish with Argyll ham, a roulade of rabbit and venison, and, for pudding, a nectarine and Talisker-whisky cheesecake. As well as the set menu, it's well worth studying the à la carte menu of seasonal specialities.

○ Open all year ☒ From Portree, follow A855 north for 25 miles; hotel is 2 miles past Staffin, on right. Private car park ↵ 1 single, 6 twin, 8 double, 2 four-poster, 2 family rooms; some in annexe; most with bathroom/WC, some with shower/WC; all with room service, hair-dryer, direct-dial telephone; TV available ✓ Restaurant, bar, lounge, drying-room, conservatory, garden; functions (max 120 people incl up to 39 residential), conferences; snooker; early suppers for children; cots, high chairs, toys, babysitting, baby-listening ⅙ Wheelchair access to hotel (1 step) and restaurant, WC (M, F), 4 ground-floor bedrooms, 1 room specially equipped for disabled people ● Smoking in bar and lounge only ▭ MasterCard, Switch, Visa £ Single £29 to £48, twin/double £58 to £116, four-poster £118 to £150, family room £78 to £116; deposit required. Bar/bistro L, D £13; set Sun L £16, D £28.50. Special breaks available

---

STRATHKINNESS Fife   map 11

Fossil House   NEW ENTRY

12–14 Main Street, Strathkinness, St Andrews KY16 9RU
TEL: 01334 850639 (AND FAX)

Welcoming B&B with amazing range of facilities near St Andrews.

'Arrive as guests, depart as friends' is the slogan of this little B&B tucked away in a village three miles from the centre of St Andrews. Alistair and Kornelia Inverarity provide exactly the right combination of a warm welcome, wonderful breakfasts and a genuine concern for their guests' comfort. Accommodation is in two separate stone buildings, once a smallholding, separated by a gravel courtyard. There are four bedrooms, done up with colourful fabrics and glowing pine, a sitting-room, a breakfast room and a sunny conservatory full of comfortable chairs and pot-plants. None of the rooms could be called spacious, or even large; moreover, every spare niche is filled by ornaments, pictures of fighter aircraft (Alistair still works at nearby RAF Leuchars), plants and *objets trouvés*. But the range of facilities is breathtaking. Take the family room (two bunk beds and a double), for example: wooden pull-along toys fill a small shelf unit, Roald Dahl books are set out ready for bedtime, and the cupboard opens to reveal a complete baby-servicing tray, with everything from nappy cream to baby-bath. For adults there are shelves of videos in the lounge, coffee-table books in the conservatory and racks of information leaflets in bedrooms and in passages. Fresh flowers are set out on your bedside table. Breakfasts exhibit the same overwhelming abundance. Here, a pair of kippers really means a pair, Aberdeen butteries take their place alongside the toast, and the range of marmalades would fill a cupboard on its own.

◑ Open all year ☑ Strathkinness is signposted off A91, west of St Andrews; house is at top of village, near pub. Private car park ⊫ 2 twin, 1 double, 1 family room; some in annexe; all with shower/WC exc family room with bathroom/WC; all with TV, hair-dryer, trouser press, fridge, clock radio ⊘ Breakfast room, 2 lounges, TV room, conservatory, garden; cots, high chairs, toys, baby-listening ♿ No wheelchair access ● No dogs; no smoking ▱ MasterCard, Visa £ Single occupancy of twin/double £25 to £30, twin/double £42 to £46, family room £55 to £63; deposit required

---

STRONTIAN Highland

map 11

Kilcamb Lodge

Strontian, Acharacle PH36 4HY
TEL: (01967) 402257   FAX: (01967) 402041

Unstuffy country house in the wilderness.

There's not much to Strontian, but it gave its name to the element strontium, which was first isolated in the hills behind the village. This is isolated countryside – away from the main tourist routes and more like the Highlands of old, with single-track roads, and ferries instead of bridges across the narrow sea lochs. The area is rich in wildlife and there are good beaches on the Ardnamurchan peninsula not far away. Peter Blakeway's small hotel makes an ideal base for exploring the area, and is properly West Highland in the relaxed air that it gives of time slipping leisurely away. Surrounded by yachting trophies and pictures going back to Peter's days racing on the ocean, you can indulge in putting together the house jigsaw puzzle on wet days, or venture out and explore the lush tangle of vegetation which encloses the house. The dinners are worth working up an appetite for. Paupiette of lemon sole with smoked eel is an example of the excellent seafood dishes on offer; to follow, there might be glazed lemon tart. The bedrooms are colourful and comfortable, in keeping with the rest of the house. 'Welcome, ambience, service and food all of high quality.'

○ Closed Dec to Feb 🔟 From A82 south of Fort William, take Corran ferry, then A861 to Strontian. Private car park 🛏️ 1 single, 7 twin/double, 3 double; suites available; annexe rooms available; all with bathroom/WC exc single with shower/WC; all with TV, hair-dryer ✅ Restaurant, lounge/bar, drawing-room, drying-room, garden; functions (max 40 people incl up to 21 residential), conferences; fishing; early suppers for children; cots, high chairs, baby-listening ♿ Wheelchair access to annexe with ground-floor bedroom/WC, access to restaurant (1 step), WC (M, F) ● No children under 8 in restaurant eves; dogs in bedrooms only, by arrangement; smoking in lounge bar only ▭ Delta, MasterCard, Switch, Visa 💷 Single £70, single occupancy of twin/double £80, twin/double £140 to £180, suite £180 (rates incl dinner); deposit required. Bar/bistro L £2 to £8. Special breaks available

---

SWINTON Borders

map 11

Wheatsheaf Hotel

Main Street, Swinton, Duns TD11 3JJ
TEL: (01890) 860257 FAX: (01890) 860688

Attractive village pub with a well-deserved reputation for fine food.

Set in the quiet countryside west of Berwick-upon-Tweed, the small village of Swinton is made up of simple, flower-bedecked cottages lining a single street. It comes to life at lunch-time, when people arrive from all over the district to eat at Alan and Julie Reid's Wheatsheaf Hotel. In most places bar food is uninventive, but what about slices of pigeon breast sitting on a piece of black pudding surrounded by fresh salad? An unusual combination, and an extremely successful one. Game and seafood feature strongly on the menu and everything is fresh and cooked to perfection; the service is fast, efficient and, above all, friendly. Were this all, it would be enough. But the bedrooms share the food's virtues of high quality and reasonable cost. The newly created Room 7 is especially nice, with windows on two sides, pale-yellow and beige décor and ample room. Other rooms are smaller but equally well decorated – most have fair or good-sized bathrooms and plenty of extras. When the bar and restaurant areas are crowded, there's not much sitting space for residents, but there is a small, peaceful garden, and a most genial atmosphere.

○ Closed Chr & 1 Jan 🔟 On B6461, 12 miles north of Berwick-upon-Tweed. Private car park 🛏️ 5 double; family rooms and suites available; 2 with bathroom/WC, 2 with shower/WC; all with TV, room service, hair-dryer ✅ Restaurant, 2 bars, lounge, conservatory, drying-room, garden; functions (max 30 people incl up to 10 residential), conferences; early suppers for children; cots, high chairs ♿ No wheelchair access ● No dogs in public rooms; smoking in bars only ▭ MasterCard, Switch, Visa 💷 Single occupancy of double £34 to £45, double £58 to £72, family room (room rate + £10 per child aged 5 to 12), suite £95; deposit required. Bar/bistro L £10, D £21.50. Special breaks available

---

The Guide *office can quickly spot when a hotelier is encouraging customers to write a letter recommending inclusion. Such reports do not further a hotel's cause.*

Mansfield House   ⟦NEW ENTRY⟧

Scotsburn Road, Tain IV19 1PR
TEL: (01862) 892052   FAX: (01862) 892260
EMAIL: mansfield@cali.co.uk
WEB SITE: www.milford/scotland/accom/h-l-1592.html/

An enthusiastic proprietor is making a success of this lovely house.

Mansfield House Hotel is a solid stone, Scottish baronial house, complete with tower and natty little turrets, on a quiet road not far from the centre of Tain. After a lifetime spent in the pharmaceutical business, much of it in Japan, Norman Lauritsen bought the hotel three years ago and is busy transforming it into an establishment of considerable character and comfort. We are already getting positive feedback: 'first-class food . . . friendly local staff . . . well-furnished rooms'. Part of the charm of the place lies in the house itself, whose interior reflects the good craftsmanship of the turn of the century. There is some fine stained glass, some stunning plasterwork, a grand staircase (the original piper's gallery may soon be restored) and a series of light, high-ceilinged bedrooms, the best of which (Haakon) has a wonderful fireplace and mantelshelf dating from 1902. More of the hotel's appeal lies in the welcoming atmosphere and the personal touches which the Lauritsens bring to it. The small dining-room (an overflow for bar meals) has been decorated with objects brought back from Japan – not just fabrics and prints, but also a basket for silkworms and brightly coloured temple charms. A residents' lounge is being completed on the first floor. The Lauritsens' son, David, does all the cooking – reasonably priced table d'hôte menus with half-a-dozen choices at each stage. Dishes range from the simple local rabbit with rosemary and white wine through the enigmatic fillet of local lamb Provost Fowler to the luxurious iced cranachan parfait with warm honey and raspberry sauces.

◗ Open all year   ⟦⟧ Approaching Tain from south, ignore first entrance and continue on A9 for ½ mile; turn right to hotel. Private car park   ⟦⟧ 1 single, 6 twin, 6 double, 1 four-poster, 4 family rooms; some in annexe; suites available; all with bathroom/WC exc single with shower/WC; all with TV, room service, hair-dryer, trouser press, direct-dial telephone   ⟦⟧ Restaurant, dining-room/bar, lounge/library, beauty salon, garden; functions (max 250 people incl up to 35 residential), conferences; leisure facilities nearby (reduced rates for guests); early suppers for children; cots, high chairs, babysitting   ⟦⟧ Wheelchair access to hotel (3 steps) and restaurant, 6 ground-floor bedrooms   ⟦⟧ No dogs in restaurant; no smoking in restaurant, dining-room and some bedrooms   ⟦⟧ Amex, Delta, MasterCard, Switch, Visa   ⟦£⟧ Single £60, single occupancy of twin/double £50 to £75, twin/double £90 to £100, four-poster/family room £100, suite £120; deposit required. Bar/bistro L, D £12.50; set L £11; alc D £25. Special breaks available

---

Denotes somewhere you can rely on a good meal – either the hotel features in the 1999 edition of our sister publication, The Good Food Guide, *or our inspectors thought the cooking impressive, whether particularly competent home cooking or more lavish cuisine.*

THURSO Highland   map 11

Forss House

Thurso KW14 7XY
TEL: (01847) 861201   FAX: (01847) 861301

Family-run, friendly fishing hotel with a lot of character.

The river from which the hotel takes its name makes its last plunge into the sea virtually under the walls of this solid, grey, lofty-chimneyed house on Scotland's northern coast. Built to withstand the gales of the Pentland Firth, the adjective 'dauntless' might well be applied to its exterior. Inside, however, everything is warm and comfortable. Many of your fellow guests are likely to be after the salmon and may be found gazing wistfully at the specimen fish that hangs above the fire in the bar. The dining-room is large and light – the best room in the house – and has an elegant Adam-style fireplace (though the Adams themselves are unlikely to have got this far north). The bedrooms, like the public rooms, are spacious and warm, with furniture as solid and practical as the house. The food is designed to appease hungry fishermen who have had to survive all day on a packed lunch. You might have sliced smoked venison with hawthorn jelly, sirloin steak stuffed with haggis in a Glenmorangie sauce, and – perennially popular – burnt raspberry cream.

◑ Closed 24 Dec to 6 Jan   🔟 On A836, 4 miles west of Thurso. Private car park
🛏 7 twin, 2 double, 1 suite; some in annexe; family rooms available; all with bathroom/WC exc 1 double with shower/WC; all with TV, room service, hair-dryer, direct-dial telephone, clock radio, some with trouser press   ✅ Dining-room, lounge/bar, drying-room, conservatory, garden; functions (max 40 people incl up to 20 residential), conferences; fishing; early suppers for children; cots, high chairs, toys, baby-listening, outdoor play area   ♿ Wheelchair access to hotel (4 steps, hotel will assist) and dining-room, WC (unisex), 6 ground-floor bedrooms, 1 room specially equipped for disabled people   ● No dogs in public rooms; no smoking in dining-room and conservatory   💳 Amex, MasterCard, Visa   £ Single occupancy of twin/double £55, twin/double £90, family room £110, suite £120; deposit required. Set D £21.50; alc L £12. Special breaks available

---

TONGUE Highland   map 11

Rhian Guest House

Tongue, Lairg IV27 4XJ
TEL: (01847) 611257

Excellent guesthouse in the far, far north.

Set on the outskirts of Tongue, under the shadow of Ben Loyal, Stephanie Mackay's guesthouse is an ideal refuge. The views of the mountain, the nearby beaches and the overall quality of this guesthouse would make it a good choice for a stopover on a grand tour of Scotland. It's a simple enough place from the outside – a traditional crofthouse which looks as though it could not possibly contain six bedrooms. Inside, bold design, featuring flowered wallpaper and good-quality furnishings, has replaced traditional simplicity; the lounge is decorated in a soothing tartan and the dining-room is a pretty, elegant place. Here Stephanie serves three-course menus with a choice at each stage. You might start with haggis in a whisky and chive sauce, follow that with venison steak in a red-wine and juniper sauce, and end up with peaches stuffed with marzipan and cinnamon. There are soups, fruit juices and a vegetarian choice as well. The bedrooms mostly have good views of Ben Loyal, and the twin room in the converted-outbuilding annexe is popular with those who like more privacy.

◑ Open all year 🔼 From the centre of Tongue, with Royal Bank on right, continue for 1 mile; hotel is at end of private track to right. Private car park 🛏 2 twin, 2 double, 2 family rooms; some in annexe; 2 with bathroom/WC (not *en suite*), 4 with shower/WC; ✦ Dining-room, lounge, drying-room, garden; cots, high chairs, outdoor play area 🚫 No wheelchair access ● No smoking ⬜ None accepted 💷 Single occupancy of twin/double £20 to £30; twin/double £36 to £40; family room £50; deposit required. Set D £14

TROON South Ayrshire	map 11

Lochgreen House

Monktonhill Road, Southwood, Troon KA10 7EN
TEL: (01292) 313343   FAX: (01292) 318661

The gourmet golfer's choice on the west coast.

The golf courses of Turnberry and Troon, both fronting the sea and both backed by good hotels, draw many visitors to the Ayrshire coast. The gourmets among them may well look to William and Catherine Costley's hotel as their first choice. It's a pleasant old country house, surrounded by woodland and lawns and showing its antiquity in its crow-step gables. Inside, it is equally distinguished, with a large sitting-room floored with rugs and lined with oil paintings. There are separate dining-rooms – including the conservatory and the oak-panelled loggia – and the food is cooked with traditional ingredients but has a hint of the exotic. Crisp sea bass with a salad of wild mushrooms and baby spinach, saddle of lamb with caramelised onions, and rhubarb steamed pudding with home-made ginger ice-cream might be examples from a menu featuring also crab, venison and trout. The bedrooms – luxurious and spacious, with coronets over the beds and ample space – are partly in the main house and partly in what used to be the old stable block.

◑ Open all year 🔼 Take B746 to Troon; hotel is on left. Private car park 🛏 15 double; some in annexe; suites available; all with bathroom/WC; all with TV, room service, hair-dryer, trouser press, direct-dial telephone ✦ 4 dining-rooms, bar, 2 sitting-rooms, garden; functions (max 70 people incl up to 30 residential), conferences; tennis; cots, high chairs 🚿 Wheelchair access to hotel and dining-rooms, WC (unisex), 7 ground-floor bedrooms, 1 room specially equipped for disabled people ● No children in dining-rooms eves; no dogs ⬜ Amex, Delta, MasterCard, Switch, Visa 💷 Single occupancy of double £99, double £140, suite £160; deposit required. Set L £19, D £30

Please let us know if an establishment has changed hands.

TURNBERRY South Ayrshire   map 11

Turnberry Hotel

Turnberry, Girvan KA26 9LT
TEL: (01655) 331000   FAX: (01655) 331706

Smooth-running, luxury golf-and-fitness hotel of impressive quality.

Like Gleneagles, Turnberry started life as a flagship hotel for a railway company, drawing the wealthy merchants of Glasgow to the famous golf course which lies between its curving bay windows and the sea. It opened in 1906, a massive, red-roofed, white-painted building set on a hillside, with seaward views to the distant coasts of Kintyre and Arran. Over the decades, its Japanese and now American owners have poured money in to maintain the luxury. Unlike Gleneagles, which has diversified in all directions, Turnberry has added only a spa and fitness centre to its golfing attraction. But what a spa! Among hushed corridors you glimpse steel machines, combination turbo massagers, sunbeds, steam rooms, saunas and pools. In the main hotel, a sequence of sitting-rooms, writing rooms and conference rooms faces the sea. The luxury is restrained: comfortable furniture, fresh flowers, every facility and immediate attention from the staff – sit down for an instant, and someone will be at your side to see what you need. The original restaurant seats 160 easily. Here the food is classic French haute cuisine: seared foie gras, confit of duck with rosemary-scented haricot beans, and iced passion-fruit soufflé, for example. A fair trudge away, above the spa, a less formal restaurant offers Mediterranean cooking, from risotto to veal sausage. Two styles of bedroom are on offer. Those over the spa are modern, pretty rooms, with light wood, cottagey wallpaper and magnificent bathrooms. In the original hotel, bedrooms – some of which are almost apartments – are a little more traditional.

◑ Open all year   ⊿ On A77, south of Ayr. Private car park   ⤶ 122 twin/double, 10 suites; family rooms available; all with bathroom/WC; all with TV, 24-hour room service, hair-dryer, direct-dial telephone, some with mini-bar, no tea/coffee-making facilities in rooms   ⊘ 3 restaurants, 4 bars, 4 lounges, drying-room, library, conservatory, games room, garden; functions (max 250 people residential/non-residential), conferences; golf, gym, sauna, solarium, heated indoor swimming-pool, tennis, putting green, snooker, pitch & putt, health spa; early suppers for children; cots, high chairs, babysitting, baby-listening   ♿ Wheelchair access to hotel (ramp) and restaurant, WC (M, F), 17 ground-floor bedrooms, 1 room specially equipped for disabled people   ● No dogs in public rooms   ▭ Amex, Delta, Diners, MasterCard, Switch, Visa   £ Single occupancy of twin/double £180 to £230, twin/double £215 to £275, family room £235 to £295, suite £265 to £590; deposit required. Set L £25, D £45; alc L £25, D £60. Special breaks available

---

The Guide *for the year 2000 will be published in the autumn of 1999. Reports on hotels are welcome at any time of the year, but are extremely valuable in the spring. Send them to* The Which? Hotel Guide, FREEPOST, 2 Marylebone Road, London NW1 1YN. *No stamp is needed if reports are posted in the UK. Our email address is: "guide.reports@which.co.uk".*

Baile-na-Cille

Timsgarry, Uig, Isle Of Lewis HS2 9JD
TEL: (01851) 672242   FAX: (01851) 672241
EMAIL: randjgollin@compuserve.com
WEB SITE: www.witb.co.uk/links/bailenacille.htm

Jovial atmosphere in this away-from-it-all family hotel.

Joanna and Richard Gollin have long been providing all-round family fun in one
of the remotest spots of the Western Isles. After cooking 60,000 meals, Joanna is
now seeking part-time relaxation as a helicopter pilot, and Richard has taken
over responsibility in the kitchen (using Joanna's recipes). The spirit of
Baile-na-Cille remains unchanged. The old manse, fronting one of the best
beaches on the remote western coast of the Isle of Lewis, is at one and the same
time a hive of activity and a place for complete relaxation. There is beach cricket
in the long summer evenings, a sitting-room stuffed with games for children,
another with classical music and a third for dreaming quietly in. The bedrooms
are found both in the main house and in an adjoining cottage. They are simple
and comfortable, with the views best from the main house. There is no menu or
wine list; state your eating preferences when booking and choose your wine
from the selection of bottles on the windowsills. You can eat in splendid
isolation, but this is the sort of place where everyone ends up round one table.

◑ Closed 10 Oct to 10 Mar   ⤵ Take B8011 to Timsgarry; in Timsgarry take second
right (signed Timsgarry/Baile-na-Cille), then second track on left (signed to hotel).
Private car park   ⤸ 2 single, 2 twin, 8 double; some in annexe; family suites
available; most with bathroom/WC; all with room service; hair-dryer available
⊘ Dining-room, 3 sitting-rooms, drying-room, study, games room, garden; functions
(max 30 people incl up to 22 residential), conferences; fishing; early suppers for
children; cots, high chairs, toys, playroom, babysitting, baby-listening   ⴹ No
wheelchair access   ● No dogs in dining-room; no smoking in dining-room and
bedrooms   ▭ MasterCard, Visa   £ Single and single occupancy of twin/double £30
to £39, twin/double £60 to £78, family room/suite £90 to £111; deposit required. Light L
£2 to £10; set D £24

*'Certainly the furnishings in the bars and lounge were attractive and
highly polished – no wonder, because far more concern was shown to these
than the customers. No sooner had you risen from a chair, or from a chair
you had moved an inch or two to be nearer to someone, than someone
dashed over, plumped up cushions and put the chair back in its rightful
position. Not an attitude designed to make you feel at home, and the staff
were often so busy doing this that they did not have any time left to attend
to the needs of customers.'*
On a hotel in the Cotswolds

Altnaharrie Inn

Ullapool IV26 2SS
TEL: (01854) 633230

Over the sea to a luxurious hideaway, with especially desirable food.

Altnaharrie Inn is legendary for being that symbol of the twentieth-century escapist dream – a place no car can reach, where the only thing to do is to lie back and relax, and where the food seems to have descended from some divine realm. Your car is abandoned on Ullapool waterfront, while a small boat – the result of a phone call to Gunn Eriksen and Fred Brown at the inn – comes creeping over the waters of Loch Broom to ferry you across to Altnaharrie. When you consider that all the hotel's supplies come by the same route, and may include food from the four corners of the earth, the operation and effort put into it seem remarkable. (The cattle drovers who once dossed down at this old inn would rub their eyes in disbelief.) There is literally nothing to do at Altnaharrie – nothing, that is, except to walk and walk over the deserted moorland. On days when it is too wet for that, there is plenty in the house to admire, from the clean, Scandinavian feel of the rooms to the beautiful objects – many created by Gunn – which are carefully posed throughout the house. There is also dinner to look forward to: asparagus soup with mousseline of asparagus and foie gras, for example, followed by squab pigeon with kohlrabi, wild mushrooms and foie gras again, and finishing, perhaps, with thin slices of pineapple on equally thin pastry, together with pineapple sorbet and two different sauces. All this comes at a price more usually found in large cities, but there you would be lucky to get such views or such good food – and everywhere would be cars.

◑ Closed early Nov to Easter ⊅ From Ullapool, phone hotel for directions and time of hotel launch. Private car park in Ullapool ⤶ 2 twin, 6 double; some in annexe; all with bathroom/WC; all with room service, hair-dryer; no tea/coffee-making facilities in rooms ⊘ Dining-room, 2 lounges, garden ⅃ No wheelchair access ● No children under 8; dogs in bedrooms only, by arrangement; no smoking ▭ Delta, MasterCard, Switch, Visa £ Twin/double £330 to £410 (rates incl dinner); deposit required

---

Ceilidh Place

14 West Argyle Street, Ullapool IV26 2TY
TEL: (01854) 612103 FAX: (01854) 612886
EMAIL: effie@ceilidh.demon.co.uk

Ullapool's social life revolves around this mix of hotel, theatre and coffee-shop.

There's always something going on. If a ceilidh is loosely defined as an event where everyone turns up and has a good time while doing something vaguely arty along the way, then the Ceilidh Place is well named. It is hard to say where the focus of this multi-faceted hotel lies – most probably in the bar and the coffee-shop. Here a mix of locals, visitors and refugees from the rain mingle throughout the day, popping out now and again to browse in the next-door bookshop, admire the paintings hung in the hotel's exhibition space or find out what kind of entertainment is on in the Clubhouse that night – it could be anything from opera to story-telling, and it's easy enough to combine a performance with dinner in the hotel's restaurant. The menus have plenty of fish, as one might expect from a town which owes its existence to herring, but also include offerings such as Highland venison with shallots and ciabatta garlic bread or fillet steak with garlic mushrooms, deep-fried onions, tomatoes and chips. The hotel fairly bustles throughout the day. But the unique charm of the place is that it is possible to escape from it upstairs, where a bright and infinitely relaxing sitting-room, with huge windows and comfortable sofas, is a haven of tranquillity. There's even a pantry next door where you can make yourself tea, or get something stronger from the honesty bar. Bedrooms are equally comfortable and peaceful, ideal for putting your feet up for a while before rejoining the party below. The atmosphere, naturally, is very much 'hail fellow, well met', but the staff keep an extra eye open for residents' needs.

○ Open all year ☒ In centre of Ullapool; turn first right past pier. Private car park ⌂ 3 single, 4 twin, 6 double; most with bathroom/WC; some with direct-dial telephone; no tea/coffee-making facilities in rooms ◇ Restaurant, 2 bars, sitting-room, garden; functions (max 60 people incl up to 45 residential), conferences; early suppers for children; cots, high chairs, toys, baby-listening ὅ No wheelchair access ● No dogs in public rooms; no smoking in restaurant and some bedrooms ⊓ Amex, Delta, Diners, MasterCard, Switch, Visa £ Single and single occupancy of twin/double £35 to £60; twin/double £70 to £120; deposit required. Bar/bistro L £5, D £12; alc D £25. Special breaks available

---

WALLS Shetland   map 11

Burrastow House

Walls, Shetland ZE2 9PD
TEL: (01595) 809307   FAX: (01595) 809213
EMAIL: burr.hs.hotel@zetnet.co.uk
WEB SITE: www.users.zetnet.co.uk/burrastow-house-hotel

A sophisticated and beautiful house miles from anywhere.

Burrastow House stands on its own, almost at the edge of the sea in one of the remote western corners of Shetland's Mainland. It is a dignified house, both inside and out, and on a clear day looks – and is – the perfect haven in the wilderness. The wildlife draws many visitors here: not only Shetland's teeming birdlife, but the seals and otters, too. Inside, there's a good library and aromatic peat fires for those days on which it is impossible to venture out, and a conservatory for when the sun shines. Everything feels comfortable, lived in and friendly – ideal if you are likely to trail back in muddy wellington boots or drenched anoraks after a day's bird-watching. Bo Simmons's food draws gourmets and critics away from metropolitan circles. Many of the ingredients are found right on her doorstep. Among the choices for the four-course dinner one evening in May were carrot, honey and ginger soup, a mousseline of salmon, scallops and catfish, sea trout with lime, and a home-made chocolate cheesecake.

This is just the kind of fare you need after walking the moors or venturing out in the hotel's boat for a spot of sea fishing. The bedrooms are well in keeping with the rest of the operation; they have plenty of space, good country furniture, rugs, wooden floors and great views.

◑ Closed Jan to Feb, last 2 weeks Oct, 25 Dec   ⯍ In Walls, drive up hill and turn left; hotel is 2 miles further on. Private car park   ⭲ 2 twin, 2 double, 1 four-poster; family rooms available; all with bathroom/WC exc 1 twin with shower/WC; all with room service, hair-dryer, some with TV   ✅ Dining-room, 2 lounges, drying-room, library, conservatory, garden; functions (max 25 people incl up to 12 residential), conferences; fishing; early suppers for children; cots, high chairs, toys, playrooms, babysitting, baby-listening, outdoor play area   ♿ Wheelchair access to hotel and dining-room, WC (unisex), 3 ground-floor bedrooms, 1 room specially equipped for disabled people ● No dogs in dining-room; no smoking in dining-room and bedrooms   ▭ Amex, Delta, MasterCard, Switch, Visa   £ Single occupancy of twin/double £35 to £55, twin/double/four-poster £70 to £110, family room from £70; deposit required. Alc L £15, D £25. Special breaks available

WALES

TAN-Y-FOEL

CAPEL GARMON

Penhelig Arms

Terrace Road, Aberdovey LL35 0LT
TEL: (01654) 767215   FAX: (01654) 767690

Friendly waterfront inn with superior cooking and rather small bedrooms.

First impressions count – and arriving at Sally and Robert Hughes's inn you notice two things: first, it is right beside the road (so is almost every house in the village), and second (and more important) the Hughes's greeting makes you feel instantly at home. Space is at a premium in the house, and bedrooms are certainly compact, though well equipped and comfortable. Noise, too, can be a problem: our inspector's room above the convivial Fisherman's Bar was not the quietest location. Yet despite these drawbacks, the Penhelig succeeds because of its friendly atmosphere and good food. You can choose between the restaurant and the bar for evening meals (for the former it's better to book). Between the two is a small lounge bar where diners order drinks before going through to the smart but homely restaurant, with its tongue-and-groove panelling, exposed stone and family photographs. Robert was once in the wine trade and has produced a well-priced and well-chosen list. Cooking is strong on seafood, like local crab or local brill grilled with anchovy butter. Our inspection main course of pepper steak was simply but tastily done and was followed by poached pears in a fudge sauce with ice-cream; our only quibble was the skimpy helpings of vegetables. One correspondent, however, found the restaurant cramped, and cooking and service variable, though she praised the bedroom.

○ Closed 25, 26 Dec   ⤵ From Machynlleth take A493 coastal road to Aberdovey; go underneath railway bridge and hotel is first on right. Private car park   ⤶ 1 single, 4 twin/double, 5 double; most with bathroom/WC, some with shower/WC; all with TV, room service, hair-dryer, direct-dial telephone   ⊘ Restaurant, bar, lounge, drying-room; golf club nearby (reduced rates for guests); early suppers for children; cots, high chairs, baby-listening   ⅙ No wheelchair access   ● No dogs in some public rooms; no smoking in restaurant and bedrooms   ▭ Delta, MasterCard, Switch, Visa   £ Single and single occupancy of twin/double £39, twin/double £69 to £79; deposit required. Bar/bistro L £6, D £9; set Sun L £12.50; alc D £19. Special breaks available

Plas Penhelig

Aberdovey LL35 0NA
TEL: (01654) 767676   FAX: (01654) 767783

Good views of the Dovey from this old-fashioned country mansion.

Coming from the cramped confines of Aberdovey village makes it all the more impressive when you drive up to this Edwardian mansion and see the panorama of the Dovey estuary. Set in 14 acres of landscaped grounds, the pebble-dashed house was built as a gentleman's residence, and David Richardson has carefully restored many original features, including the greenhouse production of peaches, nectarines, figs and apricots. Some public rooms have impressive features, particularly the beamed and panelled reception lounge with its open fire and rugs. Others don't quite match its bold style – the lounge has an electric fire – and some of the bedrooms have an old-fashioned look, the bathrooms lacking showers. Nevertheless, Room 3, with its large bay window (more a turret than a bay), has excellent views of the garden and Cardigan Bay. The dining-room is smart, if rather staid, as is the table d'hôte menu, which relies on the fresh and home-grown: cream of lettuce soup to start, perhaps, followed by grilled fillet of salmon in a butter almond sauce, then Penhelig apple and raisin crumble.

○ Closed Jan to Feb 🔁 Entering Aberdovey on A493 from Machynlleth, turn right at roundabout after railway bridge; hotel drive is to right of car park. Private car park 🛏 8 twin, 3 double; all with bathroom/WC exc 1 double with shower/WC; all with TV, room service, hair-dryer ⊘ Dining-room, bar, 2 lounges, garden; functions (max 60 people incl up to 22 residential), conferences; putting green, croquet; golf club nearby (reduced rates for guests); early suppers for children ᕼ No wheelchair access ● No children under 8 in dining-room eves; no dogs in public rooms; no smoking in dining-room and bedrooms ▭ Amex, MasterCard, Switch, Visa £ Single occupancy of twin/double £65, twin/double £118; deposit required. Bar/bistro L £5.50; set L £13.50, D £19.50 (1998 prices). Special breaks available

---

ABERGAVENNY Monmouthshire   map 4

Llanwenarth House

Govilon, Abergavenny NP7 9SF
TEL: (01873) 830289   FAX: (01873) 832199

Peaceful sixteenth-century country house close to the Brecon Beacons National Park.

Approaching this three-storey, creeper-clad house you will probably spot either a horse or a dog, or possibly both. Once you're inside, the pictures and prints soon confirm the interests of owners Bruce and Amanda Weatherill: canine and equine portraits decorate many of the rooms. The extensive grounds and gardens are put to good use, producing most of the vegetables for the kitchen, plus the soft fruit and honey. Amanda is the cook, producing classic fare like smoked salmon mousse, chicken breasts with fresh ginger and apricot sauce, chestnut ice-cream with coffee water-ice, then a Welsh cheeseboard followed by coffee and chocolates. The house is decorated throughout with care: well-chosen antique furniture in the drawing-room and dining-room plus a beautiful sweeping staircase canopied by a glass dome which Bruce restored himself. Bedrooms are spacious and decorated individually; the front room, with its mountain views and early Victorian double bed, is particularly pleasant.

○ Closed mid-Jan to end Feb (open by arrangement) 🔁 From A465 west of Abergavenny take exit to Govilon at roundabout; hotel drive is 150 yards on right. Private car park 🛏 2 twin, 2 double; family rooms available; 2 with bathroom/WC, 2 with shower/WC; all with TV, limited room service; hair dryer available ⊘ Dining-room, drawing-room, garden ᕼ Wheelchair access to hotel (1 step) and restaurant, WC (unisex), 1 ground-floor bedroom ● No children under 10; no dogs in

public rooms; smoking in drawing-room only ☐ None accepted £ Single
occupancy of twin/double £64, twin/double £78 to £80, family room (rates on
application); deposit required. Set D £23.50. Special breaks available

---

ABERSOCH Gwynedd map 7

Porth Tocyn Hotel

Bwlch Tocyn, Abersoch LL53 7BU
TEL: (01758) 713303   FAX: (01758) 713538

*Relaxing country-house hotel in beautiful location on the Lleyn
Peninsula.*

Arriving at a hotel can give a good indication of what to expect from the rest of
your stay, and first impressions of the Fletcher-Brewer family's establishment
are telling: a porter takes your baggage from the car and tea is waiting in the
room. The décor is a well-judged mix of antiques, rugs, paintings, books and
magazines spread throughout a series of sitting-rooms (hard to believe, but once
upon a time this was a row of lead-miners' cottages). Outside you have a heated
pool, tennis court and superb views of Cardigan Bay. With over 50 years of
experience behind them, the Fletcher-Brewers know a thing or two about a good
seaside holiday, not least the necessary balance between fun and tranquillity:
older children are catered for but not pandered to. Louise's five-course dinner
menus ('home cooking with flair') change daily; they might include baked
oyster and field-mushroom roulade with dill beurre blanc, followed by poached
monkfish on a red-pepper coulis with deep-fried vegetables, with chocolate
mint mousse for dessert. Bedrooms are either in the old wing (eighteenth-
century) or the new ('sixties). All are comfortable and given a bit of character
with pieces of antique furniture, as, year by year, the Dralon headboards become
fewer.

◑ Closed mid-Nov to week before Easter ⤢ 2½ miles south of Abersoch, through
hamlets of Sarn Bach and Bwlch Tocyn; follow signs to Gwesty/Hotel. Private car
park ⛐ 3 single, 11 twin/double, 2 double, 1 family room; all with bathroom/WC; all
with TV, room service, hair-dryer, direct-dial telephone; tea/coffee-making facilities
available ⊘ Dining-room, bar, 6 sitting-rooms, drying-room, TV/games room; heated
outdoor swimming-pool, tennis; early suppers for children; cots, high chairs, toys,
babysitting, baby-listening ♿ Wheelchair access to hotel (ramp) and dining-room, 3
ground-floor bedrooms ● No children under 7 in dining-room eves; no dogs in public
rooms; no smoking in dining-room ☐ MasterCard, Switch, Visa £ Single £47 to
£61, single occupancy of twin/double £62 to £83, twin/double £62 to £112, family room
£72 to £137; deposit required. Cooked B £5; bar L £6; set Sun L £17 (children £8.50), D
£22 to £29

---

*Don't forget that other hotels worth considering are listed in our
Round-ups near the back of the* Guide.

*The text of entries is based on unsolicited reports sent in by readers and
backed up by inspections. The factual details are from questionnaires the*
Guide *sends to all hotels that feature in the book.*

BEAUMARIS Isle of Anglesey map 7

Olde Bull's Head

Castle Street, Beaumaris LL58 8AP
TEL: (01248) 810329 FAX: (01248) 811294

Fine old coaching-inn with good restaurant and interesting history.

Entry to this ancient building is through the biggest door in Britain: the one from the car park at the side of the hotel. It's the sort of place that has been around for so long that everyone seems to have stayed here at some time or other: Cromwell's generals in the Civil War, Samuel Johnson on his travels, and Dickens when, as a journalist, he came to report on a shipwreck. The interior can easily carry off such an illustrious past: the bar is as snug and clubbable as it ought to be (a shame, then, that there is no hand-pulled beer). Across the stone-flagged hall is a lounge with log fire and plenty of comfortable sofas and armchairs which guests generally use earlier in the evening when perusing the menu. Dining itself takes place on the first floor in an attractive high-ceilinged room with a pleasant informal atmosphere. An inspection dinner of moules marinière, fillet of sea bass and lemon tart proved to be skilfully cooked and tasty, though the main-course helping seemed small. Service here, as throughout the hotel, is quiet and attentive. A new brasserie is planned, and a meeting room. Bedrooms all take their names from Dickens's characters and are pleasantly furnished with basics done well – strong showers, good-quality linen and comfortable beds. Mr Pickwick would surely approve.

◑ Closed 25, 26 Dec & 1 Jan   🅿 In centre of Beaumaris. Private car park 🛏 1 single, 6 twin, 7 double, 1 four-poster; one in annexe; all with bathroom/WC; all with TV, limited room service, hair-dryer, direct-dial telephone ✅ Restaurant, bar, lounge, drying-room; functions (max 60 people incl up to 29 residential); early suppers for children; cots, high chairs, baby-listening ♿ No wheelchair access ⊖ No children under 7 in restaurant eves; no dogs; no smoking in restaurant and some bedrooms ☐ Amex, Delta, MasterCard, Switch, Visa £ Single £49, single occupancy of twin/double £52, twin/double £79, four-poster £92; deposit required. Bar/bistro L £2.50 to £12.50, D £3.50 to £15; set L £11.50, D £21; alc D £28. Special breaks available

---

BENLLECH Isle of Anglesey map 7

Bryn Meirion

Amlwch Road, Benllech, Tynygongl LL74 8SR
TEL: (01248) 853118

A traditional seaside guesthouse with rooms adapted to cater for visitors with a disability.

After careers in residential care of people with a disability, Tim and Chris Holland set up their attractive, expansive bungalow to offer holidays to those in wheelchairs and their partners or carers. The Hollands run Bryn Meirion with warmth, good humour and hospitality, and many non-disabled guests thoroughly enjoy staying with them, too. Tim, in particular, has an impish sense of fun. Take a walk around the garden and you will find mannequins' legs emerging from a pond, an alien peeking out from behind a rock, and there's a 'castle', floodlit at night. All around the house there are useful gadgets and adaptations that make life easier: a bump pad that opens the door to the dining-room, tables that can accommodate a wheelchair and, of course, the specially adapted bedrooms. Guests are usually given the room that suits their needs; despite all the necessary hoists, seats and grip rails, the rooms still manage to look homely. Room 7 even has an electric hoist mounted on a ceiling monorail that can move someone in a sling from bed to living area to bathroom. Dinners are straightforward traditional cooking with plenty of roasts and pies – special needs of all kinds are catered for.

◖ Closed owners' holidays   ⤧ After crossing Britannia Bridge, take A5025 (second slip road) to Amlwch/Benllech; hotel is on right beyond village. Private car park ⤸ 3 twin, 1 four-poster, 2 family rooms, 1 suite; 3 with bathroom/WC, 4 with shower/WC; all with TV   ⥲ Dining-room/bar, TV room, conservatory, garden; functions (max 40 people incl up to 16 residential); early suppers for children, by arrangement; travel cot, high chair, toys   ♿ Wheelchair access to hotel and restaurant, WC (unisex), 7 ground-floor bedrooms specially equipped for disabled people   ● No smoking in dining-room (during meals) and bedrooms; dogs by arrangement   ▭ None accepted   £ Single occupancy of twin £26 to £28, twin/four-poster £52 to £56, family room/suite £65 to £70; deposit required. Light L £2 to £5; set D £12

BERRIEW Powys   map 7

Lion Hotel

Berriew, Welshpool SY21 8PQ
TEL: (01686) 640452   FAX: (01686) 640604

Attractive village pub with restaurant and rooms in a pretty Marches village.

The charming village of Berriew has much going for it in the picture-postcard stakes: tumbling river and stone bridge, flower-bedecked black-and-white cottages – and the Lion. It's a deservedly popular spot, and parking can be time-consuming – but it's worth it. The bar is every inch the rural drinking parlour, with all the low beams and hand-pulled beers you might want; locals claim a favoured horse used to come for a pint until recently. Less rustic is the elegant restaurant with more hefty woodwork lightened by fresh flowers and Regency-style chairs. Our inspection meal, however, was taken in the bar: a smoked fillet of mackerel followed by an excellent apple and strawberry crumble. The style is uncomplicated and unashamedly traditional, with the restaurant menu following a similar pattern. Bedrooms have plenty of character, with floral bed-crowns and curtains among the half-timbering and beams; those at the back of the house overlooking the churchyard may be quieter. There is also a good-value family room with exposed stone walls and old barn timbers.

◖ Closed 25, 26 Dec; dining-room closed Sun eve   ⤧ Turn off A483 at sign for Berriew, 5 miles south of Welshpool; hotel is 1mile on, in centre of village. Private car park; on street parking (free)   ⤸ 1 twin, 4 double, 1 four-poster, 1 family room; all with bathroom/WC exc 2 with shower/WC; all with TV, room service, hair-dryer, direct-dial telephone, one with trouser press ✓ Restaurant, bistro, bar, 2 lounges; functions (max 60 people incl up to 14 residential); fishing; early suppers for children; cots, toys, baby-listening &. No wheelchair access ● No dogs; no smoking in bedrooms ▭ Amex, Delta, MasterCard, Switch, Visa £ Single occupancy of twin/double £55, twin/double £80, four-poster £90, family room £100; deposit required. Bar/bistro L £8, D £10; set D £19. Special breaks available

---

BETWS-Y-COED Conwy

map 7

The Ferns **NEW ENTRY**

Holyhead Road, Betws-y-Coed LL24 0AN
TEL: (01690) 710587 (AND FAX)

Smart and simple B&B with thoughtful hosts.

In the busy and competitive B&B business of this tourist-oriented town, Keith and Theresa Roobottom's smart Victorian semi stands out. The décor is pretty without being fussy, as in the cottage-style breakfast room, with its teapot collection on the sills and dried-flower arrangements on the tables. Walkers make up a large part of the clientele, so there are good-value packed lunches available, along with flasks of tea or coffee and plenty of free advice on where to go from Keith – a keen walker himself. Bedrooms are sometimes compact, and decoration simple but homely: pine furniture, floral dadoes and woodchip or anaglypta wallpaper. Tea trays are stocked with biscuits and a tea towel – a thoughtful touch typical of the Roobottoms' friendly and helpful approach. Evening meals are not served, but there are plenty of alternatives within easy walking distance.

◑ Open all year ⤢ From junction of A470 and A5, turn into village; the Ferns is on left by Cotswolds outdoor shop. Private car park ⬚ 1 twin, 6 double, 2 family rooms; all with shower/WC exc 1 double with bathroom/WC; all with TV, hair-dryer ✓ Lounge, drying-room, garden &. No wheelchair access ● No children under 4; no smoking ▭ None accepted £ Single occupancy of twin/double £20 to £25, twin/double £36 to £44, family room £46 to £55; deposit required. Special breaks available

---

BROAD HAVEN Pembrokeshire

map 4

The Druidstone

Druidston Haven, Broad Haven, Haverfordwest SA62 3NE
TEL: (01437) 781221   FAX: (01437) 781133

Family-holiday hotel for the Woodstock generation.

Jane Bell's family has been at the Druidstone for 50 years now, for half of which time it has been serving up its own idiosyncratic brand of hospitality to anyone who cares to visit this beautiful corner of the Pembrokeshire coast. The house itself is mid-Victorian, with large, spacious rooms – the downstairs ones generally stuffed with bright paintings and those upstairs colourfully painted. There is a homely, sometimes scruffy, charm about the place; people typically have a sociable coffee in the kitchen or sequester themselves in the Roundhouse (out in the grounds) to complete that long-awaited first novel. Other groups organise yoga courses or go fossicking on the beach. For evening socialising, there is a slate-floored bar which was originally a pantry and a dining-room above it with sea views. The cooking has a light touch and offers vegetarian options; a dinner menu might include a spicy chicken and vegetable soup, followed by breast of duck with ginger and orange, and rounded off with a slice of raspberry cheesecake. The bedrooms are large and easily accommodate families in simple fashion, using three shared bathrooms. Outside are various cottages offering more privacy and maybe an open fire, but not all have electricity and water.

◐ Closed Mon to Thur early Nov to mid-Dec & early Jan to early Feb; dining-room closed Sun eve ⤴ From Haverfordwest, take B4341 to Broad Haven; turn right at sea; after 1½ miles turn left to Druidston Haven; hotel is 1 mile on, on left. Private car park ⤴ 2 single, 7 family rooms in hotel; other accommodation on site; no tea/coffee-making facilities in rooms ⊘ Dining-room, bar, lounge, TV room, garden; functions (max 40 people incl up to 23 residential), conferences; civil wedding licence; early suppers for children; cots, high chairs, babysitting, baby-listening ♿ Wheelchair access to hotel (ramp) and dining-room, WC (unisex), ground-floor bedrooms and bathrooms/WC in cottages ◐ No dogs or smoking in dining-room ☐ Amex, Delta, MasterCard, Switch, Visa £ Hotel rates: Single £30, single occupancy of family room £42, family room £59 to £70; deposit required. Bar L, D £5.50; alc Sun L, D £18. Special breaks available

---

BUILTH WELLS Powys map 4

Dollynwydd | NEW ENTRY

Builth Wells LD2 3RZ
TEL: (01982) 553660

A charming old farmhouse, offering homely tranquillity.

Situated on a quiet lane in idyllic, rolling countryside, Biddy Williams's seventeenth-century farmhouse has all the beams, creaky floors and inglenooks that you could ask of a rural retreat. But after extensive recent work, it also has tight-fitting windows and a smart new roof. Downstairs, there is a cosy sitting-room with a big fireplace and television available if you want it (the bedrooms are phone- and TV-free). Breakfast is taken around a shared table in the smallish dining-room next door. The eggs come from Biddy's own chickens, and the garden also provides vegetables and soft fruit for evening meals – simple, two-course affairs of roasts followed by a choice of two puddings. The bedrooms have as much character as the rooms downstairs, with old latch doors, rugs on floorboards and cottage-style décor. Of the four rooms, only one is *en suite*; the others share a large, homely bathroom.

◐ Closed Dec to Mar ⤴ In Builth Wells take B4520 signed to Upper Chapel; after 1 mile take first left signposted Tregare/Erwood; farmhouse is 200 yards down lane, on left. Private car park ⤴ 1 single, 2 twin, 1 double; 1 twin with shower/WC; ⊘ Dining-room, sitting-room, drying-room, garden ♿ No wheelchair access ◐ No children under 14; no dogs; no smoking ☐ None accepted £ Single and single occupancy of twin/double £17, twin/double £20 to £34; deposit required. Set D £9

CAPEL GARMON Conwy   map 7

Tan-y-Foel

Capel Garmon, Betws-y-Coed, Llanrwst LL26 0RE
TEL: (01690) 710507   FAX: (01690) 710681

Striking interiors and comfort in a small country-house hotel.

On a quiet hillside, where a Roman lookout post once surveyed the Conwy valley, stands Janet and Peter Pitman's slate-built, partly sixteenth-century house. Downstairs the rooms are elegant but cosy, with paintings, books, low lamps and real fires. At the rear is the dining-room, a carefully designed space with old beams and pillars at one end leading into a conservatory extension. Peter is the designer, and this room shows off his skills at their subtlest. Janet's skills are culinary: the menu offers a fixed main course with two choices before and after, which allows her to concentrate her efforts admirably. Cream of onion soup might be followed by guinea-fowl with a porcini mushroom sauce and, for dessert, a glazed lemon and lime tart with raspberry coulis. It is a small hotel, so dinner is served at 7.45pm (it seems odd, then, if staff numbers are limited, that bedrooms have no tea trays). Bedrooms are individually designed by Peter, who goes for bold colour schemes – the scarlet in Room 5 is certainly startling and modern, but in Room 9 (through the hayloft door outside) it becomes a warm colour. The other room outside the main house is Room 1: perhaps the best, with its super bathroom and *trompe l'oeil* stonework complete with cracks and ivy.

◖ Closed Chr ☒ From northbound A470, 2 miles north of Betws-y-Coed, turn right (signposted Capel Garmon/Nebo); go uphill towards village; hotel is on left. Private car park 🚪 5 double, 2 four-poster; some in annexe; all with bathroom/WC exc 1 double with shower/WC; all with TV, room service, hair-dryer, direct-dial telephone, ironing facilities; tea/coffee-making facilities available ✇ Dining-room, 2 lounges, conservatory, garden ♿ No wheelchair access ● No children under 7; no dogs; no smoking ▭ Amex, Delta, Diners, MasterCard, Switch, Visa £ Single occupancy of double £65 to £85, double £90 to £150, four-poster £120 to £150; deposit required. Set D £20/£25/£29. Special breaks available

---

CONWY Conwy   map 7

Berthlwyd Hall

Llechwedd, Conwy LL32 8DQ
TEL: (01492) 592409   FAX: (01492) 572290
EMAIL: conwy-berth@marketsite.co.uk

Friendly country-house hotel with a touch of France, close to Conwy Castle.

In the winding lanes and rolling countryside immediately outside Conwy town stands this impressive Victorian house. The driveway takes you through a small caravan park and up to Joanna and Brian Griffin's creeper-clad home. Inside, the Victorian style is maintained: there is oak panelling, stained glass and some well-chosen period furniture. But this is no stuffy recreation of the nineteenth century – the Griffins are far too good-humoured for that. The dining-room has a

Gallic twist to it, with a terracotta carpet, lemon-yellow walls and *trompe l'oeil* painting of French landscape: a suitable accompaniment to the Mediterranean-influenced menu. Starters might be grilled scallops, followed by breast of chicken sauté with woodland mushrooms and lovage in a Chardonnay sauce. Desserts avoid the heavier British puddings and favour lighter alternatives: perhaps sugared pancakes filled with orange cream mousse in a Grand Marnier and bitter orange sauce, or fresh strawberries in a meringue nest. Bedrooms are a good size, especially Room 3, with its antique bed and original claw-foot bath, and the four-poster Room 5.

○ Open all year ⊡ From A55, go over Conwy Bridge into Conwy town centre (castle on left); follow one-way system out under town walls; turn immediately left after Bangor Archway; at T-junction turn right into Sychnant Pass Road; hotel is signposted on left after 1½ miles. Private car park ⊨ 2 twin, 2 double, 1 four-poster, 2 family rooms; all with bathroom/WC; all with TV, room service, hair-dryer, trouser press, direct-dial telephone ✅ Dining-room, bar, lounge, games room, garden; functions (max 40 people incl up to 14 residential), conferences; heated outdoor swimming-pool, snooker; leisure facilities nearby (reduced rates for guests); early suppers for children; cots, high chairs, babysitting, baby-listening ♿ No wheelchair access ⬤ No dogs or smoking in public rooms and some bedrooms ⊟ Amex, Delta, Diners, MasterCard, Switch, Visa £ Single occupancy of twin/double from £60, twin/double £62 to £85, four-poster £120, family room £85; deposit required. Cooked B £5; set L £15, D £19; alc L, D £20. Special breaks available

---

CRICCIETH Gwynedd   map 7

Mynydd Ednyfed

Caernarfon Road, Criccieth LL52 0PH
TEL: (01766) 523269

Friendly family hotel close to the sea and with sports facilities.

A short drive from the small seaside resort of Criccieth stands this slate-built, 400-year-old house – a convenient spot for exploring down the Lleyn Peninsula or back up into Snowdonia. Maureen and Ian Edwards's house is modestly furnished and decorated but has good sports facilities, including an all-weather tennis court and well-equipped gym. Inside the house, an elegant staircase winds up to a small library, while downstairs are a large conservatory-style breakfast room and a more formal dining-room with a smart yellow-and-green colour scheme. The à la carte menu offers a good selection of typical country-house cooking: fresh trout fillets in tarragon and lime juice for starters, perhaps, followed by Welsh lamb noisettes in a redcurrant and rosemary glaze. Bedrooms are comfortable and welcoming, with modern pine furniture and floral fabrics. Room 5 is a useful family room, with bunk beds and toys in an adjoining room. As we went to press, this hotel was up for sale.

○ Closed 25, 26 Dec ⊡ From Criccieth take B4411 (Caernarfon road); 1 mile on, turn right into driveway. Private car park ⊨ 1 single, 2 twin, 3 double, 2 four-poster, 1 family room; most with bathroom/WC, some with shower/WC; all with TV, room service, hair-dryer, direct-dial telephone ✅ Dining-room, breakfast room/conservatory, bar, lounge, library, drying-room, garden; functions (max 100 people incl up to 19 residential), conferences; gym, solarium, tennis, table tennis; leisure facilities nearby (reduced rates for guests); early suppers for children; cots, high chairs, toys, baby-listening ♿ No wheelchair access ● No smoking in bedrooms ▭ Amex, MasterCard, Visa £ Single £35, single occupancy of twin/double £70, twin/double/four-poster £70, family room £75; deposit required. Bar D £6; alc D £18

CRICKHOWELL Powys
map 4

Bear Hotel

High Street, Crickhowell NP8 1BW
TEL: (01873) 810408   FAX: (01873) 811696

Atmospheric pub in the Brecon Beacons National Park, with good food.

If a good traditional pub needs its cosy corners with low beams, flagstone floors and brass ornaments, then Steven and Judith Hindmarsh's town-centre inn has all the right ingredients; parts of it date back to the fifteenth century. The stables have been converted into bedrooms, and the courtyard outside attractively decorated with hanging baskets and flower tubs. This well-established inn is popular with walkers, visitors and locals alike. There are two restaurants: one more traditional in feel, with exposed stonework and rugs on flagged floors; the other prettier and more modern, with lace tablecloths and leafy wallpaper. Food has an international slant to it – Moroccan spiced lamb with couscous or chicken tikka masala as main courses, perhaps – but there are also options from closer to home, such as chicken and leek pie or beef and oyster steamed pudding. Bedrooms are divided between the main house and courtyard – all have well-chosen fabrics to give a homely country-house atmosphere. One correspondent mentioned the lack of such essentials as radio, dressing table and heated towel-rail, and found the room cold overnight. More reports, please.

◑ Open all year; restaurants closed Sun eve ⊠ On A40 from Abergavenny to Brecon, in middle of Crickhowell, on bend. Private car park ↦ 37 double, 1 four-poster, 1 suite; some in annexe; all with bathroom/WC exc 5 double with shower/WC; all with TV, room service, hair-dryer, direct-dial telephone ✧ 2 restaurants, 2 bars, 2 lounges, drying-room, garden; functions (max 60 people residential/non-residential), conferences; early suppers for children; cots, high chairs, baby-listening ♿ Wheelchair access to hotel (ramp) and restaurants, WC (unisex), 8 ground-floor bedrooms ● No children under 5 in restaurants eves; no dogs in restaurants ▭ Amex, Delta, MasterCard, Switch, Visa £ Single occupancy of double £42 to £70, double £56 to £100, four-poster £100, suite £80 to £100. Bar L, D £7.50; alc L, D £25

Gliffaes Country House

Crickhowell NP8 1RH
TEL: (01874) 730371   FAX: (01874) 730463
EMAIL: calls@gliffaeshotel.com
WEB SITE: www.gliffaeshotel.com/

Grand but welcoming hotel in a dazzling setting.

The hotel's truly magnificent gardens, occupying 33 acres, are the first thing to strike you as you approach from the A40 down a long drive; especially if you catch them at rhododendron time, or decked in autumn colours. Glimpses of National Park and Usk valley scenery all around show how carefully the original owners of this late-nineteenth-century Italianate mansion chose their spot. Some may find the remorseless high-Victorian style of the place (even higher than usual, with curious campanile embellishments) a bit cheerless, but its sun-terraces and spectacular surroundings soon dispel architectural gloom. The present family can now celebrate half a century at Gliffaes. A sense of continuity prevails inside, with traditional furnishings and imposing fireplaces, but the sun-room is surprisingly upbeat, with colonial-style cane and wicker in a huge conservatory. Vegetarians get equal billing on an appetising menu using local produce. A tennis court, golf practice net, putting green, croquet lawn and fishing rights will appeal to active types.

◖ Open all year ⬈ From Crickhowell, take A40 north-west; just beyond junction with A479, turn left on to minor road; hotel is 1 mile along. Private car park 🛏 7 single, 9 twin, 6 double; some in annexe; family rooms available; all with bathroom/WC exc 3 with shower/WC; all with TV, limited room service, hair-dryer, direct-dial telephone
✓ Dining-room, bar, 2 lounges, TV room, drying-room, conservatory, games room, garden; functions (max 150 people incl up to 37 residential), conferences; civil wedding licence; fishing, golf, tennis, putting green, snooker, croquet; early suppers for children; cots, high chairs, baby-listening, outdoor play area ♿ No wheelchair access
● No dogs; no smoking in dining-room ▭ Amex, Delta, Diners, MasterCard, Switch, Visa ⌂ Single from £39, single occupancy of twin/double from £68, twin/double from £78, family room from £78 + £15 to £20 per child; deposit required. Bar L £5; Sun L £17.50, D £22.50. (Prices valid till Mar 1999.) Special breaks available

---

EGLWYSFACH Ceredigion   map 4

Ynyshir Hall

Eglwysfach, Machynlleth SY20 8TA
TEL: (01654) 781209   FAX: (01654) 781366

A top-class country-house hotel, designed with real flair and run with great friendliness.

From the moment you enter Rob and Joan Reen's white-painted Georgian mansion, you are aware of a sense of colour and light which lifts the place above its rivals. Not the country-club look for the Reens – instead there are terracotta walls, sea-blue sofas and exuberant flower displays. Even the dark bank outside the bar window offers the opportunity for an imaginative rock garden, with a splash of azalea adding colour. Rob's paintings are a large part of the style, particularly in one dining-room, where large canvases of Welsh scenes in extraordinary blues and oranges give the whole room the vibrancy of warmer climes. There are plenty of Mediterranean flourishes in the cooking, too: veal bolognese and lobster ravioli might be followed by lemon chicken with organic baby vegetables and herb gnocchi, then a dessert of espresso-coffee cream with poached pears in red wine. Most of the bedrooms are named after painters and follow the spirit of their namesakes' works. Hence Degas is decorated in a lovely yellow colour, with a big brass bed; Hogarth is darker, more plummy in hue; Monet has a ground-floor conservatory looking towards the fountain; and

Vermeer is a classic combination of deep blue and terracotta, with arched niches and reproduction Hellenic marbles – it also has one of the largest and smartest bathrooms. All rooms have plenty of extras and benefit from Rob's latest passion for buying rugs.

● Closed 5 to 20 Jan ⬀ Just west of A487, 6 miles south-west of Machynlleth. Private car park ⬅ 2 twin, 2 double, 1 four-poster, 3 suites; family rooms available; all with bathroom/WC exc 1 double with shower/WC; all with TV, room service, hair-dryer, direct-dial telephone, radio; no tea/coffee-making facilities in rooms ⬥ 2 dining-rooms, bar, lounge, garden; functions (max 20 people incl up to 12 residential), conferences; civil wedding licence; leisure facilities nearby (free and reduced rates for guests) ♿ No wheelchair access ● No children under 9; dogs in 1 bedroom only, by arrangement; smoking in bar only ▭ Amex, Delta, Diners, MasterCard, Switch, Visa £ Single occupancy of twin/double £75 to £115, twin/double £120 to £160, four-poster £140 to £170, family room £150 to £170, suite £150 to £200; deposit required. Set L from £19.50, D from £31. Special breaks available

---

FISHGUARD Pembrokeshire map 4

Manor House

Main Street, Fishguard SA65 9HG
TEL: (01348) 873260 (AND FAX)

Some characterful rooms and friendly hosts at this town-house hotel

Ralph Davies was polishing a brass Buddha when our inspector called: another item to add to the fascinating collection of artifacts with which he and his wife Beatrix have filled their Georgian town house (interesting things, rather than valuable – the vast and voluptuous pot on the landing turns out to be papier-mâché). Each bedroom benefits from the collection in different ways. Room 5 is the pick of the bunch: a spacious double with a sea view and window seat to enjoy it from, plus all the chintzy ornaments you could wish for; Room 1 jumps forward a few years to an art-deco look; Room 3 is a cosy cabin of a single. Below is a garden with sun terrace at the end, perfect for a lazy breakfast looking out over the bay. The dining-room is in the basement, and so lacks natural light, but the Davieses have been improving things of late: 'No more Spanish hacienda and Artex walls.' Instead you get an intimate atmosphere with beams, polished wood and warm colours. The three-course menu offers a good choice at each stage: perhaps stuffed and roasted red peppers to start, then a cassoulet of venison sausages, chicken and pork, followed by a brandy and mincemeat crumble.

● Closed Chr ⬀ From central roundabout in Fishguard head north (A487) towards Cardigan; hotel is 200 yards on, on left. On-street parking (free); public car park nearby (free) ⬅ 1 single, 2 twin, 4 double; family rooms available; most with bathroom/WC, 3 with shower/WC; all with TV, hair-dryer ⬥ Dining-room, bar, lounge, garden; early suppers for children; cots, high chairs ♿ No wheelchair access ● Dogs by arrangement; no smoking in public rooms ▭ Delta, MasterCard, Switch, Visa £ Single £26, single occupancy of twin/double £35, twin/double £52, family room £60; deposit required. Set D £17.50 (reductions for guests). Special breaks available

Plas Glyn-y-Mel

Lower Fishguard SA65 9LY
TEL: (01348) 872296   FAX: (01348) 874521

A country-house atmosphere at this friendly B&B, set in beautiful grounds.

The driveway leads you in, past a 200-year-old mulberry tree and some palms; on the right is the River Gwuan and on the left is Mike and Jenny Moore's Georgian house – a handsome building, with a porticoed entrance opening into a columned hall. Built for a local poet and celebrity, the house has a secluded feeling, though it's only a few minutes' walk from Lower Fishguard. Inside, the Moores have kept many original features, including double Georgian doors, panelled window casements and even a dumb waiter in the dining-room. The finest room is undoubtedly the lounge, with its corner position looking down to the Gwuan, its bright, chintzy style and well-stocked honesty bar. Upstairs, the bedrooms do not have quite the same sparkle, but are comfortable and well equipped. Breakfast is taken in the elegant dining-room; though dinners are not provided, there are plenty of restaurants a short drive away. For walkers, there is a useful drying-room – the Coast Path runs close by – and there is a 30-foot-long indoor swimming-pool.

◗ Open all year ▨ Take A487 out of centre of Fishguard towards Cardigan; go down steep hill to old harbour; turn sharp right at bottom. Private car park ⮑ 2 single, 2 twin, 2 double, 2 suites; family rooms available; most with bathroom/WC; all with TV, hair-dryer; no tea/coffee-making facilities in rooms ⌀ Dining-room, lounge, drying-room, garden; fishing, heated indoor swimming-pool; cots, high chairs
  ♿ No wheelchair access ● No dogs in public rooms ▭ None accepted
£ Single and single occupancy of twin/double £42, twin/double £70, family room £75, suite £90; deposit required

Three Main Street

3 Main Street, Fishguard SA65 9HG
TEL: (01348) 874275

Restaurant-with-rooms in a centrally located Georgian house.

Inez Ford's previous career might not have suggested becoming a hotelier as a logical next step – she was first a social worker and then a racehorse trainer – but it has certainly worked out for her and her fellow proprietor, Marion Evans. Their three-storey town house is an elegant but homely place, with rugs on floorboards, vases of flowers and lots of paintings around. A small bar at the front is next to a coffee-shop where light lunches are served; the main restaurant is at the back, offering a two- or three-course table d'hôte menu with a wide choice. Starters might include a watercress and leek soup, followed by roast Welsh lamb with a redcurrant, port and mint sauce, then finally a dessert of strawberry and rhubarb iced parfait. Of the three bedrooms, Pink is perhaps the favourite for its sea view and quiet, back-of-house position; all are carefully decorated and have some good old furniture and simple shower-rooms.

○ Closed Feb; restaurant closed Sun & Mon eves ⟋ Just off Fishguard's town square. Private car park ⟋ 1 twin, 2 double; all with shower/WC; all with TV, hair-dryer ⟋ Restaurant, bar; functions (max 12 people incl up to 6 residential), conferences; early suppers for children ⟋ No wheelchair access ● No dogs; smoking in bar only ⟋ None accepted ⟋ Single occupancy of twin/double £35, twin/double £60; deposit required. Light L £5; set L, D £19.50/£23.50

GANLLWYD Gwynedd   map 7

Plas Dolmelynllyn

Ganllwyd, Dolgellau LL40 2HP
TEL: (01341) 440273   FAX: (01341) 440640

Family-run country-house hotel, with quiet, friendly atmosphere and pleasant terraced gardens.

Jon Barkwith's grey-stone mansion is a place dedicated to quiet and gentle pursuits like walking and fishing. The house is a strange, asymmetrical construction, featuring crow-step gables over an oriel window framed by carved Indian bedposts, then a colonnade of arches and a tower worthy of the Italian Alps – except in miniature. In fact, the house is something of a stately home on a tiny scale – one where the occasional wall of woodchip paper doesn't seem out of place, no more so than the stained glass, panelling and ornate plasterwork of the dining-room. Jon's daughter, Joanna Reddicliffe, is the chef, working in a classic country-house style seen in dishes like salmon and dill terrine, duck breast in a green-peppercorn and brandy sauce, and raspberry crumble cake and, for those who get this far, Stilton with celery and oatcakes. The menu changes monthly, and offers a list of daily specials. Finish your evening with a few digestifs in the conservatory bar, but then it may not be so easy to find your room: the hotel is amusingly maze-like after so many additions and alterations during its 500-year history. It's good to see that the single rooms have had as much care and attention taken over them as the doubles: Artro is a pleasant, floral-patterned room overlooking the terraced garden; Gamlan is darker and more cosy, with that curious oriel window over the front door. The best of the doubles look out to the garden.

○ Closed Dec to Feb ⟋ 5 miles north of Dolgellau on A470 at southern end of Ganllwyd village. Private car park ⟋ 2 single, 3 double, 1 four-poster, 1 suite; all with bathroom/WC exc 1 single with shower/WC; all with TV, room service, hair-dryer, direct-dial telephone, some with trouser press ⟋ Dining-room, bar/ conservatory, lounge, drying-room, garden; functions (max 50 people incl up to 12 residential); fishing; early suppers for children; baby-listening ⟋ No wheelchair access ● Children under 8 by arrangement; dogs in some bedrooms only, by arrangement; no smoking ⟋ Amex, Diners, MasterCard, Visa ⟋ Single £45 to £60, single occupancy of double £53 to £66, double £80 to £100, four-poster/suite £100 to £115; deposit required. Bar L £6; set D £21 to £24.50. Special breaks available

---

 This denotes that the hotel is in an exceptionally peaceful situation where you can be assured of a restful stay.

GLYNARTHEN Ceredigion　　　　　　　　　　map 4

Penbontbren Farm

Glynarthen, Cardigan SA44 6PE
TEL: (01239) 810248　FAX: (01239) 811129

Quiet farm accommodation, with beautifully converted rooms and friendly hosts.

Up a long, deep lane from the coastal road, you finally come to Barrie and Nan Humphreys' secluded home, which is something more than simply a converted farmhouse and outbuildings. With its small museum and vintage agricultural tools dotted around, it is also a place of memories of a rural past. Nan remembers that past as a child, for the farm has been in her family for four generations: the brass-bound butter churn, now an ornament in the lounge, was used by her mother, and the cow's horn in reception bugled warnings during the nineteenth-century tithe wars. On one side of the farmyard, the outbuildings are now the smart restaurant, bar and lounge; on the other side are the bedrooms. The menus, in Welsh and English – for this is a Welsh-speaking farm – might start with Rhyldewis terrine (a combination of smoked fishes), followed by steak in a cassis sauce, and then a traditional dessert, like a crumble or sticky toffee pudding. There is a wide choice, with a good selection for vegetarians. Of the bedrooms, those upstairs are a bit lighter and have the extra character of the roof beams. All are prettily done out in Laura Ashley patterns, with thoughtful touches like a brief history of the room and complimentary sherry and fruit. If visitors fancy learning a few words of the national language, they could start with 'sit' and 'come here' – the Humphreys' four corgis respond only to Welsh.

◖ Closed Chr　▨ Signposted off A487 between Tany-y-groes and Sarnau, about 10 miles east of Cardigan. Private car park　⇤ 3 double, 7 family rooms; all in annexe; all with bathroom/WC; all with TV, room service, hair-dryer, direct-dial telephone
✓ Restaurant, bar, 2 lounges, games room; functions (max 55 people incl up to 25 residential), conferences; early suppers for children; cots, high chairs, playroom, baby-listening, outdoor play area　ᕫ Wheelchair access to hotel (ramp) and restaurant, 6 ground-floor bedrooms, 2 rooms specially equipped for disabled people　● No children under 5 in restaurant eves; dogs in bedrooms only, by arrangement; no smoking in restaurant　▱ Amex, Delta, Diners, MasterCard, Switch, Visa　£ Single occupancy of double £38 to £43, double £68 to £74, family room from £68; deposit required. Set D £12.50; alc D £16. Special breaks available

---

HARLECH Gwynedd　　　　　　　　　　map 7

Castle Cottage

Pen Llech, Harlech LL46 2YL
TEL: (01766) 780479 (AND FAX)

Good food and amiable hosts at this small hotel close to the castle.

Glyn and Jacqueline Roberts have somehow shoehorned a delightful small hotel into a compact village house, complete with a spacious dining-room and snug bar. The Roberts came here a decade ago, partly because they loved the place and partly because of Glyn's family connections. Though the house dates from the sixteenth century, from the outside it looks a fairly undistinguished building, with white pebble-dashed walls and dormer windows set in a modern slate roof. Inside, however, its history reveals itself in the form of thick stone walls and a vast inglenook fireplace in the dining-room, plus various types of beams and half-timbering throughout. Glyn's cooking makes good use of local seafood – lobster from Barmouth and sea bass caught off the local beach. A three-course dinner might start off in the bar with canapés and a suggested aperitif, then move on to a risotto of haddock kedgeree, followed by breast of corn-fed chicken, and finally a chocolate and pear crème brûlée. The bedrooms are all fairly compact, which is why this tends not to be a family-type hotel, despite its informal atmosphere. All are well equipped (TV on request) and characterful. The castle views, though much sought after, are limited and, besides, it's only a minute's walk from the front door.

◐ Closed 3 weeks in Feb ⬚ Just off high street, behind castle. On-street parking (free); public car park nearby (£3 per day) ⊨ 2 single, 2 twin, 2 double; 4 with bathroom/WC; TV, hair-dryer, trouser press available ✓ Dining-room, bar, lounge; early suppers for children; cots, high chairs ♿ No wheelchair access ● No dogs in public rooms; smoking in bar only ▭ Amex, Delta, MasterCard, Switch, Visa £ Single £26, single occupancy of twin/double £38, twin/double £56; deposit required. Set Sun L £13, D £21.50. Special breaks available

---

Lower Haythog Farm

Spittal, Haverfordwest SA62 5QL
TEL: (01437) 731279 (AND FAX)

Friendly hosts and immaculate rooms on this working dairy farm.

The countryside around Nesta Thomas's farm may not be the prettiest part of Pembrokeshire – it is fairly flat, arable land – but it's well placed for trips to Fishguard to the north, Tenby to the south or St Bride's Bay to the west. Then there is Nesta's warm and friendly welcome: she runs the place with plenty of good humour, encouraging guests to enjoy the farmhouse atmosphere and the excellent gardens. Inside, the house is beautifully kept, with chintzy fabrics and well-polished brasses in the sitting-room, and a large inglenook fireplace in the dining-room. Nesta's cooking takes a traditional farmhouse style as its starting point, branching out in more adventurous ways. The bedrooms are comfortable and homely, with pastel colour schemes and floral soft furnishings.

◐ Open all year ⬚ From Haverfordwest, take B4329 towards Cardigan; farm entrance is 4 miles along, just before railway bridge. Private car park ⊨ 1 single, 1 twin, 2 double, 2 family rooms; all with bathroom/WC; all with TV, hair-dryer, some with trouser press ✓ Dining-room, sitting-room, drying-room, conservatory, garden; fishing; cots, high chairs, toys, babysitting ♿ No wheelchair access ● No dogs; no smoking ▭ None accepted £ Single £20 to £25, twin/double £40 to £45, family room from £60; deposit required. Set D £12.50 to £15. Special breaks available

Old Black Lion

26 Lion Street, Hay-on-Wye HR3 5AD
TEL: (01497) 820841

*Long-established hotel and pub in a popular tourist town, with a
fine reputation for food and much historic interest.*

This traditional, old-world coaching-inn, full of creaky character and quaint,
low-slung timbering, dates from the thirteenth century. It has been attractively
renovated to provide an intimate, candlelit restaurant and comfortable hotel
accommodation for Hay-on-Wye's hordes of second-hand bibliophiles, as well
as being a popular gathering place for local residents. Its small car park (one of
the few places where you can leave a car free of charge in central Hay-on-Wye) is
constantly thronged with occupants, and you need to stay on the ball in order to
get in and out without embarrassing yourself. The bedroom accommodation is of
a good standard – cosy and traditional in the old building, but well equipped
with mod cons. The annexe bedrooms are a little quieter and more spacious than
those directly above the bar; but one winter guest reckoned that the heating
could have been put on a little earlier. Book well ahead at festival time, when
Hay-on-Wye is packed and the service can be a bit slow. Predictable snacks are
available in the bar, along with more interesting blackboard specials (like
gravad lax and white-chocolate chiffon pie); the restaurant fare is served amid a
chintzy array of jugs and ornaments. The service is agreeable and friendly and,
despite the Old Black Lion's immense popularity, the prices remain remarkably
good value.

◗ Open all year 🅿 In centre of Hay-on-Wye. Private car park 🛏 1 single, 4 twin, 4
double, 1 family room; some in annexe; 2 with bathroom/WC, 8 with shower/WC; all
with TV, hair-dryer, direct-dial telephone, radio ⊘ Restaurant, bar, lounge, garden;
fishing; early suppers for children ♿ No wheelchair access ● No children under 5;
no children under 8 in restaurant eves; no dogs in restaurant (£5 per night in bedrooms);
no smoking in restaurant or bedrooms ▭ Amex, MasterCard, Visa 💷 Single and
single occupancy of twin/double £30, twin/double £50 to £55, family room £52 to £62;
deposit required. Bar L £8, D £9.50; set Sun L £10; alc L £9.50, D £19. Special breaks
available

Llwyndu Farmhouse

Llanaber, Barmouth LL42 1RR
TEL: (01341) 280144   FAX: (01341) 281236
EMAIL: petethompson@btinternet.com

Characterful rooms and good food at this farmhouse hotel.

After the brash charms of Barmouth, just two miles south, Peter and Paula
Thompson's sixteenth-century farmhouse comes as a quiet relief: a chestnut
horse gazes over the fence, the mill wheel lies forgotten and there is very little to
disturb the rural peace. Inside the thick-walled house, the rooms are cosy and

creaky, with exposed beams and stone. One almost wishes that the weather would turn nasty and that the snow would pile up at the door just to be snug in front of the inglenook fire with a glass of whisky from the little bar in the hall. Peter's well-regarded cooking offers traditional country fare like fish pie or roasts, along with the occasional curry. The affordable menu offers at least two alternatives at each course. The bedrooms in the main house are full of cottagey character, but for extra privacy those in the Granary are preferable.

◗ Closed 25, 26 Dec; dining-room closed Sun eve ⏹ 2½ miles north of Barmouth on east side of A496. Private car park ⏪ 1 twin, 2 double, 2 four-poster, 2 family rooms; some in annexe; all with bathroom/WC exc 1 double with shower/WC; all with TV, hair-dryer ⍩ Dining-room, bar, lounge, garden; early suppers for children; cots, high chairs ⏴ No wheelchair access ● No dogs in public rooms; no smoking ▭ Delta, MasterCard, Switch, Visa £ Twin/double £58 to £60, four-poster £66 to £70, family room £64 to £68; deposit required. Set D £17. Special breaks available

---

LLANARMON DYFFRYN CEIRIOG Wrexham

map 7

West Arms

Llanarmon Dyffryn Ceiriog, Llangollen LL20 7LD
TEL: (01691) 600665   FAX: (01691) 600622

Traditional and unpretentious inn of some character.

This whitewashed sixteenth-century farmhouse with modern additions is set in the lovely Ceiriog valley and has all the ancient features you might hope for from such a venerable establishment: huge inglenook fireplaces, slate floors and blackened beams. Dark colour schemes add to the cosiness of the place. But there is more to Rod and Margaret Evans's hotel than romantic rustic décor; they can arrange fishing on the Dee, landscape painting courses, guided walks – there is even a course for stressed-out executives called 'pamper and stressbuster'. In the evenings guests can take an aperitif in the atmospheric lounge bar, which is much nicer than the uninspired coffee lounge. The three-course dinners offer two alternatives at each stage, so main dishes might be Welsh sirloin steak with a chestnut sauce, roasted monkfish tail and cod fillet, or fillet of lamb in pastry. Bedrooms have brass bedsteads and antique furnishings.

◗ Open all year ⏹ From A5, 4 miles north of Oswestry, turn west on B4500 at Chirk; follow signs to Llanarmon DC. Private car park ⏪ 4 twin, 7 double, 1 suite; family rooms available; all with bathroom/WC; all with TV, room service, hair-dryer, direct-dial telephone ⍩ Restaurant, 2 bars, 2 lounges, drying-room, conservatory, garden; functions (max 100 people incl up to 24 residential), conferences; civil wedding licence; fishing; leisure facilities nearby (reduced rates for guests); early suppers for children; cots, high chairs, babysitting ⏴ Wheelchair access to hotel and restaurant, WC (unisex), 3 ground-floor bedrooms ● No smoking or dogs in restaurant ▭ Delta, MasterCard, Switch, Visa £ Single occupancy of twin/double £40, twin/double £70, family room £88, suite £80; deposit required. Bar L, D 6.50; set Sun L £14.50, D £17.50. Special breaks available

---

Many hotels offer special rates for stays of a few nights or more. It is worth enquiring when you book.

Ty'n Rhos

Seion, Llanddeiniolen, Caernarfon LL55 3AE
TEL: (01248) 670489   FAX: (01248) 670079

Top-quality cooking and well-appointed rooms at this peaceful, low-key country hotel.

A photograph in the hall of Lynda and Nigel Kettle's country house shows the place 25 years ago as a simple farmhouse, which is what it was when they came to farm here. Since then, various additions, including an almost finished conservatory, have left the building almost unrecognisable, though the atmosphere still remains homely and small in scale. The restful sitting-room has a fine dark-slate fireplace, a ticking clock and chintzy soft furnishings, while the elegant, striped dining-room has racks of wine and views west to the hills of Anglesey. Dinners are priced according to the main course, and provide a good range of fare: cream of celeriac soup to start, perhaps, followed by breast of chicken filled with apricot, sherry and rosemary seasoning, then a baked vanilla cheesecake with a raspberry coulis and poached vanilla pear, and finally Welsh cheeses and coffee to follow. Lynda's cooking has achieved many plaudits. The bedrooms are pleasant and well equipped – you will find a china tea service and home-made biscuits – but there are few books or magazines to be seen, most guests being content to look out at the gentle, rolling countryside.

● Closed Chr, 1 week in Jan, second week in Aug   ⏻ Off B4366 in hamlet of Seion, 1½ miles north-east of Bethel. Private car park   ⏍ 3 single, 3 twin, 8 double; some in annexe; family rooms available; all with bathroom/WC exc 1 single with shower/WC; all with TV, room service, hair-dryer, direct-dial telephone   ⏏ 2 dining-rooms, bar, sitting-room, drying-room, conservatory, garden; functions (max 35 people incl up to 25 residential), conferences; early suppers for children   ⏌ Wheelchair access to hotel (1 step) and dining-rooms, 6 ground-floor bedrooms, 1 room specially equipped for disabled people   ● No children under 6; no dogs; smoking in sitting-room only   ▭ Amex, Delta, MasterCard, Switch, Visa   £ Single £49, single occupancy of twin/double £49 to £59, twin/double £70 to £90, family room (rates on application); deposit required. Set L £15, D £19.50; alc D £25. Special breaks available

Ffaldau Country House

Llandegley, Llandrindod Wells LD1 5UD
TEL: (01597) 851421 (AND FAX)

Friendly hosts and some fine old architecture at this small country farmhouse.

Like many old buildings, Leslie and Sylvia Knott's sixteenth-century farmhouse has had the benefit of some additions and renovations, so you would scarcely guess at the wonderfully atmospheric interiors from the pretty, but undistinguished, exterior. The dining-room has a huge inglenook fireplace and a homely mix of lacy tablecloths, dark, polished furniture and sepia-tinted family photographs; best of all is the beamed and bowed ceiling, like some lower deck of a Tudor galleon. Next door is a more modern bar, with books, games and a cosy log burner. Guests usually have an aperitif here while looking at the menu, dinner being served at 8pm in summer and 7.30pm in winter. Typical offerings might be home-made soup followed by local lamb with a vermouth and herb sauce, then a chocolate brandy slice with raspberry sauce – the emphasis is on home-grown and home-made food, prepared with a touch of imagination. Breakfasts are ordered the night before and offer a good selection, including kedgeree and herb sausage. The upstairs lounge area leads to the bedrooms and is a marvel of ancient timberwork – very little of it either quite vertical or horizontal; it's a comfortable eyrie of sofas, corner seats and books. The cottage-style bedrooms have their share of character, too, with Rose being the pick of them. For more privacy, there is an additional room outside overlooking the patio; although modern and comfortable, it lacks the atmosphere of those in the house.

◑ Open all year; dining-room closed Mon eve ⬈ Set back from A44 in Llandegley, 2 miles south-east of Penybont. Private car park ⬏ 2 twin, 2 double; one in annexe; 2 with bathroom/WC, 2 with shower/WC; all with hair-dryer, some with TV; trouser press available ⊘ Dining-room, lounge/bar, lounge, TV room, drying-room, garden
♿ No wheelchair access ● No children under 10; dogs in annexe bedroom only, by arrangement; smoking in lounge bar only ▭ Delta, MasterCard, Visa £ Single occupancy of twin/double £32, twin/double £40 to £48; deposit required. Light supper £7 to £10; set D £15 to £18.50

Cawdor Arms

Rhosmaen Street, Llandeilo SA19 6EN
TEL: (01558) 823500   FAX: (01558) 822399

Atmospheric public rooms and good food at this former coaching-inn.

Step through the door of this fine old coaching-inn on Llandeilo's main street and the atmosphere seems ready for the Thane of Cawdor to come stamping up to the fire and throw off his bloodstained cloak – perhaps during a murder mystery (John and Jane Silver organise them, and the Cawdor connection is genuine, dating back to the eighteenth century). The bold, masculine style of the interconnected lounges (buttoned leather chairs, oriental rugs on sturdy wooden floors) is toned down slightly in the dining-room. Since the Silvers arrived in summer 1997 they have tried to impart a lighter touch here, and it remains an elegant room, with oil paintings on the walls and a piano in the corner, sometimes played by daughter Jane (she is also one of the three chefs – Rod Peterson and Mo Bashir are the others). Dinner might start with a cream of fennel and orange soup, followed by roast Welsh beef and finally a cardamom and orange sponge with an orange butter sauce. Bedrooms are a good size but can be disappointingly old-fashioned – something the Silvers are improving with good sense and imagination. The pick of them remains the Rose Room, a spacious four-poster with large bay window overlooking the high street.

◑ Open all year ⤢ In centre of Llandeilo on A40. Private car park ⤲ 2 single, 4 twin, 8 double, 2 four-poster, 1 family room; most with bathroom/WC, some with shower/WC; all with TV, room service, hair-dryer, direct-dial telephone ⊘ Dining-room, 2 bars, 3 lounges, conference/function room; functions (max 130 people incl up to 35 residential), conferences; leisure facilities nearby (free and reduced rates for guests); early suppers for children; cots, high chairs, toys, books ♿ No wheelchair access ● Smoking in lounges only ⊟ Amex, MasterCard, Switch, Visa £ Single and single occupancy of twin/double £45, twin/double £55, four-poster £65, family room £70; deposit required. Bar L £4.50; alc L £13.50, D £20. Special breaks available

---

LLANDRILLO Denbighshire   map 7

Tyddyn Llan

Llandrillo, Corwen LL21 0ST
TEL: (01490) 440264   FAX: (01490) 440414
EMAIL: tyddynllanhotel@compuserve.com

Fine country-house hotel with excellent food and stylish interiors.

With the beautiful River Dee and Berwyn Mountains close by, it's easy to see why Peter and Bridget Kindred fell for their modest Georgian house. But it's Peter's skills as a former television set designer that have transformed the interiors into something worthy of the location. Three interlinked sitting-rooms provide a choice of relaxing spots in which to enjoy afternoon tea or after-dinner coffee. Then there is a stylish, classical feel to the dining-room, with its windows on three sides and discreetly hidden lights and speakers. The cooking is top-notch country-house fare, with a dash of French imagination and plenty of seasonal offerings: spring brings roast saddle of rabbit and autumn Brecon venison with wild-mushroom duxelles. The desserts are creative indulgences: profiteroles with a duo of chocolate sauces or a coconut-flavoured fried rice-pudding. The bedrooms are comfortably light and airy, featuring a bold use of colour and antique furniture.

◑ Open all year ⤢ From A5 at Corwen take B4401 through Cynwyd to Llandrillo; house is on right as you leave village. Private car park ⤲ 4 twin, 6 double; family rooms available; all with bathroom/WC exc 2 doubles with shower/WC; all with TV, room service, hair-dryer, direct-dial telephone, clock radio; no tea/coffee-making facilities in rooms ⊘ Dining-room, bar, 3 sitting-rooms, drying-room, garden; functions (max 90 people incl up to 20 residential), conferences; civil wedding licence; fishing, croquet; early suppers for children; cots, high chairs, babysitting, baby-listening ♿ No wheelchair access ● No dogs in public rooms; no smoking in dining-room ⊟ Amex, Diners, MasterCard, Switch, Visa £ Single occupancy of twin/double £64 to £80, twin/double £98 to £130, family room £108 to £140; deposit required. Light L £5 to £13; set L £15.50, D £27. Special breaks available

---

The text of the entries is based on inspections carried out anonymously, backed up by unsolicited reports sent in by readers. The factual details under the text are from questionnaires the Guide *sends to all hotels that feature in the book.*

Bodysgallen Hall

Llandudno LL30 1RS
TEL: (01492) 584466   FAX: (01492) 582519

Grand country house of impeccable good taste, with useful leisure facilities.

At the heart of this fine country house is the tower – a thirteenth-century edifice built as a lookout for Conwy Castle. A polite word with reception usually allows you to climb up and take in the view around the eighteenth- and nineteenth-century house. There is plenty to admire: 200 acres of grounds, including woods, a hilltop monument, a parterre garden and a walled rose garden. The house itself is just as opulent, with its imposing, tall chimneys and mullioned windows. Inside, the atmosphere is of polished elegance and calm; there is a panelled and chintzy drawing-room for afternoon tea and cakes, as well as a cosy bar and a fine dining-room, with large bay windows overlooking the ornamental gardens. The dining here is formal, with a fixed-price menu offering sophisticated country-house fare: a warm Jerusalem-artichoke mousse with truffle and tomato to start, perhaps, followed by sorbet and then roast fillet of sea bass, finishing with a hot raspberry soufflé with Welsh-honey ice-cream. 'I cannot speak too highly of the restaurant,' wrote one correspondent; 'expensive but very good value.' The bedrooms provide everything you might expect, in country-house style; there are also 16 cottage suites. In the grounds is a swish spa with pool and fitness and beauty rooms.

◑ Open all year   ⊿ Leave A55 on A470 towards Llandudno; hotel is 2 miles on, on right. Private car park   ⊨ 2 single, 16 twin/double, 1 four-poster, 16 suites; suites in annexes; family rooms available; most with bathroom/WC, 2 with shower/WC; all with TV, room service, hair-dryer, trouser press, direct-dial telephone, some with tea/coffee-making facilities   ⊘ 2 dining-rooms, bar, 2 drawing-rooms, library, garden; functions (max 40 people incl up to 35 residential), conferences; gym, sauna, solarium, heated indoor swimming-pool, beauty salon, tennis, croquet   ♿ Wheelchair access to hotel (1 step) and dining-rooms, WC, 1 ground-floor bedroom specially equipped for disabled people   ⬤ No children under 8; dogs in suites only, by arrangement; no smoking in some bedrooms   ▭ Delta, MasterCard, Switch, Visa   £ Single £95 to £100, single occupancy of twin/double £105 to £115, twin/double £130 to £145, four-poster £175 to £205, family room £175 to £195, suite £150 to £165; deposit required. Continental B £8.50, cooked B £11.50; set D £29.50; alc L £14.50. Special breaks available

---

St Tudno Hotel

Promenade, Llandudno LL30 2LP
TEL: (01492) 874411   FAX: (01492) 860407
EMAIL: sttudnohotel@btinternet.com

Superb seaside hotel with excellent food and friendly service.

Martin and Janette Bland's nineteenth-century hotel stands opposite the Victorian pier, on Llandudno's impressive, sweeping façade of whitewashed hotels. Arriving late in the day without a reservation, our inspector was impressed by the reception and service: bags were fetched from the car, and the cheerful friendliness of the staff was noted. The bedrooms are comfortable, and are well furnished with every extra that you could wish for: satellite TV, fresh milk, a complimentary quarter-bottle of champagne in the fridge, seven types of tea next to the china teacup, home-made biscuits, iced water and a bathrobe. Not that the basics are neglected: the towels are large and the shower powerful. The Blands have been here for 26 years and have honed things as their guests like them. Downstairs, the décor encompasses plenty of Victoriana, but with a light touch. Aperitifs and canapés are served in the bar before guests wander through to the 'garden'-style restaurant – a room perhaps too dimly lit for some, but elegant, with its pale-green rattan-effect chairs and crisp linen. An inspection dinner of local fish soup, turbot and raspberry fool in Drambuie proved to be excellent. The service was quiet and unobtrusive.

○ Open all year 🔼 On Llandudno's promenade, between cenotaph and pier and opposite ornamental gardens. Private car park 🛏 2 single, 8 twin, 6 double, 1 four-poster, 2 family rooms, 1 suite; all with bathroom/WC exc 2 doubles with shower/WC; all with satellite TV, room service, hair-dryer, direct-dial telephone, clock radio, some with mini-bar, trouser press ⊘ Restaurant, bar, 2 lounges, drying-room, garden; functions (max 50 people incl up to 44 residential), conferences; heated indoor swimming-pool; leisure facilities nearby (reduced rates for guests); early suppers for children; cots, high chairs, toys, babysitting, baby-listening 🚫 No wheelchair access ● No children under 5 in restaurant eves; dogs in bedrooms only, by arrangement; no smoking in restaurant, 1 lounge and some bedrooms ☐ Amex, Delta, Diners, MasterCard, Switch, Visa 💷 Single £70 to £75, single occupancy of twin/double from £85, twin/double £90 to £180, four-poster £156, family room £105 to £171, suite £250; deposit required. Bar L £7.50 to £14.50; set L £17, D £29.50; alc D £25. Special breaks available

Ty Mawr

Llanegryn, Tywyn LL36 9SY
TEL: (01654) 710507 (AND FAX)

Beautiful location for a good-quality, friendly B&B.

Lizzie and Richard Tregarthen came to this idyllic spot a decade ago after living in various places around the world – none, perhaps, as beautiful as this, with the long valley sweeping down from the front door with Cardigan Bay to the right and Cader Idris to the left. The original house burnt down long ago, and what stands beside the ruin is actually its converted barns. Inside, you find a cottage-style living-room with log fire, patio doors and huge crooked beams – family pictures, books and television add to the homely atmosphere. Breakfasts are served in a slate-floored conservatory on the corner of the house with plants all around and lovely views to the south and west. Everyone sits around one pine table – and the friendly, sociable atmosphere is helped along by the Tregarthens' civilised hospitality. The two bedrooms are not over-large but attractively furnished with plenty of pictures and books. Suppers are prepared on request –

the home-grown vegetables and freshly laid eggs providing a firm basis for traditional home cooking.

◑ Open all year **⊉** From A493 north of Tywyn, turn off to Llanegryn; after 50 yards bear left into narrow lane; at junction go left up hill, then right at next junction to top of hill; Ty Mawr is signposted on right. Private car park **⊫** 1 twin, 1 double; both with shower/WC **⊘** Living-room, conservatory, garden **⅋** No wheelchair access **◓** No children under 10; no smoking **▭** None accepted **⌷£⌷** Single occupancy of twin/double £23 to £33, twin/double £45; deposit required

---

LLANFACHRETH Gwynedd

map 7

Tŷ Isaf

Llanfachreth, Dolgellau LL40 2EA
TEL: (01341) 423261

Rural retreat offering peace, quiet and friendly hospitality.

The first welcome at Lorna Gear's farmhouse comes from Math and Mathonwy – two llamas named after a pair of legendary Celtic heroes. The Welsh connection with an unusual spin is very much the feel of this attractive stone house overlooking a pretty valley. Lorna's cousin, Lois, might tell you about the witches' chimneys in the village while Lorna cooks one of her Welsh recipes in the kitchen: perhaps brithyll-y-cig moch – trout and parsley wrapped in smoked bacon. In the bookcase next to the dining-room you'll find biographies of Indian sages and tomes on relaxation and self-healing stacked under the photographs of Lorna's ancestors; but the real healing power of this place comes from the Welsh landscape outside and Lorna's interest in people. There is a lounge and a study; the lounge used to be part of a barn where the lambs were fed when Lorna was a child. 'This room has a good feeling,' she says. Upstairs, the three bedrooms are furnished in cottagey style, with white walls, beams and small shower-rooms (though one has a hip bath).

◑ Open all year **⊉** From A470 Dolgellau bypass, take turning to Bala then first left to Dolgellau; turn right to Llanfachreth. Private car park **⊫** 1 twin, 2 double; 1 with bathroom/WC, 2 with shower/WC; all with hair-dryer **⊘** Dining-room, lounge, study, garden **⅋** No wheelchair access **◓** No children under 12; dogs in lounge and 1 bedroom only; no smoking **▭** None accepted **⌷£⌷** Single occupancy of twin/double £36, twin/double £52; deposit required. Set D £13.50

LLANFIHANGEL CRUCORNEY Monmouthshire

map 4

Penyclawdd Court

Llanfihangel Crucorney, Abergavenny NP7 7LB
TEL: (01873) 890719 FAX: (01873) 890848

A perfectly researched Tudor stage set for fantasy feasts by candlelight.

If you have no fears for your car's undercarriage (the drive is in truly dreadful condition), persevere to this listed Tudor manor house nestling in glorious sheep country below the Black Mountains. The house is impressive enough for Julia Horton Evans and Ken Peacock to charge entrance fees for guided tours, though these are modest for such an unusual place. Careful restoration over many years, and the development of the gardens in period style, have caught the attention of many conservation organisations and feature writers, and the grounds are noted for a Norman motte and bailey (once a common fortification along these Welsh borderlands), and a zodiac knot garden. The owners are as idiosyncratic as their lovely house, and as welcoming and enthusiastic. You will sleep in astonishing antique-strewn bedrooms with low-flying beams and stone flagstones (mercifully heated underfloor), dine by candlelight, and feast on home-smoked salmon or stuffed quail in true Tudor style. Jacob sheep and free-range poultry patrol the grounds. If all you want is a bed for the night, look elsewhere – Penyclawdd Court is an experience, to be savoured positively and in the right spirit.

---

❶ Open all year   ⤴ Take A465 north from Abergavenny; after 4½ miles turn left at sign for Pantygelli; after ¼ mile turn right between bungalow and Victorian house; hotel is at top of track. Private car park   🛏 3 double; all with bathroom/WC; all with TV, room service, hair-dryer   ✔ Dining-room, lounge, garden   ♿ No wheelchair access   ⬤ No children under 12; no dogs; no smoking in bedrooms; smoking in public rooms if other guests consent   ☐ MasterCard, Visa   💷 Single occupancy of double £45, double £74; deposit required. Set D £22.50 to £25. Special breaks available

---

LLANGAMMARCH WELLS Powys   map 4

Lake Country House

Llangammarch Wells LD4 4BS
TEL: (01591) 620202   FAX: (01591) 620457

Top-notch country-house hotel in superb grounds.

Jean-Pierre Mifsud, the owner of Lake Country House, was once a hotel inspector himself, and so – poacher turned gamekeeper – he knows how he likes a hotel. The house was expanded and developed during the time of the Victorian fashion for spa waters, giving it a timbered-pavilion style of architecture and fine, airy interiors. Immaculately well kept, with 50 landscaped acres of lawns, golf course and woodland, this is a country-house hotel *par excellence*; visitors' bags are carried for them, their clothes are pressed by the staff, an afternoon cake trolley tempts within the sitting-room and gentlemen always wear jackets and ties for dinner. Chef Jeremy Medley uses plenty of organic produce and local meats on the four-course table d'hôte menu; a carrot, orange and coriander soup may open proceedings, then a small quail pie in red wine might be followed by noisettes of local venison in bitter-chocolate sauce, and a glazed lemon tart might be the final choice. The bedrooms are being slowly upgraded and improved, and it is worth asking for a newer bathroom: Eugenie, for example, has a large spa bath through an archway, and smart old furniture, along with all the standard extras like sherry, books, Molton Brown soaps and fresh flowers. Also attractive are the French and Pump House suites, with chintzy floral drapes and coronets finishing off the very smart décor.

◐ Open all year ⊿ From Brecon, take B519 across Mount Eppynt (6 miles); at foot of hill turn left at crossroads; hotel is 1 mile along road. Private car park ⤙⤐ 3 twin, 3 double, 1 four-poster, 1 family room, 11 suites; all with bathroom/WC; all with TV, room service, hair-dryer, direct-dial telephone, some with trouser press; no tea/coffee-making facilities in rooms ✅ Dining-room, bar, 2 sitting-rooms, drying-room, games room, garden; functions (max 90 people incl up to 40 residential), conferences; civil wedding licence; fishing, golf, tennis, putting green, snooker, clay-pigeon shooting, croquet; leisure facilities nearby (reduced rates for guests); early suppers for children; cots, high chairs, babysitting ⎛ Wheelchair access to hotel (1 step) and dining-room, 2 ground-floor bedrooms ● No children under 7 in dining-room eves; no dogs in public rooms; no smoking in dining-room and some bedrooms ☐ Amex, Delta, Diners, MasterCard, Switch, Visa ⌸ Single occupancy of twin/double £95 to £110, twin/double £140, family room/suite £160 to £220; deposit required. Bar/bistro L £6.50; set L £17.50, D £30. Special breaks available

---

LLANGOLLEN **Denbighshire** map 7

Gales

18 Bridge Street, Llangollen LL20 8PF
TEL: (01978) 860089 FAX: (01978) 861313

Beautifully restored rooms, with snug, sociable wine bar attached.

Gales started out as a wine bar in an attractive black-and-white town house near the centre of Llangollen. Such is the success of its blend of good food, good wine and simple but stylish décor that the bedrooms now occupy the next-door house, too. They are rooms that offer astonishing value: Room 12, for example, has lovely half-timbering dating back to the eighteenth century and a bay window with seat looking down into the road; Room 10 has its original woodwork and a small lounge attached. Care has been taken to keep the character of the place intact, so there are white walls, honey-toned beams and well-chosen furniture, like the lace-winged Victorian brass bed in Room 8 – arguably the best room in the house. Gales also acts as a wine shipper, and one of the main attractions is the competitively priced wine list – plus the bistro-style food served in the cosy restaurant-bar. With its panelling, wooden pillars and log fire, this is a convivial room. The menus are chalked up on blackboards; you could start with chicken-liver and orange pâté, follow that with mustard lamb, and then choose from 200 ice-creams for dessert, including the New Zealanders' favourite, Hokey Pokey.

◐ Closed 25 Dec to 2 Jan; restaurant closed Sun eve ⊿ In Llangollen town centre. Private car park ⤙⤐ 4 twin, 9 double, 2 suites; some in annexe; family rooms available; some with bathroom/WC, most with shower/WC; all with TV, hair-dryer, direct-dial telephone ✅ Restaurant, bar; functions (max 20 people incl up to 15 residential), conferences; early suppers for children; cots, high chairs, baby-listening ⎛ No wheelchair access ● No dogs; no smoking in some bedrooms ☐ Amex, Delta, Diners, MasterCard, Switch, Visa ⌸ Single occupancy of twin/double £38, twin/double £50, family room £50, suite £58; deposit required. Bar/bistro L £8, D £12

 This denotes that you can get a twin or double room for £70 or less per night inclusive of breakfast.

map 7

Old Rectory

Llanrwst Road, Llansanffraid Glan Conwy, Colwyn Bay LL28 5LF
TEL: (01492) 580611   FAX: (01492) 584555
EMAIL: oldrect@aol.com
WEB SITE: www.wales.com/oldrectory/

Beautifully furnished house with good views and top-notch cooking.

This Georgian mansion stands on the eastern side of the Conwy valley with superb views across to Conwy Castle, the estuary and Snowdonia. Michael and Wendy Vaughan have been here since 1984 and have slowly improved the property, carefully maintaining the period and style (the house was built in the sixteenth century but later Georgianised). The dining-room – elegant, with rugs, gilt frames and antique curios dotted around – leads through to a panelled sitting-room which is a modern addition, though you would never guess. Cases of books, a piano, well-chosen period furniture and maritime paintings all add to the atmosphere. The Old Rectory is part of the Wolsey Lodge group, but diners are served at separate tables, so, although it is convivial, there is no pressure to be sociable. Wendy's cooking has gathered much praise for its tasty simplicity and good presentation. There is no choice of main course (any special requirements are sorted out when booking). You might begin with fillet of cod with potato on a pea purée with warm leek vinaigrette, then tackle a main course of roast guinea-fowl, a choice of Welsh cheeses and, finally, a raspberry tart. The pick of the bedrooms is Mahogany, with its half-tester and views to the river, but all are beautifully furnished. Tea trays have proper filter coffee, and bathrooms Gilchrist and Soames soaps. The rooms over in the coach-house have added privacy – Pine is the best, for its views across the garden to Snowdonia.

◐ Closed 10 Dec to 1 Feb   ⊉ South of Lllandudno on A470, ½ mile south of junction with A55. Private car park   ⊨⊐ 2 twin, 4 double; some in annexe; all with bathroom/WC exc 1 double with shower/WC; all with TV, room service, hair-dryer, trouser press, direct-dial telephone, ironing facilities   ⊘ Dining-room, sitting-room, garden   ⅙ No wheelchair access   ● No children under 5 exc babes in arms; dogs and smoking in coach-house bedrooms only   ⊟ Delta, MasterCard, Switch, Visa   £ Single occupancy of twin/double £99 to £129, twin/double £99 to £149; deposit required. Set D £25/£29.50. Special breaks available

map 5

Llanthony Priory

Llanthony, Abergavenny NP7 7NN
TEL: (01873) 890487   FAX: (01873) 890844

Simple accommodation in an uplifting setting of glorious National Park countryside and evocative monastic ruins.

Few hotels enjoy a more romantic or peaceful setting than Llanthony Priory. Allow plenty of time to get here: the single-track approach road gives you an exhilarating drive through breathtaking scenery, but the going is slow during popular holiday times and is not particularly recommended in winter weather or darkness. The Augustinian priory's ruined walls stand in a steep-sided valley amid the wild, bleak sheep country of the Black Mountains and date from the twelfth century. Several rooms were converted from the west front of the church in 1790, and are still served by an original Norman spiral staircase of 62 stairs (only for the spry). The service is casual and informal. The facilities are basic – even spartan – and the bedrooms are correspondingly inexpensive. All five share a single, old-fashioned bathroom, but are interestingly furnished with a mix of antiques and four-poster or half-tester beds. Dining is a communal affair at the refectory kitchen table, in a vaulted room which once constituted the outer parlour and conference room; bar snacks and real ales are served in the cellar below. All but determined vegetarians will probably enjoy the local lamb at some point. Llanthony Priory is not widely advertised as a tourist attraction, but visitors come to admire the ruins (which are freely accessible during daylight hours) and use the adjacent public car park as a walking base.

◗ Closed Mon to Thur end Oct to Easter (open New Year); dining-room closed Mon eve 🔀 From A465 at Llanfihangel Crucorney, take road signposted Llanthony Priory; hotel is within priory. Public car park nearby 🛏️ 2 twin, 1 double, 2 four-poster; tea/coffee-making facilities available ⊘ Dining-room, bar, garden; fishing, pony trekking; early suppers for children ⅙ No wheelchair access ● No children under 10; no dogs; no smoking in bedrooms ☐ None accepted £ Single occupancy of twin/double £25 to £30, twin/double/four-poster £46 to £55; deposit required. Bar/bistro L £4; alc D £13

LLANWRTYD WELLS Powys

map 4

Carlton House

Dolycoed Road, Llanwrtyd Wells LD5 4RA
TEL: (01591) 610248   FAX: (01591) 610242

Highly rated cooking at this friendly, family-run restaurant-with-rooms.

You immediately get the feel of Dr Alan and Mary Ann Gilchrist's three-storey Victorian town house on entering the panelled reception, with its restaurant adjoining – there's a fire in the grate, some shelves of well-thumbed books, and a few old curios. In summer 1998 the sitting-room and restaurant changed places and, according to Mary Ann, this gives more space for diners and a cosier feel to the sitting-room. This is a family-run hotel, where Cecily the basset hound comes to greet you, and a junior Gilchrist might poke her head out of the kitchen and ask for a snack. And the kitchen is the heart of the matter: Mary Ann's cooking gathers much praise for its sense of innovation balanced with simplicity. There is a wide choice: a light menu (where soup might be followed by pan-fried chicken, then a sticky toffee pudding), a more serious table d'hôte menu (including a dessert called 'a serious attack on chocolate') and finally the à la carte selection, which might include king prawns with asparagus tips in lemon butter before a main course of roast Welsh lamb in a herb crust and, to finish, a red-fruit pavlova. The bedrooms follow the same pattern of solid dependability with a dash of inspiration. Best of all is the striking black, gold and white of the Cherub Room, in a fine corner position at the top of the house.

◑ Closed Chr 🔁 In centre of Llanwrtyd Wells. On-street parking (free) ⚑ 1 single, 1 twin/double, 4 double, 1 suite; most with bathroom/WC, 2 with shower/WC (not all *en suite*); all with TV, clock radio ⊘ Restaurant, sitting-room; early suppers for children; high chair, baby-listening ♿ No wheelchair access ● No dogs in public rooms ▭ Delta, MasterCard, Switch, Visa £ Single £30, single occupancy of twin/double £45, twin/double £60, suite £70; deposit required. Set L £12.50 to £20, D £20; alc L, D £28. Special breaks available

---

LLYSWEN Powys map 4

Griffin Inn

Llyswen, Brecon LD3 0UR
TEL: (01874) 754241 FAX: (01874) 754592

Popular village pub in the Welsh borders, combining old-world charm with practical, up-to-date accommodation.

This fifteenth-century, family-run sporting-inn stands in the village centre at a well-used knot of roads which pause in Llyswen as if temporarily confused by the Wye's sudden change of course from south-east to north-east as it approaches the English border. The creeper-covered building attracts passers-by with its colourful gardens and parasol-topped tables, while open fires blaze a cheerful greeting inside in all but the warmest weather. The twin bars are cosily furnished, and feature horse brasses and hunting scenes; you may well find the inn's unmistakeably clad ghillie here, ready to discuss the fishing with you. Game fishing and shooting are popular topics of conversation, and there are plenty of talking points displayed on the walls. Bar snacks and full meals are served, the latter in a pleasant, cosy dining-room, at well-spaced tables. The cooking is based on local ingredients (especially salmon) and has a good reputation; our inspector's meal was unsatisfactory on several counts, however – a promising-sounding fennel risotto was very disappointing. The bedrooms (colourfully named after fishing flies, such as Silver Wilkinson) are smartly decorated in matching florals, with honey-coloured pine and cane furnishings. The bathrooms sparkle with chrome and white tiles, and towels are generously heaped on heated rails. It seems unusual not to find televisions installed in all the bedrooms in this tariff bracket (they are available on request and there is a separate TV room for residents upstairs). The Stockton family and older staff are very pleasant, but our inspector found some of the younger staff inefficient and rather off-hand in dealing with her booking.

◑ Closed 25, 26 Dec; dining-room closed Sun eve 🔁 On A470, 7 miles south-west of Hay-on-Wye. Private car park ⚑ 2 single, 3 twin, 1 double, 1 four-poster; family rooms available; all with bathroom/WC exc singles with shower/WC; all with room service, direct-dial telephone; TV, hair-dryer available ⊘ 2 dining-rooms, 2 bars, 2 lounges, TV room, drying-room, garden; conferences (max 12 residential/non-residential); leisure facilities nearby (reduced rates for guests); early suppers for children; cots, high chairs, toys, babysitting, baby-listening ♿ No wheelchair access ● No dogs in main dining-room; no smoking in main dining-room and bedrooms ☐ Amex, Delta, Diners, MasterCard, Switch, Visa ₤ Single £40, single occupancy of twin/double £45 to £50, twin/double/family room £70, four-poster £80; deposit required. Bar/bistro L £7.50 to £10.50, D £10.50 to £15; set L £10 to £15, D £15 to £20; alc D £21. Special breaks available

Llangoed Hall

Llyswen, Brecon LD3 0YP
TEL: (01874) 754525   FAX: (01874) 754545
EMAIL: llangoed_hall_co_wales_uk@compuserve.com
WEB SITE: www.llangoedhall.com/llangoed.html

No expense spared in this luxurious country-house hotel, peacefully set on the Welsh borders of the Wye Valley.

This palatial country-house hotel is peacefully set in extensive grounds, surrounded by farmland and woods. It lies just outside Llyswen, nine miles west of Hay-on-Wye. An Edwardian recreation by Sir Clough Williams-Ellis (of Portmeirion fame) of a much earlier manor house, it has now been expensively converted into a smart luxury hotel by Sir Bernard Ashley (Laura's widower). No corners have been cut in this enterprise; the scale is lavish. The public rooms and bedrooms are grand and beautifully furnished but still unfailingly cheerful and comfortable, containing a harmonious mixture of antiques and up-market ranges of Laura Ashley décor. Walls and display cases reveal evidence of Sir Bernard's considerable art collection and his passion for model steam engines. Though the hotel's trade includes a significant proportion of conferences and overseas tour groups, this does not interfere with the supremely solicitous and personal service. The food is ambitious and elegant, using some of the produce from the walled gardens. Fishing, archery and clay-pigeon shooting can be arranged, and there's even a helipad. This is an extremely comfortable retreat, though understandably no budget option.

◑ Open all year ⊉ 1 mile north of Llyswen on A470 towards Builth Wells. Private car park ⤶ 1 single, 11 twin/double, 8 four-poster, 3 suites; all with bathroom/WC; all with TV, room service, hair-dryer, direct-dial telephone; no tea/coffee-making facilities in rooms ⊘ Dining-room, 3 lounges, library, conservatory, games room, garden; functions (max 70 people incl up to 45 residential), conferences; civil wedding licence; fishing, tennis, mountain bikes, archery, clay-pigeon shooting ⅙ No wheelchair access ⬤ No children under 8; dogs in kennels only; no smoking in dining-room ☐ Amex, Delta, Diners, MasterCard, Switch, Visa ₤ Single and single occupancy of twin/double £155, twin/double/four-poster £185, suite £360; deposit required. Set L £18, D £35; alc L £20, D £38. Special breaks available

---

MAENTWROG Gwynedd   map 7

Grapes Hotel   **NEW ENTRY**

Maentwrog, Blaenau Ffestiniog LL41 4HN
TEL: (01766) 590365   FAX: (01766) 590654

Solid, uncomplicated pub-with-rooms for real-ale aficionados.

Brian and Gill Tarbox's roadside inn is first and foremost a decent pub – real ale is served from hand-pumps, there is a lot of wood panelling and exposed stone walls, and the friendly buzz of locals and visitors. Upstairs are two bars and a restaurant offering carvery-style meals; at the time of our inspection a new dining area was shaping up downstairs in the cosy cellars, demonstrating a touch of arty sophistication in its wrought-iron and wooden furniture. The bedrooms in the house are straightforward and simple, with some old features like Victorian fireplaces. Noise from the bars below might intrude, however – in which case opt for a room in the old brewery house, where bedrooms are compact and whitewashed, and have pine furniture and simple shower-rooms. Room 1 also has a diminutive lounge upstairs, with a TV and sofa.

◑ Open all year   ⏭ Turn off A487 Porthmadog road on to A496 to Harlech; pub is 200 yards along, on right. Private car park   ⌂⇥ 3 single, 3 double, 2 family rooms; some in annexe; 3 with bathroom/WC, 5 with shower/WC; all with TV, hair-dryer   ⊘ 2 restaurants, 2 bars, conservatory; functions (max 40 people incl up to 18 residential); early suppers for children; high chairs   &. No wheelchair access   ● Dogs in 1 bar and bedrooms only; no smoking in 1 restaurant   ▭ Amex, Delta, Diners, MasterCard, Switch, Visa   £ Single and single occupancy of double £25, double £50, family room £60; deposit required. Bar/bistro L, D £7; alc D £18

MILEBROOK Powys   map 4

Milebrook House

Milebrook, Knighton LD7 1LT
TEL: (01547) 528632   FAX: (01547) 520509
EMAIL: hotel@milebrook.kc3ltd.co.uk

A quiet, family-run country house, well placed for exploring the Welsh Marches.

On the outskirts of Knighton stands this largely Victorian mansion in a fine three-acre garden which owners Rodney and Beryl Marsden are slowly developing. Last year 700 trees were planted, and the new pond, simply left to mature on its own, has somehow gathered sticklebacks, frogs and newts. The house itself has a warm, homely atmosphere with more than a few hints of elegance and grandeur. One such is in the many photographs of Emperor Haile Selassie of Abyssinia – he stayed at the house in the 1930s, when it was occupied by the family of Sir Wilfred Thesiger, the desert explorer (Sir Wilfred's boyhood room, incidentally, was Room 1). The Marsdens have cleverly used pieces of antique furniture, chandeliers and gilt frames to give the right feel to the place, leavening them with more modern colours and paintings. On the corner of the house, overlooking the herb garden, is a stylish dining-room, where the table d'hôte menu offers at least three choices at each stage: maybe Carmarthen ham with melon to start, followed by rack of lamb with fresh thyme sauce, and a French lemon tart to finish. Bedrooms are in a smart country-house style, with vibrant colour schemes. In the new West Wing are downstairs rooms suitable for less mobile guests.

◐ Open all year ⊡ 2 miles east of Knighton, on A4113 Ludlow road. Private car park
⤶ 4 twin, 6 double; family rooms available; all with bathroom/WC; all with TV, room
service, direct-dial telephone, some with hair-dryer ⊘ Dining-room, bar, lounge,
drying-room, garden; functions (max 45 people incl up to 20 residential), conferences;
fishing, clay-pigeon shooting; early suppers for children ♿ Wheelchair access to
hotel (1 step) and restaurant, 2 ground-floor bedrooms, 1 specially equipped for
disabled people ⊖ No children under 8; no dogs; no smoking in bedrooms
▭ Amex, Delta, MasterCard, Switch, Visa £ Single occupancy of twin/double £48,
twin/double £70, family room £85; deposit required. Bar L £5; set L £11, D £18.50.
Special breaks available

THE MUMBLES Swansea   map 4

Hillcrest House

1 Higher Lane, The Mumbles, Swansea SA3 4NS
TEL: (01792) 363700   FAX: (01792) 363768

Smart but unstuffy small hotel close to the seaside.

Born in Scotland, raised in Canada and formerly a South African resident,
Yvonne Scott has had a varied life which is reflected in the décor of her hotel
bedrooms: England has a feminine rose theme, Scotland smart plaids and, best
of all, Safari, with its bold leopard-print fabrics, tribal carvings and a four-poster
draped with muslin to keep tsetse flies at bay. The thoughtful design extends to
useful extras like emery boards and hand lotion (the beach is a short, steep walk
away); the tea tray comes with fresh milk and a cafetière. Downstairs Yvonne has
plans to extend the African theme, but at the time of inspection there was a
homely and attractive lounge area leading into the Mediterranean-style
dining-room and bar. The three-course table d'hôte menu offers four choices at
each stage, perhaps whitebait with tartare sauce to start with, followed by rack of
lamb with rosemary and redcurrant, and finally a sticky toffee banana pudding.

◐ Closed 1 week end Dec or early Jan; restaurant closed Sun eve ⊡ From Swansea,
take coast road 4 miles to The Mumbles; turn right at second mini-roundabout (White
Rose pub); take fourth left by church (signed Langland/Caswell Bay); hotel is on left by
junction at third bend. Private car park ⤶ 1 single, 2 twin, 3 double, 1 four-poster; all
with bathroom/WC exc 2 with shower/WC; all with TV, room service, hair-dryer,
direct-dial telephone ⊘ Dining-room, bar, lounge; functions (max 30 people incl up to
13 residential); leisure facilities nearby (free and reduced rates for guests); early suppers
for children; cots, high chairs, babysitting ♿ No wheelchair access ⊖ No dogs; no
smoking in dining-room and some bedrooms ▭ Amex, Delta, MasterCard, Visa
£ Single £48, single occupancy of twin/double £53, twin/double £60 to £68,
four-poster £80; deposit required. Set D £18.50

The Guide *is totally independent, accepts no free hospitality, and
survives on the number of copies sold each year.*

Report forms are at the back of the Guide; *write a letter or email us if
you prefer. Our email address is: "guide.reports@which.net".*

Cwmtwrch Hotel & Four Seasons Restaurant   NEW ENTRY

Nantgaredig, Carmarthen SA32 7NY
TEL: (01267) 290238   FAX: (01267) 290808

A friendly B&B in beautiful countryside, with an excellent restaurant next door.

There is something missing from the view across the rolling Carmarthen hills to Paxton's Victorian folly when standing in Jenny Willmott's herb garden: no pylons. There's not much at all, in fact, to disturb the peace of the winding River Towy, which is why the Willmotts came here 23 years ago and started offering B&B at their farmhouse. Then two of their daughters set up a restaurant and wine-shipping business next door, another outbuilding made a fine little heated swimming-pool, and Jenny's five bedrooms began to look even more beguiling places in which to stay. The house itself has a Mediterranean feel, with its natural colours, terracotta pots and rugs on quarry tiles. From the large, homely breakfast room, stairs lead to a cosy lounge, where there are plenty of books and comfy chairs set around a log burner. The two bedrooms in the house are both compact and cottagey – if you want a little more room, it's better to stay in the converted barn across the yard, where the rooms have vaulted ceilings and a pleasing mix of old furniture and stone-washed colours. The Four Seasons Restaurant is a separate enterprise, but is very similar in style to the farmhouse: a straightforward, informal approach, with pine furniture and slate floors. Customers can see into the kitchen, where the much-praised cooking is done; you might opt for mussels with leeks, cider and cream to start, then chicken breast stuffed with Brie and wrapped in Carmarthen ham.

◗ Closed 24 to 27 Dec; restaurant closed Sun & Mon eves   ⟐ At Nantgaredig crossroads on A40, take B4310 north towards Brechfa; hotel is ¼ mile on, on right. Private car park   ⊨ 2 twin, 3 double; some in annexe; family rooms available; 2 with bathroom/WC, 3 with shower/WC; all with TV, some with hair-dryer   ⊘ Restaurant, breakfast room, bar, 2 lounges, drying-room, conservatory, garden; functions (max 50 people incl up to 12 residential), conferences; gym, heated indoor swimming-pool; early suppers for children; cots, high chairs   ⟐ Wheelchair access to hotel (1 step) and restaurant (ramp), 3 ground-floor bedrooms   ● No children under 8 in restaurant eves; no dogs in public rooms; no smoking in some public rooms   ▱ MasterCard, Visa   £ Single occupancy of twin/double £40, twin/double £56, family room £60; deposit required. Set L £10 to £23, D £20 to £23

Pen-y-Gwryd Hotel

Nantgwynant, Capel Curig, Caernarfon LL55 4NT
TEL: (01286) 870211

Friendly but basic climbers' retreat in lovely scenery.

This dour-looking, craggy-faced building has made itself a base camp for several strings of Everest hopefuls and a slightly smaller number of Everest conquerors. Set in implacably imposing scenery, it is not luxurious, but it does have character and a place in mountaineering history. Antique leather boots hang from the ceiling in the 'boot room', and the ice picks are not the sort with which you could prepare cocktails. There's a cosy bar, too, with an open fire, wood panelling and a model of Snowdon. The dining-room has a little more elegance about it, with silver candelabra and a grandfather clock. The five-course dinners are intended to keep feet firmly on the ground, with plenty of soups and roasts and such traditional puddings as fruit crumbles or spotted dick. The bedrooms are simply furnished but comfortable, with the occasional interesting feature like a free-standing bath on a platform. If that sounds too soft for you, there's always the mountain stream outside.

◑ Closed Nov, Dec & midweek Jan to Feb ⊿ From Betws-y-Coed, take A5 west to Capel Curig; turn left on to A4086; hotel is 4 miles on. Private car park ⊨ 1 single, 7 twin, 7 double, 1 four-poster; one in annexe; family rooms available; some with bathroom/WC, 1 with shower/WC; no tea/coffee-making facilities in rooms ⊘ Dining-room, bar, lounge, drying-room, games room, garden; functions (max 40 people incl up to 31 residential), conferences; fishing, sauna, unheated outdoor swimming-pool; early suppers for children; cots, high chairs, playroom, outdoor play area ఉ Wheelchair access to hotel and dining-room, 1 ground-floor annexe bedroom specially equipped for disabled people ● No smoking in dining-room, discouraged in bedrooms ▭ None accepted £ Single £21 to £26, single occupancy of twin/double from £21, twin/double £42 to £52, four-poster £52, family room (rates on application); deposit required. Bar/bistro L £4; set D £16

NEWPORT Pembrokeshire map 4

Cnapan

East Street, Newport SA42 0SY
TEL: (01239) 820575   FAX: (01239) 820878

Friendly, family-run hotel with a reputation for its home cooking.

The name comes from an ancient ball game played between Newport and the next village – a game now banned for causing too many injuries! It's hard to imagine such a violent activity in this quiet and friendly settlement, particularly once you're inside this pink-painted Georgian house run by two generations of one family (the Coopers and the Lloyds). The style is charmingly cottagey, with fresh flowers, displays of crockery on dressers and framed prints. It's a style that continues through to the busy restaurant, where the emphasis is on the wholesome and the home-made, with local ingredients playing an important part. Spicy fish-cakes with coriander mayonnaise might be the choice from half-a-dozen starters on the blackboard, then local lamb marinated in spiced yoghurt, followed by a very self-indulgent chocolate, coffee and whisky cake with cream. The guest rooms are carefully decorated with books, pictures and ornaments, giving them a homely feel. Room 3 is a good-value family option – an extra side room contains bunk-beds and a pine chest full of toys. Room 4 is the pick of the rest: pretty and spacious, with a big bay window overlooking the street. All rooms have well-stocked tea trays, but the mother and daughter team of Eluned Lloyd and Judith Cooper still provide new arrivals with the welcome cuppa and home-baked Welsh cakes.

○ Closed Chr, Jan (open New Year), Feb; restaurant closed Tue eve 🅰 In centre of Newport on A487. Private car park 🛏 3 twin, 1 double, 1 family room; all with shower/WC; all with TV, room service, hair-dryer ⊘ Restaurant, bar, lounge, garden; early suppers for children; cots, high chairs, toys, baby-listening ♿ No wheelchair access ● No dogs; smoking in bar only ▭ Delta, MasterCard, Visa £ Single occupancy of twin/double £27 to £36, twin/double £54, family room £63; deposit required. Bar/bistro L £7; alc D £17

NORTHOP Flintshire   map 7

Soughton Hall

Northop, Mold CH7 6AB
TEL: (01352) 840811   FAX: (01352) 840382

Grand country house set in magnificent grounds – convenient for Theatr Clwyd.

Can a bishop have a curate's egg? Built as a bishop's residence in 1714, Soughton Hall has since seen many unepiscopal additions: Islamic turrets for a start, added by an eighteenth-century traveller, and then the more recent real-ale bar in the converted stables and a wine shop. Not that the current owners, the Rodenhurst family, have betrayed the feel of the place – quite the opposite: every care has been taken to maintain and restore the period style, with wood panelling, chintz and a mix of antique and good-quality reproduction furniture. The overall effect is grand and rather impressive, no more so than in the dining-room, with its high ceiling bedecked with frescoes and a chandelier. The three-course dinner offers a good selection that pulls out all the stops: trout with fried mussels to start, perhaps, followed by a sorbet and then baked cutlets of lamb with a crab filling and herb crust. Less formal and simpler dining can be had in the Stables Bar. The bedrooms, as you would expect, are spacious and luxurious.

○ Open all year 🅰 Leave A55 at A5119 signed Mold; pass through Northop village and hotel is ½ mile further, on left. Private car park 🛏 5 twin, 7 double, 1 four-poster, 1 family room; one in annexe; all with bathroom/WC; all with TV, room service, hair-dryer, trouser press, direct-dial telephone ⊘ Dining-room, 2 bars, 3 lounges, library, conservatory, garden; functions (max 120 people incl up to 29 residential), conferences; civil wedding licence; golf, tennis ♿ No wheelchair access ● Children in dining-room by arrangement; no dogs; no smoking in bedrooms ▭ Amex, MasterCard, Switch, Visa £ Single occupancy of twin/double £80, twin/double £130, four-poster/family room £150; deposit required. Bar/bistro L £6, D £15; set L £24.50, D £32.50. Special breaks available

---

Don't expect to turn up at a small hotel assuming that a room will be available. It's always best to telephone in advance.

Where we say 'Deposit required', a hotel may instead ask for your credit card details when taking your booking.

Penally Abbey

Penally, Tenby SA70 7PY
TEL: (01834) 843033   FAX: (01834) 844714
EMAIL: penally.abbey@btinternet.com

Friendly and unstuffy country house with excellent sea views.

Set above the golf links with spectacular sea views, Steven and Eileen Warren's nineteenth-century country-house hotel gains a head start from its location, but it is the Warrens who give the place its effortlessly relaxing atmosphere. The interiors are period in style, with stained glass, ornate plasterwork and an abundance of Gothic Revival doorways, cupboards and windows. The bedrooms, too, have nice touches of grandeur. Most have four-posters, complemented by antiques and floral fabrics; a few have striking sea views. For more privacy, try those in the converted coach house, which are equally pleasant, if a little smaller. With classical columns and chandeliers, the dining-room is an elegant room, and the menu lives up to its surroundings with starters such as pears and Stilton laced with port or green-lipped mussels in garlic and white wine; main courses might include Brecon venison in cream and brandy or local pheasant.

◑ Open all year ⊞ In centre of Penally, 1 mile south-west of Tenby, just off A4139. Private car park ⟜ 1 twin, 4 double, 7 four-poster; some in annexe; all with bathroom/WC; all with TV, room service, hair-dryer, direct-dial telephone ⌦ Dining-room, bar, lounge, drying-room, conservatory, games room, garden; functions (max 38 people incl up to 24 residential), conferences; civil wedding licence; snooker; early suppers for children; cots, high chairs, toys, babysitting, baby-listening ♿ Wheelchair access (1 step) to hotel and dining-room, 2 ground-floor bedrooms ● No children under 7 in dining-room eves; no dogs; no smoking ▭ Amex, MasterCard, Switch, Visa ⚃ Single and single occupancy of twin/double £90 to £116, twin/double £100 to £124, four-poster £120 to £124; deposit required. Bar/bistro L £16; set L £18, D £26; alc L, D £26. Special breaks available

George III Hotel

Penmaenpool, Dolgellau LL40 1YD
TEL: (01341) 422525   FAX: (01341) 423565

Good country pub, with an interesting history and convivial bars.

On a blue-skied bank-holiday afternoon, the George III Hotel can be pretty busy, but that's nothing to what it must once have been, for this little waterside hamlet was once a shipbuilding centre, a railway station and a ferry terminus. Memories of former glories are preserved in the railway signals and the hotel's extra bedrooms in the old station building, a short walk away along the quay. So train enthusiasts can today have the pleasure of staying on platform one in either Parcels or Left Luggage, now smartly attractive rooms. The main building was once a ship's chandler's, a flavour of which has been retained in the restaurant, with its beams, model boat and ships' wheels. The menu offers few surprises, and perhaps less seafood than you might have hoped for, but plenty of choice. Next door is a pleasant, clubby bar, with good views, and downstairs, beside the water, is another, noisier bar, which is popular with locals and day-trippers. The bedrooms in the main building are fresh in style, with simple, comfortable furniture.

◐ Open all year ⤬ 3 miles west of Dolgellau on A493. Private car park ⌸ 4 twin, 7 double; some in annexe; family rooms available; 6 with bathroom/WC, 5 with shower/WC; all with TV, room service, hair-dryer, trouser press, direct-dial telephone, clock radio ⊗ Restaurant, 3 bars, lounge, drying-room, conservatory; functions (max 150 people incl up to 22 residential), conferences; fishing; early suppers for children; cots, high chairs ⅙ Wheelchair access to hotel (ramp) and restaurant, 5 ground-floor bedrooms ● No dogs in restaurant; dogs in some bedrooms only (£5 per night); no smoking in 1 bar and restaurant ⊟ Delta, MasterCard, Switch, Visa £ Single occupancy of twin/double £50, twin/double £94, family room £107; deposit required. Bar/bistro L, D £4 to £6; set Sun L £12; alc D £22.50. Special breaks available

---

Penmaenuchaf Hall

Penmaenpool, Dolgellau LL40 1YB
TEL: (01341) 422129   FAX: (01341) 422787

Smart, friendly country-house hotel with excellent views.

The long, rough drive up through the woods to Lorraine Fielding's and Mark Watson's Victorian mansion is worth taking slowly – it only increases the pleasure of finally emerging at this handsome slate-roofed house. Set up on the hillside, it has fine views over the Mawddach estuary and 21 acres of grounds that produce wild mushrooms, herbs and vegetables for the pot. Over the front door is the crest of the Bolton cotton magnate who had the place built, and inside there are further stately touches, such as the dark panelling and the intricately worked ceiling in the main dining-room. The roof is even a Site of Special Scientific Interest – Mark will explain! The bedrooms have plenty of country-house character – fresh floral prints mixed with well-chosen furniture – and good bright bathrooms. The pick of them, for the best views and its smart blue-and-white décor, is Newling Griffiths, which has a corner position in the roof. Downstairs a new conservatory was almost finished when we inspected, neatly filling the bay between main wing and original billiard room. At dinner there is a choice between table d'hôte and à la carte menus, the latter particularly strong on local produce, like sea trout and bream with laverbread, and lamb in a redcurrant and mint sauce.

◐ Closed second week Jan ⤬ From A470 Dolgellau bypass, turn west on A493; hotel drive is 1 mile on left. Private car park ⌸ 5 twin, 7 double, 2 four-poster; all with bathroom/WC; all with TV, room service, hair-dryer, direct-dial telephone, clock radio, some with mini-bar ⊗ 2 dining-rooms, bar, 2 lounges, drying-room, library, conservatory, games room, garden; conferences (max 50 people incl up to 14 residential), functions; civil wedding licence; fishing, snooker; early suppers for children; cots, high chairs, baby-listening, outdoor play area ⅙ No wheelchair access ● No children under 7 exc babes in arms; dogs in 1 public room and 1 bedroom only; no smoking in some public rooms and some bedrooms ⊟ Amex, Delta, Diners,

MasterCard, Switch, Visa [£] Single occupancy of twin/double £65 to £110, twin/double £100 to £145, four-poster £155; deposit required. Bar/bistro L from £3.50; set L £13/£15, D £25; alc D £30. Special breaks available

---

PONTFAEN Pembrokeshire   map 4

Tregynon Farmhouse

Gwaun Valley, Fishguard SA65 9TU
TEL: (01239) 820531   FAX: (01239) 820808
EMAIL: tregynon@uk-holidays.co.uk
WEB SITE: www.uk-holidays.co.uk/tregynon/

Fine cooking after good walks is the attraction of this rural retreat.

Nineteen years ago, Peter Heard brought his family to this idyllic corner of Pembrokeshire and to life in a sixteenth-century farmhouse on the hillside above the Gwaun Valley – home to red kites and peregrine falcons. Inside the well-kept stone house are the hotel's lounge, dining-room and bar – a cosy snug perfect for relaxing in and looking over the daily-changing table d'hôte menu after a long day's hike. The dining-room itself, on split levels, is smartly done out in deep blues, with large blackened beams and bare stone walls. There are usually three or four choices at each course (including a vegetarian option), and you might opt for cream of spinach soup to start, followed by Welsh topside of beef baked in a red-wine and port sauce, and finally a sticky toffee pudding. Coffee is taken in the lounge – another cosy room, with its large inglenook fireplace, sofas and a piano. All but one bedroom are in the barn conversion, a short walk across the yard. It offers spacious, farmhouse-style accommodation, and has white walls, black beams and lacy drapes.

◖ Closed 2 weeks in winter   ⊿ From intersection of B4313 and B4329, take B4313 towards Fishguard; then take first right and follow signs, bearing right. Private car park   ⊨ 2 double, 2 four-poster, 2 family rooms; some in annexe; all with bathroom/WC; all with TV, hair-dryer, direct-dial telephone   ⊘ Dining-room, bar, lounge, garden; conferences (max 14 people incl up to 6 residential)   ⅙ No wheelchair access   ● No children under 8; no dogs; smoking in lounge only   ▢ Delta, MasterCard, Switch, Visa   [£] Single occupancy of double £54 to £68, double £60 to £68, four-poster £72 to £76, family room from £77; deposit required. Set D £19 to £20; alc D £24.50. Special breaks available

---

PORTHKERRY Vale of Glamorgan   map 4

Egerton Grey

Porthkerry, Barry CF62 3BZ
TEL: (01446) 711666   FAX: (01446) 711690
EMAIL: info@egertongrey.co.uk
WEB SITE: www.egertongrey.co.uk

Secluded gem of a country house run with charm and efficiency.

Tucked into a little wooded vale with views down towards the railway viaduct and the sea, there is something of a lost and forgotten era about Anthony and

Magda Pitkin's early Victorian house. One almost expects a parson in a white linen jacket, clutching a butterfly net, to come bumbling across the croquet lawn. And this despite Cardiff Airport being close by. Inside, the house is grand on a small scale: the dining-room is panelled with Cuban mahogany and lit by a clerestory, the drawing-room has a chandelier and gilt-framed portraits. The overall effect, however, is intimate rather than intimidating. There is careful attention to quality and detail in the presentation of food: a typical three-course table d'hôte menu of cream of wild mushroom soup, followed by fillet of cod with a lemon crust, then a steamed toffee and banana sponge, is borne on Royal Worcester crockery while you sip from Welsh crystal glasses. The best bedrooms take in the view at the front of the house: the Blue Room has a superb Victorian shower-bath; Master Bedroom 1 has a king-sized four-poster with another good bathroom. Ornithologists might prefer Uncle Fred's Room: the vast beech tree outside the window is a haven for nuthatches.

◑ Open all year ☒ From M4 Junction 33, follow signs to airport past Barry; at small roundabout by airport turn left, then left again after 500 yards. Private car park ⌖ 1 single, 3 twins, 3 double, 2 four-poster, 1 suite; family rooms available; all with bathroom/WC exc single with shower/WC; all with satellite TV, room service, hair-dryer, trouser press, direct-dial telephone ⊘ 2 dining-rooms, drawing-room, library, conservatory, garden; functions (max 100 people incl up to 20 residential), conferences; civil wedding licence; early suppers for children; cots, high chairs, babysitting ♿ No wheelchair access ⬤ No dogs in public rooms and most bedrooms ▭ Amex, Delta, Diners, MasterCard, Switch, Visa £⃞ Single £65, single occupancy of twin/double £80, twin/double £92, four-poster/family room/suite £120; deposit required. Light L £5; set L from £10, D from £14.50; alc L, D £25. Special breaks available

---

Hotel Portmeirion

Portmeirion, Penrhyndeudraeth LL48 6ET
TEL: (01766) 770228 FAX: (01766) 771331
EMAIL: hotel@portmeirion.wales.com
WEB SITE: portmeirion.wales.com

Supremely stylish and imaginative 'village', with beautiful rooms and views.

Set close to the swimming-pool and the sound of water tumbling from the crag, this is one of the best corners of Sir Clough Williams-Ellis's evocative recreation of a Mediterranean paradise. The whole village is a holiday complex, but such is its success that it has also become a tourist attraction, with its car parks at the gate full on busy days and sightseers wandering around the picturesque lanes and alleyways of cypresses and statuary. The various rooms and houses are beautifully furnished and equipped – Port Meirion pottery features on the tea tray, of course – and there are also self-catering alternatives. The main hotel, a white, airy building overlooking the bay, takes in influences beyond the Mediterranean, and has Indian and Thai echoes in the bar. The elegant, curving restaurant has a ceiling supported by marble pillars with gilded capitals (the originals were said to have been salvaged from a wreck in the bay). Readers are unanimous in their praise of the food – the restaurant goes 'from strength to strength', according to one regular visitor, who singled out the desserts for special mention. Service, too, seems to be back on course ('excellent') after last year's gripe.

○ Open all year ⚡ In Portmeirion village. Private car park ⤺ 10 twin, 13 double, 2 four-poster, 3 family rooms, 11 suites; some in annexe; all with bathroom/WC; all with TV, room service, hair-dryer, trouser press, direct-dial telephone, some with tea/coffee-making facilities ⚶ Restaurant, bar, 3 lounges, drying-room, garden; functions (max 100 people incl up to 80 residential), conferences; civil wedding licence; golf, heated outdoor swimming-pool, tennis; leisure facilities nearby (free for guests); early suppers for children; cots, high chairs, babysitting ⚸ No wheelchair access ● No dogs; no smoking in some public rooms ▭ Amex, Delta, Diners, MasterCard, Switch, Visa £ Single occupancy of twin/double £80, twin/double £100 to £150, four-poster £140, family room £120, suite £150; deposit required. Continental B £7, cooked B £9.50; set L £13.50, D £30. Special breaks available

---

REYNOLDSTON Swansea   map 4

Fairyhill

Reynoldston, Swansea SA3 1BS
TEL: (01792) 390139   FAX: (01792) 391358

Secluded country-house hotel with a reputation for fine cooking.

In the quiet centre of the Gower peninsula stands this stone-built eighteenth-century mansion set in 24 acres of wooded grounds. The style is classic country house with modern flourishes – smart, striped wallpapers and dark, polished furniture, the sound of classical music drifting through from the dining-room. Music is quite important to the atmosphere: every bedroom has a CD player, and guests can borrow discs from the extensive library. Room 1 is perhaps the best of the bedrooms, with its corner position and telescope for spotting the various woodpeckers, buzzards and foxes that inhabit the wooded grounds; it has a good-sized old-fashioned bathroom, too. All rooms are carefully decorated in conservative but cultured style: botanical prints, books and pieces of pottery are dotted around. The three-course dinner menu offers a wide and much-praised selection, perhaps seared scallops with black fettucini to start, followed by a grilled fillet of Welsh beef with a horseradish soufflé and whisky sauce, then for dessert a banana crème brûlée.

○ Closed between Chr and New Year ⚡ Take B4295 west from Swansea for 9 miles through Gowerton and Crofty; Fairyhill is signposted to left. Private car park ⤺ 1 twin, 7 double; all with bathroom/WC; all with TV, room service, hair-dryer, direct-dial telephone, CD player; no tea/coffee-making facilities in rooms ⚶ 2 dining-rooms, bar, lounge, garden; functions (max 40 people incl up to 8 residential), conferences; civil wedding licence; early suppers for children ⚸ No wheelchair access ● No children under 8; no dogs; no smoking in dining-rooms ▭ Amex, Delta, MasterCard, Switch, Visa £ Single occupancy of twin/double £95 to £145, twin/double £110 to £160; deposit required. Set L £11.50/£14.50, D £24.50/£29.50. Special breaks available

ST BRIDES WENTLOOGE Newport   map 4

West Usk Lighthouse

Lighthouse Road, St Brides Wentlooge,
Newport NP1 9SF
TEL: (01633) 810126   FAX: (01633) 815582

Atmospheric B&B in a nineteenth-century lighthouse.

Seen across the low, flat shores of the Severn as you drive up the rough track, Frank and Danielle Sheahan's lighthouse looks rather fort-like: a short, wide tower with a narrow one emerging from the top, like a half-extended telescope pointing heavenwards. It was built in 1821, when the memory of Napoleonic wars was still fresh – hence, perhaps, the resemblance to a Martello tower. Frank has rebuilt the lantern, now a 360-degree viewing bubble 50 feet above ground. Below it the top of the wider section of the building makes a terrace roof garden, complete with *objets trouvés* and a stone Buddha. Structurally, the lighthouse is being reborn as the architect James Walker intended, but he might not recognise some of the additions: a flotation tank where you can relive the Dead Sea experience, a red telephone box that is a shower, and a water-bed in Room 3. Frank's good humour and enthusiasm has also created a superb collection of model galleons, propellors and chairs made from barrels. Not everyone may appreciate the rutted approach road, the aromatherapy sessions on offer, or the Dalek signed by Jon Pertwee, but the excellent breakfast should suit most. Best of all is the night-time, when you can climb up to the lantern balcony, hear the breakers sighing on the rocks and look across the water to another lighthouse in far-off England. 'This hotel was wonderful,' wrote one satisfied correspondent, whose only quibble was the tiny *en suite* facilities in the family room.

○ Open all year ⏏ From Newport take B4239 for St Brides; after 2 miles turn left at B&B sign into long private road. Private car park 🛏 1 single, 1 double, 1 four-poster, 1 family room; all with shower/WC; all with TV, some with hair-dryer ✔ Dining-room, bar, lounge, conservatory, garden; sea fishing, flotation tank ♿ No wheelchair access ● No dogs; no smoking ▭ Amex, Delta, MasterCard, Switch, Visa
£ Single £50, single occupancy of double £60, double/four-poster/family room £80; deposit required

TALSARNAU Gwynedd   map 7

Maes-y-Neuadd

Talsarnau LL47 6YA
TEL: (01766) 780200   FAX: (01766) 780211
EMAIL: myn@wales-snowdonia.com

A fine country-house hotel run with quiet charm.

Standing in pleasant woods and lawns tucked far away from passing coastal traffic is this fine country house whose history goes back 600 years. The oldest part is the bar, which has huge stone walls worthy of a fort and a collection of antique bottles found when the dried-up mill race was cleared – with its leather chesterfields and its log-burner, this is the place for winter evenings. Brighter and more elegant is the dining-room, which overlooks the lawns and catches the sunsets over the Lleyn Peninsula. Head chef Peter Jackson works closely with the gardeners, using home-grown vegetables (baby turnips the day we inspected) and local fish, lamb and cheeses. The full five courses might start with a salad of scallops, venison sausage and black pudding, then move on to cauliflower and Stilton soup, terrine of local fish and loin of pork. The Grand Finale, as the menu calls it, starts with Welsh cheeses and culminates in a choice of three desserts. Bedrooms are comfortably old-fashioned, with high ceilings and Snowdon views in some, thick walls and heavy drapes in all. Glaslyn and Wynne are favourites for their views and unforced, classic style.

● Open all year ⊿ 3 miles north-east of Harlech, signposted off B4573. Private car park ⊫ 1 single, 7 twin, 5 double, 1 four-poster, 2 suites; some in annexe; family rooms available; all with bathroom/WC exc single with shower/WC; all with TV, room service, hair-dryer, direct-dial telephone; no tea/coffee-making facilities in rooms ⊘ Dining-room, bar, lounge, drying-room, conservatory, garden; conferences (max 60 people incl up to 16 residential), functions; civil wedding licence; early suppers for children; cots, high chairs, baby-listening ⅙ Wheelchair access to hotel (lift and ramps) and restaurant, WC (unisex), 3 ground-floor bedrooms, 1 specially equipped for disabled people ● No children under 8 in dining-room eves; no dogs in some public rooms; no smoking in dining-room or bedrooms ▭ Amex, Delta, Diners, MasterCard, Switch, Visa £ Single £55 to £57, single occupancy of twin/double £85 to £112, twin/double/family room £119 to £175, four-poster £133 to £139, suite £146 to £167; deposit required. Set L £13.50, D £32. Special breaks available

---

TAL-Y-LLYN Gwynedd map 7

Minffordd Hotel

Tal-y-llyn, Tywyn LL36 9AJ
TEL: (01654) 761665   FAX: (01654) 761517

Pocket-sized country-house hotel with an easy, unforced style.

It would be easy to miss this unimposing, white-painted hotel as you drive past on the A487, one eye on the vast slopes of Cader Idris, the other on the winding road. But there are good reasons to halt at Mark Warner and Mary McQuillan's seventeenth-century drovers' inn. First, there is the opportunity to walk straight out of the door on to the hills; then there is the understated elegance of the rooms; and last, but certainly not least, there is Mary's thoughtful friendliness and Mark's cooking. The dining-room has the best of the historical character: with its uneven floor and beams it has great atmosphere when candlelit for dinner. Drinks are usually taken in the bar beforehand – Mary making introductions and generally helping conversation along. The 'first-rate' fixed-price menu offers an alternative at each stage – meat or fish for the main course (maybe pheasant supreme in elderberry and shallot sauce or hake poached in lemon and bay, with lobster sauce). The cooking eschews unnecessary frippery but has plenty of flavour and comes in good-sized helpings. The bedrooms offer all the comfort you could want after a hard day's hill-walking: good linen and mattresses, modern bathrooms, and a decent tea tray. There is no television – most guests tend to congregate in the bar and lounge to swap Cader Idris stories.

◐ Closed Dec to Feb 🅩 At junction of A487 and B4405, midway between Dolgellau and Machynlleth. Private car park 🛏 2 twin, 4 double; all with bathroom/WC exc 1 double with shower/WC; all with room service, hair-dryer, direct-dial telephone, clock radio, some with binoculars ⌀ Dining-room, bar, 2 lounges, garden; early suppers for children ♿ No wheelchair access ● No children under 3; no dogs; smoking in bar only ▭ Delta, MasterCard, Visa £ Single occupancy of twin/double £54 to £65, twin/double £96 to £112 (rates incl dinner); deposit required. Special breaks available

---

TINTERN Monmouthshire   map 2

Parva Farmhouse

Tintern, Chepstow NP6 6SQ
TEL: (01291) 689411   FAX: (01291) 689557

A lovely riverside location for this former farmhouse.

Beside the river in a glorious wooded vale with views along the River Wye and of the ruined abbey, Dereck and Vickie Stubbs's seventeenth-century stone house makes an ideal place for enjoying the wonderful, peaceful landscape. The age of the house is best revealed in the sitting-room, where there is a fine stone fireplace, plus cosy leather chesterfields to lounge in on chilly evenings and a small honesty bar. Reflecting the hotel's riverside position, the dining-room is decorated with fishing-rods, trout flies and piscatorial prints. Fish and seafood, of course, appear on the four-course dinner menu, alongside starters like home-made celery, apple and tomato soup, main course options of roast lamb and steaks, and a traditional sweets trolley plus Welsh and English cheeses. 'The menu is not extensive,' wrote one correspondent, 'but everything is so delicious, it's difficult to choose.' The bedrooms are well kept and comfortable, with reproduction furniture – views are divided between garden and river.

◐ Open all year 🅩 On A466 at northern edge of Tintern village. Private car park 🛏 3 twin, 2 double, 2 four-poster, 2 family rooms; all with bathroom/WC exc doubles with shower/WC; all with TV, room service, hair-dryer, direct-dial telephone, clock radio ⌀ Dining-room, sitting-room/bar, drying-room, garden; functions (max 16 people incl up to 14 residential), conferences; leisure facilities nearby (reduced rates for guests); early suppers for children; cots, high chairs, toys, babysitting, baby-listening ♿ No wheelchair access ● No dogs in public rooms ▭ Amex, MasterCard, Visa £ Single occupancy of twin/double £46, twin/double/family room £60 to £68, four-poster £68 to £78; deposit required. Set D £19.50. Special breaks available

---

WHITEBROOK Monmouthshire   map 2

Crown at Whitebrook   **NEW ENTRY**

Whitebrook, Monmouth NP5 4TX
TEL: (01600) 860254   FAX: (01600) 860607

Superlative food served in the leafy forests of the lower Wye Valley.

Deep in the densely wooded Whitebrook valley, just a mile from the Wye near Tintern, this cream-painted roadside *auberge* amply repays a detour. The original part of the house dates from the late seventeenth century, but most is 'fifties style, with an upper floor added a decade ago. It is neat and well kept, if of no great architectural beauty. Attractive gardens of lawns, rockeries and terraces surround the house, merging into steep woodlands behind. First impressions reveal a tidy but unexceptional lounge bar comfortably furnished with plenty of relaxingly arranged sofas and easy chairs, magazines and fresh flowers. It is the restaurant areas beyond that deserve most attention, however, at lunch or dinner. The combination of Sandra Bates's splendid, mainly French, cooking and her husband Roger's friendly, solicitous service has received many unexaggerated accolades. A dozen modern, well-equipped bedrooms upstairs make the Crown a peaceful, practical overnight base, and there are excellent walks and leisure facilities close at hand. Golf, riding and fishing can be arranged on request. The owners are very knowledgeable about the area and can give visitors good suggestions for exploring an interesting stretch of the Wye.

◖ Closed 2 weeks in Jan; 2 weeks in July/Aug ⊿ Leave A466 at Bigsweir bridge, 6 miles south of Monmouth; follow sign to Whitebrook; hotel is 2 miles on left. Private car park ⇤ 2 twin, 7 double, 1 four-poster; all with bathroom/WC; all with TV, hair-dryer, direct-dial telephone ⊘ Restaurant, bar, lounge, garden; functions (max 36 people incl up to 20 residential), conferences; early suppers for children; cots, high chairs, baby-listening ⅙ No wheelchair access ● No dogs in public rooms ⊟ Amex, Delta, Diners, MasterCard, Switch, Visa £ Single occupancy of twin/double £75, twin/double £120, four-poster £134 (rates incl dinner). Light L £6, set L £17. Special breaks available

Round-ups

Again this year we are including a collection of hotels that are worth considering but do not quite merit a full entry. Those marked with an asterisk are new to the *Guide* this year. We would be particularly pleased to get feedback on any hotel in the section. The price given for each hotel is the standard cost of a twin-bedded or double room with breakfast, and is the latest available as we go to press. Prices may go up at some point in 1999.

LONDON

SE3   **Bardon Lodge/Paragon Restaurant**   0181-853 4051
Handy location in Blackheath – two Victorian houses with mature gardens and parking, though lacking in character.   £90

SW1   **The Executive**   0171-581 2424
Few frills B&B, but welcoming and keenly priced for its Knightsbridge location.   £108

SW1   **Willett Hotel ***   0171-824 8415
Spruce B&B accommodation on a fairly quiet Victorian terrace yards from Sloane Square; good value for the location.   £112

SW3   **Parkes Hotel**   0171-581 9944
Plush, mainly suite accommodation on a quiet Knightsbridge street; Scandinavian ownership and staff.   £165

SW6   **Chelsea Village Hotel ***   0171-565 1400
New hotel right on top of the football club, aimed at business people; dull bedrooms, but interesting eateries.   £160

SW7   **Cranley Gardens Hotel**   0171-373 3232
Useful, mid-sized, inexpensive hotel on a smart South Kensington Victorian terrace; passable bedrooms, but some below-par bathrooms, and reports of poor breakfasts.   £109

W1   **The Montcalm**   0171-402 4288
Slick, Japanese-owned hotel with first-rate service, occupying a handsome Georgian crescent – the best upmarket accommodation in the area.   £270

ENGLAND

Abbot's Salford (Warwickshire)   **Salford Hall**   (01386) 871300
Close to the main road, a multi-gabled manor dating from the fifteenth century, with impressive public rooms.   £110

Alston (Cumbria)   **Lovelady Shield**   (01434) 381203
With enthusiastic new owners, this peaceful Georgian house high in the Pennines is having a facelift.   £107

Ashbourne-in-the-Water (Derbyshire)   **Izaak Walton Hotel**
(01335) 350555
Good location for this secluded stone–built hotel with attractive modern bedrooms.   £103

Ashford-in-the-Water (Derbyshire)   **Riverside Country House Hotel**
(01629) 814275
Pleasant location for a smart country house hotel, under new ownership.
£120–£150

Ashprington (Devon)   **Waterman's Arms**   (01803) 732214
Appetising food and decent accommodation in a characterful, friendly hostelry by the river.   £64

Aspley Guise (Bedfordshire)   **Moore Place Hotel**   (01908) 282000
A modern hotel successfully grafted on to a Georgian house in the centre of this affluent village.   £100

Bapchild (Kent)   **Hempstead House**   (01795) 428020
Good food and home comforts in an ambitious family–run establishment – more rooms and a large restaurant were due for completion as we went to press.
£72

Basingstoke (Hampshire)   **Audley's Wood Thistle Hotel**
(01256) 817555
Victorian country house, with elegant conservatory restaurant, stylish rooms, conference facilities and easy access to the M3.   £150

Bath (Bath & N.E. Somerset)   **Bath Spa Hotel**   (01225) 444424
Regency townhouse just beyond the city walls with a country-house ambience. Two restaurants, including a vaulted basement cellar.   £178

Bath (Bath & N.E. Somerset)   **Leighton House**   (01225) 314769
Victorian B&B set in attractive gardens overlooking the city, 10 minutes' walk from the centre.   £62–£70

Bellingham (Northumberland)   **Westfield House**   (01434) 220340
Homely Victorian guest house in a village on the edge of wild moorland. Caring, friendly owners and fresh décor featuring lots of pine, four-posters and brass beds.   £56

Berkswell (Warwickshire)   **Nailcote Hall**   (01203) 466174
Excellent sports facilities at this leisure-oriented Elizabethan Manor.   £135

Blackpool (Lancashire)   **Sunray Hotel**   (01253) 351937
Comfortable, tidy B&B with welcoming hosts in a quiet residential street away from the bustle of the main promenade area. Evening meals can be pre-arranged.   £52

Bledington (Gloucestershire)   **Kings Head ***   (01608) 658365
Atmospheric old pub on the village green with a roaring food trade; most bedrooms are in modern additions.   £75

Bodinnick (Cornwall)   **Old Ferry Inn**   (01726) 870237
A traditional inn in a great spot with views across the estuary to Fowey; good pub atmosphere and acceptable accommodation.   £40

Bonchurch (Isle of Wight)   **Lake Hotel**   (01983) 852613
Family-run hotel in early nineteenth-century house with extensive gardens; lots of stripped wood and polished floors.   £52

Bradford (West Yorkshire) **Restaurant Nineteen** (01274) 492559
Elegant restaurant-with-rooms in a quietly handsome suburb of Bradford overlooking Lister Park. Stylish bedrooms with striking colour schemes. Up for sale as we went to press. £70

Braithwaite (Cumbria) **Ivy House** (01768) 778338
Pleasant service and good food, but bedrooms showing signs of wear and tear. £75

Brighton (East Sussex) **Arlanda *** (01273) 699300
Centrally located on a quiet Regency square. Bedrooms are small, and bathrooms even smaller, but comfortable enough. £46–£80

Brighton (East Sussex) **Topps Hotel** (01273) 729334
New owners for a longtime favourite in an excellent location near the West Pier. Spacious rooms but rather drab furniture and décor. £84

Bristol (Bristol) **Downlands Guesthouse** 0117-962 1639
Comfortable family-run guest house in a quiet residential street convenient for the University. £45

Broadway (Worcestershire) **Leasow House** (01386) 584526
High-quality B&B, with well-equipped, cottagey bedrooms, in a fine old Cotswold farmhouse a couple of miles from Broadway. £65

Brockenhurst (Hampshire) **Whitley Ridge** (01590) 622354
Peaceful location for a former Royal hunting lodge in the heart of the New Forest, now an affable family-run hotel. £96

Brookthorpe (Gloucestershire) **Gilbert's** (01452) 812364
Homely, unfussy rooms in striking half-timbered Jacobean house. Organic breakfasts cooked on the kitchen Aga and plenty to tempt vegetarians. £48

Bryher (Isles of Scilly) **Hell Bay Hotel** (01720) 422947
Comfort and welcome in a haven of peace on the Scillies' most unspoilt island. £130

Buckingham (Buckinghamshire) **Villiers** (01280) 822444
Efficiently managed business hotel in the town centre. £99

Burpham (West Sussex) **Burpham Country Hotel *** (01903) 882160
Charming, cheery converted old vicarage in the middle of a secluded village. Enthusiastic owners and a varied menu offering Swiss specialities. The rooms are nothing special. £86

Bury St Edmunds (Suffolk) **Angel Hotel *** (01284) 753926
Traditional bustling town hotel with good improvements underway. £98

Buxton (Derbyshire) **Coningsby Guest House** (01298) 26735
Comfortable Victorian guesthouse for non-smokers, close to town centre. £55

Cambridge (Cambridgeshire) **Regent Hotel** (01223) 351470
Well-located, if unexceptional, business hotel. £80

Canterbury (Kent) **Thanington Hotel** (01227) 453227
B&B in an elegant Georgian house with indoor swimming-pool, about 10 minutes' walk from the city centre. Well-maintained if a little characterless. £70

Carterway Heads (Northumberland)   **Manor House Inn**
(01207) 255268
Well-run inn in a remote spot overlooking the Derwent reservoir. Bedrooms are basic, but food is excellent.   £43

Chagford (Devon)   **Easton Court Hotel**   (01647) 433469
Historical interest, drunken floors and plenty of character in this fabulous thatched hostelry.   £90

Chartham Hatch (Kent)   **Howfield Manor**   (01227) 738294
Twelfth-century manor house with modern extensions. Clean bright rooms but bland business atmosphere.   £88

Cheltenham (Gloucestershire)   **The Queen's ***   (01242) 514724
Cheltenham's Forte-owned, Regency grande dame has undergone a major revamp. Within the building (but under separate ownership) is the excellent new brasserie, Le Petit Blanc.   £120

Claverdon (Warwickshire)   **Ardencote Manor**   (01926) 843111
Leisure-oriented Victorian manor house with 40 acres of grounds.   £135

Clawton (Devon)   **Court Barn**   (01409) 271219
Well-proportioned, relaxing Victorian country house, with endearingly old-fashioned décor.   £80

Crantock (Cornwall)   **Crantock Bay Hotel**   (01637) 830229
Classic seaside hotel in prime spot on peninsula overlooking bay, but rooms need updating.   £57

Cropredy (Oxfordshire)   **Old Manor**   (01295) 750235
Three neat cottagey rooms in an old stone longhouse beside the Oxford canal, with ducks, geese and vintage cars for company.   £50

Crudwell (Wiltshire)   **Mayfield House**   (01666) 577409
Good value at a friendly, informal hotel set amid lawned gardens. Go for a refurbished room.   £69

Cullompton (Devon)   **Manor House**   (01884) 32281
Good rooms in a lovely old half-timbered inn, with busy town pub next door.   £60

Dorking (Surrey)   **Burford Bridge**   (01306) 884561
Upmarket Forte hotel at the foot of Box Hill. Galleried sixteenth-century tithe barn, scenic views and lovely gardens compensate for the rather characterless but comfortable rooms.   £123

Easington (North Yorkshire)   **Grinkle Park**   (01287) 640515
Victorian Gothic mansion in extensive grounds. Public rooms are suitably grand but soulless bedrooms, although smart, fail to live up to expectations. Good for conferences and weddings.   £91

Exeter (Devon)   **St Olaves Court**   (01392) 217736
Useful, characterful Georgian town hotel, with good food and refurbished bedrooms.   £88

Fleet (Dorset)   **Moonfleet Manor ***   (01305) 786948
Ambitious plans afoot to transform this family-oriented resort hotel run on similar lines to its famous sister, Woolley Grange (see page 129).   £95

Gamlingay (Cambridgeshire)   **The Emplins**   (01767) 650581
Exceptional fifteenth-century house, with old-fashioned bedrooms, run by a friendly couple.   £60

Gittisham (Devon)   **Combe House**   (01404) 540400
Fabulous faded Elizabethan pile, full of eccentricities, with huge public rooms and bedrooms. Under new ownership.   £100

Glastonbury (Somerset)   **Number 3**   (01458) 832129
Unusual B&B with bright, spacious bedrooms in the garden annexe of a substantial Georgian house close to the ruins of Glastonbury Abbey.   £70

Grange-over-Sands (Cumbria)   **Graythwaite Manor**   (015395) 32001
Friendly, family-run, old-fashioned hotel in lovely established gardens with distant bay views.   £85

Hardwicke (Herefordshire)   **The Haven**   (01497) 831254
A welcoming, reassuring guesthouse in an early Victorian vicarage at the head of the Golden Valley.   £46

Hatherleigh (Devon)   **The George**   (01837) 810454
Historical interest, drunken floors and plenty of character in this fabulous thatched hostelry.   £70

Haytor (Devon)   **Bel Alp House**   (01364) 661217
Handsome country house hotel that once belonged to a tobacco heiress provides spacious, elegant accommodation, plenty of interesting features and a grand view.   £120

Headlam (Co Durham)   **Headlam Hall**   (01325) 730238
Stone manor house, part Jacobean, part Georgian. Go for the more characterful four-poster rooms in the main house, which have antiques, stone-mullioned windows and grand fireplaces. Holidaymakers may feel lost among the business/weddings clientele.   £80

Henley-on-Thames (Oxfordshire)   **Hernes**   (01491) 573245
Ancestral home with family portraits and impressive grounds. Guests dine with the family in typical Wolsey Lodge style.   £80

Hermitage (Dorset)   **Almshouse Farm**   (01963) 210296
Comfortable rooms in a lovely sixteenth-century farmhouse set on a working farm about six miles from Sherborne.   £42

Herstmonceux (East Sussex)   **Cleavers Lyng**   (01323) 833131
Sympathetically extended redbrick Tudor cottage in a tranquil location, with great views, pretty rooms and traditional home-cooking.   £45–£55

Holford (Somerset)   **Combe House**   (01278) 741382
New owners have ambitious plans to upgrade and modernise this homely hotel with good leisure facilities close to Bridgwater.   £66

Holne (Devon)   **Church House Inn**   (01364) 631208
Cheerful, no-frills hostelry with good menu (a 'chip-free zone'), occupying pride of place in pretty, end-of-the-road village.   £50

Hopton Wafers (Shropshire)   **Crown Inn**   (01299) 270372
Civilised sixteenth-century coaching inn; bags of character, excellent food, cottagey bedrooms.   £75

Horley (Surrey)   **The Lawn**   (01293) 775751
Victorian house a couple of miles from Gatwick. No wardrobes and small bathrooms, but holiday parking is offered at £2 a night.   £45

Huntingdon (Cambridgeshire)   **Old Bridge**   (01480) 52681
Good-quality bedrooms, but a little too close to a busy road.   £90

Huxham (Devon)   **Barton Cross ***   (01392) 841245
Fetching horseshoe-shaped thatched restaurant-with-rooms; good food but bland rooms.   £90

Ireby (Cumbria)   **Overwater Hall**   (01768) 776566
Quiet Victorian building in a fine location. Outwardly grand but homely inside, offering an exceptionally friendly welcome.   £84

Isley Walton (Leicestershire)   **Donington Park Farmhouse Hotel**
(01332) 862409
Modest converted farmhouse hotel with good pub food; convenient for the racing circuit and East Midlands Airport.   £75

Kington (Herefordshire)   **Penrhos Court**   (01544) 230720
Medieval manor house providing a memorable foil for organic, health-conscious food. Individually decorated bedrooms, all named after birds, enjoy spectacular views over rolling countryside. Regular special events and cookery courses.   £75

Knowstone (Devon)   **Masons Arms**   (01398) 341231
Lovely old thatched pub, lost in a time warp, with genuine hosts and simple rooms.   £55

Lancaster (Lancashire)   **Edenbreck House**   (01524) 32464
Affordable B&B close to Lancaster station, with comfortable rooms.   £40

Lancaster (Lancashire)   **Lancaster House**   (01524) 844822
Smart rooms and impressive leisure facilities, suitable for business guests, next to Lancaster University.   £92

Leamington Spa (Warwickshire)   **Flowerdale House**   (01926) 426002
Good-value B&B in a Victorian house on the edge of town.   £42

Ledbury (Worcestershire)   **Feathers Hotel (Fuggles Bar) ***   (01531) 635266
Striking half-timbered coaching inn on the main street of Ledbury. Traditional without being tediously predictable, with attractive public rooms and well-kept bedrooms double-glazed against passing traffic.   £90

Leicester (Leicestershire)   **Spindle Lodge**   0116-233 8801
Straightforward well-priced rooms in guesthouse close to the University.   £50

Lew (Oxfordshire)   **Farmhouse Hotel**   (01993) 850297
Historic farmhouse, part of a working dairy farm, with lovely grounds, a large restaurant and light, modern furnishings.   £55

Lichfield (Staffordshire)   **Swinfen Hall**   (01543) 481494
Superb public rooms at this eighteenth-century manor house. Bedrooms are less impressive.   £95

Limpley Stoke (Wiltshire)   **Cliffe Hotel**   (01225) 723226
Main house bedrooms have the edge over annexe accommodation at this substantial stone mansion overlooking a pleasant wooded valley.   £85

Linton (West Yorkshire)   **Wood Hall**   (01937) 587271
Large-scale country house hotel with oak panels, fine wood carvings and grand staircases. Busy leisure facilities include fishing rights on River Wharfe.
£128

Little Langdale (Cumbria)   **Three Shires Inn**   (01539) 437215
Unremarkable décor but fine views, good bar food and a warm welcome at this popular walking and touring pub.   £72

Longframlington (Northumberland)   **Embleton Hall**   (01665) 570249
A friendly family-owned country house convenient for those travelling between England and Scotland on the A1. Stylish public rooms and characterful bedrooms.   £85

Long Melford (Suffolk)   **The Bull**   (01787) 378494
Authentic medieval character has been retained in the public rooms with average chain hotel bedrooms.   £95

Loughborough (Leicestershire)   **Old Manor ***   (01509) 211228
Stylish small hotel in the centre of Loughborough with smart bistro restaurant and some characterful rooms.   £92

Lowick (Cumbria)   **Lowick House**   (01229) 885227
Exceptionally beautifully kept Georgian house in fine gardens. A Wolsey Lodge – hone your social skills for well-mannered house-party hospitality.
£40

Ludlow (Shropshire)   **Dinham Hall**   (01584) 876464
Georgian hotel yards from the castle walls. Refined public areas include a recommended restaurant; bedrooms are plainer and somewhat overpriced.
£95

Lynmouth (Devon)   **Tors Hotel**   (01598) 753236
Traditional hotel in commanding spot with fabulous view; good menu and wine list but rather uninspiring, if plush, décor.   £64

Macclesfield (Cheshire)   **Chadwick House**   (01625) 615558
Privately run Georgian town-house hotel with thirteen homely rooms – most of which have en suite bathrooms.   £55

Madeley (Shropshire)   **Madeley Court**   (01952) 680068
Sixteenth-century manor house expanded and turned into a sizeable chain hotel; much of its business comes from conferences and functions.   £125

Maidencombe (Devon)   **Orestone Manor**   (01803) 328098
Interesting old house with lots of history, great view to sea over sub-tropical gardens, promising restaurant.   £110

Masham (North Yorkshire)   **King's Head**   (01765) 689295
A down-to-earth inn at the heart of an ancient market town. Major refurbishment under way late 1998.   £70

Matlock (Derbyshire)   **Red House**   (01629) 734854
Victorian house with splendid lounge and knot garden; service friendly but can be inexperienced.   £80

Minchinhampton (Gloucestershire)   **Burleigh Court ***   (01453) 883804
Spiritedly run Georgian country-house hotel in extensive grounds; public rooms have more character than bedrooms.   £85

Mockbeggar (Hampshire)   **Plantation Cottage**   (01425) 477443
Cosy and relaxing B&B in eighteenth-century cottage in a New Forest hamlet. Pretty garden, friendly proprietor and comfy rooms.   £50

Monkton Combe (Bath & N.E. Somerset)   **Combe Grove Manor** (01225) 834644
Popular for its leisure facilities and lovely views. Public areas lack atmosphere. £99

Montacute (Somerset)   **Kings Arms ***   (01935) 822513
Comfortable rooms at a friendly sixteenth-century inn a stone's throw from Montacute House.   £69

Newcastle upon Tyne (Tyne & Wear)   **Vermont Hotel** 0191-233 1010
Up-market business hotel convenient for the town centre, with fine dining on offer.   £167

Newlyn (Cornwall)   **Higher Faugan**   (01736) 362076
Old-fashioned and very peaceful turn-of-the-century country house overlooking St Michael's Mount, with fabulous gardens.   £89

Newquay (Cornwall)   **Headland Hotel**   (01637) 872211
Vast Victorian pile on windswept bluff overlooking Fistral Beach, with booming public rooms and a great view.   £124

Northampton (Northamptonshire)   **Swallow Hotel**   (01604) 768700
Efficient business-oriented motel with good spacious rooms and leisure facilities – but swimming-pool is small.   £115

Over Haddon (Derbyshire)   **Lathkil Hotel**   (01629) 812501
Convenient for walkers, a remote pub with just four rooms – lovely views of Lathkil Dale.   £70

Pangbourne (Berkshire)   **Copper Inn**   0118-984 2244
Friendly hotel with good-sized bedrooms, busy bar and an attractive French-style restaurant in centre of bustling town.   £125

Port Isaac (Cornwall)   **Slipway Hotel**   (01208) 880264
Characterful old inn in great spot in traditional Cornish fishing village – go for a room at the front, if possible.   £72

Reading (Berkshire)   **Holiday Inn**   0118-925 9988
Serviceable chain hotel right on the river on the northern edge of the city; attractive weekend rates.   £125

Rickling Green (Essex)   **Cricketers Arms**   (01799) 543210
Bland bedrooms, but a pleasant pub with great views of the cricket pitch. £66

Ripon (North Yorkshire)   **Old Deanery**   (01765) 603518
Restaurant-with-rooms in a charming, historic building directly opposite the cathedral. Cuisine has a good reputation, rooms are spacious but lack style. £100

Rotherwick (Hampshire)   **Tylney Hall**   (01256) 764881
Grandiose, turn-of-the-century manor with extensive grounds, luxurious rooms and hot-and-cold running staff tending to your every whim.   £135

Ryde (Isle of Wight) **Little Upton Farm** * (01983) 563236
Farmhouse with lovely views and three bedrooms run by Alison Johnson and her husband Howard, who tells a tale or two as he cooks breakfast. £40

Ryde (Isle of Wight) **Newnham Farm** * (01983) 882423
Secluded farmhouse with beautiful gardens and two letting bedrooms – one a spacious family room with bunk beds. Di Cleaver has put in some nice touches like a fridge for fresh milk, and bakes shortbread to greet guests. £40

Rye (East Sussex) **Mermaid Inn** (01797) 223065
Historic inn in the heart of picturesque Rye, with authentically atmospheric rooms – lots of wood panelling and creaky floors. Room 16 is the best, with its huge four-poster. £135

St Mary's (Isles of Scilly) **Tregarthen's Hotel** (01720) 422540
Comfortable old-fashioned hotel set just above the quay. £140

St Neot (Cornwall) **London Inn** * (01579) 320263
Village pub with fresh bedrooms right next to the parish church with its fine stained glass windows. £48

Salcombe (Devon) **Marine Hotel** (01548) 844444
Very comfortable traditional seaside hotel in great location overlooking estuary. £180–£210 inc dinner

Salisbury (Wiltshire) **Old Mill** (01722) 327517
Atmospheric pub-with-rooms in lovely position on water meadows, with view over to Salisbury Cathedral. £75

Scole (Norfolk) **Scole Inn** (01379) 740481
A huge seventeenth-century coaching inn with lots of period features and pleasant bedrooms. £66

Shenington (Oxfordshire) **Sugarswell Farm** (01295) 680512
Good food, intimate surroundings and three stylish and welcoming rooms at a remote farmhouse amoung the flat fields west of Banbury. £50

Shipton-under-Wychwood (Oxfordshire) **Shaven Crown**
(01993) 830330
This former fourteenth-century hospice, with basic bedrooms and an atmospheric bar, retains an authentic medieval feel. £82

Slaidburn (Lancashire) **Parrock Head** (01200) 446614
Country farmhouse hotel in attractive rural setting, with a long drive and lots of sheep; bedrooms are rather dated. £57

Snape (Suffolk) **Crown Inn** * (01728) 688324
Cosy pub and restaurant, close to the Maltings, with pleasant rooms. £50

Southsea (Hampshire) **Westfield Hall** (01705) 826971
Family-run hotel near the waterfront, with comfortable, business-like rooms and welcoming owners. Handy for the cross-Channel ferries or exploring Portsmouth. £60

Staddlebridge (North Yorkshire) **McCoy's Restaurant**
(01609) 882671
Off-beat roadside restaurant-with-rooms; modern global cuisine and heaps of 1930s character. Rooms are comfy, bold and bright but light sleepers might find noise from the busy A19 a nuisance. £90

Standish (Greater Manchester)   **Kilhey Court ***   (01257) 472100
Large, well-equipped hotel overlooking Worthington Lakes, popular for conferences and weddings. Rooms in the original Victorian building have character, those in the newer parts of the hotel are blander.   £115

Stoke-on-Trent (Staffordshire)   **Haydon House**   (01782) 711311
Family-run hotel in a Victorian terrace; executive rooms are better value than standards.   £73

Stourbridge (West Midlands)   **Talbot Hotel**   (01384) 394350
Popular former coaching inn with comfortable bedrooms.   £90

Stow-on-the-Wold (Gloucestershire)   **Grapevine Hotel**
(01451) 830344
Imaginatively furnished seventeenth-century hotel in the centre of town, but considerably overpriced. Best bedrooms are in annexes.   £148

Studland (Dorset)   **Knoll House**   (01929) 450251
Cheerful, unpretentious, family-oriented beachside mini-resort hotel complex, where children and their carers very definitely come first.   £85 inc dinner

Sturminster Newton (Dorset)   **Fiddleford Mill House ***
(01258) 472786
Spacious, comfortable bedrooms in a lovely farmhouse, with stunning listed ceiling. Friendly, laid-back hosts.   £40

Taunton (Somerset)   **Castle Hotel ***   (01823) 272671
Slick service at a creeper-clad castellated edifice where Judge Jeffreys once held Bloody Assizes. Food is justly praised, though expensive.   £127

Tewkesbury (Gloucestershire)   **Puckrup Hall**   (01684) 296200
Large chain hotel surrounded by a golf course; reasonable value if you make use of the extensive leisure facilities (golf extra but at special residential rates).   £135

Thundridge (Hertfordshire)   **Marriott Hanbury Manor**
(01920) 487722
Huge turn-of-the-century baronial-style manor providing top-of-the-range sport, games, business facilities and seclusion for the well-heeled.   £155

Ticehurst (East Sussex)   **Dale Hill Hotel & Golf Club**   (01580) 200112
Great for golfers but uninspiring for others. Modern up-market hotel, with spacious rooms, a sunny conservatory brasserie, helpful staff, health club and glorious golfing facilities.   £110

Tintagel (Cornwall)   **Old Millfloor**   (01840) 770234
Gorgeous little old mill down in dingly dell amid jungly gardens and lots of ducks; ten minutes' walk to the beach. Bedrooms share bathroom facilities.   £40

Titchwell (Norfolk)   **Titchwell Manor**   (01485) 210221
Large Victorian house on coast, with some attractive rooms; popular with golfers and bird-watchers.   £90

Totnes (Devon)   **Old Forge**   (01803) 862174
Spruce, chintzy, cute B&B; last bastion of tradition in increasingly alternative Totnes.   £56

Tring (Hertfordshire)   **Pendley Manor**   (01442) 891891
Victorian country house, with smart and spacious rooms and a summer Shakespeare festival in the landscaped grounds.   £120

Tring (Hertfordshire)   **Rose & Crown**   (01442) 824071
Rambling coaching inn opposite the church; new management has got overdue refurbishment underway.   £101

Tunbridge Wells (Kent)   **Spa Hotel**   (01892) 520331
Imposing eighteenth-century mansion, with extensive grounds and good leisure facilities, but the emphasis on corporate business means that the rooms, though pleasant, rather lack atmosphere.   £105

Uppingham (Rutland)   **Rutland House**   (01572) 822497
Pleasant small hotel in High Street; bright bedrooms.   £40

Walberswick (Suffolk)   **Bell Hotel ***   (01502) 723109
Atmospheric pub, attractive rooms, great location down by the estuary.   £60

Walkington (East Riding of Yorkshire)   **Manor House**   (01482) 881645
Victorian country house in tranquil bucolic setting. Formal, well-reputed restaurant is its trump card.   £89

Westerham (Kent)   **Kings Arms**   (01959) 562990
Elegant Georgian coaching inn, with a great cellar bar, in the centre of Domesday Book market town. Comfy rooms, welcoming atmosphere and handy for the M25.   £103

Williton (Somerset)   **White House**   (01984) 632306/632777
Acclaimed food and comfortable rooms at a roadside Georgian House (open mid-May to early November).   £74–£94

Windermere (Cumbria)   **Beaumont Hotel**   (015394) 47075
Immaculately kept but easy-going small hotel quietly located in town centre. Generous breakfasts.   £60

Windermere (Cumbria)   **The Chestnuts**   (015394) 46999
Smartly decorated B&B between Bowness and Windermere. Friendly atmosphere.   £56

Windermere (Cumbria)   **Fayrer Garden House Hotel ***
(015394) 88195
Smart country-house style and fine gardens near the shores of Windermere. Ambitious cooking and attentive service.   £44

Windsor (Berkshire)   **Sir Christopher Wren's House**
(01753) 861354
Pricy hotel and business centre in converted seventeenth-century house beside the Eton bridge; smart rooms, rococo restaurant and a riverside patio.   £175

Withypool (Somerset)   **Royal Oak**   (01643) 831506
Cosy bedrooms in atmospheric old Exmoor inn.   £82

Woburn (Bedfordshire)   **Bell Inn**   (01525) 290280
Smart but small bedrooms in a red-brick town house close to the abbey; restaurant in the pub across the street.   £70

Woodstock (Oxfordshire)   **The Laurels**   (01993) 812583
B&B with inviting rooms and easy-going hosts; on the quieter side of the town but only two minutes' walk to the centre.   £50

Woodstock (Oxfordshire)   **Star Inn**   (01993) 811373
Four attractive pine and plain cream rooms above a traditional pub; plump for Prince Albert if it is available.   £65

Woody Bay (Devon)   **Woody Bay Hotel**   (01598) 763264/763563
A slow refurbishment programme is bringing colour to this somewhat dated Victorian hotel; the location remains unrivalled, with a fabulous view down to Woody Bay. Good value.   £66

Woolacombe (Devon)   **Little Beach**   (01271) 870398
Useful seaside hotel overlooking surfers' beach. Spacious house and friendly new owners, but slightly misconceived décor.   £52

York (North Yorkshire)   **Eastons**   (01904) 626646
B&B in two Victorian terraced houses handy for old centre of York. Make sure to turn up before 6 p.m.   £50

York (North Yorkshire)   **Grange Hotel**   (01904) 644744
Regency town house just beyond city walls with country-house ambience. Two restaurants to choose from, including a vaulted basement cellar.   £125

Zeals (Wiltshire)   **Stag Cottage**   (01747) 840458
Traditional whitewashed former estate cottage, offering simple accommodation and cream teas.   £40

SCOTLAND

Aberdeen (Aberdeen)   **The Marcliffe at Pitfodels**   (01224) 861000
Aberdeen's most classy business hotel, where character is combined with efficiency.   £145

Ardvasar (Highland)   **Ardvasar Hotel**   (01471) 844223
Encouraging reports this year for this pretty old inn in south Skye. Good food and good views, but one reader mentioned noise from traffic catching the early ferry.   £70

Auchencairn (Dumfries & Galloway)   **Balcary Bay Hotel**
(01556) 640217
Seashore country-house hotel with comfortable accommodation but slightly stiff atmosphere. On the market as we went to press.   £98–£110

Auchterarder (Perthshire & Kinross)   **Auchterarder House**
(01764) 663646
Fine old country house hotel close to Gleneagles; under new management.
£160

Brodick (North Ayrshire)   **Auchrannie Country House**
(01770) 302234
Much used by coach parties, but lots of facilites, including a swimming-pool. Good bedrooms and friendly staff.   £109

Chirnside (Borders)   **Chirnside Hall**   (01890) 818219
Stone house in rolling Berwickshire countryside, well off the beaten track. A peaceful place, cheerful and comfortable.   £90

Cromarty (Highland) **Royal Hotel** (01381) 600217
The hub of this small historic town, the Royal is cosy and lively, with plain bedrooms. £58

Dunkeld (Perthshire & Kinross) **Stakis Dunkeld House**
(01350) 727771
Modern hotel with extensive leisure facilities, situated in excellent location. Mainly for business clientele and conferences, but with good-value short breaks. £140

Edinburgh (Edinburgh) **22 Murrayfield Gardens** * 0131-337 3569
A quiet, well-appointed and elegant family B&B in a Victorian house, a bus ride from the centre, with a lovely sitting-room and a pretty garden. £80

Edinburgh (Edinburgh) **The Bonham** * 0131-226 6050
A monument to contemporary style, with textured fabrics, daring lighting effects and bold colours. Too soon to tell how successful it will be, but it's certainly interesting. £165

Edinburgh (Edinburgh) **Channings** 0131-315 2226
A classy conversion of townhouses a short walk from the city centre. A slightly cramped feel to it. £150

Edinburgh (Edinburgh) **Two Saxe Coburg Place** 0131-315 4752
Quiet and pretty B&B in one of Edinburgh's most pleasing squares. Three neat bedrooms, a lovely town garden and genial hosts. £80

Galashiels (Borders) **Woodlands Country House** (01896) 754722
Lots of character to this neo-Gothic hotel. A well-run and cheerful place, mostly populated by business people. £68

Girvan (South Ayrshire) **Glen Tachur** (01465) 821223
A good discovery in the isolated moors of the south-west. Family-run, plain and friendly. £55

Glasgow (Glasgow) **The Devonshire** 0141-339 7878
Overshadowed by its famous neighbour at number 10, but a good, small, luxury hotel. £145

Glasgow (Glasgow) **Glasgow Hilton** 0141-204 5555
Big, stylish, pricey city-centre business hotel with loads of facilities. £200

Glasgow (Glasgow) **Holiday Inn** * 0141-332 0110
Good-value business hotel close to the concert hall. Nowhere much to sit, but a good bistro, and lots of digital gadgets. £103

Kinclaven (Perthshire & Kinross) **Ballathie House** (01250) 883268
Sporting and conference country-house hotel on the River Tay. Well furnished, but a slightly bland atmosphere. £190

Lochcarnan (Western Isles) **Orasay Inn** (01870) 610298
Simple and attractive modern guesthouse-style inn in good bird-watching country. It grows slowly bigger as rooms are added – now up to nine. £58

Maryculter (Aberdeen) **Maryculter House** (01224) 732124
Old riverside house, praised for its friendliness and good rooms, but one report spoke less encouragingly of the food. £95

Melrose (Borders) **Burt's Hotel** (01896) 822285
A well-run small-town hotel, very friendly, with particularly praiseworthy food. £82

Oban (Argyll & Bute)   **Kilchrenan House ***   (01631) 562663
Suberb value B&B with friendly owners. Looks a winner.   £55

Oban (Argyll & Bute)   **Knipoch Hotel**   (01852) 316251
A strange mix of styles in this long, low, lochside hotel. Professionally run, and good public rooms, but bedrooms lack character.   £154

Plockton (Highland)   **Haven Hotel ***   (01599) 544223
Comfortable small hotel in one of Scotland's prettiest villages.   £74

Port Appin (Argyll & Bute)   **Stewart Hotel**   (01631) 740268
A well-located West Highland hotel in a former shooting lodge, but the bedrooms are in a separate, less attractive building.   £69

St Fillans (Perthshire & Kinross)   **Four Seasons**   (01764) 685333
A good loch-side location and good food at this family-run hotel, but it is becoming in need of extensive refurbishment.   £88

Salen (Argyll & Bute)   **Glenforsa**   (01680) 300377
Well-located hotel in central Mull. Chalet-style buildings, fairly basic, but comfortable and friendly.   £75

Scourie (Highland)   **Scourie Hotel**   (01971) 502396
New owners with a good track record have taken over this traditional fishing hotel in west Sutherland, but are determined not to change its character.
£78

Stewarton (Argyll & Bute)   **Chapeltoun House**   (01560) 482696
Good, solid country-house hotel, convenient for Burns country.   £105

Stirling (Stirling)   **The Heritage**   (01786) 473660
Restaurant-with-rooms in a substantial Georgian house in a quiet street close to the centre of town.   £65

Stirling (Stirling)   **Stirling Highland**   (01786) 475444
Business hotel carved out from an old school. Prime location and some good design, but you still feel a bell may ring at any moment and the corridors and stairways fill up with pupils.   £155

Stornoway (Western Isles)   **Ardlonan**   (01851) 703482
Comfortable and welcoming B&B in a Victorian house. Good point for starting exploration of Lewis.   £38

Strathyre (Stirling)   **Creagan House**   (01877) 384638
Seventeenth-century farmhouse turned restaurant-with-rooms. Extraordinary home-built baronial hall and well-furnished bedrooms.   £70

Talladale (Highland)   **Loch Maree Hotel**   (01445) 760288
Traditional fishing hotel in an enviable position on one of Scotland's most beautiful lochs.   £70

Tongue (Highland)   **Ben Loyal Hotel**   (01847) 611216
Small hotel in one of the few villages on Scotland's north coast, showing signs of needing refurbishment. On the market as we went to press.

Torridon (Highland)   **Loch Torridon Hotel**   (01445) 791242
A good base for touring the West Coast. Solid and dignified, perhaps slightly lacking distinctive character.   £110

Troon (South Ayrshire)   **Highgrove House**   (01292) 312511
Edwardian villa on a hill with good views, good food and stylish bedrooms.
£85

Walkerburn (Borders)   **Tweed Valley Hotel**   (01896) 870636
Extensive refurbishment is updating the look and feel of this fishing hotel, as new owners get to grips with the place. Re-decorated bedrooms are looking good.   £110

Wick (Highland)   **Bilbster House**   (01955) 621212
Very friendly family-run home in the far, far north, with good bedrooms and a most relaxing atmosphere.   £60

WALES

Aberystwyth (Ceredigion)   **Conrah Country House**   (01970) 617941
Straightforward country-house hotel with fine views. Pleasant indoor swimming-pool, but could do with some redecoration.   £90–£120

Bontddu (Gwynedd)   **Bontddu Hall**   (01341) 430661
Victorian Gothic mansion with characterful bedrooms and great views of the Mawddach Estuary.   £100

Caersws (Powys)   **Maesmawr Hall**   (01686) 688255
Half-timbered Tudor house, much extended at the rear. Stay in the older part, particularly room 14.   £73

Capel Coch (Isle of Anglesey)   **Tre-Ysgawen Hall**   (01248) 750750
Large late-Victorian mansion with grand but rather cool atmosphere.   £117

Cardiff (Cardiff)   **The Angel**   (01222) 232633
Large city-centre Victorian hotel with imposing public rooms and well-equipped, if unimaginative bedrooms.   £125

Lampeter (Ceredigion)   **Falcondale**   (01570) 422910
Externally impressive Italianate mansion with rather uninspiring rooms.
£85

Llanarmon Dyffryn Ceiriog (Wrexham)   **Hand Hotel**   (01691) 600666
Tranquil location for this unpretentious hotel with unusual dining-room.
£70

Llanarth (Monmouthshire)   **Clytha Arms ***   (01873) 840206
Attractively converted dower house inn not far from Raglan Castle and the River Usk, serving imaginative and sophisticated food. Three pretty individually decorated Victorian-style bedrooms make it an agreeable overnight base, especially if you like teddy bears.   £50

Llandudno (Conwy)   **Henshaws Belmont Hotel**   (01492) 877770
Friendly and lively hotel on the promenade adapted to cater for those with visual impairment. Weekly bookings only.   £225 a week full board

Llangollen (Denbighshire)   **Bryn Howel**   (01978) 860331
Late-Victorian mansion with rather characterless modern additions.   £85

Llanigon (Powys)   **Old Post Office ***   (01497) 820008
Attractive terrace of 17th-century cottages in a quiet village, offering stylishly converted B&B and a vegetarian breakfast. Lovely walking country.   £40

Llanwddyn (Powys)   **Lake Vyrnwy Hotel**   (01691) 870692
Good reports this year of this friendly Victorian sporting hotel on the magnificent lake.   £95

Llanyre (Powys)   **Bell Inn ***   (01597) 823959
New owners are making steady improvements at this modern village pub with smart restaurant and fairly ordinary rooms.   £75

Newport (Newport)   **Celtic Manor**   (01633) 413000
Serious money is being spent to upgrade this business-oriented originally-Victorian hotel.   £125

Pontyclun (Rhondda Cynon Taff)   **Miskin Manor**   (01443) 224204
Victorian house built around an 11th-century manor, now business-oriented, rather bland in places but with good leisure facilities.   £110

Pumpsaint (Carmarthenshire)   **Glanrannel Park**   (01558) 685230
Bird-watchers flock to this homely Victorian hotel for the birdlife around its small lake.   £72

Pwllheli (Gwynedd)   **Plas Bodegroes**   (01758) 612363
A Georgian house with smart bedrooms and excellent food.   £120

Rossett (Wrexham)   **Llyndir Hall**   (01244) 571648
Business-oriented hotel with good leisure facilities close to Wrexham.   £110

St David's (Pembrokeshire)   **Warpool Court Hotel ***   (01437) 720300
Country-house hotel in lovely location close to coastal path but lacking character.   £130

Swansea (Swansea)   **Windsor Lodge**   (01792) 642158
Conveniently close to the centre, a Georgian house with smart restaurant and comfortable bedrooms.   £63

Tal-y-llyn (Gwynedd)   **Tynycornel Hotel**   (01654) 782282
Set in magnificent scenery, a pleasant lakeside hotel popular with fishermen, walkers and visitors to local steam railway.   £94

Trecastle (Powys)   **Castle Coaching Inn**   (01874) 636354
Friendly inn with good atmosphere; handy for walks in the Brecon Beacons.   £45

Tresaith (Ceredigion)   **Glandwr Manor**   (01239) 810197
Plain and simple hotel in quiet surroundings, good value and close to beach.   £56

Non-smoking establishments

We list below all the hotels that state they are completely non-smoking.

London
Bedknobs
Hampstead Village Guesthouse
Searcy's Roof Garden Bedrooms
Thanet Hotel

England
Alderminster, Ettington Park
Aldwincle, The Maltings
Askrigg, Helm
Babworth, The Barns
Bath, Holly Lodge
Belstone, Tor Down House
Blackwell, Blackwell Grange
Broadway, Mill Hay House
Buckland Monachorum, Store
 Cottage
Bury St Edmund, Twelve Angel
 Hill
Campsea Ashe, Old Rectory
Cannington, Blackmore Farm
Canterbury, Magnolia House
Carlisle, Number Thirty One
Chadlington, Chadlington House
Charmouth, Thatch Lodge Hotel
Cheddleton, Choir Cottage &
 Choir House
Chester, Green Bough Hotel
Chillaton, Quither Mill
Cleeve Hill, Cleeve Hill Hotel
Clifton Hampden, Plough Inn
Clun, Birches Mill
Cockermouth, Low Hall
Cockermouth, Toddell Cottage
Colchester, Hockley Place
Colyford, Swallows Eaves
Coreley, Corndene
Coventry, Crest Guesthouse
Crackington Haven, Manor Farm
Cranford St Andrew, Dairy Farm
Creed, Creed House
Crewkerne, Broadview Gardens
Crook, Birksey Brow
Crowhurst, Brakes Coppice Farm
Dent, Stone Close
Dover, Old Vicarage

East Barkwith, Bodkin Lodge
East Ord, Tree Tops
Evershot, Summer Lodge
Farnham, Museum Hotel
Frampton, Hyde Farm House
Galmpton, Maypool Park Hotel
Gislingham, Old Guildhall
Grassington, Ashfield House
Great Hucklow, Hucklow Hall
Hamsterley Forest, Grove House
Hartfield, Bolbroke Mill
Hatch Beauchamp, Farthings
Hatton, Northleigh House
Haworth, Hole Farm
Hertford, Hall House
Hexham, Dene House
High Buston, High Buston Hall
Holmesfield, Horsley Gate Hall
Hopesay, Old Rectory
Huxley, Higher Huxley Hall
Ingleby Greenhow, Manor House
 Farm
Ironbridge, Library House
Ironbridge, Severn Lodge
Kemerton, Upper Court
Kendal, Holmfield
Kenilworth, Castle Laurels
Keswick, Craglands
Keswick, The Grange
Keswick, Swinside Lodge
Kettlewell, Langcliffe Country
 House
Landewednack, Landewednack
 House
Leintwardine, Upper Buckton
 Farm
Lewes, Millers
Little Petherick, Molesworth
 Manor
Lorton, New House Farm
Lorton, Winder Hall
Lyneham, Fenwicks
Lynton, Highcliffe House
Lynton, Valley House
Malton, Newstead Grange
Martinhoe, Old Rectory

Maxstoke, Old Rectory
Meldreth, Chiswick House
Mere, Chetcombe House
Middle Chinnock, Chinnock
  House
Middleham, Greystones
Minchinhampton, Hunters Lodge
Monkton Combe, Monkshill
Montacute, Milk House
Morchard Bishop, Wigham
Mursley, Richmond Lodge
Newbiggin-on-Lune, Low Lane
  House
North Wheatley, Old Plough
Oakham, Lord Nelson's House
Oxford, Cotswold House
Palgrave, Malt House
Plymouth, Athenaeum Lodge
Portscatho, Roseland House
Ravenstonedale, Tarn House Farm
Rogate, Mizzards Farm
Ross-on-Wye, Upper Pengethley
  Farm
Rosthwaite, Hazel Bank
St Blazey, Nanscawen House
Sandhoe, The Courtyard
Selside, Low Jock Scar
Shanklin, Foxhills
Shrewley, Shrewley House
Sissinghurst, Sissinghurst Castle
  Farm
Somerton, The Lynch
Stratford-upon-Avon, Victoria Spa
  Lodge
Swaffham, Strattons
Sway, Nurse's Cottage
Tenterden, Brattle House
Threlkeld, Blease Farm
Tilston, Tilston Lodge
Torquay, Mulberry House
Towersey, Upper Green Farm
Tutbury, Mill House
Uffington, The Craven
Virginstow, Percy's at
  Coombeshead
Weobley, Ye Olde Salutation Inn
Westdean, Old Parsonage
West Down, Long House
West Malling, Scott House
Weston-under-Redcastle, The
  Citadel

West Porlock, Bales Mead
Whaplode, Guy Wells
Wheddon Cross, Raleigh Manor
Widegates, Coombe Farm
Willersey, Old Rectory
Wilmcote, Pear Tree Cottage
Winchcombe, Isbourne Manor
  House
Winchcombe, Wesley House
Windermere, The Archway
Woodstock, Holmwood
York, The Dairy
York, Holmwood House

Scotland
Aberdour, Hawkcraig House
Aboyne, Hazlehurst Lodge
Callander, Arran Lodge
Edinburgh, Drummond House
Edinburgh, Sibbet House
Fort William, Ashburn House
Haddington, Brown's Hotel
Inverness, Sealladh Sona
Inversnaid, Inversnaid Lodge
Jedburgh, Hundalee House
Kirkcudbright, Gladstone House
Lochinver, The Albannach
Melrose, Dunfermline House
Port Ellen, Glenmachrie
South Galson, Galson Farm
  Guesthouse
Spean Bridge, Old Pines
Strathkinness, Fossil House
Tongue, Rhian Guest House
Ullapool, Altnaharrie Inn

Wales
Betws-y-Coed, The Ferns
Builth Wells, Dollynwydd
Capel Garmon, Tan-y-Foel
Ganllwyd, Plas Dolmelynllyn
Haverfordwest, Lower Haythog
  Farm
Llanaber, Llwyndu Farmhouse
Llanegryn, Ty Mawr
Llanfachreth, Tŷ Isaf
Penally, Penally Abbey
St Brides Wentlooge, West Usk
  Lighthouse

Hotels licensed to hold civil weddings

Hotels in England and Wales that are licensed for civil weddings in accordance with the Marriage Act 1949 (as amended) are listed below. The situation is different in Scotland, where religious weddings may be held at any hotel or indeed anywhere else; civil weddings, however, can be held only in registrars' offices save in exceptional circumstances.

London
Cannizaro House
The Goring
The Hempel
The Howard
Park Lane Hotel
The Savoy
Searcy's Roof Garden Bedrooms
Stafford Hotel

England
Abberley, The Elms
Bath, Royal Crescent
Beaulieu, Montagu Arms
Bigbury-on-Sea, Burgh Island
Blanchland, Lord Crewe Arms
Bournemouth, Langtry House
Bray, Monkey Island Hotel
Broadway, Dormy House
Broadway, Lygon Arms
Bromsgrove, Grafton Manor
Broxted, Whitehall
Broxton, Frogg Manor
Bury St Edmunds, Ravenwood Hall
Buxton, Brookfield on Longhill
Castle Ashby, The Falcon
Castle Combe, Manor House
Charingworth, Charingworth Manor
Climping, Bailiffscourt
Colerne, Lucknam Park
Cookham Dean, Inn on the Green
Copthorne, The Copthorne
Crudwell, Crudwell Court
Cuckfield, Ockenden Manor
Dedham, Maison Talbooth
Diddlebury, Delbury Hall
Donnington, Donnington Valley Hotel
Dunsley, Dunsley Hall
Edith Weston, Normanton Park

Egham, Great Fosters
Falmouth, Penmere Manor
Fareham, Solent Hotel
Grasmere, Michael's Nook
Great Milton, Le Manoir aux Quat' Saisons
Grimston, Congham Hall
Hadley Wood, West Lodge Park
Halifax, Holdsworth House
Hambleton, Hambleton Hall
Harrogate, White House
Hassop, Hassop Hall
Hatch Beauchamp, Farthings
Hawes, Simonstone Hall
Hexham, Langley Castle
Hintlesham, Hintlesham Hall
Hunstrete, Hunstrete House
Huntsham, Huntsham Court
Hurley, Ye Olde Bell
Hurstbourne Tarrant, Esseborne Manor
Ipswich, Belstead Brook Hotel
Ipswich, Marlborough Hotel
Langar, Langar Hall
Langho, Northcote Manor
Lavenham, The Swan
Leeds, Haley's
Lewdown, Lewtrenchard Manor
Little Singleton, Mains Hall
Longhorsley, Linden Hall
Lower Beeding, South Lodge
Lymington, Stanwell House
Lyndhurst, Parkhill Hotel
Malmesbury, Old Bell Hotel
Manchester, Crowne Plaza Midland
Mawnan Smith, Budock Vean
Middleham, Waterford House
Midhurst, Angel Hotel
Midhurst, Spread Eagle
Mollington, Crabwall Manor
New Milton, Chewton Glen

685

Newquay, Trevelgue Hotel
North Huish, Brookdale House
Oakham, Barnsdale Lodge
Penrith, North Lakes Hotel
Poole, Mansion House
Quorn, Quorn Country Hotel
Ripley, Boar's Head
Romaldkirk, Rose and Crown
Ryde, Biskra Beach Hotel
St Albans, Sopwell House
St Martin's, St Martin's
St Mawes, Idle Rocks Hotel
Sandiway, Nunsmere Hall
Seaton Burn, Horton Grange
Sheffield, Whitley Hall
Shepton Mallet, Charlton House
Shrewsbury, Albright Hussey
Shurdington, The Greenway
South Molton, Whitechapel Manor
Sparsholt, Lainston House
Stamford, George of Stamford
Stapleford, Stapleford Park
Stonor, Stonor Arms
Sutton Lane Ends, Sutton Hall
Tarporley, Willington Hall
Tavistock, Horn of Plenty
Tetbury, Calcot Manor
Thornbury, Thornbury Castle
Truro, Alverton Manor
Turners Hill, Alexander House
Uckfield, Horsted Place
Ulverston, Bay Horse

Upper Slaughter, Lords of the
   Manor
Vellow, Curdon Mill
Warminster, Bishopstrow House
Welwyn Garden City, Tewin Bury
   Farmhouse
West Bexington, Manor Hotel
Whitewell, Inn at Whitewell
Windermere, Holbeck Ghyll
Woodbridge, Seckford Hall
Woolton Hill, Hollington House
Yarmouth, George Hotel

Wales

Broad Haven, The Druidstone
Crickhowell, Gliffaes Country
   House
Eglwysfach, Ynyshir Hall
Llanarmon Dyffryn Ceiriog, West
   Arms
Llandrillo, Tyddyn Llan
Llangammarch Wells, Lake
   Country House
Llyswen, Llangoed Hall
Northop, Soughton Hall
Penally, Penally Abbey
Penmaenpool, Penmaenuchaf Hall
Porthkerry, Egerton Grey
Portmeirion, Hotel Portmeirion
Reynoldston, Fairyhill
Talsarnau, Maes-y-Neuadd

Hotels with swimming-pools

Those hotels that have swimming-pools – outdoor or indoor,
heated or unheated – are listed below.

London
The Savoy

England
Alderminster, Ettington Park
Alton, Alton Towers
Appleby-in-Westmorland,
   Appleby Manor
Aylesbury, Hartwell House
Bath, Royal Crescent
Battle, PowderMills

Bepton, Park House
Bethersden, Little Hodgeham
Bigbury-on-Sea, Burgh Island
Billingshurst, Old Wharf
Birmingham, Swallow Hotel
Bolton Abbey, Devonshire Arms
Bomere Heath, Fitz Manor
Bonchurch, Peacock Vane
Bournemouth, Carlton Hotel
Bracknell, Coppid Beech Hotel
Bradford-on-Avon, Woolley
   Grange

Broadway, Barn House
Broadway, Lygon Arms
Broxted, Whitehall
Buckland, Buckland Manor
Bury St Edmunds, Ravenwood Hall
Carbis Bay, Boskerris Hotel
Castle Combe, Manor House
Charingworth, Charingworth Manor
Chittlehamholt, Highbullen
Climping, Bailiffscourt
Colchester, Hockley Place
Colerne, Lucknam Park
Copthorne, The Copthorne
Corse Lawn, Corse Lawn House
Cranbrook, Old Cloth Hall
Dunsley, Dunsley Hall East
Knoyle, Milton Farm
Easton Grey, Whatley Manor
East Portlemouth, Gara Rock
Etchingham, King John's Lodge
Evershot, Summer Lodge
Evesham, Evesham Hotel
Exeter, Southgate Hotel
Falmouth, Penmere Manor
Fareham, Solent Hotel
Ford, White Hart
Grimston, Congham Hall
Grittleton, Church House
Hambleton, Hambleton Hall
Harome, Pheasant Hotel
Harvington, Mill at Harvington
Hintlesham, Hintlesham Hall
Hinton Charterhouse, Homewood Park
Hunstrete, Hunstrete House
Huxley, Higher Huxley Hall
Ipswich, Belstead Brook Hotel
Kendal, Holmfield
Kingston Bagpuize, Fallowfields
Landewednack, Landewednack House
Longhorsley, Linden Hall
Lower Slaughter, Lower Slaughter Manor
Lyndhurst, Parkhill Hotel
Manchester, Crowne Plaza Midland
Mawnan Smith, Budock Vean
Meriden, Forest of Arden

Middle Chinnock, Chinnock House
Midhurst, Spread Eagle
Mullion, Polurrian Hotel
Newcastle upon Tyne, The Copthorne
New Milton, Chewton Glen
Newquay, Trenance Lodge
Newquay, Trevelgue Hotel
Newquay, Whipsiderry Hotel
North Newington, La Madonette
Penrith, North Lakes Hotel
Redmile, Peacock Farm
Rogate, Mizzards Farm
St Albans, Sopwell House
St Blazey, Nanscawen House
St Hilary, Ennys
St Keyne, Well House
St Margaret's at Cliffe, Wallett's Court
St Martin's, St Martin's
Salcombe, Soar Mill Cove Hotel
Salcombe, South Sands
Salcombe, Tides Reach
Sandringham, Park House
Shefford Woodlands, Fishers Farm
Shepton Mallet, Charlton House
Stapleford, Stapleford Park
Talland, Talland Bay
Tetbury, Calcot Manor
Tresco, Island Hotel
Uckfield, Horsted Place
Vellow, Curdon Mill
Ventnor, Royal Hotel
Veryan, Nare Hotel
Warminster, Bishopstrow House
Widegates, Coombe Farm
Woodbridge, Seckford Hall
Wookey Hole, Glencot House
Woolacombe, Watersmeet Hotel
Woolton Hill, Hollington House

Scotland

Auchterarder, Gleneagles
Auchterhouse, Old Mansion House
Ballater, Stakis Craigendarroch
Blairgowrie, Kinloch House
Drumnadrochit, Polmaily House
Eriska, Isle of Eriska
Inverness, Dunain Park
St Andrews, Old Course Hotel

Turnberry, Turnberry Hotel

Wales
Abersoch, Porth Tocyn Hotel
Conwy, Berthlwyd Hall
Fishguard, Plas Glyn-y-Mel

Llandudno, Bodysgallen Hall
Llandudno, St Tudno Hotel
Nantgaredig, Cwmtwrch Hotel &
 Four Seasons Restaurant
Nantgwynant, Pen-y-Gwryd Hotel
Portmeirion, Hotel Portmeirion

Index

All entries are indexed below, including those in the Round-ups. An asterisk indicates a new entry.

Writing reports

Help us to keep this *Guide* as up-to-date, as vivid and as useful to others as possible by telling us about any hotels you stay at in Britain, whether or not they appear in this *Guide*. Write a letter if you would prefer, and send brochures or other material too. Or send your reports by email to: "guide.reports@which.co.uk".

Reports received up to May 1999 will be used in the research of the 2000 edition.

Reports need not be long: just a few pithy sentences will help us sort out the best from the rest. Please comment on any of the following: the welcome, the quality of your room and of the housekeeping, points of interest about public rooms and the garden as well as any special facilities, aspects of service throughout your stay, and details of meals eaten.

In order to guard our independence we ask that reports be unsolicited by the hotelier and that you have no personal connection with the hotel.

Report form

To: The Editors, *The Which? Hotel Guide*,
FREEPOST, 2 Marylebone Road, London NW1 1YN

Name of hotel

Address

I visited this hotel on:

My report is:

(Continued overleaf)

I am not connected in any way with the management or proprietor of this hotel.

My name is:

Address:

As a result of your sending us this report form, we may send you information on **The Which? Hotel Guide** and **The Good Food Guide** in the future. If you would prefer not to receive such information, please tick this box [ ].

Report form

To: The Editors, *The Which? Hotel Guide*,
FREEPOST, 2 Marylebone Road, London NW1 1YN

Name of hotel

Address

I visited this hotel on:

My report is:

(Continued overleaf)

I am not connected in any way with the management or proprietor of this hotel.

My name is:

Address: